Table of Laplace Transforms

This table summarizes the general properties of Laplace transforms and the Laplace transforms of particular functions derived in Chapter 10.

Function	Transform	Function	Transform
$f(t)$	$F(s)$	e^{at}	$\dfrac{1}{s-a}$
$af(t) + bg(t)$	$aF(s) + bG(s)$	$t^n e^{at}$	$\dfrac{n!}{(s-a)^{n+1}}$
$f'(t)$	$sF(s) - f(0)$	$\cos kt$	$\dfrac{s}{s^2 + k^2}$
$f''(t)$	$s^2 F(s) - sf(0) - f'(0)$	$\sin kt$	$\dfrac{k}{s^2 + k^2}$
$f^{(n)}(t)$	$s^n F(s) - s^{n-1} f(0) - \cdots - f^{(n-1)}(0)$	$\cosh kt$	$\dfrac{s}{s^2 - k^2}$
$\displaystyle\int_0^t f(\tau)\,d\tau$	$\dfrac{F(s)}{s}$	$\sinh kt$	$\dfrac{k}{s^2 - k^2}$
$e^{at} f(t)$	$F(s-a)$	$e^{at} \cos kt$	$\dfrac{s-a}{(s-a)^2 + k^2}$
$u(t-a) f(t-a)$	$e^{-as} F(s)$	$e^{at} \sin kt$	$\dfrac{k}{(s-a)^2 + k^2}$
$\displaystyle\int_0^t f(\tau)g(t-\tau)\,d\tau$	$F(s)G(s)$	$\dfrac{1}{2k^3}(\sin kt - kt \cos kt)$	$\dfrac{1}{(s^2 + k^2)^2}$
$tf(t)$	$-F'(s)$	$\dfrac{t}{2k} \sin kt$	$\dfrac{s}{(s^2 + k^2)^2}$
$t^n f(t)$	$(-1)^n F^{(n)}(s)$	$\dfrac{1}{2k}(\sin kt + kt \cos kt)$	$\dfrac{s^2}{(s^2 + k^2)^2}$
$\dfrac{f(t)}{t}$	$\displaystyle\int_s^\infty F(\sigma)\,d\sigma$	$u(t-a)$	$\dfrac{e^{-as}}{s}$
$f(t),\quad \text{period } p$	$\dfrac{1}{1 - e^{-ps}} \displaystyle\int_0^p e^{-st} f(t)\,dt$	$\delta(t-a)$	e^{-as}
1	$\dfrac{1}{s}$	$(-1)^{\llbracket t/a \rrbracket}$ (square wave)	$\dfrac{1}{s} \tanh \dfrac{as}{2}$
t	$\dfrac{1}{s^2}$	$\left\llbracket \dfrac{t}{a} \right\rrbracket$ (staircase)	$\dfrac{e^{-as}}{s(1 - e^{-as})}$
t^n	$\dfrac{n!}{s^{n+1}}$		
$\dfrac{1}{\sqrt{\pi t}}$	$\dfrac{1}{\sqrt{s}}$		
t^a	$\dfrac{\Gamma(a+1)}{s^{a+1}}$		

Table of Integrals

ELEMENTARY FORMS

1. $\displaystyle\int u\,dv = uv - \int v\,du$

2. $\displaystyle\int u^n\,du = \frac{1}{n+1}u^{n+1} + C \quad \text{if } n \neq -1$

3. $\displaystyle\int \frac{du}{u} = \ln|u| + C$

4. $\displaystyle\int e^u\,du = e^u + C$

5. $\displaystyle\int a^u\,du = \frac{a^u}{\ln a} + C$

6. $\displaystyle\int \sin u\,du = -\cos u + C$

7. $\displaystyle\int \cos u\,du = \sin u + C$

8. $\displaystyle\int \sec^2 u\,du = \tan u + C$

9. $\displaystyle\int \csc^2 u\,du = -\cot u + C$

10. $\displaystyle\int \sec u \tan u\,du = \sec u + C$

11. $\displaystyle\int \csc u \cot u\,du = -\csc u + C$

12. $\displaystyle\int \tan u\,du = \ln|\sec u| + C$

13. $\displaystyle\int \cot u\,du = \ln|\sin u| + C$

14. $\displaystyle\int \sec u\,du = \ln|\sec u + \tan u| + C$

15. $\displaystyle\int \csc u\,du = \ln|\csc u - \cot u| + C$

16. $\displaystyle\int \frac{du}{\sqrt{a^2 - u^2}} = \sin^{-1}\frac{u}{a} + C$

17. $\displaystyle\int \frac{du}{a^2 + u^2} = \frac{1}{a}\tan^{-1}\frac{u}{a} + C$

18. $\displaystyle\int \frac{du}{a^2 - u^2} = \frac{1}{2a}\ln\left|\frac{u+a}{u-a}\right| + C$

TRIGONOMETRIC FORMS

19. $\displaystyle\int \sin^2 u\,du = \frac{1}{2}u - \frac{1}{4}\sin 2u + C$

20. $\displaystyle\int \cos^2 u\,du = \frac{1}{2}u + \frac{1}{4}\sin 2u + C$

21. $\displaystyle\int \tan^2 u\,du = \tan u - u + C$

22. $\displaystyle\int \cot^2 u\,du = -\cot u - u + C$

23. $\displaystyle\int \sin^3 u\,du = -\frac{1}{3}(2 + \sin^2 u)\cos u + C$

24. $\displaystyle\int \cos^3 u\,du = \frac{1}{3}(2 + \cos^2 u)\sin u + C$

25. $\displaystyle\int \tan^3 u\,du = \frac{1}{2}\tan^2 u + \ln|\cos u| + C$

26. $\displaystyle\int \cot^3 u\,du = -\frac{1}{2}\cot^2 u - \ln|\sin u| + C$

27. $\displaystyle\int \sec^3 u\,du = \frac{1}{2}\sec u \tan u + \frac{1}{2}\ln|\sec u + \tan u| + C$

28. $\displaystyle\int \csc^3 u\,du = -\frac{1}{2}\csc u \cot u + \frac{1}{2}\ln|\csc u - \cot u| + C$

29. $\displaystyle\int \sin au \sin bu\,du = \frac{\sin(a-b)u}{2(a-b)} - \frac{\sin(a+b)u}{2(a+b)} + C \quad \text{if } a^2 \neq b^2$

(Continued on Rear Endpaper)

CYLINDRICAL COORDINATES: $u = u(r, \theta, z)$, $\mathbf{v} = v_r\hat{\mathbf{e}}_r + v_\theta\hat{\mathbf{e}}_\theta + v_z\hat{\mathbf{e}}_z$

$$x = r\cos\theta, \quad y = r\sin\theta, \quad z = z$$

$$\mathbf{R} = r\hat{\mathbf{e}}_r + z\hat{\mathbf{e}}_z, \quad d\mathbf{R} = dr\hat{\mathbf{e}}_r + rd\theta\hat{\mathbf{e}}_\theta + dz\hat{\mathbf{e}}_z$$

$$dA = \begin{cases} r\,d\theta\,dz & \text{(constant-}r\text{ surface)} \\ dr\,dz & \text{(constant-}\theta\text{ surface)} \\ r\,dr\,d\theta & \text{(constant-}z\text{ surface)} \end{cases}, \qquad dV = r\,dr\,d\theta\,dz$$

$$\frac{d\hat{\mathbf{e}}_r}{d\theta} = \hat{\mathbf{e}}_\theta, \quad \frac{d\hat{\mathbf{e}}_\theta}{d\theta} = -\hat{\mathbf{e}}_r$$

$$\nabla u = \frac{\partial u}{\partial r}\hat{\mathbf{e}}_r + \frac{1}{r}\frac{\partial u}{\partial\theta}\hat{\mathbf{e}}_\theta + \frac{\partial u}{\partial z}\hat{\mathbf{e}}_z$$

$$\nabla^2 u = \frac{\partial^2 u}{\partial r^2} + \frac{1}{r}\frac{\partial u}{\partial r} + \frac{1}{r^2}\frac{\partial^2 u}{\partial\theta^2} + \frac{\partial^2 u}{\partial z^2}$$

$$\nabla\cdot\mathbf{v} = \frac{1}{r}\frac{\partial}{\partial r}(rv_r) + \frac{1}{r}\frac{\partial}{\partial\theta}v_\theta + \frac{\partial}{\partial z}v_z$$

$$\nabla\times\mathbf{v} = \left(\frac{1}{r}\frac{\partial v_z}{\partial\theta} - \frac{\partial v_\theta}{\partial z}\right)\hat{\mathbf{e}}_r + \left(\frac{\partial v_r}{\partial z} - \frac{\partial v_z}{\partial r}\right)\hat{\mathbf{e}}_\theta + \frac{1}{r}\left(\frac{\partial(rv_\theta)}{\partial r} - \frac{\partial v_r}{\partial\theta}\right)\hat{\mathbf{e}}_z$$

SPHERICAL COORDINATES: $u = u(\rho, \phi, \theta)$, $\mathbf{v} = v_\rho\hat{\mathbf{e}}_\rho + v_\phi\hat{\mathbf{e}}_\phi + v_\theta\hat{\mathbf{e}}_\theta$

$$x = \rho\sin\phi\cos\theta, \quad y = \rho\sin\phi\sin\theta, \quad z = \rho\cos\phi$$

$$\mathbf{R} = \rho\hat{\mathbf{e}}_\rho, \quad d\mathbf{R} = d\rho\hat{\mathbf{e}}_\rho + \rho d\phi\hat{\mathbf{e}}_\phi + \rho\sin\phi\,d\theta\hat{\mathbf{e}}_\theta$$

$$dA = \begin{cases} \rho^2|\sin\phi|\,d\phi\,d\theta & \text{(constant-}\rho\text{ surface)} \\ \rho|\sin\phi|\,d\rho\,d\theta & \text{(constant-}\phi\text{ surface)} \\ \rho d\rho\,d\phi & \text{(constant-}\theta\text{ surface)} \end{cases}, \qquad dV = \rho^2|\sin\phi|\,d\rho\,d\phi\,d\theta$$

$$\frac{\partial\hat{\mathbf{e}}_\rho}{\partial\rho} = 0, \qquad \frac{\partial\hat{\mathbf{e}}_\rho}{\partial\phi} = \hat{\mathbf{e}}_\phi, \qquad \frac{\partial\hat{\mathbf{e}}_\rho}{\partial\theta} = \sin\phi\,\hat{\mathbf{e}}_\theta,$$

$$\frac{\partial\hat{\mathbf{e}}_\phi}{\partial\rho} = 0, \qquad \frac{\partial\hat{\mathbf{e}}_\phi}{\partial\phi} = -\hat{\mathbf{e}}_\rho, \qquad \frac{\partial\hat{\mathbf{e}}_\phi}{\partial\theta} = \cos\phi\,\hat{\mathbf{e}}_\theta,$$

$$\frac{\partial\hat{\mathbf{e}}_\theta}{\partial\rho} = 0, \qquad \frac{\partial\hat{\mathbf{e}}_\theta}{\partial\phi} = 0, \qquad \frac{\partial\hat{\mathbf{e}}_\theta}{\partial\theta} = -\sin\phi\,\hat{\mathbf{e}}_\rho - \cos\phi\,\hat{\mathbf{e}}_\phi$$

$$\nabla u = \frac{\partial u}{\partial\rho}\hat{\mathbf{e}}_\rho + \frac{1}{\rho}\frac{\partial u}{\partial\phi}\hat{\mathbf{e}}_\phi + \frac{1}{\rho\sin\phi}\frac{\partial u}{\partial\theta}\hat{\mathbf{e}}_\theta$$

$$\nabla^2 u = \frac{1}{\rho^2}\left[\frac{\partial}{\partial\rho}\left(\rho^2\frac{\partial u}{\partial\rho}\right) + \frac{1}{\sin\phi}\frac{\partial}{\partial\phi}\left(\sin\phi\frac{\partial u}{\partial\phi}\right) + \frac{1}{\sin^2\phi}\frac{\partial^2 u}{\partial\theta^2}\right]$$

$$\nabla\cdot\mathbf{v} = \frac{1}{\rho^2}\frac{\partial}{\partial\rho}(\rho^2 v_\rho) + \frac{1}{\rho\sin\phi}\frac{\partial}{\partial\phi}(v_\phi\sin\phi) + \frac{1}{\rho\sin\phi}\frac{\partial v_\theta}{\partial\theta}$$

$$\nabla\times\mathbf{v} = \frac{1}{\rho\sin\phi}\left(\frac{\partial}{\partial\phi}(v_\theta\sin\phi) - \frac{\partial v_\phi}{\partial\theta}\right)\hat{\mathbf{e}}_\rho + \frac{1}{\rho}\left(\frac{1}{\sin\phi}\frac{\partial v_\rho}{\partial\theta} - \frac{\partial(\rho v_\theta)}{\partial\rho}\right)\hat{\mathbf{e}}_\phi + \frac{1}{\rho}\left(\frac{\partial(\rho v_\phi)}{\partial\rho} - \frac{\partial v_\rho}{\partial\phi}\right)\hat{\mathbf{e}}_\theta$$

Differential Equations & Linear Algebra

Custom Edition for California Polytechnic State University,
San Luis Obispo

Taken from:

Differential Equations & Linear Algebra, Second Edition
by C. Henry Edwards, David E. Penney

Differential Equations and Boundary Value Problems: Computing and Modeling,
Third Edition by C. Henry Edwards, David E. Penney

Advanced Engineering Mathematics, Second Edition
by Michael D. Greenberg

Taken from:

Differential Equations & Linear Algebra, Second Edition
by C. Henry Edwards, David E. Penney
Copyright © 2005, 2001 by Pearson Education, Inc.
Published by Prentice-Hall, Inc.
Upper Saddle River, New Jersey 07458

Differential Equations and Boundary Value Problems: Computing and Modeling, Third Edition
by C. Henry Edwards, David E. Penney
Copyright © 2004, 2000, 1996 by Pearson Education, Inc.
Published by Prentice-Hall, Inc.

Advanced Engineering Mathematics, Second Edition
by Michael D. Greenberg
Copyright © 1998, 1988 by Pearson Education, Inc.
Published by Prentice-Hall, Inc.

This special edition published in cooperation with Pearson Custom Publishing.

Printed in the United States of America

10 9 8 7 6

ISBN 0-536-26492-9

2006360686

MC

Please visit our web site at *www.pearsoncustom.com*

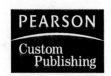

PEARSON CUSTOM PUBLISHING
75 Arlington Street, Suite 300, Boston, MA 02116
A Pearson Education Company

CONTENTS

UNIT A

DIFFERENTIAL EQUATIONS & LINEAR ALGEBRA

Second Edition

C. Henry Edwards

David E. Penney

CHAPTER 1

First-Order Differential Equations

1.1 Differential Equations and Mathematical Models

The laws of the universe are written in the language of mathematics. Algebra is sufficient to solve many static problems, but the most interesting natural phenomena involve change and are described by equations that relate changing quantities.

Because the derivative $dx/dt = f'(t)$ of the function f is the rate at which the quantity $x = f(t)$ is changing with respect to the independent variable t, it is natural that equations involving derivatives are frequently used to describe the changing universe. An equation relating an unknown function and one or more of its derivatives is called a **differential equation**.

Example 1   The differential equation

$$\frac{dx}{dt} = x^2 + t^2$$

involves both the unknown function $x(t)$ and its first derivative $x'(t) = dx/dt$. The differential equation

$$\frac{d^2y}{dx^2} + 3\frac{dy}{dx} + 7y = 0$$

involves the unknown function y of the independent variable x and the first two derivatives y' and y'' of y.   ∎

The study of differential equations has three principal goals:

1. To discover the differential equation that describes a specified physical situation.
2. To find—either exactly or approximately—the appropriate solution of that equation.
3. To interpret the solution that is found.

3

In algebra, we typically seek the unknown *numbers* that satisfy an equation such as $x^3 + 7x^2 - 11x + 41 = 0$. By contrast, in solving a differential equation, we are challenged to find the unknown *functions* $y = y(x)$ for which an identity such as $y'(x) = 2xy(x)$—that is, the differential equation

$$\frac{dy}{dx} = 2xy$$

—holds on some interval of real numbers. Ordinarily, we will want to find *all* solutions of the differential equation, if possible.

Example 2

If C is a constant and

$$y(x) = Ce^{x^2}, \tag{1}$$

then

$$\frac{dy}{dx} = C\left(2xe^{x^2}\right) = (2x)\left(Ce^{x^2}\right) = 2xy.$$

Thus every function $y(x)$ of the form in Eq. (1) *satisfies*—and thus is a solution of—the differential equation

$$\frac{dy}{dx} = 2xy \tag{2}$$

for all x. In particular, Eq. (1) defines an *infinite* family of different solutions of this differential equation, one for each choice of the arbitrary constant C. By the method of separation of variables (Section 1.4) it can be shown that every solution of the differential equation in (2) is of the form in Eq. (1). ∎

Differential Equations and Mathematical Models

The following three examples illustrate the process of translating scientific laws and principles into differential equations. In each of these examples the independent variable is time t, but we will see numerous examples in which some quantity other than time is the independent variable.

Example 3

Temperature A

Temperature T

FIGURE 1.1.1. Newton's law of cooling, Eq. (3), describes the cooling of a hot rock in water.

Newton's law of cooling may be stated in this way: The *time rate of change* (the rate of change with respect to time t) of the temperature $T(t)$ of a body is proportional to the difference between T and the temperature A of the surrounding medium (Fig. 1.1.1). That is,

$$\frac{dT}{dt} = -k(T - A), \tag{3}$$

where k is a positive constant. Observe that if $T > A$, then $dT/dt < 0$, so the temperature is a decreasing function of t and the body is cooling. But if $T < A$, then $dT/dt > 0$, so that T is increasing.

Thus the physical law is translated into a differential equation. If we are given the values of k and A, we should be able to find an explicit formula for $T(t)$, and then—with the aid of this formula—we can predict the future temperature of the body. ∎

Example 4

Torricelli's law implies that the *time rate of change* of the volume V of water in a draining tank (Fig. 1.1.2) is proportional to the square root of the depth y of water in the tank:

$$\frac{dV}{dt} = -k\sqrt{y}, \tag{4}$$

where k is a constant. If the tank is a cylinder with vertical sides and cross-sectional area A, then $V = Ay$, so $dV/dt = A \cdot (dy/dt)$. In this case Eq. (4) takes the form

$$\frac{dy}{dt} = -h\sqrt{y}, \tag{5}$$

where $h = k/A$ is a constant. ∎

Example 5	The *time rate of change* of a population $P(t)$ with constant birth and death rates is, in many simple cases, proportional to the size of the population. That is,

$$\frac{dP}{dt} = kP, \tag{6}$$

where k is the constant of proportionality. ∎

Let us discuss Example 5 further. Note first that each function of the form

$$P(t) = Ce^{kt} \tag{7}$$

is a solution of the differential equation

$$\frac{dP}{dt} = kP$$

in (6). We verify this assertion as follows:

$$P'(t) = Cke^{kt} = k\left(Ce^{kt}\right) = kP(t)$$

FIGURE 1.1.2. Torricelli's law of draining, Eq. (4), describes the draining of a water tank.

Volume V y

for all real numbers t. Because substitution of each function of the form given in (7) into Eq. (6) produces an identity, all such functions are solutions of Eq. (6).

Thus, even if the value of the constant k is known, the differential equation $dP/dt = kP$ has *infinitely many* different solutions of the form $P(t) = Ce^{kt}$, one for each choice of the "arbitrary" constant C. This is typical of differential equations. It is also fortunate, because it may allow us to use additional information to select from among all these solutions a particular one that fits the situation under study.

Example 6	Suppose that $P(t) = Ce^{kt}$ is the population of a colony of bacteria at time t, that the population at time $t = 0$ (hours, h) was 1000, and that the population doubled after 1 h. This additional information about $P(t)$ yields the following equations:

$$1000 = P(0) = Ce^0 = C,$$
$$2000 = P(1) = Ce^k.$$

It follows that $C = 1000$ and that $e^k = 2$, so $k = \ln 2 \approx 0.693147$. With this value of k the differential equation in (6) is

$$\frac{dP}{dt} = (\ln 2)P \approx (0.693147)P.$$

Substitution of $k = \ln 2$ and $C = 1000$ in Eq. (7) yields the particular solution

$$P(t) = 1000e^{(\ln 2)t} = 1000(e^{\ln 2})^t = 1000 \cdot 2^t \qquad \text{(because } e^{\ln 2} = 2\text{)}$$

that satisfies the given conditions. We can use this particular solution to predict future populations of the bacteria colony. For instance, the predicted number of bacteria in the population after one and a half hours (when $t = 1.5$) is

$$P(1.5) = 1000 \cdot 2^{3/2} \approx 2828. \qquad ∎$$

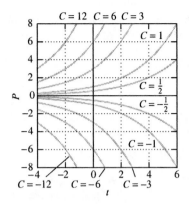

FIGURE 1.1.3. Graphs of $P(t) = Ce^{kt}$ with $k = \ln 2$.

The condition $P(0) = 1000$ in Example 6 is called an **initial condition** because we frequently write differential equations for which $t = 0$ is the "starting time." Figure 1.1.3 shows several different graphs of the form $P(t) = Ce^{kt}$ with $k = \ln 2$. The graphs of all the infinitely many solutions of $dP/dt = kP$ in fact fill the entire two-dimensional plane, and no two intersect. Moreover, the selection of any one point P_0 on the P-axis amounts to a determination of $P(0)$. Because exactly one solution passes through each such point, we see in this case that an initial condition $P(0) = P_0$ determines a unique solution agreeing with the given data.

Mathematical Models

Our brief discussion of population growth in Examples 5 and 6 illustrates the crucial process of *mathematical modeling* (Fig. 1.1.4), which involves the following:

1. The formulation of a real-world problem in mathematical terms; that is, the construction of a mathematical model.
2. The analysis or solution of the resulting mathematical problem.
3. The interpretation of the mathematical results in the context of the original real-world situation; for example, answering the question originally posed.

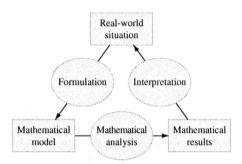

FIGURE 1.1.4. The process of mathematical modeling.

In the population example, the real-world problem is that of determining the population at some future time. A **mathematical model** consists of a list of variables (P and t) that describe the given situation, together with one or more equations relating these variables ($dP/dt = kP$, $P(0) = P_0$) that are known or are assumed to hold. The mathematical analysis consists of solving these equations (here, for P as a function of t). Finally, we apply these mathematical results to attempt to answer the original real-world question.

Nevertheless, it is possible that no one solution of the differential equation fits *all* the known information. In such a case we must suspect that the differential equation may not adequately describe the real world. For instance, the solutions of Eq. (6) are of the form $P(t) = Ce^{kt}$, where C is a positive constant, but for *no* choice of the constants k and C does $P(t)$ accurately describe the actual growth of the human population of the world over the past few centuries. We must therefore write a perhaps more complicated differential equation, one that takes into account the effects of population pressure on the birth rate, the declining food supply, and other factors. This should not be regarded as a failure of the model in Example 5, but as an insight into what additional factors must be considered in studying the growth of populations. Indeed, Eq. (6) is accurate under certain circumstances—for example, the growth of a bacterial population under conditions of unlimited food and space.

But in our population example we ignored the effects of such factors as varying birth and death rates. This made the mathematical analysis quite simple, perhaps unrealistically so. A satisfactory mathematical model is subject to two contradictory requirements: It must be sufficiently detailed to represent the real-world situation with relative accuracy, yet it must be sufficiently simple to make the mathematical analysis practical. If the model is so detailed that it fully represents the physical situation, then the mathematical analysis may be too difficult to carry out. If the model is too simple, the results may be so inaccurate as to be useless. Thus there is an inevitable tradeoff between what is physically realistic and what is mathematically possible. The construction of a model that adequately bridges this gap between realism and feasibility is therefore the most crucial and delicate step in the process. Ways must be found to simplify the model mathematically without sacrificing essential features of the real-world situation.

Mathematical models are discussed throughout this book. The remainder of this introductory section is devoted to simple examples and to standard terminology used in discussing differential equations and their solutions.

Examples and Terminology

Example 7

If C is a constant and $y(x) = 1/(C - x)$, then

$$\frac{dy}{dx} = \frac{1}{(C - x)^2} = y^2$$

if $x \neq C$. Thus

$$y(x) = \frac{1}{C - x} \tag{8}$$

defines a solution of the differential equation

$$\frac{dy}{dx} = y^2 \tag{9}$$

on any interval of real numbers not containing the point $x = C$. Actually, Eq. (8) defines a *one-parameter family* of solutions of $dy/dx = y^2$, one for each value of the arbitrary constant or "parameter" C. With $C = 1$ we get the particular solution

$$y(x) = \frac{1}{1 - x}$$

that satisfies the initial condition $y(0) = 1$. As indicated in Fig. 1.1.5, this solution is continuous on the interval $(-\infty, 1)$ but has a vertical asymptote at $x = 1$. ∎

Example 8

Verify that the function $y(x) = 2x^{1/2} - x^{1/2} \ln x$ satisfies the differential equation

$$4x^2 y'' + y = 0 \tag{10}$$

for all $x > 0$.

Solution

First we compute the derivatives

$$y'(x) = -\tfrac{1}{2} x^{-1/2} \ln x \quad \text{and} \quad y''(x) = \tfrac{1}{4} x^{-3/2} \ln x - \tfrac{1}{2} x^{-3/2}.$$

Then substitution into Eq. (10) yields

$$4x^2 y'' + y = 4x^2 \left(\tfrac{1}{4} x^{-3/2} \ln x - \tfrac{1}{2} x^{-3/2} \right) + 2x^{1/2} - x^{1/2} \ln x = 0$$

if x is positive, so the differential equation is satisfied for all $x > 0$. ∎

The fact that we can write a differential equation is not enough to guarantee that it has a solution. For example, it is clear that the differential equation

$$(y')^2 + y^2 = -1 \tag{11}$$

has *no* (real-valued) solution, because the sum of nonnegative numbers cannot be negative. For a variation on this theme, note that the equation

$$(y')^2 + y^2 = 0 \tag{12}$$

obviously has only the (real-valued) solution $y(x) \equiv 0$. In our previous examples any differential equation having at least one solution indeed had infinitely many.

The **order** of a differential equation is the order of the highest derivative that appears in it. The differential equation of Example 8 is of second order, those in Examples 2 through 7 are first-order equations, and

$$y^{(4)} + x^2 y^{(3)} + x^5 y = \sin x$$

is a fourth-order equation. The most general form of an ***nth*-order** differential equation with independent variable x and unknown function or dependent variable $y = y(x)$ is

$$F\left(x, y, y', y'', \ldots, y^{(n)}\right) = 0, \tag{13}$$

where F is a specific real-valued function of $n + 2$ variables.

Our use of the word *solution* has been until now somewhat informal. To be precise, we say that the continuous function $u = u(x)$ is a **solution** of the differential equation in (13) **on the interval** I provided that the derivatives u', u'', $\ldots$, $u^{(n)}$ exist on I and

$$F\left(x, u, u', u'', \ldots, u^{(n)}\right) = 0$$

for all x in I. For the sake of brevity, we may say that $u = u(x)$ **satisfies** the differential equation in (13) on I.

Remark: Recall from elementary calculus that a differentiable function on an open interval is necessarily continuous there. This is why only a continuous function can qualify as a (differentiable) solution of a differential equation on an interval. ∎

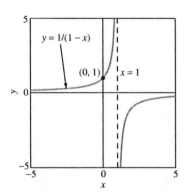

FIGURE 1.1.5. The solution of $y' = y^2$ defined by $y(x) = 1/(1-x)$.

Example 7
Continued

Figure 1.1.5 shows the two "connected" branches of the graph $y = 1/(1-x)$. The left-hand branch is the graph of a (continuous) solution of the differential equation $y' = y^2$ that is defined on the interval $(-\infty, 1)$. The right-hand branch is the graph of a *different* solution of the differential equation that is defined (and continuous) on the different interval $(1, \infty)$. So the single formula $y(x) = 1/(1-x)$ actually defines two different solutions (with different domains of definition) of the same differential equation $y' = y^2$. ∎

Example 9

If A and B are constants and

$$y(x) = A \cos 3x + B \sin 3x, \tag{14}$$

then two successive differentiations yield

$$y'(x) = -3A \sin 3x + 3B \cos 3x,$$
$$y''(x) = -9A \cos 3x - 9B \sin 3x = -9y(x)$$

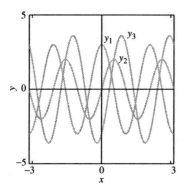

FIGURE 1.1.6. The three solutions $y_1(x) = 3\cos 3x$, $y_2(x) = 2\sin 3x$, and $y_3(x) = -3\cos 3x + 2\sin 3x$ of the differential equation $y'' + 9y = 0$.

for all x. Consequently, Eq. (14) defines what it is natural to call a *two-parameter family* of solutions of the second-order differential equation

$$y'' + 9y = 0 \tag{15}$$

on the whole real number line. Figure 1.1.6 shows the graphs of several such solutions. ∎

Although the differential equations in (11) and (12) are exceptions to the general rule, we will see that an nth-order differential equation ordinarily has an n-parameter family of solutions—one involving n different arbitrary constants or parameters.

In both Eqs. (11) and (12), the appearance of y' as an implicitly defined function causes complications. For this reason, we will ordinarily assume that any differential equation under study can be solved explicitly for the highest derivative that appears; that is, that the equation can be written in the so-called *normal form*

$$y^{(n)} = G\left(x, y, y', y'', \ldots, y^{(n-1)}\right), \tag{16}$$

where G is a real-valued function of $n + 1$ variables. In addition, we will always seek only real-valued solutions unless we warn the reader otherwise.

All the differential equations we have mentioned so far are **ordinary** differential equations, meaning that the unknown function (dependent variable) depends on only a *single* independent variable. If the dependent variable is a function of two or more independent variables, then partial derivatives are likely to be involved; if they are, the equation is called a **partial** differential equation. For example, the temperature $u = u(x, t)$ of a long thin uniform rod at the point x at time t satisfies (under appropriate simple conditions) the partial differential equation

$$\frac{\partial u}{\partial t} = k \frac{\partial^2 u}{\partial x^2},$$

where k is a constant (called the *thermal diffusivity* of the rod). In this book we will be concerned only with *ordinary* differential equations and will refer to them simply as differential equations.

In this chapter we concentrate on *first-order* differential equations of the form

$$\frac{dy}{dx} = f(x, y). \tag{17}$$

We also will sample the wide range of applications of such equations. A typical mathematical model of an applied situation will be an **initial value problem,** consisting of a differential equation of the form in (17) together with an **initial condition** $y(x_0) = y_0$. Note that we call $y(x_0) = y_0$ an initial condition whether or not $x_0 = 0$. To **solve** the initial value problem

$$\frac{dy}{dx} = f(x, y), \quad y(x_0) = y_0 \tag{18}$$

means to find a differentiable function $y = y(x)$ that satisfies both conditions in Eq. (18) on some interval containing x_0.

Example 10

Given the solution $y(x) = 1/(C - x)$ of the differential equation $dy/dx = y^2$ discussed in Example 7, solve the initial value problem

$$\frac{dy}{dx} = y^2, \quad y(1) = 2.$$

Solution   We need only find a value of C so that the solution $y(x) = 1/(C - x)$ satisfies the initial condition $y(1) = 2$. Substitution of the values $x = 1$ and $y = 2$ in the given solution yields

$$2 = y(1) = \frac{1}{C - 1},$$

so $2C - 2 = 1$, and hence $C = \frac{3}{2}$. With this value of C we obtain the desired solution

$$y(x) = \frac{1}{\frac{3}{2} - x} = \frac{2}{3 - 2x}.$$

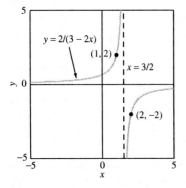

Figure 1.1.7 shows the two branches of the graph $y = 2/(3 - 2x)$. The left-hand branch is the graph on $(-\infty, \frac{3}{2})$ of the solution of the given initial value problem $y' = y^2$, $y(1) = 2$. The right-hand branch passes through the point $(2, -2)$ and is therefore the graph on $(\frac{3}{2}, \infty)$ of the solution of the different initial value problem $y' = y^2$, $y(2) = -2$. ∎

FIGURE 1.1.7. The solutions of $y' = y^2$ defined by $y(x) = 2/(3 - 2x)$.

The central question of greatest immediate interest to us is this: If we are given a differential equation known to have a solution satisfying a given initial condition, how do we actually *find* or *compute* that solution? And, once found, what can we do with it? We will see that a relatively few simple techniques—separation of variables (Section 1.4), solution of linear equations (Section 1.5), elementary substitution methods (Section 1.6)—are enough to enable us to solve a variety of first-order equations having impressive applications.

1.1 Problems

In Problems 1 through 12, verify by substitution that each given function is a solution of the given differential equation. Throughout these problems, primes denote derivatives with respect to x.

1. $y' = 3x^2$; $y = x^3 + 7$
2. $y' + 2y = 0$; $y = 3e^{-2x}$
3. $y'' + 4y = 0$; $y_1 = \cos 2x$ $y_2 = \sin 2x$
4. $y'' = 9y$; $y_1 = e^{3x}$, $y_2 = e^{-3x}$
5. $y' = y + 2e^{-x}$; $y = e^x - e^{-x}$
6. $y'' + 4y' + 4y = 0$; $y_1 = e^{-2x}$, $y_2 = xe^{-2x}$
7. $y'' - 2y' + 2y = 0$; $y_1 = e^x \cos x$, $y_2 = e^x \sin x$
8. $y'' + y = 3\cos 2x$, $y_1 = \cos x - \cos 2x$, $y_2 = \sin x - \cos 2x$
9. $y' + 2xy^2 = 0$; $y = \dfrac{1}{1 + x^2}$
10. $x^2 y'' + xy' - y = \ln x$; $y_1 = x - \ln x$, $y_2 = \dfrac{1}{x} - \ln x$
11. $x^2 y'' + 5xy' + 4y = 0$; $y_1 = \dfrac{1}{x^2}$, $y_2 = \dfrac{\ln x}{x^2}$
12. $x^2 y'' - xy' + 2y = 0$; $y_1 = x \cos(\ln x)$, $y_2 = x \sin(\ln x)$

In Problems 13 through 16, substitute $y = e^{rx}$ into the given differential equation to determine all values of the constant r for which $y = e^{rx}$ is a solution of the equation.

13. $3y' = 2y$
14. $4y'' = y$
15. $y'' + y' - 2y = 0$
16. $3y'' + 3y' - 4y = 0$

In Problems 17 through 26, first verify that $y(x)$ satisfies the given differential equation. Then determine a value of the constant C so that $y(x)$ satisfies the given initial condition. Use a computer or graphing calculator (if desired) to sketch several typical solutions of the given differential equation, and highlight the one that satisfies the given initial condition.

17. $y' + y = 0$; $y(x) = Ce^{-x}$, $y(0) = 2$
18. $y' = 2y$; $y(x) = Ce^{2x}$, $y(0) = 3$
19. $y' = y + 1$; $y(x) = Ce^x - 1$, $y(0) = 5$
20. $y' = x - y$; $y(x) = Ce^{-x} + x - 1$, $y(0) = 10$
21. $y' + 3x^2 y = 0$; $y(x) = Ce^{-x^3}$, $y(0) = 7$
22. $e^y y' = 1$; $y(x) = \ln(x + C)$, $y(0) = 0$
23. $x\dfrac{dy}{dx} + 3y = 2x^5$; $y(x) = \frac{1}{4}x^5 + Cx^{-3}$, $y(2) = 1$
24. $xy' - 3y = x^3$; $y(x) = x^3(C + \ln x)$, $y(1) = 17$
25. $y' = 3x^2(y^2 + 1)$; $y(x) = \tan(x^3 + C)$, $y(0) = 1$
26. $y' + y \tan x = \cos x$; $y(x) = (x + C)\cos x$, $y(\pi) = 0$

In Problems 27 through 31, a function $y = g(x)$ is described by some geometric property of its graph. Write a differential equation of the form $dy/dx = f(x, y)$ having the function g as its solution (or as one of its solutions).

27. The slope of the graph of g at the point (x, y) is the sum of x and y.
28. The line tangent to the graph of g at the point (x, y) intersects the x-axis at the point $(x/2, 0)$.

29. Every straight line normal to the graph of g passes through the point $(0, 1)$.

30. The graph of g is normal to every curve of the form $y = x^2 + k$ (k is a constant) where they meet.

31. The line tangent to the graph of g at (x, y) passes through the point $(-y, x)$.

In Problems 32 through 36, write—in the manner of Eqs. (3) through (6) of this section—a differential equation that is a mathematical model of the situation described.

32. The time rate of change of a population P is proportional to the square root of P.

33. The time rate of change of the velocity v of a coasting motorboat is proportional to the square of v.

34. The acceleration dv/dt of a Lamborghini is proportional to the difference between 250 km/h and the velocity of the car.

35. In a city having a fixed population of P persons, the time rate of change of the number N of those persons who have heard a certain rumor is proportional to the number of those who have not yet heard the rumor.

36. In a city with a fixed population of P persons, the time rate of change of the number N of those persons infected with a certain contagious disease is proportional to the product of the number who have the disease and the number who do not.

In Problems 37 through 42, determine by inspection at least one solution of the given differential equation. That is, use your knowledge of derivatives to make an intelligent guess. Then test your hypothesis.

37. $y'' = 0$ **38.** $y' = y$

39. $xy' + y = 3x^2$ **40.** $(y')^2 + y^2 = 1$

41. $y' + y = e^x$ **42.** $y'' + y = 0$

43. (a) If k is a constant, show that a general (1-parameter) solution of the differential equation

$$\frac{dx}{dt} = kx^2$$

is given by $x(t) = 1/(C - kt)$ where C is an arbitrary constant.

(b) Determine by inspection a solution of the initial value problem $x' = kx^2$, $x(0) = 0$.

44. (a) Continuing Problem 43, assume that k is positive, and then sketch graphs of solutions of $x' = kx^2$ with several typical positive values of $x(0)$.

(b) How would these solutions differ if the constant k were negative?

45. Suppose a population P of rodents satisfies the differential equation $dP/dt = kP^2$. Initially, there are $P(0) = 2$ rodents, and their number is increasing at the rate of $dP/dt = 1$ rodent per month when there are $P = 10$ rodents. How long will it take for this population to grow to a hundred rodents? To a thousand? What's happening here?

46. Suppose the velocity v of a motorboat coasting in water satisfies the differential equation $dv/dt = kv^2$. The initial speed of the motorboat is $v(0) = 10$ meters per second (m/s), and v is decreasing at the rate of 1 m/s² when $v = 5$ m/s. How long does it take for the velocity of the boat to decrease to 1 m/s? To $\frac{1}{10}$ m/s? When does the boat come to a stop?

47. In Example 7 we saw that $y(x) = 1/(C - x)$ defines a one-parameter family of solutions of the differential equation $dy/dx = y^2$. **(a)** Determine a value of C so that $y(10) = 10$. **(b)** Is there a value of C such that $y(0) = 0$? Can you nevertheless find by inspection a solution of $dy/dx = y^2$ such that $y(0) = 0$? **(c)** Figure 1.1.8 shows typical graphs of solutions of the form $y(x) = 1/(C - x)$. Does it appear that these solution curves fill the entire xy-plane? Can you conclude that, given any point (a, b) in the plane, the differential equation $dy/dx = y^2$ has exactly one solution $y(x)$ satisfying the condition $y(a) = b$?

48. (a) Show that $y(x) = Cx^4$ defines a one-parameter family of differentiable solutions of the differential equation $xy' = 4y$ (Fig. 1.1.9). **(b)** Show that

$$y(x) = \begin{cases} -x^4 & \text{if } x < 0, \\ x^4 & \text{if } x \geq 0 \end{cases}$$

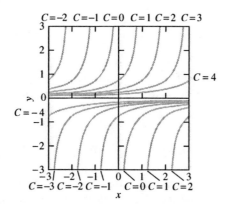

FIGURE 1.1.8. Graphs of solutions of the equation $dy/dx = y^2$.

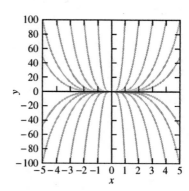

FIGURE 1.1.9. The graph $y = Cx^4$ for various values of C.

defines a differentiable solution of $xy' = 4y$ for all x, but is not of the form $y(x) = Cx^4$. **(c)** Given any two real numbers a and b, explain why—in contrast to the situation in part (c) of Problem 47—there exist infinitely many differentiable solutions of $xy' = 4y$ that all satisfy the condition $y(a) = b$.

1.2 Integrals as General and Particular Solutions

The first-order equation $dy/dx = f(x, y)$ takes an especially simple form if the function f is independent of the dependent variable y:

$$\frac{dy}{dx} = f(x). \tag{1}$$

In this special case we need only integrate both sides of Eq. (1) to obtain

$$y(x) = \int f(x)\, dx + C. \tag{2}$$

This is a **general solution** of Eq. (1), meaning that it involves an arbitrary constant C, and for every choice of C it is a solution of the differential equation in (1). If $G(x)$ is a particular antiderivative of f—that is, if $G'(x) \equiv f(x)$—then

$$y(x) = G(x) + C. \tag{3}$$

The graphs of any two such solutions $y_1(x) = G(x) + C_1$ and $y_2(x) = G(x) + C_2$ on the same interval I are "parallel" in the sense illustrated by Figs. 1.2.1 and 1.2.2. There we see that the constant C is geometrically the vertical distance between the two curves $y(x) = G(x)$ and $y(x) = G(x) + C$.

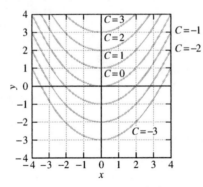

FIGURE 1.2.1. Graphs of $y = \frac{1}{4}x^2 + C$ for various values of C.

FIGURE 1.2.2. Graphs of $y = \sin x + C$ for various values of C.

To satisfy an initial condition $y(x_0) = y_0$, we need only substitute $x = x_0$ and $y = y_0$ into Eq. (3) to obtain $y_0 = G(x_0) + C$, so that $C = y_0 - G(x_0)$. With this choice of C, we obtain the **particular solution** of Eq. (1) satisfying the initial value problem

$$\frac{dy}{dx} = f(x), \quad y(x_0) = y_0.$$

We will see that this is the typical pattern for solutions of first-order differential equations. Ordinarily, we will first find a *general solution* involving an arbitrary constant C. We can then attempt to obtain, by appropriate choice of C, a *particular solution* satisfying a given initial condition $y(x_0) = y_0$.

Remark: As the term is used in the previous paragraph, a *general solution* of a first-order differential equation is simply a one-parameter family of solutions. A natural question is whether a given general solution contains *every* particular solution of the differential equation. When this is known to be true, we call it **the** general solution of the differential equation. For example, because any two antiderivatives of the same function $f(x)$ can differ only by a constant, it follows that every solution of Eq. (1) is of the form in (2). Thus Eq. (2) serves to define **the** general solution of (1). ∎

| **Example 1** | Solve the initial value problem |

$$\frac{dy}{dx} = 2x + 3, \quad y(1) = 2.$$

Solution   Integration of both sides of the differential equation as in Eq. (2) immediately yields the general solution

$$y(x) = \int (2x + 3)\, dx = x^2 + 3x + C.$$

Figure 1.2.3 shows the graph $y = x^2 + 3x + C$ for various values of C. The particular solution we seek corresponds to the curve that passes through the point $(1, 2)$, thereby satisfying the initial condition

$$y(1) = (1)^2 + 3 \cdot (1) + C = 2.$$

It follows that $C = -2$, so the desired particular solution is

$$y(x) = x^2 + 3x - 2. \qquad ∎$$

FIGURE 1.2.3. Solution curves for the differential equation in Example 1.

Second-order Equations. The observation that the special first-order equation $dy/dx = f(x)$ is readily solvable (provided that an antiderivative of f can be found) extends to second-order differential equations of the special form

$$\frac{d^2y}{dx^2} = g(x), \tag{4}$$

in which the function g on the right-hand side involves neither the dependent variable y nor its derivative dy/dx. We simply integrate once to obtain

$$\frac{dy}{dx} = \int y''(x)\, dx = \int g(x)\, dx = G(x) + C_1,$$

where G is an antiderivative of g and C_1 is an arbitrary constant. Then another integration yields

$$y(x) = \int y'(x)\, dx = \int [G(x) + C_1]\, dx = \int G(x)\, dx + C_1 x + C_2.$$

where C_2 is a second arbitrary constant. In effect, the second-order differential equation in (4) is one that can be solved by solving successively the *first-order* equations

$$\frac{dv}{dx} = g(x) \quad \text{and} \quad \frac{dy}{dx} = v(x).$$

Velocity and Acceleration

Direct integration is sufficient to allow us to solve a number of important problems concerning the motion of a particle (or *mass point*) in terms of the forces acting on it. The motion of a particle along a straight line (the x-axis) is described by its **position function**

$$x = f(t) \tag{5}$$

giving its x-coordinate at time t. The **velocity** of the particle is defined to be

➤ $$v(t) = f'(t); \quad \text{that is,} \quad v = \frac{dx}{dt}. \tag{6}$$

Its **acceleration** $a(t)$ is $a(t) = v'(t) = x''(t)$; in Leibniz notation,

➤ $$a = \frac{dv}{dt} = \frac{d^2x}{dt^2}. \tag{7}$$

Newton's *second law of motion* says that if a force $F(t)$ acts on the particle and is directed along its line of motion, then

$$ma(t) = F(t); \quad \text{that is,} \quad F = ma, \tag{8}$$

where m is the mass of the particle. If the force F is known, then the equation $x''(t) = F(t)/m$ can be integrated twice to find the position function $x(t)$ in terms of two constants of integration. These two arbitrary constants are frequently determined by the **initial position** $x_0 = x(0)$ and the **initial velocity** $v_0 = v(0)$ of the particle.

Constant Acceleration. For instance, suppose that the force F, and therefore the acceleration $a = F/m$, are *constant*. Then we begin with the equation

$$\frac{dv}{dt} = a \quad (a \text{ is a constant}) \tag{9}$$

and integrate both sides to obtain

$$v(t) = \int a \, dt = at + C_1.$$

We know that $v = v_0$ when $t = 0$, and substitution of this information into the preceding equation yields the fact that $C_1 = v_0$. So

$$v(t) = \frac{dx}{dt} = at + v_0. \tag{10}$$

A second integration gives

$$x(t) = \int v(t) \, dt = \int (at + v_0) \, dt = \tfrac{1}{2}at^2 + v_0 t + C_2,$$

and the substitution $t = 0$, $x = x_0$ gives $C_2 = x_0$. Therefore,

$$x(t) = \tfrac{1}{2}at^2 + v_0 t + x_0. \tag{11}$$

Thus, with Eq. (10) we can find the velocity, and with Eq. (11) the position, of the particle at any time t in terms of its *constant* acceleration a, its initial velocity v_0, and its initial position x_0.

Example 2   A lunar lander is falling freely toward the surface of the moon at a speed of 450 meters per second (m/s). Its retrorockets, when fired, provide a constant deceleration of 2.5 meters per second per second (m/s^2) (the gravitational acceleration produced by the moon is assumed to be included in the given deceleration). At what height above the lunar surface should the retrorockets be activated to ensure a "soft touchdown" ($v = 0$ at impact)?

Solution   We denote by $x(t)$ the height of the lunar lander above the surface, as indicated in Fig. 1.2.4. We let $t = 0$ denote the time at which the retrorockets should be fired. Then $v_0 = -450$ [m/s, negative because the height $x(t)$ is decreasing], and $a = +2.5$ because an upward thrust increases the velocity v (although it decreases the *speed* $|v|$). Then Eqs. (10) and (11) become

$$v(t) = 2.5t - 450 \tag{12}$$

and

$$x(t) = 1.25t^2 - 450t + x_0, \tag{13}$$

FIGURE 1.2.4. The lunar lander of Example 2.

where x_0 is the height of the lander above the lunar surface at the time $t = 0$ when the retrorockets should be activated.

From Eq. (12) we see that $v = 0$ (soft touchdown) occurs when $t = 450/2.5 = 180$ s (that is, 3 minutes); then substitution of $t = 180$, $x = 0$ into Eq. (13) yields

$$x_0 = 0 - (1.25)(180)^2 + 450(180) = 40,500$$

meters, that is, $x_0 = 40.5$ km $\approx 25\frac{1}{6}$ miles. Thus the retrorockets should be activated when the lunar lander is 40.5 kilometers above the surface of the moon, and it will touch down softly on the lunar surface after 3 minutes of decelerating descent. ∎

Physical Units

Numerical work requires units for the measurement of physical quantities such as distance and time. We sometimes use ad hoc units—such as distance in miles or kilometers and time in hours—in special situations (such as in a problem involving an auto trip). However, the foot-pound-second (fps) and meter-kilogram-second (mks) unit systems are used more generally in scientific and engineering problems. In fact, fps units are commonly used only in the United States (and a few other countries), while mks units constitute the standard international system of scientific units.

	fps units	mks units
Force	pound (lb)	newton (N)
Mass	slug	kilogram (kg)
Distance	foot (ft)	meter (m)
Time	second (s)	second (s)
g	32 ft/s^2	9.8 m/s^2

The last line of this table gives values for the gravitational acceleration g at the surface of the earth. Although these approximate values will suffice for most examples and problems, more precise values are 9.7805 m/s^2 and 32.088 ft/s^2 (at sea level at the equator).

Both systems are compatible with Newton's second law $F = ma$. Thus 1 N is (by definition) the force required to impart an acceleration of 1 m/s^2 to a mass of 1 kg. Similarly, 1 slug is (by definition) the mass that experiences an acceleration of 1 ft/s^2 under a force of 1 lb. (We will use mks units in all problems requiring mass units, and thus will rarely need slugs to measure mass.)

Inches and centimeters (as well as miles and kilometers) also are commonly used in describing distances. For conversions between fps and mks units it helps to remember that

$$1 \text{ in.} = 2.54 \text{ cm (exactly)} \quad \text{and} \quad 1 \text{ lb} \approx 4.448 \text{ N.}$$

For instance,

$$1 \text{ ft} = 12 \text{ in.} \times 2.54 \frac{\text{cm}}{\text{in.}} = 30.48 \text{ cm,}$$

and it follows that

$$1 \text{ mi} = 5280 \text{ ft} \times 30.48 \frac{\text{cm}}{\text{ft}} = 160934.4 \text{ cm} \approx 1.609 \text{ km.}$$

Thus a posted U.S. speed limit of 50 mi/h means that—in international terms—the legal speed limit is about $50 \times 1.609 \approx 80.45$ km/h.

Vertical Motion with Gravitational Acceleration

The **weight** W of a body is the force exerted on the body by gravity. Substitution of $a = g$ and $F = W$ in Newton's second law $F = ma$ gives

$$W = mg \tag{14}$$

for the weight W of the mass m at the surface of the earth (where $g \approx 32$ ft/s$^2 \approx 9.8$ m/s^2). For instance, a mass of $m = 20$ kg has a weight of $W = (20 \text{ kg})(9.8 \text{ m/s}^2) = 196$ N. Similarly, a mass m weighing 100 pounds has mks weight

$$W = (100 \text{ lb})(4.448 \text{ N/lb}) = 444.8 \text{ N,}$$

so its mass is

$$m = \frac{W}{g} = \frac{444.8 \text{ N}}{9.8 \text{ m/s}^2} \approx 45.4 \text{ kg.}$$

To discuss vertical motion it is natural to choose the y-axis as the coordinate system for position, frequently with $y = 0$ corresponding to "ground level." If we choose the *upward* direction as the positive direction, then the effect of gravity on a vertically moving body is to decrease its height and also to decrease its velocity $v = dy/dt$. Consequently, if we ignore air resistance, then the acceleration $a = dv/dt$ of the body is given by

$$\frac{dv}{dt} = -g. \tag{15}$$

This acceleration equation provides a starting point in many problems involving vertical motion. Successive integrations [as in Eqs. (10) and (11)] yield the velocity and height formulas

$$v(t) = -gt + v_0 \tag{16}$$

and

$$y(t) = -\tfrac{1}{2}gt^2 + v_0 t + y_0. \tag{17}$$

Here, y_0 denotes the initial ($t = 0$) height of the body and v_0 its initial velocity.

Example 3

(a) Suppose that a ball is thrown straight upward from the ground ($y_0 = 0$) with initial velocity $v_0 = 96$ (ft/s, so we use $g = 32$ ft/s^2 in fps units). Then it reaches its maximum height when its velocity [Eq. (16)] is zero,

$$v(t) = -32t + 96 = 0,$$

and thus when $t = 3$ s. Hence the maximum height that the ball attains is

$$y(3) = -\tfrac{1}{2} \cdot 32 \cdot 3^2 + 96 \cdot 3 + 0 = 144 \text{ (ft)}$$

[with the aid of Eq. (17)].

(b) If an arrow is shot straight upward from the ground with initial velocity $v_0 = 49$ (m/s, so we use $g = 9.8$ m/s^2 in mks units), then it returns to the ground when

$$y(t) = -\tfrac{1}{2} \cdot (9.8)t^2 + 49t = (4.9)t(-t + 10) = 0,$$

and thus after 10 s in the air. ∎

A Swimmer's Problem

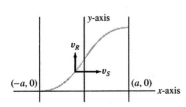

FIGURE 1.2.5. A swimmer's problem (Example 4).

Figure 1.2.5 shows a northward-flowing river of width $w = 2a$. The lines $x = \pm a$ represent the banks of the river and the y-axis its center. Suppose that the velocity v_R at which the water flows increases as one approaches the center of the river, and indeed is given in terms of distance x from the center by

$$v_R = v_0 \left(1 - \frac{x^2}{a^2} \right). \tag{18}$$

You can use Eq. (18) to verify that the water does flow the fastest at the center, where $v_R = v_0$, and that $v_R = 0$ at each riverbank.

Suppose that a swimmer starts at the point $(-a, 0)$ on the west bank and swims due east (relative to the water) with constant speed v_S. As indicated in Fig. 1.2.5, his velocity vector (relative to the ground) has horizontal component v_S and vertical component v_R. Hence the swimmer's direction angle α is given by

$$\tan \alpha = \frac{v_R}{v_S}.$$

Because $\tan \alpha = dy/dx$, substitution using (18) gives the differential equation

$$\frac{dy}{dx} = \frac{v_0}{v_S} \left(1 - \frac{x^2}{a^2} \right) \tag{19}$$

for the swimmer's trajectory $y = y(x)$ as he crosses the river.

Example 4

Suppose that the river is 1 mile wide and that its midstream velocity is $v_0 = 9$ mi/h. If the swimmer's velocity is $v_S = 3$ mi/h, then Eq. (19) takes the form

$$\frac{dy}{dx} = 3(1 - 4x^2).$$

Integration yields

$$y(x) = \int (3 - 12x^2)\, dx = 3x - 4x^3 + C$$

for the swimmer's trajectory. The initial condition $y\left(-\frac{1}{2}\right) = 0$ yields $C = 1$, so

$$y(x) = 3x - 4x^3 + 1.$$

Then

$$y\left(\tfrac{1}{2}\right) = 3\left(\tfrac{1}{2}\right) - 4\left(\tfrac{1}{2}\right)^3 + 1 = 2,$$

so the swimmer drifts 2 miles downstream while he swims 1 mile across the river. ■

1.2 Problems

In Problems 1 through 10, find a function $y = f(x)$ satisfying the given differential equation and the prescribed initial condition.

1. $\dfrac{dy}{dx} = 2x + 1;\ y(0) = 3$

2. $\dfrac{dy}{dx} = (x - 2)^2;\ y(2) = 1$

3. $\dfrac{dy}{dx} = \sqrt{x};\ y(4) = 0$

4. $\dfrac{dy}{dx} = \dfrac{1}{x^2};\ y(1) = 5$

5. $\dfrac{dy}{dx} = \dfrac{1}{\sqrt{x + 2}};\ y(2) = -1$

6. $\dfrac{dy}{dx} = x\sqrt{x^2 + 9};\ y(-4) = 0$

7. $\dfrac{dy}{dx} = \dfrac{10}{x^2 + 1};\ y(0) = 0$

8. $\dfrac{dy}{dx} = \cos 2x;\ y(0) = 1$

9. $\dfrac{dy}{dx} = \dfrac{1}{\sqrt{1 - x^2}};\ y(0) = 0$

10. $\dfrac{dy}{dx} = xe^{-x};\ y(0) = 1$

In Problems 11 through 18, find the position function $x(t)$ of a moving particle with the given acceleration $a(t)$, initial position $x_0 = x(0)$, and initial velocity $v_0 = v(0)$.

11. $a(t) = 50,\ v_0 = 10,\ x_0 = 20$
12. $a(t) = -20,\ v_0 = -15,\ x_0 = 5$
13. $a(t) = 3t,\ v_0 = 5,\ x_0 = 0$
14. $a(t) = 2t + 1,\ v_0 = -7,\ x_0 = 4$
15. $a(t) = 4(t + 3)^2,\ v_0 = -1,\ x_0 = 1$
16. $a(t) = \dfrac{1}{\sqrt{t + 4}},\ v_0 = -1,\ x_0 = 1$
17. $a(t) = \dfrac{1}{(t + 1)^3},\ v_0 = 0,\ x_0 = 0$
18. $a(t) = 50 \sin 5t,\ v_0 = -10,\ x_0 = 8$

In Problems 19 through 22, a particle starts at the origin and travels along the x-axis with the velocity function $v(t)$ whose graph is shown in Figs. 1.2.6 through 1.2.9. Sketch the graph of the resulting position function $x(t)$ for $0 \le t \le 10$.

19.
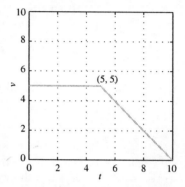

FIGURE 1.2.6. Graph of the velocity function $v(t)$ of Problem 19.

20.
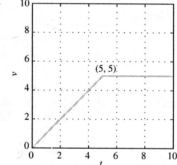

FIGURE 1.2.7. Graph of the velocity function $v(t)$ of Problem 20.

21.
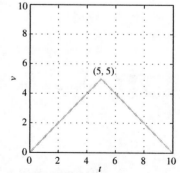

FIGURE 1.2.8. Graph of the velocity function $v(t)$ of Problem 21.

22.

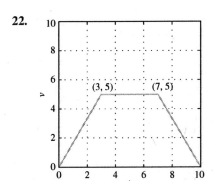

FIGURE 1.2.9. Graph of the velocity function $v(t)$ of Problem 22.

23. What is the maximum height attained by the arrow of part (b) of Example 3?

24. A ball is dropped from the top of a building 400 ft high. How long does it take to reach the ground? With what speed does the ball strike the ground?

25. The brakes of a car are applied when it is moving at 100 km/h and provide a constant deceleration of 10 meters per second per second (m/s²). How far does the car travel before coming to a stop?

26. A projectile is fired straight upward with an initial velocity of 100 m/s from the top of a building 20 m high and falls to the ground at the base of the building. Find (a) its maximum height above the ground; (b) when it passes the top of the building; (c) its total time in the air.

27. A ball is thrown straight downward from the top of a tall building. The initial speed of the ball is 10 m/s. It strikes the ground with a speed of 60 m/s. How tall is the building?

28. A baseball is thrown straight downward with an initial speed of 40 ft/s from the top of the Washington Monument (555 ft high). How long does it take to reach the ground, and with what speed does the baseball strike the ground?

29. A diesel car gradually speeds up so that for the first 10 s its acceleration is given by

$$\frac{dv}{dt} = (0.12)t^2 + (0.6)t \quad (\text{ft/s}^2).$$

If the car starts from rest ($x_0 = 0$, $v_0 = 0$), find the distance it has traveled at the end of the first 10 s and its velocity at that time.

30. A car traveling at 60 mi/h (88 ft/s) skids 176 ft after its brakes are suddenly applied. Under the assumption that the braking system provides constant deceleration, what is that deceleration? For how long does the skid continue?

31. The skid marks made by an automobile indicated that its brakes were fully applied for a distance of 75 m before it came to a stop. The car in question is known to have a constant deceleration of 20 m/s² under these conditions. How fast—in km/h—was the car traveling when the brakes were first applied?

32. Suppose that a car skids 15 m if it is moving at 50 km/h when the brakes are applied. Assuming that the car has the same constant deceleration, how far will it skid if it is moving at 100 km/h when the brakes are applied?

33. On the planet Gzyx, a ball dropped from a height of 20 ft hits the ground in 2 s. If a ball is dropped from the top of a 200-ft-tall building on Gzyx, how long will it take to hit the ground? With what speed will it hit?

34. A person can throw a ball straight upward from the surface of the earth to a maximum height of 144 ft. How high could this person throw the ball on the planet Gzyx of Problem 29?

35. A stone is dropped from rest at an initial height h above the surface of the earth. Show that the speed with which it strikes the ground is $v = \sqrt{2gh}$.

36. If a woman has enough "spring" in her legs to jump vertically to a height of 2.25 ft on the earth, how high could she jump on the moon, where the surface gravitational acceleration is (approximately) 5.3 ft/s²?

37. At noon a car starts from rest at point A and proceeds at constant acceleration along a straight road toward point B. If the car reaches B at 12:50 P.M. with a velocity of 60 mi/h, what is the distance from A to B?

38. At noon a car starts from rest at point A and proceeds with constant acceleration along a straight road toward point C, 35 miles away. If the constantly accelerated car arrives at C with a velocity of 60 mi/h, at what time does it arrive at C?

39. If $a = 0.5$ mi and $v_0 = 9$ mi/h as in Example 4, what must the swimmer's speed v_S be in order that he drifts only 1 mile downstream as he crosses the river?

40. Suppose that $a = 0.5$ mi, $v_0 = 9$ mi/h, and $v_S = 3$ mi/h as in Example 4, but that the velocity of the river is given by the fourth-degree function

$$v_R = v_0 \left(1 - \frac{x^4}{a^4} \right)$$

rather than the quadratic function in Eq. (18). Now find how far downstream the swimmer drifts as he crosses the river.

41. A bomb is dropped from a helicopter hovering at an altitude of 800 feet above the ground. From the ground directly beneath the helicopter, a projectile is fired straight upward toward the bomb, exactly 2 seconds after the bomb is released. With what initial velocity should the projectile be fired, in order to hit the bomb at an altitude of exactly 400 feet?

42. A spacecraft is in free fall toward the surface of the moon at a speed of 1000 mph (mi/h). Its retrorockets, when fired provide a constant deceleration of 20,000 mi/h². At what height above the lunar surface should the astronauts fire the retrorockets to insure a soft touchdown? (As in Example 2, ignore the moon's gravitational field.)

43. Arthur Clarke's *The Wind from the Sun* (1963) describes Diana, a spacecraft propelled by the solar wind. Its aluminized sail provides it with a constant acceleration of $0.001g = 0.0098$ m/s². Suppose this spacecraft starts from rest at time $t = 0$ and simultaneously fires a projectile (straight ahead in the same direction) that travels at one-tenth of the speed $c = 3 \times 10^8$ m/s of light. How long will it take the spacecraft to catch up with the projectile, and how far will it have traveled by then?

44. A driver involved in an accident claims he was going only 25 mph. When police tested his car, they found that when its brakes were applied at 25 mph, the car skidded only 45 feet before coming to a stop. But the driver's skid marks at the accident scene measured 210 feet. Assuming the same (constant) deceleration, determine the speed he was actually traveling just prior to the accident.

1.3 Slope Fields and Solution Curves

Consider a differential equation of the form

$$\frac{dy}{dx} = f(x, y) \tag{1}$$

where the right-hand function $f(x, y)$ involves both the independent variable x and the dependent variable y. We might think of integrating both sides in (1) with respect to x, and hence write $y(x) = \int f(x, y(x))\, dx + C$. However, this approach does not lead to a solution of the differential equation, because the indicated integral involves the *unknown* function $y(x)$ itself, and therefore cannot be evaluated explicitly. Actually, there exists *no* straightforward procedure by which a general differential equation can be solved explicitly. Indeed, the solutions of such a simple-looking differential equation as $y' = x^2 + y^2$ cannot be expressed in terms of the ordinary elementary functions studied in calculus textbooks. Nevertheless, the graphical and numerical methods of this and later sections can be used to construct *approximate* solutions of differential equations that suffice for many practical purposes.

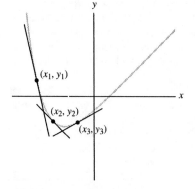

FIGURE 1.3.1. A solution curve for the differential equation $y' = x - y$ together with tangent lines having

- slope $m_1 = x_1 - y_1$ at the point (x_1, y_1);
- slope $m_2 = x_2 - y_2$ at the point (x_2, y_2); and
- slope $m_3 = x_3 - y_3$ at the point (x_3, y_3).

Slope Fields and Graphical Solutions

There is a simple geometric way to think about solutions of a given differential equation $y' = f(x, y)$. At each point (x, y) of the xy-plane, the value of $f(x, y)$ determines a slope $m = f(x, y)$. A solution of the differential equation is simply a differentiable function whose graph $y = y(x)$ has this "correct slope" at each point $(x, y(x))$ through which it passes—that is, $y'(x) = f(x, y(x))$. Thus a **solution curve** of the differential equation $y' = f(x, y)$—the graph of a solution of the equation—is simply a curve in the xy-plane whose tangent line at each point (x, y) has slope $m = f(x, y)$. For instance, Fig. 1.3.1 shows a solution curve of the differential equation $y' = x - y$ together with its tangent lines at three typical points.

This geometric viewpoint suggests a *graphical method* for constructing *approximate* solutions of the differential equation $y' = f(x, y)$. Through each of a representative collection of points (x, y) in the plane we draw a short line segment having the proper slope $m = f(x, y)$. All these line segments constitute a **slope field** (or a **direction field**) for the equation $y' = f(x, y)$.

Example 1   Figures 1.3.2(a)–(d) show slope fields and solution curves for the differential equation

$$\frac{dy}{dx} = ky \tag{2}$$

with the values $k = 2$, 0.5, -1, and -3 of the parameter k in Eq. (2). Note that each slope field yields important qualitative information about the set of all solutions of the differential equation. For instance, Figs. 1.3.2(a) and (b) suggest that each solution $y(x)$ approaches $\pm\infty$ as $x \to +\infty$ if $k > 0$, whereas Figs. 1.3.2(c) and

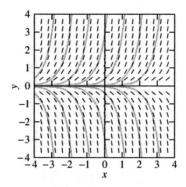

FIGURE 1.3.2(a). Slope field and solution curves for $y' = 2y$.

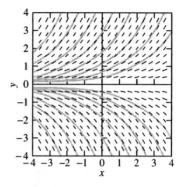

FIGURE 1.3.2(b). Slope field and solution curves for $y' = (0.5)y$.

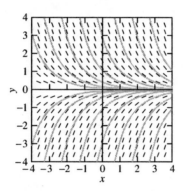

FIGURE 1.3.2(c). Slope field and solution curves for $y' = -y$.

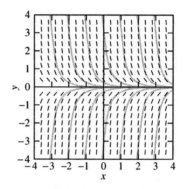

FIGURE 1.3.2(d). Slope field and solution curves for $y' = -3y$.

(d) suggest that $y(x) \to 0$ as $x \to +\infty$ if $k < 0$. Moreover, although the sign of k determines the *direction* of increase or decrease of $y(x)$, its absolute value $|k|$ appears to determine the rate of change of $y(x)$. All this is apparent from slope fields like those in Fig. 1.3.2 even without knowing that the general solution of Eq. (2) is given explicitly by $y(x) = Ce^{kx}$. ∎

A slope field suggests visually the general shapes of solution curves of the differential equation. Through each point a solution curve should proceed in such a direction that its tangent line is nearly parallel to the nearby line segments of the slope field. Starting at any initial point (a, b), we can attempt to sketch freehand an approximate solution curve that threads its way through the slope field, following the visible line segments as closely as possible.

Example 2

Construct a slope field for the differential equation $y' = x - y$ and use it to sketch an approximate solution curve that passes through the point $(-4, 4)$.

Solution

Solution Figure 1.3.3 shows a table of slopes for the given equation. The numerical slope $m = x - y$ appears at the intersection of the horizontal x-row and the vertical y-column of the table. If you inspect the pattern of upper-left to lower-right diagonals in this table, you can see that it was easily and quickly constructed. [Of course, a more complicated function $f(x, y)$ on the right-hand side of the differential equation would necessitate more complicated calculations.] Figure 1.3.4 shows

$x \backslash y$	−4	−3	−2	−1	0	1	2	3	4
−4	0	−1	−2	−3	−4	−5	−6	−7	−8
−3	1	0	−1	−2	−3	−4	−5	−6	−7
−2	2	1	0	−1	−2	−3	−4	−5	−6
−1	3	2	1	0	−1	−2	−3	−4	−5
0	4	3	2	1	0	−1	−2	−3	−4
1	5	4	3	2	1	0	−1	−2	−3
2	6	5	4	3	2	1	0	−1	−2
3	7	6	5	4	3	2	1	0	−1
4	8	7	6	5	4	3	2	1	0

FIGURE 1.3.3. Values of the slope $y' = x - y$ for $-4 \leqq x, \, y \leqq 4$.

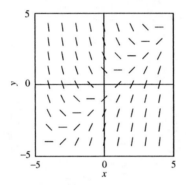

FIGURE 1.3.4. Slope field for $y' = x - y$ corresponding to the table of slopes in Fig. 1.3.3.

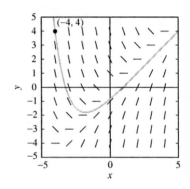

FIGURE 1.3.5. The solution curve through $(-4, 4)$.

the corresponding slope field, and Fig. 1.3.5 shows an approximate solution curve sketched through the point $(-4, 4)$ so as to follow as this slope field as closely as possible. At each point it appears to proceed in the direction indicated by the nearby line segments of the slope field. ■

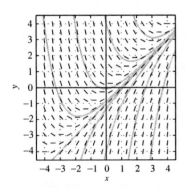

FIGURE 1.3.6. Slope field and typical solution curves for $y' = x - y$.

Although a spreadsheet program (for instance) readily constructs a table of slopes as in Fig. 1.3.3, it can be quite tedious to plot by hand a sufficient number of slope segments as in Fig. 1.3.4. However, most computer algebra systems include commands for quick and ready construction of slope fields with as many line segments as desired; such commands are illustrated in the application material for this section. The more line segments are constructed, the more accurately solution curves can be visualized and sketched. Figure 1.3.6 shows a "finer" slope field for the differential equation $y' = x - y$ of Example 2, together with typical solution curves treading through this slope field.

If you look closely at Fig. 1.3.6, you may spot a solution curve that appears to be a straight line! Indeed, you can verify that the linear function $y = x - 1$ is a solution of the equation $y' = x - y$, and it appears likely that the other solution curves approach this straight line as an asymptote as $x \to +\infty$. This inference illustrates the fact that a slope field can suggest tangible information about solutions that is not at all evident from the differential equation itself. For instance, by tracing the solution curve in this figure that passes through the point $(-4, 4)$, can you infer that $y(3) \approx 2$ for the solution $y(x)$ to the initial value problem $y' = x - y$, $y(-4) = 4$?

Applications of Slope Fields

The next two examples illustrate the use of slope fields to glean useful information in physical situations that are modeled by differential equations. Example 3 is based on the fact that a baseball moving through the air at a moderate speed v (less than about 300 ft/s) encounters air resistance that is approximately proportional to v. If the baseball is thrown straight downward from the top of a tall building or from a hovering helicopter, then it experiences both the downward acceleration of gravity and an upward acceleration of air resistance. If the y-axis is directed *downward*, then the ball's velocity $v = dy/dt$ and its gravitational acceleration $g = 32$ ft/s^2 are both positive, while its acceleration due to air resistance is negative. Hence its total acceleration is of the form

$$\frac{dv}{dt} = g - kv. \tag{3}$$

A typical value of the air resistance proportionality constant might be $k = 0.16$.

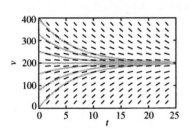

FIGURE 1.3.7. Slope field and typical solution curves for $v' = 32 - 0.16v$.

Example 3

Suppose you throw a baseball straight downward from a helicopter hovering at an altitude of 3000 feet. You wonder whether someone standing on the ground below could conceivably catch it. In order to estimate the speed with which the ball will land, you can use your laptop's computer algebra system to construct a slope field for the differential equation

$$\frac{dv}{dt} = 32 - 0.16v. \tag{4}$$

The result is shown in Fig. 1.3.7, together with a number of solution curves corresponding to different values of the initial velocity $v(0)$ with which you might throw the baseball downward. Note that all these solution curves appear to approach the horizontal line $v = 200$ as an asymptote. This implies that—however you throw it—the baseball should approach the *limiting velocity* $v = 200$ ft/s instead of accelerating indefinitely (as it would in the absence of any air resistance). The handy fact that 60 mi/h = 88 ft/s yields

$$v = 200\frac{\text{ft}}{\text{s}} \times \frac{60 \text{ mi/h}}{88 \text{ ft/s}} \approx 136.36 \ \frac{\text{mi}}{\text{h}}.$$

Perhaps a catcher accustomed to 100 mi/h fastballs would have some chance of fielding this speeding ball. ∎

Comment   If the ball's initial velocity is $v(0) = 200$, then Eq. (4) gives $v'(0) = 32 - (0.16)(200) = 0$ so the ball experiences *no* initial acceleration. Its velocity therefore remains unchanged, and hence $v(t) \equiv 200$ is a constant "equilibrium solution" of the differential equation. If the initial velocity is greater than 200, then the initial acceleration given by Eq. (4) is negative, so the ball slows down as it falls. But if the initial velocity is less than 200, then the initial acceleration given by (4) is positive, so the ball speeds up as it falls. It therefore seems reasonable that, because of air resistance, the baseball will approach a limiting velocity of 200 ft/s—whatever initial velocity it starts with. You might like to verify that—in the absence of air resistance—this ball would hit the ground at over 300 mi/h. ∎

In Section 2.1 we will discuss in detail the logistic differential equation

$$\frac{dP}{dt} = kP(M - P) \tag{5}$$

that often is used to model a population $P(t)$ that inhabits an environment with *carrying capacity* M. This means that M is the maximum population that this environment can sustain on a long-term basis (in terms of the maximum available food, for instance).

Example 4

If we take $k = 0.0004$ and $M = 150$, then the logistic equation in (5) takes the form

$$\frac{dP}{dt} = 0.0004P(150 - P) = 0.06P - 0.0004P^2. \tag{6}$$

The positive term $0.06P$ on the right in (6) corresponds to natural growth at a 6% annual rate (with time t measured in years). The negative term $-0.0004P^2$ represents the inhibition of growth due to limited resources in the environment.

Figure 1.3.8 shows a slope field for Eq. (6), together with a number of solution curves corresponding to possible different values of the initial population $P(0)$. Note that all these solution curves appear to approach the horizontal line $P = 150$ as an asymptote. This implies that—whatever the initial population—the population $P(t)$ approaches the *limiting population* $P = 150$ as $t \to \infty$. ∎

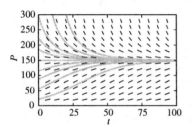

FIGURE 1.3.8. Slope field and typical solution curves for $P' = 0.06P - 0.0004P^2$.

Comment If the initial population is $P(0) = 150$, then Eq. (6) gives

$$P'(0) = 0.0004(150)(150 - 150) = 0,$$

so the population experiences *no* initial (instantaneous) change. It therefore remains unchanged, and hence $P(t) \equiv 150$ is a constant "equilibrium solution" of the differential equation. If the initial population is greater than 150, then the initial rate of change given by (6) is negative, so the population immediately begins to decrease. But if the initial population is less than 150, then the initial rate of change given by (6) is positive, so the population immediately begins to increase. It therefore seems reasonable to conclude that the population will approach a limiting value of 150—whatever the (positive) initial population. ∎

Existence and Uniqueness of Solutions

Before we spend much time attempting to solve a given differential equation, it is wise to know that solutions actually *exist*. We may also want to know whether there is only one solution of the equation satisfying a given initial condition—that is, whether its solutions are *unique*.

Example 5

(a) [Failure of existence] The initial value problem

$$y' = \frac{1}{x}, \quad y(0) = 0 \tag{7}$$

has *no* solution, because no solution $y(x) = \int (1/x)\,dx = \ln|x| + C$ of the differential equation is defined at $x = 0$.

(b) [Failure of uniqueness] On the other hand, you can readily verify that the initial value problem

$$y' = 2\sqrt{y}, \quad y(0) = 0 \tag{8}$$

has the *two* different solutions $y_1(x) = x^2$ and $y_2(x) \equiv 0$ (see Problem 27). ∎

Example 5 illustrates the fact that, before we can speak of "the" solution of an initial value problem, we need to know that it has *one and only one* solution. Questions of existence and uniqueness of solutions also bear on the process of mathematical modeling. Suppose that we are studying a physical system whose behavior is completely determined by certain initial conditions, but that our proposed mathematical model involves a differential equation *not* having a unique solution satisfying those conditions. This raises an immediate question as to whether the mathematical model adequately represents the physical system.

The theorem stated below implies that the initial value problem $y' = f(x, y)$, $y(a) = b$ has one and only one solution defined near the point $x = a$ on the x-axis, provided that both the function f and its partial derivative $\partial f / \partial y$ are continuous near the point (a, b) in the xy-plane. Methods of proving existence and uniqueness theorems are discussed in Appendix A.

THEOREM 1: Existence and Uniqueness of Solutions

Suppose that both the function $f(x, y)$ and its partial derivative $D_y f(x, y)$ are continuous on some rectangle R in the xy-plane that contains the point (a, b) in its interior. Then, for some open interval I containing the point a, the initial value problem

$$\frac{dy}{dx} = f(x, y), \quad y(a) = b \qquad (9)$$

has one and only one solution that is defined on the interval I. ▲

Remark 1: In the case of the differential equation $dy/dx = -y$ of Example 1 and Fig. 1.3.2(c), both the function $f(x, y) = -y$ and the partial derivative $\partial f / \partial y = -1$ are continuous everywhere, so Theorem 1 implies the existence of a unique solution for any initial data (a, b). Although the theorem ensures existence only on some open interval containing $x = a$, each solution $y(x) = Ce^{-x}$ actually is defined for all x.

Remark 2: In the case of the differential equation $dy/dx = -2\sqrt{y}$ of Example 5(b) and Eq. (8), the function $f(x, y) = -2\sqrt{y}$ is continuous wherever $y > 0$, but the partial derivative $\partial f / \partial y = 1/\sqrt{y}$ is discontinuous when $y = 0$, and hence at the point $(0, 0)$. This is why it is possible for there to exist two different solutions $y_1(x) = x^2$ and $y_2(x) \equiv 0$, each of which satisfies the initial condition $y(0) = 0$.

Remark 3: In Example 7 of Section 1.1 we examined the especially simple differential equation $dy/dx = y^2$. Here we have $f(x, y) = y^2$ and $\partial f / \partial y = 2y$. Both of these functions are continuous everywhere in the xy-plane, and in particular on the rectangle $-2 < x < 2$, $0 < y < 2$. Because the point $(0, 1)$ lies in the interior of this rectangle, Theorem 1 guarantees a unique solution—necessarily a continuous function—of the initial value problem

$$\frac{dy}{dx} = y^2, \quad y(0) = 1 \qquad (10)$$

on some open x-interval containing $a = 0$. Indeed this is the solution

$$y(x) = \frac{1}{1 - x}$$

that we discussed in Example 7. But $y(x) = 1/(1 - x)$ is discontinuous at $x = 1$, so our unique continuous solution does not exist on the entire interval $-2 < x < 2$. Thus the solution interval I of Theorem 1 may not be as wide as the rectangle R where f and $\partial f / \partial y$ are continuous. Geometrically, the reason is that the solution curve provided by the theorem may leave the rectangle—wherein solutions of the differential equation are guaranteed to exist—before it reaches the one or both ends of the interval (see Fig. 1.3.9). ∎

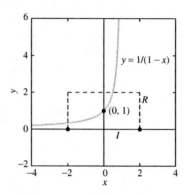

FIGURE 1.3.9. The solution curve through the initial point $(0, 1)$ leaves the rectangle R before it reaches the right end of the interval I.

The following example shows that, if the function $f(x, y)$ and/or its partial derivative $\partial f / \partial y$ fail to satisfy the continuity hypothesis of Theorem 1, then the initial value problem in (9) may have *either* no solution *or* many—even infinitely many—solutions.

Example 6 Consider the first-order differential equation

$$x \frac{dy}{dx} = 2y. \tag{11}$$

Applying Theorem 1 with $f(x, y) = 2y/x$ and $\partial f / \partial y = 2/x$, we conclude that Eq. (11) must have a unique solution near any point in the xy-plane where $x \neq 0$. Indeed, we see immediately by substitution in (11) that

$$y(x) = Cx^2 \tag{12}$$

satisfies Eq. (11) for any value of the constant C and for all values of the variable x. In particular, the initial value problem

$$x \frac{dy}{dx} = 2y, \quad y(0) = 0 \tag{13}$$

has infinitely many different solutions, whose solution curves are the parabolas $y = Cx^2$ illustrated in Fig. 1.3.10. (In case $C = 0$ the "parabola" is actually the x-axis $y = 0$.)

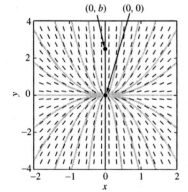

FIGURE 1.3.10. There are infinitely many solution curves through the point $(0, 0)$, but no solution curves through the point $(0, b)$ if $b \neq 0$.

Observe that all these parabolas pass through the origin $(0, 0)$, but none of them passes through any other point on the y-axis. It follows that the initial value problem in (13) has infinitely many solutions, but the initial value problem

$$x \frac{dy}{dx} = 2y, \quad y(0) = b \tag{14}$$

has no solution if $b \neq 0$.

Finally, note that through any point off the y-axis there passes only one of the parabolas $y = Cx^2$. Hence, if $a \neq 0$, then the initial value problem

$$x \frac{dy}{dx} = 2y, \quad y(a) = b \tag{15}$$

has a unique solution on any interval that contains the point $x = a$ but not the origin $x = 0$ In summary, the initial value problem in (15) has

- a unique solution near (a, b) if $a \neq 0$;
- no solution if $a = 0$ but $b \neq 0$;
- infinitely many solutions if $a = b = 0$.   ■

Still more can be said about the initial value problem in (15). Consider a typical initial point off the y-axis—for instance the point $(-1, 1)$ indicated in Fig. 1.3.11. Then for any value of the constant C the function defined by

$$y(x) = \begin{cases} x^2 & \text{if } x \leq 0, \\ Cx^2 & \text{if } x > 0 \end{cases} \tag{16}$$

is continuous and satisfies the initial value problem

$$x \frac{dy}{dx} = 2y, \quad y(-1) = 1. \tag{17}$$

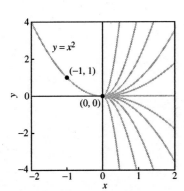

FIGURE 1.3.11. There are infinitely many solution curves through the point $(1, -1)$.

For a particular value of C, the solution curve defined by (16) consists of the left half of the parabola $y = x^2$ and the right half of the parabola $y = Cx^2$. Thus the unique solution curve near $(-1, 1)$ branches at the origin into the infinitely many solution curves illustrated in Fig. 1.3.11.

We therefore see that Theorem 1 (if its hypotheses are satisfied) guarantees uniqueness of the solution near the initial point (a, b), but a solution curve through (a, b) may eventually branch elsewhere so that uniqueness is lost. Thus a solution may exist on a larger interval than one on which the solution is unique. For instance, the solution $y(x) = x^2$ of the initial value problem in (17) exists on the whole x-axis, but this solution is unique only on the negative x-axis $-\infty < x < 0$.

1.3 Problems

In Problems 1 through 10 (Figures 1.3.12–1.3.21), we have provided the slope field of the indicated differential equation, together with one or more solution curves. Sketch likely solution curves through the additional points marked in each slope field.

1. $\dfrac{dy}{dx} = -y - \sin x$

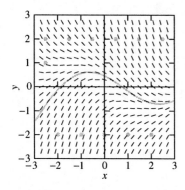

FIGURE 1.3.12.

2. $\dfrac{dy}{dx} = x + y$

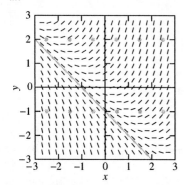

FIGURE 1.3.13.

3. $\dfrac{dy}{dx} = y - \sin x$

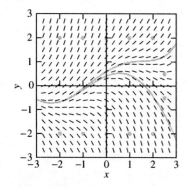

FIGURE 1.3.14.

4. $\dfrac{dy}{dx} = x - y$

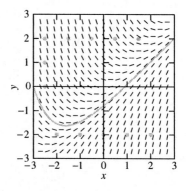

FIGURE 1.3.15.

5. $\dfrac{dy}{dx} = y - x + 1$

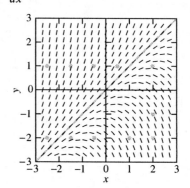

FIGURE 1.3.16.

6. $\dfrac{dy}{dx} = x - y + 1$

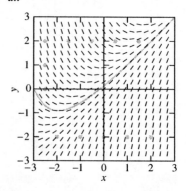

FIGURE 1.3.17.

7. $\dfrac{dy}{dx} = \sin x + \sin y$

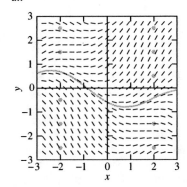

FIGURE 1.3.18.

8. $\dfrac{dy}{dx} = x^2 - y$

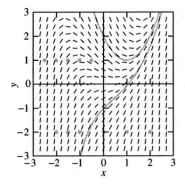

FIGURE 1.3.19.

9. $\dfrac{dy}{dx} = x^2 - y - 2$

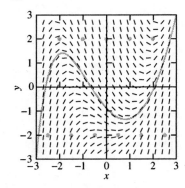

FIGURE 1.3.20.

10. $\dfrac{dy}{dx} = -x^2 + \sin y$

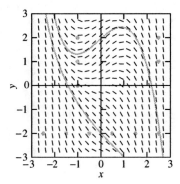

FIGURE 1.3.21.

In Problems 11 through 20, determine whether Theorem 1 does or does not guarantee existence of a solution of the given initial value problem. If existence is guaranteed, determine whether Theorem 1 does or does not guarantee uniqueness of that solution.

11. $\dfrac{dy}{dx} = 2x^2 y^2;\quad y(1) = -1$

12. $\dfrac{dy}{dx} = x \ln y;\quad y(1) = 1$

13. $\dfrac{dy}{dx} = \sqrt[3]{y};\quad y(0) = 1$

14. $\dfrac{dy}{dx} = \sqrt[3]{y};\quad y(0) = 0$

15. $\dfrac{dy}{dx} = \sqrt{x - y};\quad y(2) = 2$

16. $\dfrac{dy}{dx} = \sqrt{x - y};\quad y(2) = 1$

17. $y\dfrac{dy}{dx} = x - 1;\quad y(0) = 1$

18. $y\dfrac{dy}{dx} = x - 1;\quad y(1) = 0$

19. $\dfrac{dy}{dx} = \ln(1 + y^2);\quad y(0) = 0$

20. $\dfrac{dy}{dx} = x^2 - y^2;\quad y(0) = 1$

In Problems 21 and 22, first use the method of Example 2 to construct a slope field for the given differential equation. Then sketch the solution curve corresponding to the given initial condition. Finally, use this solution curve to estimate the desired value of the solution $y(x)$.

21. $y' = x + y,\quad y(0) = 0;\quad y(-4) = ?$
22. $y' = y - x,\quad y(4) = 0;\quad y(-4) = ?$

Problems 23 and 24 are like Problems 21 and 22, but now use a computer algebra system to plot and print out a slope field for the given differential equation. If you wish (and know how) you can check your manually sketched solution curve by plotting it with the computer.

23. $y' = x^2 + y^2 - 1$, $y(0) = 0$; $y(2) =?$

24. $y' = x + \frac{1}{2}y^2$, $y(-2) = 0$; $y(2) =?$

25. You bail out of the helicopter of Example 3 and pull the ripcord of your parachute. Now $k = 1.6$ in Eq. (3), so your downward velocity satisfies the initial value problem

$$\frac{dv}{dt} = 32 - 1.6v, \quad v(0) = 0.$$

In order to investigate your chances of survival, construct a slope field for this differential equation and sketch the appropriate solution curve. What will your limiting velocity be? Will a strategically located haystack do any good? How long will it take you to reach 95% of your limiting velocity?

26. Suppose the deer population $P(t)$ in a small forest satisfies the logistic equation

$$\frac{dP}{dt} = 0.0225P - 0.0003P^2.$$

Construct a slope field and appropriate solution curve to answer the following questions: If there are 25 deer at time $t = 0$ and t is measured in months, how long will it take the number of deer to double? What will be the limiting deer population?

The next seven problems illustrate the fact that, if the hypotheses of Theorem 1 are not satisfied, then the initial value problem $y' = f(x, y)$, $y(a) = b$ may have either no solutions, finitely many solutions, or infinitely many solutions.

27. (a) Verify that if c is a constant, then the function defined piecewise by

$$y(x) = \begin{cases} 0 & \text{for } x \leq c, \\ (x - c)^2 & \text{for } x > c \end{cases}$$

satisfies the differential equation $y' = 2\sqrt{y}$ for all x (including the point $x = c$). Construct a figure illustrating the fact that the initial value problem $y' = 2\sqrt{y}$, $y(0) = 0$ has infinitely many different solutions. **(b)** For what values of b does the initial value problem $y' = 2\sqrt{y}$, $y(0) = b$ have (i) no solution, (ii) a unique solution that is defined for all x?

28. Verify that if k is a constant, then the function $y(x) \equiv kx$ satisfies the differential equation $xy' = y$ for all x. Construct a slope field and several of these straight line solution curves. Then determine (in terms of a and b) how many different solutions the initial value problem $xy' = y$, $y(a) = b$ has—one, none, or infinitely many.

29. Verify that if c is a constant, then the function defined piecewise by

$$y(x) = \begin{cases} 0 & \text{for } x \leq c, \\ (x - c)^3 & \text{for } x > c \end{cases}$$

satisfies the differential equation $y' = 3y^{2/3}$ for all x. Can you also use the "left half" of the cubic $y = (x - c)^3$ in piecing together a solution curve of the differential equation? (See Fig. 1.3.22.) Sketch a variety of such solution curves. Is there a point (a, b) of the xy-plane such that the initial value problem $y' = 3y^{2/3}$, $y(a) = b$ has either no solution or a unique solution that is defined for all x? Reconcile your answer with Theorem 1.

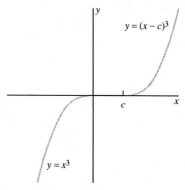

FIGURE 1.3.22. A suggestion for Problem 29.

30. Verify that if c is a constant, then the function defined piecewise by

$$y(x) = \begin{cases} +1 & \text{if } x \leq c, \\ \cos(x - c) & \text{if } c < x < c + \pi, \\ -1 & \text{if } x \geq c \end{cases}$$

satisfies the differential equation $y' = -\sqrt{1 - y^2}$ for all x. (Perhaps a preliminary sketch with $c = 0$ will be helpful.) Sketch a variety of such solution curves. Then determine (in terms of a and b) how many different solutions the initial value problem $y' = -\sqrt{1 - y^2}$, $y(a) = b$ has.

31. Carry out an investigation similar to that in Problem 30, except with the differential equation $y' = +\sqrt{1 - y^2}$. Does it suffice simply to replace $\cos(x - c)$ with $\sin(x - c)$ in piecing together a solution that is defined for all x?

32. Verify that if $c > 0$, then the function defined piecewise by

$$y(x) = \begin{cases} 0 & \text{if } x^2 \leq c, \\ (x^2 - c)^2 & \text{if } x^2 > c \end{cases}$$

satisfies the differential equation $y' = 4x\sqrt{y}$ for all x. Sketch a variety of such solution curves for different values of c. Then determine (in terms of a and b) how many different solutions the initial value problem $y' = 4x\sqrt{y}$, $y(a) = b$ has.

33. If $c \neq 0$ verify that the function defined by $y(x) = x/(cx - 1)$ (with graph illustrated in Fig. 1.3.23) satisfies the differential equation $x^2 y' + y^2 = 0$ if $x \neq 1/c$. Sketch a variety of such solution curves for different values of c. Also, note the constant-valued function $y(x) \equiv 0$ that does not result from any choice of the constant c. Finally, determine (in terms of a and b) how many different solutions the initial value problem $x^2 y' + y^2 = 0$, $y(a) = b$ has.

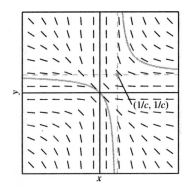

FIGURE 1.3.23. Slope field for $x^2 y' + y^2 = 0$ and graph of a solution $y(x) = x/(cx - 1)$.

1.3 Application: Computer-Generated Slope Fields and Solution Curves

Widely available computer algebra systems and technical computing environments include facilities to automate the construction of slope fields and solution curves, as do some graphing calculators (see Fig. 1.3.24).

FIGURE 1.3.24. Slope field and solution curves for the differential equation

$$\frac{dy}{dx} = \sin(x - y)$$

with initial points $(0, b)$, $b = -3, -1, -2, 0, 2, 4$ and window $-5 \leq x, y \leq 5$ on a TI-89 graphing calculator.

The applications manual accompanying this textbook includes discussion of *Maple*®, *Mathematica*®, and MATLAB®resources for the investigation of differential equations. For instance, the *Maple* command

```
with(DEtools):
DEplot(diff(y(x),x)=sin(x-y(x)), y(x), x=-5..5, y=-5..5);
```

and the *Mathematica* command

```
<< Graphics\PlotField.m
PlotVectorField[{1, Sin[x-y]}, {x, -5, 5}, {y, -5, 5}]
```

produce slope fields similar to the one shown in Fig. 1.3.25. Figure 1.3.25 itself was generated with the MATLAB program **dfield** (John Polking and David Arnold, *Ordinary Differential Equations Using* MATLAB [3rd edition], Prentice Hall, 2004)

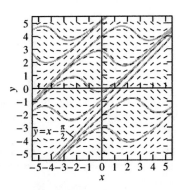

FIGURE 1.3.25. Computer-generated slope field and solution curves for the differential equation $y' = \sin(x - y)$.

that is freely available for educational use (**math.rice.edu/~dfield**). When a differential equation is entered in the **dfield** setup menu (Fig. 1.3.26), you can (with mouse button clicks) plot both a slope field and the solution curve (or curves) through any desired point (or points). Another freely available and user-friendly MATLAB-based ODE (ordinary differential equations) package with impressive graphical capabilities is **Iode** (**www.math.uiuc.edu/iode**).

FIGURE 1.3.26. MATLAB **dfield** setup to construct slope field and solution curves for $y' = \sin(x - y)$.

Use a graphing calculator or computer system in the following investigations. You might warm up by generating the slope fields and some solution curves for Problems 1 through 10 in this section.

INVESTIGATION A: Plot a slope field and typical solution curves for the differential equation $dy/dx = \sin(x - y)$, but with a larger window than that of Fig. 1.3.25. With $-10 \leq x \leq 10$, $-10 \leq y \leq 10$, for instance, a number of apparent straight line solution curves should be visible.

(a) Substitute $y = ax + b$ in the differential equation to determine what the coefficients a and b must be in order to get a solution.

(b) A computer algebra system gives the general solution

$$y(x) = x - 2\tan^{-1}\left(\frac{x - 2 - C}{x - C}\right).$$

Can you determine a value of the arbitrary constant C that yields the linear solution $y = x - (\pi/2)$ corresponding to the initial condition $y(\pi/2) = 0$?

INVESTIGATION B: For your own personal investigation, let n be the *smallest* digit in your student ID number that is greater than 1, and consider the differential equation

$$\frac{dy}{dx} = \frac{1}{n}\cos(x - ny).$$

(a) First investigate [as in part (a) of Investigation A] the possibility of straight line solutions.

(b) Then generate a slope field for this differential equation, with the viewing window chosen so that you can picture some of these straight lines, plus a sufficient number of nonlinear solution curves that you can formulate a conjecture about what happens to $y(x)$ as $x \to +\infty$. State your inference as plainly as you can. Given the initial value $y(0) = y_0$, try to predict (perhaps in terms of y_0) how $y(x)$ behaves as $x \to +\infty$.

(c) A computer algebra system gives the general solution

$$y(x) = \frac{1}{n}\left[x + 2\tan^{-1}\left(\frac{1}{x - C}\right)\right].$$

Can you make a connection between this symbolic solution and your graphically generated solution curves (straight lines or otherwise)?

1.4 Separable Equations and Applications

The first-order differential equation

$$\frac{dy}{dx} = H(x, y) \tag{1}$$

is called **separable** provided that $H(x, y)$ can be written as the product of a function of x and a function of y:

➤ $$\frac{dy}{dx} = g(x)h(y) = \frac{g(x)}{f(y)},$$

where $h(y) = 1/f(y)$. In this case the variables x and y can be *separated*—isolated on opposite sides of an equation—by writing informally the equation

$$f(y)\,dy = g(x)\,dx,$$

which we understand to be concise notation for the differential equation

$$f(y)\frac{dy}{dx} = g(x). \tag{2}$$

In principle, it is easy to solve this special type of differential equation simply by integrating both sides with respect to x:

$$\int f(y(x))\frac{dy}{dx}\,dx = \int g(x)\,dx + C;$$

equivalently, the substitution $y = y(x)$, $dy = y'(x)dx$ gives

$$\int f(y)\,dy = \int g(x)\,dx + C. \tag{3}$$

All that is required now is that the antiderivatives

$$F(y) = \int f(y)\,dy \quad \text{and} \quad G(x) = \int g(x)\,dx$$

can be found. To see that Eqs. (2) and (3) are equivalent, note the following consequence of the chain rule:

$$D_x[F(y(x))] = F'(y(x))y'(x) = f(y)\frac{dy}{dx} = g(x) = D_x[G(x)],$$

which in turn is equivalent to

$$F(y(x)) = G(x) + C, \tag{4}$$

because two functions have the same derivative on an interval if and only if they differ by a constant on that interval.

Example 1 Solve the initial value problem

$$\frac{dy}{dx} = -6xy, \quad y(0) = 7.$$

Solution Informally, we divide both sides of the differential equation by y and multiply each side by dx to get

$$\frac{dy}{y} = -6x\,dx.$$

Hence

$$\int \frac{dy}{y} = \int (-6x)\,dx;$$
$$\ln|y| = -3x^2 + C.$$

We see from the initial condition $y(0) = 7$ that $y(x)$ is positive near $x = 0$, so we may delete the absolute value symbols:

$$\ln y = -3x^2 + C,$$

and hence

$$y(x) = e^{-3x^2+C} = e^{-3x^2}e^C = Ae^{-3x^2},$$

where $A = e^C$. The condition $y(0) = 7$ yields $A = 7$ so the desired solution is

$$y(x) = 7e^{-3x^2}.$$

This is the upper emphasized solution curve shown in Fig. 1.4.1. ■

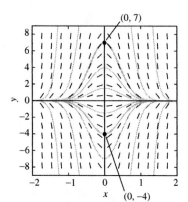

FIGURE 1.4.1. Slope field and solution curves for $y' = -6xy$ in Example 1.

Remark: Suppose, instead, that the initial condition in Example 1 had been $y(0) = -4$. Then it would follow that $y(x)$ is *negative* near $x = 0$. We should therefore replace $|y|$ with $-y$ in the integrated equation $\ln|y| = -3x^2 + C$ to obtain

$$\ln(-y) = -3x^2 + C.$$

The initial condition then yields $C = \ln 4$, so $\ln(-y) = -3x^2 + \ln 4$, and hence

$$y(x) = -4e^{-3x^2}.$$

This is the lower emphasized solution curve in Fig. 1.4.1. ■

Example 2   Solve the differential equation

$$\frac{dy}{dx} = \frac{4 - 2x}{3y^2 - 5}. \tag{5}$$

Solution   When we separate the variables and integrate both sides, we get

$$\int (3y^2 - 5)\, dy = \int (4 - 2x)\, dx;$$
$$y^3 - 5y = 4x - x^2 + C. \tag{6}$$

This equation is not readily solved for y as an explicit function of x.   ∎

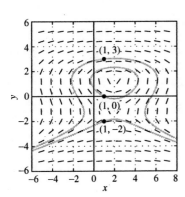

FIGURE 1.4.2. Slope field and solution curves for $y' = (4 - 2x)/(3y^2 - 5)$ in Example 2.

As Example 2 illustrates, it may or may not be possible or practical to solve Eq. (4) explicitly for y in terms of x. If not, then we call (4) an *implicit solution* of the differential equation in (2). Thus Eq. (6) gives an implicit solution of the differential equation in (5). Although it is not convenient to solve Eq. (6) explicitly in terms of x, we see that each solution curve $y = y(x)$ lies on a contour (or level) curve where the function

$$H(x, y) = x^2 - 4x + y^3 - 5y$$

is constant. Figure 1.4.2 shows several of these contour curves.

Example 3   To solve the initial value problem

$$\frac{dy}{dx} = \frac{4 - 2x}{3y^2 - 5}, \quad y(1) = 3, \tag{7}$$

we substitute $x = 1$ and $y = 3$ in Eq. (6) and get $C = 9$. Thus the desired particular solution $y(x)$ is defined implicitly by the equation

$$y^3 - 5y = 4x - x^2 + 9. \tag{8}$$

The corresponding solution curve $y = y(x)$ lies on the upper contour curve in Fig. 1.4.2—the one passing through $(1, 3)$. Because the graph of a differentiable solution cannot have a vertical tangent line anywhere, it appears from the figure that this particular solution is defined on the interval $(-1, 5)$ but not on the interval $(-3, 7)$.   ∎

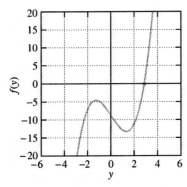

FIGURE 1.4.3. Graph of $f(y) = y^3 - 5y - 9$.

Remark 1:   When a specific value of x is substituted in Eq. (8), we can attempt to solve numerically for y. For instance, $x = 4$ yields the equation

$$f(y) = y^3 - 5y - 9 = 0.$$

Figure 1.4.3 shows the graph of f. With a graphing calculator we can solve for the single real root $y \approx 2.8552$. This yields the value $y(4) \approx 2.8552$ of the particular solution in Example 3.

Remark 2:   If the initial condition in (7) is replaced with the condition $y(1) = 0$, then the resulting particular solution of the differential equation in (5) lies on the lower "half" of the oval contour curve in Fig. 1.4.2. It appears that this particular solution through $(1, 0)$ is defined on the interval $(0, 4)$ but not on the interval $(-1, 5)$. On the other hand, with the initial condition $y(1) = -2$ we get the lower contour curve in Fig. 1.4.2. This particular solution is defined for all x. Thus the initial condition can determine whether a particular solution is defined on the whole real line or only on some bounded interval. With a computer algebra system one can readily calculate a table of values of the y-solutions of Eq. (8) for x-values at desired increments from $x = -1$ to $x = 5$ (for instance). Such a table of values serves effectively as a "numerical solution" of the initial value problem in (7). ∎

Implicit Solutions and Singular Solutions

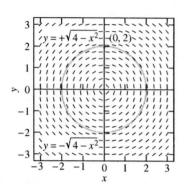

In general, the equation $K(x, y) = 0$ is called an **implicit solution** of a differential equation if it is satisfied (on some interval) by some solution $y = y(x)$ of the differential equation. But note that a particular solution $y = y(x)$ of $K(x, y) = 0$ may or may not satisfy a given initial condition. For example, differentiation of $x^2 + y^2 = 4$ yields

$$x + y\frac{dy}{dx} = 0,$$

so $x^2 + y^2 = 4$ is an implicit solution of the differential equation $x + yy' = 0$. But only the first of the two explicit solutions

$$y(x) = +\sqrt{4 - x^2} \quad \text{and} \quad y(x) = -\sqrt{4 - x^2}$$

FIGURE 1.4.4. Slope field and solution curves for $y' = -x/y$.

satisfies the initial condition $y(0) = 2$ (Fig. 1.4.4).

The argument preceding Example 1 shows that every particular solution of Eq. (2) satisfies Eq. (4) for some choice of C; *this* is why it is appropriate to call (4) the **general solution** of Eq. (2).

Warning: Suppose, however, that we begin with the differential equation

$$\frac{dy}{dx} = g(x)h(y) \tag{9}$$

and divide by $h(y)$ to obtain the separated equation

$$\frac{1}{h(y)}\frac{dy}{dx} = g(x). \tag{10}$$

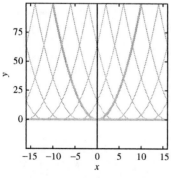

If y_0 is a root of the equation $h(y) = 0$—that is, if $h(y_0) = 0$—then the constant function $y(x) \equiv y_0$ is clearly a solution of Eq. (9) but may *not* be contained in the general solution of Eq. (10). Thus solutions of a differential equation may be lost upon division by a vanishing factor. (Indeed, false solutions may be gained upon multiplication by a vanishing factor. This phenomenon is similar to the introduction of extraneous roots in solving algebraic equations.)

In Section 1.5 we shall see that every particular solution of a *linear* first-order differential equation is contained in its general solution. By contrast, it is common for a nonlinear first-order differential equation to have both a general solution involving an arbitrary constant C and one or several particular solutions that cannot be obtained by selecting a value for C. These exceptional solutions are frequently called **singular solutions**. In Problem 30 we ask you to show that the general solution of the differential equation $(y')^2 = 4y$ yields the family of parabolas $y = (x - C)^2$ illustrated in Fig. 1.4.5, and to observe that the constant-valued function $y(x) \equiv 0$ is a singular solution that cannot be obtained from the general solution by any choice of the arbitrary constant C.

FIGURE 1.4.5. The general solution curves $y = (x - C)^2$ and the singular solution curve $y = 0$ of the differential equation $(y')^2 = 4y$.

Example 4 Find all solutions of the differential equation

$$\frac{dy}{dx} = 6x(y-1)^{2/3}.$$

Solution Separation of variables gives

$$\int \frac{1}{3(y-1)^{2/3}}\, dy = \int 2x\, dx;$$

$$(y-1)^{1/3} = x^2 + C;$$

$$y(x) = 1 + (x^2 + C)^3.$$

Positive values of the arbitrary constant C give the solution curves in Fig. 1.4.6 that lie above the line $y = 1$, whereas negative values yield those that dip below it. The value $C = 0$ gives the solution $y(x) = 1 + x^6$, but *no* value of C gives the singular solution $y(x) \equiv 1$ that was lost when the variables were separated. Note that the two different solutions $y(x) \equiv 1$ and $y(x) = 1 + (x^2 - 1)^3$ both satisfy the initial condition $y(1) = 1$. Indeed, the whole singular solution curve $y = 1$ consists of points where the solution is not unique and where the function $f(x, y) = 6x(y-1)^{2/3}$ is not differentiable. ∎

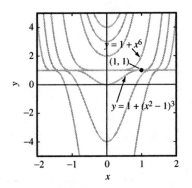

FIGURE 1.4.6. General and singular solution curves for $y' = 6x(y-1)^{2/3}$.

Natural Growth and Decay

The differential equation

$$\frac{dx}{dt} = kx \quad (k \text{ a constant}) \tag{11}$$

serves as a mathematical model for a remarkably wide range of natural phenomena—any involving a quantity whose time rate of change is proportional to its current size. Here are some examples.

POPULATION GROWTH: Suppose that $P(t)$ is the number of individuals in a population (of humans, or insects, or bacteria) having *constant* birth and death rates β and δ (in births or deaths per individual per unit of time). Then, during a short time interval Δt, approximately $\beta P(t)\Delta t$ births and $\delta P(t)\Delta t$ deaths occur, so the change in $P(t)$ is given approximately by

$$\Delta P \approx (\beta - \delta)P(t)\Delta t,$$

and therefore

$$\frac{dP}{dt} = \lim_{\Delta t \to 0} \frac{\Delta P}{\Delta t} = kP, \tag{12}$$

where $k = \beta - \delta$.

COMPOUND INTEREST: Let $A(t)$ be the number of dollars in a savings account at time t (in years), and suppose that the interest is *compounded continuously* at an annual interest rate r. (Note that 10% annual interest means that $r = 0.10$.) Continuous compounding means that during a short time interval Δt, the amount of interest added to the account is approximately $\Delta A = rA(t)\Delta t$, so that

$$\frac{dA}{dt} = \lim_{\Delta t \to 0} \frac{\Delta A}{\Delta t} = rA. \tag{13}$$

RADIOACTIVE DECAY: Consider a sample of material that contains $N(t)$ atoms of a certain radioactive isotope at time t. It has been observed that a constant fraction of those radioactive atoms will spontaneously decay (into atoms of another element or into another isotope of the same element) during each unit of time. Consequently, the sample behaves exactly like a population with a constant death rate and no births. To write a model for $N(t)$, we use Eq. (12) with N in place of P, with $k > 0$ in place of δ, and with $\beta = 0$. We thus get the differential equation

$$\frac{dN}{dt} = -kN. \tag{14}$$

The value of k depends on the particular radioactive isotope.

The key to the method of *radiocarbon dating* is that a constant proportion of the carbon atoms in any living creature is made up of the radioactive isotope ^{14}C of carbon. This proportion remains constant because the fraction of ^{14}C in the atmosphere remains almost constant, and living matter is continuously taking up carbon from the air or is consuming other living matter containing the same constant ratio of ^{14}C atoms to ordinary ^{12}C atoms. This same ratio permeates all life, because organic processes seem to make no distinction between the two isotopes.

The ratio of ^{14}C to normal carbon remains constant in the atmosphere because, although ^{14}C is radioactive and slowly decays, the amount is continuously replenished through the conversion of ^{14}N (ordinary nitrogen) to ^{14}C by cosmic rays bombarding the upper atmosphere. Over the long history of the planet, this decay and replenishment process has come into nearly steady state.

Of course, when a living organism dies, it ceases its metabolism of carbon and the process of radioactive decay begins to deplete its ^{14}C content. There is no replenishment of this ^{14}C, and consequently the ratio of ^{14}C to normal carbon begins to drop. By measuring this ratio, the amount of time elapsed since the death of the organism can be estimated. For such purposes it is necessary to measure the **decay constant** k. For ^{14}C, it is known that $k \approx 0.0001216$ if t is measured in years.

(Matters are not as simple as we have made them appear. In applying the technique of radiocarbon dating, extreme care must be taken to avoid contaminating the sample with organic matter or even with ordinary fresh air. In addition, the cosmic ray levels apparently have not been constant, so the ratio of ^{14}C in the atmosphere has varied over the past centuries. By using independent methods of dating samples, researchers in this area have compiled tables of correction factors to enhance the accuracy of this process.)

DRUG ELIMINATION: In many cases the amount $A(t)$ of a certain drug in the bloodstream, measured by the excess over the natural level of the drug, will decline at a rate proportional to the current excess amount. That is,

$$\frac{dA}{dt} = -\lambda A, \tag{15}$$

where $\lambda > 0$. The parameter λ is called the **elimination constant** of the drug.

The Natural Growth Equation

The prototype differential equation $dx/dt = kx$ with $x(t) > 0$ and k a constant (either negative or positive) is readily solved by separating the variables and integrating:

$$\int \frac{1}{x}\, dx = \int k\, dt;$$

$$\ln x = kt + C.$$

Then we solve for x:

$$e^{\ln x} = e^{kt+C}; \quad x = x(t) = e^C e^{kt} = Ae^{kt}.$$

Because C is a constant, so is $A = e^C$. It is also clear that $A = x(0) = x_0$, so the particular solution of Eq. (11) with the initial condition $x(0) = x_0$ is simply

➤
$$x(t) = x_0 e^{kt}. \tag{16}$$

Because of the presence of the natural exponential function in its solution, the differential equation

➤
$$\frac{dx}{dt} = kx \tag{17}$$

is often called the **exponential** or **natural growth equation**. Figure 1.4.7 shows a typical graph of $x(t)$ in the case $k > 0$; the case $k < 0$ is illustrated in Fig. 1.4.8.

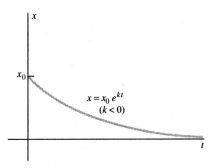

FIGURE 1.4.7. Natural growth.   **FIGURE 1.4.8.** Natural decay.

Example 5   According to data listed at **www.census.gov**, the world's total population reached 6 billion persons in mid-1999 and was then increasing at the rate of about 212 thousand persons each day. Assuming that natural population growth at this rate continues, we want to answer these questions:

(a) What is the annual growth rate k?
(b) What will be the world population at the middle of the twenty-first century?
(c) How long will it take the world population to increase tenfold—thereby reaching the 60 billion that some demographers believe to be the maximum for which the planet can provide adequate food supplies?

Solution   **(a)** We measure the world population $P(t)$ in billions and measure time in years. We take $t = 0$ to correspond to (mid) 1999, so $P_0 = 6$. The fact that P is increasing by 212,000, or 0.000212 billion, persons per day at time $t = 0$ means that

$$P'(0) = (0.000212)(365.25) \approx 0.07743$$

billion per year. From the natural growth equation $P' = kP$ with $t = 0$ we now obtain

$$k = \frac{P'(0)}{P(0)} \approx \frac{0.07743}{6} \approx 0.0129.$$

Thus the world population was growing at the rate of about 1.29% annually in 1999. This value of k gives the world population function

$$P(t) = 6e^{0.0129t}.$$

(b) With $t = 51$ we obtain the prediction

$$P(51) = 6e^{(0.0129)(51)} \approx 11.58 \text{ (billion)}$$

for the world population in mid-2050 (so the population will almost have doubled in the just over a half-century since 1999).

(c) The world population should reach 60 billion when

$$60 = 6e^{0.0129t}; \quad \text{that is, when } t = \frac{\ln 10}{0.0129} \approx 178;$$

and thus in the year 2177. ∎

Note: Actually, the rate of growth of the world population is expected to slow somewhat during the next half-century, and the best current prediction for the 2050 population is "only" 9.1 billion. A simple mathematical model cannot be expected to mirror precisely the complexity of the real world.

The decay constant of a radioactive isotope is often specified in terms of another empirical constant, the *half-life* of the isotope, because this parameter is more convenient. The **half-life** τ of a radioactive isotope is the time required for *half* of it to decay. To find the relationship between k and τ, we set $t = \tau$ and $N = \frac{1}{2}N_0$ in the equation $N(t) = N_0 e^{kt}$, so that $\frac{1}{2}N_0 = N_0 e^{k\tau}$. When we solve for τ, we find that

$$\tau = \frac{\ln 2}{k}. \tag{18}$$

For example, the half-life of ^{14}C is $\tau \approx (\ln 2)/(0.0001216)$, approximately 5700 years.

Example 6   A specimen of charcoal found at Stonehenge turns out to contain 63% as much ^{14}C as a sample of present-day charcoal of equal mass. What is the age of the sample?

Solution   We take $t = 0$ as the time of the death of the tree from which the Stonehenge charcoal was made and N_0 as the number of ^{14}C atoms that the Stonehenge sample contained then. We are given that $N = (0.63)N_0$ now, so we solve the equation $(0.63)N_0 = N_0 e^{-kt}$ with the value $k = 0.0001216$. Thus we find that

$$t = -\frac{\ln(0.63)}{0.0001216} \approx 3800 \text{ (years)}.$$

Thus the sample is about 3800 years old. If it has any connection with the builders of Stonehenge, our computations suggest that this observatory, monument, or temple—whichever it may be—dates from 1800 B.C. or earlier. ∎

Cooling and Heating

According to Newton's law of cooling [Eq. (3) of Section 1.1], the time rate of change of the temperature $T(t)$ of a body immersed in a medium of constant temperature A is proportional to the difference $A - T$. That is,

$$\frac{dT}{dt} = k(A - T), \tag{19}$$

where k is a positive constant. This is an instance of the linear first-order differential equation with constant coefficients:

➤
$$\frac{dx}{dt} = ax + b. \tag{20}$$

It includes the exponential equation as a special case ($b = 0$) and is also easy to solve by separation of variables.

Example 7 A 4-lb roast, initially at 50°F, is placed in a 375°F oven at 5:00 P.M. After 75 minutes it is found that the temperature $T(t)$ of the roast is 125°F. When will the roast be 150°F (medium rare)?

Solution We take time t in minutes, with $t = 0$ corresponding to 5:00 P.M. We also assume (somewhat unrealistically) that at any instant the temperature $T(t)$ of the roast is uniform throughout. We have $T(t) < A = 375$, $T(0) = 50$, and $T(75) = 125$. Hence

$$\frac{dT}{dt} = k(375 - T);$$

$$\int \frac{1}{375 - T}\, dT = \int k\, dt;$$

$$-\ln(375 - T) = kt + C;$$

$$375 - T = Be^{-kt}.$$

Now $T(0) = 50$ implies that $B = 325$, so $T(t) = 375 - 325e^{-kt}$. We also know that $T = 125$ when $t = 75$. Substitution of these values in the preceding equation yields

$$k = -\tfrac{1}{75} \ln \left(\tfrac{250}{325} \right) \approx 0.0035.$$

Hence we finally solve the equation

$$150 = 375 - 325e^{(-0.0035)t}$$

for $t = -[\ln(225/325)]/(0.0035) \approx 105$ (min), the total cooking time required. Because the roast was placed in the oven at 5:00 P.M., it should be removed at about 6:45 P.M. ∎

Torricelli's Law

Suppose that a water tank has a hole with area a at its bottom, from which water is leaking. Denote by $y(t)$ the depth of water in the tank at time t, and by $V(t)$ the volume of water in the tank then. It is plausible—and true, under ideal conditions—that the velocity of water exiting through the hole is

$$v = \sqrt{2gy}, \tag{21}$$

which is the velocity a drop of water would acquire in falling freely from the surface of the water to the hole (see Problem 35 of Section 1.2). One can derive this formula beginning with the assumption that the sum of the kinetic and potential energy of the system remains constant. Under real conditions, taking into account the constriction of a water jet from an orifice, $v = c\sqrt{2gy}$, where c is an empirical constant between 0 and 1 (usually about 0.6 for a small continuous stream of water). For simplicity we take $c = 1$ in the following discussion.

As a consequence of Eq. (21), we have

➤
$$\frac{dV}{dt} = -av = -a\sqrt{2gy}; \tag{22a}$$

equivalently,

➤
$$\frac{dV}{dt} = -k\sqrt{y}, \quad \text{where} \quad k = a\sqrt{2g}. \tag{22b}$$

This is a statement of Torricelli's law for a draining tank. If $A(y)$ denotes the horizontal cross-sectional area of the tank at height y above the hole, the method of volume by cross sections gives

$$V = \int_0^y A(y)\,dy,$$

so the fundamental theorem of calculus implies that $dV/dy = A(y)$ and therefore that

$$\frac{dV}{dt} = \frac{dV}{dy} \cdot \frac{dy}{dt} = A(y)\frac{dy}{dt}. \tag{23}$$

From Eqs. (22) and (23) we finally obtain

$$A(y)\frac{dy}{dt} = -a\sqrt{2gy} = -k\sqrt{y}, \tag{24}$$

an alternative form of Torricelli's law. ■

Example 8 A hemispherical bowl has top radius 4 ft and at time $t = 0$ is full of water. At that moment a circular hole with diameter 1 in. is opened in the bottom of the tank. How long will it take for all the water to drain from the tank?

Solution From the right triangle in Fig. 1.4.9, we see that

$$A(y) = \pi r^2 = \pi\left[16 - (4 - y)^2\right] = \pi(8y - y^2).$$

With $g = 32$ ft/s^2, Eq. (24) becomes

$$\pi(8y - y^2)\frac{dy}{dt} = -\pi \left(\tfrac{1}{24}\right)^2 \sqrt{2 \cdot 32 y};$$

$$\int (8y^{1/2} - y^{3/2})\, dy = -\int \tfrac{1}{72}\, dt;$$

$$\tfrac{16}{3}y^{3/2} - \tfrac{2}{5}y^{5/2} = -\tfrac{1}{72}t + C.$$

Now $y(0) = 4$, so

$$C = \tfrac{16}{3} \cdot 4^{3/2} - \tfrac{2}{5} \cdot 4^{5/2} = \tfrac{448}{15}.$$

The tank is empty when $y = 0$, thus when

$$t = 72 \cdot \tfrac{448}{15} \approx 2150 \ (\text{s});$$

that is, about 35 min 50 s. So it takes slightly less than 36 min for the tank to drain. ∎

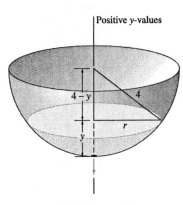

Positive *y*-values

$4 - y$

4

r

y

FIGURE 1.4.9. Draining a hemispherical tank.

1.4 Problems

Find general solutions (implicit if necessary, explicit if convenient) of the differential equations in Problems 1 through 18. Primes denote derivatives with respect to x.

1. $\dfrac{dy}{dx} + 2xy = 0$

2. $\dfrac{dy}{dx} + 2xy^2 = 0$

3. $\dfrac{dy}{dx} = y \sin x$

4. $(1 + x)\dfrac{dy}{dx} = 4y$

5. $2\sqrt{x}\,\dfrac{dy}{dx} = \sqrt{1 - y^2}$

6. $\dfrac{dy}{dx} = 3\sqrt{xy}$

7. $\dfrac{dy}{dx} = (64xy)^{1/3}$

8. $\dfrac{dy}{dx} = 2x \sec y$

9. $(1 - x^2)\dfrac{dy}{dx} = 2y$

10. $(1 + x)^2 \dfrac{dy}{dx} = (1 + y)^2$

11. $y' = xy^3$

12. $yy' = x(y^2 + 1)$

13. $y^3 \dfrac{dy}{dx} = (y^4 + 1)\cos x$

14. $\dfrac{dy}{dx} = \dfrac{1 + \sqrt{x}}{1 + \sqrt{y}}$

15. $\dfrac{dy}{dx} = \dfrac{(x - 1)y^5}{x^2(2y^3 - y)}$

16. $(x^2 + 1)(\tan y)y' = x$

17. $y' = 1 + x + y + xy$ (*Suggestion*: Factor the right-hand side.)

18. $x^2 y' = 1 - x^2 + y^2 - x^2 y^2$

Find explicit particular solutions of the initial value problems in Problems 19 through 28.

19. $\dfrac{dy}{dx} = ye^x, \quad y(0) = 2e$

20. $\dfrac{dy}{dx} = 3x^2(y^2 + 1), \quad y(0) = 1$

21. $2y\dfrac{dy}{dx} = \dfrac{x}{\sqrt{x^2 - 16}}, \quad y(5) = 2$

22. $\dfrac{dy}{dx} = 4x^3 y - y, \quad y(1) = -3$

23. $\dfrac{dy}{dx} + 1 = 2y, \quad y(1) = 1$

24. $(\tan x)\dfrac{dy}{dx} = y, \quad y\left(\tfrac{1}{2}\pi\right) = \tfrac{1}{2}\pi$

25. $x\dfrac{dy}{dx} - y = 2x^2 y, \quad y(1) = 1$

26. $\dfrac{dy}{dx} = 2xy^2 + 3x^2 y^2, \quad y(1) = -1$

27. $\dfrac{dy}{dx} = 6e^{2x - y}, \quad y(0) = 0$

28. $2\sqrt{x}\,\dfrac{dy}{dx} = \cos^2 y, \quad y(4) = \pi/4$

29. (a) Find a general solution of the differential equation $dy/dx = y^2$. (b) Find a singular solution that is not included in the general solution. (c) Inspect a sketch of typical solution curves to determine the points (a, b) for which the initial value problem $y' = y^2$, $y(a) = b$ has a unique solution.

30. Solve the differential equation $(dy/dx)^2 = 4y$ to verify the general solution curves and singular solution curve that are illustrated in Fig. 1.4.5. Then determine the points (a, b) in the plane for which the initial value problem $(y')^2 = 4y$, $y(a) = b$ has (a) no solution, (b) infinitely many solutions that are defined for all x, (c) on some neighborhood of the point $x = a$, only finitely many solutions.

31. Discuss the difference between the differential equations $(dy/dx)^2 = 4y$ and $dy/dx = 2\sqrt{y}$. Do they have the same solution curves? Why or why not? Determine the points (a, b) in the plane for which the initial value problem $y' = 2\sqrt{y}$, $y(a) = b$ has (a) no solution, (c) a unique solution, (b) infinitely many solutions.

32. Find a general solution and any singular solutions of the differential equation $dy/dx = y\sqrt{y^2 - 1}$. Determine the points (a, b) in the plane for which the initial value problem $y' = y\sqrt{y^2 - 1}$, $y(a) = b$ has **(a)** no solution, **(c)** a unique solution, **(b)** infinitely many solutions.

33. *(Population growth)* A certain city had a population of 25,000 in 1960 and a population of 30,000 in 1970. Assume that its population will continue to grow exponentially at a constant rate. What population can its city planners expect in the year 2000?

34. *(Population growth)* In a certain culture of bacteria, the number of bacteria increased sixfold in 10 h. How long did it take for the population to double?

35. *(Radiocarbon dating)* Carbon extracted from an ancient skull contained only one-sixth as much ^{14}C as carbon extracted from present-day bone. How old is the skull?

36. *(Radiocarbon dating)* Carbon taken from a purported relic of the time of Christ contained 4.6×10^{10} atoms of ^{14}C per gram. Carbon extracted from a present-day specimen of the same substance contained 5.0×10^{10} atoms of ^{14}C per gram. Compute the approximate age of the relic. What is your opinion as to its authenticity?

37. *(Continuously compounded interest)* Upon the birth of their first child, a couple deposited $5000 in an account that pays 8% interest compounded continuously. The interest payments are allowed to accumulate. How much will the account contain on the child's eighteenth birthday?

38. *(Continuously compounded interest)* Suppose that you discover in your attic an overdue library book on which your grandfather owed a fine of 30 cents 100 years ago. If an overdue fine grows exponentially at a 5% annual rate compounded continuously, how much would you have to pay if you returned the book today?

39. *(Drug elimination)* Suppose that sodium pentobarbitol is used to anesthetize a dog. The dog is anesthetized when its bloodstream contains at least 45 milligrams (mg) of sodium pentobarbitol per kilogram of the dog's body weight. Suppose also that sodium pentobarbitol is eliminated exponentially from the dog's bloodstream, with a half-life of 5 h. What single dose should be administered in order to anesthetize a 50-kg dog for 1 h?

40. The half-life of radioactive cobalt is 5.27 years. Suppose that a nuclear accident has left the level of cobalt radiation in a certain region at 100 times the level acceptable for human habitation. How long will it be until the region is again habitable? (Ignore the probable presence of other radioactive isotopes.)

41. Suppose that a mineral body formed in an ancient cataclysm—perhaps the formation of the earth itself—originally contained the uranium isotope ^{238}U (which has a half-life of 4.51×10^9 years) but no lead, the end product of the radioactive decay of ^{238}U. If today the ratio of ^{238}U atoms to lead atoms in the mineral body is 0.9, when did the cataclysm occur?

42. A certain moon rock was found to contain equal numbers of potassium and argon atoms. Assume that all the argon is the result of radioactive decay of potassium (its half-life is about 1.28×10^9 years) and that one of every

nine potassium atom disintegrations yields an argon atom. What is the age of the rock, measured from the time it contained only potassium?

43. A pitcher of buttermilk initially at 25°C is to be cooled by setting it on the front porch, where the temperature if 0°C. Suppose that the temperature of the buttermilk has dropped to 15°C after 20 min. When will it be at 5°C?

44. When sugar is dissolved in water, the amount A that remains undissolved after t minutes satisfies the differential equation $dA/dt = -kA$ $(k > 0)$. If 25% of the sugar dissolves after 1 min, how long does it take for half of the sugar to dissolve?

45. The intensity I of light at a depth of x meters below the surface of a lake satisfies the differential equation $dI/dx = (-1.4)I$. **(a)** At what depth is the intensity half the intensity I_0 at the surface (where $x = 0$)? **(b)** What is the intensity at a depth of 10 m (as a fraction of I_0)? **(c)** At what depth will the intensity be 1% of that at the surface?

46. The barometric pressure p (in inches of mercury) at an altitude x miles above sea level satisfies the initial value problem $dp/dx = (-0.2)p$, $p(0) = 29.92$. **(a)** Calculate the barometric pressure at 10,000 ft and again at 30,000 ft. **(b)** Without prior conditioning, few people can survive when the pressure drops to less than 15 in. of mercury. How high is that?

47. A certain piece of dubious information about phenylethylamine in the drinking water began to spread one day in a city with a population of 100,000. Within a week, 10,000 people had heard this rumor. Assume that the rate of increase of the number who have heard the rumor is proportional to the number who have not yet heard it. How long will it be until half the population of the city has heard the rumor?

48. According to one cosmological theory, there were equal amounts of the two uranium isotopes ^{235}U and ^{238}U at the creation of the universe in the "big bang." At present there are 137.7 atoms of ^{238}U for each atom of ^{235}U. Using the half-lives 4.51×10^9 years for ^{238}U and 7.10×10^8 years for ^{235}U, calculate the age of the universe.

49. A cake is removed from an oven at 210°F and left to cool at room temperature, which is 70°F. After 30 min the temperature of the cake is 140°F. When will it be 100°F?

50. The amount $A(t)$ of atmospheric pollutants in a certain mountain valley grows naturally and is tripling every 7.5 years.

   (a) If the initial amount is 10 pu (pollutant units), write a formula for $A(t)$ giving the amount (in pu) present after t years.

   (b) What will be the amount (in pu) of pollutants present in the valley atmosphere after 5 years?

   (c) If it will be dangerous to stay in the valley when the amount of pollutants reaches 100 pu, how long will this take?

51. An accident at a nuclear power plant has left the surrounding area polluted with radioactive material that decays naturally. The initial amount of radioactive material present is 15 su (safe units), and 5 months later it is still 10 su.

(a) Write a formula giving the amount $A(t)$ of radioactive material (in su) remaining after t months.

(b) What amount of radioactive material will remain after 8 months?

(c) How long—total number of months or fraction thereof—will it be until $A = 1$ su, so it is safe for people to return to the area?

52. There are now about 3300 different human "language families" in the whole world. Assume that all these are derived from a single original language, and that a language family develops into 1.5 language families every 6 thousand years. About how long ago was the single original human language spoken?

53. Thousands of years ago ancestors of the Native Americans crossed the Bering Strait from Asia and entered the western hemisphere. Since then, they have fanned out across North and South America. The single language that the original Native Americans spoke has since split into many Indian "language families." Assume (as in Problem 52) that the number of these language families has been multiplied by 1.5 every 6000 years. There are now 150 Native American language families in the western hemisphere. About when did the ancestors of today's Native Americans arrive?

54. A tank is shaped like a vertical cylinder; it initially contains water to a depth of 9 ft, and a bottom plug is removed at time $t = 0$ (hours). After 1 h the depth of the water has dropped to 4 ft. How long does it take for all the water to drain from the tank?

55. Suppose that the tank of Problem 48 has a radius of 3 ft and that its bottom hole is circular with radius 1 in. How long will it take the water (initially 9 ft deep) to drain completely?

56. At time $t = 0$ the bottom plug (at the vertex) of a full conical water tank 16 ft high is removed. After 1 h the water in the tank is 9 ft deep. When will the tank be empty?

57. Suppose that a cylindrical tank initially containing V_0 gallons of water drains (through a bottom hole) in T minutes. Use Torricelli's law to show that the volume of water in the tank after $t \leq T$ minutes is $V = V_0 \left[1 - (t/T)\right]^2$.

58. A water tank has the shape obtained by revolving the curve $y = x^{4/3}$ around the y-axis. A plug at the bottom is removed at 12 noon, when the depth of water in the tank is 12 ft. At 1 P.M. the depth of the water is 6 ft. When will the tank be empty?

59. A water tank has the shape obtained by revolving the parabola $x^2 = by$ around the y-axis. The water depth is 4 ft at 12 noon, when a circular plug in the bottom of the tank is removed. At 1 P.M. the depth of the water is 1 ft. (a) Find the depth $y(t)$ of water remaining after t hours. (b) When will the tank be empty? (c) If the initial radius

of the top surface of the water is 2 ft, what is the radius of the circular hole in the bottom?

60. A cylindrical tank with length 5 ft and radius 3 ft is situated with its axis horizontal. If a circular bottom hole with a radius of 1 in. is opened and the tank is initially half full of xylene, how long will it take for the liquid to drain completely?

61. A spherical tank of radius 4 ft is full of gasoline when a circular bottom hole with radius 1 in. is opened. How long will be required for all the gasoline to drain from the tank?

62. Suppose that an initially full hemispherical water tank of radius 1 m has its flat side as its bottom. It has a bottom hole of radius 1 cm. If this bottom hole is opened at 1 P.M., when will the tank be empty?

63. Consider the initially full hemispherical water tank of Example 8, except that the radius r of its circular bottom hole is now unknown. At 1 P.M. the bottom hole is opened and at 1:30 P.M. the depth of water in the tank is 2 ft. (a) Use Torricelli's law in the form $dV/dt = -(0.6)\pi r^2 \sqrt{2gy}$ (taking constriction into account) to determine when the tank will be empty. (b) What is the radius of the bottom hole?

64. (The clepsydra, or water clock) A 12-h water clock is to be designed with the dimensions shown in Fig. 1.4.10, shaped like the surface obtained by revolving the curve $y = f(x)$ around the y-axis. What should be this curve, and what should be the radius of the circular bottom hole, in order that the water level will fall at the constant rate of 4 inches per hour (in./h)?

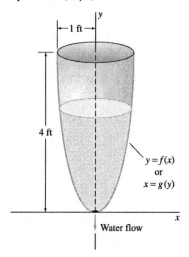

FIGURE 1.4.10. The clepsydra.

65. Just before midday the body of an apparent homicide victim is found in a room that is kept at a constant temperature of 70°F. At 12 noon the temperature of the body is 80°F and at 1 P.M. it is 75°F. Assume that the temperature of the body at the time of death was 98.6°F and that it has cooled in accord with Newton's law. What was the time of death?

66. Early one morning it began to snow at a constant rate. At 7 A.M. a snowplow set off to clear a road. By 8 A.M. it had traveled 2 miles, but it took two more hours (until 10 A.M.) for the snowplow to go an additional 2 miles. (a) Let $t = 0$ when it began to snow and let x denote the distance traveled by the snowplow at time t. Assuming that the snowplow clears snow from the road at a constant rate (in cubic feet per hour, say), show that

$$k\frac{dx}{dt} = \frac{1}{t}$$

where k is a constant. (b) What time did it start snowing? (*Answer:* 6 A.M.)

67. A snowplow sets off at 7 A.M. as in Problem 60. Suppose now that by 8 A.M. it had traveled 4 miles and that by 9 A.M. it had moved an additional 3 miles. What time did it start snowing? This is a more difficult snowplow problem because now a transcendental equation must be solved numerically to find the value of k. (*Answer:* 4:27 A.M.)

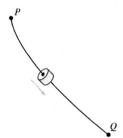

FIGURE 1.4.11. A bead sliding down a wire—the brachistochrone problem.

68. Figure 1.4.11 shows a bead sliding down a frictionless wire from point P to point Q. The *brachistochrone problem* asks what shape the wire should be in order to minimize the bead's time of descent from P to Q. In June of 1696, John Bernoulli proposed this problem as a public challenge, with a 6-month deadline (later extended to Easter 1697 at George Leibniz's request). Isaac Newton, then retired from academic life and serving as Warden of the Mint in London, received Bernoulli's challenge on January 29, 1697. The very next day he communicated his own solution—the curve of minimal descent time is an arc of an inverted cycloid—to the Royal Society of London. For a modern derivation of this result, suppose the bead starts from rest at the origin P and let $y = y(x)$ be the equation of the desired curve in a coordinate system with the y-axis pointing downward. Then a mechanical analogue of Snell's law in optics implies that

$$\frac{\sin \alpha}{v} = \text{constant}, \qquad \text{(i)}$$

where α denotes the angle of deflection (from the vertical) of the tangent line to the curve—so $\cot \alpha = y'(x)$ (why?)—and $v = \sqrt{2gy}$ is the bead's velocity when it has descended a distance y vertically (from KE $= \frac{1}{2}mv^2 = mgy = -$PE).

(a) First derive from Eq. (i) the differential equation

$$\frac{dy}{dx} = \sqrt{\frac{2a - y}{y}}, \qquad \text{(ii)}$$

where a is an appropriate positive constant.

(b) Substitute $y = 2a \sin^2 t$, $dy = 4a \sin t \cos t\, dt$ in (ii) to derive the solution

$$x = a(2t - \sin 2t), \quad y = a(1 - \cos 2t) \qquad \text{(iii)}$$

for which $t = y = 0$ when $x = 0$. Finally, the substitution of $\theta = 2a$ in (iii) yields the standard parametric equations $x = a(\theta - \sin \theta)$, $y = a(1 - \cos \theta)$ of the cycloid that is generated by a point on the rim of a circular wheel of radius a as it rolls along the x-axis. [See Example 5 in Section 10.4 of Edwards and Penney, *Calculus*, 6th edition (Upper Saddle River, NJ: Prentice Hall, 2002).]

69. Suppose a uniform flexible cable is suspended between two points $(\pm L, H)$ at equal heights located symmetrically on either side of the x-axis (Fig. 1.4.12). Principles of physics can be used to show that the shape $y = y(x)$ of the hanging cable satisfies the differential equation

$$a\frac{d^2 y}{dx^2} = \sqrt{1 + \left(\frac{dy}{dx}\right)^2},$$

where the constant $a = T/\rho$ is the ratio of the cable's tension T at its lowest point $x = 0$ (where $y'(0) = 0$) and its (constant) linear density ρ. If we substitute $v = dy/dx$, $dv/dx = d^2 y/dx^2$ in this second-order differential equation, we get the first-order equation

$$a\frac{dv}{dx} = \sqrt{1 + v^2}.$$

Solve this differential equation for $y'(x) = v(x) = \sinh(x/a)$. Then integrate to get the shape function

$$y(x) = a \cosh\left(\frac{x}{a}\right) + C$$

of the hanging cable. This curve is called a *catenary*, from the Latin word for *chain*.

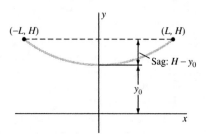

FIGURE 1.4.12. The catenary.

1.4 Application: The Logistic Equation

As in Eq. (3) of this section, the solution of a separable differential equation reduces to the evaluation of two indefinite integrals. It is tempting to use a symbolic algebra system for this purpose. We illustrate this approach using the *logistic differential equation*

$$\frac{dx}{dt} = ax - bx^2 \tag{1}$$

that models a population $x(t)$ with births (per unit time) proportional to x and deaths proportional to x^2. Here we concentrate on the solution of Eq. (1) and defer discussion of population applications to Section 2.1.

If $a = 0.01$ and $b = 0.0001$, for instance, Eq. (1) is

$$\frac{dx}{dt} = (0.01)x - (0.0001)x^2 = \frac{x}{10000}(100 - x). \tag{2}$$

Separation of variables leads to

$$\int \frac{1}{x(100 - x)}\, dx = \int \frac{1}{10000}\, dt = \frac{t}{10000} + C. \tag{3}$$

FIGURE 1.4.13. TI-89 screen showing the integral in Eq. (3).

We can evaluate the integral on the left by using the *Maple* command

    `int(1/(x*(100 - x)), x);`

the *Mathematica* command

    `Integrate[ 1/(x*(100 - x)), x ]`

or the MATLAB command

    `syms x;   int(1/(x*(100 - x)))`

Any computer algebra system gives a result of the form

$$\frac{1}{100}\ln x - \frac{1}{100}\ln(x - 100) = \frac{t}{10000} + C \tag{4}$$

equivalent to the graphing calculator result shown in Fig. 1.4.13.

You can now apply the initial condition $x(0) = x_0$, combine logarithms, and finally exponentiate to solve Eq. (4) for the particular solution

$$x(t) = \frac{100 x_0 e^{t/100}}{100 - x_0 + x_0 e^{t/100}} \tag{5}$$

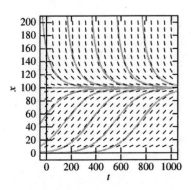

FIGURE 1.4.14. Slope field and solution curves for $x' = (0.01)x - (0.0001)x^2$.

of Eq. (2). The slope field and solution curves shown in Fig. 1.4.14 suggest that, whatever is the initial value x_0, the solution $x(t)$ approaches 100 as $t \to +\infty$. Can you use Eq. (5) to verify this conjecture?

INVESTIGATION: For your own personal logistic equation, take $a = m/n$ and $b = 1/n$ in Eq. (1), with m and n being the *largest* two distinct digits (in either order) in your student ID number.

(a) First generate a slope field for your differential equation and include a sufficient number of solution curves that you can see what happens to the population as $t \to +\infty$. State your inference plainly.

(b) Next use a computer algebra system to solve the differential equation symbolically; then use the symbolic solution to find the limit of $x(t)$ as $t \to +\infty$. Was your graphically based inference correct?

(c) Finally, state and solve a numerical problem using the symbolic solution. For instance, how long does it take x to grow from a selected initial value x_0 to a given target value x_1?

1.5 Linear First-Order Equations

In Section 1.4 we saw how to solve a separable differential equation by integrating *after* multiplying both sides by an appropriate factor. For instance, to solve the equation

$$\frac{dy}{dx} = 2xy \quad (y > 0),$$ (1)

we multiply both sides by the factor $1/y$ to get

$$\frac{1}{y} \cdot \frac{dy}{dx} = 2x; \quad \text{that is,} \quad D_x (\ln y) = D_x \left(x^2\right).$$ (2)

Because each side of the equation in (2) is recognizable as a *derivative* (with respect to the independent variable x), all that remains are two simple integrations, which yield $\ln y = x^2 + C$. For this reason, the function $\rho(y) = 1/y$ is called an *integrating factor* for the original equation in (1). An **integrating factor** for a differential equation is a function $\rho(x, y)$ such that the multiplication of each side of the differential equation by $\rho(x, y)$ yields an equation in which each side is recognizable as a derivative.

With the aid of the appropriate integrating factor, there is a standard technique for solving the **linear first-order equation**

$$\blacktriangleright \qquad \frac{dy}{dx} + P(x)y = Q(x)$$ (3)

on an interval on which the coefficient functions $P(x)$ and $Q(x)$ are continuous. We multiply each side in Eq. (3) by the integrating factor

$$\blacktriangleright \qquad \rho(x) = e^{\int P(x)\,dx}.$$ (4)

The result is

$$e^{\int P(x)\,dx} \frac{dy}{dx} + P(x)e^{\int P(x)\,dx} y = Q(x)e^{\int P(x)\,dx}.$$ (5)

Because

$$D_x \left[\int P(x)\,dx\right] = P(x),$$

the left-hand side is the derivative of the *product* $y(x) \cdot e^{\int P(x)\,dx}$, so Eq. (5) is equivalent to

$$D_x \left[y(x) \cdot e^{\int P(x)\,dx} \right] = Q(x) e^{\int P(x)\,dx}.$$

Integration of both sides of this equation gives

$$y(x) e^{\int P(x)\,dx} = \int \left(Q(x) e^{\int P(x)\,dx} \right)\,dx + C.$$

Finally, solving for y, we obtain the general solution of the linear first-order equation in (3):

$$y(x) = e^{-\int P(x)\,dx} \left[\int \left(Q(x) e^{\int P(x)\,dx} \right)\,dx + C \right]. \tag{6}$$

This formula should **not** be memorized. In a specific problem it generally is simpler to use the *method* by which we developed the formula. That is, in order to solve an equation that can be written in the form in Eq. (3) with the coefficient functions $P(x)$ and $Q(x)$ displayed explicitly, you should attempt to carry out the following steps.

METHOD: SOLUTION OF FIRST-ORDER LINEAR EQUATIONS

1. Begin by calculating the integrating factor $\rho(x) = e^{\int P(x)\,dx}$.
2. Then multiply both sides of the differential equation by $\rho(x)$.
3. Next, recognize the left-hand side of the resulting equation as the derivative of a product:
$$D_x [\rho(x)y(x)] = \rho(x)Q(x).$$
4. Finally, integrate this equation,

$$\rho(x)y(x) = \int \rho(x)Q(x)\,dx + C;$$

then solve for y to obtain the general solution of the original differential equation.

Remark 1:   Given an initial condition $y(x_0) = y_0$, you can (as usual) substitute $x = x_0$ and $y = y_0$ into the general solution and solve for the value of C yielding the particular solution that satisfies this initial condition.

Remark 2:   You need not supply explicitly a constant of integration when you find the integrating factor $\rho(x)$. For if we replace

$$\int P(x)\,dx \quad \text{with} \quad \int P(x)\,dx + K$$

in Eq. (4), the result is

$$\rho(x) = e^{K + \int P(x)\,dx} = e^K e^{\int P(x)\,dx}.$$

But the constant factor e^K does not affect materially the result of multiplying both sides of the differential equation in (3) by $\rho(x)$, so we might as well take $K = 0$. You may therefore choose for $\int P(x)\,dx$ *any* convenient antiderivative of $P(x)$, without bothering to add a constant of integration. ■

Example 1

Solve the initial value problem

$$\frac{dy}{dx} - y = \tfrac{11}{8}e^{-x/3}, \quad y(0) = -1.$$

Solution

Here we have $P(x) \equiv -1$ and $Q(x) = \tfrac{11}{8}e^{-x/3}$, so the integrating factor is

$$\rho(x) = e^{\int (-1)\,dx} = e^{-x}.$$

Multiplication of both sides of the given equation by e^{-x} yields

$$e^{-x}\frac{dy}{dx} - e^{-x}y = \tfrac{11}{8}e^{-4x/3}, \tag{7}$$

which we recognize as

$$\frac{d}{dx}\left(e^{-x}y\right) = \tfrac{11}{8}e^{-4x/3}.$$

Hence integration with respect to x gives

$$e^{-x}y = \int \tfrac{11}{8}e^{-4x/3}\,dx = -\tfrac{33}{32}e^{-4x/3} + C,$$

and multiplication by e^x gives the general solution

$$y(x) = Ce^x - \tfrac{33}{32}e^{-x/3}. \tag{8}$$

Substitution of $x = 0$ and $y = -1$ now gives $C = \tfrac{1}{32}$, so the desired particular solution is

$$y(x) = \tfrac{1}{32}e^x - \tfrac{33}{32}e^{-x/3} = \tfrac{1}{32}\left(e^x - 33e^{-x/3}\right). \quad \blacksquare$$

Remark: Figure 1.5.1 shows a slope field and typical solution curves for Eq. (7), including the one passing through the point $(0, -1)$. Note that some solutions grow rapidly in the positive direction as x increases, while others grow rapidly in the negative direction. The behavior of a given solution curve is determined by its initial condition $y(0) = y_0$. The two types of behavior are separated by the particular solution $y(x) = -\tfrac{33}{32}e^{-x/3}$ for which $C = 0$ in Eq. (8), so $y_0 = -\tfrac{33}{32}$ for the solution curve that is dashed in Fig. 1.5.1. If $y_0 > -\tfrac{33}{32}$, then $C > 0$ in Eq. (8), so the term e^x eventually dominates the behavior of $y(x)$, and hence $y(x) \to +\infty$ as $x \to +\infty$. But if $y_0 < -\tfrac{33}{32}$, then $C < 0$, so both terms in $y(x)$ are negative and therefore $y(x) \to -\infty$ as $x \to +\infty$. Thus the initial condition $y_0 = -\tfrac{33}{32}$ is *critical* in the sense that solutions that start above $-\tfrac{33}{32}$ on the y-axis grow in the positive direction, while solutions that start lower than $-\tfrac{33}{32}$ grow in the negative direction as $x \to +\infty$. The interpretation of a mathematical model often hinges on finding such a critical condition that separates one kind of behavior of a solution from a different kind of behavior. $\quad \blacksquare$

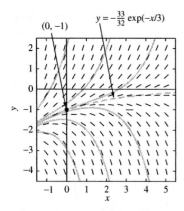

$y = -\tfrac{33}{32}\exp(-x/3)$

$(0, -1)$

FIGURE 1.5.1. Slope field and solution curves for $y' = y + \tfrac{11}{8}e^{-x/3}$.

Example 2

Find a general solution of

$$(x^2 + 1)\frac{dy}{dx} + 3xy = 6x. \tag{9}$$

Solution   After division of both sides of the equation by $x^2 + 1$, we recognize the result

$$\frac{dy}{dx} + \frac{3x}{x^2+1}y = \frac{6x}{x^2+1}$$

as a first-order linear equation with $P(x) = 3x/(x^2 + 1)$ and $Q(x) = 6x/(x^2 + 1)$. Multiplication by

$$\rho(x) = \exp\left(\int \frac{3x}{x^2+1}\,dx\right) = \exp\left(\tfrac{3}{2}\ln(x^2+1)\right) = (x^2+1)^{3/2}$$

yields

$$(x^2+1)^{3/2}\frac{dy}{dx} + 3x(x^2+1)^{1/2}y = 6x(x^2+1)^{1/2},$$

and thus

$$D_x\left[(x^2+1)^{3/2}y\right] = 6x(x^2+1)^{1/2}.$$

Integration then yields

$$(x^2+1)^{3/2}y = \int 6x(x^2+1)^{1/2}\,dx = 2(x^2+1)^{3/2} + C.$$

Multiplication of both sides by $(x^2+1)^{-3/2}$ gives the general solution

$$y(x) = 2 + C(x^2+1)^{-3/2}. \tag{10}$$

■

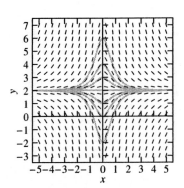

FIGURE 1.5.2. Slope field and solution curves for the differential equation in Eq. (9).

Remark: Figure 1.5.2 shows a slope field and typical solution curves for Eq. (9). Note that, as $x \to +\infty$, all other solution curves approach the constant solution curve $y(x) \equiv 2$ that corresponds to $C = 0$ in Eq. (10). This constant solution can be described as an *equilibrium solution* of the differential equation, because $y(0) = 2$ implies that $y(x) = 2$ for all x (and thus the value of the solution remains forever where it starts). ■

A Closer Look at the Method

The preceding derivation of the solution in Eq. (6) of the linear first-order equation $y' + Py = Q$ bears closer examination. Suppose that the coefficient functions $P(x)$ and $Q(x)$ are continuous on the (possibly unbounded) open interval I. Then the antiderivatives

$$\int P(x)\,dx \quad \text{and} \quad \int \left(Q(x)e^{\int P(x)\,dx}\right) dx$$

exist on I. Our derivation of Eq. (6) shows that *if* $y = y(x)$ is a solution of Eq. (3) on I, *then* $y(x)$ is given by the formula in Eq. (6) for some choice of the constant C. Conversely, you may verify by direct substitution (Problem 31) that the function $y(x)$ given in Eq. (6) satisfies Eq. (3). Finally, given a point x_0 of I and any number y_0, there is—as previously noted—a unique value of C such that $y(x_0) = y_0$. Consequently, we have proved the following existence-uniqueness theorem.

THEOREM 1: The Linear First-Order Equation

If the functions $P(x)$ and $Q(x)$ are continuous on the open interval I containing the point x_0, then the initial value problem

$$\frac{dy}{dx} + P(x)y = Q(x), \quad y(x_0) = y_0 \tag{11}$$

has a unique solution $y(x)$ on I, given by the formula in Eq. (6) with an appropriate value of C. ▲

Remark 1: Theorem 1 gives a solution on the *entire* interval I for a *linear* differential equation, in contrast with Theorem 1 of Section 1.3, which guarantees only a solution on a possibly smaller interval.

Remark 2: Theorem 1 tells us that every solution of Eq. (3) is included in the general solution given in Eq. (6). Thus a *linear* first-order differential equation has *no* singular solutions.

Remark 3: The appropriate value of the constant C in Eq. (6)—as needed to solve the initial value problem in Eq. (11)—can be selected "automatically" by writing

$$\rho(x) = \exp\left(\int_{x_0}^{x} P(t)\,dt\right),$$

$$y(x) = \frac{1}{\rho(x)}\left[y_0 + \int_{x_0}^{x} \rho(t)Q(t)\,dt\right]. \tag{12}$$

The indicated limits x_0 and x effect a choice of indefinite integrals in Eq. (6) that guarantees in advance that $\rho(x_0) = 1$ and that $y(x_0) = y_0$ [as you can verify directly by substituting $x = x_0$ in Eq. (12)]. ■

Example 3

Solve the initial value problem

$$x^2\frac{dy}{dx} + xy = \sin x, \quad y(1) = y_0. \tag{13}$$

Solution Division by x^2 gives the linear first-order equation

$$\frac{dy}{dx} + \frac{1}{x}y = \frac{\sin x}{x^2}$$

with $P(x) = 1/x$ and $Q(x) = (\sin x)/x^2$. With $x_0 = 1$ the integrating factor in (12) is

$$\rho(x) = \exp\left(\int_{1}^{x}\frac{1}{t}\,dt\right) = \exp(\ln x) = x,$$

so the desired particular solution is given by

$$y(x) = \frac{1}{x}\left[y_0 + \int_{1}^{x}\frac{\sin t}{t}\,dt\right]. \tag{14}$$

In accord with Theorem 1, this solution is defined on the whole positive x-axis. ■

Comment: In general, an integral such as the one in Eq. (14) would (for given x) need to be approximated numerically—using Simpson's rule, for instance—to find the value $y(x)$ of the solution at x. In this case, however, we have the sine integral function

$$\text{Si}(x) = \int_0^x \frac{\sin t}{t}\, dt,$$

which appears with sufficient frequency in applications that its values have been tabulated. A good set of tables of special functions is Abramowitz and Stegun, *Handbook of Mathematical Functions* (New York: Dover, 1965). Then the particular solution in Eq. (14) reduces to

$$y(x) = \frac{1}{x}\left[y_0 + \int_0^x \frac{\sin t}{t}\, dt - \int_0^1 \frac{\sin t}{t}\, dt \right] = \frac{1}{x}\left[y_0 + \text{Si}(x) - \text{Si}(1) \right]. \qquad (15)$$

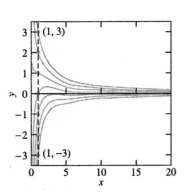

FIGURE 1.5.3. Typical solution curves defined by Eq. (15).

The sine integral function is available in most scientific computing systems and can be used to plot typical solution curves defined by Eq. (15). Figure 1.5.3 shows a selection of solution curves with initial values $y(1) = y_0$ ranging from $y_0 = -3$ to $y_0 = 3$. It appears that on each solution curve, $y(x) \to 0$ as $x \to +\infty$, and this is in fact true because the sine integral function is bounded. ∎

In the sequel we will see that it is the exception—rather than the rule—when a solution of a differential equation can be expressed in terms of elementary functions. We will study various devices for obtaining good approximations to the values of the nonelementary functions we encounter. In Chapter 2 we will discuss numerical integration of differential equations in some detail.

Mixture Problems

As a first application of linear first-order equations, we consider a tank containing a solution—a mixture of solute and solvent—such as salt dissolved in water. There is both inflow and outflow, and we want to compute the *amount* $x(t)$ of solute in the tank at time t, given the amount $x(0) = x_0$ at time $t = 0$. Suppose that solution with a concentration of c_i grams of solute per liter of solution flows into the tank at the constant rate of r_i liters per second, and that the solution in the tank—kept thoroughly mixed by stirring—flows out at the constant rate of r_o liters per second.

To set up a differential equation for $x(t)$, we estimate the change Δx in x during the brief time interval $[t, t + \Delta t]$. The amount of solute that flows into the tank during Δt seconds is $r_i c_i \Delta t$ grams. To check this, note how the cancellation of dimensions checks our computations:

$$\left(r_i\, \frac{\text{liters}}{\text{second}} \right) \left(c_i\, \frac{\text{grams}}{\text{liter}} \right) (\Delta t\ \text{seconds})$$

Input: r_i L/s, c_i g/L

Amount $x(t)$
Volume $V(t)$
Concentration $c_o(t) = \frac{x}{V}$

Output:
r_o L/s,
c_o g/L

FIGURE 1.5.4. The single-tank mixture problem.

yields a quantity measured in grams.

The amount of solute that flows out of the tank during the same time interval depends on the concentration $c_o(t)$ of solute in the solution at time t. But as noted in Fig. 1.5.4, $c_o(t) = x(t)/V(t)$, where $V(t)$ denotes the volume (not constant unless $r_i = r_o$) of solution in the tank at time t. Then

$$\Delta x = \{\text{grams input}\} - \{\text{grams output}\} \approx r_i c_i \Delta t - r_o c_o \Delta t.$$

We now divide by Δt:

$$\frac{\Delta x}{\Delta t} \approx r_i c_i - r_o c_o.$$

Finally, we take the limit as $\Delta t \to 0$; if all the functions involved are continuous and $x(t)$ is differentiable, then the error in this approximation also approaches zero, and we obtain the differential equation

$$\frac{dx}{dt} = r_i c_i - r_o c_o, \tag{16}$$

in which r_i, c_i, and r_o are constants, but c_o denotes the variable concentration

$$c_o(t) = \frac{x(t)}{V(t)} \tag{17}$$

of solute in the tank at time t. Thus the amount $x(t)$ of solute in the tank satisfies the differential equation

$$\frac{dx}{dt} = r_i c_i - \frac{r_o}{V} x. \tag{18}$$

If $V_0 = V(0)$, then $V(t) = V_0 + (r_i - r_o)t$, so Eq. (18) is a linear first-order differential equation for the amount $x(t)$ of solute in the tank at time t.

Important: Equation (18) need not be committed to memory. It is the process we used to obtain that equation—examination of the behavior of the system over a short time interval $[t, t + \Delta t]$—that you should strive to understand, because it is a very useful tool for obtaining all sorts of differential equations.

Remark: It was convenient for us to use g/L mass/volume units in deriving Eq. (18). But any other consistent system of units can be used to measure amounts of solute and volumes of solution. In the following example we measure both in cubic kilometers. ∎

Example 4 Assume that Lake Erie has a volume of 480 km³ and that its rate of inflow (from Lake Huron) and outflow (to Lake Ontario) are both 350 km³ per year. Suppose that at the time $t = 0$ (years), the pollutant concentration of Lake Erie—caused by past industrial pollution that has now been ordered to cease—is five times that of Lake Huron. If the outflow henceforth is perfectly mixed lake water, how long will it take to reduce the pollution concentration in Lake Erie to twice that of Lake Huron?

Solution Here we have

$$V = 480 \quad (\text{km}^3),$$
$$r_i = r_o = r = 350 \ (\text{km}^3/\text{yr}),$$
$$c_i = c \ (\text{the pollutant concentration of Lake Huron}), \text{and}$$
$$x_0 = x(0) = 5cV,$$

and the question is this: When is $x(t) = 2cV$? With this notation, Eq. (18) is the separable equation

$$\frac{dx}{dt} = rc - \frac{r}{V} x, \tag{19}$$

which we rewrite in the linear first-order form

$$\frac{dx}{dt} + px = q \tag{20}$$

with constant coefficients $p = r/V$, $q = rc$, and integrating factor $\rho = e^{pt}$. You can either solve this equation directly or apply the formula in (12). The latter gives

$$x(t) = e^{-pt} \left[x_0 + \int_0^t q e^{pt} \, dt \right] = e^{-pt} \left[x_0 + \frac{q}{p} \left(e^{pt} - 1 \right) \right]$$

$$= e^{-rt/V} \left[5cV + \frac{rc}{r/V} \left(e^{rt/V} - 1 \right) \right];$$

$$x(t) = cV + 4cV e^{-rt/V}. \tag{21}$$

To find when $x(t) = 2cV$, we therefore need only solve the equation

$$cV + 4cV e^{-rt/V} = 2cV \quad \text{for} \quad t = \frac{V}{r} \ln 4 = \frac{480}{350} \ln 4 \approx 1.901 \text{ (years)}. \qquad \blacksquare$$

| **Example 5** | A 120-gallon (gal) tank initially contains 90 lb of salt dissolved in 90 gal of water. Brine containing 2 lb/gal of salt flows into the tank at the rate of 4 gal/min, and the well-stirred mixture flows out of the tank at the rate of 3 gal/min. How much salt does the tank contain when it is full? |

Solution The interesting feature of this example is that, due to the differing rates of inflow and outflow, the volume of brine in the tank increases steadily with $V(t) = 90 + t$ gallons. The change Δx in the amount x of salt in the tank from time t to time $t + \Delta t$ (minutes) is given by

$$\Delta x \approx (4)(2)\Delta t - 3 \left(\frac{x}{90 + t} \right) \Delta t,$$

so our differential equation is

$$\frac{dx}{dt} + \frac{3}{90 + t} x = 8.$$

An integrating factor is

$$\rho(x) = \exp \left(\int \frac{3}{90 + t} \, dt \right) = e^{3 \ln(90+t)} = (90 + t)^3,$$

which gives

$$D_t \left[(90 + t)^3 x \right] = 8(90 + t)^3;$$
$$(90 + t)^3 x = 2(90 + t)^4 + C.$$

Substitution of $x(0) = 90$ gives $C = -(90)^4$, so the amount of salt in the tank at time t is

$$x(t) = 2(90 + t) - \frac{90^4}{(90 + t)^3}.$$

The tank is full after 30 min, and when $t = 30$, we have

$$x(30) = 2(90 + 30) - \frac{90^4}{120^3} \approx 202 \text{ (lb)}$$

of salt in the tank. $\qquad \blacksquare$

1.5 Problems

Find general solutions of the differential equations in Problems 1 through 25. If an initial condition is given, find the corresponding particular solution. Throughout, primes denote derivatives with respect to x.

1. $y' + y = 2$, $y(0) = 0$
2. $y' - 2y = 3e^{2x}$, $y(0) = 0$
3. $y' + 3y = 2xe^{-3x}$
4. $y' - 2xy = e^{x^2}$
5. $xy' + 2y = 3x$, $y(1) = 5$
6. $xy' + 5y = 7x^2$, $y(2) = 5$
7. $2xy' + y = 10\sqrt{x}$
8. $3xy' + y = 12x$
9. $xy' - y = x$, $y(1) = 7$
10. $2xy' - 3y = 9x^3$
11. $xy' + y = 3xy$, $y(1) = 0$
12. $xy' + 3y = 2x^5$, $y(2) = 1$
13. $y' + y = e^x$, $y(0) = 1$
14. $xy' - 3y = x^3$, $y(1) = 10$
15. $y' + 2xy = x$, $y(0) = -2$
16. $y' = (1 - y)\cos x$, $y(\pi) = 2$
17. $(1 + x)y' + y = \cos x$, $y(0) = 1$
18. $xy' = 2y + x^3 \cos x$
19. $y' + y \cot x = \cos x$
20. $y' = 1 + x + y + xy$, $y(0) = 0$
21. $xy' = 3y + x^4 \cos x$, $y(2\pi) = 0$
22. $y' = 2xy + 3x^2 \exp(x^2)$, $y(0) = 5$
23. $xy' + (2x - 3)y = 4x^4$
24. $(x^2 + 4)y' + 3xy = x$, $y(0) = 1$
25. $(x^2 + 1)\dfrac{dy}{dx} + 3x^3 y = 6x \exp\left(-\tfrac{3}{2}x^2\right)$, $y(0) = 1$

Solve the differential equations in Problems 26 through 28 by regarding y as the independent variable rather than x.

26. $(1 - 4xy^2)\dfrac{dy}{dx} = y^3$ 27. $(x + ye^y)\dfrac{dy}{dx} = 1$

28. $(1 + 2xy)\dfrac{dy}{dx} = 1 + y^2$

29. Express the general solution of $dy/dx = 1 + 2xy$ in terms of the **error function**

$$\text{erf}(x) = \frac{2}{\sqrt{\pi}} \int_0^x e^{-t^2}\, dt.$$

30. Express the solution of the initial value problem

$$2x\frac{dy}{dx} = y + 2x \cos x, \quad y(1) = 0$$

as an integral as in Example 3 of this section.

31. **(a)** Show that

$$y_c(x) = Ce^{-\int P(x)\, dx}$$

is a general solution of $dy/dx + P(x)y = 0$.   **(b)** Show that

$$y_p(x) = e^{-\int P(x)\, dx}\left[\int \left(Q(x)e^{\int P(x)\, dx}\right) dx\right]$$

is a particular solution of $dy/dx + P(x)y = Q(x)$.
(c) Suppose that $y_c(x)$ is any general solution of $dy/dx + P(x)y = 0$ and that $y_p(x)$ is any particular solution of $dy/dx + P(x)y = Q(x)$. Show that $y(x) = y_c(x) + y_p(x)$ is a general solution of $dy/dx + P(x)y = Q(x)$.

32. **(a)** Find constants A and B such that $y_p(x) = A \sin x + B \cos x$ is a solution of $dy/dx + y = 2 \sin x$.   **(b)** Use the result of part (a) and the method of Problem 31 to find the general solution of $dy/dx + y = 2 \sin x$.   **(c)** Solve the initial value problem $dy/dx + y = 2 \sin x$, $y(0) = 1$.

33. A tank contains 1000 liters (L) of a solution consisting of 100 kg of salt dissolved in water. Pure water is pumped into the tank at the rate of 5 L/s, and the mixture—kept uniform by stirring— is pumped out at the same rate. How long will it be until only 10 kg of salt remains in the tank?

34. Consider a reservoir with a volume of 8 billion cubic feet (ft^3) and an initial pollutant concentration of 0.25%. There is a daily inflow of 500 million ft^3 of water with a pollutant concentration of 0.05% and an equal daily outflow of the well-mixed water in the reservoir. How long will it take to reduce the pollutant concentration in the reservoir to 0.10%?

35. Rework Example 4 for the case of Lake Ontario. The only differences are that this lake has a volume of 1640 km^3 and an inflow-outflow rate of 410 km^3/year.

36. A tank initially contains 60 gal of pure water. Brine containing 1 lb of salt per gallon enters the tank at 2 gal/min, and the (perfectly mixed) solution leaves the tank at 3 gal/min; thus the tank is empty after exactly 1 h. **(a)** Find the amount of salt in the tank after t minutes. **(b)** What is the maximum amount of salt ever in the tank?

37. A 400-gal tank initially contains 100 gal of brine containing 50 lb of salt. Brine containing 1 lb of salt per gallon enters the tank at the rate of 5 gal/s, and the well-mixed brine in the tank flows out at the rate of 3 gal/s. How much salt will the tank contain when it is full of brine?

38. Consider the *cascade* of two tanks shown in Fig. 1.5.5, with $V_1 = 100$ (gal) and $V_2 = 200$ (gal) the volumes of brine in the two tanks. Each tank also initially contains 50 lb of salt. The three flow rates indicated in the figure are each 5 gal/min, with pure water flowing into tank 1. **(a)** Find the amount $x(t)$ of salt in tank 1 at time t. **(b)** Suppose that $y(t)$ is the amount of salt in tank 2 at time t. Show first that

$$\frac{dy}{dt} = \frac{5x}{100} - \frac{5y}{200},$$

and then solve for $y(t)$, using the function $x(t)$ found in part (a). **(c)** Finally, find the maximum amount of salt ever in tank 2.

FIGURE 1.5.5. A cascade of two tanks.

39. Suppose that in the cascade shown in Fig. 1.5.5, tank 1 initially contains 100 gal of pure ethanol and tank 2 initially contains 100 gal of pure water. Pure water flows into tank 1 at 10 gal/min, and the other two flow rates are also 10 gal/min. **(a)** Find the amounts $x(t)$ and $y(t)$ of ethanol in the two tanks at time $t \geq 0$. **(b)** Find the maximum amount of ethanol ever in tank 2.

40. A multiple cascade is shown in Fig. 1.5.6. At time $t = 0$, tank 0 contains 1 gal of ethanol and 1 gal of water; all the remaining tanks contain 2 gal of pure water each. Pure water is pumped into tank 0 at 1 gal/min, and the varying mixture in each tank is pumped into the one below it at the same rate. Assume, as usual, that the mixtures are kept perfectly uniform by stirring. Let $x_n(t)$ denote the amount of ethanol in tank n at time t.

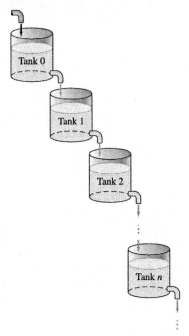

FIGURE 1.5.6. A multiple cascade.

(a) Show that $x_0(t) = e^{-t/2}$. **(b)** Show by induction on n

that

$$x_n(t) = \frac{t^n e^{-t/2}}{n! \, 2^n} \quad \text{for } n > 0.$$

(c) Show that the maximum value of $x_n(t)$ for $n > 0$ is $M_n = n^n e^{-n}/n!$. **(d)** Conclude from **Stirling's approximation** $n! \approx n^n e^{-n} \sqrt{2\pi n}$ that $M_n \approx (2\pi n)^{-1/2}$.

41. A 30-year-old woman accepts an engineering position with a starting salary of \$30,000 per year. Her salary $S(t)$ increases exponentially, with $S(t) = 30 e^{t/20}$ thousand dollars after t years. Meanwhile, 12% of her salary is deposited continuously in a retirement account, which accumulates interest at a continuous annual rate of 6%. **(a)** Estimate ΔA in terms of Δt to derive the differential equation satisfied by the amount $A(t)$ in her retirement account after t years. **(b)** Compute $A(40)$, the amount available for her retirement at age 70.

42. Suppose that a falling hailstone with density $\delta = 1$ starts from rest with negligible radius $r = 0$. Thereafter its radius is $r = kt$ (k is a constant) as it grows by accretion during its fall. Set up and solve the initial value problem

$$\frac{d}{dt}(mv) = mg, \quad v(0) = 0,$$

where m is the variable mass of the hailstone, $v = dy/dt$ is its velocity, and the positive y-axis points downward. Then show that $dv/dt = g/4$. Thus the hailstone falls as though it were under *one-fourth* the influence of gravity.

43. Figure 1.5.7 shows a slope field and typical solution curves for the equation $y' = x - y$. **(a)** Show that every solution curve approaches the straight line $y = x - 1$ as $x \to +\infty$. **(b)** For each of the five values $y_1 = 3.998$, 3.999, 4.000, 4.001, and 4.002, determine the initial value y_0 (accurate to four decimal places) such that $y(5) = y_1$ for the solution satisfying the initial condition $y(-5) = y_0$.

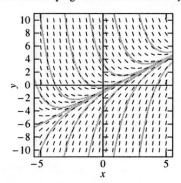

FIGURE 1.5.7. Slope field and solution curves for $y' = x - y$.

44. Figure 1.5.8 shows a slope field and typical solution curves for the equation $y' = x + y$. **(a)** Show that every solution curve approaches the straight line $y = -x - 1$ as $x \to -\infty$. **(b)** For each of the five values $y_1 = -10, -5$, 0, 5, and 10, determine the initial value y_0 (accurate to five decimal places) such that $y(5) = y_1$ for the solution satisfying the initial condition $y(-5) = y_0$.

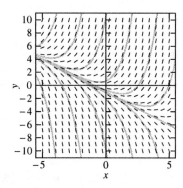

FIGURE 1.5.8. Slope field and solution curves for $y' = x + y$.

Problems 45 and 46 deal with a shallow reservoir that has a one square kilometer water surface and an average water depth of 2 meters. Initially it is filled with fresh water, but at time $t = 0$ water contaminated with a liquid pollutant begins flowing into the reservoir at the rate of 200 thousand cubic meters per month. The well-mixed water in the reservoir flows out at the same rate. Your first task is to find the amount $x(t)$ of pollutant (in millions of liters) in the reservoir after t months.

45. The incoming water has a pollutant concentration of $c(t) = 10$ liters per cubic meter (L/m^3). Verify that the graph of $x(t)$ resembles the steadily rising curve in Fig. 1.5.9, which approaches asymptotically the graph of

the equilibrium solution $x(t) \equiv 20$ that corresponds to the reservoir's long-term pollutant content. How long does it take the pollutant concentration in the reservoir to reach 5 L/m^3?

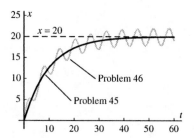

FIGURE 1.5.9. Graphs of solutions in Problems 45 and 46.

46. The incoming water has pollutant concentration $c(t) = 10(1 + \cos t)$ L/m^3 that varies between 0 and 20, with an average concentration of 10 L/m^3 and a period of oscillation of slightly over $6\frac{1}{4}$ months. Does it seem predictable that the lake's polutant content should ultimately oscillate periodically about an average level of 20 million liters? Verify that the graph of $x(t)$ does, indeed, resemble the oscillatory curve shown in Fig. 1.5.9. How long does it take the pollutant concentration in the reservoir to reach 5 L/m^3?

1.5 Application: Indoor Temperature Oscillations

For an interesting applied problem that involves the solution of a linear differential equation, consider indoor temperature oscillations that are driven by outdoor temperature oscillations of the form

$$A(t) = a_0 + a_1 \cos \omega t + b_1 \sin \omega t. \tag{1}$$

If $\omega = \pi/12$, then these oscillations have a period of 24 hours (so that the cycle of outdoor temperatures repeats itself daily). For instance, for a typical July day in Athens, GA with a minimum temperature of 70°F when $t = 4$ (4 A.M.) and a maximum of 90°F when $t = 16$ (4 P.M.), we would take

$$A(t) = 80 - 10 \cos \omega(t - 4) = 80 - 5 \cos \omega t - 5\sqrt{3} \sin \omega t. \tag{2}$$

We derived Eq. (2) by using the identity $\cos(\alpha - \beta) = \cos \alpha \cos \beta + \sin \alpha \sin \beta$ to get $a_0 = 80$, $a_1 = -5$, and $b_1 = -5\sqrt{3}$ in Eq. (1).

If we write Newton's law of cooling [Eq. (3) of Section 1.1] for the corresponding indoor temperature $u(t)$ at time t, but with the outside temperature $A(t)$ given by Eq. (1) instead of a constant ambient temperature A, we get the linear first-order differential equation

$$\frac{du}{dt} = -k(u - A(t));$$

that is,

$$\frac{du}{dt} + ku = k(a_0 + a_1 \cos \omega t + b_1 \sin \omega t) \tag{3}$$

with coefficient functions $P(t) \equiv k$ and $Q(t) = kA(t)$. Typical values of the proportionality constant k range from 0.2 to 0.5 (although k might be greater than 0.5 for a poorly insulated building with open windows, or less than 0.2 for a well-insulated building with tightly sealed windows).

SCENARIO: Suppose that our air conditioner fails at time $t_0 = 0$ one midnight, and we cannot afford to have it repaired until payday at the end of the month. We therefore want to investigate the resulting indoor temperatures that we must endure for the next several days.

Begin your investigation by solving Eq. (3) with the initial condition $u(0) = u_0$ (the indoor temperature at the time of the failure of the air conditioner). You may want to use the integral formulas in 49 and 50 of the endpapers, or possibly a computer algebra system. You should get the solution

$$u(t) = a_0 + c_0 e^{-kt} + c_1 \cos \omega t + d_1 \sin \omega t, \tag{4}$$

where

$$c_0 = u_0 - a_0 - \frac{k^2 a_1 - k\omega b_1}{k^2 + \omega^2},$$

$$c_1 = \frac{k^2 a_1 - k\omega b_1}{k^2 + \omega^2}, \quad d_1 = \frac{k\omega a_1 + k^2 b_1}{k^2 + \omega^2}$$

with $\omega = \pi/12$.

With $a_0 = 80$, $a_1 = -5$, $b_1 = -5\sqrt{3}$ [as in Eq. (2)], $\omega = \pi/12$, and $k = 0.2$ (for instance), this solution reduces (approximately) to

$$u(t) = 80 + e^{-t/5}(u_0 - 82.3351) + (2.3351)\cos\frac{\pi t}{12} - (5.6036)\sin\frac{\pi t}{12}. \tag{5}$$

Observe first that the damped exponential term in Eq. (5) approaches zero as $t \to +\infty$, leaving the long-term "steady periodic" solution

$$u_{\text{sp}}(t) = 80 + (2.3351)\cos\frac{\pi t}{12} - (5.6036)\sin\frac{\pi t}{12}. \tag{6}$$

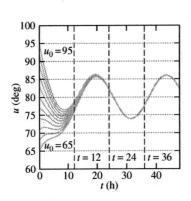

FIGURE 1.5.10. Solution curves given by Eq. (5) with $u_0 = 65, 68, 71, \ldots, 92, 95$.

Consequently, the long-term indoor temperatures oscillate every 24 hours around the same average temperature 80°F as the average outdoor temperature.

Figure 1.5.10 shows a number of solution curves corresponding to possible initial temperatures u_0 ranging from 65°F to 95°F. Observe that—whatever the initial temperature—the indoor temperature "settles down" within about 18 hours to a periodic daily oscillation. But the amplitude of temperature variation is less indoors than outdoors. Indeed, using the trigonometric identity mentioned earlier, Eq. (6) can be rewritten (verify this!) as

$$u(t) = 80 - (6.0707)\cos\left(\frac{\pi t}{12} - 1.9656\right)$$

$$= 80 - (6.0707)\cos\frac{\pi}{12}(t - 7.5082). \tag{7}$$

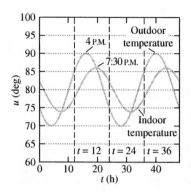

FIGURE 1.5.11. Comparison of indoor and outdoor temperature oscillations.

Do you see that this implies that the indoor temperature varies between a minimum of about 74°F and a maximum of about 86°F?

Finally, comparison of Eqs. (2) and (7) indicates that the indoor temperature lags behind the outdoor temperature by about $7.5082 - 4 \approx 3.5$ hours, as illustrated in Fig. 1.5.11. Thus the temperature inside the house continues to rise until about 7:30 P.M. each evening, so the hottest part of the day inside is early evening rather than late afternoon (as outside).

For a personal problem to investigate, carry out a similar analysis using average July daily maximum/minimum figures for your own locale and a value of k appropriate to your own home. You might also consider a winter day instead of a summer day. (What is the winter-summer difference for the indoor temperature problem?)

1.6 Substitution Methods and Exact Equations

The first-order differential equations we have solved in the previous sections have all been either separable or linear. But many applications involve differential equations that are neither separable nor linear. In this section we illustrate (mainly with examples) substitution methods that sometimes can be used to transform a given differential equation into one that we already know how to solve.

For instance, the differential equation

$$\frac{dy}{dx} = f(x, y), \tag{1}$$

with dependent variable y and independent variable x, may contain a conspicuous combination

$$v = \alpha(x, y) \tag{2}$$

of x and y that suggests itself as a new independent variable v. Thus the differential equation

$$\frac{dy}{dx} = (x + y + 3)^2$$

practically demands the substitution $v = x + y + 3$ of the form in Eq. (2).

If the substitution relation in Eq. (2) can be solved for

$$y = \beta(x, v), \tag{3}$$

then application of the chain rule—regarding v as an (unknown) function of x—yields

$$\frac{dy}{dx} = \frac{\partial \beta}{\partial x}\frac{dx}{dx} + \frac{\partial \beta}{\partial v}\frac{dv}{dx} = \beta_x + \beta_v \frac{dv}{dx}, \tag{4}$$

where the partial derivatives $\partial \beta / \partial x = \beta_x(x, v)$ and $\partial \beta / \partial v = \beta_v(x, v)$ are *known* functions of x and v. If we substitute the right-hand side in (4) for dy/dx in Eq. (1) and then solve for dv/dx, the result is a *new* differential equation of the form

$$\frac{dv}{dx} = g(x, v) \tag{5}$$

with *new* dependent variable v. If this new equation is either separable or linear, then we can apply the methods of preceding sections to solve it.

If $v = v(x)$ is a solution of Eq. (5), then $y = \beta(x, v(x))$ will be a solution of the original Eq. (1). The trick is to select a substitution such that the transformed Eq. (5) is one we can solve. Even when possible, this is not always easy; it may require a fair amount of ingenuity or trial and error.

Example 1 Solve the differential equation

$$\frac{dy}{dx} = (x + y + 3)^2.$$

Solution As indicated earlier, let's try the substitution

$$v = x + y + 3; \quad \text{that is,} \quad y = v - x - 3.$$

Then

$$\frac{dy}{dx} = \frac{dv}{dx} - 1,$$

so the transformed equation is

$$\frac{dv}{dx} = 1 + v^2.$$

This is a separable equation, and we have no difficulty in obtaining its solution

$$x = \int \frac{dv}{1 + v^2} = \tan^{-1} v + C.$$

So $v = \tan(x - C)$. Because $v = x + y + 3$, the general solution of the original equation $dy/dx = (x + y + 3)^2$ is $x + y + 3 = \tan(x - C)$; that is,

$$y(x) = \tan(x - C) - x - 3. \qquad \blacksquare$$

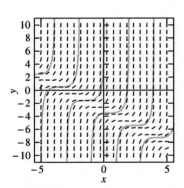

FIGURE 1.6.1. Slope field and solution curves for $y' = (x + y + 3)^2$.

Remark: Figure 1.6.1 shows a slope field and typical solution curves for the differential equation of Example 1. We see that, although the function $f(x, y) = (x+y+3)^2$ is continuously differentiable for all x and y, each solution is continuous only on a bounded interval. In particular, because the tangent function is continuous on the open interval $(-\pi/2, \pi/2)$, the particular solution with arbitrary constant value C is continuous on the interval where $-\pi/2 < x - C < \pi/2$; that is, $C - \pi/2 < x < C + \pi/2$. $\qquad \blacksquare$

Example 1 illustrates the fact that any differential equation of the form

$$\frac{dy}{dx} = F(ax + by + c) \tag{6}$$

can be transformed into a separable equation by use of the substitution $v = ax + by + c$ (see Problem 31). The paragraphs that follow deal with other classes of first-order equations for which there are standard substitutions that are known to succeed.

Homogeneous Equations

A **homogeneous** first-order differential equation is one that can be written in the form

➤
$$\frac{dy}{dx} = F\left(\frac{y}{x}\right). \tag{7}$$

If we make the substitutions

$$v = \frac{y}{x}, \quad y = vx, \quad \frac{dy}{dx} = v + x\frac{dv}{dx}, \tag{8}$$

then Eq. (7) is transformed into the *separable* equation

$$x\frac{dv}{dx} = F(v) - v.$$

Thus every homogeneous first-order differential equation can be reduced to an integration problem by means of the substitutions in (8).

Example 2 Solve the differential equation

$$2xy\frac{dy}{dx} = 4x^2 + 3y^2.$$

Solution This equation is neither separable nor linear, but we recognize it as a homogeneous equation by writing it in the form

$$\frac{dy}{dx} = \frac{4x^2 + 3y^2}{2xy} = 2\left(\frac{x}{y}\right) + \frac{3}{2}\left(\frac{y}{x}\right).$$

The substitutions in (8) then take the form

$$y = vx, \quad \frac{dy}{dx} = v + x\frac{dv}{dx}, \quad v = \frac{y}{x}, \quad \text{and} \quad \frac{1}{v} = \frac{x}{y}.$$

These yield

$$v + x\frac{dv}{dx} = \frac{2}{v} + \frac{3}{2}v,$$

and hence

$$x\frac{dv}{dx} = \frac{2}{v} + \frac{v}{2} = \frac{v^2 + 4}{2v};$$

$$\int \frac{2v}{v^2 + 4}\,dv = \int \frac{1}{x}\,dx;$$

$$\ln(v^2 + 4) = \ln|x| + \ln C.$$

We apply the exponential function to both sides of the last equation to obtain

$$v^2 + 4 = C|x|;$$

$$\frac{y^2}{x^2} + 4 = C|x|;$$

$$y^2 + 4x^2 = kx^3.$$

Note that the left-hand side of this equation is necessarily nonnegative. It follows that $k > 0$ in the case of solutions that are defined for $x > 0$, while $k < 0$ for solutions where $x < 0$. Indeed, the family of solution curves illustrated in Fig. 1.6.2 exhibits symmetry about both coordinate axes. Actually, there are positive-valued and negative-valued solutions of the forms $y(x) = \pm\sqrt{kx^3 - 4x^2}$ that are defined for $x > 4/k$ if the constant k is positive, for $x < 4/k$ if k is negative. ■

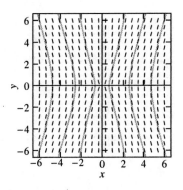

FIGURE 1.6.2. Slope field and solution curves for $2xyy' = 4x^2 + 3y^2$.

Example 3   Solve the initial value problem

$$x\frac{dy}{dx} = y + \sqrt{x^2 - y^2}, \quad y(x_0) = 0$$

where $x_0 > 0$.

Solution   We divide both sides by x and find that

$$\frac{dy}{dx} = \frac{y}{x} + \sqrt{1 - \left(\frac{y}{x}\right)^2},$$

so we make the substitutions in (8); we get

$$v + x\frac{dv}{dx} = v + \sqrt{1 - v^2};$$

$$\int \frac{1}{\sqrt{1 - v^2}}\, dv = \int \frac{1}{x}\, dx;$$

$$\sin^{-1} v = \ln x + C.$$

We need not write $\ln|x|$ because $x > 0$ near $x = x_0 > 0$. Now note that $v(x_0) = y(x_0)/x_0 = 0$, so $C = \sin^{-1} 0 - \ln x_0 = -\ln x_0$. Hence

$$v = \frac{y}{x} = \sin(\ln x - \ln x_0) = \sin\left(\ln\frac{x}{x_0}\right),$$

and therefore

$$y(x) = x \sin\left(\ln\frac{x}{x_0}\right)$$

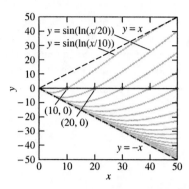

FIGURE 1.6.3. Solution curves for $xy' = y + \sqrt{x^2 - y^2}$.

is the desired particular solution. Because the range of $\sin^{-1} v = \ln(x/x_0)$ is the interval $-\pi/2 \leq \ln(x/x_0) \leq \pi/2$, it follows that this particular solution is defined on the interval $x_0 e^{-\pi/2} \leq x \leq x_0 e^{\pi/2}$. Figure 1.6.3 shows some typical solution curves. Because of the radical in the differential equation, these solution curves are confined to the indicated triangular region $x \geq |y|$. You can check that the boundary lines $y = x$ and $y = -x$ (for $x > 0$) are singular solution curves that consist of points of tangency with the solution curves found earlier. ∎

Bernoulli Equations

A first-order differential equation of the form

➤
$$\frac{dy}{dx} + P(x)y = Q(x)y^n \tag{9}$$

is called a **Bernoulli equation.** If either $n = 0$ or $n = 1$, then Eq. (9) is linear. Otherwise, as we ask you to show in Problem 56, the substitution

➤
$$v = y^{1-n} \tag{10}$$

transforms Eq. (9) into the linear equation

$$\frac{dv}{dx} + (1 - n)P(x)v = (1 - n)Q(x).$$

Rather than memorizing the form of this transformed equation, it is more efficient to make the substitution in Eq. (10) explicitly, as in the following examples.

Example 4

If we rewrite the homogeneous equation $2xyy' = 4x^2 + 3y^2$ of Example 2 in the form

$$\frac{dy}{dx} - \frac{3}{2x}y = \frac{2x}{y},$$

we see that it is also a Bernoulli equation with $P(x) = -3/(2x)$, $Q(x) = 2x$, $n = -1$, and $1 - n = 2$. Hence we substitute

$$v = y^2, \quad y = v^{1/2}, \quad \text{and} \quad \frac{dy}{dx} = \frac{dy}{dv}\frac{dv}{dx} = \frac{1}{2}v^{-1/2}\frac{dv}{dx}.$$

This gives

$$\frac{1}{2}v^{-1/2}\frac{dv}{dx} - \frac{3}{2x}v^{1/2} = 2xv^{-1/2}.$$

Then multiplication by $2v^{1/2}$ produces the linear equation

$$\frac{dv}{dx} - \frac{3}{x}v = 4x$$

with integrating factor $\rho = e^{\int(-3/x)\,dx} = x^{-3}$. So we obtain

$$D_x(x^{-3}v) = \frac{4}{x^2};$$

$$x^{-3}v = -\frac{4}{x} + C;$$

$$x^{-3}y^2 = -\frac{4}{x} + C;$$

$$y^2 = -4x^2 + Cx^3.$$

∎

Example 5 The equation

$$x\frac{dy}{dx} + 6y = 3xy^{4/3}$$

is neither separable nor linear nor homogeneous, but it is a Bernoulli equation with $n = \frac{4}{3}$, $1 - n = -\frac{1}{3}$. The substitutions

$$v = y^{-1/3}, \quad y = v^{-3}, \quad \text{and} \quad \frac{dy}{dx} = \frac{dy}{dv}\frac{dv}{dx} = -3v^{-4}\frac{dv}{dx}$$

transform it into

$$-3xv^{-4}\frac{dv}{dx} + 6v^{-3} = 3xv^{-4}.$$

Division by $-3xv^{-4}$ yields the linear equation

$$\frac{dv}{dx} - \frac{2}{x}v = -1$$

with integrating factor $\rho = e^{\int(-2/x)\,dx} = x^{-2}$. This gives

$$D_x(x^{-2}v) = -\frac{1}{x^2}; \quad x^{-2}v = \frac{1}{x} + C; \quad v = x + Cx^2;$$

and finally,

$$y(x) = \frac{1}{(x + Cx^2)^3}. \qquad \blacksquare$$

Example 6 The equation

$$2xe^{2y}\frac{dy}{dx} = 3x^4 + e^{2y} \tag{11}$$

is neither separable, nor linear, nor homogeneous, nor is it a Bernoulli equation. But we observe that y appears only in the combinations e^{2y} and $D_x(e^{2y}) = 2e^{2y}y'$. This prompts the substitution

$$v = e^{2y}, \quad \frac{dv}{dx} = 2e^{2y}\frac{dy}{dx}$$

that transforms Eq. (11) into the linear equation $xv'(x) = 3x^4 + v(x)$; that is,

$$\frac{dv}{dx} - \frac{1}{x}v = 3x^3.$$

After multiplying by the integrating factor $\rho = 1/x$, we find that

$$\frac{1}{x}v = \int 3x^2\,dx = x^3 + C, \quad \text{so} \quad e^{2y} = v = x^4 + Cx,$$

and hence

$$y(x) = \tfrac{1}{2}\ln\left|x^4 + Cx\right|. \qquad \blacksquare$$

Flight Trajectories

Suppose that an airplane departs from the point $(a, 0)$ located due east of its intended destination—an airport located at the origin $(0, 0)$. The plane travels with constant speed v_0 relative to the wind, which is blowing due north with constant speed w. As indicated in Fig. 1.6.4, we assume that the plane's pilot maintains its heading directly toward the origin.

Figure 1.6.5 helps us derive the plane's velocity components relative to the ground. They are

$$\frac{dx}{dt} = -v_0 \cos \theta = -\frac{v_0 x}{\sqrt{x^2 + y^2}},$$

$$\frac{dy}{dt} = -v_0 \sin \theta + w = -\frac{v_0 y}{\sqrt{x^2 + y^2}} + w.$$

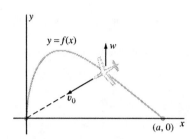

FIGURE 1.6.4. The airplane headed for the origin.

Hence the trajectory $y = f(x)$ of the plane satisfies the differential equation

$$\frac{dy}{dx} = \frac{dy/dt}{dx/dt} = \frac{1}{v_0 x} \left(v_0 y - w \sqrt{x^2 + y^2} \right). \tag{12}$$

If we set

$$k = \frac{w}{v_0}, \tag{13}$$

the ratio of the windspeed to the plane's airspeed, then Eq. (12) takes the homogeneous form

$$\frac{dy}{dx} = \frac{y}{x} - k \left[1 + \left(\frac{y}{x} \right)^2 \right]^{1/2}. \tag{14}$$

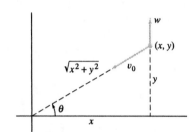

FIGURE 1.6.5. The components of the velocity vector of the airplane.

The substitution $y = xv$, $y' = v + xv'$ then leads routinely to

$$\int \frac{dv}{\sqrt{1 + v^2}} = -\int \frac{k}{x} \, dx. \tag{15}$$

By trigonometric substitution, or by consulting a table for the integral on the left, we find that

$$\ln \left(v + \sqrt{1 + v^2} \right) = -k \ln x + C, \tag{16}$$

and the initial condition $v(a) = y(a)/a = 0$ yields

$$C = k \ln a. \tag{17}$$

According to Problem 68, the result of substituting (17) in Eq. (16) and then solving for v is

$$v = \frac{1}{2} \left[\left(\frac{x}{a} \right)^{-k} - \left(\frac{x}{a} \right)^{k} \right]. \tag{18}$$

Because $y = xv$, we finally obtain

$$y(x) = \frac{a}{2} \left[\left(\frac{x}{a} \right)^{1-k} - \left(\frac{x}{a} \right)^{1+k} \right] \tag{19}$$

for the equation of the plane's trajectory.

Note that only in the case $k < 1$ (that is, $w < v_0$) does the curve in Eq. (19) pass through the origin, so that the plane reaches its destination. If $w = v_0$ (so that $k = 1$), then Eq. (19) takes the form $y(x) = \frac{1}{2}a(1 - x^2/a^2)$, so the plane's trajectory approaches the point $(0, a/2)$ rather than $(0, 0)$. The situation is even worse if $w > v_0$ (so $k > 1$)—in this case it follows from Eq. (19) that $y \to +\infty$ as $x \to 0$.

Example 7

If $a = 200$ mi, $v_0 = 500$ mi/h, and $w = 100$ mi/h, then $k = w/v_0 = \frac{1}{5}$, so the plane will succeed in reaching the airport at $(0, 0)$. With these values, Eq. (19) yields

$$y(x) = 100 \left[\left(\frac{x}{200} \right)^{4/5} - \left(\frac{x}{200} \right)^{6/5} \right]. \tag{20}$$

Now suppose that we want to find the maximum amount by which the plane is blown off course during its trip. That is, what is the maximum value of $y(x)$ for $0 \leq x \leq 200$?

Solution Differentiation of the function in Eq. (20) yields

$$\frac{dy}{dx} = \frac{1}{2} \left[\frac{4}{5} \left(\frac{x}{200} \right)^{-1/5} - \frac{6}{5} \left(\frac{x}{200} \right)^{1/5} \right],$$

and we readily solve the equation $y'(x) = 0$ to obtain $(x/200)^{2/5} = \frac{2}{3}$. Hence

$$y_{\max} = 100 \left[\left(\frac{2}{3} \right)^2 - \left(\frac{2}{3} \right)^3 \right] = \frac{400}{27} \approx 14.81.$$

Thus the plane is blown almost 15 mi north at one point during its westward journey. [The graph of the function in Eq. (20) is the one used to construct Fig. 1.6.4. The vertical scale there is exaggerated by a factor of 4.] ■

Exact Differential Equations

We have seen that a general solution $y(x)$ of a first-order differential equation is often defined implicitly by an equation of the form

$$F(x, y(x)) = C, \tag{21}$$

where C is a constant. On the other hand, given the identity in (21), we can recover the original differential equation by differentiating each side with respect to x. Provided that Eq. (21) implicitly defines y as a differentiable function of x, this gives the original differential equation in the form

$$\frac{\partial F}{\partial x} + \frac{\partial F}{\partial y} \frac{dy}{dx} = 0;$$

that is,

$$M(x, y) + N(x, y) \frac{dy}{dx} = 0, \tag{22}$$

where $M(x, y) = F_x(x, y)$ and $N(x, y) = F_y(x, y)$.

It is sometimes convenient to rewrite Eq. (22) in the more symmetric form

➤ $$M(x, y)\, dx + N(x, y)\, dy = 0,\qquad(23)$$

called its **differential** form. The general first-order differential equation $y' = f(x, y)$ can be written in this form with $M = f(x, y)$ and $N \equiv -1$. The preceding discussion shows that, *if* there exists a function $F(x, y)$ such that

$$\frac{\partial F}{\partial x} = M \quad \text{and} \quad \frac{\partial F}{\partial y} = N,$$

then the equation

➤ $$F(x, y) = C$$

implicitly defines a general solution of Eq. (23). In this case, Eq. (23) is called an **exact differential equation**—the differential

$$dF = F_x\, dx + F_y\, dy$$

of $F(x, y)$ is exactly $M\, dx + N\, dy$.

Natural questions are these: How can we determine whether the differential equation in (23) is exact? And if it is exact, how can we find the function F such that $F_x = M$ and $F_y = N$? To answer the first question, let us recall that if the mixed second-order partial derivatives F_{xy} and F_{yx} are continuous on an open set in the xy-plane, then they are equal: $F_{xy} = F_{yx}$. If Eq. (23) is exact and M and N have continuous partial derivatives, it then follows that

$$\frac{\partial M}{\partial y} = F_{xy} = F_{yx} = \frac{\partial N}{\partial x}.$$

Thus the equation

➤ $$\frac{\partial M}{\partial y} = \frac{\partial N}{\partial x}\qquad(24)$$

is a *necessary condition* that the differential equation $M\, dx + N\, dy = 0$ be exact. That is, if $M_y \neq N_x$, then the differential equation in question is not exact, so we need not attempt to find a function $F(x, y)$ such that $F_x = M$ and $F_y = N$—there is no such function.

Example 8

The differential equation

$$y^3\, dx + 3xy^2\, dy = 0\qquad(25)$$

is exact because we can immediately see that the function $F(x, y) = xy^3$ has the property that $F_x = y^3$ and $F_y = 3xy^2$. Thus a general solution of Eq. (25) is

$$xy^3 = C;$$

if you prefer, $y(x) = kx^{-1/3}$. ∎

But suppose that we divide each term of the differential equation in Example 8 by y^2 to obtain

$$y\,dx + 3x\,dy = 0. \tag{26}$$

This equation is not exact because, with $M = y$ and $N = 3x$, we have

$$\frac{\partial M}{\partial y} = 1 \neq 3 = \frac{\partial N}{\partial x}.$$

Hence the necessary condition in Eq. (24) is not satisfied.

We are confronted with a curious situation here. The differential equations in (25) and (26) are essentially equivalent, and they have exactly the same solutions, yet one is exact and the other is not. In brief, whether a given differential equation is exact or not is related to the precise form $M\,dx + N\,dy = 0$ in which it is written. Theorem 1 tells us that (subject to differentiability conditions usually satisfied in practice) the necessary condition in (24) is also a *sufficient* condition for exactness. In other words, if $M_y = N_x$, then the differential equation $M\,dx + N\,dy = 0$ is exact.

THEOREM 1: Criterion for Exactness

Suppose that the functions $M(x, y)$ and $N(x, y)$ are continuous and have continuous first-order partial derivatives in the open rectangle $R: a < x < b,\ c < y < d$. Then the differential equation

$$M(x, y)\,dx + N(x, y)\,dy = 0 \tag{23}$$

is exact in R if and only if

$$\frac{\partial M}{\partial y} = \frac{\partial N}{\partial x} \tag{24}$$

at each point of R. That is, there exists a function $F(x, y)$ defined on R with $\partial F/\partial x = M$ and $\partial F/\partial y = N$ if and only if Eq. (24) holds on R.

Proof: We have seen already that it is necessary for Eq. (24) to hold if Eq. (23) is to be exact. To prove the converse, we must show that if Eq. (24) holds, then we can construct a function $F(x, y)$ such that $\partial F/\partial x = M$ and $\partial F/\partial y = N$. Note first that, for *any* function $g(y)$, the function

$$F(x, y) = \int M(x, y)\,dx + g(y) \tag{27}$$

satisfies the condition $\partial F/\partial x = M$. [In Eq. (27), the notation $\int M(x, y)\,dx$ denotes an antiderivative of $M(x, y)$ with respect to x.] We plan to choose $g(y)$ so that

$$N = \frac{\partial F}{\partial y} = \left(\frac{\partial}{\partial y} \int M(x, y)\,dx \right) + g'(y)$$

as well; that is, so that

$$g'(y) = N - \frac{\partial}{\partial y} \int M(x, y)\,dx. \tag{28}$$

To see that there *is* such a function of y, it suffices to show that the right-hand side in Eq. (28) is a function of y alone. We can then find $g(y)$ by integrating with respect to y. Because the right-hand side in Eq. (28) is defined on a rectangle, and hence on an interval as a function of x, it suffices to show that its derivative with respect to x is identically zero. But

$$\frac{\partial}{\partial x}\left(N - \frac{\partial}{\partial y}\int M(x, y)\, dx\right) = \frac{\partial N}{\partial x} - \frac{\partial}{\partial x}\frac{\partial}{\partial y}\int M(x, y)\, dx$$

$$= \frac{\partial N}{\partial x} - \frac{\partial}{\partial y}\frac{\partial}{\partial x}\int M(x, y)\, dx$$

$$= \frac{\partial N}{\partial x} - \frac{\partial M}{\partial y} = 0$$

by hypothesis. So we can, indeed, find the desired function $g(y)$ by integrating Eq. (28). We substitute this result in Eq. (27) to obtain

$$F(x, y) = \int M(x, y)\, dx + \int\left(N(x, y) - \frac{\partial}{\partial y}\int M(x, y)\, dx\right) dy \qquad (29)$$

as the desired function with $F_x = M$ and $F_y = N$.   ▲

Instead of memorizing Eq. (29), it is usually better to solve an exact equation $M\, dx + N\, dy = 0$ by carrying out the process indicated by Eqs. (27) and (28). First we integrate $M(x, y)$ with respect to x and write

$$F(x, y) = \int M(x, y)\, dx + g(y),$$

thinking of the function $g(y)$ as an "arbitrary constant of integration" as far as the variable x is concerned. Then we determine $g(y)$ by imposing the condition that $\partial F/\partial y = N(x, y)$. This yields a general solution in the implicit form $F(x, y) = C$.

Example 9   Solve the differential equation

$$(6xy - y^3)\, dx + (4y + 3x^2 - 3xy^2)\, dy = 0. \qquad (30)$$

Solution   Let $M(x, y) = 6xy - y^3$ and $N(x, y) = 4y + 3x^2 - 3xy^2$. The given equation is exact because

$$\frac{\partial M}{\partial y} = 6x - 3y^2 = \frac{\partial N}{\partial x}.$$

Integrating $\partial F/\partial x = M(x, y)$ with respect to x, we get

$$F(x, y) = \int(6xy - y^3)\, dx = 3x^2 y - xy^3 + g(y).$$

Then we differentiate with respect to y and set $\partial F/\partial y = N(x, y)$. This yields

$$\frac{\partial F}{\partial y} = 3x^2 - 3xy^2 + g'(y) = 4y + 3x^2 - 3xy^2,$$

and it follows that $g'(y) = 4y$. Hence $g(y) = 2y^2 + C_1$, and thus

$$F(x, y) = 3x^2y - xy^3 + 2y^2 + C_1.$$

Therefore, a general solution of the differential equation is defined implicitly by the equation

$$3x^2y - xy^3 + 2y^2 = C \qquad (31)$$

(we have absorbed the constant C_1 into the constant C). ∎

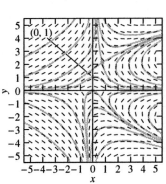

FIGURE 1.6.6. Slope field and solution curves for the exact equation in Example 9.

Remark: Figure 1.6.6 shows a rather complicated structure of solution curves for the differential equation of Example 9. The solution satisfying a given initial condition $y(x_0) = y_0$ is defined implicitly by Eq. (31), with C determined by substituting $x = x_0$ and $y = y_0$ in the equation. For instance, the particular solution satisfying $y(0) = 1$ is defined implicitly by the equation $3x^2y - xy^3 + 2y^2 = 2$. The other two special points in the figure—at $(0, 0)$ and near $(0.75, 2.12)$—are ones where both coefficient functions in Eq. (30) vanish, so the theorem of Section 1.3 does not guarantee a unique solution. ∎

Reducible Second-Order Equations

A *second-order differential equation* involves the second derivative of the unknown function $y(x)$, and thus has the general form

$$F(x, y, y', y'') = 0. \qquad (32)$$

If *either* the dependent variable y *or* the independent variable x is missing from a second-order equation, then it is easily reduced by a simple substitution to a first-order equation that may be solvable by the methods of this chapter.

Dependent Variable y Missing. If y is missing, then Eq. (32) takes the form

➤ $$F(x, y', y'') = 0. \qquad (33)$$

Then the substitution

➤ $$p = y' = \frac{dy}{dx}, \quad y'' = \frac{dp}{dx} \qquad (34)$$

results in the *first-order* differential equation

$$F(x, p, p') = 0.$$

If we can solve this equation for a general solution $p(x, C_1)$ involving an arbitrary constant C_1, then we need only write

$$y(x) = \int y'(x)\,dx = \int p(x, C_1)\,dx + C_2$$

to get a solution of Eq. (33) that involves two arbitrary constants C_1 and C_2 (as is to be expected in the case of a second-order differential equation).

Example 10 Solve the equation $xy'' + 2y' = 6x$ in which the dependent variable y is missing.

Solution The substitution defined in (34) gives the first-order equation

$$x\frac{dp}{dx} + 2p = 6x; \quad \text{that is,} \quad \frac{dp}{dx} + \frac{2}{x}p = 6.$$

Observing that the equation on the right here is linear, we multiply by its integrating factor $\rho = \exp\left(\int(2/x)\,dx\right) = e^{2\ln x} = x^2$ and get

$$D_x(x^2 p) = 6x^2,$$
$$x^2 p = 2x^3 + C_1,$$
$$p = \frac{dy}{dx} = 2x + \frac{C_1}{x^2}.$$

A final integration with respect to x yields the general solution

$$y(x) = x^2 + \frac{C_1}{x} + C_2$$

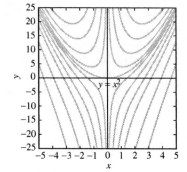

FIGURE 1.6.7. Solution curves of the form $y = x^2 + \dfrac{C_1}{x}$ for $C_1 = 0,\ \pm 3,\ \pm 10,\ \pm 20,\ \pm 35,\ \pm 60,\ \pm 100.$

of the second-order equation $xy'' + 2y' = 6x$. Solution curves with $C_1 = 0$ are simply vertical translates of the parabola $y = x^2$. Figure 1.6.7 shows typical solution curves with $C_2 = 0$. Solution curves with C_1 and C_2 both nonzero are vertical translates of those shown in Fig. 1.6.7. ∎

Independent Variable x Missing. If x is missing, then Eq. (32) takes the form

$$F(y, y', y'') = 0. \tag{35}$$

Then the substitution

$$p = y' = \frac{dy}{dx}, \quad y'' = \frac{dp}{dx} = \frac{dp}{dy}\frac{dy}{dx} = p\frac{dp}{dy} \tag{36}$$

results in the *first-order* differential equation

$$F\left(y, p, p\frac{dp}{dy}\right) = 0$$

for p as a function of y. If we can solve this equation for a general solution $p(y, C_1)$ involving an arbitrary constant C_1, then (assuming that $y' \neq 0$) we need only write

$$x(y) = \int \frac{dx}{dy}\,dx = \int \frac{1}{dy/dx}\,dx = \int \frac{1}{p}\,dy = \int \frac{dy}{p(y, C_1)} + C_2.$$

If the final integral $P = \int (1/p)\,dy$ can be evaluated, the result is an implicit solution $x(y) = P(y, C_1) + C_2$ of our second-order differential equation.

Example 11	Solve the equation $yy'' = (y')^2$ in which the independent variable x is missing.

Solution   We assume temporarily that y and y' are both nonnegative, and then point out at the end that this restriction is unnecessary. The substitution defined in (36) gives the first-order equation

$$yp\frac{dp}{dx} = p^2.$$

Then separation of variables gives

$$\int \frac{dp}{p} = \int \frac{dy}{y},$$

$$\ln p = \ln y + C \quad \text{(because } y > 0 \text{ and } p = y' > 0\text{)},$$

$$p = C_1 y$$

where $C_1 = e^C$. Hence

$$\frac{dx}{dy} = \frac{1}{p} = \frac{1}{C_1 y},$$

$$C_1 x = \int \frac{dy}{y} = \ln y + C_1.$$

The resulting general solution of the second-order equation $yy'' = (y')^2$ is

$$y(x) = \exp(C_1 x - C_2) = Ae^{Bx},$$

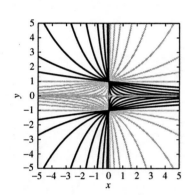

FIGURE 1.6.8. The solution curves $y = Ae^{Bx}$ with $B = 0$ and $A = 0, \pm 1$ are the horizontal lines $y = 0, \pm 1$. The exponential curves with $B > 0$ and $A = \pm 1$ are in color, those with $B < 0$ and $A = \pm 1$ are black.

where $A = e^{-C_2}$ and $B = C_1$. Despite our temporary assumptions, which imply that the constants A and B are both positive, we readily verify that $y(x) = Ae^{Bx}$ satisfies $yy'' = (y')^2$ for *all* real values of A and B. With $B = 0$ and different values of A, we get all horizontal lines in the plane as solution curves. The upper half of Fig. 1.6.8 shows the solution curves obtained with $A = 1$ (for instance) and different positive values of B. With $A = -1$ these solution curves are reflected in the x-axis. And with negative values of B they are reflected in the y-axis. In particular, we see that we get solutions of $yy'' = (y')^2$ allowing both positive and negative possibilities for both y and y'. ∎

1.6 Problems

Find general solutions of the differential equations in Problems 1 through 30. Primes denote derivatives with respect to x throughout.

1. $(x + y)y' = x - y$
2. $2xyy' = x^2 + 2y^2$
3. $xy' = y + 2\sqrt{xy}$
4. $(x - y)y' = x + y$
5. $x(x + y)y' = y(x - y)$
6. $(x + 2y)y' = y$
7. $xy^2 y' = x^3 + y^3$
8. $x^2 y' = xy + x^2 e^{y/x}$
9. $x^2 y' = xy + y^2$
10. $xyy' = x^2 + 3y^2$
11. $(x^2 - y^2)y' = 2xy$
12. $xyy' = y^2 + x\sqrt{4x^2 + y^2}$
13. $xy' = y + \sqrt{x^2 + y^2}$
14. $yy' + x = \sqrt{x^2 + y^2}$
15. $x(x + y)y' + y(3x + y) = 0$

16. $y' = \sqrt{x + y + 1}$
17. $y' = (4x + y)^2$
18. $(x + y)y' = 1$
19. $x^2 y' + 2xy = 5y^3$
20. $y^2 y' + 2xy^3 = 6x$
21. $y' = y + y^3$
22. $x^2 y' + 2xy = 5y^4$
23. $xy' + 6y = 3xy^{4/3}$
24. $2xy' + y^3 e^{-2x} = 2xy$
25. $y^2(xy' + y)(1 + x^4)^{1/2} = x$
26. $3y^2 y' + y^3 = e^{-x}$
27. $3xy^2 y' = 3x^4 + y^3$
28. $xe^y y' = 2(e^y + x^3 e^{2x})$
29. $(2x \sin y \cos y)y' = 4x^2 + \sin^2 y$
30. $(x + e^y)y' = xe^{-y} - 1$

In Problems 31 through 42, verify that the given differential equation is exact; then solve it.

31. $(2x + 3y)\,dx + (3x + 2y)\,dy = 0$

32. $(4x - y)\,dx + (6y - x)\,dy = 0$

33. $(3x^2 + 2y^2)\,dx + (4xy + 6y^2)\,dy = 0$

34. $(2xy^2 + 3x^2)\,dx + (2x^2 y + 4y^3)\,dy = 0$

35. $\left(x^3 + \dfrac{y}{x}\right)dx + (y^2 + \ln x)\,dy = 0$

36. $(1 + ye^{xy})\,dx + (2y + xe^{xy})\,dy = 0$

37. $(\cos x + \ln y)\,dx + \left(\dfrac{x}{y} + e^y\right)dy = 0$

38. $(x + \tan^{-1} y)\,dx + \dfrac{x + y}{1 + y^2}\,dy = 0$

39. $(3x^2 y^3 + y^4)\,dx + (3x^3 y^2 + y^4 + 4xy^3)\,dy = 0$

40. $(e^x \sin y + \tan y)\,dx + (e^x \cos y + x \sec^2 y)\,dy = 0$

41. $\left(\dfrac{2x}{y} - \dfrac{3y^2}{x^4}\right)dx + \left(\dfrac{2y}{x^3} - \dfrac{x^2}{y^2} + \dfrac{1}{\sqrt{y}}\right)dy = 0$

42. $\dfrac{2x^{5/2} - 3y^{5/3}}{2x^{5/2} y^{2/3}}\,dx + \dfrac{3y^{5/3} - 2x^{5/2}}{3x^{3/2} y^{5/3}}\,dy = 0$

Find a general solution of each reducible second-order differential equation in Problems 43–54. Assume x, y and/or y′ positive where helpful (as in Example 11).

43. $xy'' = y'$ **44.** $yy'' + (y')^2 = 0$

45. $y'' + 4y = 0$ **46.** $xy'' + y' = 4x$

47. $y'' = (y')^2$ **48.** $x^2 y'' + 3xy' = 2$

49. $yy'' + (y')^2 = yy'$ **50.** $y'' = (x + y')^2$

51. $y'' = 2y(y')^3$ **52.** $y^3 y'' = 1$

53. $y'' = 2yy'$ **54.** $yy'' = 3(y')^2$

55. Show that the substitution $v = ax + by + c$ transforms the differential equation $dy/dx = F(ax + by + c)$ into a separable equation.

56. Suppose that $n \neq 0$ and $n \neq 1$. Show that the substitution $v = y^{1-n}$ transforms the Bernoulli equation $dy/dx + P(x)y = Q(x)y^n$ into the linear equation

$$\frac{dv}{dx} + (1 - n)P(x)v(x) = (1 - n)Q(x).$$

57. Show that the substitution $v = \ln y$ transforms the differential equation $dy/dx + P(x)y = Q(x)(y \ln y)$ into the linear equation $dv/dx + P(x) = Q(x)v(x)$.

58. Use the idea in Problem 57 to solve the equation

$$x\frac{dy}{dx} - 4x^2 y + 2y \ln y = 0.$$

59. Solve the differential equation

$$\frac{dy}{dx} = \frac{x - y - 1}{x + y + 3}$$

by finding h and k so that the substitutions $x = u + h$, $y = v + k$ transform it into the homogeneous equation

$$\frac{dv}{du} = \frac{u - v}{u + v}.$$

60. Use the method in Problem 59 to solve the differential equation

$$\frac{dy}{dx} = \frac{2y - x + 7}{4x - 3y - 18}.$$

61. Make an appropriate substitution to find a solution of the equation $dy/dx = \sin(x - y)$. Does this general solution contain the linear solution $y(x) = x - \pi/2$ that is readily verified by substitution in the differential equation?

62. Show that the solution curves of the differential equation

$$\frac{dy}{dx} = -\frac{y(2x^3 - y^3)}{x(2y^3 - x^3)}$$

are of the form $x^3 + y^3 = 3Cxy$.

63. The equation $dy/dx = A(x)y^2 + B(x)y + C(x)$ is called a **Riccati equation.** Suppose that one particular solution $y_1(x)$ of this equation is known. Show that the substitution

$$y = y_1 + \frac{1}{v}$$

transforms the Riccati equation into the *linear* equation

$$\frac{dv}{dx} + (B + 2Ay_1)v = -A.$$

Use the method of Problem 63 to solve the equations in Problems 64 and 65, given that $y_1(x) = x$ is a solution of each.

64. $\dfrac{dy}{dx} + y^2 = 1 + x^2$

65. $\dfrac{dy}{dx} + 2xy = 1 + x^2 + y^2$

66. An equation of the form

$$y = xy' + g(y') \tag{37}$$

is called a **Clairaut equation.** Show that the one-parameter family of straight lines described by

$$y(x) = Cx + g(C) \tag{38}$$

is a general solution of Eq. (37).

67. Consider the Clairaut equation

$$y = xy' - \tfrac{1}{4}(y')^2$$

for which $g(y') = -\tfrac{1}{4}(y')^2$ in Eq. (37). Show that the line

$$y = Cx - \tfrac{1}{4}C^2$$

is tangent to the parabola $y = x^2$ at the point $\left(\tfrac{1}{2}C, \tfrac{1}{4}C^2\right)$. Explain why this implies that $y = x^2$ is a singular solution of the given Clairaut equation. This singular solution and the one-parameter family of straight line solutions are illustrated in Fig. 1.6.9.

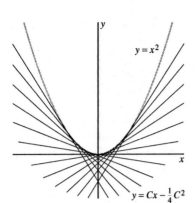

FIGURE 1.6.9. Solutions of the Clairaut equation of Problem 67. The "typical" straight line with equation $y = Cx - \frac{1}{4}C^2$ is tangent to the parabola at the point $(\frac{1}{2}C, \frac{1}{4}C^2)$.

68. Derive Eq. (18) in this section from Eqs. (16) and (17).

69. In the situation of Example 7, suppose that $a = 100$ mi, $v_0 = 400$ mi/h, and $w = 40$ mi/h. Now how far northward does the wind blow the airplane?

70. As in the text discussion, suppose that an airplane maintains a heading toward an airport at the origin. If $v_0 = 500$ mi/h and $w = 50$ mi/h (with the wind blowing due north), and the plane begins at the point $(200, 150)$, show that its trajectory is described by

$$y + \sqrt{x^2 + y^2} = 2(200 x^9)^{1/10}.$$

71. A river 100 ft wide is flowing north at w feet per second. A dog starts at $(100, 0)$ and swims at $v_0 = 4$ ft/s, always heading toward a tree at $(0, 0)$ on the west bank directly across from the dog's starting point. **(a)** If $w = 2$ ft/s, show that the dog reaches the tree. **(b)** If $w = 4$ ft/s, show that the dog reaches instead the point on the west bank 50 ft north of the tree. **(c)** If $w = 6$ ft/s, show that the dog never reaches the west bank.

72. In the calculus of plane curves, one learns that the *curvature* κ of the curve $y = y(x)$ at the point (x, y) is given by

$$\kappa = \frac{|y''(x)|}{[1 + y'(x)^2]^{3/2}},$$

and that the curvature of a circle of radius r is $\kappa = 1/r$. [See Example 3 in Section 12.6 of Edwards and Penney, *Calculus*, 6th edition (Upper Saddle River, NJ: Prentice Hall, 2002).] Conversely, substitute $\rho = y'$ to derive a general solution of the second-order differential equation

$$ry'' = [1 + (y')^2]^{3/2}$$

(with r constant) in the form

$$(x - a)^2 + (y - b)^2 = r^2.$$

Thus a circle of radius r (or a part thereof) is the *only* plane curve with constant curvature $1/r$.

1.6 Application: Computer Algebra Solutions

Computer algebra systems typically include commands for the "automatic" solution of differential equations. But two different such systems often give different results whose equivalence is not clear, and a single system may give the solution in an overly complicated form. Consequently, computer algebra solutions of differential equations often require considerable "processing" or simplification by a human user in order to yield concrete and applicable information. Here we illustrate these issues using the interesting differential equation

$$\frac{dy}{dx} = \sin(x - y) \tag{1}$$

that appeared in the Section 1.3 Application. The *Maple* command

```
dsolve( D(y)(x) = sin(x - y(x)), y(x));
```

yields the simple and attractive result

$$y(x) = x - 2\tan^{-1}\left(\frac{x - 2 - C1}{x - C1}\right) \tag{2}$$

that was cited there. But the supposedly equivalent *Mathematica* command

```
DSolve[ y'[x] == Sin[x - y[x]], y[x], x]
```

returns the more complicated result

$$y(x) = x \pm 2\cos^{-1}\left(\pm\frac{\sqrt{4 + 4x + x^2 + 4C1 + 2xC1 + C1^2}}{\sqrt{4 + 4x + 2x^2 + 4C1 + 4xC1 + 2C1^2}}\right). \tag{3}$$

This apparent disparity is not unusual, and with another differential equation *Mathematica* might well produce the simpler form of the solution. As an alternative to attempting to reconcile the results in Eqs. (2) and (3), a common tactic is to simplify the differential equation before submitting it to a computer algebra system.

EXERCISE 1: Show that the plausible substitution $v = x - y$ in Eq. (1) yields the separable equation

$$\frac{dv}{dx} = 1 - \sin v. \tag{4}$$

Now the *Mathematica* command

```
Integrate[1/(1 - Sin[v]), v] // TrigReduce
```

yields

$$\int \frac{1}{1 - \sin v}\, dv = \frac{\cos v}{1 - \sin v} \tag{5}$$

(*Mathematica* omits the constant of integration unless you specifically ask for it.)

EXERCISE 2: Apply the trigonometric identities $\sin 2A = 2\sin A\cos A$ and $\cos 2A = \cos^2 A - \sin^2 A$ to deduce from Eq. (5) that

$$\int \frac{1}{1 - \sin v}\, dv = \frac{1 + \tan(v/2)}{1 - \tan(v/2)} + C. \tag{6}$$

EXERCISE 3: Deduce from (6) that Eq. (4) has the general solution

$$v(x) = 2\tan^{-1}\left(\frac{x - 1 + C}{x + 1 + C}\right),$$

and hence that Eq. (1) has the general solution

$$y(x) = x - 2\tan^{-1}\left(\frac{x - 1 + C}{x + 1 + C}\right). \tag{7}$$

FIGURE 1.6.10. Implicit solution of $y' = \sin(x - y)$ generated by a TI-89 graphing calculator.

EXERCISE 4: Finally, reconcile the forms in Eq. (2) and Eq. (7). What is the relation between the constants C and $C1$?

EXERCISE 5: Show that the integral in Eq. (5) yields immediately the graphing calculator implicit solution shown in Fig. 1.6.10.

INVESTIGATION: For your own personal differential equation, let p and q be two distinct nonzero digits in your student ID number, and consider the differential equation

$$\frac{dy}{dx} = \frac{1}{p}\cos(x - qy). \tag{8}$$

(a) Find a symbolic general solution using a computer algebra system and/or some combination of the techniques listed in this project.

(b) Determine the symbolic particular solution corresponding to several typical initial conditions of the form $y(x_0) = y_0$.

(c) Determine the possible values of a and b such that the straight line $y = ax + b$ is a solution curve of Eq. (8).

(d) Plot a direction field and some typical solution curves. Can you make a connection between the symbolic solution and your (linear and nonlinear) solution curves?

Chapter 1: Summary

In this chapter we have discussed applications of and solution methods for several important types of first-order differential equations, including those that are separable (Section 1.4), linear (Section 1.5), or exact (Section 1.6). In Section 1.6 we also discussed substitution techniques that can sometimes be used to transform a given first-order differential equation into one that is either separable, linear, or exact.

Lest it appear that these methods constitute a "grab bag" of special and unrelated techniques, it is important to note that they are all versions of a single idea. Given a differential equation

$$f(x, y, y') = 0, \tag{1}$$

we attempt to write it in the form

$$\frac{d}{dx}[G(x, y)] = 0. \tag{2}$$

It is precisely to obtain the form in Eq. (2) that we multiply the terms in Eq. (1) by an appropriate integrating factor (even if all we are doing is separating the variables). But once we have found a function $G(x, y)$ such that Eqs. (1) and (2) are equivalent, a general solution is defined implicitly by means of the equation

$$G(x, y) = C \tag{3}$$

that one obtains by integrating Eq. (2).

Given a specific first-order differential equation to be solved, we can attack it by means of the following steps:

- Is it *separable*? If so, separate the variables and integrate (Section 1.4).
- Is it *linear*? That is, can it be written in the form

$$\frac{dy}{dx} + P(x)y = Q(x)?$$

If so, multiply by the integrating factor $\rho = \exp\left(\int P\,dx\right)$ of Section 1.5.

- Is it *exact*? That is, when the equation is written in the form $M\,dx + N\,dy = 0$, is $\partial M/\partial y = \partial N/\partial x$ (Section 1.6)?
- If the equation as it stands is not separable, linear, or exact, is there a plausible substitution that will make it so? For instance, is it homogeneous (Section 1.6)?

Many first-order differential equations succumb to the line of attack outlined here. Nevertheless, many more do not. Because of the wide availability of computers, numerical techniques are commonly used to *approximate* the solutions of differential equations that cannot be solved readily or explicitly by the methods of this chapter. Indeed, most of the solution curves shown in figures in this chapter were plotted using numerical approximations rather than exact solutions. Several numerical methods for the appropriate solution of differential equations will be discussed in Chapter 2.

Chapter 1: Review Problems

Find general solutions of the differential equations in Problems 1 through 30. Primes denote derivatives with respect to x.

1. $x^3 + 3y - xy' = 0$

2. $xy^2 + 3y^2 - x^2y' = 0$

3. $xy + y^2 - x^2y' = 0$

4. $2xy^3 + e^x + (3x^2y^2 + \sin y)y' = 0$

5. $3y + x^4y' = 2xy$ **6.** $2xy^2 + x^2y' = y^2$

7. $2x^2y + x^3y' = 1$ **8.** $2xy + x^2y' = y^2$

9. $xy' + 2y = 6x^2\sqrt{y}$

10. $y' = 1 + x^2 + y^2 + x^2y^2$

11. $x^2y' = xy + 3y^2$

12. $6xy^3 + 2y^4 + (9x^2y^2 + 8xy^3)y' = 0$

13. $4xy^2 + y' = 5x^4y^2$ **14.** $x^3y' = x^2y - y^3$

15. $y' + 3y = 3x^2e^{-3x}$ **16.** $y' = x^2 - 2xy + y^2$

17. $e^x + ye^{xy} + (e^y + xe^{yx})y' = 0$

18. $2x^2y - x^3y' = y^3$

19. $3x^5y^2 + x^3y' = 2y^2$

20. $xy' + 3y = 3x^{-3/2}$

21. $(x^2 - 1)y' + (x - 1)y = 1$

22. $xy' = 6y + 12x^4y^{2/3}$

23. $e^y + y\cos x + (xe^y + \sin x)y' = 0$

24. $9x^2y^2 + x^{3/2}y' = y^2$

25. $2y + (x + 1)y' = 3x + 3$

26. $9x^{1/2}y^{4/3} - 12x^{1/5}y^{3/2} + (8x^{3/2}y^{1/3} - 15x^{6/5}y^{1/2})y' = 0$

27. $3y + x^3y^4 + 3xy' = 0$

28. $y + xy' = 2e^{2x}$

29. $(2x + 1)y' + y = (2x + 1)^{3/2}$

30. $y' = \sqrt{x + y}$

Each of the differential equations in Problems 31 through 36 is of two different types considered in this chapter—separable, linear, homogeneous, Bernoulli, exact, and so on. Hence, derive general solutions for each of these equations in two different ways; then reconcile your results.

31. $\dfrac{dy}{dx} = 3(y + 7)x^2$ **32.** $\dfrac{dy}{dx} = xy^3 - xy$

33. $\dfrac{dy}{dx} = -\dfrac{3x^2 + 2y^2}{4xy}$ **34.** $\dfrac{dy}{dx} = \dfrac{x + 3y}{y - 3x}$

35. $\dfrac{dy}{dx} = \dfrac{2xy + 2x}{x^2 + 1}$ **36.** $\dfrac{dy}{dx} = \dfrac{\sqrt{y} - y}{\tan x}$

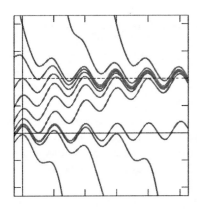

CHAPTER 2

Mathematical Models and Numerical Methods

2.1 Population Models

In Section 1.4 we introduced the exponential differential equation $dP/dt = kP$, with solution $P(t) = P_0 e^{kt}$, as a mathematical model for natural population growth that occurs as a result of constant birth and death rates. Here we present a more general population model that accommodates birth and death rates that are not necessarily constant. As before, however, our population function $P(t)$ will be a *continuous* approximation to the actual population, which of course grows by integral increments.

Suppose that the population changes only by the occurrence of births and deaths—there is no immigration or emigration from outside the country or environment under consideration. It is customary to track the growth or decline of a population in terms of its *birth rate* and *death rate* functions defined as follows:

- $\beta(t)$ is the number of births per unit of population per unit of time at time t;
- $\delta(t)$ is the number of deaths per unit of population per unit of time at time t.

Then the numbers of births and deaths that occur during the time interval $[t, t + \Delta t]$ is given (approximately) by

births: $\beta(t) \cdot P(t) \cdot \Delta t$, deaths: $\delta(t) \cdot P(t) \cdot \Delta t$.

Hence the change ΔP in the population during the time interval $[t, t + \Delta t]$ of length Δt is

$$\Delta P = \{births\} - \{deaths\} \approx \beta(t) \cdot P(t) \cdot \Delta t - \delta(t) \cdot P(t) \cdot \Delta t,$$

so

$$\frac{\Delta P}{\Delta t} \approx [\beta(t) - \delta(t)] P(t).$$

79

The error in this approximation should approach zero as $\Delta t \to 0$, so—taking the limit—we get the differential equation

$$\frac{dP}{dt} = (\beta - \delta)P, \tag{1}$$

in which we write $\beta = \beta(t)$, $\delta = \delta(t)$, and $P = P(t)$ for brevity. Equation (1) is the **general population equation.** If β and δ are constant, Eq. (1) reduces to the natural growth equation with $k = \beta - \delta$. But it also includes the possibility that β and δ are variable functions of t. The birth and death rates need not be known in advance; they may well depend on the unknown function $P(t)$.

Example 1

Suppose that an alligator population numbers 100 initially and that its death rate is $\delta = 0$ (so none of the alligators is dying). If the birth rate is $\beta = (0.0005)P$—and thus increases as the population does—then Eq. (1) gives the initial value problem

$$\frac{dP}{dt} = (0.0005)P^2, \quad P(0) = 100$$

(with t in years). Then upon separating the variables we get

$$\int \frac{1}{P^2}\, dP = \int (0.0005)\, dt;$$

$$-\frac{1}{P} = (0.0005)t + C.$$

Substitution of $t = 0$, $P = 100$ gives $C = -1/100$, and then we readily solve for

$$P(t) = \frac{2000}{20 - t}.$$

For instance, $P(10) = 2000/10 = 200$, so after 10 years the alligator population has doubled. But we see that $P \to +\infty$ as $t \to 20$, so a real "population explosion" occurs in 20 years. Indeed, the direction field and solution curves shown in Fig. 2.1.1 indicate that a population explosion always occurs, whatever the size of the (positive) initial population $P(0) = P_0$. In particular, it appears that the population always becomes unbounded in a *finite* period of time. ∎

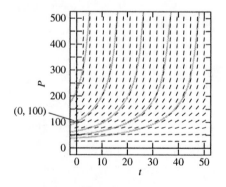

FIGURE 2.1.1. Slope field and solution curves for the equation $dP/dt = (0.0005)P^2$ in Example 1.

Bounded Populations and the Logistic Equation

In situations as diverse as the human population of a nation and a fruit fly population in a closed container, it is often observed that the birth rate decreases as the population itself increases. The reasons may range from increased scientific or cultural sophistication to a limited food supply. Suppose, for example, that the birth rate β is a *linear* decreasing function of the population size P, so that $\beta = \beta_0 - \beta_1 P$, where β_0 and β_1 are positive constants. If the death rate $\delta = \delta_0$ remains constant, then Eq. (1) takes the form

$$\frac{dP}{dt} = (\beta_0 - \beta_1 P - \delta_0)P;$$

that is,

$$\frac{dP}{dt} = aP - bP^2, \tag{2}$$

where $a = \beta_0 - \delta_0$ and $b = \beta_1$.

If the coefficients a and b are both positive, then Eq. (2) is called the **logistic equation.** For the purpose of relating the behavior of the population $P(t)$ to the values of the parameters in the equation, it is useful to rewrite the logistic equation in the form

$$\frac{dP}{dt} = kP(M - P), \tag{3}$$

where $k = b$ and $M = a/b$ are constants.

Example 2

In Example 4 of Section 1.3 we explored graphically a population that is modeled by the logistic equation

$$\frac{dP}{dt} = 0.0004P(150 - P) = 0.06P - 0.0004P^2. \tag{4}$$

To solve this differential equation symbolically, we separate the variables and integrate. We get

$$\int \frac{dP}{P(150 - P)} = \int 0.0004\,dt,$$

$$\frac{1}{150} \int \left(\frac{1}{P} + \frac{1}{150 - P} \right) dP = \int 0.0004\,dt, \qquad \text{[partial fractions]}$$

$$\ln|P| - \ln|150 - P| = 0.06t + C,$$

$$\frac{P}{150 - P} = \pm e^C e^{0.06t} = Be^{0.06t} \quad \text{[where } B = \pm e^C].$$

If we substitute $t = 0$ and $P = P_0 \neq 150$ into this last equation, we find that $B = P_0/(150 - P_0)$. Hence

$$\frac{P}{150 - P} = \frac{P_0 e^{0.06t}}{150 - P_0}.$$

Finally, this equation is easy to solve for the population

$$P(t) = \frac{150 P_0}{P_0 + (150 - P_0)e^{-0.06t}} \tag{5}$$

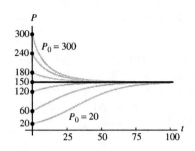

FIGURE 2.1.2. Typical solution curves for the logistic equation $P' = 0.06P - 0.0004P^2$.

at time t in terms of the initial population $P_0 = P(0)$. Figure 2.1.2 shows a number of solution curves corresponding to different values of the initial population ranging from $P_0 = 20$ to $P_0 = 300$. Note that all these solution curves appear to approach the horizontal line $P = 150$ as an asymptote. Indeed, you should be able to see directly from Eq. (5) that $\lim_{t \to \infty} P(t) = 150$, whatever the initial value $P_0 > 0$. ∎

Limiting Populations and Carrying Capacity

The finite limiting population noted in Example 2 is characteristic of logistic populations. In Problem 32 we ask you to use the method of solution of Example 2 to show that the solution of the logistic initial value problem

$$\frac{dP}{dt} = kP(M - P), \quad P(0) = P_0 \tag{6}$$

is

$$P(t) = \frac{MP_0}{P_0 + (M - P_0)e^{-kMt}}. \tag{7}$$

Actual animal populations are positive valued. If $P_0 = M$, then (7) reduces to the unchanging (constant-valued) "equilibrium population" $P(t) \equiv M$. Otherwise, the behavior of a logistic population depends on whether $0 < P_0 < M$ or $P_0 > M$. If $0 < P_0 < M$, then we see from (6) and (7) that $P' > 0$ and

$$P(t) = \frac{MP_0}{P_0 + (M - P_0)e^{-kMt}} = \frac{MP_0}{P_0 + \{\text{pos. number}\}} < \frac{MP_0}{P_0} = M.$$

However, if $P_0 > M$, then we see from (6) and (7) that $P' < 0$ and

$$P(t) = \frac{MP_0}{P_0 + (M - P_0)e^{-kMt}} = \frac{MP_0}{P_0 + \{\text{neg. number}\}} > \frac{MP_0}{P_0} = M.$$

In either case, the denominator is positive for $t > 0$ (why?), and the "positive number" or "negative number" $(M - P_0)e^{-kMt} \to 0$ as $t \to +\infty$. It follows that

$$\lim_{t \to +\infty} P(t) = \frac{MP_0}{P_0 + 0} = M. \tag{8}$$

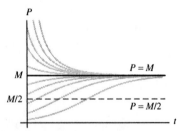

FIGURE 2.1.3. Typical solution curves for the logistic equation $P' = kP(M - P)$. Each solution curve that starts below the line $P = M/2$ has an inflection point on this line. (See Problem 34.)

Thus a population that satisfies the logistic equation does *not* grow without bound like a naturally growing population modeled by the exponential equation $P' = kP$. Instead, it approaches the finite **limiting population** M as $t \to +\infty$. As illustrated by the typical logistic solution curves in Fig. 2.1.3, the population $P(t)$ steadily increases and approaches M from below if $0 < P_0 < M$, but steadily decreases and approaches M from above if $P_0 > M$. Sometimes M is called the **carrying capacity** of the environment, considering it to be the maximum population that the environment can support on a long-term basis.

Example 3

Suppose that in 1885 the population of a certain country was 50 million and was growing at the rate of 750,000 people per year at that time. Suppose also that in 1940 its population was 100 million and was then growing at the rate of 1 million per year. Assume that this population satisfies the logistic equation. Determine both the limiting population M and the predicted population for the year 2000.

Solution

We substitute the two given pairs of data in Eq. (3) and find that

$$0.75 = 50k(M - 50), \quad 1.00 = 100k(M - 100).$$

We solve simultaneously for $M = 200$ and $k = 0.0001$. Thus the limiting population of the country in question is 200 million. With these values of M and k, and with $t = 0$ corresponding to the year 1940 (in which $P_0 = 100$), we find that—according to Eq. (7)—the population in the year 2000 will be

$$P(60) = \frac{100 \cdot 200}{100 + (200 - 100)e^{-(0.0001)(200)(60)}},$$

about 153.7 million people. ∎

Historical Note

The logistic equation was introduced (around 1840) by the Belgian mathematician and demographer P. F. Verhulst as a possible model for human population growth. In the next two examples we compare natural growth and logistic model fits to the 19th century U.S. population census data, then compare projections for the 20th century.

Example 4

The U.S. population in 1800 was 5.308 million and in 1900 was 76.212 million. If we take $P_0 = 5.308$ (with $t = 0$ in 1800) in the natural growth model $P(t) = P_0 e^{rt}$ and substitute $t = 100$, $P = 76.212$, we find that

$$76.212 = 5.308e^{100r}, \quad \text{so} \quad r = \frac{1}{100} \ln \frac{76.212}{5.308} \approx 0.026643.$$

Thus our natural growth model for the U.S. population during the 19th century is

$$P(t) = (5.308)e^{(0.026643)t} \tag{9}$$

(with t in years and P in millions). Because $e^{0.026643} \approx 1.02700$, the average population growth between 1800 and 1900 was about 2.7% per year. ∎

Example 5

The U.S. population in 1850 was 23.192 million. If we take $P_0 = 5.308$ and substitute the data pairs $t = 50$, $P = 23.192$ (for 1850) and $t = 100$, $P = 76.212$ (for 1900) in the logistic model formula in Eq. (7), we get the two equations

$$\frac{(5.308)M}{5.308 + (M - 5.308)e^{-50kM}} = 23.192,$$

$$\frac{(5.308)M}{5.308 + (M - 5.308)e^{-100kM}} = 76.212 \tag{10}$$

in the two unknowns k and M. Nonlinear systems like this ordinarily are solved numerically using an appropriate computer system. But with the right algebraic trick (Problem 36 in this section) the equations in (10) can be solved manually for $k = 0.000167716$, $M = 188.121$. Substitution of these values in Eq. (7) yields the logistic model

$$P(t) = \frac{998.546}{5.308 + (182.813)e^{-(0.031551)t}}. \tag{11}$$

The table in Fig. 2.1.4 compares the actual 1800–1990 U.S. census population figures with those predicted by the exponential growth model in (9) and the logistic model in (11). Both agree well with the 19th-century figures. But the exponential model diverges appreciably from the census data in the early decades of the 20th century, whereas the logistic model remains accurate until 1940. By the end of the 20th century the exponential model vastly overestimates the actual U.S. population—predicting over a billion in the year 2000—whereas the logistic model somewhat underestimates it.

In order to measure the extent to which a given model fits actual data, it is customary to define the **average error** (in the model) as *the square root of the average of the squares of the individual errors* (the latter appearing in the fourth and sixth columns of the table in Fig. 2.1.4). Using only the 1800–1900 data, this definition gives 3.162 for the average error in the exponential model, while the average error

Year	Actual U.S. Pop.	Exponential Model	Exponential Error	Logistic Model	Logistic Error
1800	5.308	5.308	0.000	5.308	0.000
1810	7.240	6.929	0.311	7.202	0.038
1820	9.638	9.044	0.594	9.735	−0.097
1830	12.861	11.805	1.056	13.095	−0.234
1840	17.064	15.409	1.655	17.501	−0.437
1850	23.192	20.113	3.079	23.192	0.000
1860	31.443	26.253	5.190	30.405	1.038
1870	38.558	34.268	4.290	39.326	−0.768
1880	50.189	44.730	5.459	50.034	0.155
1890	62.980	58.387	4.593	62.435	0.545
1900	76.212	76.212	0.000	76.213	−0.001
1910	92.228	99.479	−7.251	90.834	1.394
1920	106.022	129.849	−23.827	105.612	0.410
1930	123.203	169.492	−46.289	119.834	3.369
1940	132.165	221.237	−89.072	132.886	−0.721
1950	151.326	288.780	−137.454	144.354	6.972
1960	179.323	376.943	−197.620	154.052	25.271
1970	203.302	492.023	−288.721	161.990	41.312
1980	226.542	642.236	−415.694	168.316	58.226
1990	248.710	838.308	−589.598	173.252	76.458
2000	281.422	1094.240	−812.818	177.038	104.384

FIGURE 2.1.4. Comparison of exponential growth and logistic models with U.S. census populations (in millions).

in the logistic model is only 0.452. Consequently, even in 1900 we might well have anticipated that the logistic model would predict the U.S. population growth during the 20th century more accurately than the exponential model. ■

The moral of Examples 4 and 5 is simply that one should not expect too much of models that are based on severely limited information (such as just a pair of data points). Much of the science of *statistics* is devoted to the analysis of large "data sets" to formulate useful (and perhaps reliable) mathematical models.

More Applications of the Logistic Equation

We next describe some situations that illustrate the varied circumstances in which the logistic equation is a satisfactory mathematical model.

1. *Limited environment situation.* A certain environment can support a population of at most M individuals. It is then reasonable to expect the growth rate $\beta - \delta$ (the combined birth and death rates) to be proportional to $M - P$, because we may think of $M - P$ as the potential for further expansion. Then $\beta - \delta = k(M - P)$, so that

    $$\frac{dP}{dt} = (\beta - \delta)P = kP(M - P).$$

    The classic example of a limited environment situation is a fruit fly population in a closed container.

2. *Competition situation.* If the birth rate β is constant but the death rate δ is proportional to P, so that $\delta = \alpha P$, then

    $$\frac{dP}{dt} = (\beta - \alpha P)P = kP(M - P).$$

    This might be a reasonable working hypothesis in a study of a cannibalistic population, in which all deaths result from chance encounters between individuals. Of course, competition between individuals is not usually so deadly, nor its effects so immediate and decisive.

3. *Joint proportion situation.* Let $P(t)$ denote the number of individuals in a constant-size susceptible population M who are infected with a certain contagious and incurable disease. The disease is spread by chance encounters. Then $P'(t)$ should be proportional to the product of the number P of individuals having the disease and the number $M - P$ of those not having it, and therefore $dP/dt = kP(M - P)$. Again we discover that the mathematical model is the logistic equation. The mathematical description of the spread of a rumor in a population of M individuals is identical.

Example 6 Suppose that at time $t = 0$, 10 thousand people in a city with population $M = 100$ thousand people have heard a certain rumor. After 1 week the number $P(t)$ of those who have heard it has increased to $P(1) = 20$ thousand. Assuming that $P(t)$ satisfies a logistic equation, when will 80% of the city's population have heard the rumor?

Solution Substituting $P_0 = 10$ and $M = 100$ (thousand) in Eq. (7), we get

$$P(t) = \frac{1000}{10 + 90e^{-100kt}}. \tag{12}$$

Then substitution of $t = 1$, $P = 20$ gives the equation

$$20 = \frac{1000}{10 + 90e^{-100k}}$$

that is readily solved for

$$e^{-100k} = \tfrac{4}{9}, \quad \text{so} \quad k = \tfrac{1}{100} \ln \tfrac{9}{4} \approx 0.008109.$$

With $P(t) = 80$, Eq. (12) takes the form

$$80 = \frac{1000}{10 + 90e^{-100kt}},$$

which we solve for $e^{-100kt} = \tfrac{1}{36}$. It follows that 80% of the population has heard the rumor when

$$t = \frac{\ln 36}{100k} = \frac{\ln 36}{\ln \tfrac{9}{4}} \approx 4.42,$$

thus after about 4 weeks and 3 days. ∎

Doomsday versus Extinction

Consider a population $P(t)$ of unsophisticated animals in which females rely solely on chance encounters to meet males for reproductive purposes. It is reasonable to expect such encounters to occur at a rate that is proportional to the product of the number $P/2$ of males and the number $P/2$ of females, hence at a rate proportional to P^2. We therefore assume that births occur at the rate kP^2 (per unit time, with k constant). The birth rate (births/time/population) is then given by $\beta = kP$. If the death rate δ is constant, then the general population equation in (1) yields the differential equation

➤
$$\frac{dP}{dt} = kP^2 - \delta P = kP(P - M) \tag{13}$$

(where $M = \delta/k > 0$) as a mathematical model of the population.

Note that the right-hand side in Eq. (13) is the *negative* of the right-hand side in the logistic equation in (3). We will see that the constant M is now a **threshold population**, with the way the population behaves in the future depending critically on whether the initial population P_0 is less than or greater than M.

Example 7   Consider an animal population $P(t)$ that is modeled by the equation

$$\frac{dP}{dt} = 0.0004P(P - 150) = 0.0004P^2 - 0.06P. \tag{14}$$

We want to find $P(t)$ if (a) $P(0) = 200$; (b) $P(0) = 100$.

Solution   To solve the equation in (14), we separate the variables and integrate. We get

$$\int \frac{dP}{P(P-150)} = \int 0.0004\, dt,$$

$$-\frac{1}{150} \int \left(\frac{1}{P} - \frac{1}{P-150} \right) dP = \int 0.0004\, dt, \quad \text{[partial fractions]}$$

$$\ln|P| - \ln|P - 150| = -0.06t + C,$$

$$\frac{P}{P-150} = \pm e^C e^{-0.06t} = Be^{-0.06t} \qquad \text{[where } B = \pm e^C\text{]}. \qquad (15)$$

(a) Substitution of $t = 0$ and $P = 200$ into (15) gives $B = 4$. With this value of B we solve Eq. (15) for

$$P(t) = \frac{600e^{-0.06t}}{4e^{-0.06t} - 1}. \qquad (16)$$

Note that, as t increases and approaches $T = \ln(4)/0.06 \approx 23.105$, the positive denominator on the right in (16) decreases and approaches 0. Consequently $P(t) \to +\infty$ as $t \to T^-$. This is a *doomsday* situation—a real population *explosion*.
(b) Substitution of $t = 0$ and $P = 100$ into (15) gives $B = -2$. With this value of B we solve Eq. (15) for

$$P(t) = \frac{300e^{-0.06t}}{2e^{-0.06t} + 1} = \frac{300}{2 + e^{0.06t}}. \qquad (17)$$

Note that, as t increases without bound, the positive denominator on the right in (16) approaches $+\infty$. Consequently, $P(t) \to 0$ as $t \to +\infty$. This is an (eventual) *extinction* situation. ∎

Thus the population in Example 7 either explodes or is an endangered species threatened with extinction, depending on whether or not its initial size exceeds the threshold population $M = 150$. An approximation to this phenomenon is sometimes observed with animal populations, such as the alligator population in certain areas of the southern United States.

Figure 2.1.5 shows typical solution curves that illustrate the two possibilities for a population $P(t)$ satisfying Eq. (13). If $P_0 = M$ (exactly!), then the population remains constant. However, this equilibrium situation is very unstable. If P_0 exceeds M (even slightly), then $P(t)$ rapidly increases without bound, whereas if the initial (positive) population is less than M (however slightly), then it decreases (more gradually) toward zero as $t \to +\infty$. See Problem 33.

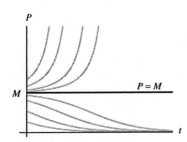

FIGURE 2.1.5. Typical solution curves for the explosion-extinction equation $P' = kP(P - M)$.

2.1 Problems

Separate variables and use partial fractions to solve the initial value problems in Problems 1–8. Use either the exact solution or a computer-generated slope field to sketch the graphs of several solutions of the given differential equation, and highlight the indicated particular solution.

1. $\dfrac{dx}{dt} = x - x^2$, $x(0) = 2$ **2.** $\dfrac{dx}{dt} = 10x - x^2$, $x(0) = 1$

3. $\dfrac{dx}{dt} = 1 - x^2$, $x(0) = 3$ **4.** $\dfrac{dx}{dt} = 9 - 4x^2$, $x(0) = 0$

5. $\dfrac{dx}{dt} = 3x(5 - x)$, $x(0) = 8$

6. $\dfrac{dx}{dt} = 3x(x - 5)$, $x(0) = 2$

7. $\dfrac{dx}{dt} = 4x(7 - x)$, $x(0) = 11$

8. $\dfrac{dx}{dt} = 7x(x - 13)$, $x(0) = 17$

9. The time rate of change of a rabbit population P is proportional to the square root of P. At time $t = 0$ (months) the population numbers 100 rabbits and is increasing at the rate of 20 rabbits per month. How many rabbits will there be one year later?

10. Suppose that the fish population $P(t)$ in a lake is attacked by a disease at time $t = 0$, with the result that the fish cease to reproduce (so that the birth rate is $\beta = 0$) and the death rate δ (deaths per week per fish) is thereafter proportional to $1/\sqrt{P}$. If there were initially 900 fish in the lake and 441 were left after 6 weeks, how long did it take all the fish in the lake to die?

11. Suppose that when a certain lake is stocked with fish, the birth and death rates β and δ are both inversely proportional to $\sqrt{P}$. **(a)** Show that

$$P(t) = \left(\tfrac{1}{2}kt + \sqrt{P_0} \right)^2,$$

where k is a constant. **(b)** If $P_0 = 100$ and after 6 months there are 169 fish in the lake, how many will there be after 1 year?

12. The time rate of change of an alligator population P in a swamp is proportional to the square of P. The swamp contained a dozen alligators in 1988, two dozen in 1998. When will there be four dozen alligators in the swamp? What happens thereafter?

13. Consider a prolific breed of rabbits whose birth and death rates, β and δ, are each proportional to the rabbit population $P = P(t)$, with $\beta > \delta$. **(a)** Show that

$$P(t) = \frac{P_0}{1 - kP_0 t}, \quad k \text{ constant.}$$

Note that $P(t) \to +\infty$ as $t \to 1/(kP_0)$. This is doomsday.
(b) Suppose that $P_0 = 6$ and that there are nine rabbits after ten months. When does doomsday occur?

14. Repeat part (a) of Problem 13 in the case $\beta < \delta$. What now happens to the rabbit population in the long run?

15. Consider a population $P(t)$ satisfying the logistic equation $dP/dt = aP - bP^2$, where $B = aP$ is the time rate at which births occur and $D = bP^2$ is the rate at which deaths occur. If the initial population is $P(0) = P_0$, and B_0 births per month and D_0 deaths per month are occurring at time $t = 0$, show that the limiting population is $M = B_0 P_0 / D_0$.

16. Consider a rabbit population $P(t)$ satisfying the logistic equation as in Problem 15. If the initial population is 120 rabbits and there are 8 births per month and 6 deaths per month occurring at time $t = 0$, how many months does it take for $P(t)$ to reach 95% of the limiting population M?

17. Consider a rabbit population $P(t)$ satisfying the logistic equation as in Problem 15. If the initial population is 240 rabbits and there are 9 births per month and 12 deaths per month occurring at time $t = 0$, how many months does it take for $P(t)$ to reach 105% of the limiting population M?

18. Consider a population $P(t)$ satisfying the extinction-explosion equation $dP/dt = aP^2 - bP$, where $B = aP^2$ is the time rate at which births occur and $D = bP$ is the rate at which deaths occur. If the initial population is $P(0) = P_0$ and B_0 births per month and D_0 deaths per month are occurring at time $t = 0$, show that the threshold population is $M = D_0 P_0 / B_0$.

19. Consider an alligator population $P(t)$ satisfying the extinction/explosion equation as in Problem 18. If the initial population is 100 alligators and there are 10 births per month and 9 deaths per months occurring at time $t = 0$, how many months does it take for $P(t)$ to reach 10 times the threshold population M?

20. Consider an alligator population $P(t)$ satisfying the extinction/explosion equation as in Problem 18. If the initial population is 110 alligators and there are 11 births per month and 12 deaths per month occurring at time $t = 0$, how many months does it take for $P(t)$ to reach 10% of the threshold population M?

21. Suppose that the population $P(t)$ of a country satisfies the differential equation $dP/dt = kP(200 - P)$ with k constant. Its population in 1940 was 100 million and was then growing at the rate of 1 million per year. Predict this country's population for the year 2000.

22. Suppose that at time $t = 0$, half of a "logistic" population of 100,000 persons have heard a certain rumor, and that the number of those who have heard it is then increasing at the rate of 1000 persons per day. How long will it take for this rumor to spread to 80% of the population? [*Suggestion:* Find the value of k by substituting $P(0)$ and $P'(0)$ in the logistic equation, Eq. (3).]

23. As the salt KNO_3 dissolves in methanol, the number $x(t)$ of grams of the salt in a solution after t seconds satisfies the differential equation $dx/dt = 0.8x - 0.004x^2$.

   (a) What is the maximum amount of the salt that will ever dissolve in the methanol?

(b) If $x = 50$ when $t = 0$, how long will it take for an additional 50 g of salt to dissolve?

24. Suppose that a community contains 15,000 people who are susceptible to Michaud's syndrome, a contagious disease. At time $t = 0$ the number $N(t)$ of people who have developed Michaud's syndrome is 5000 and is increasing at the rate of 500 per day. Assume that $N'(t)$ is proportional to the product of the numbers of those who have caught the disease and of those who have not. How long will it take for another 5000 people to develop Michaud's syndrome?

25. The data in the table in Fig. 2.1.6 are given for a certain population $P(t)$ that satisfies the logistic equation in (3). **(a)** What is the limiting population M? [*Suggestion*: Use the approximation

$$P'(t) \approx \frac{P(t+h) - P(t-h)}{2h}$$

with $h = 1$ to estimate the values of $P'(t)$ when $P = 25.00$ and when $P = 47.54$. Then substitute these values in the logistic equation and solve for k and M.] **(b)** Use the values of k and M found in part (a) to determine when $P = 75$. (*Suggestion*: Take $t = 0$ to correspond to the year 1925.)

Year	P (millions)
1924	24.63
1925	25.00
1926	25.38
⋮	⋮
1974	47.04
1975	47.54
1976	48.04

FIGURE 2.1.6. Population data for Problem 25.

26. A population $P(t)$ of small rodents has birth rate $\beta = (0.001)P$ (births per month per rodent) and *constant* death rate δ. If $P(0) = 100$ and $P'(0) = 8$, how long (in months) will it take this population to double to 200 rodents? (*Suggestion*: First find the value of δ.)

27. Consider an animal population $P(t)$ with constant death rate $\delta = 0.01$ (deaths per animal per month) and with birth rate β proportional to P. Suppose that $P(0) = 200$ and $P'(0) = 2$. **(a)** When is $P = 1000$? **(b)** When does doomsday occur?

28. Suppose that the number $x(t)$ (with t in months) of alligators in a swamp satisfies the differential equation $dP/dt = 0.0001x^2 - 0.01x$.

(a) If initially there are 25 alligators in the swamp, solve this differential equation to determine what happens to the alligator population in the long run.

(b) Repeat part (a), except with 150 alligators initially.

29. During the period from 1790 to 1930, the U.S. population $P(t)$ (t in years) grew from 3.9 million to 123.2 million. Throughout this period, $P(t)$ remained close to the solution of the initial value problem

$$\frac{dP}{dt} = 0.03135P - 0.0001489P^2, \quad P(0) = 3.9.$$

(a) What 1930 population does this logistic equation predict?

(b) What limiting population does it predict?

(c) Has this logistic equation continued since 1930 to accurately model the U.S. population?

[This problem is based on a computation by Verhulst, who in 1845 used the 1790–1840 U.S. population data to predict accurately the U.S. population through the year 1930 (long after his own death, of course).]

30. A tumor may be regarded as a population of multiplying cells. It is found empirically that the "birth rate" of the cells in a tumor decreases exponentially with time, so that $\beta(t) = \beta_0 e^{-\alpha t}$ (where α and β_0 are positive constants), and hence

$$\frac{dP}{dt} = \beta_0 e^{-\alpha t} P, \quad P(0) = P_0.$$

Solve this initial value problem for

$$P(t) = P_0 \exp\left(\frac{\beta_0}{\alpha}(1 - e^{-\alpha t})\right).$$

Observe that $P(t)$ approaches the finite limiting population $P_0 \exp(\beta_0/\alpha)$ as $t \to +\infty$.

31. For the tumor of Problem 30, suppose that at time $t = 0$ there are $P_0 = 10^6$ cells and that $P(t)$ is then increasing at the rate of 3×10^5 cells per month. After 6 months the tumor has doubled (in size and in number of cells). Solve numerically for α, and then find the limiting population of the tumor.

32. Derive the solution

$$P(t) = \frac{MP_0}{P_0 + (M - P_0)e^{-kMt}}$$

of the logistic initial value problem $P' = kP(M - P)$, $P(0) = P_0$. Make it clear how your derivation depends on whether $0 < P_0 < M$ or $P_0 > M$.

33. (a) Derive the solution

$$P(t) = \frac{MP_0}{P_0 + (M - P_0)e^{kMt}}$$

of the extinction-explosion initial value problem $P' = kP(P - M)$, $P(0) = P_0$.

(b) How does the behavior of $P(t)$ as t increases depend on whether $0 < P_0 < M$ or $P_0 > M$?

34. If $P(t)$ satisfies the logistic equation in (3), use the chain rule to show that

$$P''(t) = 2k^2 P(P - \tfrac{1}{2}M)(P - M).$$

Conclude that $P'' > 0$ if $0 < P < \tfrac{1}{2}M$; $P'' = 0$ if $P = \tfrac{1}{2}M$; $P'' < 0$ if $\tfrac{1}{2}M < P < M$; and $P'' > 0$ if $P > M$. In particular, it follows that any solution curve that crosses the line $P = \tfrac{1}{2}M$ has an inflection point where it crosses that line, and therefore resembles one of the lower S-shaped curves in Fig. 2.1.3.

35. Consider two population functions $P_1(t)$ and $P_2(t)$, both of which satisfy the logistic equation with the same limiting population M, but with different values k_1 and k_2 of the constant k in Eq. (3). Assume that $k_1 < k_2$. Which population approaches M the most rapidly? You can reason *geometrically* by examining slope fields (especially if appropriate software is available), *symbolically* by analyzing the solution given in Eq. (7), or *numerically* by substituting successive values of t.

36. To solve the two equations in (10) for the values of k and M, begin by solving the first equation for the quantity $x = e^{-50kM}$ and the second equation for $x^2 = e^{-100kM}$. Upon equating the two resulting expressions for x^2 in terms of M, you get an equation that is readily solved for M. With M now known, either of the original equations is readily solved for k. This technique can be used to "fit" the logistic equation to any three population values P_0, P_1, and P_2 corresponding to *equally* spaced times $t_0 = 0$, t_1, and $t_2 = 2t_1$.

37. Use the method of Problem 36 to fit the logistic equation to the actual U.S. population data (Fig. 2.1.4) for the years 1850, 1900, and 1950. Solve the resulting logistic equation and compare the predicted and actual populations for the years 1990 and 2000.

38. Fit the logistic equation to the actual U.S. population data (Fig. 2.1.4) for the years 1900, 1930, and 1960. Solve the resulting logistic equation, then compare the predicted and actual populations for the years 1980, 1990, and 2000.

39. Birth and death rates of animal populations typically are not constant; instead, they vary periodically with the passage of seasons. Find $P(t)$ if the population P satisfies the differential equation

$$\frac{dP}{dt} = (k + b\cos 2\pi t)P,$$

where t is in years and k and b are positive constants. Thus the growth rate function $r(t) = k + b\cos 2\pi t$ varies periodically about its mean value k. Construct a graph that contrasts the growth of this population with one that has the same initial value P_0 but satisfies the natural growth equation $P' = kP$ (same constant k). How would the two populations compare after the passage of many years?

2.1 Application: Logistic Modeling of Population Data

These investigations deal with the problem of fitting a logistic model to given population data. Thus we want to determine the numerical constants a and b so that the solution $P(t)$ of the initial value problem

$$\frac{dP}{dt} = aP + bP^2, \quad P(0) = P_0 \tag{1}$$

approximates the given values P_0, P_1, ..., P_n of the population at the times $t_0 = 0$, t_1, ..., t_n. If we rewrite Eq. (1) (the logistic equation with $kM = a$ and $k = -b$) in the form

$$\frac{1}{P}\frac{dP}{dt} = a + bP, \tag{2}$$

then we see that the points

$$\left(P(t_i), \frac{P'(t_i)}{P(t_i)} \right), \quad i = 0, 1, 2, \ldots, n,$$

should all lie on the straight line with y-intercept a and slope b [as determined by the function of P on the right-hand side in Eq. (2)].

This observation provides a way to find a and b. If we can determine the approximate values of the derivatives $P'_1, P'_2, \ldots$ corresponding to the given population data, then we can proceed with the following agenda:

- First plot the points $(P_1, P_1'/P_1)$, $(P_2, P_2'/P_2)$, ... on a sheet of graph paper with horizontal P-axis.
- Then use a ruler to draw a straight line that appears to approximate these points well.
- Finally, measure this straight line's y-intercept a and slope b.

But where are we to find the needed values of the derivative $P'(t)$ of the (as yet) unknown function P? It is easiest to use the approximation

$$P_i' = \frac{P_{i+1} - P_{i-1}}{t_{i+1} - t_{i-1}} \tag{3}$$

suggested by Fig. 2.1.7. For instance, if we take $i = 0$ corresponding to the year 1790, then the U.S. population data in Fig. 2.1.8 give

$$P_1' = \frac{P_2 - P_0}{t_2 - t_0} = \frac{7.240 - 3.929}{20} \approx 0.166$$

for the slope at (t_1, P_1) corresponding to the year 1800.

Year	i	t_i	Population P_i	Slope P_i'
1790	0	−10	3.929	
1800	1	0	5.308	0.166
1810	2	10	7.240	0.217
1820	3	20	9.638	0.281
1830	4	30	12.861	0.371
1840	5	40	17.064	0.517
1850	6	50	23.192	0.719
1860	7	60	31.443	0.768
1870	8	70	38.558	0.937
1880	9	80	50.189	1.221
1890	10	90	62.980	1.301
1900	11	100	76.212	1.462
1910	12	110	92.228	

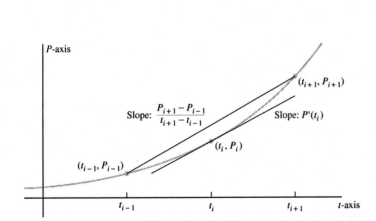

FIGURE 2.1.7. The symmetric difference approximation $\dfrac{P_{i+1} - P_{i-1}}{t_{i+1} - t_{i-1}}$ to the derivative $P'(t_i)$.

FIGURE 2.1.8. U.S. population data (in millions) and approximate slopes.

INVESTIGATION A: Use Eq. (3) to verify the slope figures shown in the final column of the table in Fig. 2.1.8; then plot the points $(P_1, P_1'/P_1)$, ..., $(P_{11}, P_{11}'/P_{11})$ indicated by the asterisks in Fig. 2.1.9. If an appropriate graphing calculator, spreadsheet, or computer program is available, use it to find the straight line $y = a + bP$ as in (2) that best fits these points. If not, draw your own straight line approximating these points, and then measure its intercept a and slope b as accurately as you can. Next, solve the logistic equation in (1) with these numerical parameters, taking $t = 0$ corresponding to the year 1800. Finally, compare the predicted 20th century U.S. population figures with the actual data listed in Fig. 2.1.4.

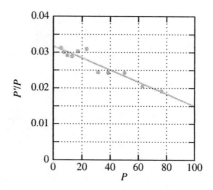

FIGURE 2.1.9. Points and approximating straight line for U.S. population data from 1800 to 1900.

INVESTIGATION B: Repeat Investigation A, but take $t = 0$ in 1900 and use only 20th century population data. Do you get a better approximation for the U.S. population during the final decades of the 20th century?

INVESTIGATION C: Model similarly the world population data shown in Fig. 2.1.10. The Population Division of the United Nations predicts a world population of 8.177 billion in the year 2025. What do you predict?

Year	World Population (billions)
1960	3.049
1965	3.358
1970	3.721
1975	4.103
1980	4.473
1985	4.882
1990	5.249
1995	5.679
2000	6.127

FIGURE 2.1.10. World population data.

2.2 Equilibrium Solutions and Stability

In previous sections we have often used explicit solutions of differential equations to answer specific numerical questions. But even when a given differential equation is difficult or impossible to solve explicitly, it often is possible to extract *qualitative* information about general properties of its solutions. For example, we may be able to establish that every solution $x(t)$ grows without bound as $t \to +\infty$, or approaches a finite limit, or is a periodic function of t. In this section we introduce—mainly by consideration of simple differential equations that *can* be solved explicitly—some of the more important qualitative questions that can sometimes be answered for equations that are difficult or impossible to solve.

Example 1

Let $x(t)$ denote the temperature of a body with initial temperature $x(0) = x_0$. At time $t = 0$ this body is immersed in a medium with constant temperature A. Assuming Newton's law of cooling,

$$\frac{dx}{dt} = -k(x - A) \qquad (k > 0 \quad \text{constant}), \tag{1}$$

we readily solve (by separation of variables) for the explicit solution

$$x(t) = A + (x_0 - A)e^{-kt}.$$

It follows immediately that

$$\lim_{t \to \infty} x(t) = A, \tag{2}$$

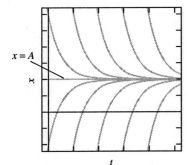

$x = A$

x

FIGURE 2.2.1. Typical solution curves for the equation of Newton's law of cooling, $dx/dt = -k(x - A)$.

so the temperature of the body approaches that of the surrounding medium (as is evident to one's intuition). Note that the constant function $x(t) \equiv A$ is a solution of Eq. (1); it corresponds to the temperature of the body when it is in thermal equilibrium with the surrounding medium. In Fig. 2.2.1 the limit in (2) means that every other solution curve approaches the equilibrium solution curve $x = A$ asymptotically as $t \to +\infty$. ∎

$x' > 0$ $x' < 0$

$x < A$ $x = A$ $x > A$

FIGURE 2.2.2. Phase diagram for the equation $dx/dt = f(x) = k(A - x)$.

Remark: The behavior of solutions of Eq. (1) is summarized briefly by the **phase diagram** in Fig. 2.2.2. The right-hand side $f(x) = -k(x - A) = k(A - x)$ is positive if $x < A$, negative if $x > A$. This observation corresponds to the fact that solutions starting above the line $x = A$ and those starting below it both approach the limiting solution $x(t) \equiv A$ as t increases (as indicated by the arrows). ∎

In Section 2.1 we introduced the general population equation

$$\frac{dx}{dt} = (\beta - \delta)x, \tag{3}$$

where β and δ are the birth and death rates, respectively, in births or deaths per individual per unit of time. The question of whether a population $x(t)$ is bounded or unbounded as $t \to +\infty$ is of evident interest. In many situations—like the logistic and explosion/extinction populations of Section 2.1—the birth and death rates are known functions of x. Then Eq. (3) takes the form

$$\frac{dx}{dt} = f(x). \tag{4}$$

This is an **autonomous** first-order differential equation—one in which the independent variable t does not appear explicitly. As in Example 1, the solutions of the equation $f(x) = 0$ play an important role and are called **critical points** of the autonomous differential equation $dx/dt = f(x)$.

If $x = c$ is a critical point of Eq. (4), then the differential equation has the constant solution $x(t) \equiv c$. A constant solution of a differential equation is sometimes called an **equilibrium solution** (one may think of a population that remains constant because it is in "equilibrium" with its environment). Thus the critical point $x = c$, a number, corresponds to the equilibrium solution $x(t) \equiv c$, a constant-valued function.

Example 2 illustrates the fact that the qualitative behavior (as t increases) of the solutions of an autonomous first-order equation can be described in terms of its critical points.

Example 2

Consider the logistic differential equation

$$\frac{dx}{dt} = kx(M - x) \tag{5}$$

(with $k > 0$ and $M > 0$). It has two critical points—the solutions $x = 0$ and $x = M$ of the equation

$$f(x) = kx(M - x) = 0.$$

In Section 2.1 we discussed the logistic-equation solution

$$x(t) = \frac{M x_0}{x_0 + (M - x_0)e^{-kMt}} \tag{6}$$

satisfying the initial condition $x(0) = x_0$. Note that the initial values $x_0 = 0$ and $x_0 = M$ yield the equilibrium solutions $x(t) \equiv 0$ and $x(t) \equiv M$ of Eq. (5).

We observed in Section 2.1 that if $x_0 > 0$, then $x(t) \to M$ as $t \to +\infty$. But if $x_0 < 0$, then the denominator in Eq. (6) initially is positive but vanishes when

$$t = t_1 = \frac{1}{kM} \ln \frac{M - x_0}{-x_0} > 0.$$

Because the numerator in (6) is negative in this case, it follows that

$$\lim_{t \to t_1^-} x(t) = -\infty \quad \text{if} \quad x_0 < 0.$$

It follows that the solution curves of the logistic equation in (5) look as illustrated in Fig. 2.2.3. ∎

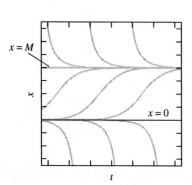

$x = M$

x

$x = 0$

t

FIGURE 2.2.3. Typical solution curves for the logistic equation $dx/dt = kx(M - x)$.

Stability of Critical Points

Figure 2.2.3 illustrates the concept of *stability*. A critical point $x = c$ of an autonomous first-order equation is said to be *stable* provided that, if the initial value x_0 is sufficiently close to c, then $x(t)$ remains close to c for all $t > 0$. More precisely, the critical point c is **stable** if, for each $\epsilon > 0$, there exists $\delta > 0$ such that

$$|x_0 - c| < \delta \quad \text{implies that} \quad |x(t) - c| < \epsilon \tag{7}$$

for all $t > 0$. The critical point $x = c$ is **unstable** if it is not stable.

Figure 2.2.4 shows a "wider view" of the solution curves of a logistic equation with $k = 1$ and $M = 4$. Note that the strip $3.5 < x < 4.5$ enclosing the stable equilibrium curve $x = 4$ acts like a *funnel*—solution curves (moving from left to right) enter this strip and thereafter remain within it. By contrast, the strip $-0.5 < x < 0.5$ enclosing the unstable solution curve $x = 0$ acts like a *spout*—solution curves leave this strip and thereafter remain outside it. Thus the critical point $x = M$ is stable, whereas the critical point $x = 0$ is unstable.

FIGURE 2.2.4. Solution curves, funnel, and spout for $dx/dt = 4x - x^2$.

$x' < 0 \qquad x' > 0 \qquad x' < 0$

$x = 0 \qquad\qquad x = M$
Unstable $\qquad\qquad$ Stable

FIGURE 2.2.5. Phase diagram for the logistic equation $dx/dt = f(x) = kx(M - x)$.

Remark 1: We can summarize the behavior of solutions of the logistic equation in (5)—in terms of their initial values—by means of the phase diagram shown in Fig. 2.2.5. It indicates that $x(t) \to M$ as $t \to +\infty$ if either $x_0 > M$ or $0 < x_0 < M$, whereas $x(t) \to -\infty$ as t increases if $x_0 < 0$. The fact that M is a stable critical point would be important, for instance, if we wished to conduct an experiment with a population of M bacteria. It is impossible to count precisely M bacteria for M large, but any initially positive population will approach M as t increases.

Remark 2:   Related to the stability of the limiting solution $M = a/b$ of the logistic equation

$$\frac{dx}{dt} = ax - bx^2 \tag{8}$$

is the "predictability" of M for an actual population. The coefficients a and b are unlikely to be known precisely for an actual population. But if they are replaced with close approximations $a^\star$ and $b^\star$—derived perhaps from empirical measurements—then the approximate limiting population $M^\star = a^\star/b^\star$ will be close to the actual limiting population $M = a/b$. We may therefore say that the value M of the limiting population predicted by a logistic equation not only is a stable critical point of the differential equation; this value also is "stable" with respect to small perturbations of the constant coefficients in the equation. (Note that one of these two statements involves changes in the initial value x_0; the other involves changes in the coefficients a and b.)   ■

Example 3   Consider now the explosion/extinction equation

$$\frac{dx}{dt} = kx(x - M) \tag{9}$$

of Eq. (10) in Section 2.1. Like the logistic equation, it has the two critical points $x = 0$ and $x = M$ corresponding to the equilibrium solutions $x(t) \equiv 0$ and $x(t) \equiv M$. According to Problem 33 in Section 2.1, its solution with $x(0) = x_0$ is given by

$$x(t) = \frac{M x_0}{x_0 + (M - x_0)e^{kMt}} \tag{10}$$

(with only a single difference in sign from the logistic solution in (6)). If $x_0 < M$, then (because the coefficient of the exponential in the denominator is positive) it follows immediately from Eq. (10) that $x(t) \to 0$ as $t \to +\infty$. But if $x_0 > M$, then the denominator in (10) initially is positive, but vanishes when

$$t = t_1 = \frac{1}{kM} \ln \frac{x_0}{x_0 - M} > 0.$$

Because the numerator in (10) is positive in this case, it follows that

$$\lim_{t \to t_1^-} x(t) = +\infty \quad \text{if} \quad x_0 > M.$$

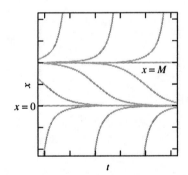

FIGURE 2.2.6. Typical solution curves for the explosion/extinction equation $dx/dt = kx(x - M)$.

Therefore, the solution curves of the explosion/extinction equation in (9) look as illustrated in Fig. 2.2.6. A narrow band along the equilibrium curve $x = 0$ (as in Fig. 2.2.4) would serve as a funnel, while a band along the solution curve $x = M$ would serve as a spout for solutions. The behavior of the solutions of Eq. (9) is summarized by the phase diagram in Fig. 2.2.7, where we see that the critical point $x = 0$ is stable and the critical point $x = M$ is unstable.   ■

FIGURE 2.2.7. Phase diagram for the explosion/extinction equation $dx/dt = f(x) = kx(x - M)$.

Harvesting a Logistic Population

The autonomous differential equation

$$\frac{dx}{dt} = ax - bx^2 - h \tag{11}$$

(with a, b, and h all positive) may be considered to describe a logistic population *with harvesting*. For instance, we might think of the population of fish in a lake from which h fish per year are removed by fishing.

Example 4 Let us rewrite Eq. (11) in the form

$$\frac{dx}{dt} = kx(M - x) - h, \tag{12}$$

which exhibits the limiting population M in the case $h = 0$ of no harvesting. Assuming hereafter that $h > 0$, we can solve the quadratic equation $-kx^2 + kMx - h = 0$ for the two critical points

$$H, N = \frac{kM \pm \sqrt{(kM)^2 - 4hk}}{2k} = \frac{1}{2}\left(M \pm \sqrt{M^2 - 4h/k}\right), \tag{13}$$

assuming that the harvesting rate h is sufficiently small that $4h < kM^2$, so both roots H and N are real with $0 < H < N < M$. Then we can rewrite Eq. (12) in the form

$$\frac{dx}{dt} = k(N - x)(x - H). \tag{14}$$

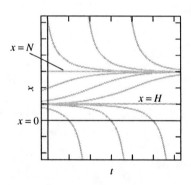

For instance, the number of critical points of the equation may change abruptly as the value of a parameter is changed. In Problem 24 we ask you to solve this equation for the solution

$$x(t) = \frac{N(x_0 - H) - H(x_0 - N)e^{-k(N-H)t}}{(x_0 - H) - (x_0 - N)e^{-k(N-H)t}} \tag{15}$$

in terms of the initial value $x(0) = x_0$.

Note that the exponent $-k(N - H)t$ is negative for $t > 0$. If $x_0 > N$ then each of the coefficients within parentheses in Eq. (15) is positive; it follows that

$$\text{If} \quad x_0 > N \quad \text{then} \quad x(t) \to N \quad \text{as} \quad t \to +\infty. \tag{16}$$

FIGURE 2.2.8. Typical solution curves for the logistic harvesting equation $dx/dt = k(N - x)(x - H)$.

In Problem 25 we ask you to deduce also from Eq. (15) that

$$\text{If} \quad H < x_0 < N \quad \text{then} \quad x(t) \to N \quad \text{as} \quad t \to +\infty, \quad \text{whereas} \tag{17}$$

$$\text{if} \quad x_0 < H \quad \text{then} \quad x(t) \to -\infty \quad \text{as} \quad t \to t_1 \tag{18}$$

for a positive value t_1 that depends on x_0. It follows that the solution curves of Eq. (12)—still assuming that $4h < kM^2$—look as illustrated in Fig. 2.2.8. (Can you visualize a funnel along the line $x = N$ and a spout along the line $x = H$?) Thus the constant solution $x(t) \equiv N$ is an equilibrium *limiting solution*, whereas $x(t) \equiv H$ is a *threshold solution* that separates different behaviors—the population approaches N if $x_0 > H$, while it becomes extinct because of harvesting if $x_0 < H$. Finally, the stable critical point $x = N$ and the unstable critical point $x = H$ are illustrated in the phase diagram in Fig. 2.2.9. ∎

FIGURE 2.2.9. Phase diagram for the logistic harvesting equation $dx/dt = f(x) = k(N - x)(x - H)$.

Example 5

For a concrete application of our stability conclusions in Example 4, suppose that $k = 1$ and $M = 4$ for a logistic population $x(t)$ of fish in a lake, measured in hundreds after t years. Without any fishing at all, the lake would eventually contain nearly 400 fish, whatever the initial population. Now suppose that $h = 3$, so that 300 fish are "harvested" annually (at a constant rate throughout the year). Equation (12) is then $dx/dt = x(4 - x) - 3$, and the quadratic equation

$$-x^2 + 4x - 3 = (3 - x)(x - 1) = 0$$

has solutions $H = 1$ and $N = 3$. Thus the threshold population is 100 fish and the (new) limiting population is 300 fish. In short, if the lake is stocked initially with more than 100 fish, then as t increases the fish population will approach a limiting value of 300 fish. But if the lake is stocked initially with fewer than 100 fish, then the lake will be "fished out" and the fish will disappear entirely within a finite period of time. ∎

Bifurcation and Dependence on Parameters

A biological or physical system that is modeled by a differential equation may depend crucially on the numerical values of certain coefficients or parameters that appear in the equation. For instance, the number of critical points of the equation may change abruptly as the value of a parameter is changed.

Example 6

The differential equation

$$\frac{dx}{dt} = x(4 - x) - h \tag{19}$$

(with x in hundreds) models the harvesting of a logistic population with $k = 1$ and limiting population $M = 4$ (hundred). In Example 5 we considered the case of harvesting level $h = 3$, and found that the new limiting population is $N = 3$ hundred and the threshold population is $H = 1$ hundred. Typical solution curves, including the equilibrium solutions $x(t) \equiv 3$ and $x(t) \equiv 1$, then look like those pictured in Fig. 2.2.8.

Now let's investigate the dependence of this picture upon the harvesting level h. According to Eq. (13) with $k = 1$ and $M = 4$, the limiting and threshold populations N and H are given by

$$H, N = \frac{1}{2}\left(4 \pm \sqrt{16 - 4h}\right) = 2 \pm \sqrt{4 - h}. \tag{20}$$

If $h < 4$—we can consider negative values of h to describe stocking rather than harvesting the fish—then there are distinct equilibrium solutions $x(t) \equiv N$ and $x(t) \equiv H$ with $N > H$ as in Fig. 2.2.8.

But if $h = 4$, then Eq. (20) gives $N = H = 2$, so the differential equation has only the single equilibrium solution $x(t) \equiv 2$. In this case the solution curves of the equation look like those illustrated in Fig. 2.2.10. If the initial number x_0 (in hundreds) of fish exceeds 2, then the population approaches a limiting population of 2 (hundred fish). However, any initial population $x_0 < 2$ (hundred) results in extinction with the fish dying out as a consequence of the harvesting of 4 hundred fish annually.

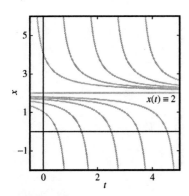

FIGURE 2.2.10. Solution curves of the equation $x' = x(4 - x) - h$ with critical harvesting $h = 4$.

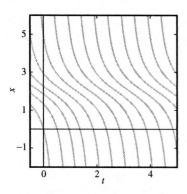

FIGURE 2.2.11. Solution curves of the equation $x' = x(4 - x) - h$ with excessive harvesting $h = 5$.

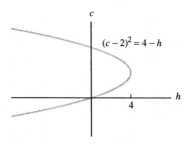

FIGURE 2.2.12. The parabola $(c - 2)^2 = 4 - h$ is the bifurcation diagram for the differential equation $x' = x(4 - x) - h$.

If, finally, $h > 4$, then the quadratic equation corresponding to (20) has no real solutions and the differential equation in (19) has no equilibrium solutions. The solution curves then look like those illustrated in Fig. 2.2.11, and (whatever the initial number of fish) the population dies out as a result of the excessive harvesting. ∎

If we imagine turning a dial to gradually increase the value of the parameter h in Eq. (10), then the picture of the solution curves changes from one like Fig. 2.2.8 with $h < 4$, to Fig. 2.2.10 with $h = 4$, to one like Fig. 2.2.11 with $h > 4$. Thus the differential equation has

- two critical points if $h < 4$;
- one critical point if $h = 4$;
- no critical point if $h > 4$.

The value $h = 4$—for which the qualitative nature of the solutions changes as h increases—is called a **bifurcation point** for the differential equation containing the parameter h. A common way to visualize the corresponding "bifurcation" in the solutions is to plot the **bifurcation diagram** consisting of all points (h, c), where c is a critical point of the equation $x' = x(4 - x) + h$. For instance, if we rewrite Eq. (20) as

$$c = 2 \pm \sqrt{4 - h},$$
$$(c - 2)^2 = 4 - h,$$

where either $c = N$ or $c = H$, then we get the equation of the parabola that is shown in Fig. 2.2.12. This parabola is then the bifurcation diagram for our differential equation that models a logistic fish population with harvesting at the level specified by the parameter h.

2.2 Problems

In Problems 1 through 12, first solve the equation $f(x) = 0$ to find the critical points of the given autonomous differential equation $dx/dt = f(x)$. Then analyze the sign of $f(x)$ to determine whether each critical point is stable or unstable, and construct the corresponding phase diagram for the differential equation. Next, solve the differential equation explicitly for $x(t)$ in terms of t. Finally, use either the exact solution or a computer-generated slope field to sketch typical solution curves for the given differential equation, and verify visually the stability of each critical point.

1. $\dfrac{dx}{dt} = x - 4$

2. $\dfrac{dx}{dt} = 3 - x$

3. $\dfrac{dx}{dt} = x^2 - 4x$

4. $\dfrac{dx}{dt} = 3x - x^2$

5. $\dfrac{dx}{dt} = x^2 - 4$

6. $\dfrac{dx}{dt} = 9 - x^2$

7. $\dfrac{dx}{dt} = (x - 2)^2$

8. $\dfrac{dx}{dt} = -(3 - x)^2$

9. $\dfrac{dx}{dt} = x^2 - 5x + 4$

10. $\dfrac{dx}{dt} = 7x - x^2 - 10$

11. $\dfrac{dx}{dt} = (x - 1)^3$

12. $\dfrac{dx}{dt} = (2 - x)^3$

In Problems 13 through 18, use a computer system or graphing calculator to plot a slope field and/or enough solution curves to indicate the stability or instability of each critical point of the given differential equation.

13. $\dfrac{dx}{dt} = (x + 2)(x - 2)^2$

14. $\dfrac{dx}{dt} = x(x^2 - 4)$

15. $\dfrac{dx}{dt} = (x^2 - 4)^2$

16. $\dfrac{dx}{dt} = (x^2 - 4)^3$

17. $\dfrac{dx}{dt} = x^2(x^2 - 4)$

18. $\dfrac{dx}{dt} = x^3(x^2 - 4)$

19. The differential equation $dx/dt = \frac{1}{10}x(10 - x) - h$ models a logistic population with harvesting at rate h. Determine (as in Example 6) the dependence of the number of critical points on the parameter h, and then construct a bifurcation diagram like Fig. 2.2.12.

20. The differential equation $dx/dt = \frac{1}{100}x(x - 5) + s$ models a population with stocking at rate s. Determine the dependence of the number of critical points c on the parameter s,

and then construct the corresponding bifurcation diagram in the sc-plane.

21. Consider the differential equation $dx/dt = kx - x^3$. **(a)** If $k \leq 0$, show that the only critical value $c = 0$ of x is stable. **(b)** If $k > 0$, show that the critical point $c = 0$ is now unstable, but that the critical points $c = \pm\sqrt{k}$ are stable. Thus the qualitative nature of the solutions changes at $k = 0$ as the parameter k increases, and so $k = 0$ is a bifurcation point for the differential equation with parameter k. The plot of all points of the form (k, c) where c is a critical point of the equation $x' = kx - x^3$ is the "pitchfork diagram" shown in Fig. 2.2.13.

22. Consider the differential equation $dx/dt = x + kx^3$ containing the parameter k. Analyze (as in Problem 21) the dependence of the number and nature of the critical points on the value of k, and construct the corresponding bifurcation diagram.

23. Suppose that the logistic equation $dx/dt = kx(M - x)$ models a population $x(t)$ of fish in a lake after t months during which no fishing occurs. Now suppose that, because of fishing, fish are removed from the lake at the rate of hx fish per month (with h a positive constant). Thus fish are "harvested" at a rate proportional to the existing fish population, rather than at the constant rate of Example 4. **(a)** If $0 < h < kM$, show that the population is still logistic. What is the new limiting population? **(b)** If $h \geq kM$, show that $x(t) \to 0$ are $t \to +\infty$, so the lake is eventually fished out.

24. Separate variables in the logistic harvesting equation $dx/dt = k(N - x)(x - H)$ and then use partial fractions to derive the solution given in Eq. (15).

25. Use the alternative forms

$$x(t) = \frac{N(x_0 - H) + H(N - x_0)e^{-k(N-H)t}}{(x_0 - H) + (N - x_0)e^{-k(N-H)t}}$$

$$= \frac{H(N - x_0)e^{-k(N-H)t} - N(H - x_0)}{(N - x_0)e^{-k(N-H)t} - (H - x_0)}$$

of the solution in (15) to establish the conclusions stated in (17) and (18).

Example 4 dealt with the case $4h > kM^2$ in the equation $dx/dt = kx(M - x) - h$ that describes constant-rate harvesting of a logistic population. Problems 26 and 27 deal with the other cases.

26. If $4h = kM^2$, show that typical solution curves look as illustrated in Fig. 2.2.14. Thus if $x_0 \geq M/2$, then $x(t) \to M/2$ as $t \to +\infty$. But if $x_0 < M/2$, then $x(t) = 0$ after a finite period of time, so the lake is fished out. The critical point $x = M/2$ might be called *semistable*, because it looks stable from one side, unstable from the other.

27. If $4h > kM^2$, show that $x(t) = 0$ after a finite period of time, so the lake is fished out (whatever the initial population). *Suggestion:* Complete the square to rewrite the differential equation in the form $dx/dt = -k[(x-a)^2 + b^2]$. Then solve explicitly by separation of variables. The results of this and the previous problem (together with Example 4) show that $h = \frac{1}{4}kM^2$ is a critical harvesting rate for a logistic population. At any lesser harvesting rate the population approaches a limiting population N that is less than M (why?), whereas at any greater harvesting rate the population reaches extinction.

28. This problem deals with the differential equation $dx/dt = kx(x - M) - h$ that models the harvesting of an unsophisticated population (such as alligators). Show that this equation can be rewritten in the form $dx/dt = k(x - H)(x - K)$, where

$$H = \frac{1}{2}\left(M + \sqrt{M^2 + 4h/k}\right) > 0,$$

$$K = \frac{1}{2}\left(M - \sqrt{M^2 + 4h/k}\right) < 0.$$

Show that typical solution curves look as illustrated in Fig. 2.2.15.

29. Consider the two differential equations

$$\frac{dx}{dt} = (x - a)(x - b)(x - c) \qquad (21)$$

and

$$\frac{dx}{dt} = (a - x)(b - x)(c - x), \qquad (22)$$

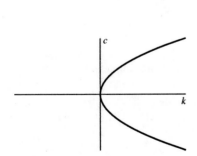

FIGURE 2.2.13. Bifurcation diagram for $dx/dt = kx - x^3$.

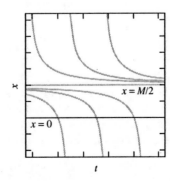

FIGURE 2.2.14. Solution curves for harvesting a logistic population with $4h = kM^2$.

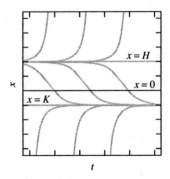

FIGURE 2.2.15. Solution curves for harvesting a population of alligators.

each having the critical points *a*, *b*, and *c*; suppose that *a* < *b* < *c*. For one of these equations, only the critical point *b* is stable; for the other equation, *b* is the only unstable critical point. Construct phase diagrams for the two equations to determine which is which. Without attempting to solve either equation explicitly, make rough sketches of typical solution curves for each. You should see two funnels and a spout in one case, two spouts and a funnel in the other.

2.3 Acceleration-Velocity Models

In Section 1.2 we discussed vertical motion of a mass *m* near the surface of the earth under the influence of constant gravitational acceleration. If we neglect any effects of air resistance, then Newton's second law ($F = ma$) implies that the velocity *v* of the mass *m* satisfies the equation

$$m\frac{dv}{dt} = F_G, \tag{1}$$

where $F_G = -mg$ is the (downward-directed) force of gravity, where the gravitational acceleration is $g \approx 9.8$ m/s^2 (in mks units; $g \approx 32$ ft/s^2 in fps units).

Example 1   Suppose that a crossbow bolt is shot straight upward from the ground ($y_0 = 0$) with initial velocity $v_0 = 49$ (m/s). Then Eq. (1) with $g = 9.8$ gives

$$\frac{dv}{dt} = -9.8, \quad \text{so} \quad v(t) = -(9.8)t + v_0 = -(9.8)t + 49.$$

Hence the bolt's height function $y(t)$ is given by

$$y(t) = \int[-(9.8)t + 49]\,dt = -(4.9)t^2 + 49t + y_0 = -(4.9)t^2 + 49t.$$

The bolt reaches its maximum height when $v = -(9.8)t + 49 = 0$, hence when $t = 5$ (s). Thus its maximum height is

$$y_{max} = y(5) = -(4.9)(5^2) + (49)(5) = 122.5 \text{ (m)}.$$

The bolt returns to the ground when $y = -(4.9)t(t - 10) = 0$, and thus after 10 seconds aloft. ∎

Now we want to take account of air resistance in a problem like Example 1. The force F_R exerted by air resistance on the moving mass *m* must be added in Eq. (1), so now

$$m\frac{dv}{dt} = F_G + F_R. \tag{2}$$

Newton showed in his *Principia Mathematica* that certain simple physical assumptions imply that F_R is proportional to the *square* of the velocity: $F_R = kv^2$. But empirical investigations indicate that the actual dependence of air resistance on velocity can be quite complicated. For many purposes it suffices to assume that

$$F_R = kv^p,$$

where $1 \leq p \leq 2$ and the value of *k* depends on the size and shape of the body, as well as the density and viscosity of the air. Generally speaking, $p = 1$ for relatively low speeds and $p = 2$ for high speeds, whereas $1 < p < 2$ for intermediate speeds. But how slow "low speed" and how fast "high speed" are depend on the same factors that determine the value of the coefficient k.

Thus air resistance is a complicated physical phenomenon. But the simplifying assumption that F_R is exactly of the form given here, with either $p = 1$ or $p = 2$, yields a tractable mathematical model that exhibits the most important qualitative features of motion with resistance.

Resistance Proportional to Velocity

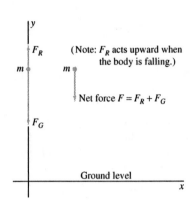

FIGURE 2.3.1. Vertical motion with air resistance.

Let us first consider the vertical motion of a body with mass m near the surface of the earth, subject to two forces: a downward gravitational force F_G and a force F_R of air resistance that is proportional to velocity (so that $p = 1$) and of course directed opposite the direction of motion of the body. If we set up a coordinate system with the positive y-direction upward and with $y = 0$ at ground level, then $F_G = -mg$ and

$$F_R = -kv, \qquad (3)$$

where k is a positive constant and $v = dy/dt$ is the velocity of the body. Note that the minus sign in Eq. (3) makes F_R positive (an upward force) if the body is falling (v is negative) and makes F_R negative (a downward force) if the body is rising (v is positive). As indicated in Fig. 2.3.1, the net force acting on the body is then

$$F = F_R + F_G = -kv - mg,$$

and Newton's law of motion $F = m(dv/dt)$ yields the equation

$$m\frac{dv}{dt} = -kv - mg.$$

Thus

$$\frac{dv}{dt} = -\rho v - g, \qquad (4)$$

where $\rho = k/m > 0$. You should verify for yourself that if the positive y-axis were directed downward, then Eq. (4) would take the form $dv/dt = -\rho v + g$.

Equation (4) is a separable first-order differential equation, and its solution is

$$v(t) = \left(v_0 + \frac{g}{\rho}\right)e^{-\rho t} - \frac{g}{\rho}. \qquad (5)$$

Here, $v_0 = v(0)$ is the initial velocity of the body. Note that

$$v_\tau = \lim_{t \to \infty} v(t) = -\frac{g}{\rho}. \qquad (6)$$

Thus the speed of a body falling with air resistance does *not* increase indefinitely; instead, it approaches a *finite* limiting speed, or **terminal speed,**

$$|v_\tau| = \frac{g}{\rho} = \frac{mg}{k}. \qquad (7)$$

This fact is what makes a parachute a practical invention; it even helps explain the occasional survival of people who fall without parachutes from high-flying airplanes. We now rewrite Eq. (5) in the form

$$\frac{dy}{dt} = (v_0 - v_\tau)e^{-\rho t} + v_\tau. \tag{8}$$

Integration gives

$$y(t) = -\frac{1}{\rho}(v_0 - v_\tau)e^{-\rho t} + v_\tau t + C.$$

We substitute 0 for t and let $y_0 = y(0)$ denote the initial height of the body. Thus we find that $C = y_0 + (v_0 - v_\tau)/\rho$, and so

$$y(t) = y_0 + v_\tau t + \frac{1}{\rho}(v_0 - v_\tau)(1 - e^{-\rho t}). \tag{9}$$

Equations (8) and (9) give the velocity v and height y of a body moving vertically under the influence of gravity and air resistance. The formulas depend on the initial height y_0 of the body, its initial velocity v_0, and the *drag coefficient* ρ, the constant such that the acceleration due to air resistance is $a_R = -\rho v$. The two equations also involve the terminal velocity v_τ defined in Eq. (6).

For a person descending with the aid of a parachute, a typical value of ρ is 1.5, which corresponds to a terminal speed of $|v_\tau| \approx 21.3$ ft/s, or about 14.5 mi/h. With an unbuttoned overcoat flapping in the wind in place of a parachute, an unlucky skydiver might increase ρ to perhaps as much as 0.5, which gives a terminal speed of $|v_\tau| \approx 65$ ft/s, about 44 mi/h. See Problems 10 and 11 for some parachute-jump computations.

Example 2   We again consider a bolt shot straight upward with initial velocity $v_0 = 49$ m/s from a crossbow at ground level. But now we take air resistance into account, with $\rho = 0.04$ in Eq. (4). We ask how the resulting maximum height and time aloft compare with the values found in Example 1.

Solution   We substitute $y_0 = 0$, $v_0 = 49$, and $v_\tau = -g/\rho = -245$ in Eqs. (5) and (9), and obtain

$$v(t) = 294e^{-t/25} - 245,$$
$$y(t) = 7350 - 245t - 7350e^{-t/25}.$$

To find the time required for the bolt to reach its maximum height (when $v = 0$), we solve the equation
$$v(t) = 294e^{-t/25} - 245 = 0$$

for $t_m = 25\ln(294/245) \approx 4.558$ (s). Its maximum height is then $y_{max} = v(t_m) \approx$ 108.280 meters (as opposed to 122.5 meters without air resistance). To find when the bolt strikes the ground, we must solve the equation

$$y(t) = 7350 - 245t - 7350e^{-t/25} = 0.$$

Using Newton's method, we can begin with the initial guess $t_0 = 10$ and carry out the iteration $t_{n+1} = t_n - y(t_n)/y'(t_n)$ to generate successive approximations to the root. Or we can simply use the **Solve** command on a calculator or computer. We find that the bolt is in the air for $t_f \approx 9.411$ seconds (as opposed to 10 seconds without air resistance). It hits the ground with a reduced speed of $|v(t_f)| \approx 43.227$ m/s (as opposed to its initial velocity of 49 m/s).

Thus the effect of air resistance is to decrease the bolt's maximum height, the total time spent aloft, and its final impact speed. Note also that the bolt now spends more time in descent ($t_f - t_m \approx 4.853$ s) than in ascent ($t_m \approx 4.558$ s). ∎

Resistance Proportional to Square of Velocity

Now we assume that the force of air resistance is proportional to the *square* of the velocity:

$$F_R = \pm kv^2, \tag{10}$$

with $k > 0$. The choice of signs here depends on the direction of motion, which the force of resistance always opposes. Taking the positive y-direction as upward, $F_R < 0$ for upward motion (when $v > 0$) while $F_R > 0$ for downward motion (when $v < 0$). Thus the sign of F_R is always opposite that of v, so we can rewrite Eq. (10) as

$$F_R = -kv|v|. \tag{10'}$$

Then Newton's second law gives

$$m\frac{dv}{dt} = F_G + F_R = -mg - kv|v|;$$

that is,

$$\frac{dv}{dt} = -g - \rho v|v|, \tag{11}$$

where $\rho = k/m > 0$. We must discuss the cases of upward and downward motion separately.

UPWARD MOTION: Suppose that a projectile is launched straight upward from the initial position y_0 with initial velocity $v_0 > 0$. Then Eq. (11) with $v > 0$ gives the differential equation

$$\frac{dv}{dt} = -g - \rho v^2 = -g\left(1 + \frac{\rho}{g}v^2\right). \tag{12}$$

In Problem 13 we ask you to make the substitution $u = v\sqrt{\rho/g}$ and apply the familiar integral

$$\int \frac{1}{1+u^2}\,du = \tan^{-1}u + C$$

to derive the projectile's velocity function

$$v(t) = \sqrt{\frac{g}{\rho}}\tan\left(C_1 - t\sqrt{\rho g}\right) \quad \text{with} \quad C_1 = \tan^{-1}\left(v_0\sqrt{\frac{\rho}{g}}\right). \tag{13}$$

Because $\int \tan u\,du = -\ln|\cos u| + C$, a second integration (see Problem 14) yields the position function

$$y(t) = y_0 + \frac{1}{\rho}\ln\left|\frac{\cos\left(C_1 - t\sqrt{\rho g}\right)}{\cos C_1}\right|. \tag{14}$$

DOWNWARD MOTION: Suppose that a projectile is launched (or dropped) straight downward from the initial position y_0 with initial velocity $v_0 \leq 0$. Then Eq. (11) with $v < 0$ gives the differential equation

$$\frac{dv}{dt} = -g + \rho v^2 = -g\left(1 - \frac{\rho}{g}v^2\right). \tag{15}$$

In Problem 15 we ask you to make the substitution $u = v\sqrt{\rho/g}$ and apply the integral

$$\int \frac{1}{1 - u^2}\, du = \tanh^{-1} u + C$$

to derive the projectile's velocity function

$$v(t) = \sqrt{\frac{g}{\rho}}\tanh\left(C_2 - t\sqrt{\rho g}\right) \quad \text{with} \quad C_2 = \tanh^{-1}\left(v_0\sqrt{\frac{\rho}{g}}\right). \tag{16}$$

Because $\int \tanh u\, du = \ln|\cosh u| + C$, another integration (Problem 16) yields the position function

$$y(t) = y_0 - \frac{1}{\rho}\ln\left|\frac{\cosh\left(C_2 - t\sqrt{\rho g}\right)}{\cosh C_2}\right|. \tag{17}$$

[Note the analogy between Eqs. (16) and (17) and Eqs. (13) and (14) for upward motion.]

If $v_0 = 0$, then $C_2 = 0$, so $v(t) = -\sqrt{g/\rho}\tanh\left(t\sqrt{\rho g}\right)$. Because

$$\lim_{x\to\infty} \tanh x = \lim_{x\to\infty}\frac{\sinh x}{\cosh x} = \lim_{x\to\infty}\frac{\frac{1}{2}(e^x - e^{-x})}{\frac{1}{2}(e^x + e^{-x})} = 1,$$

it follows that in the case of downward motion the body approaches the terminal speed

$$|v_\tau| = \sqrt{\frac{g}{\rho}} \tag{18}$$

[as compared with $|v_\tau| = g/\rho$ in the case of downward motion with linear resistance described by Eq. (4)].

| Example 3 |

We consider once more a bolt shot straight upward with initial velocity $v_0 = 49$ m/s from a crossbow at ground level, as in Example 2. But now we assume air resistance proportional to the square of the velocity, with $\rho = 0.0011$ in Eqs. (12) and (15). In Problems 17 and 18 we ask you to verify the entries in the last line of the following table.

Air Resistance	Maximum Height (ft)	Time Aloft (s)	Ascent Time (s)	Descent Time (s)	Impact Speed (ft/s)
0.0	122.5	10	5	5	49
$(0.04)v$	108.28	9.41	4.56	4.85	43.23
$(0.0011)v^2$	108.47	9.41	4.61	4.80	43.49

Comparison of the last two lines of data here indicates little difference—for the motion of our crossbow bolt—between linear air resistance and air resistance proportional to the square of the velocity. And in Fig. 2.3.2, where the corresponding

FIGURE 2.3.2. The height functions in Example 1 (without air resistance), Example 2 (with linear air resistance), and Example 3 (with air resistance proportional to the square of the velocity) are all plotted. The graphs of the latter two are visually indistinguishable.

height functions are graphed, the difference is hardly visible. However, the difference between linear and nonlinear resistance can be significant in more complex situations—such as, for instance, the atmospheric reentry and descent of a space vehicle. ∎

Variable Gravitational Acceleration

Unless a projectile in vertical motion remains in the immediate vicinity of the earth's surface, the gravitational acceleration acting on it is not constant. According to Newton's law of gravitation, the gravitational force of attraction between two point masses M and m located at a distance r apart is given by

$$F = \frac{GMm}{r^2},$$ (19)

where G is a certain empirical constant ($G \approx 6.6726 \times 10^{-11}$ N·(m/kg)^2 in mks units). The formula is also valid if either or both of the two masses are homogeneous spheres; in this case, the distance r is measured between the centers of the spheres.

The following example is similar to Example 2 in Section 1.2, but now we take account of lunar gravity.

Example 4

A lunar lander is free-falling toward the moon, and at an altitude of 53 kilometers above the lunar surface its downward velocity is measured at 1477 km/h. Its retro-rockets, when fired in free space, provide a deceleration of $T = 4$ m/s^2. At what height above the lunar surface should the retrorockets be activated to ensure a "soft touchdown" ($v = 0$ at impact)?

Solution

Let $r(t)$ denote the lander's distance from the center of the moon at time t (Fig. 2.3.3). When we combine the (constant) thrust acceleration T and the (negative) lunar acceleration $F/m = GM/r^2$ of Eq. (19), we get the (acceleration) differential equation

$$\frac{d^2r}{dt^2} = T - \frac{GM}{r^2},$$ (20)

where $M = 7.35 \times 10^{22}$ (kg) is the mass of the moon, which has a radius of $R = 1.74 \times 10^6$ meters (or 1740 km, a little over a quarter of the earth's radius).

Noting that this second-order differential equation does not involve the independent variable t, we substitute

$$v = \frac{dr}{dt}, \quad \frac{d^2r}{dt^2} = \frac{dv}{dt} = \frac{dv}{dr} \cdot \frac{dr}{dt} = v\frac{dv}{dr}$$

[as in Eq. (36) of Section 1.6] and obtain the first-order equation

$$v\frac{dv}{dr} = T - \frac{GM}{r^2}$$

with the new independent variable r. Integration with respect to r now yields the equation

$$\frac{1}{2}v^2 = Tr + \frac{GM}{r} + C \tag{21}$$

that we can apply both before ignition ($T = 0$) and after ignition ($T = 4$).

Before ignition: Substitution of $T = 0$ in (21) gives the equation

$$\frac{1}{2}v^2 = \frac{GM}{r} + C_1, \tag{21a}$$

where the constant is given by $C_1 = v_0^2/2 - GM/r_0$ with

$$v_0 = -1477\frac{km}{h} \times 1000\frac{m}{km} \times \frac{1\ h}{3600\ s} = -\frac{14770}{36}\frac{m}{s}$$

and $r_0 = (1.74 \times 10^6) + 53000 = 1.793 \times 10^6$ m (from the initial velocity-position measurement).

After ignition: Substitution of $T = 4$ and $v = 0$, $r = R$ (at touchdown) into (21) gives

$$\frac{1}{2}v^2 = 4r + \frac{GM}{r} + C_2, \tag{21b}$$

where the constant $C_2 = -4R - GM/R$ is obtained by substituting the values $v = 0$, $r = R$ at touchdown.

At the instant of ignition the lunar lander's position and velocity satisfy both (21a) and (21b). Therefore, we can find its desired height h above the lunar surface at ignition by equating the right-hand sides in (21a) and (21b). This gives $r = \frac{1}{4}(C_1 - C_2) = 1.78187 \times 10^6$ and finally $h = r - R = 41870$ meters (that is, 41.87 kilometers—just over 26 miles). Moreover, substitution of this value of r in (21a) gives the velocity $v = -450$ m/s at the instant of ignition. ■

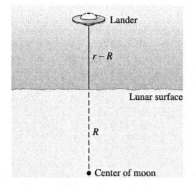

FIGURE 2.3.3. The lunar lander descending to the surface of the moon.

Escape Velocity

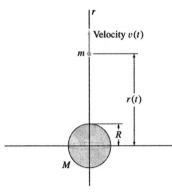

In his novel *From the Earth to the Moon* (1865), Jules Verne raised the question of the initial velocity necesary for a projectile fired from the surface of the earth to reach the moon. Similarly, we can ask what initial velocity v_0 is necessary for the projectile to escape from the earth altogether. This will be so if its velocity $v = dr/dt$ remains *positive* for all $t > 0$, so it continues forever to move away from the earth. With $r(t)$ denoting the projectile's distance from the earth's center at time t (Fig. 2.3.4), we have the equation

$$\frac{dv}{dt} = \frac{d^2r}{dt^2} = -\frac{GM}{r^2}, \tag{22}$$

FIGURE 2.3.4. A mass m at a great distance from the earth.

similar to Eq. (20), but with $T = 0$ (no thrust) and with $M = 5.975 \times 10^{24}$ (kg) denoting the mass of the earth, which has an equatorial radius of $R = 6.378 \times 10^6$ (m). Substitution of the chain rule expression $dv/dt = v(dv/dr)$ as in Example 4 gives

$$v\frac{dv}{dr} = -\frac{GM}{r^2}.$$

Then integration of both sides with respect to r yields

$$\frac{1}{2}v^2 = \frac{GM}{r} + C.$$

Now $v = v_0$ and $r = R$ when $t = 0$, so $C = \frac{1}{2}v_0^2 - GM/R$, and hence solution for v^2 gives

$$v^2 = v_0^2 + 2GM\left(\frac{1}{r} - \frac{1}{R}\right). \tag{23}$$

This implicit solution of Eq. (22) determines the projectile's velocity v as a function of its distance r from the earth's center. In particular,

$$v^2 > v_0^2 - \frac{2GM}{R},$$

so v will remain positive provided that $v_0^2 \geqq 2GM/R$. Therefore, the **escape velocity** from the earth is given by

$$v_0 = \sqrt{\frac{2GM}{R}}. \tag{24}$$

In Problem 27 we ask you to show that, if the projectile's initial velocity exceeds $\sqrt{2GM/R}$, then $r(t) \to \infty$ as $t \to \infty$, so it does, indeed, "escape" from the earth. With the given values of G and the earth's mass M and radius R, this gives $v_0 \approx 11180$ (m/s) (about 36680 ft/s, about 6.95 mi/s, about 25000 mi/h).

Remark: Equation (24) gives the escape velocity for any other (spherical) planetary body when we use *its* mass and radius. For instance, when we use the mass M and radius R for the moon given in Example 4, we find that escape velocity from the lunar surface is $v_0 \approx 2375$ m/s. This is just over one-fifth of the escape velocity from the earth's surface, a fact that greatly facilitates the return trip ("From the Moon to the Earth"). ∎

2.3 Problems

1. The acceleration of a Maserati is proportional to the difference between 250 km/h and the velocity of this sports car. If this machine can accelerate from rest to 100 km/h in 10 s, how long will it take for the car to accelerate from rest to 200 km/h?

2. Suppose that a body moves through a resisting medium with resistance proportional to its velocity v, so that $dv/dt = -kv$. **(a)** Show that its velocity and position at time t are given by

$$v(t) = v_0 e^{-kt}$$

and

$$x(t) = x_0 + \left(\frac{v_0}{k}\right)(1 - e^{-kt}).$$

(b) Conclude that the body travels only a finite distance, and find that distance.

3. Suppose that a motorboat is moving at 40 ft/s when its motor suddenly quits, and that 10 s later the boat has slowed to 20 ft/s. Assume, as in Problem 2, that the resistance it encounters while coasting is proportional to its velocity. How far will the boat coast in all?

4. Consider a body that moves horizontally through a medium whose resistance is proportional to the *square* of the velocity v, so that $dv/dt = -kv^2$. Show that

$$v(t) = \frac{v_0}{1 + v_0 kt}$$

and that

$$x(t) = x_0 + \frac{1}{k}\ln(1 + v_0 kt).$$

Note that, in contrast with the result of Problem 2, $x(t) \to +\infty$ as $t \to +\infty$.

5. Assuming resistance proportional to the square of the velocity (as in Problem 4), how far does the motorboat of Problem 3 coast in the first minute after its motor quits?

6. Assume that a body moving with velocity v encounters resistance of the form $dv/dt = -kv^{3/2}$. Show that

$$v(t) = \frac{4v_0}{\left(kt\sqrt{v_0} + 2\right)^2}$$

and that

$$x(t) = x_0 + \frac{2}{k}\sqrt{v_0}\left(1 - \frac{2}{kt\sqrt{v_0} + 2}\right).$$

Conclude that under a $\frac{3}{2}$-power resistance a body coasts only a finite distance before coming to a stop.

7. Suppose that a car starts from rest, its engine providing an acceleration of 10 ft/s², while air resistance provides 0.1 ft/s² of deceleration for each foot per second of the car's velocity. **(a)** Find the car's maximum possible (limiting) velocity. **(b)** Find how long it takes the car to attain 90% of its limiting velocity and how far it travels while doing so.

8. Rework both parts of Problem 7, with the sole difference that the deceleration due to air resistance now is $(0.001)v^2$ ft/s² when the car's velocity is v feet per second.

9. A motorboat weighs 32,000 lb and its motor provides a thrust of 5000 lb. Assume that the water resistance is 100 pounds for each foot per second of the speed v of the boat. Then

$$1000\frac{dv}{dt} = 5000 - 100v.$$

If the boat starts from rest, what is the maximum velocity that it can attain?

10. A woman bails out of an airplane at an altitude of 10,000 ft, falls freely for 20 s, then opens her parachute. How long will it take her to reach the ground? Assume linear air resistance ρv ft/s², taking $\rho = 0.15$ without the parachute and $\rho = 1.5$ with the parachute. (*Suggestion*: First determine her height and velocity when the parachute opens.)

11. According to a newspaper account, a paratrooper survived a training jump from 1200 ft when his parachute failed to open but provided some resistance by flapping unopened in the wind. Allegedly he hit the ground at 100 mi/h after falling for 8 s. Test the accuracy of this account. [*Suggestion*: Find ρ in Eq. (4) by assuming a terminal velocity of 100 mi/h. Then calculate the time required to fall 1200 ft.]

12. It is proposed to dispose of nuclear wastes—in drums with weight $W = 640$ lb and volume 8 ft³—by dropping them into the ocean ($v_0 = 0$). The force equation for a drum falling through water is

$$m\frac{dv}{dt} = -W + B + F_R,$$

where the buoyant force B is equal to the weight (at 62.5 lb/ft³) of the volume of water displaced by the drum (Archimedes' principle) and F_R is the force of water resistance, found empirically to be 1 lb for each foot per second of the velocity of a drum. If the drums are likely to burst upon an impact of more than 75 ft/s, what is the maximum depth to which they can be dropped in the ocean without likelihood of bursting?

13. Separate variables in Eq. (12) and substitute $u = v\sqrt{\rho/g}$ to obtain the upward-motion velocity function given in Eq. (13) with initial condition $v(0) = v_0$.

14. Integrate the velocity function in Eq. (13) to obtain the upward-motion position function given in Eq. (14) with initial condition $y(0) = y_0$.

15. Separate variables in Eq. (15) and substitute $u = v\sqrt{\rho/g}$ to obtain the downward-motion velocity function given in Eq. (16) with initial condition $v(0) = v_0$.

16. Integrate the velocity function in Eq. (16) to obtain the downward-motion position function given in Eq. (17) with initial condition $y(0) = y_0$.

17. Consider the crossbow bolt of Example 3, shot straight upward from the ground ($y = 0$) at time $t = 0$ with initial velocity $v_0 = 49$ m/s. Take $g = 9.8$ m/s^2 and $\rho = 0.0011$ in Eq. (12). Then use Eqs. (13) and (14) to show that the bolt reaches its maximum height of about 108.47 m in about 4.61 s.

18. Continuing Problem 17, suppose that the bolt is now dropped ($v_0 = 0$) from a height of $y_0 = 108.47$ m. Then use Eqs. (16) and (17) to show that it hits the ground about 4.80 s later with an impact speed of about 43.49 m/s.

19. A motorboat starts from rest (initial velocity $v(0) = v_0 = 0$). Its motor provides a constant acceleration of 4 ft/s^2, but water resistance causes a deceleration of $v^2/400$ ft/s^2. Find v when $t = 10$ s, and also find the *limiting velocity* as $t \to +\infty$ (that is, the maximum possible speed of the boat).

20. An arrow is shot straight upward from the ground with an initial velocity of 160 ft/s. It experiences both the deceleration of gravity and deceleration $v^2/800$ due to air resistance. How high in the air does it go?

21. If a ball is projected upward from the ground with initial velocity v_0, deduce from Eq. (14) that the maximum height it attains is

$$y_{max} = \frac{1}{2\rho} \ln\left(1 + \frac{\rho v_0^2}{g}\right).$$

22. Suppose that $\rho = 0.075$ (in fps units, with $g = 32$ ft/s^2) in Eq. (15) for a paratrooper falling with parachute open. If he jumps from an altitude of 10,000 ft and opens his parachute immediately, what will be his terminal speed? How long will it take him to reach the ground?

23. Suppose that the paratrooper of Problem 22 falls freely for 30 s with $\rho = 0.00075$ before opening his parachute. How long will it now take him to reach the ground?

24. The mass of the sun is 329,320 times that of the earth and its radius is 109 times the radius of the earth. (a) To what radius (in meters) would the earth have to be compressed in order for it to become a *black hole*—the escape velocity from its surface equal to the velocity $c = 3 \times 10^8$ m/s of light? (b) Repeat part (a) with the sun in place of the earth.

25. (a) Show that if a projectile is launched straight upward from the surface of the earth with initial velocity v_0 less than escape velocity $\sqrt{2GM/R}$, then the maximum distance from the center of the earth attained by the projectile is

$$r_{max} = \frac{2GMR}{2GM - Rv_0^2},$$

where M and R are the mass and radius of the earth, respectively. (b) With what initial velocity v_0 must such a projectile be launched to yield a maximum altitude of 100 kilometers above the surface of the earth? (c) Find the maximum distance from the center of the earth, expressed in terms of earth radii, attained by a projectile launched from the surface of the earth with 90% of escape velocity.

26. Suppose that you are stranded—your rocket engine has failed—on an asteroid of diameter 3 miles, with density equal to that of the earth with radius 3960 miles. If you have enough spring in your legs to jump 4 feet straight up on earth while wearing your space suit, can you blast off from this asteroid using leg power alone?

27. (a) Suppose a projectile is launched vertically from the surface $r = R$ of the earth with initial velocity $v_0 = \sqrt{2GM/R}$ so $v_0^2 = k^2/R$, where $k^2 = 2GM$. Then solve the differential equation $dr/dt = k/\sqrt{r}$ [from Eq. (23) in this section] explicitly to deduce that $r(t) \to \infty$ as $t \to \infty$.

(b) If the projectile is launched vertically with initial velocity $v_0 > \sqrt{2GM/R}$, deduce that

$$\frac{dr}{dt} = \sqrt{\frac{k^2}{r} + \alpha} > \frac{k}{\sqrt{r}}.$$

Why does it again follow that $r(t) \to \infty$ as $t \to \infty$?

28. (a) Suppose that a body is dropped ($v_0 = 0$) from a distance $r_0 > R$ from the earth's center, so its acceleration is $dv/dt = -GM/r^2$. Ignoring air resistance, show that it reaches the height $r < r_0$ at time

$$t = \sqrt{\frac{r_0}{2GM}}\left(\sqrt{rr_0 - r^2} + r_0 \cos^{-1}\sqrt{\frac{r}{r_0}}\right).$$

[*Suggestion:* Substitute $r = r_0 \cos^2 \theta$ to evaluate $\int \sqrt{r/(r_0 - r)}\, dr$.] (b) If a body is dropped from a height of 1000 km above the earth's surface and air resistance is neglected, how long does it take to fall and with what speed will it strike the earth's surface?

29. Suppose that a projectile is fired straight upward from the surface of the earth with initial velocity $v_0 < \sqrt{2GM/R}$. Then its height $y(t)$ above the surface satisfies the initial value problem

$$\frac{d^2y}{dt^2} = -\frac{GM}{(y + R)^2}; \quad y(0) = 0, \quad y'(0) = v_0.$$

Substitute $dv/dt = v(dv/dy)$ and then integrate to obtain

$$v^2 = v_0^2 - \frac{2GMy}{R(R + y)}$$

for the velocity v of the projectile at height y. What maximum altitude does it reach if its initial velocity is 1 km/s?

30. In Jules Verne's original problem, the projectile launched from the surface of the earth is attracted by both the earth and the moon, so its distance $r(t)$ from the center of the earth satisfies the initial value problem

$$\frac{d^2r}{dt^2} = -\frac{GM_e}{r^2} + \frac{GM_m}{(S - r)^2}; \quad r(0) = R, \quad r'(0) = v_0$$

where M_e and M_m denote the masses of the earth and the moon, respectively; R is the radius of the earth and $S = 384,400$ km is the distance between the centers of the earth and the moon. To reach the moon, the projectile must only just pass the point between the moon and earth where its net acceleration vanishes. Thereafter it is "under the control" of the moon and falls from there to the lunar surface. Find the *minimal* launch velocity v_0 that suffices for the projectile to make it "From the Earth to the Moon."

2.3 Application: Rocket Propulsion

FIGURE 2.3.5. An ascending rocket.

Suppose that the rocket of Fig.2.3.5 blasts off straight upward from the surface of the earth at time $t = 0$. We want to calculate its height y and velocity $v = dy/dt$ at time t. The rocket is propelled by exhaust gases that exit (rearward) with constant speed c (relative to the rocket). Because of the combustion of its fuel, the mass $m = m(t)$ of the rocket is variable.

To derive the equation of motion of the rocket, we use Newton's second law in the form

$$\frac{dP}{dt} = F \tag{1}$$

where P is momentum (the product of mass and velocity) and F denotes net external force (gravity, air resistance, etc.). If m is constant, then Eq. (1) takes the standard form $F = m(dv/dt) = ma$.

But here m is not constant. Suppose m changes to $m + \Delta m$ and v to $v + \Delta v$ during the short time interval from t to $t + \Delta t$. Then the change in the momentum *of the rocket itself* is

$$\Delta P \approx (m + \Delta m)(v + \Delta v) - mv = m\,\Delta v + v\,\Delta m + \Delta m\,\Delta v.$$

But the system also includes the exhaust gases expelled during this time interval, with mass $-\Delta m$ and approximate velocity $v - c$. Hence the total change in momentum during the time interval Δt is

$$\Delta P \approx (m\,\Delta v + v\,\Delta m + \Delta m\,\Delta v) + (-\Delta m)(v - c)$$
$$= m\,\Delta v + c\,\Delta m + \Delta m\,\Delta v.$$

If we divide by Δt and take the limit as $\Delta t \to 0$ and then substitute the resulting expression for dP/dt in (1), we get the **rocket propulsion equation**

$$m\frac{dv}{dt} + c\frac{dm}{dt} = F. \tag{2}$$

If $F = F_G + F_R$, where $F_G = -mg$ is a constant force of gravity and $F_R = -kv$ is a force of air resistance proportional to velocity, then Eq. (2) finally gives

$$m\frac{dv}{dt} + c\frac{dm}{dt} = -mg - kv. \tag{3}$$

Constant Thrust

Now suppose that the rocket fuel is consumed at the constant "burn rate" β during the time interval $[0, t_1]$, during which time the mass of the rocket decreases from m_0 to m_1. Thus

$$m(0) = m_0, \qquad m(t_1) = m_1,$$
$$m(t) = m_0 - \beta t, \qquad \frac{dm}{dt} = -\beta \quad \text{for } t \le t_1, \tag{4}$$

with burnout occurring at time $t = t_1$.

PROBLEM 1 Substitute the expressions in (4) into Eq. (3) to obtain the differential equation

$$(m_0 - \beta t)\frac{dv}{dt} + kv = \beta c - (m_0 - \beta t)g. \tag{5}$$

Solve this linear equation for

$$v(t) = v_0 M^{k/\beta} + \frac{\beta c}{k}(1 - M^{k/\beta}) + \frac{gm_0}{\beta - k}(1 - M^{k/\beta}), \tag{6}$$

where $v_0 = v(0)$ and

$$M = \frac{m(t)}{m_0} = \frac{m_0 - \beta t}{m_0}$$

denotes the rocket's **fractional mass** at time t.

No Resistance

PROBLEM 2 For the case of no air resistance, set $k = 0$ in Eq. (5) and integrate to obtain

$$v(t) = v_0 - gt + c \ln \frac{m_0}{m_0 - \beta t}. \tag{7}$$

Because $m_0 - \beta t_1 = m_1$, it follows that the velocity of the rocket at burnout ($t = t_1$) is

$$v_1 = v(t_1) = v_0 - gt_1 + c \ln \frac{m_0}{m_1}. \tag{8}$$

PROBLEM 3 Start with Eq. (7) and integrate to obtain

$$y(t) = (v_0 + c)t - \frac{1}{2}gt^2 - \frac{c}{\beta}(m_0 - \beta t) \ln \frac{m_0}{m_0 - \beta t}. \tag{9}$$

It follows that the rocket's altitude at burnout is

$$y_1 = y(t_1) = (v_0 + c)t_1 - \frac{1}{2}gt_1^2 - \frac{cm_1}{\beta} \ln \frac{m_0}{m_1}. \tag{10}$$

PROBLEM 4 The V-2 rocket that was used to attack London in World War II had an initial mass of 12,850 kg, of which 68.5% was fuel. This fuel burned uniformly for 70 seconds with an exhaust velocity of 2 km/s. Assume it encounters air resistance of 1.45 N per m/s of velocity. Then find the velocity and altitude of the V-2 at burnout under the assumption that it is launched vertically upward from rest on the ground.

Free Space

Suppose finally that the rocket is accelerating in free space, where there is neither gravity nor resistance, so $g = k = 0$. With $g = 0$ in Eq. (8) we see that, as the mass of the rocket decreases from m_0 to m_1, its increase in velocity is

$$\Delta v = v_1 - v_0 = c \ln \frac{m_0}{m_1}. \tag{11}$$

Note that Δv depends only on the exhaust gas speed c and the initial-to-final mass ratio m_0/m_1 but does not depend on the burn rate β. For example, if the rocket blasts off from rest ($v_0 = 0$) and $c = 5$ km/s and $m_0/m_1 = 20$, then its velocity at burnout is $v_1 = 5 \ln 20 \approx 15$ km/s. Thus if a rocket initially consists predominantly of fuel, then it can attain velocities significantly greater than the (relative) velocity of its exhaust gases.

2.4 Numerical Approximation: Euler's Method

It is the exception rather than the rule when a differential equation of the general form

$$\frac{dy}{dx} = f(x, y)$$

can be solved exactly and explicitly by elementary methods like those discussed in Chapter 1. For example, consider the simple equation

$$\frac{dy}{dx} = e^{-x^2}. \tag{1}$$

A solution of Eq. (1) is simply an antiderivative of e^{-x^2}. But it is known that every antiderivative of $f(x) = e^{-x^2}$ is a **nonelementary** function—one that cannot be expressed as a finite combination of the familiar functions of elementary calculus. Hence no particular solution of Eq. (1) is finitely expressible in terms of elementary functions. Any attempt to use the symbolic techniques of Chapter 1 to find a simple explicit formula for a solution of (1) is therefore doomed to failure.

As a possible alternative, a computer plotter can be programmed to draw a solution curve that starts at the initial point (x_0, y_0) and attempts to thread its way through the slope field of a given differential equation $y' = f(x, y)$. The procedure the plotter carries out can be described as follows.

- The plotter pen starts at the initial point (x_0, y_0) and moves a tiny distance along the slope segment though (x_0, y_0). This takes it to the point (x_1, y_1).
- At (x_1, y_1) the pen changes direction and now moves a tiny distance along the slope segment through this new starting point (x_1, y_1). This takes it to the next starting point (x_2, y_2).
- At (x_2, y_2) the pen changes direction again and now moves a tiny distance along the slope segment through (x_2, y_2). This takes it to the next starting point (x_3, y_3).

Fig. 2.4.1 illustrates the result of continuing in this fashion—by a sequence of discrete straight-line steps from one starting point to the next. In this figure we see a polygonal curve consisting of line segments that connect the successive points $(x_0, y_0), (x_1, y_1), (x_2, y_2), (x_3, y_3), \ldots$. However, suppose that each "tiny distance" the pen travels along a slope segment—before the midcourse correction that sends it along a fresh new slope segment—is so very small that the naked eye cannot distinguish the individual line segments constituting the polygonal curve. Then the resulting polygonal curve looks like a smooth, continuously turning solution curve of the differential equation. Indeed, this is (in essence) how most of the solution curves shown in the figures of Chapter 1 were computer generated.

Euler did not have a computer plotter (in the 18th century), and his idea was to do all this numerically rather than graphically. In order to approximate the solution of the initial value problem

$$\frac{dy}{dx} = f(x, y), \quad y(x_0) = y_0, \tag{2}$$

we first choose a fixed (horizontal) **step size** h to use in making each step from one point to the next. Suppose we've started at the initial point (x_0, y_0) and after

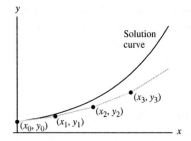

FIGURE 2.4.1. The first few steps in approximating a solution curve.

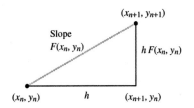

FIGURE 2.4.2. The step from (x_n, y_n) to (x_{n+1}, y_{n+1}).

n steps have reached the point (x_n, y_n). Then the step from (x_n, y_n) to the next point (x_{n+1}, y_{n+1}) is illustrated in Fig. 2.4.2. The slope of the direction segment through (x_n, y_n) is $m = f(x_n, y_n)$. Hence a horizontal change of h from x_n to x_{n+1} corresponds to a vertical change of $m \cdot h = h \cdot f(x_n, y_n)$ from y_n to y_{n+1}. Therefore the coordinates of the new point (x_{n+1}, y_{n+1}) are given in terms of the old coordinates by

$$x_{n+1} = x_n + h, \quad y_{n+1} = y_n + h \cdot f(x_n, y_n).$$

Given the initial value problem in (2), **Euler's method** with step size h consists of starting with the initial point (x_0, y_0) and applying the formulas

$$x_1 = x_0 + h \qquad y_1 = y_0 + h \cdot f(x_0, y_0)$$
$$x_2 = x_1 + h \qquad y_2 = y_1 + h \cdot f(x_1, y_1)$$
$$x_3 = x_2 + h \qquad y_3 = y_2 + h \cdot f(x_2, y_2)$$
$$\vdots \qquad\qquad \vdots$$
$$\vdots \qquad\qquad \vdots$$

to calculate successive points (x_1, y_1), (x_2, y_2), (x_3, y_3), ... on an approximate solution curve.

However, we ordinarily do not sketch the corresponding polygonal approximation. Instead, the numerical result of applying Euler's method is the sequence of *approximations*

$$y_1, y_2, y_3, \ldots, y_n, \ldots$$

to the *true values*

$$y(x_1), y(x_2), y(x_3), \ldots, y(x_n), \ldots$$

at the points $x_1, x_2, x_3, \ldots, x_n, \ldots$ of the *exact* (though unknown) solution $y(x)$ of the initial value problem. These results typically are presented in the form of a table of approximate values of the desired solution.

ALGORITHM: The Euler Method

Given the initial value problem

➤
$$\frac{dy}{dx} = f(x, y), \quad y(x_0) = y_0, \tag{2}$$

Euler's method with step size h consists of applying the iterative formula

➤
$$y_{n+1} = y_n + h \cdot f(x_n, y_n) \quad (n \geq 0) \tag{3}$$

to calculate successive approximations y_1, y_2, y_3, ... to the [true] values $y(x_1)$, $y(x_2)$, $y(x_3)$, ... of the [exact] solution $y = y(x)$ at the points x_1, x_2, x_3, ..., respectively.   ▲

The iterative formula in (3) tells us how to make the typical step from y_n to y_{n+1} and is the heart of Euler's method. Although the most important applications of Euler's method are to nonlinear equations, we first illustrate the method with a simple initial value problem whose exact solution is available for purpose of comparison of approximate and actual solutions.

Example 1 Apply Euler's method to approximate the solution of the initial value problem

$$\frac{dy}{dx} = x + \frac{1}{5}y, \quad y(0) = -3, \tag{4}$$

(a) first with step size $h = 1$ on the interval $[0, 5]$,
(b) then with step size $h = 0.2$ on the interval $[0, 1]$.

Solution **(a)** With $x_0 = 0$, $y_0 = -3$, $f(x, y) = x + \frac{1}{5}y$, and $h = 1$ the iterative formula in (3) yields the approximate values

$$y_1 = y_0 + h \cdot [x_0 + \tfrac{1}{5}y_0] = (-3) + (1)[0 + \tfrac{1}{5}(-3)] = -3.6,$$
$$y_2 = y_1 + h \cdot [x_1 + \tfrac{1}{5}y_1] = (-3.6) + (1)[1 + \tfrac{1}{5}(-3.6)] = -3.32,$$
$$y_3 = y_2 + h \cdot [x_2 + \tfrac{1}{5}y_2] = (-3.32) + (1)[2 + \tfrac{1}{5}(-3.32)] = -1.984,$$
$$y_4 = y_3 + h \cdot [x_3 + \tfrac{1}{5}y_3] = (-1.984) + (1)[3 + \tfrac{1}{5}(-1.984)] = 0.6192, \quad \text{and}$$
$$y_5 = y_4 + h \cdot [x_4 + \tfrac{1}{5}y_4] = (0.6912) + (1)[4 + \tfrac{1}{5}(0.6912)] \approx 4.7430$$

at the points $x_1 = 1$, $x_2 = 2$, $x_3 = 3$, $x_4 = 4$, and $x_5 = 5$. Note how the result of each calculation feeds into the next one. The resulting table of approximate values is

x	0	1	2	3	4	5
Approx. y	-3	-3.6	-3.32	-1.984	0.6912	4.7430

Figure 2.4.3 shows the graph of this approximation, together with the graphs of the Euler approximations obtained with step sizes $h = 0.2$ and 0.05, as well as the graph of the exact solution

$$y(x) = 22e^{x/5} - 5x - 25$$

that is readily found using the linear-equation technique of Section 1.5. We see that decreasing the step size increases the accuracy, but with any single approximation, the accuracy decreases with distance from the initial point.

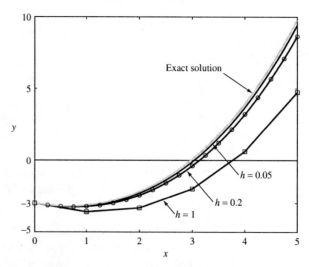

FIGURE 2.4.3. Graphs of Euler approximations with step sizes $h = 1$, $h = 0.2$, and $h = 0.05$.

(b) Starting afresh with $x_0 = 0$, $y_0 = -3$, $f(x, y) = x + \frac{1}{5}y$, and $h = 0.2$, we get the approximate values

$$y_1 = y_0 + h \cdot [x_0 + \tfrac{1}{5}y_0] = (-3) + (0.2)[0 + \tfrac{1}{5}(-3)] = -3.12,$$

$$y_2 = y_1 + h \cdot [x_1 + \tfrac{1}{5}y_1] = (-3.12) + (0.2)[0.2 + \tfrac{1}{5}(-3.12)] \approx -3.205,$$

$$y_3 = y_2 + h \cdot [x_2 + \tfrac{1}{5}y_2] \approx (-3.205) + (0.2)[0.4 + \tfrac{1}{5}(-3.205)] \approx -3.253,$$

$$y_4 = y_3 + h \cdot [x_3 + \tfrac{1}{5}y_3] \approx (-3.253) + (0.2)[0.6 + \tfrac{1}{5}(-3.253)] \approx -3.263,$$

$$y_5 = y_4 + h \cdot [x_4 + \tfrac{1}{5}y_4] \approx (-3.263) + (0.2)[0.8 + \tfrac{1}{5}(-3.263)] \approx -3.234$$

at the points $x_1 = 0.2$, $x_2 = 0.4$, $x_3 = 0.6$, $x_4 = 0.8$, and $x_5 = 1$. The resulting table of approximate values is

x	0	0.2	0.4	0.6	0.8	1
Approx. y	−3	−3.12	−3.205	−3.253	−3.263	−3.234

■

High accuracy with Euler's method usually requires a very small step size hence and a larger number of steps than can reasonably be carried out by hand. The application material for this section contains calculator and computer programs for automating Euler's method. One of these programs was used to calculate the table entries shown in Fig. 2.4.4. We see that 500 Euler steps (with step size $h = 0.002$) from $x = 0$ to $x = 1$ yield values that are accurate to within 0.001.

x	Approx y with $h = 0.2$	Approx y with $h = 0.02$	Approx y with $h = 0.002$	Actual value of y
0	−3.000	−3.000	−3.000	−3.000
0.2	−3.120	−3.104	−3.102	−3.102
0.4	−3.205	−3.172	−3.168	−3.168
0.6	−3.253	−3.201	−3.196	−3.195
0.8	−3.263	−3.191	−3.184	−3.183
1	−3.234	−3.140	−3.130	−3.129

FIGURE 2.4.4. Euler approximations with step sizes $h = 0.2$, $h = 0.02$, and $h = 0.002$.

Example 2   Suppose the baseball of Example 3 in Section 1.3 is simply dropped (instead of being thrown downward) from the helicopter. Then its velocity $v(t)$ after t seconds satisfies the initial value problem

$$\frac{dv}{dt} = 32 - 0.16v, \quad v(0) = 0. \tag{5}$$

We use Euler's method with $h = 1$ to track the ball's increasing velocity at 1-second intervals for the first 10 seconds of fall. With $t_0 = 0$, $v_0 = 0$, $F(t, v) = 32 - 0.16v$, and $h = 1$ the iterative formula in (3) yields the approximate values

$$v_1 = v_0 + h \cdot [32 - 0.16v_0] = (0) + (1)[32 - 0.16(0)] = 32,$$

$$v_2 = v_1 + h \cdot [32 - 0.16v_1] = (32) + (1)[32 - 0.16(32)] = 58.88,$$

$$v_3 = v_2 + h \cdot [32 - 0.16v_2] = (58.88) + (1)[32 - 0.16(58.88)] \approx 81.46,$$

$$v_4 = v_3 + h \cdot [32 - 0.16v_3] = (81.46) + (1)[32 - 0.16(81.46)] \approx 100.43, \text{ and}$$

$$v_5 = v_4 + h \cdot [32 - 0.16v_4] = (100.43) + (1)[32 - 0.16(100.43)] \approx 116.36.$$

Continuing in this fashion, we complete the $h = 1$ column of v-values shown in the table of Fig. 2.4.5—where we have rounded off velocity entries to the nearest foot per second. The values corresponding to $h = 0.1$ were calculated using a computer, and we see that they are accurate to within about 1 ft/s. Note also that after 10 seconds the falling ball has attained about 80% of its limiting velocity of 200 ft/s.

∎

t	Approx v with $h = 1$	Approx v with $h = 0.1$	Actual value of v
1	32	30	30
2	59	55	55
3	81	77	76
4	100	95	95
5	116	111	110
6	130	124	123
7	141	135	135
8	150	145	144
9	158	153	153
10	165	160	160

FIGURE 2.4.5. Euler approximations in Example 2 with step sizes $h = 1$ and $h = 0.1$.

Local and Cumulative Errors

There are several sources of error in Euler's method that may make the approximation y_n to $y(x_n)$ unreliable for large values of n, those for which x_n is not sufficiently close to x_0. The error in the linear approximation formula

$$y(x_{n+1}) \approx y_n + h \cdot f(x_n, y_n) = y_{n+1} \tag{6}$$

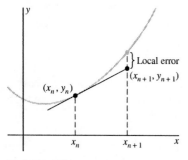

FIGURE 2.4.6. The local error in Euler's method.

is the amount by which the tangent line at (x_n, y_n) departs from the solution curve through (x_n, y_n), as illustrated in Fig. 2.4.6. This error, introduced at each step in the process, is called the **local error** in Euler's method.

The local error indicated in Fig. 2.4.6 *would be* the total error in y_{n+1} *if* the starting point y_n in (6) were an exact value, rather than merely an approximation to the actual value $y(x_n)$. But y_n itself suffers from the accumulated effects of all the local errors introduced at the previous steps. Thus the tangent line in Fig. 2.4.6 is tangent to the "wrong" solution curve—the one through (x_n, y_n) rather than the actual solution curve through the initial point (x_0, y_0). Figure 2.4.7 illustrates this **cumulative error** in Euler's method; it is the amount by which the polygonal stepwise path from (x_0, y_0) departs from the actual solution curve through (x_0, y_0).

The usual way of attempting to reduce the cumulative error in Euler's method is to decrease the step size h. The table in Fig. 2.4.8 shows the results obtained in approximating the exact solution $y(x) = 2e^x - x - 1$ of the initial value problem

$$\frac{dy}{dx} = x + y, \quad y(0) = 1,$$

using the successively smaller step sizes $h = 0.1$, $h = 0.02$, $h = 0.005$, and $h = 0.001$. We show computed values only at intervals of $\Delta x = 0.1$. For instance,

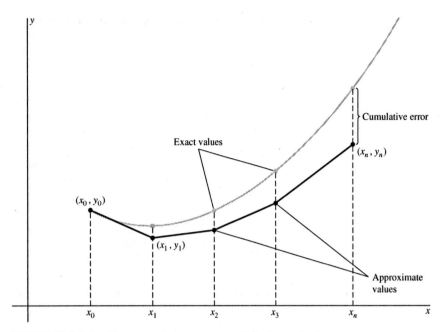

FIGURE 2.4.7. The cumulative error in Euler's method.

x	y with $h = 0.1$	y with $h = 0.02$	y with $h = 0.005$	y with $h = 0.001$	Actual y
0.1	1.1000	1.1082	1.1098	1.1102	1.1103
0.2	1.2200	1.2380	1.2416	1.2426	1.2428
0.3	1.3620	1.3917	1.3977	1.3993	1.3997
0.4	1.5282	1.5719	1.5807	1.5831	1.5836
0.5	1.7210	1.7812	1.7933	1.7966	1.7974
0.6	1.9461	2.0227	2.0388	2.0431	2.0442
0.7	2.1974	2.2998	2.3205	2.3261	2.3275
0.8	2.4872	2.6161	2.6422	2.6493	2.6511
0.9	2.8159	2.9757	3.0082	3.0170	3.0192
1.0	3.1875	3.3832	3.4230	3.4238	3.4266

FIGURE 2.4.8. Approximating the solution of $dy/dx = x + y$, $y(0) = 1$ with successively smaller step sizes.

with $h = 0.001$, the computation required 1000 Euler steps, but the value y_n is shown only when n is a multiple of 100, so that x_n is an integral multiple of 0.1.

By scanning the column in Fig. 2.4.8 we observe that, for each fixed step size h, the error $y_{\text{actual}} - y_{\text{approx}}$ increases as x gets farther from the starting point $x_0 = 0$. But by scanning the rows of the table we see that for each fixed x, the error decreases as the step size h is reduced. The percentage errors at the final point $x = 1$ range from 7.25% with $h = 0.1$ down to only 0.08% with $h = 0.001$. Thus the smaller the step size, the more slowly does the error grow with increasing distance from the starting point.

The column of data for $h = 0.1$ in Fig. 2.4.8 requires only 10 steps, so Euler's method can be carried out with a hand-held calculator. But 50 steps are required to reach $x = 1$ with $h = 0.02$, 200 steps with $h = 0.005$, and 1000 steps with

$h = 0.001$. A computer is almost always used to implement Euler's method when more than 10 or 20 steps are required. Once an appropriate computer program has been written, one step size is—in principle—just as convenient as another; after all, the computer hardly cares how many steps it is asked to carry out.

Why, then, do we not simply choose an exceedingly small step size (such as $h = 10^{-12}$), with the expectation that very great accuracy will result? There are two reasons for not doing so. The first is obvious: the time required for the computation. For example, the data in Fig. 2.4.8 were obtained using a hand-held calculator that carried out nine Euler steps per second. Thus it required slightly over one second to approximate $y(1)$ with $h = 0.1$ and about 1 min 50 s with $h = 0.001$. But with $h = 10^{-12}$ it would require over 3000 years!

The second reason is more subtle. In addition to the local and cumulative errors discussed previously, the computer itself will contribute **roundoff error** at each stage because only finitely many significant digits can be used in each calculation. An Euler's method computation with $h = 0.0001$ will introduce roundoff errors 1000 times as often as one with $h = 0.1$. Hence with certain differential equations, $h = 0.1$ might actually produce more accurate results than those obtained with $h = 0.0001$, because the cumulative effect of roundoff error in the latter case might exceed combined cumulative and roundoff error in the case $h = 0.1$.

The "best" choice of h is difficult to determine in practice as well as in theory. It depends on the nature of the function $f(x, y)$ in the initial value problem in (2), on the exact code in which the program is written, and on the specific computer used. With a step size that is too large, the approximations inherent in Euler's method may not be sufficiently accurate, whereas if h is too small, then roundoff errors may accumulate to an unacceptable degree or the program may require too much time to be practical. The subject of *error propagation* in numerical algorithms is treated in numerical analysis courses and textbooks.

The computations in Fig. 2.4.8 illustrate the common strategy of applying a numerical algorithm, such as Euler's method, several times in succession, beginning with a selected number n of subintervals for the first application, then doubling n for each succeeding application of the method. Visual comparison of successive results often can provide an "intuitive feel" for their accuracy. In the next two examples we present graphically the results of successive applications of Euler's method.

Example 3

The exact solution of the logistic initial value problem

$$\frac{dy}{dx} = \tfrac{1}{3}y(8 - y), \quad y(0) = 1$$

is $y(x) = 8/(1 + 7e^{-8x/3})$. Figure 2.4.9 shows both the exact solution curve and approximate solution curves obtained by applying Euler's method on the interval $0 \leq x \leq 5$ with $n = 5$, $n = 10$, and $n = 20$ subintervals. Each of these "curves" actually consists of line segments joining successive points (x_n, y_n) and (x_{n+1}, y_{n+1}). The Euler approximation with 5 subintervals is poor, and the approximation with 10 subintervals also overshoots the limiting value $y = 8$ of the solution before leveling off, but with 20 subintervals we obtain fairly good qualitative agreement with the actual behavior of the solution. ∎

Example 4

The exact solution of the initial value problem

$$\frac{dy}{dx} = y \cos x, \quad y(0) = 1$$

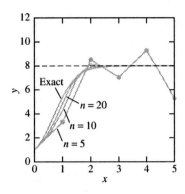

FIGURE 2.4.9. Approximating a logistic solution using Euler's method with $n = 5$, $n = 10$, and $n = 20$ subintervals.

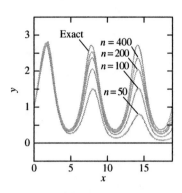

FIGURE 2.4.10. Approximating the exact solution $y = e^{\sin x}$ using Euler's method with 50, 100, 200, and 400 subintervals.

is the periodic function $y(x) = e^{\sin x}$. Figure 2.4.10 shows both the exact solution curve and approximate solution curves obtained by applying Euler's method on the interval $0 \leq x \leq 6\pi$ with $n = 50$, $n = 100$, $n = 200$, and $n = 400$ subintervals. Even with this many subintervals, Euler's method evidently has considerable difficulty keeping up with the oscillations in the actual solution. Consequently, the more accurate methods discussed in succeeding sections are needed for serious numerical investigations. ∎

A Word of Caution

The data shown in Fig. 2.4.8 indicate that Euler's method works well in approximating the solution of $dy/dx = x + y$, $y(0) = 1$ on the interval $[0, 1]$. That is, for each fixed x it appears that the approximate values approach the actual value of $y(x)$ as the step size h is decreased. For instance, the approximate values in the rows corresponding to $x = 0.3$ and $x = 0.5$ suggest that $y(0.3) \approx 1.40$ and $y(0.5) \approx 1.80$, in accord with the actual values shown in the final column of the table.

Example 5, in contrast, shows that some initial value problems are not so well behaved.

Example 5 Use Euler's method to approximate the solution of the initial value problem

$$\frac{dy}{dx} = x^2 + y^2, \quad y(0) = 1 \tag{7}$$

on the interval $[0, 1]$.

Solution Here $f(x, y) = x^2 + y^2$, so the iterative formula of Euler's method is

$$y_{n+1} = y_n + h \cdot (x_n^2 + y_n^2). \tag{8}$$

With step size $h = 0.1$ we obtain

$$y_1 = 1 + (0.1) \cdot [(0)^2 + (1)^2] = 1.1,$$
$$y_2 = 1.1 + (0.1) \cdot [(0.1)^2 + (1.1)^2] = 1.222,$$
$$y_3 = 1.222 + (0.1) \cdot [(0.2)^2 + (1.222)^2] \approx 1.3753,$$

and so forth. Rounded to four decimal places, the first ten values obtained in this manner are

$$y_1 = 1.1000 \qquad y_6 = 2.1995$$
$$y_2 = 1.2220 \qquad y_7 = 2.7193$$
$$y_3 = 1.3753 \qquad y_8 = 3.5078$$
$$y_4 = 1.5735 \qquad y_9 = 4.8023$$
$$y_5 = 1.8371 \qquad y_{10} = 7.1895.$$

But instead of naively accepting these results as accurate approximations, we decided to use a computer to repeat the computations with smaller values of h. The table in Fig. 2.4.11 shows the results obtained with step sizes $h = 0.1$, $h = 0.02$, and $h = 0.005$. Observe that now the "stability" of the procedure in Example 1 is missing. Indeed, it seems obvious that something is going wrong near $x = 1$.

Figure 2.4.12 provides a graphical clue to the difficulty. It shows a slope field for $dy/dx = x^2 + y^2$, together with a solution curve through $(0, 1)$ plotted using one of the more accurate approximation methods of the following two sections. It appears that this solution curve may have a vertical asymptote near $x = 0.97$. Indeed, an exact solution using Bessel functions (see Problem 34 in Section 11.4) can be used to show that $y(x) \to +\infty$ as $x \to 0.969811$ (approximately). Although Euler's method gives values (albeit spurious ones) at $x = 1$, the actual solution does not exist on the entire interval $[0, 1]$. Moreover, Euler's method is unable to "keep up" with the rapid changes in $y(x)$ that occur as x approaches the infinite discontinuity near 0.969811. ∎

x	y with $h = 0.1$	y with $h = 0.02$	y with $h = 0.005$
0.1	1.1000	1.1088	1.1108
0.2	1.2220	1.2458	1.2512
0.3	1.3753	1.4243	1.4357
0.4	1.5735	1.6658	1.6882
0.5	1.8371	2.0074	2.0512
0.6	2.1995	2.5201	2.6104
0.7	2.7193	3.3612	3.5706
0.8	3.5078	4.9601	5.5763
0.9	4.8023	9.0000	12.2061
1.0	7.1895	30.9167	1502.2090

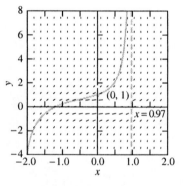

FIGURE 2.4.11. Attempting to approximate the solution of $dy/dx = x^2 + y^2$, $y(0) = 1$.

FIGURE 2.4.12. Solution of $dy/dx = x^2 + y^2$, $y(0) = 1$.

The moral of Example 5 is that there are pitfalls in the numerical solution of certain initial value problems. Certainly it's pointless to attempt to approximate a solution on an interval where it doesn't even exist (or where it is not unique, in which case there's no general way to predict which way the numerical approximations will branch at a point of nonuniqueness). We should never accept as accurate the results of applying Euler's method with a single fixed step size h. A second "run" with smaller step size ($h/2$, say, or $h/5$, or $h/10$) may give seemingly consistent results, thereby suggesting their accuracy, or it may—as in Example 5—reveal the presence of some hidden difficulty in the problem. Many problems simply require the more accurate and powerful methods that are discussed in the final two sections of this chapter.

2.4 Problems

In Problems 1 through 10, an initial value problem and its exact solution $y(x)$ are given. Apply Euler's method twice to approximate to this solution on the interval $[0, \frac{1}{2}]$, first with step size $h = 0.25$, then with step size $h = 0.1$. Compare the 3-decimal-place values of the two approximations at $x = \frac{1}{2}$ with the value $y(\frac{1}{2})$ of the actual solution.

1. $y' = -y$, $y(0) = 2$; $y(x) = 2e^{-x}$
2. $y' = 2y$, $y(0) = \frac{1}{2}$; $y(x) = \frac{1}{2}e^{2x}$
3. $y' = y + 1$, $y(0) = 1$; $y(x) = 2e^x - 1$
4. $y' = x - y$, $y(0) = 1$; $y(x) = 2e^{-x} + x - 1$
5. $y' = y - x - 1$, $y(0) = 1$; $y(x) = 2 + x - e^x$
6. $y' = -2xy$, $y(0) = 2$; $y(x) = 2e^{-x^2}$
7. $y' = -3x^2y$, $y(0) = 3$; $y(x) = 3e^{-x^3}$
8. $y' = e^{-y}$, $y(0) = 0$; $y(x) = \ln(x + 1)$
9. $y' = \frac{1}{4}(1 + y^2)$, $y(0) = 1$; $y(x) = \tan\frac{1}{4}(x + \pi)$
10. $y' = 2xy^2$, $y(0) = 1$; $y(x) = \dfrac{1}{1 - x^2}$

Note: The application following this problem set lists illustrative calculator/computer programs that can be used in the remaining problems.

A programmable calculator or a computer will be useful for Problems 11 through 16. In each problem find the exact solution of the given initial value problem. Then apply Euler's method twice to approximate (to four decimal places) this solution on the given interval, first with step size $h = 0.01$, then with step size $h = 0.005$. Make a table showing the approximate values and the actual value, together with the percentage error in the more accurate approximation, for x an integral multiple of 0.2. Throughout, primes denote derivatives with respect to x.

11. $y' = y - 2$, $y(0) = 1$; $0 \leq x \leq 1$
12. $y' = \frac{1}{2}(y - 1)^2$, $y(0) = 2$; $0 \leq x \leq 1$
13. $yy' = 2x^3$, $y(1) = 3$; $1 \leq x \leq 2$
14. $xy' = y^2$, $y(1) = 1$; $1 \leq x \leq 2$
15. $xy' = 3x - 2y$, $y(2) = 3$; $2 \leq x \leq 3$
16. $y^2y' = 2x^5$, $y(2) = 3$; $2 \leq x \leq 3$

A computer with a printer is required for Problems 17 through 24. In these initial value problems, use Euler's method with step sizes $h = 0.1$, 0.02, 0.004, and 0.0008 to approximate to four decimal places the values of the solution at ten equally spaced points of the given interval. Print the results in tabular form with appropriate headings to make it easy to gauge the effect of varying the step size h. Throughout, primes denote derivatives with respect to x.

17. $y' = x^2 + y^2$, $y(0) = 0$; $0 \leq x \leq 1$
18. $y' = x^2 - y^2$, $y(0) = 1$; $0 \leq x \leq 2$
19. $y' = x + \sqrt{y}$, $y(0) = 1$; $0 \leq x \leq 2$
20. $y' = x + \sqrt[3]{y}$, $y(0) = -1$; $0 \leq x \leq 2$
21. $y' = \ln y$, $y(1) = 2$; $1 \leq x \leq 2$
22. $y' = x^{2/3} + y^{2/3}$, $y(0) = 1$; $0 \leq x \leq 2$
23. $y' = \sin x + \cos y$, $y(0) = 0$; $0 \leq x \leq 1$
24. $y' = \dfrac{x}{1 + y^2}$, $y(-1) = 1$; $-1 \leq x \leq 1$

25. You bail out of the helicopter of Example 2 and immediately pull the ripcord of your parachute. Now $k = 1.6$ in Eq. (5), so your downward velocity satisfies the initial value problem

$$\frac{dv}{dt} = 32 - 1.6v, \quad v(0) = 0$$

(with t in seconds and v in ft/s). Use Euler's method with a programmable calculator or computer to approximate the solution for $0 \leq t \leq 2$, first with step size $h = 0.01$ and then with $h = 0.005$, rounding off approximate v-values to 1 decimal place. What percentage of the limiting velocity 20 ft/sec has been attained after 1 second? After 2 seconds?

26. Suppose the deer population $P(t)$ in a small forest initially numbers 25 and satisfies the logistic equation

$$\frac{dP}{dt} = 0.0225P - 0.0003P^2$$

(with t in months). Use Euler's method with a programmable calculator or computer to approximate the solution for 10 years, first with step size $h = 1$ and then with $h = 0.5$, rounding off approximate P-values to integral numbers of deer. What percentage of the limiting population of 75 deer has been attained after 5 years? After 10 years?

Use Euler's method with a computer system to find the desired solution values in Problems 27 and 28. Start with step size $h = 0.1$, and then use successively smaller step sizes until successive approximate solution values at $x = 2$ agree rounded off to 2 decimal places.

27. $y' = x^2 + y^2 - 1$, $y(0) = 0$; $y(2) = ?$
28. $y' = x + \frac{1}{2}y^2$, $y(-2) = 0$; $y(2) = ?$

29. Consider the initial value problem

$$7x\frac{dy}{dx} + y = 0, \quad y(-1) = 1.$$

(a) Solve this problem for the exact solution

$$y(x) = -\frac{1}{x^{1/7}},$$

which has an infinite discontinuity at $x = 0$. **(b)** Apply Euler's method with step size $h = 0.15$ to approximate this solution on the interval $-1 \le x \le 0.5$. Note that, from these data alone, you might not suspect any difficulty near $x = 0$. The reason is that the numerical approximation "jumps across the discontinuity" to another solution of $7xy' + y = 0$ for $x > 0$. **(c)** Finally, apply Euler's method with step sizes $h = 0.03$ and $h = 0.006$, but still printing results only at the original points $x = -1.00, -0.85, -0.70, \ldots, 1.20, 1.35$. and 1.50. Would you now suspect a discontinuity in the exact solution?

30. Apply Euler's method with successively smaller step sizes on the interval $[0, 2]$ to verify empirically that the solution of the initial value problem

$$\frac{dy}{dx} = x^2 + y^2, \quad y(0) = 0$$

has a vertical asymptote near $x = 2.003147$. [Contrast this with Example 2, in which $y(0) = 1$.]

31. The general solution of the equation

$$\frac{dy}{dx} = (1 + y^2)\cos x$$

is $y(x) = \tan(C + \sin x)$. With the initial condition $y(0) = 0$ the solution $y(x) = \tan(\sin x)$ is well behaved. But with $y(0) = 1$ the solution $y(x) = \tan\left(\frac{1}{4}\pi + \sin x\right)$ has a vertical asymptote at $x = \sin^{-1}(\pi/4) \approx 0.90334$. Use Euler's method to verify this fact empirically.

2.4 Application: Implementing Euler's Method

Construction of a calculator or computer program to implement a numerical algorithm can sharpen one's understanding of the algorithm. Figure 2.4.13 lists TI-89 and BASIC programs implementing Euler's method to approximate the solution of the initial value problem

$$\frac{dy}{dx} = x + y, \quad y(0) = 1$$

considered in this section. The comments provided in the final column should make these programs intelligible even if you have little familiarity with the BASIC and TI calculator programming languages.

TI-89	BASIC	Comment
`:euler()`	`Program EULER`	`Program title`
`:Prgm`		
`:10→n`	`N = 10`	`Number of steps`
`:0→x`	`X = 0`	`Initial x`
`:1→y`	`Y = 1`	`Initial y`
`:1→x1`	`X1 = 1`	`Final x`
`:(x1-x)/n→h`	`H = (X1-X)/N`	`Step size`
`:For i,1,n,1`	`FOR I=1 TO N`	`Begin loop`
`:x+y→f`	`F = X + Y`	`Function value`
`:y+h*f→y`	`Y = Y + H*F`	`Euler iteration`
`:x+h→x`	`X = X + H`	`New x`
`:Disp x,y`	`PRINT X,Y`	`Display results`
`:EndFor`	`NEXT I`	`End loop`
`:EndPrgm`	`END`	`End program`

FIGURE 2.4.13. TI-89 and BASIC Euler's method programs.

To increase the number of steps (and thereby decrease the step size), you need only change the value of **N** specified in the first line of the program. To apply Euler's method to a different equation $dy/dx = f(x, y)$, you need only change the single line that calculates the function value **F**.

Any other procedural programming language (such as FORTRAN or Pascal) would follow the pattern illustrated by the parallel lines of TI-89 and BASIC code in Fig. 2.4.13. Some of the modern functional programming languages mirror standard mathematical notation even more closely. Figure 2.4.14 shows a MATLAB implementation of Euler's method. The **euler** function takes as input the initial value **x**, the initial value **y**, the final value **x1** of x, and the desired number **n** of subintervals. For instance, the MATLAB command

```
[X, Y] = euler(0, 1, 1, 10)
```

then generates the x_n- and y_n-data shown in the first two columns of the table of Fig. 2.4.8.

```
function yp = f(x,y)
yp = x + y;                    % yp = y'

function [X,Y] = euler(x,y,x1,n)
h = (x1 - x)/n;                % step size
X = x;                         % initial x
Y = y;                         % initial y
for i = 1:n                    % begin loop
    y = y + h*f(x,y);          % Euler iteration
    x = x + h;                 % new x
    X = [X;x];                 % update x-column
    Y = [Y;y];                 % update y-column
    end                        % end loop
```

FIGURE 2.4.14. MATLAB implementation of Euler's method.

You should begin this project by implementing Euler's method with your own calculator or computer system. Test your program by first applying it to the initial value problem in Example 1, then to some of the problems for this section.

Famous Numbers Investigation

The following problems describe the numbers $e \approx 2.71828$, $\ln 2 \approx 0.69315$, and $\pi \approx 3.14159$ as specific values of solutions of certain initial value problems. In each case, apply Euler's method with $n = 50, 100, 200, \ldots$ subintervals (doubling n each time). How many subintervals are needed to obtain—twice in succession—the correct value of the target number rounded to three decimal places?

1. The number $e = y(1)$, where $y(x)$ is the solution of the initial value problem $dy/dx = y$, $y(0) = 1$.
2. The number $\ln 2 = y(2)$, where $y(x)$ is the solution of the initial value problem $dy/dx = 1/x$, $y(1) = 0$.
3. The number $\pi = y(1)$, where $y(x)$ is the solution of the initial value problem $dy/dx = 4/(1 + x^2)$, $y(0) = 0$.

Also explain in each problem what the point is—why the indicated famous number is the expected numerical result.

2.5 A Closer Look at the Euler Method

The Euler method as presented in Section 2.4 is not often used in practice, mainly because more accurate methods are available. But Euler's method has the advantage of simplicity, and a careful study of this method yields insights into the workings of more accurate methods, because many of the latter are extensions or refinements of the Euler method.

To compare two different methods of numerical approximation, we need some way to measure the accuracy of each. Theorem 1 tells what degree of accuracy we can expect when we use Euler's method.

THEOREM 1: The Error in the Euler Method

Suppose that the initial value problem

$$\frac{dy}{dx} = f(x, y), \quad y(x_0) = y_0 \tag{1}$$

has a unique solution $y(x)$ on the closed interval $[a, b]$ with $a = x_0$, and assume that $y(x)$ has a continuous second derivative on $[a, b]$. (This would follow from the assumption that f, f_x, and f_y are all continuous for $a \leqq x \leqq b$ and $c \leqq y \leqq d$, where $c \leqq y(x) \leqq d$ for all x in $[a, b]$.) Then there exists a constant C such that the following is true: If the approximations y_1, y_2, y_3, ..., y_k to the actual values $y(x_1)$, $y(x_2)$, $y(x_3)$, ..., $y(x_k)$ at points of $[a, b]$ are computed using Euler's method with step size $h > 0$, then

$$|y_n - y(x_n)| \leqq Ch \tag{2}$$

for each $n = 1, 2, 3, \ldots, k$. ▲

Remark: The **error**

$$y_{\text{actual}} - y_{\text{approx}} = y(x_n) - y_n$$

in (2) denotes the (cumulative) error in Euler's method after n steps in the approximation, *exclusive* of roundoff error (as though we were using a perfect machine that made no roundoff errors). The theorem can be summarized by saying that *the error in Euler's method is of order* h; that is, the error is bounded by a (predetermined) constant C multiplied by the step size h. It follows, for instance, that (on a given closed interval) halving the step size cuts the maximum error in half; similarly, with step size $h/10$ we get 10 times the accuracy (that is, $1/10$ the maximum error) as with step size h. Consequently, we can—in principle—get any degree of accuracy we want by choosing h sufficiently small. ■

We will omit the proof of this theorem, but one can be found in Chapter 7 of G. Birkhoff and G.-C. Rota, *Ordinary Differential Equations,* 4th ed. (New York: John Wiley, 1989). The constant C deserves some comment. Because C tends to increase as the maximum value of $|y''(x)|$ on $[a, b]$ increases, it follows that C must depend in a fairly complicated way on y, and actual computation of a value of C such that the inequality in (2) holds is usually impractical. In practice, the following type of procedure is commonly employed.

1. Apply Euler's method to the initial value problem in (1) with a reasonable value of h.

2. Repeat with $h/2$, $h/4$, and so forth, at each stage halving the step size for the next application of Euler's method.

3. Continue until the results obtained at one stage agree—to an appropriate number of significant digits—with those obtained at the previous stage. Then the approximate values obtained at this stage are considered likely to be accurate to the indicated number of significant digits.

Example 1 Carry out this procedure with the initial value problem

$$\frac{dy}{dx} = -\frac{2xy}{1+x^2}, \quad y(0) = 1 \tag{3}$$

to approximate accurately the value $y(1)$ of the solution at $x = 1$.

Solution Using an Euler method program, perhaps one of those listed in Figs. 2.4.13 and 2.4.14, we begin with a step size $h = 0.04$ requiring $n = 25$ steps to reach $x = 1$. The table in Fig. 2.5.1 shows the approximate values of $y(1)$ obtained with successively smaller values of h. The data suggest that the true value of $y(1)$ is exactly 0.5. Indeed, the exact solution of the initial value problem in (3) is $y(x) = 1/(1 + x^2)$, so the true value of $y(1)$ is exactly $\frac{1}{2}$. ■

h	Approximate $y(1)$	Actual $y(1)$	|Error|$/h$
0.04	0.50451	0.50000	0.11
0.02	0.50220	0.50000	0.11
0.01	0.50109	0.50000	0.11
0.005	0.50054	0.50000	0.11
0.0025	0.50027	0.50000	0.11
0.00125	0.50013	0.50000	0.10
0.000625	0.50007	0.50000	0.11
0.0003125	0.50003	0.50000	0.10

FIGURE 2.5.1. Table of values in Example 1.

The final column of the table in Fig. 2.5.1 displays the ratio of the magnitude of the error to h; that is, $|y_{\text{actual}} - y_{\text{approx}}|/h$. Observe how the data in this column substantiate Theorem 1—in this computation, the error bound in (2) appears to hold with a value of C slightly larger than 0.1.

An Improvement in Euler's Method

As Fig. 2.5.2 shows, Euler's method is rather unsymmetrical. It uses the predicted slope $k = f(x_n, y_n)$ of the graph of the solution at the left-hand endpoint of the interval $[x_n, x_n + h]$ as if it were the actual slope of the solution over that entire interval. We now turn our attention to a way in which increased accuracy can easily be obtained; it is known as the *improved Euler method*.

Given the initial value problem

$$\frac{dy}{dx} = f(x, y), \quad y(x_0) = y_0, \tag{4}$$

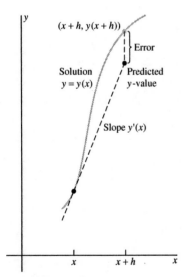

FIGURE 2.5.2. True and predicted values in Euler's method.

suppose that after carrying out n steps with step size h we have computed the approximation y_n to the actual value $y(x_n)$ of the solution at $x_n = x_0 + nh$. We can use the Euler method to obtain a first estimate—which we now call u_{n+1} rather than y_{n+1}—of the value of the solution at $x_{n+1} = x_n + h$. Thus

➤
$$u_{n+1} = y_n + h \cdot f(x_n, y_n) = y_n + h \cdot k_1.$$

Now that $u_{n+1} \approx y(x_{n+1})$ has been computed, we can take

➤
$$k_2 = f(x_{n+1}, u_{n+1})$$

as a second estimate of the slope of the solution curve $y = y(x)$ at $x = x_{n+1}$.

Of course, the approximate slope $k_1 = f(x_n, y_n)$ at $x = x_n$ has already been calculated. Why not *average* these two slopes to obtain a more accurate estimate of the average slope of the solution curve over the entire subinterval $[x_n, x_{n+1}]$? This idea is the essence of the *improved* Euler method. Figure 2.5.3 shows the geometry behind this method.

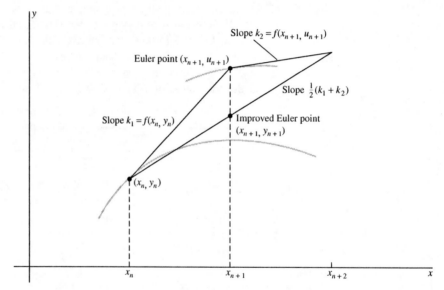

FIGURE 2.5.3. The improved Euler method: Average the slopes of the tangent lines at (x_n, y_n) and (x_{n+1}, u_{n+1}).

ALGORITHM: The Improved Euler Method

Given the initial value problem

$$\frac{dy}{dx} = f(x, y), \quad y(x_0) = y_0,$$

the **improved Euler method with step size** h consists in applying the iterative formulas

$$\begin{aligned}
k_1 &= f(x_n, y_n), \\
u_{n+1} &= y_n + h \cdot k_1, \\
k_2 &= f(x_{n+1}, u_{n+1}), \\
y_{n+1} &= y_n + h \cdot \tfrac{1}{2}(k_1 + k_2)
\end{aligned} \qquad (5)$$

to compute successive approximations y_1, y_2, y_3, ... to the (true) values $y(x_1)$, $y(x_2)$, $y(x_3)$, ... of the (exact) solution $y = y(x)$ at the points x_1, x_2, x_3, ..., respectively.   ▲

Remark: The final formula in (5) takes the "Euler form"

$$y_{n+1} = y_n + h \cdot k$$

if we write

$$k = \frac{k_1 + k_2}{2}$$

for the approximate *average slope* on the interval $[x_n, x_{n+1}]$.   ■

The improved Euler method is one of a class of numerical techniques known as **predictor-corrector** methods. First a predictor u_{n+1} of the next y-value is computed; then it is used to correct itself. Thus the **improved Euler method** with step size h consists of using the **predictor**

➤ $$u_{n+1} = y_n + h \cdot f(x_n, y_n) \tag{6}$$

and the **corrector**

➤ $$y_{n+1} = y_n + h \cdot \tfrac{1}{2} [f(x_n, y_n) + f(x_{n+1}, u_{n+1})] \tag{7}$$

iteratively to compute successive approximations y_1, y_2, y_2, ... to the values $y(x_1)$, $y(x_2)$, $y(x_3)$, ... of the actual solution of the initial value problem in (4).

Remark: Each improved Euler step requires two evaluations of the function $f(x, y)$, as compared with the single function evaluation required for an ordinary Euler step. We naturally wonder whether this doubled computational labor is worth the trouble.

Answer: Under the assumption that the exact solution $y = y(x)$ of the initial value problem in (4) has a continuous third derivative, it can be proved—see Chapter 7 of Birkhoff and Rota—that the error in the improved Euler method is of order h^2. This means that on a given bounded interval $[a, b]$, each approximate value y_n satisfies the inequality

➤ $$|y(x_n) - y_n| \leqq Ch^2, \tag{8}$$

where the constant C does not depend on h. Because h^2 is much smaller than h if h itself is small, this means that the improved Euler method is more accurate than Euler's method itself. This advantage is offset by the fact that about twice as many computations are required. But the factor h^2 in (8) means that halving the step size results in 1/4 the maximum error, and with step size $h/10$ we get 100 times the accuracy (that is, 1/100 the maximum error) as with step size h.   ■

Example 2 Figure 2.4.8 shows results of applying Euler's method to the initial value problem

$$\frac{dy}{dx} = x + y, \quad y(0) = 1 \tag{9}$$

with exact solution $y(x) = 2e^x - x - 1$. With $f(x, y) = x + y$ in Eqs. (6) and (7), the predictor-corrector formulas for the improved Euler method are

$$u_{n+1} = y_n + h \cdot (x_n + y_n),$$
$$y_{n+1} = y_n + h \cdot \tfrac{1}{2} [(x_n + y_n) + (x_{n+1} + u_{n+1})].$$

With step size $h = 0.1$ we calculate

$$u_1 = 1 + (0.1) \cdot (0 + 1) = 1.1,$$
$$y_1 = 1 + (0.05) \cdot [(0 + 1) + (0.1 + 1.1)] = 1.11,$$
$$u_2 = 1.11 + (0.1) \cdot (0.1 + 1.11) = 1.231,$$
$$y_2 = 1.11 + (0.05) \cdot [(0.1 + 1.11) + (0.2 + 1.231)] = 1.24205,$$

and so forth. The table in Fig. 2.5.4 compares the results obtained using the improved Euler method with those obtained previously using the "unimproved" Euler method. When the same step size $h = 0.1$ is used, the error in the Euler approximation to $y(1)$ is 7.25%, but the error in the improved Euler approximation is only 0.24%.

x	Euler method, $h = 0.1$ Values of y	Euler method, $h = 0.005$ Values of y	Improved Euler, $h = 0.1$ Values of y	Actual y
0.1	1.1000	1.1098	1.1100	1.1103
0.2	1.2200	1.2416	1.2421	1.2428
0.3	1.3620	1.3977	1.3985	1.3997
0.4	1.5282	1.5807	1.5818	1.5836
0.5	1.7210	1.7933	1.7949	1.7974
0.6	1.9431	2.0388	2.0409	2.0442
0.7	2.1974	2.3205	2.3231	2.3275
0.8	2.4872	2.6422	2.6456	2.6511
0.9	2.8159	3.0082	3.0124	3.0192
1.0	3.1875	3.4230	3.4282	3.4366

FIGURE 2.5.4. Euler and improved Euler approximations to the solution of $dy/dx = x + y$, $y(0) = 1$.

x	Improved Euler, Approximate y	Actual y
0.0	1.00000	1.00000
0.1	1.11034	1.11034
0.2	1.24280	1.24281
0.3	1.39971	1.39972
0.4	1.58364	1.58365
0.5	1.79744	1.79744
0.6	2.04423	2.04424
0.7	2.32749	2.32751
0.8	2.65107	2.65108
0.9	3.01919	3.01921
1.0	3.43654	3.43656

FIGURE 2.5.5. Improved Euler approximation to the solution of Eq. (9) with step size $h = 0.005$.

Indeed, the improved Euler method with $h = 0.1$ is more accurate (in this example) than the original Euler method with $h = 0.005$. The latter requires 200 evaluations of the function $f(x, y)$, but the former requires only 20 such evaluations, so in this case the improved Euler method yields greater accuracy with only about one-tenth the work.

Figure 2.5.5 shows the results obtained when the improved Euler method is applied to the initial value problem in (9) using step size $h = 0.005$. Accuracy of five significant figures is apparent in the table. This suggests that, in contrast with the original Euler method, the improved Euler method is sufficiently accurate for certain practical applications—such as plotting solution curves. ■

An improved Euler program (similar to the ones listed in the application material for this section) was used to compute approximations to the exact value

$y(1) = 0.5$ of the solution $y(x) = 1/(1 + x^2)$ of the initial value problem

$$\frac{dy}{dx} = -\frac{2xy}{1 + x^2}, \quad y(0) = 1 \tag{3}$$

of Example 1. The results obtained by successively halving the step size appear in the table in Fig. 2.5.6. Note that the final column of this table impressively corroborates the form of the error bound in (8), and that each halving of the step size reduces the error by a factor of almost exactly 4, as should happen if the error is proportional to h^2.

h	Improved Euler Approximation to $y(1)$	Error	$|Error|/h^2$
0.04	0.500195903	−0.000195903	0.12
0.02	0.500049494	−0.000049494	0.12
0.01	0.500012437	−0.000012437	0.12
0.005	0.500003117	−0.000003117	0.12
0.0025	0.500000780	−0.000000780	0.12
0.00125	0.500000195	−0.000000195	0.12
0.000625	0.500000049	−0.000000049	0.12
0.0003125	0.500000012	−0.000000012	0.12

FIGURE 2.5.6. Improved Euler approximation to $y(1)$ for $dy/dx = -2xy/(1 + x^2)$, $y(0) = 1$.

In the following two examples we exhibit graphical results obtained by employing this strategy of successively halving the step size and thus doubling the number of subintervals of a fixed interval on which we are approximating a solution.

Example 3

In Example 3 of Section 2.4 we applied Euler's method to the logistic initial value problem

$$\frac{dy}{dx} = \tfrac{1}{3}y(8 - y), \quad y(0) = 1.$$

Figure 2.4.9 shows an obvious difference between the exact solution $y(x) = 8/(1 + 7e^{-8x/3})$ and the Euler approximation on $0 \leq x \leq 5$ using $n = 20$ subintervals. Figure 2.5.7 shows approximate solution curves plotted using the improved Euler's method.

The approximation with five subintervals is still bad—perhaps worse! It appears to level off considerably short of the actual limiting population $M = 8$. You should carry out at least the first two improved Euler steps manually to see for yourself how it happens that, after increasing appropriately during the first step, the approximate solution *decreases* in the second step rather than continuing to increase (as it should). In the project for this section we ask you to show empirically that the improved Euler approximate solution with step size $h = 1$ levels off at $y \approx 4.3542$.

In contrast, the approximate solution curve with $n = 20$ subintervals tracks the exact solution curve rather closely, and with $n = 40$ subintervals the exact and approximate solution curves are indistinguishable in Fig. 2.5.7. The table in Fig. 2.5.8 indicates that the improved Euler approximation with $n = 200$ subintervals is accurate rounded to three decimal places (that is, four significant digits) on the interval

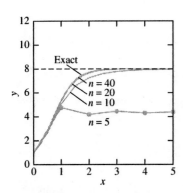

FIGURE 2.5.7. Approximating a logistic solution using the improved Euler method with $n = 5$, $n = 10$, $n = 20$, and $n = 40$ subintervals.

x	Actual $y(x)$	Improved Euler with $n = 200$
0	1.0000	1.0000
1	5.3822	5.3809
2	7.7385	7.7379
3	7.9813	7.9812
4	7.9987	7.9987
5	7.9999	7.9999

FIGURE 2.5.8. Using the improved Euler method to approximate the actual solution of the initial value problem in Example 3.

$0 \leqq x \leqq 5$. Because discrepancies in the fourth significant digit are not visually apparent at the resolution of an ordinary computer screen, the improved Euler method (using several hundred subintervals) is considered adequate for many graphical purposes. ■

Example 4   In Example 4 of Section 2.4 we applied Euler's method to the initial value problem

$$\frac{dy}{dx} = y \cos x, \quad y(0) = 1.$$

Figure 2.4.10 shows obvious visual differences between the periodic exact solution $y(x) = e^{\sin x}$ and the Euler approximations on $0 \leqq x \leqq 6\pi$ with as many as $n = 400$ subintervals.

Figure 2.5.9 shows the exact solution curve and approximate solution curves plotted using the improved Euler method with $n = 50$, $n = 100$, and $n = 200$ subintervals. The approximation obtained with $n = 200$ is indistinguishable from the exact solution curve, and the approximation with $n = 100$ is only barely distinguishable from it. ■

Although Figs. 2.5.7 and 2.5.9 indicate that the improved Euler method can provide accuracy that suffices for many graphical purposes, it does not provide the higher-precision numerical accuracy that sometimes is needed for more careful investigations. For instance, consider again the initial value problem

$$\frac{dy}{dx} = -\frac{2xy}{1 + x^2}, \quad y(0) = 1$$

of Example 1. The final column of the table in Fig. 2.5.6 suggests that, if the improved Euler method is used on the interval $0 \leqq x \leqq 1$ with n subintervals and step size $h = 1/n$, then the resulting error E in the final approximation $y_n \approx y(1)$ is given by

$$E = |y(1) - y_n| \approx (0.12)h^2 = \frac{0.12}{n^2}.$$

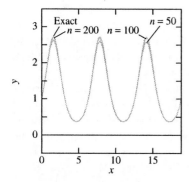

FIGURE 2.5.9. Approximating the exact solution $y = e^{\sin x}$ using the improved Euler method with $n = 50$, 100, and 200 subintervals.

If so, then 12-place accuracy (for instance) in the value $y(1)$ would require that $(0.12)n^{-2} < 5 \times 10^{-13}$, which means that $n \geqq 489{,}898$. Thus, roughly half a million steps of length $h \approx 0.000002$ would be required. Aside from the possible impracticality of this many steps (using available computational resources), the roundoff error resulting from so many successive steps might well overwhelm the cumulative error predicted by theory (which assumes exact computations in each separate step). Consequently, still more accurate methods than the improved Euler method are needed for such high-precision computations. Such a method is presented in Section 2.6.

2.5 Problems

A hand-held calculator will suffice for Problems 1 through 10, where an initial value problem and its exact solution are given. Apply the improved Euler method to approximate this solution on the interval [0, 0.5] with step size h = 0.1. Construct a table showing 4-decimal place values of the approximate solution and actual solution at the points x = 0.1, 0.2, 0.3, 0.4, 0.5.

1. $y' = -y$, $y(0) = 2$; $y(x) = 2e^{-x}$
2. $y' = 2y$, $y(0) = \frac{1}{2}$; $y(x) = \frac{1}{2}e^{2x}$
3. $y' = y + 1$, $y(0) = 1$; $y(x) = 2e^x - 1$
4. $y' = x - y$, $y(0) = 1$; $y(x) = 2e^{-x} + x - 1$
5. $y' = y - x - 1$, $y(0) = 1$; $y(x) = 2 + x - e^x$
6. $y' = -2xy$, $y(0) = 2$; $y(x) = 2e^{-x^2}$
7. $y' = -3x^2 y$, $y(0) = 3$; $y(x) = 3e^{-x^3}$
8. $y' = e^{-y}$, $y(0) = 0$; $y(x) = \ln(x + 1)$
9. $y' = \frac{1}{4}(1 + y^2)$, $y(0) = 1$; $y(x) = \tan\frac{1}{4}(x + \pi)$
10. $y' = 2xy^2$, $y(0) = 1$; $y(x) = \dfrac{1}{1 - x^2}$

Note: The application following this problem set lists illustrative calculator/computer programs that can be used in Problems 11 through 24.

A programmable calculator or a computer will be useful for Problems 11 through 16. In each problem find the exact solution of the given initial value problem. Then apply the improved Euler method twice to approximate (to five decimal places) this solution on the given interval, first with step size h = 0.01, then with step size h = 0.005. Make a table showing the approximate values and the actual value, together with the percentage error in the more accurate approximations, for x an integral multiple of 0.2. Throughout, primes denote derivatives with respect to x.

11. $y' = y - 2$, $y(0) = 1$; $0 \le x \le 1$
12. $y' = \frac{1}{2}(y - 1)^2$, $y(0) = 2$; $0 \le x \le 1$
13. $yy' = 2x^3$, $y(1) = 3$; $1 \le x \le 2$
14. $xy' = y^2$, $y(1) = 1$; $1 \le x \le 2$
15. $xy' = 3x - 2y$, $y(2) = 3$; $2 \le x \le 3$
16. $y^2 y' = 2x^5$, $y(2) = 3$; $2 \le x \le 3$

A computer with a printer is required for Problems 17 through 24. In these initial value problems, use the improved Euler method with step sizes h = 0.1, 0.02, 0.004, and 0.0008 to approximate to five decimal places the values of the solution at ten equally spaced points of the given interval. Print the results in tabular form with appropriate headings to make it easy to gauge the effect of varying the step size h. Throughout, primes denote derivatives with respect to x.

17. $y' = x^2 + y^2$, $y(0) = 0$; $0 \le x \le 1$
18. $y' = x^2 - y^2$, $y(0) = 1$; $0 \le x \le 2$
19. $y' = x + \sqrt{y}$, $y(0) = 1$; $0 \le x \le 2$
20. $y' = x + \sqrt[3]{y}$, $y(0) = -1$; $0 \le x \le 2$
21. $y' = \ln y$, $y(1) = 2$; $1 \le x \le 2$
22. $y' = x^{2/3} + y^{2/3}$, $y(0) = 1$; $0 \le x \le 2$
23. $y' = \sin x + \cos y$, $y(0) = 0$; $0 \le x \le 1$
24. $y' = \dfrac{x}{1 + y^2}$, $y(-1) = 1$; $-1 \le x \le 1$

25. As in Problem 25 of Section 2.4, you bail out a helicopter and immediately open your parachute, so your downward velocity satisfies the initial value problem

$$\frac{dv}{dt} = 32 - 1.6v, \quad v(0) = 0$$

(with t in seconds and v in ft/s). Use the improved Euler method with a programmable calculator or computer to approximate the solution for $0 \le t \le 2$, first with step size $h = 0.01$ and then with $h = 0.005$, rounding off approximate v-values to 3 decimal places. What percentage of the limiting velocity 20 ft/s has been attained after 1 second? After 2 seconds?

26. As in Problem 26 of Section 2.4, suppose the deer population $P(t)$ in a small forest initially numbers 25 and satisfies the logistic equation

$$\frac{dP}{dt} = 0.0225P - 0.0003P^2$$

(with t in months). Use the improved Euler method with a programmable calculator or computer to approximate the solution for 10 years, first with step size $h = 1$ and then with $h = 0.5$, rounding off approximate P-values to 3 decimal places. What percentage of the limiting population of 75 deer has been attained after 5 years? After 10 years?

Use the improved Euler method with a computer system to find the desired solution values in Problems 27 and 28. Start with step size h = 0.1, and then use successively smaller step sizes until successive approximate solution values at x = 2 agree rounded off to 4 decimal places.

27. $y' = x^2 + y^2 - 1$, $y(0) = 0$; $y(2) = ?$
28. $y' = x + \frac{1}{2}y^2$, $y(-2) = 0$; $y(2) = ?$

29. Consider the crossbow bolt of Example 2 in Section 2.3, shot straight upward from the ground with an initial velocity of 49 m/s. Because of linear air resistance, its velocity function $v(t)$ satisfies the initial value problem

$$\frac{dv}{dt} = -(0.04)v - 9.8, \quad v(0) = 49$$

with exact solution $v(t) = 294e^{-t/25} - 245$. Use a calculator or computer implementation of the improved Euler method to approximate $v(t)$ for $0 \leq t \leq 10$ using both $n = 50$ and $n = 100$ subintervals. Display the results at intervals of 1 second. Do the two approximations—each rounded to two decimal places—agree both with each other and with the exact solution? If the exact solution were unavailable, explain how you could use the improved Euler method to approximate closely **(a)** the bolt's time of ascent to its apex (given in Section 2.3 as 4.56 s) and **(b)** its impact velocity after 9.41 s in the air.

30. Consider now the crossbow bolt of Example 3 in Section 2.3. It still is shot straight upward from the ground with an initial velocity of 49 m/s, but because of air resistance proportional to the square of its velocity, its velocity function $v(t)$ satisfies the initial value problem

$$\frac{dv}{dt} = -(0.0011)v|v| - 9.8, \quad v(0) = 49.$$

The symbolic solution discussed in Section 2.3 required separate investigations of the bolt's ascent and its descent, with $v(t)$ given by a tangent function during ascent and by a hyperbolic tangent function during descent. But the improved Euler method requires no such distinction. Use a calculator or computer implementation of the improved Euler method to approximate $v(t)$ for $0 \leq t \leq 10$ using both $n = 100$ and $n = 200$ subintervals. Display the results at intervals of 1 second. Do the two approximations—each rounded to two decimal places—agree with each other? If an exact solution were unavailable, explain how you could use the improved Euler method to approximate closely **(a)** the bolt's time of ascent to its apex (given in Section 2.3 as 4.61 s) and **(b)** its impact velocity after 9.41 s in the air.

2.5 Application: Improved Euler Implementation

Figure 2.5.10 lists TI-89 and BASIC programs implementing the improved Euler method to approximate the solution of the initial value problem

$$\frac{dy}{dx} = x + y, \quad y(0) = 1$$

considered in Example 2 of this section. The comments provided in the final column should make these programs intelligible even if you have little familiarity with the BASIC and TI programming languages.

To apply the improved Euler method to a differential equation $dy/dx = f(x, y)$, one need only change the initial line of the program, in which the function f is defined. To increase the number of steps (and thereby decrease the step size) one need only change the value of **N** specified in the second line of the program.

Figure 2.5.11 exhibits one MATLAB implementation of the improved Euler method. The **impeuler** function takes as input the initial value **x**, the initial value **y**, the final value **x1** of x, and the desired number **n** of subintervals. As output it produces the resulting column vectors **X** and **Y** of x- and y-values. For instance, the MATLAB command

```
[X, Y] = impeuler(0, 1, 1, 10)
```

then generates the first and fourth columns of data shown in the table of Fig. 2.5.4.

You should begin this project by implementing the improved Euler method with your own calculator or computer system. Test your program by first applying it to the initial value problem of Example 1, then to some of the problems for this section.

Famous Numbers Revisited

The following problems describe the numbers $e \approx 2.7182818$, $\ln 2 \approx 0.6931472$, and $\pi \approx 3.1415927$ as specific values of certain initial value problems. In each case,

TI-89	BASIC	Comment
`:impeuler()`	`Program IMPEULER`	Program title
`:Prgm`		
`:Define f(x,y)=x+y`	`DEF FN F(X,Y) = X + Y`	Define function f
`:10→n`	`N = 10`	Number of steps
`:0→x`	`X = 0`	Initial x
`:1→y`	`Y = 1`	Initial y
`:1→x1`	`X1 = 1`	Final x
`:(x1-x)/n→h`	`H = (X1-X)/N`	Step size
`:For i,1,n,1`	`FOR I=1 TO N`	Begin loop
`:y→y0`	`Y0 = Y`	Save previous y
`:f(x,y)→k1`	`K1 = FNF(X,Y)`	First slope
`:y0+h*k1→y`	`Y = Y0 + H*K1`	Predictor
`:x+h→x`	`X = X + H`	New x
`:f(x,y)→k2`	`K2 = FNF(X,Y)`	Second slope
`:(k1+k2)/2→k`	`K = (K1 + K2)/2`	Average slope
`:y0+h*k→y`	`Y = Y0 + H*K`	Corrector
`:Disp x,y`	`PRINT X,Y`	Display results
`:EndFor`	`NEXT I`	End loop
`:EndPrgm`	`END`	End program

FIGURE 2.5.10. TI-89 and BASIC improved Euler programs.

```
function yp = f(x,y)
yp = x + y;                          % yp = y'

function [X,Y] = impeuler(x,y,x1,n)
h = (x1 - x)/n;                      % step size
X = x;                               % initial x
Y = y;                               % initial y
for i = 1:n;                         % begin loop
    k1 = f(x,y);                     % first slope
    k2 = f(x+h,y+h*k1);              % second slope
    k = (k1 + k2)/2;;                % average slope
    x = x + h;                       % new x
    y = y + h*k;                     % new y
    X = [X;x];                       % update x-column
    Y = [Y;y];                       % update y-column
end                                  % end loop
```

FIGURE 2.5.11. MATLAB implementation of improved Euler method.

apply the improved Euler method with $n = 10, 20, 40, \ldots$ subintervals (doubling n each time). How many subintervals are needed to obtain—twice in succession—the correct value of the target number rounded to five decimal places?

   1. The number $e = y(1)$, where $y(x)$ is the solution of the initial value problem $dy/dx = y$, $y(0) = 1$.

2. The number $\ln 2 = y(2)$, where $y(x)$ is the solution of the initial value problem $dy/dx = 1/x$, $y(1) = 0$.

3. The number $\pi = y(1)$, where $y(x)$ is the solution of the initial value problem $dy/dx = 4/(1 + x^2)$, $y(0) = 0$.

Logistic Population Investigation

Apply your improved Euler program to the initial value problem $dy/dx = \frac{1}{3}y(8 - y)$, $y(0) = 1$ of Example 3. In particular, verify (as claimed) that the approximate solution with step size $h = 1$ levels off at $y \approx 4.3542$ rather than at the limiting value $y = 8$ of the exact solution. Perhaps a table of values for $0 \leq x \leq 100$ will make this apparent.

For your own logistic population to investigate, consider the initial value problem

$$\frac{dy}{dx} = \frac{1}{n}y(m - y), \quad y(0) = 1,$$

where m and n are (for instance) the largest and smallest nonzero digits in your student ID number. Does the improved Euler approximation with step size $h = 1$ level off at the "correct" limiting value of the exact solution? If not, find a smaller value of h so that it does.

Periodic Harvesting and Restocking

The differential equation

$$\frac{dy}{dt} = ky(M - y) - h\sin\left(\frac{2\pi t}{P}\right)$$

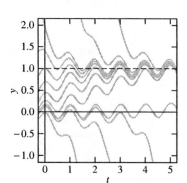

FIGURE 2.5.12. Solution curves of $dy/dt = y(1 - y) - \sin 2\pi t$.

models a logistic population that is periodically harvested and restocked with period P and maximal harvesting/restocking rate h. A numerical approximation program was used to plot the typical solution curves for the case $k = M = h = P = 1$ that are shown in Fig. 2.5.12. This figure suggests—although it does not prove—the existence of a threshold initial population such that

- Beginning with an initial population above this threshold, the population oscillates (perhaps with period P?) around the (unharvested) stable limiting population $y(t) \equiv M$, whereas
- The population dies out if it begins with an initial population below this threshold.

Use an appropriate plotting utility to investigate your own logistic population with periodic harvesting and restocking (selecting typical values of the parameters k, M, h, and P). Do the observations indicated here appear to hold for your population?

2.6 The Runge-Kutta Method

We now discuss a method for approximating the solution $y = y(x)$ of the initial value problem

$$\frac{dy}{dx} = f(x, y), \quad y(x_0) = y_0 \qquad (1)$$

that is considerably more accurate than the improved Euler method and is more widely used in practice than any of the numerical methods discussed in Sections 2.4 and 2.5. It is called the *Runge-Kutta method*, after the German mathematicians who developed it, Carl Runge (1856–1927) and Wilhelm Kutta (1867–1944).

With the usual notation, suppose that we have computed the approximations y_1, y_2, y_3, ..., y_n to the actual values $y(x_1)$, $y(x_2)$, $y(x_3)$, ..., $y(x_n)$ and now want to compute $y_{n+1} \approx y(x_{n+1})$. Then

$$y(x_{n+1}) - y(x_n) = \int_{x_n}^{x_{n+1}} y'(x)\, dx = \int_{x_n}^{x_n+h} y'(x)\, dx \tag{2}$$

by the fundamental theorem of calculus. Next, Simpson's rule for numerical integration yields

$$y(x_{n+1}) - y(x_n) \approx \frac{h}{6}\left[y'(x_n) + 4y'\left(x_n + \frac{h}{2}\right) + y'(x_{n+1}) \right]. \tag{3}$$

Hence we want to define y_{n+1} so that

$$y_{n+1} \approx y_n + \frac{h}{6}\left[y'(x_n) + 2y'\left(x_n + \frac{h}{2}\right) + 2y'\left(x_n + \frac{h}{2}\right) + y'(x_{n+1}) \right]; \tag{4}$$

we have split $4y'\left(x_n + \frac{1}{2}h\right)$ into a sum of two terms because we intend to approximate the slope $y'\left(x_n + \frac{1}{2}h\right)$ at the midpoint $x_n + \frac{1}{2}h$ of the interval $[x_n, x_{n+1}]$ in two different ways.

On the right-hand side in (4), we replace the [true] slope values $y'(x_n)$, $y'\left(x_n + \frac{1}{2}h\right)$, $y'\left(x_n + \frac{1}{2}h\right)$, and $y'(x_{n+1})$, respectively, with the following estimates.

➤
$$k_1 = f(x_n, y_n) \tag{5a}$$

- This is the Euler method slope at x_n.

➤
$$k_2 = f\left(x_n + \tfrac{1}{2}h, y_n + \tfrac{1}{2}hk_1\right) \tag{5b}$$

- This is an estimate of the slope at the midpoint of the interval $[x_n, x_{n+1}]$ using the Euler method to predict the ordinate there.

➤
$$k_3 = f\left(x_n + \tfrac{1}{2}h, y_n + \tfrac{1}{2}hk_2\right) \tag{5c}$$

- This is an improved Euler value for the slope at the midpoint.

➤
$$k_4 = f(x_{n+1}, y_n + hk_3) \tag{5d}$$

- This is the Euler method slope at x_{n+1}, using the improved slope k_3 at the midpoint to step to x_{n+1}.

When these substitutions are made in (4), the result is the iterative formula

➤
$$y_{n+1} = y_n + \frac{h}{6}(k_1 + 2k_2 + 2k_3 + k_4). \tag{6}$$

The use of this formula to compute the approximations y_1, y_2, y_3, ... successively constitutes the **Runge-Kutta method.** Note that Eq. (6) takes the "Euler form"

$$y_{n+1} = y_n + h \cdot k$$

if we write

$$k = \frac{1}{6}(k_1 + 2k_2 + 2k_3 + k_4) \tag{7}$$

for the approximate *average slope* on the interval $[x_n, x_{n+1}]$.

The Runge-Kutta method is a *fourth-order* method—it can be proved that the cumulative error on a bounded interval $[a, b]$ with $a = x_0$ is of order h^4. [Thus the iteration in (6) is sometimes called the *fourth-order* Runge-Kutta method because it is possible to develop Runge-Kutta methods of other orders.] That is,

➤
$$|y(x_n) - y_n| \leqq Ch^4, \tag{8}$$

where the constant C depends on the function $f(x, y)$ and the interval $[a, b]$, but does not depend on the step size h. The following example illustrates this high accuracy in comparison with the lower-order accuracy of our previous numerical methods.

Example 1 We first apply the Runge-Kutta method to the illustrative initial value problem

$$\frac{dy}{dx} = x + y, \quad y(0) = 1 \tag{9}$$

that we considered in Fig. 2.4.8 of Section 2.4 and again in Example 2 of Section 2.5. The exact solution of this problem is $y(x) = 2e^x - x - 1$. To make a point we use $h = 0.5$, a larger step size than in any previous example, so only two steps are required to go from $x = 0$ to $x = 1$.

In the first step we use the formulas in (5) and (6) to calculate

$$k_1 = 0 + 1 = 1,$$
$$k_2 = (0 + 0.25) + (1 + (0.25) \cdot (1)) = 1.5,$$
$$k_3 = (0 + 0.25) + (1 + (0.25) \cdot (1.5)) = 1.625,$$
$$k_4 = (0.5) + (1 + (0.5) \cdot (1.625)) = 2.3125,$$

and then

$$y_1 = 1 + \frac{0.5}{6}[1 + 2 \cdot (1.5) + 2 \cdot (1.625) + 2.3125] \approx 1.7969.$$

Similarly, the second step yields $y_2 \approx 3.4347$.

| | **Improved Euler** | | **Runge-Kutta** | | |
x	y with $h = 0.1$	Percent Error	y with $h = 0.5$	Percent Error	Actual y
0.0	1.0000	0.00%	1.0000	0.00%	1.0000
0.5	1.7949	0.14%	1.7969	0.03%	1.7974
1.0	3.4282	0.24%	3.4347	0.05%	3.4366

FIGURE 2.6.1. Runge-Kutta and improved Euler results for the initial value problem $dy/dx = x + y$, $y(0) = 1$.

Figure 2.6.1 presents these results together with the results (from Fig. 2.5.4) of applying the improved Euler method with step size $h = 0.1$. We see that even with the larger step size, the Runge-Kutta method gives (for this problem) four to five times the accuracy (in terms of relative percentage errors) of the improved Euler method. ∎

It is customary to measure the computational labor involved in solving $dy/dx = f(x, y)$ numerically by counting the number of evaluations of the function $f(x, y)$ that are required. In Example 1, the Runge-Kutta method required eight evaluations of $f(x, y) = x + y$ (four at each step), whereas the improved Euler method required 20 such evaluations (two for each of 10 steps). Thus the Runge-Kutta method gave over four times the accuracy with only 40% of the labor.

Computer programs implementing the Runge-Kutta method are listed in the project material for this section. Figure 2.6.2 shows the results obtained by applying the improved Euler and Runge-Kutta methods to the problem $dy/dx = x+y$, $y(0) = 1$ with the same step size $h = 0.1$. The relative error in the improved Euler value at $x = 1$ is about 0.24%, but for the Runge-Kutta value it is 0.00012%. In this comparison the Runge-Kutta method is about 2000 times as accurate, but requires only twice as many function evaluations, as the improved Euler method.

x	Improved Euler y	Runge-Kutta y	Actual y
0.1	1.1100	1.110342	1.110342
0.2	1.2421	1.242805	1.242806
0.3	1.3985	1.399717	1.399718
0.4	1.5818	1.583648	1.583649
0.5	1.7949	1.797441	1.797443
0.6	2.0409	2.044236	2.044238
0.7	2.3231	2.327503	2.327505
0.8	2.6456	2.651079	2.651082
0.9	3.0124	3.019203	3.019206
1.0	3.4282	3.436559	3.436564

FIGURE 2.6.2. Runge-Kutta and improved Euler results for the initial value problem $dy/dx = x + y$, $y(0) = 1$, with the same step size $h = 0.1$.

The error bound

$$|y(x_n) - y_n| \leqq Ch^4 \tag{8}$$

for the Runge-Kutta method results in a rapid decrease in the magnitude of errors when the step size h is reduced (except for the possibility that very small step sizes may result in unacceptable roundoff errors). It follows from the inequality in (8) that (on a fixed bounded interval) halving the step size decreases the absolute error by a factor of $\left(\frac{1}{2}\right)^4 = \frac{1}{16}$. Consequently, the common practice of successively halving the step size until the computed results "stabilize" is particularly effective with the Runge-Kutta method.

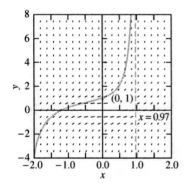

FIGURE 2.6.3. Solutions of $dy/dx = x^2 + y^2$, $y(0) = 1$.

Example 2

In Example 5 of Section 2.4 we saw that Euler's method is not adequate to approximate the solution $y(x)$ of the initial value problem

$$\frac{dy}{dx} = x^2 + y^2, \quad y(0) = 1 \tag{10}$$

as x approaches the infinite discontinuity near $x = 0.969811$ (see Fig. 2.6.3). Now we apply the Runge-Kutta method to this initial value problem.

Figure 2.6.4 shows Runge-Kutta results on the interval $[0.0, 0.9]$, computed with step sizes $h = 0.1$, $h = 0.05$, and $h = 0.025$. There is still some difficulty near $x = 0.9$, but it seems safe to conclude from these data that $y(0.5) \approx 2.0670$.

x	y with $h = 0.1$	y with $h = 0.05$	y with $h = 0.025$
0.1	1.1115	1.1115	1.1115
0.3	1.4397	1.4397	1.4397
0.5	2.0670	2.0670	2.0670
0.7	3.6522	3.6529	3.6529
0.9	14.0218	14.2712	14.3021

FIGURE 2.6.4. Approximating the solution of the initial value problem in Eq. (10).

We therefore begin anew and apply the Runge-Kutta method to the initial value problem

$$\frac{dy}{dx} = x^2 + y^2, \quad y(0.5) = 2.0670. \tag{11}$$

Figure 2.6.5 shows results on the interval $[0.5, 0.9]$, obtained with step sizes $h = 0.01$, $h = 0.005$, and $h = 0.0025$. We now conclude that $y(0.9) \approx 14.3049$.

x	y with $h = 0.01$	y with $h = 0.005$	y with $h = 0.0025$
0.5	2.0670	2.0670	2.0670
0.6	2.6440	2.6440	2.6440
0.7	3.6529	3.6529	3.6529
0.8	5.8486	5.8486	5.8486
0.9	14.3048	14.3049	14.3049

FIGURE 2.6.5. Approximating the solution of the initial value problem in Eq. (11).

Finally, Fig. 2.6.6 shows results on the interval $[0.90, 0.95]$ for the initial value problem

$$\frac{dy}{dx} = x^2 + y^2, \quad y(0.9) = 14.3049, \tag{12}$$

x	y with $h = 0.002$	y with $h = 0.001$	y with $h = 0.0005$
0.90	14.3049	14.3049	14.3049
0.91	16.7024	16.7024	16.7024
0.92	20.0617	20.0617	20.0617
0.93	25.1073	25.1073	25.1073
0.94	33.5363	33.5363	33.5363
0.95	50.4722	50.4723	50.4723

FIGURE 2.6.6. Approximating the solution of the initial value problem in Eq. (12).

obtained using step sizes $h = 0.002$, $h = 0.001$, and $h = 0.0005$. Our final approximate result is $y(0.95) \approx 50.4723$. The actual value of the solution at $x = 0.95$ is $y(0.95) \approx 50.471867$. Our slight overestimate results mainly from the fact that the four-place initial value in (12) is (in effect) the result of rounding *up* the actual value $y(0.9) \approx 14.304864$; such errors are magnified considerably as we approach the vertical asymptote. ∎

Example 3   A skydiver with a mass of 60 kg jumps from a helicopter hovering at an initial altitude of 5 kilometers. Assume that she falls vertically with initial velocity zero and experiences an upward force F_R of air resistance given in terms of her velocity v (in meters per second) by

$$F_R = (0.0096)(100v + 10v^2 + v^3)$$

(in newtons, and with the coordinate axis directed downward so that $v > 0$ during her descent to the ground). If she does not open her parachute, what will be her terminal velocity? How fast will she be falling after 5 s have elapsed? After 10 s? After 20 s?

Solution   Newton's law $F = ma$ gives

$$m\frac{dv}{dt} = mg - F_R;$$

that is,

$$60\frac{dv}{dt} = (60)(9.8) - (0.0096)(100v + 10v^2 + v^3) \tag{13}$$

because $m = 60$ and $g = 9.8$. Thus the velocity function $v(t)$ satisfies the initial value problem

$$\frac{dv}{dt} = f(v), \quad v(0) = 0, \tag{14}$$

where

$$f(v) = 9.8 - (0.00016)(100v + 10v^2 + v^3). \tag{15}$$

The skydiver reaches her terminal velocity when the forces of gravity and air resistance balance, so $f(v) = 0$. We can therefore calculate her terminal velocity immediately by solving the equation

$$f(v) = 9.8 - (0.00016)(100v + 10v^2 + v^3) = 0. \tag{16}$$

FIGURE 2.6.7. Graph of $f(v) = $ $9.8 - (0.00016)(100v + 10v^2 + v^3)$.

Figure 2.6.7 shows the graph of the function $f(v)$ and exhibits the single real solution $v \approx 35.5780$ (found graphically or by using a calculator or computer **Solve** procedure). Thus the skydiver's terminal speed is approximately 35.578 m/s, about 128 km/h (almost 80 mi/h).

Figure 2.6.8 shows the results of Runge-Kutta approximations to the solution of the initial value problem in (14); the step sizes $h = 0.2$ and $h = 0.1$ yield the same results (to three decimal places). Observe that the terminal velocity is effectively attained in only 15 s. But the skydiver's velocity is 91.85% of her terminal velocity after only 5 s, and 99.78% after 10 s. ∎

The final example of this section contains a *warning*: For certain types of initial value problems, the numerical methods we have discussed are not nearly so successful as in the previous examples.

t (s)	v (m/s)	t (s)	v (m/s)
0	0	11	35.541
1	9.636	12	35.560
2	18.386	13	35.569
3	25.299	14	35.574
4	29.949	15	35.576
5	32.678	16	35.577
6	34.137	17	35.578
7	34.875	18	35.578
8	35.239	19	35.578
9	35.415	20	35.578
10	35.500		

FIGURE 2.6.8.   The skydiver's velocity data.

Example 4   Consider the seemingly innocuous initial value problem

$$\frac{dy}{dx} = 5y - 6e^{-x}, \quad y(0) = 1 \tag{17}$$

whose exact solution is $y(x) = e^{-x}$. The table in Fig. 2.6.9 shows the results obtained by applying the Runge-Kutta method on the interval $[0,4]$ with step sizes $h = 0.2$, $h = 0.1$, and $h = 0.05$. Obviously these attempts are spectacularly unsuccessful. Although $y(x) = e^{-x} \to 0$ as $x \to +\infty$, it appears that our numerical approximations are headed toward $-\infty$ rather than zero.

x	Runge-Kutta y with $h = 0.2$	Runge-Kutta y with $h = 0.1$	Runge-Kutta y with $h = 0.05$	Actual y
0.4	0.66880	0.67020	0.67031	0.67032
0.8	0.43713	0.44833	0.44926	0.44933
1.2	0.21099	0.29376	0.30067	0.30199
1.6	−0.46019	0.14697	0.19802	0.20190
2.0	−4.72142	−0.27026	0.10668	0.13534
2.4	−35.53415	−2.90419	−0.12102	0.09072
2.8	−261.25023	−22.05352	−1.50367	0.06081
3.2	−1,916.69395	−163.25077	−11.51868	0.04076
3.6	−14059.35494	−1205.71249	−85.38156	0.02732
4.0	−103,126.5270	−8903.12866	−631.03934	0.01832

FIGURE 2.6.9.   Runge-Kutta attempts to solve numerically the initial value problem in Eq. (17).

The explanation lies in the fact that the general solution of the equation $dy/dx = 5y - 6e^{-x}$ is

$$y(x) = e^{-x} + Ce^{5x}. \tag{18}$$

The particular solution of (17) satisfying the initial condition $y(0) = 1$ is obtained with $C = 0$. But any departure, however small, from the exact solution

$y(x) = e^{-x}$—even if due only to roundoff error—introduces [in effect] a nonzero value of C in Eq. (18). And as indicated in Fig. 2.6.10, all solution curves of the form in (18) with $C \neq 0$ diverge rapidly away from the one with $C = 0$, even if their initial values are close to 1. ∎

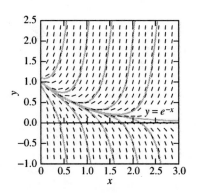

FIGURE 2.6.10. Direction field and solution curves for $dy/dx = 5y - 6e^{-x}$.

Difficulties of the sort illustrated by Example 4 sometimes are unavoidable, but one can at least hope to recognize such a problem when it appears. Approximate values whose order of magnitude varies with changing step size are a common indicator of such instability. These difficulties are discussed in numerical analysis textbooks and are the subject of current research in the field.

2.6 Problems

A hand-held calculator will suffice for Problems 1 through 10, where an initial value problem and its exact solution are given. Apply the Runge-Kutta method to approximate this solution on the interval [0, 0.5] with step size $h = 0.25$. Construct a table showing 5-decimal place values of the approximate solution and actual solution at the points $x = 0.25$ and 0.5.

1. $y' = -y$, $y(0) = 2$; $y(x) = 2e^{-x}$
2. $y' = 2y$, $y(0) = \frac{1}{2}$; $y(x) = \frac{1}{2}e^{2x}$
3. $y' = y + 1$, $y(0) = 1$; $y(x) = 2e^x - 1$
4. $y' = x - y$, $y(0) = 1$; $y(x) = 2e^{-x} + x - 1$
5. $y' = y - x - 1$, $y(0) = 1$; $y(x) = 2 + x - e^x$
6. $y' = -2xy$, $y(0) = 2$; $y(x) = 2e^{-x^2}$
7. $y' = -3x^2 y$, $y(0) = 3$; $y(x) = 3e^{-x^3}$
8. $y' = e^{-y}$, $y(0) = 0$; $y(x) = \ln(x + 1)$
9. $y' = \frac{1}{4}(1 + y^2)$, $y(0) = 1$; $y(x) = \tan\frac{1}{4}(x + \pi)$
10. $y' = 2xy^2$, $y(0) = 1$; $y(x) = \dfrac{1}{1 - x^2}$

Note: *The application following this problem set lists illustrative calculator/computer programs that can be used in the remaining problems.*

A programmable calculator or a computer will be useful for Problems 11 through 16. In each problem find the exact solution of the given initial value problem. Then apply the Runge-Kutta method twice to approximate (to five decimal places)

this solution on the given interval, first with step size $h = 0.2$, then with step size $h = 0.1$. Make a table showing the approximate values and the actual value, together with the percentage error in the more accurate approximation, for x an integral multiple of 0.2. Throughout, primes denote derivatives with respect to x.

11. $y' = y - 2$, $y(0) = 1$; $0 \leq x \leq 1$
12. $y' = \frac{1}{2}(y - 1)^2$, $y(0) = 2$; $0 \leq x \leq 1$
13. $yy' = 2x^3$, $y(1) = 3$; $1 \leq x \leq 2$
14. $xy' = y^2$, $y(1) = 1$; $1 \leq x \leq 2$
15. $xy' = 3x - 2y$, $y(2) = 3$; $2 \leq x \leq 3$
16. $y^2 y' = 2x^5$, $y(2) = 3$; $2 \leq x \leq 3$

A computer with a printer is required for Problems 17 through 24. In these initial value problems, use the Runge-Kutta method with step sizes $h = 0.2$, 0.1, 0.05, and 0.025 to approximate to six decimal places the values of the solution at five equally spaced points of the given interval. Print the results in tabular form with appropriate headings to make it easy to gauge the effect of varying the step size h. Throughout, primes denote derivatives with respect to x.

17. $y' = x^2 + y^2$, $y(0) = 0$; $0 \leq x \leq 1$
18. $y' = x^2 - y^2$, $y(0) = 1$; $0 \leq x \leq 2$
19. $y' = x + \sqrt{y}$, $y(0) = 1$; $0 \leq x \leq 2$

20. $y' = x + \sqrt[3]{y}$, $y(0) = -1$; $0 \leq x \leq 2$

21. $y' = \ln y$, $y(1) = 2$; $1 \leq x \leq 2$

22. $y' = x^{2/3} + y^{2/3}$, $y(0) = 1$; $0 \leq x \leq 2$

23. $y' = \sin x + \cos y$, $y(0) = 0$; $0 \leq x \leq 1$

24. $y' = \dfrac{x}{1 + y^2}$, $y(-1) = 1$; $-1 \leq x \leq 1$

25. As in Problem 25 of Section 2.5, you bail out a helicopter and immediately open your parachute, so your downward velocity satisfies the initial value problem

$$\frac{dv}{dt} = 32 - 1.6v, \quad v(0) = 0$$

(with t in seconds and v in ft/s). Use the Runge-Kutta method with a programmable calculator or computer to approximate the solution for $0 \leq t \leq 2$, first with step size $h = 0.1$ and then with $h = 0.05$, rounding off approximate v-values to 3 decimal places. What percentage of the limiting velocity 20 ft/s has been attained after 1 second? After 2 seconds?

26. As in Problem 26 of Section 2.5, suppose the deer population $P(t)$ in a small forest initially numbers 25 and satisfies the logistic equation

$$\frac{dP}{dt} = 0.0225P - 0.0003P^2$$

(with t in months). Use the Runge-Kutta method with a programmable calculator or computer to approximate the solution for 10 years, first with step size $h = 6$ and then with $h = 3$, rounding off approximate P-values to 4 decimal places. What percentage of the limiting population of 75 deer has been attained after 5 years? After 10 years?

Use the Runge-Kutta method with a computer system to find the desired solution values in Problems 27 and 28. Start with step size $h = 1$, and then use successively smaller step sizes until successive approximate solution values at $x = 2$ agree rounded off to 5 decimal places.

27. $y' = x^2 + y^2 - 1$, $y(0) = 0$; $y(2) = ?$

28. $y' = x + \frac{1}{2}y^2$, $y(-2) = 0$; $y(2) = ?$

Velocity-Acceleration Problems

In Problems 25 and 26, the linear acceleration $a = dv/dt$ of a moving particle is given by a formula $dv/dt = f(t, v)$, where the velocity $v = dy/dt$ is the derivative of the function $y = y(t)$ giving the position of the particle at time t. Suppose that the velocity $v(t)$ is approximated using the Runge-Kutta method to solve numerically the initial value problem

$$\frac{dv}{dt} = f(t, v), \quad v(0) = v_0. \tag{19}$$

That is, starting with $t_0 = 0$ and v_0, the formulas in Eqs. (5) and (6) are applied—with t and v in place of x and y—to calculate the successive approximate velocity values v_1, v_2, v_3, ..., v_m at the successive times t_1, t_2, t_3, ..., t_m (with $t_{n+1} = t_n + h$). Now suppose that we also want to approximate

the distance $y(t)$ traveled by the particle. We can do this by beginning with the initial position $y(0) = y_0$ and calculating

$$y_{n+1} = y_n + v_n h + \tfrac{1}{2}a_n h^2 \tag{20}$$

($n = 1, 2, 3, ...$), where $a_n = f(t_n, v_n) \approx v'(t_n)$ is the particle's approximate acceleration at time t_n. The formula in (20) would give the correct increment (from y_n to y_{n+1}) if the acceleration a_n remained constant during the time interval $[t_n, t_{n+1}]$.

Thus, once a table of approximate velocities has been calculated, Eq. (20) provides a simple way to calculate a table of corresponding successive positions. This process is illustrated in the project for this section, by beginning with the velocity data in Fig. 2.6.8 (Example 3) and proceeding to follow the skydiver's position during her descent to the ground.

29. Consider again the crossbow bolt of Example 2 in Section 2.3, shot straight upward from the ground with an initial velocity of 49 m/s. Because of linear air resistance, its velocity function $v = dy/dt$ satisfies the initial value problem

$$\frac{dv}{dt} = -(0.04)v - 9.8, \quad v(0) = 49$$

with exact solution $v(t) = 294e^{-t/25} - 245$. **(a)** Use a calculator or computer implementation of the Runge-Kutta method to approximate $v(t)$ for $0 \leq t \leq 10$ using both $n = 100$ and $n = 200$ subintervals. Display the results at intervals of 1 second. Do the two approximations—each rounded to four decimal places—agree both with each other and with the exact solution? **(b)** Now use the velocity data from part (a) to approximate $y(t)$ for $0 \leq t \leq 10$ using $n = 200$ subintervals. Display the results at intervals of 1 second. Do these approximate position values—each rounded to two decimal places—agree with the exact solution

$$y(t) = 7350\left(1 - e^{-t/25}\right) - 245t?$$

(c) If the exact solution were unavailable, explain how you could use the Runge-Kutta method to approximate closely the bolt's times of ascent and descent and the maximum height it attains.

30. Now consider again the crossbow bolt of Example 3 in Section 2.3. It still is shot straight upward from the ground with an initial velocity of 49 m/s, but because of air resistance proportional to the square of its velocity, its velocity function $v(t)$ satisfies the initial value problem

$$\frac{dv}{dt} = -(0.0011)v|v| - 9.8, \quad v(0) = 49.$$

Beginning with this initial value problem, repeat parts (a) through (c) of Problem 25 [except that you may need $n = 200$ subintervals to get four-place accuracy in part (a) and $n = 400$ subintervals for two-place accuracy in part (b)]. According to the results of Problems 17 and 18 in Section 2.3, the bolt's velocity and position functions during ascent and descent are given by the following formulas.

Ascent:
$v(t) = (94.388) \tan(0.478837 - [0.103827]t)$,
$y(t) = 108.465$
$\quad + (909.091) \ln (\cos(0.478837 - [0.103827]t))$

Descent:
$v(t) = -(94.388) \tanh(0.103827[t - 4.6119])$,
$y(t) = 108.465$
$\quad - (909.091) \ln (\cosh(0.103827[t - 4.6119]))$

2.6 Application: Runge-Kutta Implementation

Figure 2.6.11 lists TI-89 and BASIC programs implementing the Runge-Kutta method to approximate the solution of the initial value problem

$$\frac{dy}{dx} = x + y, \quad y(0) = 1$$

considered in Example 1 of this section. The comments provided in the final column should make these programs intelligible even if you have little familiarity with the BASIC and TI programming languages.

TI-89	BASIC	Comment
`:rk()`	`Program RK`	`Program title`
`:Prgm`		
`:Define f(x,y)=x+y`	`DEF FN F(X,Y) = X + Y`	`Define function f`
`:10→n`	`N = 10`	`Number of steps`
`:0→x`	`X = 0`	`Initial x`
`:1→y`	`Y = 1`	`Initial y`
`:1→x1`	`X1 = 1`	`Final x`
`:(x1-x)/n→h`	`H = (X1-X)/N`	`Step size`
`:For i,1,n,1`	`FOR I=1 TO N`	`Begin loop`
`:x→x0`	`X0 = X`	`Save previous x`
`:y→y0`	`Y0 = Y`	`Save previous y`
`:f(x,y)→k1`	`K1 = FNF(X,Y)`	`First slope`
`:x0+h/2→x`	`X = X0 + H/2`	`Midpoint`
`:y0+h*k1/2→y`	`Y = Y0 + H*K1/2`	`Midpt predictor`
`:f(x,y)→k2`	`K2 = FNF(X,Y)`	`Second slope`
`:y0+h*k2/2→y`	`Y = Y0 + H*K2/2`	`Midpt predictor`
`:f(x,y)→k3`	`K3 = FNF(X,Y)`	`Third slope`
`:x0+h→x`	`X = X0 + H`	`New x`
`:y0+h*k3→y`	`Y = Y0 + H*K3`	`Endpt predictor`
`:f(x,y)→k4`	`K4 = FNF(X,Y)`	`Fourth slope`
`:(k1+2*k2+2*k3` `+k4)/6→k`	`K = (K1+2*K2+2*K3` `+K4)/6`	`Average slope`
`:y0+h*k→y`	`Y = Y0 + H*K`	`Corrector`
`:Disp x,y`	`PRINT X,Y`	`Display results`
`:EndFor`	`NEXT I`	`End loop`
`:EndPrgm`	`END`	`End program`

FIGURE 2.6.11. TI-89 and BASIC Runge-Kutta programs.

To apply the Runge-Kutta method to a different equation $dy/dx = f(x, y)$, we need only change the initial line of the program, in which the function f is defined. To increase the number of steps (and thereby decrease the step size), one need only change the value of **N** specified in the second line of the program.

Figure 2.6.12 exhibits a MATLAB implementation of the Runge-Kutta method. Suppose that the function f describing the differential equation $y' = f(x, y)$ has been defined. Then the **rk** function takes as input the initial value **x**, the initial value **y**, the final value **x1** of x, and the desired number **n** of subintervals. As output it produces the resulting column vectors **X** and **Y** of x- and y-values. For instance, the MATLAB command

```
[X, Y] = rk(0, 1, 1, 10)
```

then generates the first and third columns of data shown in the table in Fig. 2.6.2.

```
function yp = f(x,y)
yp = x + y;                    % yp = y'

function [X,Y] = rk(x,y,x1,n)
h = (x1 - x)/n;                % step size
X = x;                         % initial x
Y = y;                         % initial y
for i = 1:n                    % begin loop
    k1 = f(x,y);               % first slope
    k2 = f(x+h/2,y+h*k1/2);    % second slope
    k3 = f(x+h/2,y+h*k2/2);    % third slope
    k4 = f(x+h,y+h*k3);        % fourth slope
    k  = (k1+2*k2+2*k3+k4)/6;  % average slope
    x  = x + h;                % new x
    y  = y + h*k;              % new y
    X = [X;x];                 % update x-column
    Y = [Y;y];                 % update y-column
end                            % end loop
```

FIGURE 2.6.12. MATLAB implementation of the Runge-Kutta method.

You should begin this project by implementing the Runge-Kutta method with your own calculator or computer system. Test your program by applying it first to the initial value problem in Example 1, then to some of the problems for this section.

Famous Numbers Revisited, One Last Time

The following problems describe the numbers

$$e \approx 2.71828182846, \quad \ln 2 \approx 0.69314718056, \quad \text{and} \quad \pi \approx 3.14159265359$$

as specific values of certain initial value problems. In each case, apply the Runge-Kutta method with $n = 10, 20, 40, \ldots$ subintervals (doubling n each time). How many subintervals are needed to obtain—twice in succession—the correct value of the target number rounded to nine decimal places?

1. The number $e = y(1)$, where $y(x)$ is the solution of the initial value problem $dy/dx = y$, $y(0) = 1$.
2. The number $\ln 2 = y(2)$, where $y(x)$ is the solution of the initial value problem $dy/dx = 1/x$, $y(1) = 0$.

3. The number $\pi = y(1)$, where $y(x)$ is the solution of the initial value problem $dy/dx = 4/(1 + x^2)$, $y(0) = 0$.

The Skydiver's Descent

The following MATLAB function describes the skydiver's acceleration function in Example 3.

```
function    vp = f(t,v)
vp = 9.8 - 0.00016*(100*v + 10*v^2 + v^3);
```

Then the commands

t (s)	v (m/s)	y (m)
0	0	0
2	18.386	18.984
4	29.949	68.825
6	34.137	133.763
8	35.239	203.392
10	35.500	274.192
12	35.560	345.266
14	35.574	416.403
16	35.577	487.555
18	35.578	558.710
20	35.578	629.866

FIGURE 2.6.13. The skydiver's velocity and position data.

```
k = 200                        % 200 subintervals
[t,v] = rk(0, 20, 0, k);       % Runge-Kutta approximation
[t(1:10:k+1); v(1:10:k+1)]     % Display every 10th entry
```

produce the table of approximate velocities shown in Fig. 2.6.8. Finally, the commands

```
y = zeros(k+1,1):                    % initialize y
h = 0.1;                             % step size
for n = 1:k                          % for n = 1 to k
  a = f(t(n),v(n)):                  % acceleration
  y(n+1) = y(n) + v(n)*h + 0.5*a*h^2;   % Equation (20)
end                                  % end loop
[t(1:20:k+1),v(1:20:k+1),y(1:20:k+1)]   % each 20th entry
```

carry out the position function calculations described in Eq. (20) in the instructions for Problems 25 and 26. The results of these calculations are shown in the table in Fig. 2.6.13. It appears that the skydiver falls 629.866 m during her first 20 s of descent, and then free falls the remaining 4370.134 meters to the ground at her terminal speed of 35.578 m/s. Hence her total time of descent is $20 + (4370.134/35.578) \approx 142.833$ s, or about 2 min 23 s.

For an individual problem to solve after implementing these methods using an available computer system, analyze your own skydive (perhaps from a different height), using your own mass m and a plausible air resistance force of the form $F_R = av + bv^2 + cv^3$.

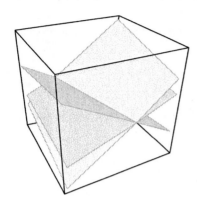

C H A P T E R 3

Linear Systems and Matrices

3.1 Introduction to Linear Systems

The subject of **linear algebra** centers around the problem of solving systems of (algebraic) *linear equations*. In high school algebra the *method of elimination* is used to solve systems of two and three (simultaneous) linear equations, with attention ordinarily confined to systems that have one and only one solution, with applications to "word problems" that have one and only one "answer." In this section we introduce some of the basic terminology of linear algebra by reviewing the elementary technique of elimination from a slightly more general viewpoint. In subsequent sections we apply this same technique to the solution of systems involving many linear equations in many unknowns. The applications of the method of elimination are diverse and important, because so many mathematical problems involve the solution of systems of linear equations.

Recall that if a, b, and c are constants with a and b not both zero, then the graph of the equation

$$ax + by = c \tag{1}$$

is a (straight) *line* in the xy-plane. For this reason, an equation of the form in (1) is called a **linear equation** in the **variables** x and y. Similarly, an equation that can be written in the form

$$ax + by + cz = d \tag{2}$$

is called **linear** in the three variables x, y, and z (even though its graph in xyz-space is a plane rather than a line). Thus the equations

$$3x - 2y = 5 \quad \text{and} \quad x - 7y + 5z = -11$$

are linear, because they involve only the first powers of the variables. By contrast, the equations

$$x + y + xy = 5 \quad \text{and} \quad x^2 + y^3 + \sqrt{z} = 1$$

146

are *not* linear, because they cannot be rewritten to eliminate the higher powers, roots, and products of the variables.

Two Equations in Two Unknowns

A **system** of linear equations (also called a **linear system**) is simply a finite collection of linear equations involving certain variables. Sometimes we refer to the variables as the "unknowns" in the system. Thus a system of two linear equations in two unknowns x and y may be written in the form

$$a_1 x + b_1 y = c_1$$
$$a_2 x + b_2 y = c_2. \tag{3}$$

By a **solution** of the system in (3) is meant a pair (x, y) of values—normally real numbers—that satisfy *both* equations *simultaneously*.

Example 1 The values $x = 2$, $y = -1$ constitute a solution of the system

$$2x - y = 5$$
$$x + 2y = 0 \tag{4}$$

because both $2(2) - (-1) = 5$ and $(2) + 2(-1) = 0$. The values $x = 3$, $y = 1$ satisfy the first equation in (4) but do not satisfy the second. Hence $(3, 1)$ is not a solution of the system in (4). ∎

Example 2 The linear system

$$x + y = 1$$
$$2x + 2y = 3 \tag{5}$$

has no solution at all, because if $x + y = 1$, then $2x + 2y = 2$, and so $2x + 2y \neq 3$. Thus, two numbers that satisfy the first equation in (5) cannot simultaneously satisfy the second. ∎

A linear system is said to be **consistent** if it has at least one solution and **inconsistent** if it has none. Thus the system in Example 1 is consistent, whereas the system in Example 2 is inconsistent.

Three Possibilities

Given a system of linear equations, we ask: What is the set of all solutions of the system? In brief, what is the **solution set** of the system?

In the case of a linear system

$$a_1 x + b_1 y = c_1$$
$$a_2 x + b_2 y = c_2 \tag{6}$$

of two equations in two unknowns, we can use our knowledge of elementary geometry to sort out the possibilities for its solution set. Let L_1 and L_2 denote the straight line graphs of the two equations in (6). Then exactly one of the following situations must hold.

- The lines L_1 and L_2 intersect at a single point (as in Figure 3.1.1).
- The lines L_1 and L_2 are parallel nonintersecting lines (as in Figure 3.1.2).
- The lines L_1 and L_2 coincide—they actually are the same line (see Figure 3.1.3).

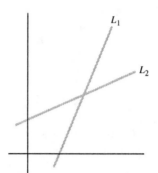

FIGURE 3.1.1. Two intersecting lines: a unique solution.

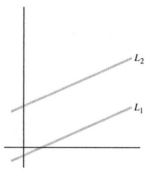

FIGURE 3.1.2. Two parallel lines: no solution.

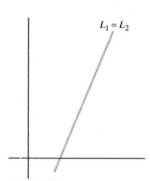

FIGURE 3.1.3. Two coincident lines: infinitely many solutions.

A pair (x, y) of real numbers constitutes a solution of the system in (6) if and only if the point (x, y) in the coordinate plane lies on *both* the two lines L_1 and L_2. In the case shown in Figure 3.1.1, there is exactly one such point. In the case shown in Figure 3.1.2, there is no such point, and in the case in Figure 3.1.3, there are infinitely many such points—every point on the line $L_1 = L_2$ is such a point. We therefore see that there are just *three possibilities* for a linear system of two equations in two unknowns: It has either

- exactly one solution;
- no solution; or
- infinitely many solutions.

It is a fundamental fact of linear algebra (which we will establish in Section 3.3) that, however many equations and variables may appear in a linear system, precisely these same three possibilities occur: A system of m linear equations in n variables either has a **unique** solution (that is, exactly one solution), or it has no solution, or it has infinitely many solutions. Thus it is impossible, for instance, for a linear system to have exactly 2 solutions or to have exactly 17 solutions.

The Method of Elimination

The next three examples illustrate how we can use the elementary method of elimination to solve a system of two equations in two unknowns. To **solve** a system means to determine what its solution set is. The basic idea of the method is this: First, we add an appropriate constant multiple of the first equation to the second equation. The idea is to choose the constant in such a way as to eliminate the variable x from the second equation. Next, the new second equation contains only the variable y, so we readily solve it for the value of y. Finally, we determine the value of x by substitution of this value of y in the first equation.

Example 3   In order to solve the system

$$5x + 3y = 1$$
$$x - 2y = 8, \tag{7}$$

we first interchange the two equations:

$$x - 2y = 8$$
$$5x + 3y = 1.$$

Then we multiply the first equation by -5 and add the resulting terms to the second (without changing the first equation). The result is

$$x - 2y = \quad 8$$
$$13y = -39. \tag{8}$$

Now the second equation immediately yields the value $y = -3$, and *back substitution* of this value in the first equation yields

$$x = 2y + 8 = 2(-3) + 8 = 2.$$

Taking it as obvious (for the moment) that the systems in (7) and (8) have the same solution set, we conclude that the original system in (7) has the *unique solution* $x = 2$, $y = -3$.   ■

Example 4   To solve the system

$$2x + 6y = \quad 4$$
$$3x + 9y = 11, \tag{9}$$

we first multiply the first equation by $\frac{1}{2}$ and get

$$x + 3y = \quad 2$$
$$3x + 9y = 11.$$

We next multiply the first equation by -3 and add each term to the corresponding term in the second equation. The result is

$$x + 3y = 2$$
$$0 = 5. \tag{10}$$

What, however, are we to make of the new second equation, $0 = 5$? The system in (10) actually is

$$x + 3y = 2$$
$$0x + 0y = 5.$$

Because 0 is simply not equal to 5, there are *no* values of x and y that satisfy the second equation. Hence there certainly can be no values that satisfy both simultaneously. We conclude that the original system in (9) has *no solution*.   ■

Example 5   If, instead of the system in (9), we had begun in Example 4 with the system

$$2x + 6y = 4$$
$$3x + 9y = 6 \tag{11}$$

and performed the same operations, we would have obtained, instead of (10), the system

$$x + 3y = 2$$
$$0 = 0. \tag{12}$$

Here, $0 = 0$ is shorthand for the equation

$$0x + 0y = 0,$$

which is satisfied by *all* values of x and y. In terms of restrictions or conditions on x and y, one of our original two equations has in effect disappeared, leaving us with the single equation

$$x + 3y = 2. \tag{13}$$

Of course this is hardly surprising, because each equation in (11) is a multiple of the one in (13); in some sense we really had only one equation to begin with. At any rate, we can substitute any value of y we please in (13) and then solve for x. Thus our system in (11) has *infinitely many solutions*. To describe them explicitly, let us write $y = t$, where the **parameter** t is a new independent variable that we will use to generate solution pairs (x, y). Then Equation (13) yields $x = 2 - 3t$, so our infinite solution set of the system in (11) may be described as follows:

$$x = 2 - 3t, \quad y = t$$

as the arbitrary parameter t ranges over the set of all real numbers. For instance, $t = 2$ yields the solution $(-4, 2)$, and $t = -3$ yields the solution $(11, -3)$. ∎

COMMENT   These three examples illustrate the basic features of the method of elimination, which involves "transforming" a given linear system by means of a sequence of successive steps. Each of these steps consists of performing one of the following three **elementary operations**:

1. Multiply one equation by a nonzero constant.
2. Interchange two equations.
3. Add a constant multiple of (the terms of) one equation to (corresponding terms of) another equation.

In subsequent sections of this chapter we discuss the systematic use of these elementary operations to eliminate variables successively in any linear system, whatever the number of equations and variables. In this way we will see that every linear system corresponds to precisely one of the three situations illustrated in Examples 3–5. That is, either

- we discover (as in Example 3) a unique solution of the system; or
- we eventually arrive at an inconsistent equation (as in Example 4), so that the system has no solution; or
- we find that the original system has infinitely many solutions.

Three Equations in Three Unknowns

In the case of a system of three linear equations in three variables x, y, and z, we may proceed as follows: Assuming that the first equation involves x, use the first equation to eliminate x from the second and third equations by adding appropriate multiples of the first equation. Then, assuming that the new second equation involves y, use the new second equation to eliminate y from the new third equation. Solve the new third equation for z, back-substitute in the second equation to determine y, and, finally, back-substitute y and z in the first equation to find x. The following two examples illustrate this procedure.

| **Example 6** | Solve the linear system |

$$\begin{aligned} x + 2y + z &= 4 \\ 3x + 8y + 7z &= 20 \\ 2x + 7y + 9z &= 23. \end{aligned} \tag{14}$$

Solution First, we add -3 times the first equation to the second equation; the result is

$$\begin{aligned} x + 2y + z &= 4 \\ 2y + 4z &= 8 \\ 2x + 7y + 9z &= 23. \end{aligned}$$

Then addition of -2 times the first equation to the third equation yields

$$\begin{aligned} x + 2y + z &= 4 \\ 2y + 4z &= 8 \\ 3y + 7z &= 15. \end{aligned}$$

We have now eliminated x from the second and third equations. To simplify the process of eliminating y from the third equation, we multiply the second equation by $\frac{1}{2}$, to obtain

$$\begin{aligned} x + 2y + z &= 4 \\ y + 2z &= 4 \\ 3y + 7z &= 15. \end{aligned}$$

Finally, addition of -3 times the second equation to the third equation gives

$$\begin{aligned} x + 2y + z &= 4 \\ y + 2z &= 4 \\ z &= 3. \end{aligned} \tag{15}$$

This system has a *triangular* form that makes its solution easy. By back substitution of $z = 3$ in the second equation in (15), we find that

$$y = 4 - 2z = 4 - 2(3) = -2;$$

then the first equation yields

$$\begin{aligned} x &= 4 - 2y - z \\ &= 4 - 2(-2) - (3) = 5. \end{aligned}$$

Thus our original system in (14) has the unique solution $x = 5$, $y = -2$, $z = 3$. ∎

COMMENT   The steps by which we transformed (14) into (15) show that every solution of the system in (14) is a solution of the system in (15). But these steps can be reversed to show similarly that every solution of the system in (15) is also a solution of the system in (14). Thus the two systems are equivalent in the sense that they have the same solution set. The computation at the end of Example 6 shows that (15) has the unique solution $(x, y, z) = (5, -2, 3)$, and it follows that this also is the unique solution of the original system in (14).

Example 7   Solve the system

$$
\begin{aligned}
3x - 8y + 10z &= 22 \\
x - 3y + 2z &= 5 \\
2x - 9y - 8z &= -11.
\end{aligned}
\tag{16}
$$

Solution   In order to avoid fractions in the elimination of x, we first interchange the first two equations to get

$$
\begin{aligned}
x - 3y + 2z &= 5 \\
3x - 8y + 10z &= 22 \\
2x - 9y - 8z &= -11.
\end{aligned}
$$

Addition of -3 times the first equation to the second gives

$$
\begin{aligned}
x - 3y + 2z &= 5 \\
y + 4z &= 7 \\
2x - 9y - 8z &= -11,
\end{aligned}
$$

and then addition of -2 times the first equation to the third equation gives

$$
\begin{aligned}
x - 3y + 2z &= 5 \\
y + 4z &= 7 \\
-3y - 12z &= -21.
\end{aligned}
$$

Finally, addition of 3 times the second equation to the third equation yields

$$
\begin{aligned}
x - 3y + 2z &= 5 \\
y + 4z &= 7 \\
0 &= 0.
\end{aligned}
\tag{17}
$$

Because the third equation has disappeared, we can choose $z = t$ arbitrarily and then solve for x and y:

$$
\begin{aligned}
y &= 7 - 4z = 7 - 4t, \\
x &= 5 + 3y - 2z \\
&= 5 + 3(7 - 4t) - 2t = 26 - 14t.
\end{aligned}
$$

Thus our original system in (16) has infinitely many solutions. Moreover, one convenient way of describing them is this:

$$
x = 26 - 14t, \quad y = 7 - 4t, \quad z = t.
\tag{18}
$$

The arbitrary parameter t can take on all real number values, and in so doing generates all the (infinitely many) solutions of the original system in (16). Figure 3.1.4 shows the three planes corresponding to the three equations in (16). These planes intersect in a straight line that is parameterized by the equations in (18). ∎

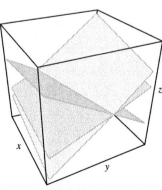

FIGURE 3.1.4. The three planes of Example 7.

A Differential Equations Application

In Chapter 1 we saw that a general solution of a first-order differential equation involves an arbitrary constant that must be determined in order to satisfy a given initial condition. The next example illustrates the fact that a general solution of a second-order differential equation typically involves *two* arbitrary constants. An initial value problem for such a differential equation ordinarily involves *two* initial conditions, whose imposition leads to a system of two equations with the two arbitrary constants as unknowns.

Example 8 If A and B are constants and

$$y(x) = Ae^{3x} + Be^{-3x}, \tag{19}$$

then differentiation yields

$$y'(x) = 3Ae^{3x} - 3Be^{-3x} \tag{20}$$

and

$$y''(x) = 9Ae^{3x} + 9Be^{-3x} = 9y(x).$$

Thus the function $y(x)$ defined by (19) satisfies the second-order differential equation

$$y'' - 9y = 0. \tag{21}$$

Now, suppose that we want to solve the initial value problem consisting of this equation and the two initial conditions

$$y(0) = 7, \quad y'(0) = 9. \tag{22}$$

Then substitution of $x = 0$ in (19) and (20) yields the linear system

$$\begin{aligned} A + \quad B &= 7 \\ 3A - 3B &= 9 \end{aligned}$$

that we readily solve for $A = 5$, $B = 2$. It follows that the particular function

$$y(x) = 5e^{3x} + 2e^{-3x}$$

satisfies both the differential equation (21) and the initial conditions in (22). ■

In Chapter 5 we will study higher-order differential equations and initial value problems in detail, after developing the necessary methods of linear algebra in the intervening chapters.

3.1 Problems

In each of Problems 1–22, use the method of elimination to determine whether the given linear system is consistent or inconsistent. For each consistent system, find the solution if it is unique; otherwise, describe the infinite solution set in terms of an arbitrary parameter t (as in Examples 5 and 7).

1. $x + 3y = 9$
$2x + y = 8$

2. $3x + 2y = 9$
$x - y = 8$

3. $2x + 3y = 1$
$3x + 5y = 3$

4. $5x - 6y = 1$
$6x - 5y = 10$

5. $x + 2y = 4$
$2x + 4y = 9$

6. $4x - 2y = 4$
$6x - 3y = 7$

7. $x - 4y = -10$
$-2x + 8y = 20$

8. $3x - 6y = 12$
$2x - 4y = 8$

9. $x + 5y + z = 2$
$2x + y - 2z = 1$
$x + 7y + 2z = 3$

10. $x + 3y + 2z = 2$
$2x + 7y + 7z = -1$
$2x + 5y + 2z = 7$

11. $2x + 7y + 3z = 11$
$x + 3y + 2z = 2$
$3x + 7y + 9z = -12$

12. $3x + 5y - z = 13$
$2x + 7y + z = 28$
$x + 7y + 2z = 32$

13. $3x + 9y + 7z = 0$
$2x + 7y + 4z = 0$
$2x + 6y + 5z = 0$

14. $4x + 9y + 12z = -1$
$3x + y + 16z = -46$
$2x + 7y + 3z = 19$

15. $x + 3y + 2z = 5$
$x - y + 3z = 3$
$3x + y + 8z = 10$

16. $x - 3y + 2z = 6$
$x + 4y - z = 4$
$5x + 6y + z = 20$

17. $2x - y + 4z = 7$
$3x + 2y - 2z = 3$
$5x + y + 2z = 15$

18. $x + 5y + 6z = 3$
$5x + 2y - 10z = 1$
$8x + 17y + 8z = 5$

19. $x - 2y + z = 2$
$2x - y - 4z = 13$
$x - y - z = 5$

20. $2x + 3y + 7z = 15$
$x + 4y + z = 20$
$x + 2y + 3z = 10$

21. $x + y - z = 5$
$3x + y + 3z = 11$
$4x + y + 5z = 14$

22. $4x - 2y + 6z = 0$
$x - y - z = 0$
$2x - y + 3z = 0$

In each of Problems 23–30, a second-order differential equation and its general solution y(x) are given. Determine the constants A and B so as to find a solution of the differential equation that satisfies the given initial conditions involving y(0) and y'(0).

23. $y'' + 4y = 0$, $y(x) = A\cos 2x + B\sin 2x$,
$y(0) = 3$, $y'(0) = 8$

24. $y'' - 9y = 0$, $y(x) = A\cosh 3x + B\sinh 3x$,
$y(0) = 5$, $y'(0) = 12$

25. $y'' - 25y = 0$, $y(x) = Ae^{5x} + Be^{-5x}$,
$y(0) = 10$, $y'(0) = 20$

26. $y'' - 121y = 0$, $y(x) = Ae^{11x} + Be^{-11x}$,
$y(0) = 44$, $y'(0) = 22$

27. $y'' + 2y' - 15y = 0$, $y(x) = Ae^{3x} + Be^{-5x}$,
$y(0) = 40$, $y'(0) = -16$

28. $y'' - 10y' + 21y = 0$, $y(x) = Ae^{3x} + Be^{7x}$,
$y(0) = 15$, $y'(0) = 13$

29. $6y'' - 5y' + y = 0$, $y(x) = Ae^{x/2} + Be^{x/3}$,
$y(0) = 7$, $y'(0) = 11$

30. $15y'' + y' - 28y = 0$, $y(x) = Ae^{4x/3} + Be^{-7x/5}$,
$y(0) = 41$, $y'(0) = 164$

31. A system of the form

$$a_1 x + b_1 y = 0$$
$$a_2 x + b_2 y = 0,$$

in which the constants on the right-hand side are all zero, is said to be **homogeneous**. Explain by geometric reasoning why such a system has either a unique solution or infinitely many solutions.

32. Consider the system

$$a_1 x + b_1 y + c_1 z = d_1$$
$$a_2 x + b_2 y + c_2 z = d_2$$

of two equations in three unknowns.

(a) Use the fact that the graph of each such equation is a plane in xyz-space to explain why such a system always has either no solution or infinitely many solutions.

(b) Explain why the system must have infinitely many solutions if $d_1 = 0 = d_2$.

33. The linear system

$$a_1 x + b_1 y = c_1$$
$$a_2 x + b_2 y = c_2$$
$$a_3 x + b_3 y = c_3$$

of three equations in two unknowns represents three lines L_1, L_2, and L_3 in the xy-plane. Figure 3.1.5 shows six possible configurations of these three lines. In each case describe the solution set of the system.

34. Consider the linear system

$$a_1 x + b_1 y + c_1 z = d_1$$
$$a_2 x + b_2 y + c_2 z = d_2$$
$$a_3 x + b_3 y + c_3 z = d_3$$

of three equations in three unknowns to represent three planes P_1, P_2, and P_3 in xyz-space. Describe the solution set of the system in each of the following cases.

(a) The three planes are parallel and distinct.

(b) The three planes coincide—$P_1 = P_2 = P_3$.

(c) P_1 and P_2 coincide and are parallel to P_3.

(d) P_1 and P_2 intersect in a line L that is parallel to P_3.

(e) P_1 and P_2 intersect in a line L that lies in P_3.

(f) P_1 and P_2 intersect in a line L that intersects P_3 in a single point.

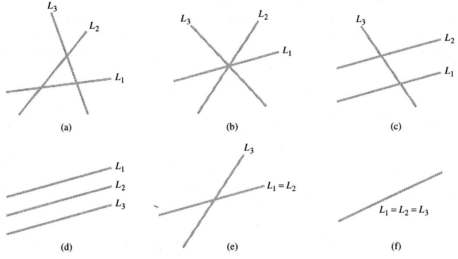

FIGURE 3.1.5. Three lines in the plane (Problem 33).

3.2 Matrices and Gaussian Elimination

In Example 6 of Section 3.1 we applied the method of elimination to solve the linear system

$$1x + 2y + 1z = 4$$
$$3x + 8y + 7z = 20 \tag{1}$$
$$2x + 7y + 9z = 23.$$

There we employed elementary operations to transform this system into the equivalent system

$$1x + 2y + 1z = 4$$
$$0x + 1y + 2z = 4 \tag{2}$$
$$0x + 0y + 1z = 3,$$

which we found easy to solve by back substitution. Here we have printed in color the coefficients and constants (including the 0s and 1s that would normally be omitted) because everything else—the symbols x, y, and z for the variables and the $+$ and $=$ signs—is excess baggage that means only extra writing, for we can keep track of these symbols mentally. In effect, in Example 6 we used an appropriate sequence of operations to transform the array

$$\begin{bmatrix} 1 & 2 & 1 & 4 \\ 3 & 8 & 7 & 20 \\ 2 & 7 & 9 & 23 \end{bmatrix} \tag{3}$$

of coefficients and constants in (1) into the array

$$\begin{bmatrix} 1 & 2 & 1 & 4 \\ 0 & 1 & 2 & 4 \\ 0 & 0 & 1 & 3 \end{bmatrix} \tag{4}$$

of constants and coefficients in (2).

Rectangular arrays of numbers like those in (3) and (4) are called *matrices*. Thus, a **matrix** is simply a rectangular array of numbers, which are called the **entries** or **elements** of the matrix. The **size**, or **shape**, of a matrix is specified by telling how many horizontal **rows** and vertical **columns** it has. Each matrix in (3) and (4) has three rows and four columns; therefore, each is a 3×4 (read "three by four") matrix. We *always* specify *first* the number of rows and *then* the number of columns.

Example 1   The matrices

$$
\begin{bmatrix} 3 & -7 \\ -2 & 5 \end{bmatrix}
\qquad
\begin{bmatrix} 3 & 0 & -1 & 5 \end{bmatrix}
\qquad
\begin{bmatrix} 2 \\ 0 \\ -3 \end{bmatrix}
$$

have sizes 2×2, 1×4, and 3×1, respectively.   ∎

Coefficient Matrices

A general system of m linear equations in the n variables $x_1, x_2, \ldots, x_n$ may be written in the form

$$
\begin{aligned}
a_{11}x_1 + a_{12}x_2 + a_{13}x_3 + \cdots + a_{1n}x_n &= b_1 \\
a_{21}x_1 + a_{22}x_2 + a_{23}x_3 + \cdots + a_{2n}x_n &= b_2 \\
&\vdots \\
a_{m1}x_1 + a_{m2}x_2 + a_{m3}x_3 + \cdots + a_{mn}x_n &= b_m.
\end{aligned}
\tag{5}
$$

Observe that a_{ij} denotes the (constant) coefficient in the ith equation of the jth variable x_j and that b_i denotes the constant on the right-hand side in the ith equation. Thus the first subscript i refers to the equation and the second subscript j to the variable. For instance, a_{32} denotes the coefficient of x_2 in the 3rd equation. This scheme of systematic double subscripts enables us to specify readily the location of each coefficient in a system with many equations and variables. It also helps us get rid of the excess baggage in (5) by focusing our attention on the coefficients.

The **coefficient matrix** of the linear system in (5) is the $m \times n$ matrix

$$
\mathbf{A} = \begin{bmatrix}
a_{11} & a_{12} & a_{13} & \cdots & a_{1n} \\
a_{21} & a_{22} & a_{23} & \cdots & a_{2n} \\
\vdots & \vdots & \vdots & \ddots & \vdots \\
a_{m1} & a_{m2} & a_{m3} & \cdots & a_{mn}
\end{bmatrix}.
\tag{6}
$$

We will use **boldface** capital letters to denote matrices and lowercase letters to denote numbers. When we want to refer more briefly to the matrix $\mathbf{A}$ and its entries, we can write

$$
\mathbf{A} = \begin{bmatrix} a_{ij} \end{bmatrix}.
\tag{7}
$$

The first subscript i specifies the row and the second subscript j the column of $\mathbf{A}$ in which the element a_{ij} appears:

First subscript	Second subscript
Row	Column

Although double subscripts may seem tedious when first encountered, their usefulness should not be underestimated. For instance, they are consistent with the notation used in most programming languages. Many practical applications lead to linear systems with hundreds or even thousands of variables and equations. In a typical computer system, the coefficient matrix $\mathbf{A}$ of such a system would be represented by a two-dimensional array in which $A(i, j)$ denotes a_{ij}. With this approach, the computer can store a 100×100 matrix in the same way that it stores a 3×3 matrix.

The matrices in (3) and (4) include not only the coefficients but also the constants on the right-hand sides in the corresponding linear systems in (1) and (2). Let us write

$$\mathbf{b} = \begin{bmatrix} b_1 \\ b_2 \\ \vdots \\ b_m \end{bmatrix} \tag{8}$$

for the column of constants in the general system in (5). An $m \times 1$ matrix—that is, one with a single column—is often called a **(column) vector** and is denoted by a boldface letter. When we adjoin the constant vector $\mathbf{b}$ to the coefficient matrix $\mathbf{A}$ (as a final column), we get the matrix

$$\begin{bmatrix} \mathbf{A} & \mathbf{b} \end{bmatrix} = \begin{bmatrix} a_{11} & a_{12} & \cdots & a_{1n} & b_1 \\ a_{21} & a_{22} & \cdots & a_{2n} & b_2 \\ \vdots & \vdots & \ddots & \vdots & \vdots \\ a_{m1} & a_{m2} & \cdots & a_{mn} & b_m \end{bmatrix}. \tag{9}$$

This $m \times (n + 1)$ matrix is called the **augmented coefficient matrix**, or simply the augmented matrix, of the $m \times n$ system in (5).

Although it takes a good deal of notation to describe the augmented matrix of a *general* linear system, it is a very simple matter to write the augmented matrix of a *particular* system. If the system is written in chalk on a blackboard with the variables in the same order in each equation, we merely erase all the x_j's and the plus and equal signs (retaining a minus sign for each negative coefficient) and insert a zero in each spot where a variable is missing in an equation.

| Example 2 | The augmented coefficient matrix of the system |

$$\begin{aligned} 2x_1 + 3x_2 - 7x_3 + 4x_4 &= 6 \\ x_2 + 3x_3 - 5x_4 &= 0 \\ -x_1 + 2x_2 \qquad\quad - 9x_4 &= 17 \end{aligned}$$

of three equations in four variables is the 3×5 matrix

$$\begin{bmatrix} 2 & 3 & -7 & 4 & 6 \\ 0 & 1 & 3 & -5 & 0 \\ -1 & 2 & 0 & -9 & 17 \end{bmatrix}.$$

∎

Elementary Row Operations

In Section 3.1 we described the three elementary operations that are used in the method of elimination. To each of these corresponds an *elementary row operation* on the augmented matrix of the system. For instance, when we interchange two equations in the system, we interchange the corresponding two rows of its augmented coefficient matrix.

Definition: Elementary Row Operations

The following are the three types of **elementary row operations** on the matrix **A**:

1. Multiply any (single) row of **A** by a nonzero constant.

2. Interchange two rows of **A**.

3. Add a constant multiple of one row of **A** to another row.

Figure 3.2.1 shows notation that we use to describe elementary row operations briefly. For instance,

$$\begin{bmatrix} 1 & 2 \\ 3 & 4 \end{bmatrix} \xrightarrow{\;(3)R_1 + R_2\;} \begin{bmatrix} 1 & 2 \\ 6 & 10 \end{bmatrix} \tag{10}$$

shows the result of adding 3 times row 1 to row 2. Note that, when we perform the operation $(c)R_p + R_q$ on a matrix, adding c times row p to row q, row p itself remains unchanged.

Type	Row Operation	Notation
1	Multiply row p by c	cR_p
2	Interchange row p and row q	$\text{SWAP}(R_p, R_q)$
3	Add c times row p to row q	$(c)R_p + R_q$

FIGURE 3.2.1. Notation for elementary row operations.

Example 3 To solve the system

$$\begin{aligned} x_1 + 2x_2 + x_3 &= 4 \\ 3x_1 + 8x_2 + 7x_3 &= 20 \\ 2x_1 + 7x_2 + 9x_3 &= 23, \end{aligned} \tag{11}$$

whose augmented coefficient matrix is exhibited in (3), we carry out the following sequence of elementary row operations, corresponding to the steps in the solution of Example 6 in Section 3.1:

$$\begin{bmatrix} 1 & 2 & 1 & 4 \\ 3 & 8 & 7 & 20 \\ 2 & 7 & 9 & 23 \end{bmatrix} \tag{12}$$

$$\xrightarrow{\;(-3)R_1 + R_2\;} \begin{bmatrix} 1 & 2 & 1 & 4 \\ 0 & 2 & 4 & 8 \\ 2 & 7 & 9 & 23 \end{bmatrix}$$

$$\xrightarrow{\ (-2)R_1 + R_3\ } \begin{bmatrix} 1 & 2 & 1 & 4 \\ 0 & 2 & 4 & 8 \\ 0 & 3 & 7 & 15 \end{bmatrix}$$

$$\xrightarrow{\ \left(\frac{1}{2}\right)R_2\ } \begin{bmatrix} 1 & 2 & 1 & 4 \\ 0 & 1 & 2 & 4 \\ 0 & 3 & 7 & 15 \end{bmatrix}$$

$$\xrightarrow{\ (-3)R_2 + R_3\ } \begin{bmatrix} 1 & 2 & 1 & 4 \\ 0 & 1 & 2 & 4 \\ 0 & 0 & 1 & 3 \end{bmatrix}. \tag{13}$$

The final matrix here is the augmented coefficient matrix of the system

$$\begin{aligned} x_1 + 2x_2 + \ x_3 &= 4 \\ x_2 + 2x_3 &= 4. \\ x_3 &= 3 \end{aligned} \tag{14}$$

whose unique solution (readily found by back substitution) is $x_1 = 5$, $x_2 = -2$, $x_3 = 3$. ∎

It is not quite self-evident that a sequence of elementary row operations produces a linear system having the same solution set as the original system. To state the pertinent result concisely, we need the following definition.

Definition: Row-Equivalent Matrices

Two matrices are called **row equivalent** if one can be obtained from the other by a (finite) sequence of elementary row operations.

Thus the two matrices in (10) are row equivalent, as are the two matrices in (12) and (13). In Problem 29 we ask you to show that if **B** can be obtained from **A** by elementary row operations, then **A** can be obtained from **B** by elementary row operations. This follows from the observation that row operations are "reversible." In Problem 30 we suggest a proof of the following theorem.

THEOREM 1: Equivalent Systems and Equivalent Matrices

If the augmented coefficient matrices of two linear systems are row equivalent, then the two systems have the same solution set.   ▲

Thus, the linear systems in (11) and (14) have the same solution set, because their augmented matrices in (12) and (13) are row equivalent.

Echelon Matrices

Up to this point we have been somewhat informal in our description of the method of elimination. Its objective is to transform a given linear system, by elementary row operations, into one for which back substitution leads easily and routinely to a solution. The following definition tells what should be the appearance of the augmented coefficient matrix of the transformed system.

> **Definition: Echelon Matrix**
>
> The matrix **E** is called an **echelon matrix** provided it has the following two properties:
>
> 1. Every row of **E** that consists entirely of zeros (if any) lies *beneath* every row that contains a nonzero element.
> 2. In each row of **E** that contains a nonzero element, the *first* nonzero element lies strictly to the *right* of the first nonzero element in the preceding row (if there is a preceding row).

Echelon matrices are sometimes called *row-echelon matrices*. Property 1 says that if **E** has any all-zero rows, then they are grouped together at the bottom of the matrix. The first (from the left) *nonzero* element in each of the other rows is called its **leading entry**. Property 2 says that the leading entries form a "descending staircase" pattern from upper left to lower right, as in the following echelon matrix.

$$\mathbf{E} = \begin{bmatrix} 2 & -1 & 0 & 4 & 7 \\ 0 & 1 & 2 & 0 & -5 \\ 0 & 0 & 0 & 3 & 0 \\ 0 & 0 & 0 & 0 & 0 \end{bmatrix}$$

Here we have highlighted the leading entries and indicated the descending staircase pattern.

The following list exhibits *all* possibilities for the form of a 3×3 echelon matrix, with asterisks denoting the (nonzero) leading entries; a # denotes an element that may be either zero or nonzero.

$$\begin{bmatrix} * & \# & \# \\ 0 & * & \# \\ 0 & 0 & * \end{bmatrix} \quad \begin{bmatrix} 0 & 0 & 0 \\ 0 & 0 & 0 \\ 0 & 0 & 0 \end{bmatrix}$$

$$\begin{bmatrix} * & \# & \# \\ 0 & * & \# \\ 0 & 0 & 0 \end{bmatrix} \quad \begin{bmatrix} * & \# & \# \\ 0 & 0 & * \\ 0 & 0 & 0 \end{bmatrix} \quad \begin{bmatrix} 0 & * & \# \\ 0 & 0 & * \\ 0 & 0 & 0 \end{bmatrix}$$

$$\begin{bmatrix} * & \# & \# \\ 0 & 0 & 0 \\ 0 & 0 & 0 \end{bmatrix} \quad \begin{bmatrix} 0 & * & \# \\ 0 & 0 & 0 \\ 0 & 0 & 0 \end{bmatrix} \quad \begin{bmatrix} 0 & 0 & * \\ 0 & 0 & 0 \\ 0 & 0 & 0 \end{bmatrix}$$

It follows from Properties 1 and 2 that the elements *beneath* any leading entry in the same column are all zero. The matrices

$$\mathbf{A} = \begin{bmatrix} 1 & 3 & -2 \\ 0 & 0 & 0 \\ 0 & 1 & 5 \end{bmatrix} \quad \text{and} \quad \mathbf{B} = \begin{bmatrix} 0 & 1 & 5 \\ 1 & 3 & -2 \\ 0 & 0 & 0 \end{bmatrix}$$

are not echelon matrices because **A** does not have Property 1 and **B** does not have Property 2.

Suppose that a linear system is in **echelon form**—its augmented matrix is an echelon matrix. Then those variables that correspond to *columns* containing leading entries are called **leading variables**; all the other variables are called **free variables**.

The following algorithm describes the process of **back substitution** to solve such a system.

ALGORITHM: Back Substitution

To solve a consistent linear system in echelon form by back substitution, carry out the following steps.

1. Set each free variable equal to an arbitrary parameter (a different parameter for each free variable).
2. Solve the *final* (nonzero) equation for its leading variable.
3. Substitute the result in the next-to-last equation and then solve for its leading variable.
4. Continuing in this fashion, work upward through the system of equations until all variables have been determined. ▲

Example 4 The augmented coefficient matrix of the system

$$
\begin{aligned}
x_1 - 2x_2 + 3x_3 + 2x_4 + \; x_5 &= 10 \\
x_3 \qquad\quad + 2x_5 &= -3 \\
x_4 - 4x_5 &= \;\; 7
\end{aligned} \tag{15}
$$

is the echelon matrix

$$
\begin{bmatrix}
1 & -2 & 3 & 2 & 1 & 10 \\
0 & 0 & 1 & 0 & 2 & -3 \\
0 & 0 & 0 & 1 & -4 & 7
\end{bmatrix}. \tag{16}
$$

The leading entries are in the first, third, and fourth columns. Hence x_1, x_3, and x_4 are the leading variables and x_2 and x_5 are the free variables. To solve the system by back substitution, we first write

$$
x_2 = s, \quad x_5 = t, \tag{17a}
$$

where s and t are arbitrary parameters. Then the third equation in (15) gives

$$
x_4 = 7 + 4x_5 = 7 + 4t; \tag{17b}
$$

the second equation gives

$$
x_3 = -3 - 2x_5 = -3 - 2t; \tag{17c}
$$

finally, the first equation in (15) yields

$$
\begin{aligned}
x_1 &= 10 + 2x_2 - 3x_3 - 2x_4 - x_5 \\
&= 10 + 2s - 3(-3 - 2t) - 2(7 + 4t) - t.
\end{aligned}
$$

Therefore

$$
x_1 = 5 + 2s - 3t. \tag{17d}
$$

Thus the system in (15) has an infinite solution set consisting of all $(x_1, x_2, x_3, x_4, x_5)$ given in terms of the two parameters s and t as follows:

$$x_1 = 5 + 2s - 3t$$
$$x_2 = s$$
$$x_3 = -3 - 2t$$
$$x_4 = 7 + 4t$$
$$x_5 = t.$$

For instance, with $s = 2$ and $t = 1$ we get the solution $x_1 = 6$, $x_2 = 2$, $x_3 = -5$, $x_4 = 11$, and $x_5 = 1$. ∎

Gaussian Elimination

Because we can use back substitution to solve any linear system already in echelon form, it remains only to establish that we can transform any matrix (using elementary row operations) into an echelon matrix. The procedure that we have already illustrated in several examples is known as **Gaussian elimination**. The following systematic description of the procedure makes it clear that it succeeds with *any* given matrix **A**.

ALGORITHM: Gaussian Elimination

1. Locate the first column of **A** that contains a nonzero element.
2. If the first (top) entry in this column is zero, interchange the first row of **A** with a row in which the corresponding entry is nonzero.
3. Now the first entry in our column is nonzero. Replace the entries below it in the same column with zeros by adding appropriate multiples of the first row of **A** to lower rows.
4. After Steps 1–3, the matrix looks like the matrix below, although there may be several initial columns of zeros or even none at all. Perform Steps 1–3 on the indicated lower right matrix $\mathbf{A}_1$.
5. Repeat this cycle of steps until an echelon matrix is obtained.

$$\mathbf{A} = \begin{bmatrix} 0 & * & \# & \# & \cdots & \# \\ 0 & 0 & & & & \\ 0 & 0 & & \mathbf{A}_1 & & \\ \vdots & \vdots & & & & \\ 0 & 0 & & & & \end{bmatrix} \qquad \blacktriangle$$

In brief, we work on the matrix **A** one column at a time, from left to right. In each column containing a leading entry (perhaps after a row interchange), we "clear out" the nonzero elements below it and then move on to the next column.

Example 5   To solve the system

$$\begin{aligned} x_1 - 2x_2 + 3x_3 + 2x_4 + x_5 &= 10 \\ 2x_1 - 4x_2 + 8x_3 + 3x_4 + 10x_5 &= 7 \\ 3x_1 - 6x_2 + 10x_3 + 6x_4 + 5x_5 &= 27, \end{aligned} \qquad (18)$$

we reduce its augmented coefficient matrix to echelon form as follows.

$$\begin{bmatrix} 1 & -2 & 3 & 2 & 1 & 10 \\ 2 & -4 & 8 & 3 & 10 & 7 \\ 3 & -6 & 10 & 6 & 5 & 27 \end{bmatrix}$$

$$\xrightarrow{\;(-2)R_1 + R_2\;} \begin{bmatrix} 1 & -2 & 3 & 2 & 1 & 10 \\ 0 & 0 & 2 & -1 & 8 & -13 \\ 3 & -6 & 10 & 6 & 5 & 27 \end{bmatrix}$$

$$\xrightarrow{\;(-3)R_1 + R_3\;} \begin{bmatrix} 1 & -2 & 3 & 2 & 1 & 10 \\ 0 & 0 & 2 & -1 & 8 & -13 \\ 0 & 0 & 1 & 0 & 2 & -3 \end{bmatrix}$$

$$\xrightarrow{\;\text{SWAP}(R_2, R_3)\;} \begin{bmatrix} 1 & -2 & 3 & 2 & 1 & 10 \\ 0 & 0 & 1 & 0 & 2 & -3 \\ 0 & 0 & 2 & -1 & 8 & -13 \end{bmatrix}$$

$$\xrightarrow{\;(-2)R_2 + R_3\;} \begin{bmatrix} 1 & -2 & 3 & 2 & 1 & 10 \\ 0 & 0 & 1 & 0 & 2 & -3 \\ 0 & 0 & 0 & -1 & 4 & -7 \end{bmatrix}$$

$$\xrightarrow{\;(-1)R_3\;} \begin{bmatrix} 1 & -2 & 3 & 2 & 1 & 10 \\ 0 & 0 & 1 & 0 & 2 & -3 \\ 0 & 0 & 0 & 1 & -4 & 7 \end{bmatrix}$$

Our final result is the echelon matrix in (16), so by Eqs. (17a)–(17d) in Example 4, the infinite solution set of the system in (18) is described in terms of arbitrary parameters s and t as follows:

$$\begin{aligned} x_1 &= 5 + 2s - 3t \\ x_2 &= s \\ x_3 &= -3 - 2t \\ x_4 &= 7 + 4t \\ x_5 &= t. \end{aligned} \qquad (19)$$

Thus, the substitution of any two specific values for s and t in (19) yields a particular solution $(x_1, x_2, x_3, x_4, x_5)$ of the system, and each of the system's infinitely many different solutions is the result of some such substitution. ∎

Examples 3 and 5 illustrate the ways in which Gaussian elimination can result in either a unique solution or infinitely many solutions. If the reduction of the augmented matrix to echelon form leads to a row of the form

$$0 \quad 0 \quad \cdots \quad 0 \quad 0 \quad *,$$

where the asterisk denotes a nonzero entry in the last column, then we have an inconsistent equation,

$$0x_1 + 0x_2 + \cdots + 0x_n = *,$$

and therefore the system has no solution.

Remark: We use algorithms such as the back substitution and Gaussian elimination algorithms of this section to outline the basic computational procedures of linear algebra. In modern numerical work, these procedures often are implemented on a computer. For instance, linear systems of more than four equations are usually solved in practice by using a computer to carry out the process of Gaussian elimination.

3.2 Problems

The linear systems in Problems 1–10 are in echelon form. Solve each by back substitution.

1. $x_1 + x_2 + 2x_3 = 5$
$\quad x_2 + 3x_3 = 6$
$\quad\quad x_3 = 2$

2. $2x_1 - 5x_2 + x_3 = 2$
$\quad 3x_2 - 2x_3 = 9$
$\quad\quad x_3 = -3$

3. $x_1 - 3x_2 + 4x_3 = 7$
$\quad x_2 - 5x_3 = 2$

4. $x_1 - 5x_2 + 2x_3 = 10$
$\quad x_2 - 7x_3 = 5$

5. $x_1 + x_2 - 2x_3 + x_4 = 9$
$\quad x_2 - x_3 + 2x_4 = 1$
$\quad\quad x_3 - 3x_4 = 5$

6. $x_1 - 2x_2 + 5x_3 - 3x_4 = 7$
$\quad x_2 - 3x_3 + 2x_4 = 3$
$\quad\quad x_4 = -4$

7. $x_1 + 2x_2 + 4x_3 - 5x_4 = 17$
$\quad x_2 - 2x_3 + 7x_4 = 7$

8. $x_1 - 10x_2 + 3x_3 - 13x_4 = 5$
$\quad x_3 + 3x_4 = 10$

9. $2x_1 + x_2 + x_3 + x_4 = 6$
$\quad 3x_2 - x_3 - 2x_4 = 2$
$\quad\quad 3x_3 + 4x_4 = 9$
$\quad\quad\quad x_4 = 6$

10. $x_1 - 5x_2 + 2x_3 - 7x_4 + 11x_5 = 0$
$\quad x_2 - 13x_3 + 3x_4 - 7x_5 = 0$
$\quad\quad x_4 - 5x_5 = 0$

In Problems 11–22, use elementary row operations to transform each augmented coefficient matrix to echelon form. Then solve the system by back substitution.

11. $2x_1 + 8x_2 + 3x_3 = 2$
$\quad x_1 + 3x_2 + 2x_3 = 5$
$\quad 2x_1 + 7x_2 + 4x_3 = 8$

12. $3x_1 + x_2 - 3x_3 = 6$
$\quad 2x_1 + 7x_2 + x_3 = -9$
$\quad 2x_1 + 5x_2 = -5$

13. $x_1 + 3x_2 + 3x_3 = 13$
$\quad 2x_1 + 5x_2 + 4x_3 = 23$
$\quad 2x_1 + 7x_2 + 8x_3 = 29$

14. $3x_1 - 6x_2 - 2x_3 = 1$
$\quad 2x_1 - 4x_2 + x_3 = 17$
$\quad x_1 - 2x_2 - 2x_3 = -9$

15. $3x_1 + x_2 - 3x_3 = -4$
$\quad x_1 + x_2 + x_3 = 1$
$\quad 5x_1 + 6x_2 + 8x_3 = 8$

16. $2x_1 + 5x_2 + 12x_3 = 6$
$\quad 3x_1 + x_2 + 5x_3 = 12$
$\quad 5x_1 + 8x_2 + 21x_3 = 17$

17. $x_1 - 4x_2 - 3x_3 - 3x_4 = 4$
$\quad 2x_1 - 6x_2 - 5x_3 - 5x_4 = 5$
$\quad 3x_1 - x_2 - 4x_3 - 5x_4 = -7$

18. $3x_1 - 6x_2 + x_3 + 13x_4 = 15$
$\quad 3x_1 - 6x_2 + 3x_3 + 21x_4 = 21$
$\quad 2x_1 - 4x_2 + 5x_3 + 26x_4 = 23$

19. $3x_1 + x_2 + x_3 + 6x_4 = 14$
$\quad x_1 - 2x_2 + 5x_3 - 5x_4 = -7$
$\quad 4x_1 + x_2 + 2x_3 + 7x_4 = 17$

20. $2x_1 + 4x_2 - x_3 - 2x_4 + 2x_5 = 6$
$\quad x_1 + 3x_2 + 2x_3 - 7x_4 + 3x_5 = 9$
$\quad 5x_1 + 8x_2 - 7x_3 + 6x_4 + x_5 = 4$

21. $x_1 + x_2 + x_3 = 6$
$\quad 2x_1 - 2x_2 - 5x_3 = -13$
$\quad 3x_1 + x_3 + x_4 = 13$
$\quad 4x_1 - 2x_2 - 3x_3 + x_4 = 1$

22. $4x_1 - 2x_2 - 3x_3 + x_4 = 3$
$\quad 2x_1 - 2x_2 - 5x_3 = -10$
$\quad 4x_1 + x_2 + 2x_3 + x_4 = 17$
$\quad 3x_1 + x_3 + x_4 = 12$

In Problems 23–27, determine for what values of k each system has (a) a unique solution; (b) no solution; (c) infinitely many solutions.

23. $3x + 2y = 1$
$\quad 6x + 4y = k$

24. $3x + 2y = 0$
$\quad 6x + ky = 0$

25. $3x + 2y = 11$
$\quad 6x + ky = 21$

26. $3x + 2y = 1$
$\quad 7x + 5y = k$

27. $x + 2y + z = 3$
$\quad 2x - y - 3z = 5$
$\quad 4x + 3y - z = k$

28. Under what condition on the constants a, b, and c does the system

$$2x - y + 3z = a$$
$$x + 2y + z = b$$
$$7x + 4y + 9z = c$$

have a unique solution? No solution? Infinitely many solutions?

29. This problem deals with the reversibility of elementary row operations.

(a) If the elementary row operation cR_p changes the matrix **A** to the matrix **B**, show that $(1/c)R_p$ changes **B** to **A**.

(b) If $\text{SWAP}(R_p, R_q)$ changes **A** to **B**, show that $\text{SWAP}(R_p, R_q)$ also changes **B** to **A**.

(c) If $cR_p + R_q$ changes **A** to **B**, show that $(-c)R_p + R_q$ changes **B** to **A**.

(d) Conclude that if **A** can be transformed into **B** by a finite sequence of elementary row operations, then **B** can similarly be transformed into **A**.

30. This problem outlines a proof that two linear systems LS_1 and LS_2 are equivalent (that is, have the same solution set) if their augmented coefficient matrices $\mathbf{A}_1$ and $\mathbf{A}_2$ are row equivalent.

(a) If a *single* elementary row operation transforms $\mathbf{A}_1$ to $\mathbf{A}_2$, show directly—considering separately the three

cases—that every solution of LS_1 is also a solution of LS_2.

(b) Explain why it now follows from Problem 29 that every solution of either system is also a solution of the other system; thus the two systems have the same solution set.

3.2 Application: Automated Row Operations

Computer algebra systems are often used to ease the labor of matrix computations, including elementary row operations. The 3×4 augmented coefficient matrix of Example 3 can be entered with the *Maple* command

```
with(linalg):
A := array( [[1, 2, 1,  4],
             [3, 8, 7, 20],
             [2, 7, 9, 23]] );
```

or the *Mathematica* command

```
A = {{1, 2, 1,  4},
     {3, 8, 7, 20},
     {2, 7, 9, 23}}
```

or the MATLAB command

```
A = [1 2 1  4
     3 8 7 20
     2 7 9 23]
```

The *Maple* **linalg** package has built-in elementary row operations that can be used to carry out the reduction of **A** exhibited in Example 3, as follows:

```
A := addrow(A,1,2,-3);        # (-3)R1 + R2
A := addrow(A,1,3,-2);        # (-2)R1 + R3
A := mulrow(A,2,1/2);         # (1/2)R2
A := addrow(A,2,3,-3);        # (-3)R2 + R3
```

The inserted remarks, which follow the notation of Fig. 3.2.1, should make clear the structure of these row operations in *Maple*.

In *Mathematica* the ith row of the matrix **A** is denoted by **A[[i]]**, and we can operate directly on rows to carry out the reduction of Example 3, as follows:

```
A[[2]] = (-3)A[[1]] + A[[2]];     (*  (-3)R1 + R2  *)
A[[3]] = (-2)A[[1]] + A[[3]];     (*  (-2)R1 + R3  *)
A[[2]] = (1/2)A[[2]];             (*    (1/2)R2    *)
A[[3]] = (-3)A[[2]] + A[[3]];     (*  (-3)R2 + R3  *)
```

In MATLAB, the ith row of the matrix **A** is denoted by **A(i,:)**, and we can operate similarly on rows to carry out the reduction to echelon form, as follows:

```
A(2,:) = (-3)*A(1,:) + A(2,:)     %  (-3)R1 + R2
A(3,:) = (-2)*A(1,:) + A(3,:)     %  (-2)R1 + R3
A(2,:) = (1/2)*A(2,:)             %    (1/2)R2
A(3,:) = (-3)*A(2,:) + A(3,:)     %  (-3)R2 + R3
```

You should verify (by using the computer algebra system of your choice) that these operations yield the echelon matrix

$$\begin{bmatrix} 1 & 2 & 1 & 4 \\ 0 & 1 & 2 & 4 \\ 0 & 0 & 1 & 3 \end{bmatrix}.$$

If you wanted to interchange the 1st and 3rd rows—and proceed to solve the corresponding system by "forward substitution" rather than back substitution—this could be done as follows:

`A := swaprow(A,1,3);`	(Maple)
`A[[{1,3}]] = A[[{3,1}]];`	(Mathematica)
`A([1 3],:) = A([3 1],:)`	(MATLAB)

These "automated" elementary row operations can be used in Problems 11–22 of this section.

3.3 Reduced Row-Echelon Matrices

The result of the process of Gaussian elimination described in Section 3.2 is not uniquely determined. That is, two different sequences of elementary row operations, both starting with the same matrix **A**, may yield two different echelon matrices, each of course still row equivalent to **A**. For instance, the two echelon matrices

$$\begin{bmatrix} 1 & 2 & 3 \\ 0 & 4 & 5 \\ 0 & 0 & 6 \end{bmatrix} \quad \text{and} \quad \begin{bmatrix} 1 & 1 & 1 \\ 0 & 2 & 2 \\ 0 & 0 & 3 \end{bmatrix} \tag{1}$$

are readily seen (as in Problem 31) to be row equivalent. Hence it is possible to begin with an appropriate 3×3 matrix and derive by Gaussian elimination either of the two different echelon matrices in (1).

A full understanding of the structure of systems of linear equations depends on the definition of a special class of echelon matrices, a class having the property that every matrix in it is row equivalent to one and only one of these special echelon matrices. Recall that an echelon matrix **E** is one that has the following two properties:

1. Every all-zero row of **E** lies beneath every row that contains a nonzero element.
2. The leading nonzero entry in each row lies to the right of the leading nonzero entry in the preceding row.

A *reduced* echelon matrix (sometimes called a reduced row-echelon matrix) has two additional properties.

Definition: Reduced Echelon Matrix

A **reduced echelon matrix** **E** is an echelon matrix that has—in addition to Properties 1 and 2—the following properties:

3. Each leading entry of **E** is 1.
4. Each leading entry of **E** is the only nonzero element in its column.

A matrix is said to be in **reduced echelon form** if it is a reduced echelon matrix. Similarly, a linear system is in **reduced echelon form** if its augmented coefficient matrix is a reduced echelon matrix.

Example 1 The following matrices are reduced echelon matrices.

$$\begin{bmatrix} 1 & 0 \\ 0 & 1 \end{bmatrix} \qquad \begin{bmatrix} 1 & 0 & -3 & 0 \\ 0 & 1 & 4 & 0 \\ 0 & 0 & 0 & 1 \end{bmatrix}$$

$$\begin{bmatrix} 1 & -2 & 0 \\ 0 & 0 & 1 \\ 0 & 0 & 0 \end{bmatrix} \qquad \begin{bmatrix} 1 & 0 & -7 \\ 0 & 1 & 5 \\ 0 & 0 & 0 \end{bmatrix}$$

The echelon matrices

$$A = \begin{bmatrix} 1 & 0 & 0 \\ 0 & 2 & 0 \\ 0 & 0 & 0 \end{bmatrix} \quad \text{and} \quad B = \begin{bmatrix} 1 & 0 & 2 \\ 0 & 1 & 0 \\ 0 & 0 & 1 \end{bmatrix}$$

are not in *reduced* echelon form, because **A** does not have Property 3 and **B** does not have Property 4. ∎

The process of transforming a matrix **A** into reduced echelon form is called **Gauss-Jordan elimination**.

ALGORITHM: Gauss-Jordan Elimination

1. First transform **A** into echelon form by Gaussian elimination.
2. Then divide each element of each nonzero *row* by its leading entry (to satisfy Property 3).
3. Finally, use each leading 1 to "clear out" any remaining nonzero elements in its *column* (to satisfy Property 4). ▲

The reduced echelon form of a matrix *is* unique. The special class of matrices that we mentioned at the beginning of this discussion is simply the class of all reduced echelon matrices. A proof of the following theorem may be found in Section 4.2 of B. Noble and J. W. Daniel, *Applied Linear Algebra*, 3rd ed. (Upper Saddle River, N.J.: Prentice Hall, 1988).

THEOREM 1: Unique Reduced Echelon Form

Every matrix is row equivalent to one and only one reduced echelon matrix. ▲

Example 2 Find the reduced echelon form of the matrix

$$A = \begin{bmatrix} 1 & 2 & 1 & 4 \\ 3 & 8 & 7 & 20 \\ 2 & 7 & 9 & 23 \end{bmatrix}.$$

Solution In Example 3 of Section 3.2 we found the echelon form

$$\begin{bmatrix} 1 & 2 & 1 & 4 \\ 0 & 1 & 2 & 4 \\ 0 & 0 & 1 & 3 \end{bmatrix},$$

which already satisfies Property 3. To clear out columns 2 and 3 (in order to satisfy Property 4), we continue the reduction as follows.

$$\begin{bmatrix} 1 & 2 & 1 & 4 \\ 0 & 1 & 2 & 4 \\ 0 & 0 & 1 & 3 \end{bmatrix} \xrightarrow{(-2)R_2 + R_1} \begin{bmatrix} 1 & 0 & -3 & -4 \\ 0 & 1 & 2 & 4 \\ 0 & 0 & 1 & 3 \end{bmatrix}$$

$$\xrightarrow{(-2)R_3 + R_2} \begin{bmatrix} 1 & 0 & -3 & -4 \\ 0 & 1 & 0 & -2 \\ 0 & 0 & 1 & 3 \end{bmatrix}$$

$$\xrightarrow{(3)R_3 + R_1} \begin{bmatrix} 1 & 0 & 0 & 5 \\ 0 & 1 & 0 & -2 \\ 0 & 0 & 1 & 3 \end{bmatrix}$$

For instance, we see immediately from this reduced echelon form that the linear system

$$x + 2y + z = 4$$
$$3x + 8y + 7z = 20$$
$$2x + 7y + 9z = 23$$

with augmented coefficient matrix **A** has the unique solution $x = 5$, $y = -2$, $z = 3$. ∎

Example 3 To use Gauss-Jordan elimination to solve the linear system

$$x_1 + x_2 + x_3 + x_4 = 12$$
$$x_1 + 2x_2 \quad\quad + 5x_4 = 17 \quad\quad\quad (2)$$
$$3x_1 + 2x_2 + 4x_3 - x_4 = 31,$$

we transform its augmented coefficient matrix into *reduced* echelon form, as follows:

$$\begin{bmatrix} 1 & 1 & 1 & 1 & 12 \\ 1 & 2 & 0 & 5 & 17 \\ 3 & 2 & 4 & -1 & 31 \end{bmatrix} \xrightarrow{(-1)R_1 + R_2} \begin{bmatrix} 1 & 1 & 1 & 1 & 12 \\ 0 & 1 & -1 & 4 & 5 \\ 3 & 2 & 4 & -1 & 31 \end{bmatrix}$$

$$\xrightarrow{(-3)R_1 + R_3} \begin{bmatrix} 1 & 1 & 1 & 1 & 12 \\ 0 & 1 & -1 & 4 & 5 \\ 0 & -1 & 1 & -4 & -5 \end{bmatrix}$$

$$\xrightarrow{(1)R_2 + R_3} \begin{bmatrix} 1 & 1 & 1 & 1 & 12 \\ 0 & 1 & -1 & 4 & 5 \\ 0 & 0 & 0 & 0 & 0 \end{bmatrix}$$

$$\xrightarrow{(-1)R_2 + R_1} \begin{bmatrix} 1 & 0 & 2 & -3 & 7 \\ 0 & 1 & -1 & 4 & 5 \\ 0 & 0 & 0 & 0 & 0 \end{bmatrix}.$$

Thus the reduced echelon form of the system in (2) is

$$
\begin{aligned}
x_1 \quad + 2x_3 - 3x_4 &= 7 \\
x_2 - \quad x_3 + 4x_4 &= 5 \\
0 &= 0.
\end{aligned}
\tag{3}
$$

The leading variables are x_1 and x_2; the free variables are x_3 and x_4. If we set

$$
x_3 = s \quad \text{and} \quad x_4 = t,
$$

then (3) immediately yields

$$
\begin{aligned}
x_1 &= 7 - 2s + 3t, \\
x_2 &= 5 + \quad s - 4t.
\end{aligned}
$$
■

As a practical matter, Gauss-Jordan elimination generally offers no significant computational advantage over Gaussian elimination (transformation to nonreduced echelon form) followed by back substitution. Therefore, Gaussian elimination is commonly employed in practical procedures and in computer programs used to solve linear systems numerically.

The Three Possibilities

The chief importance of Gauss-Jordan elimination stems from the fact that the reduced echelon form of a general linear system

$$
\begin{aligned}
a_{11}x_1 + a_{12}x_2 + a_{13}x_3 + \cdots + a_{1n}x_n &= b_1 \\
a_{21}x_1 + a_{22}x_2 + a_{23}x_3 + \cdots + a_{2n}x_n &= b_2 \\
&\ \ \vdots \\
a_{m1}x_1 + a_{m2}x_2 + a_{m3}x_3 + \cdots + a_{mn}x_n &= b_m
\end{aligned}
\tag{4}
$$

most clearly exhibits its underlying structure and enables us most readily to answer questions about the number and type of its solutions. If the leading variables are $x_{j_1}, x_{j_2}, \ldots, x_{j_r}$, then the reduced echelon form of the system in (4) looks like

$$
\begin{aligned}
x_{j_1} \qquad\qquad\qquad\qquad + \sum c_{1j}x_j &= d_1 \\
x_{j_2} \qquad\qquad\quad + \sum c_{2j}x_j &= d_2 \\
\ddots \qquad\qquad\qquad\quad \vdots \\
x_{j_r} + \sum c_{rj}x_j &= d_r \\
0 &= d_{r+1} \\
\vdots \\
0 &= d_m
\end{aligned}
\tag{5}
$$

where the summations involve only the free variables.

The system is consistent if and only if the constants $d_{r+1}, d_{r+2}, \ldots, d_m$ in (5) are all zero. If this is so, and if $r < n$, then there are free variables that we can set equal to arbitrary parameters. If the system is consistent, and if $r = n$, then the summations in (5) disappear and we have the unique solution $x_1 = d_1, x_2 = d_2, \ldots, x_n = d_n$. These observations establish the following result, to which we have already alluded.

THEOREM 2: The Three Possibilities

A linear system of equations either has a unique solution, has no solution, or has infinitely many solutions. ▲

Homogeneous Systems

The linear system in (4) is called **homogeneous** provided that the constants $b_1, b_2, \ldots, b_m$ on the right-hand side are all zero. Thus a homogeneous system of m equations in n variables has the form

$$
\begin{aligned}
a_{11}x_1 + a_{12}x_2 + a_{13}x_3 + \cdots + a_{1n}x_n &= 0 \\
a_{21}x_1 + a_{22}x_2 + a_{23}x_3 + \cdots + a_{2n}x_n &= 0 \\
&\ \ \vdots \\
a_{m1}x_1 + a_{m2}x_2 + a_{m3}x_3 + \cdots + a_{mn}x_n &= 0.
\end{aligned}
\tag{6}
$$

Every homogeneous system obviously has at least the **trivial solution**

$$
x_1 = 0, \quad x_2 = 0, \ldots, x_n = 0.
\tag{7}
$$

Thus we know from the outset that *every homogeneous linear system either has only the trivial solution or has infinitely many solutions.* If it has a *nontrivial* solution—one with not every x_i equal to zero—then it must have infinitely many solutions.

An important special case, in which a nontrivial solution is guaranteed, is that of a homogeneous system with *more variables than equations*: $m < n$. To see why there must be a solution, consider the reduced echelon system in (5) with the constants on the right-hand side all zero (because the original system is homogeneous). The number r of leading variables is at most the number m of equations (because there is at most one leading variable per equation). If $m < n$, it then follows that $r < n$, so there is at least one free variable that can be set equal to an arbitrary parameter, thereby yielding infinitely many solutions. This argument establishes the following key result.

THEOREM 3: Homogeneous Systems with More Variables than Equations

Every homogeneous linear system with more variables than equations has infinitely many solutions. ▲

Example 4

The homogeneous linear system

$$
\begin{aligned}
47x_1 - 73x_2 + 56x_3 + 21x_4 &= 0 \\
19x_1 + 81x_2 - 17x_3 - 99x_4 &= 0 \\
53x_1 + 62x_2 + 39x_3 + 25x_4 &= 0
\end{aligned}
$$

of three equations in four unknowns necessarily has infinitely many solutions. The only question (which we could answer by reducing the system to echelon form) is whether the system has one, two, or three free variables. ■

The situation is different for a *nonhomogeneous* system with more variables than equations. The simple example

$$x_1 + x_2 + x_3 = 0$$
$$x_1 + x_2 + x_3 = 1$$

shows that such a system may be inconsistent. But if it is consistent—meaning that $d_{r+1} = \cdots = d_m = 0$ in the reduced echelon form in (5)—then the fact that $m < n$ implies (just as in the proof of Theorem 3) that there is at least one free variable, and that the system therefore has infinitely many solutions. Hence *every nonhomogeneous system with more variables than equations either has no solution or has infinitely many solutions.*

Equal Numbers of Equations and Variables

An especially important case in the theory of linear systems is that of a homogeneous system

$$
\begin{aligned}
a_{11}x_1 + a_{12}x_2 + a_{13}x_3 + \cdots + a_{1n}x_n &= 0 \\
a_{21}x_1 + a_{22}x_2 + a_{23}x_3 + \cdots + a_{2n}x_n &= 0 \\
&\vdots \\
a_{n1}x_1 + a_{n2}x_2 + a_{n3}x_3 + \cdots + a_{nn}x_n &= 0
\end{aligned}
\tag{8}
$$

with the *same* number n of variables and equations. The coefficient matrix $\mathbf{A} = [a_{ij}]$ then has the same number of rows and columns and thus is an $n \times n$ **square matrix**.

Here we are most interested in the situation when (8) has *only* the trivial solution $x_1 = x_2 = \cdots = x_n = 0$. This occurs if and only if the reduced echelon system contains *no* free variables. That is, all n of the variables $x_1, x_2, \ldots, x_n$ must be leading variables. Because the system consists of exactly n equations, we conclude that the reduced echelon system is simply

$$
\begin{aligned}
x_1 \qquad\qquad\qquad\quad &= 0 \\
x_2 \qquad\qquad\quad &= 0 \\
x_3 \qquad\quad &= 0 \\
\ddots \qquad &\vdots \\
x_n &= 0,
\end{aligned}
$$

and, therefore, that the reduced echelon form of the coefficient matrix $\mathbf{A}$ is the matrix

$$
\begin{bmatrix}
1 & 0 & 0 & \cdots & 0 \\
0 & 1 & 0 & \cdots & 0 \\
0 & 0 & 1 & \cdots & 0 \\
\vdots & \vdots & \vdots & \ddots & \vdots \\
0 & 0 & 0 & \cdots & 1
\end{bmatrix}.
\tag{9}
$$

Such a (square) matrix, with 1s on its **principal diagonal** (the one from upper left to lower right) and zeros elsewhere, is called an **identity matrix** (for reasons given in Section 3.5). For instance, the 2×2 and 3×3 identity matrices are

$$
\begin{bmatrix} 1 & 0 \\ 0 & 1 \end{bmatrix} \quad \text{and} \quad \begin{bmatrix} 1 & 0 & 0 \\ 0 & 1 & 0 \\ 0 & 0 & 1 \end{bmatrix}.
$$

The matrix in (9) is the $n \times n$ identity matrix. With this terminology, the preceding argument establishes the following theorem.

THEOREM 4: Homogeneous Systems with Unique Solutions

Let $\mathbf{A}$ be an $n \times n$ matrix. Then the homogeneous system with coefficient matrix $\mathbf{A}$ has only the trivial solution if and only if $\mathbf{A}$ is row equivalent to the $n \times n$ identity matrix. ▲

Example 5 The computation in Example 2 (disregarding the fourth column in each matrix there) shows that the matrix

$$\mathbf{A} = \begin{bmatrix} 1 & 2 & 1 \\ 3 & 8 & 7 \\ 2 & 7 & 9 \end{bmatrix}$$

is row equivalent to the 3×3 identity matrix. Hence Theorem 4 implies that the homogeneous system

$$\begin{aligned} x_1 + 2x_2 + \ x_3 &= 0 \\ 3x_1 + 8x_2 + 7x_3 &= 0 \\ 2x_1 + 7x_2 + 9x_3 &= 0 \end{aligned}$$

with coefficient matrix $\mathbf{A}$ has only the trivial solution $x_1 = x_2 = x_3 = 0$. ■

3.3 Problems

Find the reduced echelon form of each of the matrices given in Problems 1–20.

1. $\begin{bmatrix} 1 & 2 \\ 3 & 7 \end{bmatrix}$

2. $\begin{bmatrix} 3 & 7 \\ 2 & 5 \end{bmatrix}$

3. $\begin{bmatrix} 3 & 7 & 15 \\ 2 & 5 & 11 \end{bmatrix}$

4. $\begin{bmatrix} 3 & 7 & -1 \\ 5 & 2 & 8 \end{bmatrix}$

5. $\begin{bmatrix} 1 & 2 & -11 \\ 2 & 3 & -19 \end{bmatrix}$

6. $\begin{bmatrix} 1 & -2 & 19 \\ 4 & -7 & 70 \end{bmatrix}$

7. $\begin{bmatrix} 1 & 2 & 3 \\ 1 & 4 & 1 \\ 2 & 1 & 9 \end{bmatrix}$

8. $\begin{bmatrix} 1 & -4 & -5 \\ 3 & -9 & 3 \\ 1 & -2 & 3 \end{bmatrix}$

9. $\begin{bmatrix} 5 & 2 & 18 \\ 0 & 1 & 4 \\ 4 & 1 & 12 \end{bmatrix}$

10. $\begin{bmatrix} 5 & 2 & -5 \\ 9 & 4 & -7 \\ 4 & 1 & -7 \end{bmatrix}$

11. $\begin{bmatrix} 3 & 9 & 1 \\ 2 & 6 & 7 \\ 1 & 3 & -6 \end{bmatrix}$

12. $\begin{bmatrix} 1 & -4 & -2 \\ 3 & -12 & 1 \\ 2 & -8 & 5 \end{bmatrix}$

13. $\begin{bmatrix} 2 & 7 & 4 & 0 \\ 1 & 3 & 2 & 1 \\ 2 & 6 & 5 & 4 \end{bmatrix}$

14. $\begin{bmatrix} 1 & 3 & 2 & 5 \\ 2 & 5 & 2 & 3 \\ 2 & 7 & 7 & 22 \end{bmatrix}$

15. $\begin{bmatrix} 2 & 2 & 4 & 2 \\ 1 & -1 & -4 & 3 \\ 2 & 7 & 19 & -3 \end{bmatrix}$

16. $\begin{bmatrix} 1 & 3 & 15 & 7 \\ 2 & 4 & 22 & 8 \\ 2 & 7 & 34 & 17 \end{bmatrix}$

17. $\begin{bmatrix} 1 & 1 & 1 & -1 & -4 \\ 1 & -2 & -2 & 8 & -1 \\ 2 & 3 & -1 & 3 & 11 \end{bmatrix}$

18. $\begin{bmatrix} 1 & -2 & -5 & -12 & 1 \\ 2 & 3 & 18 & 11 & 9 \\ 2 & 5 & 26 & 21 & 11 \end{bmatrix}$

19. $\begin{bmatrix} 2 & 7 & -10 & -19 & 13 \\ 1 & 3 & -4 & -8 & 6 \\ 1 & 0 & 2 & 1 & 3 \end{bmatrix}$

20. $\begin{bmatrix} 3 & 6 & 1 & 7 & 13 \\ 5 & 10 & 8 & 18 & 47 \\ 2 & 4 & 5 & 9 & 26 \end{bmatrix}$

21–30. Use the method of Gauss-Jordan elimination (transforming the augmented matrix into reduced echelon form) to solve Problems 11–20 in Section 3.2.

31. Show that the two matrices in (1) are both row equivalent to the 3×3 identity matrix.

32. Show that the 2×2 matrix

$$\mathbf{A} = \begin{bmatrix} a & b \\ c & d \end{bmatrix}$$

is row equivalent to the 2×2 identity matrix provided that $ad - bc \neq 0$.

33. List all possible reduced row-echelon forms of a 2×2 matrix, using asterisks to indicate elements that may be either zero or nonzero.

34. List all possible reduced row-echelon forms of a 3×3 matrix, using asterisks to indicate elements that may be either zero or nonzero.

35. Consider the homogeneous system

$$ax + by = 0$$
$$cx + dy = 0.$$

(a) If $x = x_0$ and $y = y_0$ is a solution and k is a real number, then show that $x = kx_0$ and $y = ky_0$ is also a solution.

(b) If $x = x_1$, $y = y_1$ and $x = x_2$, $y = y_2$ are both solutions, then show that $x = x_1 + x_2$, $y = y_1 + y_2$ is a solution.

36. Suppose that $ad - bc \neq 0$ in the homogeneous system of Problem 35. Use Problem 32 to show that its only solution is the trivial solution.

37. Show that the homogeneous system in Problem 35 has a nontrivial solution if and only if $ad - bc = 0$.

38. Use the result of Problem 37 to find all values of c for which the homogeneous system

$$(c + 2)x + \quad\quad 3y = 0$$
$$2x + (c - 3)y = 0$$

has a nontrivial solution.

39. Consider a *homogeneous* system of three equations in three unknowns. Suppose that the third equation is the sum of some multiple of the first equation and some multiple of the second equation. Show that the system has a nontrivial solution.

40. Let **E** be an echelon matrix that is row equivalent to the matrix **A**. Show that **E** has the same number of nonzero rows as does the reduced echelon form **E*** of **A**. Thus the number of nonzero rows in an echelon form of **A** is an "invariant" of the matrix **A**. *Suggestion*: Consider reducing **E** to **E***.

3.3 Application: Automated Row Reduction

Most computer algebra systems include commands for the immediate reduction of matrices to reduced echelon form. For instance, if the matrix

$$\mathbf{A} = \begin{bmatrix} 1 & 2 & 1 & 4 \\ 3 & 8 & 7 & 20 \\ 2 & 7 & 9 & 23 \end{bmatrix}$$

of Example 2 has been entered—as illustrated in the 3.2 Application—then the *Maple* command

```
with(linalg): R := rref(A);
```

or the *Mathematica* command

```
R = RowReduce[A]
```

or the MATLAB command

```
R = rref(A)
```

produces the reduced echelon matrix

FIGURE 3.3.1. Finding a reduced row-echelon matrix with a TI-92 calculator.

$$\mathbf{R} = \begin{bmatrix} 1 & 0 & 0 & 5 \\ 0 & 1 & 0 & -2 \\ 0 & 0 & 1 & 3 \end{bmatrix}$$

that exhibits the solution of the linear system having augmented coefficient matrix **A**. The same calculation is illustrated in the calculator screen of Fig. 3.3.1. Solve similarly the systems in the following problems (which apparently would be somewhat tedious to solve by manual row reduction):

1. $17x + 42y - 36z = 213$
$13x + 45y - 34z = 226$
$12x + 47y - 35z = 197$

2. $32x + 57y - 41z = 713$
$23x + 43y - 37z = 130$
$42x - 61y + 39z = 221$

3. $231x + 157y - 241z = 420$
$323x + 181y - 375z = 412$
$542x + 161y - 759z = 419$

4. $837x + 667y - 729z = 1659$
$152x - 179y - 975z = 1630$
$542x + 328y - 759z = 1645$

5. $49w - 57x + 37y - 59z = 97$
$73w - 15x - 19y - 22z = 99$
$52w - 51x + 14y - 29z = 89$
$13w - 27x + 27y - 25z = 73$

6. $64w - 57x + 97y - 67z = 485$
$92w + 77x - 34y - 37z = 486$
$44w - 34x + 53y - 34z = 465$
$27w + 57x - 69y + 29z = 464$

3.4 Matrix Operations

As yet, we have used matrices only to simplify our record keeping in the solution of linear systems. But it turns out that matrices can be added and multiplied in ways similar to the ways in which numbers are added and multiplied and that these operations with matrices have far-reaching applications.

At the level of this text everyone "knows" that $2 + 3 = 5$, and we do not dwell on the underlying meaning of this equation. But in the case of matrices we must begin with precise definitions of what the familiar language of algebra is to mean when it is applied to matrices rather than to numbers.

Two matrices **A** and **B** *of the same size*— the same number of rows and the same number of columns—are called **equal** provided that each element of **A** is equal to the corresponding element of **B**. Thus two matrices of the same size are equal provided they are *elementwise equal*, and we write $\mathbf{A} = \mathbf{B}$ to denote equality of the two matrices **A** and **B**.

Example 1 If

$$\mathbf{A} = \begin{bmatrix} 3 & 4 \\ 5 & 6 \end{bmatrix}, \quad \mathbf{B} = \begin{bmatrix} 3 & 4 \\ 5 & 7 \end{bmatrix}, \quad \text{and} \quad \mathbf{C} = \begin{bmatrix} 3 & 4 & 7 \\ 5 & 6 & 8 \end{bmatrix},$$

then $\mathbf{A} \neq \mathbf{B}$ because $a_{22} = 6$, whereas $b_{22} = 7$, and $\mathbf{A} \neq \mathbf{C}$ because the matrices **A** and **C** are not of the same size. ∎

The next two definitions are further examples of "doing it elementwise."

Definition: Addition of Matrices

If $\mathbf{A} = \begin{bmatrix} a_{ij} \end{bmatrix}$ and $\mathbf{B} = \begin{bmatrix} b_{ij} \end{bmatrix}$ are matrices *of the same size*, then their **sum A + B** is the matrix obtained by adding corresponding elements of the matrices **A** and **B**. That is,

$$\mathbf{A} + \mathbf{B} = \begin{bmatrix} a_{ij} + b_{ij} \end{bmatrix}, \tag{1}$$

where the notation on the right signifies that the element in the ith row and jth column of the matrix $\mathbf{A} + \mathbf{B}$ is $a_{ij} + b_{ij}$.

Example 2 If

$$\mathbf{A} = \begin{bmatrix} 3 & 0 & -1 \\ 2 & -7 & 5 \end{bmatrix}, \quad \mathbf{B} = \begin{bmatrix} 4 & -3 & 6 \\ 9 & 0 & -2 \end{bmatrix}, \quad \text{and} \quad \mathbf{C} = \begin{bmatrix} 3 & -2 \\ -1 & 6 \end{bmatrix},$$

then

$$A + B = \begin{bmatrix} 7 & -3 & 5 \\ 11 & -7 & 3 \end{bmatrix},$$

but the sum $A + C$ is not defined because the matrices A and C are not of the same size. ∎

Definition: Multiplication of a Matrix by a Number

If $A = \begin{bmatrix} a_{ij} \end{bmatrix}$ is a matrix and c is a number, then cA is the matrix obtained by multiplying each element of A by c. That is,

$$cA = \begin{bmatrix} ca_{ij} \end{bmatrix}. \tag{2}$$

We also write

$$-A = (-1)A \quad \text{and} \quad A - B = A + (-B).$$

Example 3   If A and B are the 2×3 matrices of Example 2, then

$$3A = \begin{bmatrix} 9 & 0 & -3 \\ 6 & -21 & 15 \end{bmatrix}, \quad -B = \begin{bmatrix} -4 & 3 & -6 \\ -9 & 0 & 2 \end{bmatrix},$$

and

$$3A - B = \begin{bmatrix} 5 & 3 & -9 \\ -3 & -21 & 17 \end{bmatrix}. \quad ∎$$

Vectors

Our first application of these matrix operations is to vectors. As mentioned in Section 3.2, a **column vector** (or simply **vector**) is merely an $n \times 1$ matrix, one having a single column. We normally use boldface lowercase letters, rather than lightface uppercase letters, to denote vectors. If

$$a = \begin{bmatrix} 6 \\ -2 \\ 5 \end{bmatrix} \quad \text{and} \quad b = \begin{bmatrix} -2 \\ 3 \\ -4 \end{bmatrix},$$

we can form such combinations as

$$3a + 2b = \begin{bmatrix} 18 \\ -6 \\ 15 \end{bmatrix} + \begin{bmatrix} -4 \\ 6 \\ -8 \end{bmatrix} = \begin{bmatrix} 14 \\ 0 \\ 7 \end{bmatrix}.$$

Largely for typographical reasons, we sometimes write

$$a = \begin{bmatrix} a_1 \\ a_2 \\ \vdots \\ a_n \end{bmatrix} = (a_1, a_2, \ldots, a_n). \tag{3}$$

That is, $(a_1, a_2, \ldots, a_n)$ is simply another notation for the *column* vector with elements $a_1, a_2, \ldots, a_n$. It should not be confused with the *row vector*

$$\begin{bmatrix} a_1 & a_2 & \cdots & a_n \end{bmatrix}. \tag{4}$$

A **row vector** is a $1 \times n$ (rather than $n \times 1$) matrix having a single row, and

$$(3, 2, 1) = \begin{bmatrix} 3 \\ 2 \\ 1 \end{bmatrix} \neq \begin{bmatrix} 3 & 2 & 1 \end{bmatrix}$$

because the two matrices here have different sizes (even though they have the same elements).

Now consider the linear system

$$\begin{aligned}
a_{11}x_1 + a_{12}x_2 + a_{13}x_3 + \cdots + a_{1n}x_n &= b_1 \\
a_{21}x_1 + a_{22}x_2 + a_{23}x_3 + \cdots + a_{2n}x_n &= b_2 \\
&\vdots \\
a_{m1}x_1 + a_{m2}x_2 + a_{m3}x_3 + \cdots + a_{mn}x_n &= b_m
\end{aligned} \tag{5}$$

of m equations in n variables. We may regard a solution of this system as a *vector*

$$\mathbf{x} = \begin{bmatrix} x_1 \\ x_2 \\ x_3 \\ \vdots \\ x_n \end{bmatrix} = (x_1, x_2, x_3, \ldots, x_n) \tag{6}$$

whose elements satisfy each of the equations in (5). If we want to refer explicitly to the number of elements, we may call $\mathbf{x}$ an **n-vector**.

Example 4 Consider the homogeneous system

$$\begin{aligned}
x_1 + 3x_2 - 15x_3 + 7x_4 &= 0 \\
x_1 + 4x_2 - 19x_3 + 10x_4 &= 0 \\
2x_1 + 5x_2 - 26x_3 + 11x_4 &= 0.
\end{aligned} \tag{7}$$

We find readily that the reduced echelon form of the augmented coefficient matrix of this system is

$$\begin{bmatrix}
1 & 0 & -3 & -2 & 0 \\
0 & 1 & -4 & 3 & 0 \\
0 & 0 & 0 & 0 & 0
\end{bmatrix}.$$

Hence x_1 and x_2 are leading variables and x_3 and x_4 are free variables. In the manner of Sections 3.2 and 3.3, we therefore see that the infinite solution set of the system in (7) is described by the equations

$$\begin{aligned}
x_4 &= t, \\
x_3 &= s, \\
x_2 &= 4s - 3t, \\
x_1 &= 3s + 2t
\end{aligned} \tag{8}$$

in terms of the arbitrary parameters s and t.

Now let us write the solution $\mathbf{x} = (x_1, x_2, x_3, x_4)$ in vector notation. The equations in (8) yield

$$\mathbf{x} = \begin{bmatrix} x_1 \\ x_2 \\ x_3 \\ x_4 \end{bmatrix} = \begin{bmatrix} 3s + 2t \\ 4s - 3t \\ s \\ t \end{bmatrix},$$

and "separating" the s and t parts gives

$$\mathbf{x} = \begin{bmatrix} 3s \\ 4s \\ s \\ 0 \end{bmatrix} + \begin{bmatrix} 2t \\ -3t \\ 0 \\ t \end{bmatrix} = s \begin{bmatrix} 3 \\ 4 \\ 1 \\ 0 \end{bmatrix} + t \begin{bmatrix} 2 \\ -3 \\ 0 \\ 1 \end{bmatrix}$$

—that is,

$$\mathbf{x} = s(3, 4, 1, 0) + t(2, -3, 0, 1) = s\mathbf{x}_1 + t\mathbf{x}_2. \tag{9}$$

Equation (9) expresses in **vector form** the general solution of the linear system in (7). It says that the vector $\mathbf{x}$ is a solution if and only if $\mathbf{x}$ is a *linear combination*—a sum of multiples—of the particular solutions $\mathbf{x}_1 = (3, 4, 1, 0)$ and $\mathbf{x}_2 = (2, -3, 0, 1)$. The parameters s and t are simply the coefficients in this "sum of multiples." ∎

In the same manner as that in which we derived Eq. (9) from the equations in (8), the general solution of every homogeneous linear system can be expressed as a linear combination of particular solution vectors. For this reason (as well as others), linear combinations of vectors will play a central role in succeeding chapters.

Matrix Multiplication

The first surprise is that matrices are *not* multiplied elementwise. The initial purpose of matrix multiplication is to simplify the notation for systems of linear equations. If we write

$$\mathbf{A} = \begin{bmatrix} a_{ij} \end{bmatrix}, \quad \mathbf{x} = \begin{bmatrix} x_1 \\ x_2 \\ \vdots \\ x_n \end{bmatrix}, \quad \text{and} \quad \mathbf{b} = \begin{bmatrix} b_1 \\ b_2 \\ \vdots \\ b_m \end{bmatrix}, \tag{10}$$

then $\mathbf{A}$, $\mathbf{x}$, and $\mathbf{b}$ are, respectively, the coefficient matrix, the unknown vector, and the constant vector for the linear system in (5). We want to define the matrix product $\mathbf{Ax}$ in such a way that the entire system of linear equations reduces to the single matrix equation

$$\mathbf{Ax} = \mathbf{b}. \tag{11}$$

The first step is to define the product of a *row* vector $\mathbf{a}$ and a *column* vector $\mathbf{b}$,

$$\mathbf{a} = \begin{bmatrix} a_1 & a_2 & \cdots & a_n \end{bmatrix} \quad \text{and} \quad \mathbf{b} = \begin{bmatrix} b_1 \\ b_2 \\ \vdots \\ b_n \end{bmatrix},$$

each having n elements. In this case, the product $\mathbf{ab}$ is *defined* to be

$$\mathbf{ab} = a_1 b_1 + a_2 b_2 + \cdots + a_n b_n. \tag{12}$$

Thus $\mathbf{ab}$ is the *sum of products* of corresponding elements of $\mathbf{a}$ and $\mathbf{b}$. For instance,

$$\begin{bmatrix} 2 & -3 \end{bmatrix} \begin{bmatrix} 3 \\ 5 \end{bmatrix} = (2)(3) + (-3)(5) = -9$$

and

$$\begin{bmatrix} 3 & 0 & -1 & 7 \end{bmatrix} \begin{bmatrix} 5 \\ 2 \\ -3 \\ 4 \end{bmatrix} = 3 \cdot 5 + 0 \cdot 2 + (-1)(-3) + 7 \cdot 4 = 46.$$

Note that if

$$\mathbf{a} = \begin{bmatrix} a_1 & a_2 & \cdots & a_n \end{bmatrix} \quad \text{and} \quad \mathbf{x} = \begin{bmatrix} x_1 \\ x_2 \\ \vdots \\ x_n \end{bmatrix},$$

then

$$\mathbf{ax} = a_1 x_1 + a_2 x_2 + \cdots + a_n x_n.$$

Hence the single equation

$$a_1 x_1 + a_2 x_2 + \cdots + a_n x_n = b \tag{13}$$

reduces to the equation

$$\mathbf{ax} = b, \tag{14}$$

which is a step toward the objective expressed in Eq. (11). This observation is the underlying motivation for the following definition.

Definition: Matrix Multiplication

Suppose that $\mathbf{A}$ is an $m \times p$ matrix and $\mathbf{B}$ is a $p \times n$ matrix. Then the **product** $\mathbf{AB}$ is the $m \times n$ matrix defined as follows: The element of $\mathbf{AB}$ in its ith row and jth column is the *sum of products* of corresponding elements in the ith row of $\mathbf{A}$ and the jth column of $\mathbf{B}$.

That is, if the ith row of $\mathbf{A}$ is

$$\begin{bmatrix} a_{i1} & a_{i2} & a_{i3} & \cdots & a_{ip} \end{bmatrix}$$

and the jth column of $\mathbf{B}$ is

$$\begin{bmatrix} b_{1j} \\ b_{2j} \\ b_{3j} \\ \vdots \\ b_{pj} \end{bmatrix},$$

then the element in the ith row and jth column of the product $\mathbf{AB}$ is

$$a_{i1} b_{1j} + a_{i2} b_{2j} + a_{i3} b_{3j} + \cdots + a_{ip} b_{pj}.$$

Example 5

If

$$A = \begin{bmatrix} 2 & -1 \\ -4 & 3 \end{bmatrix} \quad \text{and} \quad B = \begin{bmatrix} 1 & 5 \\ 3 & 7 \end{bmatrix}$$

then $m = p = n = 2$, so **AB** will also be a 2×2 matrix. To find **AB**, we calculate sums of products as follows:

$$\text{AB, row 1, column 1}: \quad (2)(1) + (-1)(3) = -1;$$
$$\text{AB, row 1, column 2}: \quad (2)(5) + (-1)(7) = 3;$$
$$\text{AB, row 2, column 1}: \quad (-4)(1) + (3)(3) = 5;$$
$$\text{AB, row 2, column 2}: \quad (-4)(5) + (3)(7) = 1.$$

Thus

$$AB = \begin{bmatrix} -1 & 3 \\ 5 & 1 \end{bmatrix}. \qquad \blacksquare$$

For your first practice with matrix multiplication, you should compute

$$BA = \begin{bmatrix} 1 & 5 \\ 3 & 7 \end{bmatrix} \begin{bmatrix} 2 & -1 \\ -4 & 3 \end{bmatrix} = \begin{bmatrix} -18 & 14 \\ -22 & 18 \end{bmatrix}.$$

Note that $AB \neq BA$. This shows that multiplication of matrices is *not* commutative! We must therefore be careful about the order in which we write the matrices in a matrix product.

The definition of the matrix product bears careful examination to see how it fits together. First, the fact that **A** is $m \times p$ and **B** is $p \times n$ implies that the number of *columns* of **A** is equal to the number of *rows* of **B**. If so, then the size of the product **AB** is obtained by a sort of cancellation of the "inside" dimensions:

$$\begin{array}{ccccc} \mathbf{A} & \text{times} & \mathbf{B} & = & \mathbf{AB} \\ m \times p & & p \times n & & m \times n. \end{array}$$

These "cancel."

If the inside dimensions are not equal, then the product **AB** is *not defined*.

Example 6

If **A** is a 3×2 matrix and **B** is a 2×3 matrix, then **AB** will be a 3×3 matrix, whereas **BA** will be a 2×2 matrix. If **C** is a 3×5 matrix and **D** is a 5×7 matrix, then **CD** will be a 3×7 matrix, but **DC** is undefined. $\qquad \blacksquare$

To emphasize the fact that the *ij*th element of **AB** is the product of the *i*th row of **A** and the *j*th column of **B**, we can write

$$AB = \begin{bmatrix} \text{---} \mathbf{a}_1 \text{---} \\ \text{---} \mathbf{a}_2 \text{---} \\ \vdots \\ \text{---} \mathbf{a}_i \text{---} \\ \vdots \\ \text{---} \mathbf{a}_m \text{---} \end{bmatrix} \begin{bmatrix} \mathbf{b}_1 & \mathbf{b}_2 & \cdots & \mathbf{b}_j & \cdots & \mathbf{b}_n \end{bmatrix},$$

where $\mathbf{a}_1, \mathbf{a}_2, \ldots, \mathbf{a}_m$ denote the m **row vectors** of $\mathbf{A}$ and $\mathbf{b}_1, \mathbf{b}_2, \ldots, \mathbf{b}_n$ denote the n **column vectors** of $\mathbf{B}$. More briefly, if

$$\mathbf{A} = \begin{bmatrix} \mathbf{a}_1 \\ \mathbf{a}_2 \\ \vdots \\ \mathbf{a}_m \end{bmatrix} \quad \text{and} \quad \mathbf{B} = \begin{bmatrix} \mathbf{b}_1 & \mathbf{b}_2 & \cdots & \mathbf{b}_n \end{bmatrix}$$

in terms of the rows of $\mathbf{A}$ and the columns of $\mathbf{B}$, then

$$\mathbf{AB} = \begin{bmatrix} \mathbf{a}_i \mathbf{b}_j \end{bmatrix}. \tag{15}$$

Therefore, as mentioned earlier, the ijth element $\mathbf{a}_i \mathbf{b}_j$ of $\mathbf{AB}$ is given in terms of elements of $\mathbf{A}$ and $\mathbf{B}$ by

$$\mathbf{a}_i \mathbf{b}_j = \begin{bmatrix} a_{i1} & a_{i2} & \cdots & a_{ip} \end{bmatrix} \begin{bmatrix} b_{1j} \\ b_{2j} \\ \vdots \\ b_{pj} \end{bmatrix} = a_{i1}b_{1j} + a_{i2}b_{2j} + \cdots + a_{ip}b_{pj}.$$

That is,

$$\mathbf{a}_i \mathbf{b}_j = \sum_{k=1}^{p} a_{ik}b_{kj}. \tag{16}$$

One can visualize "pouring the ith row of $\mathbf{A}$ down the jth column of $\mathbf{B}$" until elements match in pairs, then forming the sum of the products of these pairs, to obtain the element c_{ij} of the matrix $\mathbf{C} = \mathbf{AB}$.

SUGGESTION The key to accuracy and confidence in computing matrix products lies in doing it systematically. Always perform your computations in the same order. *First* calculate the elements of the *first* row of $\mathbf{AB}$ by multiplying the *first* row of $\mathbf{A}$ by the successive columns of $\mathbf{B}$; *second*, calculate the elements of the *second* row of $\mathbf{AB}$ by multiplying the *second* row of $\mathbf{A}$ by the successive columns of $\mathbf{B}$; and so forth.

Computing systems often are used for the calculation of products of "large" matrices. If the matrices $\mathbf{A}$ and $\mathbf{B}$, with appropriate sizes, have been entered—as illustrated in the 3.2 Application—then the *Maple* command

```
with(linalg) : C := multiply(A,B),
```

or the *Mathematica* command

```
C = A.B,
```

or the MATLAB command

```
C = A*B
```

immediately yield the product matrix $\mathbf{C} = \mathbf{AB}$.

Matrix Equations

If $\mathbf{A} = \begin{bmatrix} a_{ij} \end{bmatrix}$ is an $m \times n$ coefficient matrix and $\mathbf{x} = (x_1, x_2, \ldots, x_n)$ is an $n \times 1$ variable (column) matrix, then the product $\mathbf{Ax}$ is the $m \times 1$ matrix

$$\mathbf{Ax} = \begin{bmatrix} a_{11} & a_{12} & \cdots & a_{1n} \\ a_{21} & a_{22} & \cdots & a_{2n} \\ \vdots & \vdots & \ddots & \vdots \\ a_{m1} & a_{m2} & \cdots & a_{mn} \end{bmatrix} \begin{bmatrix} x_1 \\ x_2 \\ \vdots \\ x_n \end{bmatrix}$$

$$= \begin{bmatrix} a_{11}x_1 + a_{12}x_2 + \cdots + a_{1n}x_n \\ a_{21}x_1 + a_{22}x_2 + \cdots + a_{2n}x_n \\ \vdots \\ a_{m1}x_1 + a_{m2}x_2 + \cdots + a_{mn}x_n \end{bmatrix} \overset{(?)}{=} \begin{bmatrix} b_1 \\ b_2 \\ \vdots \\ b_m \end{bmatrix} = \mathbf{b}.$$

We therefore see that

$$\mathbf{Ax} = \mathbf{b} \tag{17}$$

if and only if $\mathbf{x} = (x_1, x_2, \ldots, x_n)$ is a solution of the linear system in (5). Thus, matrix multiplication enables us to "boil down" a system of m scalar equations in n unknowns to the single matrix equation in (17), which is analogous in notation to the single scalar equation $ax = b$ in a single variable x.

Example 7

The system

$$\begin{aligned} 3x_1 - 4x_2 + x_3 + 7x_4 &= 10 \\ 4x_1 \qquad - 5x_3 + 2x_4 &= 0 \\ x_1 + 9x_2 + 2x_3 - 6x_4 &= 5 \end{aligned}$$

of three equations in four unknowns is equivalent to the single matrix equation

$$\begin{bmatrix} 3 & -4 & 1 & 7 \\ 4 & 0 & -5 & 2 \\ 1 & 9 & 2 & -6 \end{bmatrix} \begin{bmatrix} x_1 \\ x_2 \\ x_3 \\ x_4 \end{bmatrix} = \begin{bmatrix} 10 \\ 0 \\ 5 \end{bmatrix}. \qquad ∎$$

Matrix Algebra

The definitions of matrix addition and multiplication can be used to establish the rules of matrix algebra listed in the following theorem.

THEOREM 1: Rules of Matrix Algebra

If $\mathbf{A}$, $\mathbf{B}$, and $\mathbf{C}$ are matrices of appropriate sizes to make the indicated operations possible, then the following identities hold.

Commutative law of addition:	$\mathbf{A} + \mathbf{B} = \mathbf{B} + \mathbf{A}$
Associative law of addition:	$\mathbf{A} + (\mathbf{B} + \mathbf{C}) = (\mathbf{A} + \mathbf{B}) + \mathbf{C}$
Associative law of multiplication:	$\mathbf{A}(\mathbf{BC}) = (\mathbf{AB})\mathbf{C}$
Distributive laws:	$\mathbf{A}(\mathbf{B} + \mathbf{C}) = \mathbf{AB} + \mathbf{AC}$

and

$$(\mathbf{A} + \mathbf{B})\mathbf{C} = \mathbf{AC} + \mathbf{BC} \qquad ▲$$

The only verification that is not entirely routine is that of the associative law of multiplication; see Problem 44 for an outline. Each of the others follows quickly from the corresponding law for the ordinary arithmetic of real numbers. As an illustration, we prove the first distributive law. Suppose that $\mathbf{A} = \begin{bmatrix} a_{ij} \end{bmatrix}$ is an $m \times p$ matrix and that $\mathbf{B} = \begin{bmatrix} b_{ij} \end{bmatrix}$ and $\mathbf{C} = \begin{bmatrix} c_{ij} \end{bmatrix}$ are $p \times n$ matrices. Then

$$\mathbf{B} + \mathbf{C} = \begin{bmatrix} b_{ij} + c_{ij} \end{bmatrix},$$

so by (16) the ijth element of the $m \times n$ matrix $\mathbf{A}(\mathbf{B} + \mathbf{C})$ is

$$\sum_{k=1}^{p} a_{ik}(b_{kj} + c_{kj}). \tag{18}$$

The ijth element of the $m \times n$ matrix $\mathbf{AB} + \mathbf{AC}$ is

$$\sum_{k=1}^{p} a_{ik}b_{kj} + \sum_{k=1}^{p} a_{ik}c_{kj} = \sum_{k=1}^{p} (a_{ik}b_{kj} + a_{ik}c_{kj}). \tag{19}$$

But the distributive law for real numbers, $a(b + c) = ab + ac$, tells us that corresponding terms of the sums in (18) and (19) are equal. Hence, the ijth terms of the two $m \times n$ matrices $\mathbf{A}(\mathbf{B} + \mathbf{C})$ and $\mathbf{AB} + \mathbf{AC}$ are equal, and so these matrices are equal: $\mathbf{A}(\mathbf{B} + \mathbf{C}) = \mathbf{AB} + \mathbf{AC}$.

If a and b are real numbers, then rules such as

$$(a + b)\mathbf{C} = a\mathbf{C} + b\mathbf{C}, \quad (ab)\mathbf{C} = a(b\mathbf{C}), \quad a(\mathbf{BC}) = (a\mathbf{B})\mathbf{C}$$

are even easier to verify. What all these rules amount to is this: *In matrix manipulations, pairs of parentheses can be inserted or deleted in the same ways as in the ordinary algebra of real numbers.*

But not all of the rules of "ordinary" algebra carry over to matrix algebra. In Example 5 we saw that multiplication of matrices is *not* commutative—in general, $\mathbf{AB} \neq \mathbf{BA}$. Other exceptions are associated with zero matrices. A **zero matrix** is one whose elements are *all* zero, such as

$$\begin{bmatrix} 0 & 0 \\ 0 & 0 \end{bmatrix}, \quad \begin{bmatrix} 0 & 0 & 0 \\ 0 & 0 & 0 \end{bmatrix}, \quad \begin{bmatrix} 0 & 0 \\ 0 & 0 \\ 0 & 0 \end{bmatrix}, \quad \begin{bmatrix} 0 \\ 0 \end{bmatrix}.$$

We ordinarily denote a zero matrix (whatever its size) by $\mathbf{0}$. It should be clear that for any matrix $\mathbf{A}$,

$$\mathbf{0} + \mathbf{A} = \mathbf{A} = \mathbf{A} + \mathbf{0}, \quad \mathbf{A0} = \mathbf{0}, \quad \text{and} \quad \mathbf{0A} = \mathbf{0},$$

where in each case $\mathbf{0}$ is a zero matrix of appropriate size. Thus zero matrices appear to play a role in the arithmetic of matrices similar to the role of the real number 0 in ordinary arithmetic.

For real numbers, the following two rules are familiar:

- If $ab = ac$ and $a \neq 0$, then $b = c$
    (the "cancellation law").
- If $ad = 0$, then either $a = 0$ or $d = 0$.

The following example shows that matrices do *not* obey either of these rules.

Example 8   If

$$A = \begin{bmatrix} 4 & 1 & -2 & 7 \\ 3 & 1 & -1 & 5 \end{bmatrix}, \quad B = \begin{bmatrix} 1 & 5 \\ 3 & -1 \\ -2 & 4 \\ 2 & -3 \end{bmatrix}, \quad \text{and} \quad C = \begin{bmatrix} 3 & 4 \\ 2 & 1 \\ -2 & 3 \\ 1 & -3 \end{bmatrix},$$

then $B \neq C$, but

$$AB = \begin{bmatrix} 25 & -10 \\ 18 & -5 \end{bmatrix} = AC. \qquad \text{(Check this!)}$$

Thus the cancellation law does not generally hold for matrices. If

$$D = B - C = \begin{bmatrix} -2 & 1 \\ 1 & -2 \\ 0 & 1 \\ 1 & 0 \end{bmatrix},$$

then

$$AD = \begin{bmatrix} 0 & 0 \\ 0 & 0 \end{bmatrix} = 0,$$

despite the fact that neither A nor D is a zero matrix. See Problems 31–38 for additional ways in which the algebra of matrices differs significantly from the familiar algebra of real numbers. ∎

Recall that an *identity matrix* is a square matrix I that has ones on its principal diagonal and zeros elsewhere. Identity matrices play a role in matrix arithmetic which is strongly analogous to that of the real number 1, for which $a \cdot 1 = 1 \cdot a = a$ for all values of the real number a. For instance,

$$\begin{bmatrix} a & b \\ c & d \end{bmatrix} \begin{bmatrix} 1 & 0 \\ 0 & 1 \end{bmatrix} = \begin{bmatrix} 1 & 0 \\ 0 & 1 \end{bmatrix} \begin{bmatrix} a & b \\ c & d \end{bmatrix} = \begin{bmatrix} a & b \\ c & d \end{bmatrix}.$$

Similarly, if

$$A = \begin{bmatrix} a_{11} & a_{12} & a_{13} \\ a_{21} & a_{22} & a_{23} \\ a_{31} & a_{32} & a_{33} \end{bmatrix} \quad \text{and} \quad I = \begin{bmatrix} 1 & 0 & 0 \\ 0 & 1 & 0 \\ 0 & 0 & 1 \end{bmatrix},$$

then $AI = IA = A$. For instance, the element in the second row and third column of AI is

$$(a_{21})(0) + (a_{22})(0) + (a_{23})(1) = a_{23}.$$

If a is a nonzero real number and $b = a^{-1}$, then $ab = ba = 1$. Given a nonzero square matrix A, the question as to whether there exists an *inverse matrix* B, one such that $AB = BA = I$, is more complicated and is investigated in Section 3.5.

3.4 Problems

In Problems 1–4, two matrices $\mathbf{A}$ and $\mathbf{B}$ and two numbers c and d are given. Compute the matrix $c\mathbf{A} + d\mathbf{B}$.

1. $\mathbf{A} = \begin{bmatrix} 3 & -5 \\ 2 & 7 \end{bmatrix}$, $\mathbf{B} = \begin{bmatrix} -1 & 0 \\ 3 & -4 \end{bmatrix}$, $c = 3$, $d = 4$

2. $\mathbf{A} = \begin{bmatrix} 2 & 0 & -3 \\ -1 & 5 & 6 \end{bmatrix}$, $\mathbf{B} = \begin{bmatrix} -2 & 3 & 1 \\ 7 & 1 & 5 \end{bmatrix}$, $c = 5$, $d = -3$

3. $\mathbf{A} = \begin{bmatrix} 5 & 0 \\ 0 & 7 \\ 3 & -1 \end{bmatrix}$, $\mathbf{B} = \begin{bmatrix} -4 & 5 \\ 3 & 2 \\ 7 & 4 \end{bmatrix}$, $c = -2$, $d = 4$

4. $\mathbf{A} = \begin{bmatrix} 2 & -1 & 0 \\ 4 & 0 & -3 \\ 5 & -2 & 7 \end{bmatrix}$, $\mathbf{B} = \begin{bmatrix} 6 & -3 & -4 \\ 5 & 2 & -1 \\ 0 & 7 & 9 \end{bmatrix}$, $c = 7$, $d = 5$

In Problems 5–12, two matrices $\mathbf{A}$ and $\mathbf{B}$ are given. Calculate whichever of the matrices $\mathbf{AB}$ and $\mathbf{BA}$ is defined.

5. $\mathbf{A} = \begin{bmatrix} 2 & -1 \\ 3 & 2 \end{bmatrix}$, $\mathbf{B} = \begin{bmatrix} -4 & 2 \\ 1 & 3 \end{bmatrix}$

6. $\mathbf{A} = \begin{bmatrix} 1 & 0 & -3 \\ 3 & 2 & 4 \\ 2 & -3 & 5 \end{bmatrix}$, $\mathbf{B} = \begin{bmatrix} 7 & -4 & 3 \\ 1 & 5 & -2 \\ 0 & 3 & 9 \end{bmatrix}$

7. $\mathbf{A} = \begin{bmatrix} 1 & 2 & 3 \end{bmatrix}$, $\mathbf{B} = \begin{bmatrix} 3 \\ 4 \\ 5 \end{bmatrix}$

8. $\mathbf{A} = \begin{bmatrix} 1 & 0 & 3 \\ 2 & -5 & 4 \end{bmatrix}$, $\mathbf{B} = \begin{bmatrix} 3 & 0 \\ -1 & 4 \\ 6 & 5 \end{bmatrix}$

9. $\mathbf{A} = \begin{bmatrix} 3 \\ -2 \end{bmatrix}$, $\mathbf{B} = \begin{bmatrix} 0 & -2 \\ 3 & 1 \\ -4 & 5 \end{bmatrix}$

10. $\mathbf{A} = \begin{bmatrix} 2 & 1 \\ 4 & 3 \end{bmatrix}$, $\mathbf{B} = \begin{bmatrix} -1 & 0 & 4 \\ 3 & -2 & 5 \end{bmatrix}$

11. $\mathbf{A} = \begin{bmatrix} 3 & -5 \end{bmatrix}$, $\mathbf{B} = \begin{bmatrix} 2 & 7 & 5 & 6 \\ -1 & 4 & 2 & 3 \end{bmatrix}$

12. $\mathbf{A} = \begin{bmatrix} 1 & 0 & 3 & -2 \end{bmatrix}$, $\mathbf{B} = \begin{bmatrix} 2 & -7 & 5 \\ 3 & 9 & 10 \end{bmatrix}$

In Problems 13–16, three matrices $\mathbf{A}$, $\mathbf{B}$, and $\mathbf{C}$ are given. Verify by computation of both sides the associative law $\mathbf{A(BC)} = (\mathbf{AB})\mathbf{C}$.

13. $\mathbf{A} = \begin{bmatrix} 3 & 1 \\ -1 & 4 \end{bmatrix}$, $\mathbf{B} = \begin{bmatrix} 2 & 5 \\ -3 & 1 \end{bmatrix}$, $\mathbf{C} = \begin{bmatrix} 0 & 1 \\ 2 & 3 \end{bmatrix}$

14. $\mathbf{A} = \begin{bmatrix} 2 & -1 \end{bmatrix}$, $\mathbf{B} = \begin{bmatrix} 2 & 5 \\ -3 & 1 \end{bmatrix}$, $\mathbf{C} = \begin{bmatrix} 6 \\ -5 \end{bmatrix}$

15. $\mathbf{A} = \begin{bmatrix} 3 \\ 2 \end{bmatrix}$, $\mathbf{B} = \begin{bmatrix} 1 & -1 & 2 \end{bmatrix}$, $\mathbf{C} = \begin{bmatrix} 2 & 0 \\ 0 & 3 \\ 1 & 4 \end{bmatrix}$

16. $\mathbf{A} = \begin{bmatrix} 2 & 0 \\ 0 & 3 \\ 1 & 4 \end{bmatrix}$, $\mathbf{B} = \begin{bmatrix} 1 & -1 \\ 3 & -2 \end{bmatrix}$, $\mathbf{C} = \begin{bmatrix} 1 & 0 & -1 & 2 \\ 3 & 2 & 0 & 1 \end{bmatrix}$

In Problems 17–22, first write each given homogeneous system in the matrix form $\mathbf{Ax} = \mathbf{0}$. Then find the solution in vector form, as in Eq. (9).

17. $\begin{aligned} x_1 \quad - 5x_3 + 4x_4 &= 0 \\ x_2 + 2x_3 - 7x_4 &= 0 \end{aligned}$

18. $\begin{aligned} x_1 - 3x_2 \quad + 6x_4 &= 0 \\ x_3 + 9x_4 &= 0 \end{aligned}$

19. $\begin{aligned} x_1 \quad\quad + 3x_4 - x_5 &= 0 \\ x_2 \quad - 2x_4 + 6x_5 &= 0 \\ x_3 + x_4 - 8x_5 &= 0 \end{aligned}$

20. $\begin{aligned} x_1 - 3x_2 \quad\quad + 7x_5 &= 0 \\ x_3 \quad - 2x_5 &= 0 \\ x_4 - 10x_5 &= 0 \end{aligned}$

21. $\begin{aligned} x_1 \quad - x_3 + 2x_4 + 7x_5 &= 0 \\ x_2 + 2x_3 - 3x_4 + 4x_5 &= 0 \end{aligned}$

22. $\begin{aligned} x_1 - x_2 \quad + 7x_4 + 3x_5 &= 0 \\ x_3 - x_4 - 2x_5 &= 0 \end{aligned}$

23. Let
$$\mathbf{A} = \begin{bmatrix} 2 & 1 \\ 3 & 2 \end{bmatrix}, \quad \mathbf{B} = \begin{bmatrix} a & b \\ c & d \end{bmatrix},$$
and
$$\mathbf{I} = \begin{bmatrix} 1 & 0 \\ 0 & 1 \end{bmatrix}.$$

Find $\mathbf{B}$ so that $\mathbf{AB} = \mathbf{I} = \mathbf{BA}$ as follows: First equate entries on the two sides of the equation $\mathbf{AB} = \mathbf{I}$. Then solve the resulting four equations for a, b, c, and d. Finally verify that $\mathbf{BA} = \mathbf{I}$ as well.

24. Repeat Problem 23, but with $\mathbf{A}$ replaced by the matrix
$$\mathbf{A} = \begin{bmatrix} 3 & 4 \\ 5 & 7 \end{bmatrix}.$$

25. Repeat Problem 23, but with $\mathbf{A}$ replaced by the matrix
$$\mathbf{A} = \begin{bmatrix} 5 & 7 \\ 2 & 3 \end{bmatrix}.$$

26. Use the technique of Problem 23 to show that if
$$\mathbf{A} = \begin{bmatrix} 1 & -2 \\ -2 & 4 \end{bmatrix},$$
then there does not exist a matrix $\mathbf{B}$ such that $\mathbf{AB} = \mathbf{I}$. *Suggestion:* Show that the system of four equations in a, b, c, and d is inconsistent.

27. A **diagonal matrix** is a square matrix of the form
$$\begin{bmatrix} a_1 & 0 & 0 & \cdots & 0 \\ 0 & a_2 & 0 & \cdots & 0 \\ 0 & 0 & a_3 & \cdots & 0 \\ \vdots & \vdots & \vdots & \ddots & \vdots \\ 0 & 0 & 0 & \cdots & a_n \end{bmatrix},$$

in which every element off the main diagonal is zero. Show that the product **AB** of two $n \times n$ diagonal matrices **A** and **B** is again a diagonal matrix. State a concise rule for quickly computing **AB**. Is it clear that **AB** = **BA**? Explain.

28. The positive integral powers of a square matrix **A** are defined as follows:

$$\mathbf{A}^1 = \mathbf{A}, \qquad \mathbf{A}^2 = \mathbf{AA}, \qquad \mathbf{A}^3 = \mathbf{AA}^2,$$
$$\mathbf{A}^4 = \mathbf{AA}^3, \dots, \qquad\qquad \mathbf{A}^{n+1} = \mathbf{AA}^n, \dots.$$

Suppose that r and s are positive integers. Prove that $\mathbf{A}^r \mathbf{A}^s = \mathbf{A}^{r+s}$ and that $(\mathbf{A}^r)^s = \mathbf{A}^{rs}$ (in close analogy with the laws of exponents for real numbers).

29. If $\mathbf{A} = \begin{bmatrix} a & b \\ c & d \end{bmatrix}$, then show that

$$\mathbf{A}^2 = (a + d)\mathbf{A} - (ad - bc)\mathbf{I},$$

where **I** denotes the 2×2 identity matrix.

30. The formula in Problem 29 can be used to compute $\mathbf{A}^2$ without an explicit matrix multiplication. It follows that

$$\mathbf{A}^3 = (a + d)\mathbf{A}^2 - (ad - bc)\mathbf{A}$$

without an explicit matrix multiplication,

$$\mathbf{A}^4 = (a + d)\mathbf{A}^3 - (ad - bc)\mathbf{A}^2,$$

and so on. Use this method to compute $\mathbf{A}^2$, $\mathbf{A}^3$, $\mathbf{A}^4$, and $\mathbf{A}^5$ given

$$\mathbf{A} = \begin{bmatrix} 2 & 1 \\ 1 & 2 \end{bmatrix}.$$

Problems 31–38 illustrate ways in which the algebra of matrices is not *analogous to the algebra of real numbers.*

31. (a) Suppose that **A** and **B** are the matrices of Example 5. Show that $(\mathbf{A} + \mathbf{B})(\mathbf{A} - \mathbf{B}) \neq \mathbf{A}^2 - \mathbf{B}^2$.
    (b) Suppose that **A** and **B** are square matrices with the property that **AB** = **BA**. Show that $(\mathbf{A} + \mathbf{B})(\mathbf{A} - \mathbf{B}) = \mathbf{A}^2 - \mathbf{B}^2$.

32. (a) Suppose that **A** and **B** are the matrices of Example 5. Show that $(\mathbf{A} + \mathbf{B})^2 \neq \mathbf{A}^2 + 2\mathbf{AB} + \mathbf{B}^2$.
    (b) Suppose that **A** and **B** are square matrices such that **AB** = **BA**. Show that $(\mathbf{A} + \mathbf{B})^2 = \mathbf{A}^2 + 2\mathbf{AB} + \mathbf{B}^2$.

33. Find four different 2×2 matrices **A**, with each main diagonal element either $+1$ or -1, such that $\mathbf{A}^2 = \mathbf{I}$.

34. Find a 2×2 matrix **A** with each element $+1$ or -1 such that $\mathbf{A}^2 = \mathbf{0}$. The formula of Problem 29 may be helpful.

35. Use the formula of Problem 29 to find a 2×2 matrix **A** such that $\mathbf{A} \neq \mathbf{0}$ and $\mathbf{A} \neq \mathbf{I}$ but such that $\mathbf{A}^2 = \mathbf{A}$.

36. Find a 2×2 matrix **A** with each main diagonal element zero such that $\mathbf{A}^2 = \mathbf{I}$.

37. Find a 2×2 matrix **A** with each main diagonal element zero such that $\mathbf{A}^2 = -\mathbf{I}$.

38. This is a continuation of the previous two problems. Find two nonzero 2×2 matrices **A** and **B** such that $\mathbf{A}^2 + \mathbf{B}^2 = \mathbf{0}$.

39. Use matrix multiplication to show that if $\mathbf{x}_1$ and $\mathbf{x}_2$ are two solutions of the homogeneous system $\mathbf{Ax} = \mathbf{0}$ and c_1 and c_2 are real numbers, then $c_1\mathbf{x}_1 + c_2\mathbf{x}_2$ is also a solution.

40. (a) Use matrix multiplication to show that if $\mathbf{x}_0$ is a solution of the homogeneous system $\mathbf{Ax} = \mathbf{0}$ and $\mathbf{x}_1$ is a solution of the nonhomogeneous system $\mathbf{Ax} = \mathbf{b}$, then $\mathbf{x}_0 + \mathbf{x}_1$ is also a solution of the nonhomogeneous system.
    (b) Suppose that $\mathbf{x}_1$ and $\mathbf{x}_2$ are solutions of the nonhomogeneous system of part (a). Show that $\mathbf{x}_1 - \mathbf{x}_2$ is a solution of the homogeneous system $\mathbf{Ax} = \mathbf{0}$.

41. This is a continuation of Problem 32. Show that if **A** and **B** are square matrices such that **AB** = **BA**, then

$$(\mathbf{A} + \mathbf{B})^3 = \mathbf{A}^3 + 3\mathbf{A}^2\mathbf{B} + 3\mathbf{AB}^2 + \mathbf{B}^3$$

and

$$(\mathbf{A} + \mathbf{B})^4 = \mathbf{A}^4 + 4\mathbf{A}^3\mathbf{B} + 6\mathbf{A}^2\mathbf{B}^2 + 4\mathbf{AB}^3 + \mathbf{B}^4.$$

42. Let

$$\mathbf{A} = \begin{bmatrix} 1 & 2 & 0 \\ 0 & 1 & 2 \\ 0 & 0 & 1 \end{bmatrix}$$
$$= \begin{bmatrix} 1 & 0 & 0 \\ 0 & 1 & 0 \\ 0 & 0 & 1 \end{bmatrix} + \begin{bmatrix} 0 & 2 & 0 \\ 0 & 0 & 2 \\ 0 & 0 & 0 \end{bmatrix} = \mathbf{I} + \mathbf{N}.$$

(a) Show that $\mathbf{N}^2 \neq \mathbf{0}$ but $\mathbf{N}^3 = \mathbf{0}$.
(b) Use the binomial formulas of Problem 41 to compute

$$\mathbf{A}^2 = (\mathbf{I} + \mathbf{N})^2 = \mathbf{I} + 2\mathbf{N} + \mathbf{N}^2,$$
$$\mathbf{A}^3 = (\mathbf{I} + \mathbf{N})^3 = \mathbf{I} + 3\mathbf{N} + 3\mathbf{N}^2,$$

and

$$\mathbf{A}^4 = (\mathbf{I} + \mathbf{N})^4 = \mathbf{I} + 4\mathbf{N} + 6\mathbf{N}^2.$$

43. Consider the 3×3 matrix

$$\mathbf{A} = \begin{bmatrix} 2 & -1 & -1 \\ -1 & 2 & -1 \\ -1 & -1 & 2 \end{bmatrix}.$$

First verify by direct computation that $\mathbf{A}^2 = 3\mathbf{A}$. Then conclude that $\mathbf{A}^{n+1} = 3^n\mathbf{A}$ for every positive integer n.

44. Let $\mathbf{A} = \begin{bmatrix} a_{hi} \end{bmatrix}$, $\mathbf{B} = \begin{bmatrix} b_{ij} \end{bmatrix}$, and $\mathbf{C} = \begin{bmatrix} c_{jk} \end{bmatrix}$ be matrices of sizes $m \times n$, $n \times p$, and $p \times q$, respectively. To establish the associative law $\mathbf{A(BC)} = \mathbf{(AB)C}$, proceed as follows. By Equation (16) the hjth element of **AB** is

$$\sum_{i=1}^{n} a_{hi}b_{ij}.$$

By another application of Equation (16), the hkth element of **(AB)C** is

$$\sum_{j=1}^{p} \left(\sum_{i=1}^{n} a_{hi}b_{ij} \right) c_{jk} = \sum_{i=1}^{n} \sum_{j=1}^{p} a_{hi}b_{ij}c_{jk}.$$

Show similarly that the double sum on the right is also equal to the hkth element of **A(BC)**. Hence the $m \times q$ matrices **(AB)C** and **A(BC)** are equal.

3.5 Inverses of Matrices

Recall that the $n \times n$ **identity matrix** is the diagonal matrix

$$\mathbf{I} = \begin{bmatrix} 1 & 0 & 0 & \cdots & 0 \\ 0 & 1 & 0 & \cdots & 0 \\ 0 & 0 & 1 & \cdots & 0 \\ \vdots & \vdots & \vdots & \ddots & \vdots \\ 0 & 0 & 0 & \cdots & 1 \end{bmatrix} \tag{1}$$

having 1s on its main diagonal and 0s elsewhere. It is not difficult to deduce directly from the definition of the matrix product that $\mathbf{I}$ acts like an identity for matrix multiplication:

$$\mathbf{AI} = \mathbf{A} \quad \text{and} \quad \mathbf{IB} = \mathbf{B} \tag{2}$$

if the sizes of $\mathbf{A}$ and $\mathbf{B}$ are such that the products $\mathbf{AI}$ and $\mathbf{IB}$ are defined. It is, nevertheless, instructive to derive the identities in (2) formally from the two basic facts about matrix multiplication that we state below. First, recall that the notation

$$\mathbf{A} = \begin{bmatrix} \mathbf{a}_1 & \mathbf{a}_2 & \mathbf{a}_3 & \cdots & \mathbf{a}_n \end{bmatrix} \tag{3}$$

expresses the $m \times n$ matrix $\mathbf{A}$ in terms of its column vectors $\mathbf{a}_1, \mathbf{a}_2, \mathbf{a}_3, \ldots,$ and $\mathbf{a}_n$.

Fact 1 **$\mathbf{Ax}$** *in terms of columns of* **$\mathbf{A}$**

If $\mathbf{A} = \begin{bmatrix} \mathbf{a}_1 & \mathbf{a}_2 & \cdots & \mathbf{a}_n \end{bmatrix}$ and $\mathbf{x} = (x_1, x_2, \ldots, x_n)$ is an n-vector, then

$$\mathbf{Ax} = x_1\mathbf{a}_1 + x_2\mathbf{a}_2 + \cdots + x_n\mathbf{a}_n. \tag{4}$$

The reason is that when each row vector of $\mathbf{A}$ is multiplied by the column vector $\mathbf{x}$, its jth element is multiplied by x_j.

Fact 2 **$\mathbf{AB}$** *in terms of columns of* **$\mathbf{B}$**

If $\mathbf{A}$ is an $m \times n$ matrix $\mathbf{B} = \begin{bmatrix} \mathbf{b}_1 & \mathbf{b}_2 & \cdots & \mathbf{b}_p \end{bmatrix}$ is an $n \times p$ matrix, then

$$\mathbf{AB} = \begin{bmatrix} \mathbf{Ab}_1 & \mathbf{Ab}_2 & \cdots & \mathbf{Ab}_p \end{bmatrix}. \tag{5}$$

That is, *the jth column of $\mathbf{AB}$ is the product of $\mathbf{A}$ and the jth column of $\mathbf{B}$.* The reason is that the elements of the jth column of $\mathbf{AB}$ are obtained by multiplying the individual rows of $\mathbf{A}$ by the jth column of $\mathbf{B}$.

Example 1 The third column of the product $\mathbf{AB}$ of the matrices

$$\mathbf{A} = \begin{bmatrix} 2 & -1 & 0 \\ 4 & 0 & 3 \end{bmatrix} \quad \text{and} \quad \mathbf{B} = \begin{bmatrix} 3 & 7 & 5 & -4 \\ -2 & 6 & 3 & 6 \\ 5 & 1 & -2 & -1 \end{bmatrix}$$

is

$$\mathbf{Ab}_3 = \begin{bmatrix} 2 & -1 & 0 \\ 4 & 0 & 3 \end{bmatrix} \begin{bmatrix} 5 \\ 3 \\ -2 \end{bmatrix} = \begin{bmatrix} 7 \\ 14 \end{bmatrix}. \qquad \blacksquare$$

To prove that $\mathbf{AI} = \mathbf{A}$, note first that

$$\mathbf{I} = \begin{bmatrix} \mathbf{e}_1 & \mathbf{e}_2 & \cdots & \mathbf{e}_n \end{bmatrix}, \tag{6}$$

where the jth column vector of $\mathbf{I}$ is the jth **basic unit vector**

$$\mathbf{e}_j = \begin{bmatrix} 0 \\ \vdots \\ 1 \\ \vdots \\ 0 \end{bmatrix} \leftarrow j\text{th entry.} \tag{7}$$

If $\mathbf{A} = \begin{bmatrix} \mathbf{a}_1 & \mathbf{a}_2 & \cdots & \mathbf{a}_n \end{bmatrix}$, then Fact 1 yields

$$\mathbf{Ae}_j = 0 \cdot \mathbf{a}_1 + \cdots + 1 \cdot \mathbf{a}_j + \cdots + 0 \cdot \mathbf{a}_n = \mathbf{a}_j. \tag{8}$$

Hence Fact 2 gives

$$\mathbf{AI} = \mathbf{A} \begin{bmatrix} \mathbf{e}_1 & \mathbf{e}_2 & \cdots & \mathbf{e}_n \end{bmatrix}$$
$$= \begin{bmatrix} \mathbf{Ae}_1 & \mathbf{Ae}_2 & \cdots & \mathbf{Ae}_n \end{bmatrix} = \begin{bmatrix} \mathbf{a}_1 & \mathbf{a}_2 & \cdots & \mathbf{a}_n \end{bmatrix};$$

that is, $\mathbf{AI} = \mathbf{A}$. The proof that $\mathbf{IB} = \mathbf{B}$ is similar. (See Problems 41 and 42.)

The Inverse Matrix $\mathbf{A}^{-1}$

If $a \neq 0$, then there is a number $b = a^{-1} = 1/a$ such that $ab = ba = 1$. Given a nonzero matrix $\mathbf{A}$, we therefore wonder whether there is a matrix $\mathbf{B}$ such that $\mathbf{AB} = \mathbf{BA} = \mathbf{I}$. The following two examples show that the answer to this question depends upon the particular matrix $\mathbf{A}$.

Example 2 If

$$\mathbf{A} = \begin{bmatrix} 4 & 9 \\ 3 & 7 \end{bmatrix} \quad \text{and} \quad \mathbf{B} = \begin{bmatrix} 7 & -9 \\ -3 & 4 \end{bmatrix},$$

then

$$\mathbf{AB} = \begin{bmatrix} 4 & 9 \\ 3 & 7 \end{bmatrix} \begin{bmatrix} 7 & -9 \\ -3 & 4 \end{bmatrix} = \begin{bmatrix} 1 & 0 \\ 0 & 1 \end{bmatrix} = \mathbf{I};$$

$\mathbf{BA} = \mathbf{I}$ by a similar computation.   ∎

Example 3 Let

$$\mathbf{A} = \begin{bmatrix} 1 & -3 \\ -2 & 6 \end{bmatrix} \quad \text{and} \quad \mathbf{B} = \begin{bmatrix} a & b \\ c & d \end{bmatrix}.$$

If the matrix $\mathbf{B}$ had the property that $\mathbf{AB} = \mathbf{BA} = \mathbf{I}$, then

$$\mathbf{AB} = \begin{bmatrix} 1 & -3 \\ -2 & 6 \end{bmatrix} \begin{bmatrix} a & b \\ c & d \end{bmatrix}$$
$$= \begin{bmatrix} a - 3c & b - 3d \\ -2a + 6c & -2b + 6d \end{bmatrix} = \begin{bmatrix} 1 & 0 \\ 0 & 1 \end{bmatrix}.$$

But upon equating corresponding elements of **AB** and the 2×2 identity matrix in the last line, we find that

$$a - 3c = 1 \qquad \text{and} \qquad b - 3d = 0$$
$$-2a + 6c = 0 \qquad \qquad -2b + 6d = 1.$$

It is clear that these equations are inconsistent. Thus there can exist *no* 2×2 matrix **B** such that **AB = I**. ∎

Definition: Invertible Matrix

The square matrix **A** is called **invertible** if there exists a matrix **B** such that

$$\mathbf{AB} = \mathbf{BA} = \mathbf{I}.$$

Thus the matrix **A** of Example 2 is invertible, whereas the matrix **A** of Example 3 is not invertible.

A matrix **B** such that **AB = BA = I** is called an **inverse matrix** of the matrix **A**. The following theorem says that no matrix can have two different inverse matrices.

THEOREM 1: Uniqueness of Inverse Matrices

If the matrix **A** is invertible, then there exists precisely one matrix **B** such that **AB = BA = I**.

Proof: If **C** is a (possibly different) matrix such that **AC = CA = I** as well, then

$$\mathbf{C} = \mathbf{CI} = \mathbf{C(AB)} = \mathbf{(CA)B} = \mathbf{IB} = \mathbf{B}.$$

Thus **C** is in fact the same matrix as **B**. ▲

The unique inverse of an invertible matrix **A** is denoted by $\mathbf{A}^{-1}$. Thus we say in Example 2 that

$$\text{If} \quad \mathbf{A} = \begin{bmatrix} 4 & 9 \\ 3 & 7 \end{bmatrix} \quad \text{then} \quad \mathbf{A}^{-1} = \begin{bmatrix} 7 & -9 \\ -3 & 4 \end{bmatrix}.$$

In the case of a 2×2 matrix **A**, it is easy to determine whether or not **A** is invertible and to find $\mathbf{A}^{-1}$ if it exists. In Problems 36 and 37 we ask you to verify the following result.

THEOREM 2: Inverses of 2 x 2 Matrices

The 2×2 matrix

$$\mathbf{A} = \begin{bmatrix} a & b \\ c & d \end{bmatrix}$$

is invertible if and only if $ad - bc \neq 0$, in which case

$$\mathbf{A}^{-1} = \frac{1}{ad - bc} \begin{bmatrix} d & -b \\ -c & a \end{bmatrix}. \tag{9}$$

▲

Equation (9) gives us the following prescription for writing the inverse of an invertible 2×2 matrix:

- First, interchange the two main diagonal entries.
- Then, change the signs of the two off-diagonal elements.
- Finally, divide each element of the resulting matrix by $ad - bc$.

You might check that this is how $\mathbf{B} = \mathbf{A}^{-1}$ is obtained from $\mathbf{A}$ in Example 2 (in which $ad - bc = 1$).

Example 4   If

$$\mathbf{A} = \begin{bmatrix} 4 & 6 \\ 5 & 9 \end{bmatrix},$$

then $ad - bc = 36 - 30 = 6 \neq 0$, so

$$\mathbf{A}^{-1} = \frac{1}{6} \begin{bmatrix} 9 & -6 \\ -5 & 4 \end{bmatrix} = \begin{bmatrix} \frac{3}{2} & -1 \\ -\frac{5}{6} & \frac{2}{3} \end{bmatrix}. \qquad \blacksquare$$

Arbitrary integral powers of a square matrix $\mathbf{A}$ are defined as follows, though in the case of a negative exponent we must assume that $\mathbf{A}$ is also invertible. If n is a positive integer, we define

$$\mathbf{A}^0 = \mathbf{I} \quad \text{and} \quad \mathbf{A}^1 = \mathbf{A};$$
$$\mathbf{A}^{n+1} = \mathbf{A}^n \mathbf{A} \quad \text{for } n \geq 1;$$
$$\mathbf{A}^{-n} = (\mathbf{A}^{-1})^n.$$

In Problem 28 of Section 3.4, we asked you to verify the laws of exponents

$$\mathbf{A}^r \mathbf{A}^s = \mathbf{A}^{r+s}, \quad (\mathbf{A}^r)^s = \mathbf{A}^{rs} \qquad (10)$$

in the case of positive integral exponents, and Problem 31 of this section deals with the case of negative integral exponents. In Problem 29 we ask you to establish parts (a) and (b) of the following theorem.

THEOREM 3: Algebra of Inverse Matrices

If the matrices $\mathbf{A}$ and $\mathbf{B}$ of the same size are invertible, then

(a) $\mathbf{A}^{-1}$ is invertible and $(A^{-1})^{-1} = \mathbf{A}$;

(b) If n is a nonnegative integer, then $\mathbf{A}^n$ is invertible and $(\mathbf{A}^n)^{-1} = (\mathbf{A}^{-1})^n$;

(c) The product $\mathbf{AB}$ is invertible and

$$(\mathbf{AB})^{-1} = \mathbf{B}^{-1}\mathbf{A}^{-1}. \qquad (11)$$

***Proof of* (c):**

$$(\mathbf{AB})(\mathbf{B}^{-1}\mathbf{A}^{-1}) = \mathbf{A}(\mathbf{BB}^{-1})\mathbf{A}^{-1} = \mathbf{AIA}^{-1} = \mathbf{AA}^{-1} = \mathbf{I};$$
$$(\mathbf{B}^{-1}\mathbf{A}^{-1})(\mathbf{AB}) = \mathbf{B}^{-1}(\mathbf{A}^{-1}\mathbf{A})\mathbf{B} = \mathbf{B}^{-1}\mathbf{IB} = \mathbf{B}^{-1}\mathbf{B} = \mathbf{I}.$$

Thus we get $\mathbf{I}$ when we multiply $\mathbf{AB}$ *on either side* by $\mathbf{B}^{-1}\mathbf{A}^{-1}$. Because the inverse of the matrix $\mathbf{AB}$ is unique, this proves that $\mathbf{AB}$ is invertible and that its inverse matrix is $\mathbf{B}^{-1}\mathbf{A}^{-1}$. $\qquad \blacktriangle$

In mathematics it is frequently important to note the surprises. The surprise in Eq. (11) is the reversal of the natural order of the factors in the right-hand side. You should now be able to show that

$$(\mathbf{ABC})^{-1} = \mathbf{C}^{-1}\mathbf{B}^{-1}\mathbf{A}^{-1}.$$

In general, any product of invertible matrices of the same size is again invertible, and the inverse of a product of invertible matrices is the product *in reverse order* of their inverses.

THEOREM 4: Inverse Matrix Solution of Ax = b

If the $n \times n$ matrix $\mathbf{A}$ is invertible, then for any n-vector $\mathbf{b}$ the system

$$\mathbf{Ax} = \mathbf{b} \tag{12}$$

has the unique solution

$$\mathbf{x} = \mathbf{A}^{-1}\mathbf{b} \tag{13}$$

that is obtained by multiplying both sides in (12) on the left by the matrix $\mathbf{A}^{-1}$.

Proof: We must show that $\mathbf{x} = \mathbf{A}^{-1}\mathbf{b}$ is a solution and that it is the only solution of Eq. (12). First, the computation

$$\mathbf{A}(\mathbf{A}^{-1}\mathbf{b}) = (\mathbf{AA}^{-1})\mathbf{b} = \mathbf{Ib} = \mathbf{b}$$

shows that $\mathbf{x} = \mathbf{A}^{-1}\mathbf{b}$ *is* a solution. Second, if $\mathbf{x}_1$ is any (possibly different) solution, we observe that multiplication of each side of the equation $\mathbf{Ax}_1 = \mathbf{b}$ on the left by $\mathbf{A}^{-1}$ yields $\mathbf{x}_1 = \mathbf{A}^{-1}\mathbf{b}$, and hence $\mathbf{x}_1$ is the same solution as $\mathbf{x}$ after all. ▲

Example 5 To solve the system

$$4x_1 + 6x_2 = 6$$
$$5x_1 + 9x_2 = 18,$$

we use the inverse of the coefficient matrix

$$\mathbf{A} = \begin{bmatrix} 4 & 6 \\ 5 & 9 \end{bmatrix}$$

that we found in Example 4. Then Eq. (13) yields

$$\mathbf{x} = \mathbf{A}^{-1}\mathbf{b} = \begin{bmatrix} 4 & 6 \\ 5 & 9 \end{bmatrix}^{-1} \begin{bmatrix} 6 \\ 18 \end{bmatrix}$$

$$= \begin{bmatrix} \frac{3}{2} & -1 \\ -\frac{5}{6} & \frac{2}{3} \end{bmatrix} \begin{bmatrix} 6 \\ 18 \end{bmatrix} = \begin{bmatrix} -9 \\ 7 \end{bmatrix}.$$

Thus $x_1 = -9$, $x_2 = 7$ is the unique solution. ■

How to Find A^{-1}

Theorem 2 tells us only how to invert 2×2 matrices. The development of a method for inverting larger matrices involves a special class of matrices, which we define next.

Definition: Elementary Matrix

The $n \times n$ matrix **E** is called an **elementary matrix** if it can be obtained by performing a *single* elementary row operation on the $n \times n$ identity matrix **I**.

Example 6

We obtain some typical elementary matrices as follows.

$$\begin{bmatrix} 1 & 0 \\ 0 & 1 \end{bmatrix} \xrightarrow{\ (3)R_1\ } \begin{bmatrix} 3 & 0 \\ 0 & 1 \end{bmatrix} = \mathbf{E}_1$$

$$\begin{bmatrix} 1 & 0 & 0 \\ 0 & 1 & 0 \\ 0 & 0 & 1 \end{bmatrix} \xrightarrow{\ (2)R_1 + R_3\ } \begin{bmatrix} 1 & 0 & 0 \\ 0 & 1 & 0 \\ 2 & 0 & 1 \end{bmatrix} = \mathbf{E}_2$$

$$\begin{bmatrix} 1 & 0 & 0 \\ 0 & 1 & 0 \\ 0 & 0 & 1 \end{bmatrix} \xrightarrow{\ \text{SWAP}(R_1, R_2)\ } \begin{bmatrix} 0 & 1 & 0 \\ 1 & 0 & 0 \\ 0 & 0 & 1 \end{bmatrix} = \mathbf{E}_3$$

The three elementary matrices $\mathbf{E}_1$, $\mathbf{E}_2$, and $\mathbf{E}_3$ correspond to three typical elementary row operations. ∎

Now, suppose that the $m \times m$ elementary matrix **E** corresponds to a certain elementary row operation. It turns out that if we perform this same operation on an arbitrary $m \times n$ matrix **A**, we get the product matrix **EA** that results upon multiplying **A** on the *left* by the matrix **E**. Thus we can carry out an elementary row operation by means of left multiplication by the corresponding elementary matrix. Problems 38–40 illustrate typical cases in the proof of the following theorem.

THEOREM 5: Elementary Matrices and Row Operations

If an elementary row operation is performed on the $m \times n$ matrix **A**, then the result is the product matrix **EA**, where **E** is the elementary matrix obtained by performing the same row operation on the $m \times m$ identity matrix. ▲

Elementary row operations are reversible. That is, to every elementary row operation there corresponds an *inverse* elementary row operation that cancels its effects (see Figure 3.5.1). It follows that *every elementary matrix is invertible*. To see why, let **E** be a given elementary matrix and let $\mathbf{E}_1$ be the elementary matrix corresponding to the inverse of the row operation that transforms **I** into **E**. Then the inverse operation transforms **E** to **I**, so Theorem 5 implies that $\mathbf{E}_1\mathbf{E} = \mathbf{I}$. We see similarly that $\mathbf{E}\mathbf{E}_1 = \mathbf{I}$. Hence, the elementary matrix **E** is invertible with $\mathbf{E}^{-1} = \mathbf{E}_1$.

Elementary matrices are not ordinarily used for computational purposes; it is simpler to carry out row operations directly than to multiply by elementary matrices. Instead, their principal role is in the proof of the following theorem, which leads in turn to a practical method for inverting matrices.

Elementary Row Operation	Inverse Operation
$(c)R_i$	$\dfrac{1}{c}R_i$
SWAP(R_i, R_j)	SWAP(R_i, R_j)
$(c)R_i + R_j$	$(-c)R_i + R_j$

FIGURE 3.5.1. Inverse elementary row operations.

THEOREM 6: Invertible Matrices and Row Operations

The $n \times n$ matrix $\mathbf{A}$ is invertible if and only if it is row equivalent to the $n \times n$ identity matrix $\mathbf{I}$.

Proof: Assume first that $\mathbf{A}$ is invertible. Then, by Theorem 4 (with $\mathbf{b} = \mathbf{0}$), it follows that $\mathbf{Ax} = \mathbf{0}$ has only the trivial solution $\mathbf{x} = \mathbf{0}$. But Theorem 4 in Section 3.3 implies that this is so (if and) only if $\mathbf{A}$ is row equivalent to $\mathbf{I}$.

Now assume, conversely, that $\mathbf{A}$ is row equivalent to $\mathbf{I}$. That is, there is a finite sequence of elementary row operations that transforms $\mathbf{A}$ into $\mathbf{I}$. According to Theorem 5, each of these operations can be performed by multiplying on the left by the corresponding elementary matrix. If $\mathbf{E}_1, \mathbf{E}_2, \ldots, \mathbf{E}_k$ are the elementary matrices corresponding to these row operations, it follows that

$$\mathbf{E}_k \mathbf{E}_{k-1} \cdots \mathbf{E}_2 \mathbf{E}_1 \mathbf{A} = \mathbf{I}. \tag{14}$$

If we now multiply each side in Eq. (14) by the inverse matrices $(\mathbf{E}_k)^{-1}$, $(\mathbf{E}_{k-1})^{-1}$, $\ldots$, $(\mathbf{E}_2)^{-1}$, $(\mathbf{E}_1)^{-1}$ in turn, we find that

$$\mathbf{A} = (\mathbf{E}_1)^{-1}(\mathbf{E}_2)^{-1} \cdots (\mathbf{E}_{k-1})^{-1}(\mathbf{E}_k)^{-1}. \tag{15}$$

Thus $\mathbf{A}$ is a product of invertible elementary matrices, and it follows from part (c) of Theorem 3 that $\mathbf{A}$ is invertible. ▲

The proof of Theorem 6 actually tells us *how to find* the inverse matrix of $\mathbf{A}$. If we invert each side in Eq. (15) (remembering to reverse the order on the right), we get

$$\mathbf{A}^{-1} = \mathbf{E}_k \mathbf{E}_{k-1} \cdots \mathbf{E}_2 \mathbf{E}_1 \mathbf{I}. \tag{16}$$

Because each left multiplication by an elementary matrix is equivalent to performing the corresponding row operation, we see by comparison of Eqs. (14) and (16) that *the same sequence of elementary row operations that transforms $\mathbf{A}$ into $\mathbf{I}$ also transforms $\mathbf{I}$ into $\mathbf{A}^{-1}$*.

ALGORITHM: Finding A⁻¹

To find the inverse $\mathbf{A}^{-1}$ of the invertible $n \times n$ matrix $\mathbf{A}$, find a sequence of elementary row operations that reduces $\mathbf{A}$ to the $n \times n$ identity matrix $\mathbf{I}$. Then apply the same sequence of operations in the same order to $\mathbf{I}$ to transform it into $\mathbf{A}^{-1}$. ▲

As a practical matter, it generally is more convenient to carry out the two reductions—from $\mathbf{A}$ to $\mathbf{I}$ and from $\mathbf{I}$ to $\mathbf{A}^{-1}$—in parallel, as illustrated in our next example.

Example 7

Find the inverse of the 3×3 matrix

$$\mathbf{A} = \begin{bmatrix} 4 & 3 & 2 \\ 5 & 6 & 3 \\ 3 & 5 & 2 \end{bmatrix}.$$

Solution

We want to reduce $\mathbf{A}$ to the 3×3 identity matrix $\mathbf{I}$ while simultaneously performing the same sequence of row operations on $\mathbf{I}$ to obtain $\mathbf{A}^{-1}$. In order to carry out this process efficiently, we adjoin $\mathbf{I}$ on the right of $\mathbf{A}$ to form the 3×6 matrix

$$\begin{bmatrix} 4 & 3 & 2 & \vdots & 1 & 0 & 0 \\ 5 & 6 & 3 & \vdots & 0 & 1 & 0 \\ 3 & 5 & 2 & \vdots & 0 & 0 & 1 \end{bmatrix}.$$

We now apply the following sequence of elementary row operations to this 3×6 matrix (designed to transform its left half into the 3×3 identity matrix).

$$\xrightarrow{\;(-1)R_3 + R_1\;} \begin{bmatrix} 1 & -2 & 0 & \vdots & 1 & 0 & -1 \\ 5 & 6 & 3 & \vdots & 0 & 1 & 0 \\ 3 & 5 & 2 & \vdots & 0 & 0 & 1 \end{bmatrix}$$

$$\xrightarrow{\;(-1)R_3 + R_2\;} \begin{bmatrix} 1 & -2 & 0 & \vdots & 1 & 0 & -1 \\ 2 & 1 & 1 & \vdots & 0 & 1 & -1 \\ 3 & 5 & 2 & \vdots & 0 & 0 & 1 \end{bmatrix}$$

$$\xrightarrow{\;(-2)R_1 + R_2\;} \begin{bmatrix} 1 & -2 & 0 & \vdots & 1 & 0 & -1 \\ 0 & 5 & 1 & \vdots & -2 & 1 & 1 \\ 3 & 5 & 2 & \vdots & 0 & 0 & 1 \end{bmatrix}$$

$$\xrightarrow{\;(-3)R_1 + R_3\;} \begin{bmatrix} 1 & -2 & 0 & \vdots & 1 & 0 & -1 \\ 0 & 5 & 1 & \vdots & -2 & 1 & 1 \\ 0 & 11 & 2 & \vdots & -3 & 0 & 4 \end{bmatrix}$$

$$\xrightarrow{\;(-2)R_2 + R_3\;} \begin{bmatrix} 1 & -2 & 0 & \vdots & 1 & 0 & -1 \\ 0 & 5 & 1 & \vdots & -2 & 1 & 1 \\ 0 & 1 & 0 & \vdots & 1 & -2 & 2 \end{bmatrix}$$

$$\xrightarrow{\;\text{SWAP}(R_2, R_3)\;} \begin{bmatrix} 1 & -2 & 0 & \vdots & 1 & 0 & -1 \\ 0 & 1 & 0 & \vdots & 1 & -2 & 2 \\ 0 & 5 & 1 & \vdots & -2 & 1 & 1 \end{bmatrix}$$

$$\xrightarrow{\;(2)R_2 + R_1\;} \begin{bmatrix} 1 & 0 & 0 & \vdots & 3 & -4 & 3 \\ 0 & 1 & 0 & \vdots & 1 & -2 & 2 \\ 0 & 5 & 1 & \vdots & -2 & 1 & 1 \end{bmatrix}$$

$$\xrightarrow{\;(-5)R_2 + R_3\;} \begin{bmatrix} 1 & 0 & 0 & \vdots & 3 & -4 & 3 \\ 0 & 1 & 0 & \vdots & 1 & -2 & 2 \\ 0 & 0 & 1 & \vdots & -7 & 11 & -9 \end{bmatrix}$$

Now that we have reduced the left half of the 3×6 matrix to $\mathbf{I}$, we simply examine its right half to see that the inverse of $\mathbf{A}$ is

$$\mathbf{A}^{-1} = \begin{bmatrix} 3 & -4 & 3 \\ 1 & -2 & 2 \\ -7 & 11 & -9 \end{bmatrix}. \qquad \blacksquare$$

Remark: Ordinarily, we do not know in advance whether a given square matrix is invertible or not. To find out, we attempt to carry out the reduction process illustrated in Example 7. If we succeed in reducing $\mathbf{A}$ to $\mathbf{I}$, then $\mathbf{A}$ is invertible and thereby we find $\mathbf{A}^{-1}$. Otherwise—if, somewhere along the way, an all-zero row appears in the left half—we conclude that $\mathbf{A}$ is not row equivalent to $\mathbf{I}$, and therefore (by Theorem 6) $\mathbf{A}$ is not invertible.

Matrix Equations

In certain applications, one needs to solve a system $\mathbf{Ax} = \mathbf{b}$ of n equations in n unknowns several times in succession—with the same $n \times n$ coefficient matrix $\mathbf{A}$ each time, but with different constant vectors $\mathbf{b}_1, \mathbf{b}_2, \ldots, \mathbf{b}_k$ on the right. Thus we want to find solution vectors $\mathbf{x}_1, \mathbf{x}_2, \ldots, \mathbf{x}_k$ such that

$$\mathbf{Ax}_1 = \mathbf{b}_1, \quad \mathbf{Ax}_2 = \mathbf{b}_2, \quad \ldots, \quad \mathbf{Ax}_k = \mathbf{b}_k. \tag{17}$$

By Fact 2 at the beginning of this section,

$$\begin{bmatrix} \mathbf{Ax}_1 & \mathbf{Ax}_2 & \cdots & \mathbf{Ax}_k \end{bmatrix} = \mathbf{A} \begin{bmatrix} \mathbf{x}_1 & \mathbf{x}_2 & \cdots & \mathbf{x}_k \end{bmatrix}.$$

So the k equations in (17) are equivalent to the single matrix equation

$$\mathbf{AX} = \mathbf{B}, \tag{18}$$

where
$$\mathbf{X} = \begin{bmatrix} \mathbf{x}_1 & \mathbf{x}_2 & \cdots & \mathbf{x}_k \end{bmatrix} \quad \text{and} \quad \mathbf{B} = \begin{bmatrix} \mathbf{b}_1 & \mathbf{b}_2 & \cdots & \mathbf{b}_k \end{bmatrix}.$$

If $\mathbf{A}$ is invertible and we know $\mathbf{A}^{-1}$, we can find the $n \times k$ matrix of "unknowns" by multiplying each term in Equation (18) on the left by $\mathbf{A}^{-1}$:

$$\mathbf{X} = \mathbf{A}^{-1}\mathbf{B}. \tag{19}$$

Note that this equation is a generalization of Eq. (13) in Theorem 4. If $k = 1$, it usually is simplest to solve the system by Gaussian elimination, but when several different solutions are sought, it may be simpler to find $\mathbf{A}^{-1}$ first and then to apply (19).

Example 8 Find a 3×4 matrix $\mathbf{X}$ such that

$$\begin{bmatrix} 4 & 3 & 2 \\ 5 & 6 & 3 \\ 3 & 5 & 2 \end{bmatrix} \mathbf{X} = \begin{bmatrix} 3 & -1 & 2 & 6 \\ 7 & 4 & 1 & 5 \\ 5 & 2 & 4 & 1 \end{bmatrix}.$$

Solution   The coefficient matrix is the matrix **A** whose inverse we found in Example 7, so Eq. (19) yields

$$\mathbf{X} = \mathbf{A}^{-1}\mathbf{B} = \begin{bmatrix} 3 & -4 & 3 \\ 1 & -2 & 2 \\ -7 & 11 & -9 \end{bmatrix} \begin{bmatrix} 3 & -1 & 2 & 6 \\ 7 & 4 & 1 & 5 \\ 5 & 2 & 4 & 1 \end{bmatrix},$$

and hence

$$\mathbf{X} = \begin{bmatrix} -4 & -13 & 14 & 1 \\ -1 & -5 & 8 & -2 \\ 11 & 33 & -39 & 4 \end{bmatrix}.$$

By looking at the third columns of **B** and **X**, for instance, we see that the solution of

$$4x_1 + 3x_2 + 2x_3 = 2$$
$$5x_1 + 6x_2 + 3x_3 = 1$$
$$3x_1 + 5x_2 + 2x_3 = 4$$

is $x_1 = 14$, $x_2 = 8$, $x_3 = -39$.   ∎

Nonsingular Matrices

Theorem 6 tells us that the square matrix **A** is invertible if and only if it is row equivalent to the identity matrix **I**, and Theorem 4 in Section 3.3 implies that the latter is true if and only if the system $\mathbf{Ax} = \mathbf{0}$ has only the trivial solution $\mathbf{x} = \mathbf{0}$. A square matrix having these equivalent properties is sometimes called a **nonsingular matrix**.

THEOREM 7: Properties of Nonsingular Matrices

The following properties of an $n \times n$ matrix **A** are equivalent.

(a) **A** is invertible.

(b) **A** is row equivalent to the $n \times n$ identity matrix **I**.

(c) $\mathbf{Ax} = \mathbf{0}$ has only the trivial solution.

(d) For every n-vector **b**, the system $\mathbf{Ax} = \mathbf{b}$ has a unique solution.

(e) For every n-vector **b**, the system $\mathbf{Ax} = \mathbf{b}$ is consistent.

Proof: By the remarks preceding the statement of Theorem 7, we already know that properties (a), (b), and (c) are equivalent—if **A** has any one of these properties, then it also has the other two. We can, therefore, complete the proof by establishing the chain of logical implications

$$(c) \Rightarrow (d) \Rightarrow (e) \Rightarrow (a).$$

That is, we need to show that if **A** has property (c), then it has property (d), and, similarly, that (d) implies (e) and that (e) implies (a).

(c) $\Rightarrow$ (d): We already know that (c) implies (a), and Theorem 4 says that (a) implies (d). Therefore, (c) implies (d).

(d) $\Rightarrow$ (e): This is obvious, because if the system $\mathbf{Ax} = \mathbf{b}$ has a unique solution, then it certainly has a solution, and thus is consistent.

(e) $\Rightarrow$ (a): Given the hypothesis that $\mathbf{Ax} = \mathbf{b}$ is consistent for every $\mathbf{b}$, we must prove that $\mathbf{A}$ is invertible. Let $\mathbf{b} = \mathbf{e}_j$, the jth column vector of the identity matrix $\mathbf{I}$. Then the consistency of $\mathbf{Ax} = \mathbf{e}_j$ yields an n-vector $\mathbf{x}_j$ such that

$$\mathbf{Ax}_j = \mathbf{e}_j. \tag{20}$$

Let the vectors $\mathbf{x}_1, \mathbf{x}_2, \ldots, \mathbf{x}_n$ be obtained in this way for $j = 1, 2, \ldots, n$, and let $\mathbf{B}$ be the $n \times n$ matrix with these vectors as its columns:

$$\mathbf{B} = \begin{bmatrix} \mathbf{x}_1 & \mathbf{x}_2 & \ldots & \mathbf{x}_n \end{bmatrix}.$$

Then

$$\begin{aligned} \mathbf{AB} &= \mathbf{A} \begin{bmatrix} \mathbf{x}_1 & \mathbf{x}_2 & \cdots & \mathbf{x}_n \end{bmatrix} \\ &= \begin{bmatrix} \mathbf{Ax}_1 & \mathbf{Ax}_2 & \cdots & \mathbf{Ax}_n \end{bmatrix} \\ &= \begin{bmatrix} \mathbf{e}_1 & \mathbf{e}_2 & \cdots & \mathbf{e}_n \end{bmatrix} \qquad \text{[by (20)]}. \end{aligned}$$

Therefore, $\mathbf{AB} = \mathbf{I}$, and thus we have found a matrix $\mathbf{B}$ such that $\mathbf{AB} = \mathbf{I}$.

We next show that $\mathbf{B}$ is invertible by showing that $\mathbf{Bx} = \mathbf{0}$ has only the trivial solution [and by using the fact that property (c) implies property (a)]. But if $\mathbf{Bx} = \mathbf{0}$, then

$$\mathbf{A(Bx)} = \mathbf{A0} = \mathbf{0},$$

which implies that $\mathbf{Ix} = \mathbf{0}$ and thus that $\mathbf{x} = \mathbf{0}$. So $\mathbf{B}$ is indeed invertible. We can therefore multiply each term in the equation $\mathbf{AB} = \mathbf{I}$ on the right by $\mathbf{B}^{-1}$ to get

$$\mathbf{ABB}^{-1} = \mathbf{IB}^{-1},$$

so that $\mathbf{A} = \mathbf{B}^{-1}$. Thus $\mathbf{A}$ is the inverse of an invertible matrix, and so is itself invertible. This establishes that property (e) implies property (a), and therefore we have completed the proof.   ▲

The proof of Theorem 7 is a bit long, but it summarizes most of the basic theory of Chapter 1 and is therefore well worth the effort. Indeed, this theorem is one of the central theorems of elementary linear algebra, and we will need to refer to it repeatedly in subsequent chapters.

3.5 Problems

In Problems 1–8, first apply the formulas in (9) to find $\mathbf{A}^{-1}$. Then use $\mathbf{A}^{-1}$ (as in Example 5) to solve the system $\mathbf{Ax} = \mathbf{b}$.

1. $\mathbf{A} = \begin{bmatrix} 3 & 2 \\ 4 & 3 \end{bmatrix}$, $\mathbf{b} = \begin{bmatrix} 5 \\ 6 \end{bmatrix}$

2. $\mathbf{A} = \begin{bmatrix} 3 & 7 \\ 2 & 5 \end{bmatrix}$, $\mathbf{b} = \begin{bmatrix} -1 \\ 3 \end{bmatrix}$

3. $\mathbf{A} = \begin{bmatrix} 6 & 7 \\ 5 & 6 \end{bmatrix}$, $\mathbf{b} = \begin{bmatrix} 2 \\ -3 \end{bmatrix}$

4. $\mathbf{A} = \begin{bmatrix} 5 & 12 \\ 7 & 17 \end{bmatrix}$, $\mathbf{b} = \begin{bmatrix} 5 \\ 5 \end{bmatrix}$

5. $\mathbf{A} = \begin{bmatrix} 3 & 2 \\ 5 & 4 \end{bmatrix}$, $\mathbf{b} = \begin{bmatrix} 5 \\ 6 \end{bmatrix}$

6. $\mathbf{A} = \begin{bmatrix} 4 & 7 \\ 3 & 6 \end{bmatrix}$, $\mathbf{b} = \begin{bmatrix} 10 \\ 5 \end{bmatrix}$

7. $\mathbf{A} = \begin{bmatrix} 7 & 9 \\ 5 & 7 \end{bmatrix}$, $\mathbf{b} = \begin{bmatrix} 3 \\ 2 \end{bmatrix}$

8. $\mathbf{A} = \begin{bmatrix} 8 & 15 \\ 5 & 10 \end{bmatrix}$, $\mathbf{b} = \begin{bmatrix} 7 \\ 3 \end{bmatrix}$

In Problems 9–22, use the method of Example 7 to find the inverse $\mathbf{A}^{-1}$ of each given matrix $\mathbf{A}$.

9. $\begin{bmatrix} 5 & 6 \\ 4 & 5 \end{bmatrix}$ **10.** $\begin{bmatrix} 5 & 7 \\ 4 & 6 \end{bmatrix}$

11. $\begin{bmatrix} 1 & 5 & 1 \\ 2 & 5 & 0 \\ 2 & 7 & 1 \end{bmatrix}$ **12.** $\begin{bmatrix} 1 & 3 & 2 \\ 2 & 8 & 3 \\ 3 & 10 & 6 \end{bmatrix}$

13. $\begin{bmatrix} 2 & 7 & 3 \\ 1 & 3 & 2 \\ 3 & 7 & 9 \end{bmatrix}$ **14.** $\begin{bmatrix} 3 & 5 & 6 \\ 2 & 4 & 3 \\ 2 & 3 & 5 \end{bmatrix}$

15. $\begin{bmatrix} 1 & 1 & 5 \\ 1 & 4 & 13 \\ 3 & 2 & 12 \end{bmatrix}$ **16.** $\begin{bmatrix} 1 & -3 & -3 \\ -1 & 1 & 2 \\ 2 & -3 & -3 \end{bmatrix}$

17. $\begin{bmatrix} 1 & -3 & 0 \\ -1 & 2 & -1 \\ 0 & -2 & 2 \end{bmatrix}$ **18.** $\begin{bmatrix} 1 & -2 & 2 \\ 3 & 0 & 1 \\ 1 & -1 & 2 \end{bmatrix}$

19. $\begin{bmatrix} 1 & 4 & 3 \\ 1 & 4 & 5 \\ 2 & 5 & 1 \end{bmatrix}$ **20.** $\begin{bmatrix} 2 & 0 & -1 \\ 1 & 0 & 3 \\ 1 & 1 & 1 \end{bmatrix}$

21. $\begin{bmatrix} 0 & 0 & 1 & 0 \\ 1 & 0 & 0 & 0 \\ 0 & 1 & 2 & 0 \\ 3 & 0 & 0 & 1 \end{bmatrix}$ **22.** $\begin{bmatrix} 4 & 0 & 1 & 1 \\ 3 & 1 & 3 & 1 \\ 0 & 1 & 2 & 0 \\ 3 & 2 & 4 & 1 \end{bmatrix}$

In Problems 23–28, use the method of Example 8 to find a matrix **X** *such that* **AX = B**.

23. $\mathbf{A} = \begin{bmatrix} 4 & 3 \\ 5 & 4 \end{bmatrix}, \mathbf{B} = \begin{bmatrix} 1 & 3 & -5 \\ -1 & -2 & 5 \end{bmatrix}$

24. $\mathbf{A} = \begin{bmatrix} 7 & 6 \\ 8 & 7 \end{bmatrix}, \mathbf{B} = \begin{bmatrix} 2 & 0 & 4 \\ 0 & 5 & -3 \end{bmatrix}$

25. $\mathbf{A} = \begin{bmatrix} 1 & 4 & 1 \\ 2 & 8 & 3 \\ 2 & 7 & 4 \end{bmatrix}, \mathbf{B} = \begin{bmatrix} 1 & 0 & 3 \\ 0 & 2 & 2 \\ -1 & 1 & 0 \end{bmatrix}$

26. $\mathbf{A} = \begin{bmatrix} 1 & 5 & 1 \\ 2 & 1 & -2 \\ 1 & 7 & 2 \end{bmatrix}, \mathbf{B} = \begin{bmatrix} 2 & 0 & 1 \\ 0 & 3 & 0 \\ 1 & 0 & 2 \end{bmatrix}$

27. $\mathbf{A} = \begin{bmatrix} 1 & -2 & 3 \\ 2 & 1 & 7 \\ 2 & 2 & 7 \end{bmatrix}, \mathbf{B} = \begin{bmatrix} 0 & 0 & 1 & 1 \\ 0 & 1 & 0 & 1 \\ 1 & 0 & 1 & 0 \end{bmatrix}$

28. $\mathbf{A} = \begin{bmatrix} 6 & 5 & 3 \\ 5 & 3 & 2 \\ 3 & 4 & 2 \end{bmatrix}, \mathbf{B} = \begin{bmatrix} 2 & 1 & 0 & 2 \\ -1 & 3 & 5 & 0 \\ 1 & 1 & 0 & 5 \end{bmatrix}$

29. Verify parts (a) and (b) of Theorem 3.

30. Suppose that **A**, **B**, and **C** are invertible matrices of the same size. Show that the product **ABC** is invertible and that $(\mathbf{ABC})^{-1} = \mathbf{C}^{-1}\mathbf{B}^{-1}\mathbf{A}^{-1}$.

31. Suppose that **A** is an invertible matrix and that r and s are negative integers. Verify that $\mathbf{A}^r\mathbf{A}^s = \mathbf{A}^{r+s}$ and that $(\mathbf{A}^r)^s = \mathbf{A}^{rs}$.

32. Prove that if **A** is an invertible matrix and **AB = AC**, then **B = C**. Thus *invertible* matrices can be canceled.

33. Let **A** be an $n \times n$ matrix such that **Ax = x** for every n-vector **x**. Show that **A = I**.

34. Show that a diagonal matrix is invertible if and only if each diagonal element is nonzero. In this case, state concisely how the inverse matrix is obtained.

35. Let **A** be an $n \times n$ matrix with either a row or a column consisting only of zeros. Show that **A** is not invertible.

36. Show that $\mathbf{A} = \begin{bmatrix} a & b \\ c & d \end{bmatrix}$ is not invertible if $ad - bc = 0$.

37. Suppose that $ad - bc \neq 0$ and $\mathbf{A}^{-1}$ is defined as in Equation (9). Verify directly that $\mathbf{AA}^{-1} = \mathbf{A}^{-1}\mathbf{A} = \mathbf{I}$.

38. Let **E** be the elementary matrix $\mathbf{E}_1$ of Example 6. If **A** is a 2×2 matrix, show that **EA** is the result of multiplying the first row of **A** by 3.

39. Let **E** be the elementary matrix $\mathbf{E}_2$ of Example 6 and suppose that **A** is a 3×3 matrix. Show that **EA** is the result upon adding twice the first row of **A** to its third row.

40. Let **E** be the elementary matrix $\mathbf{E}_3$ of Example 6. Show that **EA** is the result of interchanging the first two rows of the matrix **A**.

41. Show that the ith row of the product **AB** is $\mathbf{A}_i\mathbf{B}$, where $\mathbf{A}_i$ is the ith row of the matrix **A**.

42. Apply the result of Problem 41 to show that if **B** is an $m \times n$ matrix and **I** is the $m \times m$ identity matrix, then **IB = B**.

43. Suppose that the matrices **A** and **B** are row equivalent. Use Theorem 5 to prove that **B = GA**, where **G** is a product of elementary matrices.

44. Show that every invertible matrix is a product of elementary matrices.

45. Extract from the proof of Theorem 7 a self-contained proof of the following fact: If **A** and **B** are square matrices such that **AB = I**, then **A** and **B** are invertible.

46. Deduce from the result of Problem 45 that if **A** and **B** are square matrices whose product **AB** is invertible, then **A** and **B** are themselves invertible.

3.5 Application: Automated Solution of Linear Systems

Linear systems with more than two or three equations are most frequently solved with the aid of calculators or computers. If an $n \times n$ linear system is written in the matrix form **Ax = b**, then we need to calculate first the inverse matrix $\mathbf{A}^{-1}$ and then the matrix product $\mathbf{x} = \mathbf{A}^{-1}\mathbf{b}$. Suppose the $n \times n$ matrix **A** and the column vector **b** have been entered (as illustrated in the 3.2 Application). If **A** is invertible, then the inverse matrix $\mathbf{A}^{-1}$ is calculated by the *Maple* command `with(linalg): inverse(A)`, the *Mathematica* command `Inverse[A]`, or the MATLAB command

inv(A). Consequently, the solution vector **x** is calculated by the *Maple* command

$$\texttt{with(linalg): x := multiply(inverse(A),b);}$$

or the *Mathematica* command

$$\texttt{x = Inverse[A].b}$$

or the MATLAB command

$$\texttt{x = inv(A)*b}$$

FIGURE 3.5.2. TI-92 solution of a linear system $\mathbf{Ax} = \mathbf{b}$.

Figure 3.5.2 illustrates a similar calculator solution of the linear system

$$3x_1 - 2x_2 + 7x_3 + 5x_4 = 505$$
$$2x_1 + 4x_2 - x_3 + 6x_4 = 435$$
$$5x_1 + x_2 + 7x_3 - 3x_4 = 286$$
$$4x_1 - 6x_2 - 8x_3 + 9x_4 = 445$$

for the solution $x_1 = 59$, $x_2 = 13$, $x_3 = 17$, $x_4 = 47$.

Use an available calculator or computer system to solve the linear systems in Problems 1–6 of the 3.3 Application. The applied problems below are elementary in character—resembling the "word problems" of high school algebra—but might illustrate the practical advantages of automated solutions.

1. You are walking down the street minding your own business when you spot a small but heavy leather bag lying on the sidewalk. It turns out to contain U.S. Mint American Eagle gold coins of the following types:

   • One-half ounce gold coins that sell for $285 each,
   • One-quarter ounce gold coins that sell for $150 each, and
   • One-tenth ounce gold coins that sell for $70 each.

   A bank receipt found in the bag certifies that it contains 258 such coins with a total weight of 67 ounces and a total value of exactly $40,145. How many coins of each type are there?

2. Now you really strike it rich! You find a bag containing one-ounce U.S. American Eagle gold coins valued at $550 each, together with half-ounce and quarter-ounce coins valued as in the preceding problem. If this bag contains a total of 365 coins with a total weight of exactly 11 pounds and a total value of $100,130, how many gold coins of each type are there?

3. A commercial customer orders 81 gallons of paint that contains equal amounts of red paint, green paint, and blue paint—and, hence, could be prepared by mixing 27 gallons of each. However, the store wishes to prepare this order by mixing three types of paint that are already available in large quantity:

   • a *reddish* paint that is a mixture of 50% red, 25% green, and 25% blue paint;
   • a *greenish* paint that is 12.5% red, 75% green, and 12.5% blue paint; and
   • a *bluish* paint that is 20% red, 20% green, and 60% blue paint.

   How many gallons of each are needed to prepare the customer's order?

4. Now the paint store receives a really big order—for 244 gallons of paint that is 1/2 red paint, 1/4 green paint, and 1/4 blue paint. The store has three already-mixed

types of paint available in large quantity—the greenish paint and the bluish paint of the preceding problem, plus a reddish paint that is 2/3 red paint, 1/6 green paint, and 1/6 blue paint. How many gallons of each must be mixed in order to fill this order?

5. A tour busload of 45 people attended two Florida theme parks on successive days. On Day 1 the entrance fee was $15 per adult, $8 per child, $12 per senior citizen and the total charge was $558. On Day 2 the entrance fee was $20 per adult, $12 per child, $17 per senior citizen and the total charge was $771. How many adults, children, and senior citizens were on this tour bus?

6. For some crazy reason, the lunches bought at the first theme park were totaled separately for the adults, children, and seniors. The adults ordered 34 hot dogs, 15 French fries, and 24 soft drinks for a total bill of $70.85. The children ordered 20 hot dogs, 14 French fries, and 15 soft drinks for a total bill of $46.65. The senior citizens ordered 11 hot dogs, 10 French fries, and 12 soft drinks for a total bill of $30.05. What were the prices of a hot dog, an order of French fries, and a soft drink?

7. A fast-food restaurant sells four types of sandwiches—hamburgers, cheeseburgers, roast beef, and chicken—and has four cash registers. At the end of each day, each cash register tallies the number of each type of sandwich sold, and the total sandwich receipts for the day. The four cash register operators work at different speeds, and one day's totals were as follows:

	Hamburgers	**Cheeseburgers**	**Roast Beef**	**Chicken**	**Receipts**
Register 1	37	44	17	23	$232.99
Register 2	28	35	13	17	$178.97
Register 3	32	39	19	21	$215.99
Register 4	47	51	25	29	$294.38

What was the price of each of the four types of sandwiches?

8. The fast-food restaurant of the preceding problem adds a ham sandwich to its menu and, because of increased business, it also adds a fifth cash register and reduces prices. After this expansion, one day's totals were as follows:

	Hamburgers	**Cheeseburgers**	**Roast Beef**	**Chicken**	**Ham**	**Receipts**
Register 1	41	49	22	26	19	$292.79
Register 2	34	39	18	20	16	$236.73
Register 3	36	43	23	24	18	$270.70
Register 4	49	52	26	31	24	$340.19
Register 5	52	55	24	28	25	$341.64

What were the new prices of the five types of sandwiches?

3.6 Determinants

In Theorem 2 of Section 3.5 we saw that the 2×2 matrix

$$\mathbf{A} = \begin{bmatrix} a & b \\ c & d \end{bmatrix}$$

is invertible if and only if $ad - bc \neq 0$. The number $ad - bc$ is called the **determinant** of the 2×2 matrix $\mathbf{A}$. There are several common notations for determinants:

$$\det \mathbf{A} = \det \begin{bmatrix} a & b \\ c & d \end{bmatrix} = \begin{vmatrix} a & b \\ c & d \end{vmatrix} = ad - bc. \tag{1}$$

In particular, note the vertical bars that distinguish a determinant from a matrix. Sometimes we write $\det(\mathbf{A})$ to emphasize that (1) defines a function which associates a number $|\mathbf{A}|$ with each 2×2 matrix $\mathbf{A}$.

Example 1

$$\begin{vmatrix} 3 & 7 \\ 4 & -6 \end{vmatrix} = (3)(-6) - (4)(7) = -46 \qquad \blacksquare$$

Determinants are often used in elementary algebra to solve a 2×2 system of the form

$$\begin{aligned} a_{11}x + a_{12}y &= b_1 \\ a_{21}x + a_{22}y &= b_2. \end{aligned} \tag{2}$$

It follows from Theorems 2 and 7 in Section 3.5 that this system has a unique solution if and only if its **coefficient determinant**—the determinant of its coefficient matrix $\mathbf{A}$—is nonzero:

$$\det \mathbf{A} = \begin{vmatrix} a_{11} & a_{12} \\ a_{21} & a_{22} \end{vmatrix} \neq 0. \tag{3}$$

Then **Cramer's rule** says that this unique solution is given by

$$x = \frac{\begin{vmatrix} b_1 & a_{12} \\ b_2 & a_{22} \end{vmatrix}}{\begin{vmatrix} a_{11} & a_{12} \\ a_{21} & a_{22} \end{vmatrix}}, \qquad y = \frac{\begin{vmatrix} a_{11} & b_1 \\ a_{21} & b_2 \end{vmatrix}}{\begin{vmatrix} a_{11} & a_{12} \\ a_{21} & a_{22} \end{vmatrix}}. \tag{4}$$

Thus Cramer's rule gives each of x and y as a quotient of two determinants, the denominator in each case being the determinant of the coefficient matrix. In the numerator for x the coefficients a_{11} and a_{21} of x are replaced with the right-side coefficients b_1 and b_2, whereas in the numerator for y the coefficients of y are replaced with b_1 and b_2.

The proof of Cramer's rule is a routine calculation—to verify that evaluation of the determinant in (4) gives the same expressions for x and y as are gotten by solution of (2) by the method of elimination.

Example 2   To apply Cramer's rule to solve the system

$$7x + 8y = 5$$
$$6x + 9y = 4$$

with coefficient determinant

$$\begin{vmatrix} 7 & 8 \\ 6 & 9 \end{vmatrix} = 15,$$

we simply substitute in the equations in (4) to get

$$x = \frac{\begin{vmatrix} 5 & 8 \\ 4 & 9 \end{vmatrix}}{15} = \frac{13}{15}, \qquad y = \frac{\begin{vmatrix} 7 & 5 \\ 6 & 4 \end{vmatrix}}{15} = -\frac{2}{15}.$$ ∎

Higher-Order Determinants

We define 3×3 determinants in terms of 2×2 determinants, 4×4 determinants in terms of 3×3 determinants, and so on. This type of definition—one dimension at a time, with the definition in each dimension depending on its meaning in lower dimensions—is called an *inductive definition*.

The determinant $\det \mathbf{A} = |a_{ij}|$ of a 3×3 matrix $\mathbf{A} = \begin{bmatrix} a_{ij} \end{bmatrix}$ is defined as follows:

$$\begin{vmatrix} a_{11} & a_{12} & a_{13} \\ a_{21} & a_{22} & a_{23} \\ a_{31} & a_{32} & a_{33} \end{vmatrix} = a_{11} \begin{vmatrix} a_{22} & a_{23} \\ a_{32} & a_{33} \end{vmatrix} - a_{12} \begin{vmatrix} a_{21} & a_{23} \\ a_{31} & a_{33} \end{vmatrix} + a_{13} \begin{vmatrix} a_{21} & a_{22} \\ a_{31} & a_{32} \end{vmatrix}. \quad (5)$$

Note the single minus sign on the right-hand side. The three 2×2 determinants in (5) are multiplied by the elements a_{11}, a_{12}, and a_{13} along the *first row* of the matrix $\mathbf{A}$. Each of these elements a_{1j} is multiplied by the determinant of the 2×2 submatrix of $\mathbf{A}$ that remains after the row and column containing a_{1j} are deleted.

Example 3

$$\begin{vmatrix} 5 & -2 & -3 \\ 4 & 0 & 1 \\ 3 & -1 & 2 \end{vmatrix} = (5) \begin{vmatrix} 0 & 1 \\ -1 & 2 \end{vmatrix} - (-2) \begin{vmatrix} 4 & 1 \\ 3 & 2 \end{vmatrix} + (-3) \begin{vmatrix} 4 & 0 \\ 3 & -1 \end{vmatrix}$$

$$= (5)(1) + (2)(5) - (3)(-4) = 27.$$ ∎

The definition of higher-order determinants is simplified by the following notation and terminology.

Definition: Minors and Cofactors

Let $\mathbf{A} = \left[a_{ij} \right]$ be an $n \times n$ matrix. The ijth **minor** of $\mathbf{A}$ (also called the **minor** of a_{ij}) is the determinant M_{ij} of the $(n-1) \times (n-1)$ submatrix that remains after deleting the ith row and the jth column of $\mathbf{A}$. The ijth **cofactor** A_{ij} of $\mathbf{A}$ (or the **cofactor** of a_{ij}) is defined to be

$$A_{ij} = (-1)^{i+j} M_{ij}. \tag{6}$$

For example, the minor of a_{12} in a 3×3 matrix is

$$M_{12} = \begin{vmatrix} a_{11} & a_{12} & a_{13} \\ a_{21} & a_{22} & a_{23} \\ a_{31} & a_{32} & a_{33} \end{vmatrix} = \begin{vmatrix} a_{21} & a_{23} \\ a_{31} & a_{33} \end{vmatrix}.$$

The minor of a_{32} in a 4×4 matrix is

$$M_{32} = \begin{vmatrix} a_{11} & a_{12} & a_{13} & a_{14} \\ a_{21} & a_{22} & a_{23} & a_{24} \\ a_{31} & a_{32} & a_{33} & a_{34} \\ a_{41} & a_{42} & a_{43} & a_{44} \end{vmatrix} = \begin{vmatrix} a_{11} & a_{13} & a_{14} \\ a_{21} & a_{23} & a_{24} \\ a_{41} & a_{43} & a_{44} \end{vmatrix}.$$

According to Eq. (6), the cofactor A_{ij} is obtained by attaching the sign $(-1)^{i+j}$ to the minor M_{ij}. This sign is most easily remembered as the one that appears in the ijth position in checkerboard arrays such as

$$\begin{bmatrix} + & - & + \\ - & + & - \\ + & - & + \end{bmatrix} \quad \text{and} \quad \begin{bmatrix} + & - & + & - \\ - & + & - & + \\ + & - & + & - \\ - & + & - & + \end{bmatrix}.$$

Note that a plus sign always appears in the upper left corner and that the signs alternate horizontally and vertically. In the 4×4 case, for instance,

$$A_{11} = +M_{11}, \quad A_{12} = -M_{12}, \quad A_{13} = +M_{13}, \quad A_{14} = -M_{14},$$
$$A_{21} = -M_{21}, \quad A_{22} = +M_{22}, \quad A_{23} = -M_{23}, \quad A_{24} = +M_{24},$$

and so forth.

With this notation, the definition of 3×3 determinants in (5) can be rewritten as

$$\begin{aligned} \det \mathbf{A} &= a_{11} M_{11} - a_{12} M_{12} + a_{13} M_{13} \\ &= a_{11} A_{11} + a_{12} A_{12} + a_{13} A_{13}. \end{aligned} \tag{7}$$

The last formula is the **cofactor expansion** of $\det \mathbf{A}$ along the *first row* of $\mathbf{A}$. Its natural generalization yields the definition of the determinant of an $n \times n$ matrix, under the inductive assumption that $(n-1) \times (n-1)$ determinants have already been defined.

Definition: $n \times n$ Determinants

The **determinant** $\det \mathbf{A} = |a_{ij}|$ of an $n \times n$ matrix $\mathbf{A} = \begin{bmatrix} a_{ij} \end{bmatrix}$ is defined as

$$\det \mathbf{A} = a_{11} A_{11} + a_{12} A_{12} + \cdots + a_{1n} A_{1n}. \tag{8}$$

Thus we multiply each element of the first row of $\mathbf{A}$ by its cofactor and then add these n products to get $\det \mathbf{A}$.

In numerical computations, it frequently is more convenient to work first with minors rather than with cofactors and then attach signs in accord with the checkerboard pattern illustrated previously. Note that determinants have been defined only for *square* matrices.

Example 4   To evaluate the determinant of

$$\mathbf{A} = \begin{bmatrix} 2 & 0 & 0 & -3 \\ 0 & -1 & 0 & 0 \\ 7 & 4 & 3 & 5 \\ -6 & 2 & 2 & 4 \end{bmatrix},$$

we observe that there are only two nonzero terms in the cofactor expansion along the first row. We need not compute the cofactors of zeros, because they will be multiplied by zero in computing the determinant; hence

$$\det \mathbf{A} = +(2) \begin{vmatrix} -1 & 0 & 0 \\ 4 & 3 & 5 \\ 2 & 2 & 4 \end{vmatrix} - (-3) \begin{vmatrix} 0 & -1 & 0 \\ 7 & 4 & 3 \\ -6 & 2 & 2 \end{vmatrix}.$$

Each of the 3×3 determinants on the right-hand side has only a single nonzero term in its cofactor expansion along the first row, so

$$\det \mathbf{A} = (2)(-1) \begin{vmatrix} 3 & 5 \\ 2 & 4 \end{vmatrix} + (3)(+1) \begin{vmatrix} 7 & 3 \\ -6 & 2 \end{vmatrix}$$
$$= (-2)(12 - 10) + (3)(14 + 18) = 92. \qquad \blacksquare$$

Note that, if we could expand along the second row in Example 4, there would be only a single 3×3 determinant to evaluate. It is in fact true that a determinant can be evaluated by expansion along *any* row or column. The proof of the following theorem is included in Appendix B.

THEOREM 1: Cofactor Expansions of Determinants

The determinant of an $n \times n$ matrix $\mathbf{A} = \begin{bmatrix} a_{ij} \end{bmatrix}$ can be obtained by expansion along any row or column. The cofactor expansion along the ith row is

$$\det \mathbf{A} = a_{i1} A_{i1} + a_{i2} A_{i2} + \cdots + a_{in} A_{in}. \tag{9}$$

The cofactor expansion along the jth column is

$$\det \mathbf{A} = a_{1j} A_{1j} + a_{2j} A_{2j} + \cdots + a_{nj} A_{nj}. \tag{10}$$

▲

The formulas in (9) and (10) provide $2n$ different cofactor expansions of an $n \times n$ determinant. For $n = 3$, for instance, we have

$$
\begin{aligned}
\det \mathbf{A} &= a_{11}A_{11} + a_{12}A_{12} + a_{13}A_{13} \\
&= a_{21}A_{21} + a_{22}A_{22} + a_{23}A_{23} \\
&= a_{31}A_{31} + a_{32}A_{32} + a_{33}A_{33} \\
&= a_{11}A_{11} + a_{21}A_{21} + a_{31}A_{31} \\
&= a_{12}A_{12} + a_{22}A_{22} + a_{32}A_{32} \\
&= a_{13}A_{13} + a_{23}A_{23} + a_{33}A_{33}.
\end{aligned}
$$

In a specific example, we naturally attempt to choose the expansion that requires the least computational labor.

Example 5   To evaluate the determinant of

$$
\mathbf{A} = \begin{bmatrix} 7 & 6 & 0 \\ 9 & -3 & 2 \\ 4 & 5 & 0 \end{bmatrix},
$$

we expand along the third column, because it has only a single nonzero entry. Thus

$$
\det \mathbf{A} = -(2) \begin{vmatrix} 7 & 6 \\ 4 & 5 \end{vmatrix} = (-2)(35 - 24) = -22. \qquad \blacksquare
$$

In addition to providing ways of evaluating determinants, the theorem on cofactor expansions is a valuable tool for investigating the general properties of determinants. For instance, it follows immediately from the formulas in (9) and (10) that, *if the square matrix* $\mathbf{A}$ *has either an all-zero row or an all-zero column, then* $\det \mathbf{A} = 0$. For example, by expanding along the second row we see immediately that

$$
\begin{vmatrix} 17 & 33 & -24 \\ 0 & 0 & 0 \\ 80 & -62 & 41 \end{vmatrix} = 0.
$$

Row and Column Properties

We now list seven properties of determinants that simplify their computation. Each of these properties is readily verified directly in the case of 2×2 determinants. Just as our definition of $n \times n$ determinants was inductive, the following discussion of Properties 1–7 of determinants is inductive. That is, we suppose that $n \geq 3$ and that these properties have already been verified for $(n-1) \times (n-1)$ determinants.

PROPERTY 1:   If the $n \times n$ matrix $\mathbf{B}$ is obtained from $\mathbf{A}$ by multiplying a single row (or a column) of $\mathbf{A}$ by the constant k, then $\det \mathbf{B} = k \det \mathbf{A}$.

For instance, if the ith row of $\mathbf{A}$ is multiplied by k, then the elements *off* the ith row of $\mathbf{A}$ are unchanged. Hence for each $j = 1, 2, \ldots, n$, the ijth cofactors of $\mathbf{A}$ and $\mathbf{B}$ are equal: $A_{ij} = B_{ij}$. Therefore, expansion of $\mathbf{B}$ along the ith row gives

$$
\begin{aligned}
\det \mathbf{B} &= (ka_{i1})B_{i1} + (ka_{i2})B_{i2} + \cdots + (ka_{in})B_{in} \\
&= k(a_{i1}A_{i1} + a_{i2}A_{i2} + \cdots + a_{in}A_{in}),
\end{aligned}
$$

and thus $\det \mathbf{B} = k \det \mathbf{A}$.

Property 1 implies simply that a constant can be factored out of a single row or column of a determinant. Thus we see that

$$
\begin{vmatrix} 7 & 15 & -17 \\ -2 & 9 & 6 \\ 5 & -12 & 10 \end{vmatrix} = (3) \begin{vmatrix} 7 & 5 & -17 \\ -2 & 3 & 6 \\ 5 & -4 & 10 \end{vmatrix}
$$

by factoring 3 out of the second column.

PROPERTY 2: If the $n \times n$ matrix **B** is obtained from **A** by interchanging two rows (or two columns), then $\det \mathbf{B} = -\det \mathbf{A}$.

To see why this is so, suppose (for instance) that the first row is *not* one of the two that are interchanged (recall that $n \geq 3$). Then for each $j = 1, 2, \ldots, n$, the cofactor B_{1j} is obtained by interchanging two rows of the cofactor A_{1j}. Therefore, $B_{1j} = -A_{1j}$ by Property 2 for $(n-1) \times (n-1)$ determinants. Because $b_{1j} = a_{1j}$ for each j, it follows by expanding along the first row that

$$
\begin{aligned}
\det \mathbf{B} &= b_{11}B_{11} + b_{12}B_{12} + \cdots + b_{1n}B_{1n} \\
&= a_{11}(-A_{11}) + a_{12}(-A_{12}) + \cdots + a_{1n}(-A_{1n}) \\
&= -(a_{11}A_{11} + a_{12}A_{12} + \cdots + a_{1n}A_{1n}),
\end{aligned}
$$

and thus $\det \mathbf{B} = -\det \mathbf{A}$.

PROPERTY 3: If two rows (or two columns) of the $n \times n$ matrix **A** are identical, then $\det \mathbf{A} = 0$.

To see why, let **B** denote the matrix obtained by interchanging the two identical rows of **A**. Then $\mathbf{B} = \mathbf{A}$, so $\det \mathbf{B} = \det \mathbf{A}$. But Property 2 implies that $\det \mathbf{B} = -\det \mathbf{A}$. Thus $\det \mathbf{A} = -\det \mathbf{A}$, and it follows immediately that $\det \mathbf{A} = 0$.

PROPERTY 4: Suppose that the $n \times n$ matrices $\mathbf{A}_1$, $\mathbf{A}_2$, and **B** are identical except for their ith rows—that is, the other $n-1$ rows of the three matrices are identical—and that the ith row of **B** is the sum of the ith rows of $\mathbf{A}_1$ and $\mathbf{A}_2$. Then

$$
\det \mathbf{B} = \det \mathbf{A}_1 + \det \mathbf{A}_2.
$$

This result also holds if columns are involved instead of rows.

Property 4 is readily established by expanding **B** along its ith row. In Problem 45 we ask you to supply the details for a typical case. The main importance (at this point) of Property 4 is that it implies the following property relating determinants and elementary row operations.

PROPERTY 5: If the $n \times n$ matrix **B** is obtained by adding a constant multiple of one row (or column) of **A** to another row (or column) of **A**, then $\det \mathbf{B} = \det \mathbf{A}$.

Thus the value of a determinant is *not* changed either by the type of elementary row operation described or by the corresponding type of elementary column operation. The following computation with 3×3 matrices illustrates the general proof of Property 5. Let

$$
\mathbf{A} = \begin{bmatrix} a_{11} & a_{12} & a_{13} \\ a_{21} & a_{22} & a_{23} \\ a_{31} & a_{32} & a_{33} \end{bmatrix} \quad \text{and} \quad \mathbf{B} = \begin{bmatrix} a_{11} & a_{12} & a_{13} + ka_{11} \\ a_{21} & a_{22} & a_{23} + ka_{21} \\ a_{31} & a_{32} & a_{33} + ka_{31} \end{bmatrix}.
$$

So **B** is the result of adding k times the first column of **A** to its third column. Then

$$\det \mathbf{B} = \begin{vmatrix} a_{11} & a_{12} & a_{13} + ka_{11} \\ a_{21} & a_{22} & a_{23} + ka_{21} \\ a_{31} & a_{32} & a_{33} + ka_{31} \end{vmatrix} \tag{11}$$

$$= \begin{vmatrix} a_{11} & a_{12} & a_{13} \\ a_{21} & a_{22} & a_{23} \\ a_{31} & a_{32} & a_{33} \end{vmatrix} + k \begin{vmatrix} a_{11} & a_{12} & a_{11} \\ a_{21} & a_{22} & a_{21} \\ a_{31} & a_{32} & a_{31} \end{vmatrix}.$$

Here we first applied Property 4 and then factored k out of the second summand with the aid of Property 1. Now the first determinant on the right-hand side in (11) is simply $\det \mathbf{A}$, whereas the second determinant is zero (by Property 3—its first and third columns are identical). We therefore have shown that $\det \mathbf{B} = \det \mathbf{A}$, as desired.

Although we use only elementary row operations in reducing a matrix to echelon form, Properties 1, 2, and 5 imply that we may use both elementary row operations and the analogous elementary column operations in simplifying the evaluation of determinants.

Example 6   The matrix

$$\mathbf{A} = \begin{bmatrix} 2 & -3 & -4 \\ -1 & 4 & 2 \\ 3 & 10 & 1 \end{bmatrix}$$

has no zero elements to simplify the computation of its determinant *as it stands*, but we notice that we can "knock out" the first two elements of its third column by adding twice the first column to the third column. This gives

$$\det \mathbf{A} = \begin{vmatrix} 2 & -3 & -4 \\ -1 & 4 & 2 \\ 3 & 10 & 1 \end{vmatrix} = \begin{vmatrix} 2 & -3 & 0 \\ -1 & 4 & 0 \\ 3 & 10 & 7 \end{vmatrix}$$

$$= (+7) \begin{vmatrix} 2 & -3 \\ -1 & 4 \end{vmatrix} = 35.$$

The moral of the example is this: Evaluate determinants with your eyes open. ■

An **upper triangular matrix** is a square matrix having only zeros *below* its main diagonal. A **lower triangular matrix** is a square matrix having only zeros *above* its main diagonal. A **triangular matrix** is one like

$$\begin{bmatrix} 3 & 6 & 10 \\ 0 & 5 & 8 \\ 0 & 0 & 7 \end{bmatrix} \quad \text{or} \quad \begin{bmatrix} 1 & 0 & 0 \\ 3 & 7 & 0 \\ 4 & 6 & 5 \end{bmatrix};$$

thus a triangular matrix is one that is either upper triangular or lower triangular. The next property tells us that determinants of triangular matrices are especially easy to evaluate.

PROPERTY 6:   The determinant of a triangular matrix is equal to the product of its diagonal elements.

The reason is that the determinant of any triangular matrix can be evaluated as in the following computation:

$$
\begin{vmatrix} 3 & 11 & 9 & 2 \\ 0 & -2 & 8 & -6 \\ 0 & 0 & 5 & 17 \\ 0 & 0 & 0 & -4 \end{vmatrix} = (3) \begin{vmatrix} -2 & 8 & -6 \\ 0 & 5 & 17 \\ 0 & 0 & -4 \end{vmatrix}
$$

$$
= (3)(-2) \begin{vmatrix} 5 & 17 \\ 0 & -4 \end{vmatrix} = (3)(-2)(5)(-4) = 120.
$$

At each step we expand along the first column and pick up another diagonal element as a factor of the determinant.

Example 7

To evaluate

$$
\begin{vmatrix} 2 & -1 & 3 \\ -2 & 1 & 5 \\ 4 & -2 & 10 \end{vmatrix},
$$

we first add the first row to the second and then subtract twice the first row from the third. This yields

$$
\begin{vmatrix} 2 & -1 & 3 \\ -2 & 1 & 5 \\ 4 & -2 & 10 \end{vmatrix} = \begin{vmatrix} 2 & -1 & 3 \\ 0 & 0 & 8 \\ 0 & 0 & 4 \end{vmatrix} = 0,
$$

because we produced a triangular matrix having a zero on its main diagonal. (Can you see an even quicker way to do it by keeping your eyes open?) ■

The Transpose of a Matrix

The transpose $\mathbf{A}^T$ of a 2×2 matrix $\mathbf{A}$ is obtained by interchanging its off-diagonal elements:

$$
\text{If}\quad \mathbf{A} = \begin{bmatrix} a & b \\ c & d \end{bmatrix} \quad \text{then}\quad \mathbf{A}^T = \begin{bmatrix} a & c \\ b & d \end{bmatrix}. \tag{12}
$$

More generally, the **transpose** of the $m \times n$ matrix $\mathbf{A} = \begin{bmatrix} a_{ij} \end{bmatrix}$ is the $n \times m$ matrix $\mathbf{A}^T$ defined by

$$
\mathbf{A}^T = \begin{bmatrix} a_{ji} \end{bmatrix}. \tag{13}
$$

Note the reversal of subscripts; this means that the element of $\mathbf{A}^T$ in its jth row and ith column is the element of $\mathbf{A}$ in the ith row and the jth column of $\mathbf{A}$. Hence the rows of the transpose $\mathbf{A}^T$ are (in order) the columns of $\mathbf{A}$, and the columns of $\mathbf{A}^T$ are the rows of $\mathbf{A}$. Thus we obtain $\mathbf{A}^T$ by changing the rows of $\mathbf{A}$ into columns. For instance,

$$
\begin{bmatrix} 2 & 0 & 5 \\ 4 & -1 & 7 \end{bmatrix}^T = \begin{bmatrix} 2 & 4 \\ 0 & -1 \\ 5 & 7 \end{bmatrix}
$$

and

$$
\begin{bmatrix} 7 & -2 & 6 \\ 1 & 2 & 3 \\ 5 & 0 & 4 \end{bmatrix}^T = \begin{bmatrix} 7 & 1 & 5 \\ -2 & 2 & 0 \\ 6 & 3 & 4 \end{bmatrix}.
$$

If the matrix $\mathbf{A}$ is square then we get $\mathbf{A}^T$ by interchanging elements of $\mathbf{A}$ that are located symmetrically with respect to its main diagonal. Thus $\mathbf{A}^T$ is the mirror reflection of $\mathbf{A}$ through its main diagonal.

In Problems 47 and 48 we ask you to verify the following properties of the transpose operation (under the assumption that $\mathbf{A}$ and $\mathbf{B}$ are matrices of appropriate sizes and c is a number):

(i) $(\mathbf{A}^T)^T = \mathbf{A}$;

(ii) $(\mathbf{A} + \mathbf{B})^T = \mathbf{A}^T + \mathbf{B}^T$;

(iii) $(c\mathbf{A})^T = c\mathbf{A}^T$;

(iv) $(\mathbf{AB})^T = \mathbf{B}^T\mathbf{A}^T$.

PROPERTY 7:   If $\mathbf{A}$ is a square matrix, then $\det(\mathbf{A}^T) = \det\mathbf{A}$.

This property of determinants can be verified by writing the cofactor expansion of $\det\mathbf{A}$ along its first *row* and the cofactor expansion of $\det(\mathbf{A}^T)$ along its first *column*. When this is done, we see that the two expansions are identical, because the rows of $\mathbf{A}$ are the columns of $\mathbf{A}^T$ (as in Problem 49).

Determinants and Invertibility

We began this section with the remark that a 2×2 matrix $\mathbf{A}$ is invertible if and only if its determinant is nonzero: $|\mathbf{A}| \neq 0$. This result holds more generally for $n \times n$ matrices.

THEOREM 2: Determinants and Invertibility

The $n \times n$ matrix $\mathbf{A}$ is invertible if and only if $\det\mathbf{A} \neq 0$.   ▲

This theorem (along with the others in this section) is proved in Appendix B. So now we can add the statement that $\det\mathbf{A} \neq 0$ to the list of equivalent properties of nonsingular matrices stated in Theorem 7 of Section 3.5. Indeed, some texts *define* the square matrix $\mathbf{A}$ to be nonsingular if and only if $\det\mathbf{A} \neq 0$.

Example 8   According to Problem 61, the determinant of the matrix

$$\mathbf{V} = \begin{bmatrix} 1 & a & a^2 \\ 1 & b & b^2 \\ 1 & c & c^2 \end{bmatrix}$$

is

$$|\mathbf{V}| = (b - a)(c - a)(c - b).$$

Note that $|\mathbf{V}| \neq 0$ if and only if the three numbers a, b, and c are *distinct*. Hence it follows from Theorem 2 that $\mathbf{V}$ is invertible if and only if a, b, and c are distinct. For instance, with $a = -2$, $b = 3$, and $c = -4$ we see that the matrix

$$\begin{bmatrix} 1 & -2 & 4 \\ 1 & 3 & 9 \\ 1 & -4 & 16 \end{bmatrix}$$

is invertible.   ∎

The connection between nonzero determinants and matrix invertibility is closely related to the fact that the determinant function "respects" matrix multiplication in the sense of the following theorem.

THEOREM 3: Determinants and Matrix Products

If **A** and **B** are $n \times n$ matrices, then

$$|\mathbf{AB}| = |\mathbf{A}|\,|\mathbf{B}|. \tag{14}$$

▲

The fact that $|\mathbf{AB}| = |\mathbf{A}|\,|\mathbf{B}|$ seems so natural that we might fail to note that it is also quite remarkable. Contrast the simplicity of the equation $|\mathbf{AB}| = |\mathbf{A}|\,|\mathbf{B}|$ with the complexity of the seemingly unrelated definitions of determinants and matrix products. For another contrast, we can mention that $|\mathbf{A} + \mathbf{B}|$ is generally *not* equal to $|\mathbf{A}| + |\mathbf{B}|$. (Pick a pair of 2×2 matrices and calculate their determinants and that of their sum.)

As a first application of Theorem 3, we can calculate the determinant of the *inverse* of an invertible matrix **A**:

$$\mathbf{AA}^{-1} = \mathbf{I},$$

so

$$|\mathbf{A}|\,|\mathbf{A}^{-1}| = |\mathbf{AA}^{-1}| = |\mathbf{I}| = 1,$$

and therefore

$$|\mathbf{A}^{-1}| = \frac{1}{|\mathbf{A}|}. \tag{15}$$

Now $|\mathbf{A}| \neq 0$ because **A** is invertible. Thus $\det(\mathbf{A}^{-1})$ *is the reciprocal of* $\det \mathbf{A}$.

Example 9   The determinant of

$$\mathbf{A} = \begin{bmatrix} 2 & 2 & -2 & 0 \\ -4 & 2 & 3 & 1 \\ 0 & 4 & -1 & -4 \\ 3 & 1 & 3 & -1 \end{bmatrix}$$

happens to be $|\mathbf{A}| = 320 \neq 0$. Hence **A** is invertible, and *without* finding $\mathbf{A}^{-1}$ we know from Eq. (15) that $|\mathbf{A}^{-1}| = 1/320$.   ■

Cramer's Rule for $n \times n$ Systems

Suppose that we need to solve the $n \times n$ linear system

$$\mathbf{Ax} = \mathbf{b}, \tag{16}$$

where

$$\mathbf{A} = \begin{bmatrix} a_{ij} \end{bmatrix}, \quad \mathbf{x} = \begin{bmatrix} x_1 \\ x_2 \\ \vdots \\ x_n \end{bmatrix}, \quad \text{and} \quad \mathbf{b} = \begin{bmatrix} b_1 \\ b_2 \\ \vdots \\ b_n \end{bmatrix}.$$

We assume that the coefficient matrix **A** is invertible, so we know in advance that a unique solution **x** of (16) exists. The question is how to write **x** explicitly in terms of the coefficients a_{ij} and the constants b_i. In the following discussion, we think of **x** as a fixed (though as yet unknown) vector.

If we denote by $\mathbf{a}_1, \mathbf{a}_2, \ldots, \mathbf{a}_n$ the column vectors of the $n \times n$ matrix **A**, then

$$\mathbf{A} = \begin{bmatrix} \mathbf{a}_1 & \mathbf{a}_2 & \cdots & \mathbf{a}_n \end{bmatrix}.$$

The desired formula for the ith unknown x_i involves the determinant of the matrix $\begin{bmatrix} \mathbf{a}_1 & \cdots & \mathbf{b} & \cdots & \mathbf{a}_n \end{bmatrix}$ that is obtained upon replacing the ith column $\mathbf{a}_i$ of **A** with the constant vector **b**.

THEOREM 4: Cramer's Rule

Consider the $n \times n$ linear system $\mathbf{Ax} = \mathbf{b}$, with

$$\mathbf{A} = \begin{bmatrix} \mathbf{a}_1 & \mathbf{a}_2 & \cdots & \mathbf{a}_n \end{bmatrix}.$$

If $|\mathbf{A}| \neq 0$, then the ith entry of the unique solution $\mathbf{x} = (x_1, x_2, \ldots, x_n)$ is given by

$$
\begin{aligned}
x_i &= \frac{\begin{vmatrix} \mathbf{a}_1 & \cdots & \mathbf{b} & \cdots & \mathbf{a}_n \end{vmatrix}}{|\mathbf{A}|} \\
&= \frac{1}{|\mathbf{A}|} \begin{vmatrix} a_{11} & \cdots & b_1 & \cdots & a_{1n} \\ a_{21} & \cdots & b_2 & \cdots & a_{2n} \\ \vdots & \ddots & \vdots & \ddots & \vdots \\ a_{n1} & \cdots & b_n & \cdots & a_{nn} \end{vmatrix},
\end{aligned}
\tag{17}
$$

where in the last expression the constant vector **b** replaces the ith column vector $\mathbf{a}_i$ of **A**. ▲

For instance, the unique solution (x_1, x_2, x_3) of the 3×3 system

$$
\begin{aligned}
a_{11}x_1 + a_{12}x_2 + a_{13}x_3 &= b_1 \\
a_{21}x_1 + a_{22}x_2 + a_{23}x_3 &= b_2 \\
a_{31}x_1 + a_{32}x_2 + a_{33}x_3 &= b_3
\end{aligned}
\tag{18}
$$

with $|\mathbf{A}| = |a_{ij}| \neq 0$ is given by the formulas

$$
x_1 = \frac{1}{|\mathbf{A}|} \begin{vmatrix} b_1 & a_{12} & a_{13} \\ b_2 & a_{22} & a_{23} \\ b_3 & a_{32} & a_{33} \end{vmatrix},
$$

$$
x_2 = \frac{1}{|\mathbf{A}|} \begin{vmatrix} a_{11} & b_1 & a_{13} \\ a_{21} & b_2 & a_{23} \\ a_{31} & b_3 & a_{33} \end{vmatrix}
\tag{19}
$$

$$
x_3 = \frac{1}{|\mathbf{A}|} \begin{vmatrix} a_{11} & a_{12} & b_1 \\ a_{21} & a_{22} & b_2 \\ a_{31} & a_{32} & b_3 \end{vmatrix}.
$$

Example 10   Use Cramer's rule to solve the system

$$x_1 + 4x_2 + 5x_3 = 2$$
$$4x_1 + 2x_2 + 5x_3 = 3$$
$$-3x_1 + 3x_2 - x_3 = 1.$$

Solution   We find that

$$|\mathbf{A}| = \begin{vmatrix} 1 & 4 & 5 \\ 4 & 2 & 5 \\ -3 & 3 & -1 \end{vmatrix} = 29;$$

then the formulas in (19) yield

$$x_1 = \frac{1}{29} \begin{vmatrix} 2 & 4 & 5 \\ 3 & 2 & 5 \\ 1 & 3 & -1 \end{vmatrix} = \frac{33}{29},$$

$$x_2 = \frac{1}{29} \begin{vmatrix} 1 & 2 & 5 \\ 4 & 3 & 5 \\ -3 & 1 & -1 \end{vmatrix} = \frac{35}{29},$$

and

$$x_3 = \frac{1}{29} \begin{vmatrix} 1 & 4 & 2 \\ 4 & 2 & 3 \\ -3 & 3 & 1 \end{vmatrix} = -\frac{23}{29}.$$ ∎

Inverses and the Adjoint Matrix

The inverse $\mathbf{A}^{-1}$ of the invertible $n \times n$ matrix $\mathbf{A}$ can be found by solving the matrix equation

$$\mathbf{AX} = \mathbf{I}. \tag{20}$$

If we write the coefficient matrix $\mathbf{A} = \begin{bmatrix} \mathbf{a}_1 & \mathbf{a}_2 & \cdots & \mathbf{a}_n \end{bmatrix}$, the unknown matrix $\mathbf{X} = \begin{bmatrix} \mathbf{x}_1 & \mathbf{x}_2 & \cdots & \mathbf{x}_n \end{bmatrix}$, and the identity matrix $\mathbf{I} = \begin{bmatrix} \mathbf{e}_1 & \mathbf{e}_2 & \cdots & \mathbf{e}_n \end{bmatrix}$ in terms of their columns, then (20) says that

$$\mathbf{Ax}_j = \mathbf{e}_j \tag{21}$$

for $j = 1, 2, \ldots, n$. Each of these n equations can then be solved explicitly using Cramer's rule. In particular, Eq. (17) says that the ith element of the column matrix $\mathbf{x}_j$ is given by

$$x_{ij} = \frac{\begin{vmatrix} \mathbf{a}_1 & \cdots & \mathbf{a}_{i-1} & \mathbf{e}_j & \mathbf{a}_{i+1} & \cdots & \mathbf{a}_n \end{vmatrix}}{|\mathbf{A}|} \tag{22}$$

for $i, j = 1, 2, \ldots, n$. When these results are assembled (Appendix B), we get an explicit formula for the inverse matrix.

THEOREM 5: The Inverse Matrix

The inverse of the invertible matrix **A** is given by the formula

$$\mathbf{A}^{-1} = \frac{\left[A_{ij} \right]^T}{|\mathbf{A}|}, \tag{23}$$

where, as usual, A_{ij} denotes the ijth cofactor of **A**; that is, A_{ij} is the product of $(-1)^{i+j}$ and the ijth minor determinant of **A**. ▲

We see in (23) the *transpose* of the **cofactor matrix** $\left[A_{ij} \right]$ of the $n \times n$ matrix **A**. This transposed cofactor matrix is called the **adjoint matrix** of **A** and is denoted by

$$\text{adj } \mathbf{A} = \left[A_{ij} \right]^T = \left[A_{ji} \right]. \tag{24}$$

Example 11 Apply the formula in (23) to find the inverse of the matrix

$$\mathbf{A} = \begin{bmatrix} 1 & 4 & 5 \\ 4 & 2 & 5 \\ -3 & 3 & -1 \end{bmatrix}$$

of Example 10, in which we saw that $|\mathbf{A}| = 29$.

Solution First we calculate the cofactors of **A**, arranging our computations in a natural 3×3 array:

$$A_{11} = + \begin{vmatrix} 2 & 5 \\ 3 & -1 \end{vmatrix} = -17, \quad A_{12} = - \begin{vmatrix} 4 & 5 \\ -3 & -1 \end{vmatrix} = -11, \quad A_{13} = + \begin{vmatrix} 4 & 2 \\ -3 & 3 \end{vmatrix} = 18,$$

$$A_{21} = - \begin{vmatrix} 4 & 5 \\ 3 & -1 \end{vmatrix} = 19, \quad A_{22} = + \begin{vmatrix} 1 & 5 \\ -3 & -1 \end{vmatrix} = 14, \quad A_{23} = - \begin{vmatrix} 1 & 4 \\ -3 & 3 \end{vmatrix} = -15,$$

$$A_{31} = + \begin{vmatrix} 4 & 5 \\ 2 & 5 \end{vmatrix} = 10, \quad A_{32} = - \begin{vmatrix} 1 & 5 \\ 4 & 5 \end{vmatrix} = 15, \quad A_{33} = + \begin{vmatrix} 1 & 4 \\ 4 & 2 \end{vmatrix} = -14.$$

(Note the familiar checkerboard pattern of signs.) Thus the cofactor matrix of **A** is

$$\left[A_{ij} \right] = \begin{bmatrix} -17 & -11 & 18 \\ 19 & 14 & -15 \\ 10 & 15 & -14 \end{bmatrix}.$$

Next, we interchange rows and columns to obtain the adjoint matrix

$$\text{adj } \mathbf{A} = \left[A_{ij} \right]^T = \begin{bmatrix} -17 & 19 & 10 \\ -11 & 14 & 15 \\ 18 & -15 & -14 \end{bmatrix}.$$

Finally, in accord with Eq. (23), we divide by $|\mathbf{A}| = 29$ to get the inverse matrix

$$\mathbf{A}^{-1} = \frac{1}{29} \begin{bmatrix} -17 & 19 & 10 \\ -11 & 14 & 15 \\ 18 & -15 & -14 \end{bmatrix}. \quad \blacksquare$$

Computational Efficiency

The amount of labor required to complete a numerical calculation is measured by the number of arithmetical operations it involves. So let us count just the number of multiplications required to evaluate an $n \times n$ determinant using cofactor expansions. If $n = 5$, for instance, then the cofactor expansion along a row or column requires computations of *five* 4×4 determinants. A cofactor expansion of each of these five 4×4 determinants involves *four* 3×3 determinants. Each of these four 3×3 determinants leads to *three* 2×2 determinants, and finally each of these 2×2 determinants requires *two* multiplications for its evaluation. Hence the total number of multiplications required to evaluate the original 5×5 determinant is

$$5 \cdot 4 \cdot 3 \cdot 2 = 5! = 120.$$

In general, *the number of multiplications required to evaluate an $n \times n$ determinant completely by cofactor expansions is*

$$n! = n \cdot (n-1) \cdots 3 \cdot 2 \cdot 1 \qquad (n \text{ factorial}).$$

Thus, if we ignore the smaller number of additions involved, then our *operations count* for an $n \times n$ determinant is $n!$. For instance, the evaluation of a 25×25 determinant by cofactor expansion would require about $25! \approx 1.55 \times 10^{25}$ operations. If we used a supercomputer capable of a billion operations per second this task would require about $(1.55 \times 10^{16})/(365.25 \times 24 \times 3600) \approx 492$ million years! This same supercomputer would require about 9.64×10^{47} years—incomparably longer than the estimated age of the universe (perhaps 20 billion years)—to evaluate a 50×50 determinant by cofactor expansion. Contemporary scientific and engineering applications routinely involve matrices of size 1000×1000 (or larger) whose cofactor expansions would require incomprehensibly long times with any conceivable computer.

However, a typical 1998 desktop computer, using MATLAB and performing "only" about 40 million operations per second, calculates the determinant or inverse of a randomly generated 100×100 matrix almost instantaneously. How is this possible? Obviously not by using cofactor expansions!

The answer is that determinants are much more efficiently calculated by Gaussian elimination—that is, by reduction to triangular form, so that only the product of the remaining diagonal elements need be calculated. Similarly, the inverse of the invertible matrix $\mathbf{A}$ is much more efficiently calculated by reduction of the augmented matrix $\begin{bmatrix} \mathbf{A} & \mathbf{I} \end{bmatrix}$ to reduced echelon form (as in Section 3.5) than by use of Cramer's rule (as in Theorem 5 here). A careful count reveals that the number of arithmetic operations required to reduce an $n \times n$ matrix to echelon form is of the order of n^3 rather than $n!$. As indicated in the table of Fig. 3.6.1, n^3 is dramatically smaller than $n!$ if n is fairly large. Consequently, cofactor expansions of determinants and Cramer's rule for the solution of systems are primarily of theoretical importance, and are seldom used in numerical problems where n is greater than 3 or 4.

n	5	10	25	50	100
$\frac{2}{3}n^3$	83	667	10,417	83,333	666,667
$n!$	120	3,628,800	1.55×10^{25}	3.04×10^{64}	9.33×10^{157}

FIGURE 3.6.1. Approximate operations counts for evaluating an $n \times n$ determinant by Gaussian elimination ($\frac{2}{3}n^3$) and by cofactor expansion ($n!$).

3.6 Problems

Use cofactor expansions to evaluate the determinants in Problems 1–6. Expand along the row or column that minimizes the amount of computation that is required.

1. $\begin{vmatrix} 0 & 0 & 3 \\ 4 & 0 & 0 \\ 0 & 5 & 0 \end{vmatrix}$

2. $\begin{vmatrix} 2 & 1 & 0 \\ 1 & 2 & 1 \\ 0 & 1 & 2 \end{vmatrix}$

3. $\begin{vmatrix} 1 & 0 & 0 & 0 \\ 2 & 0 & 5 & 0 \\ 3 & 6 & 9 & 8 \\ 4 & 0 & 10 & 7 \end{vmatrix}$

4. $\begin{vmatrix} 5 & 11 & 8 & 7 \\ 3 & -2 & 6 & 23 \\ 0 & 0 & 0 & -3 \\ 0 & 4 & 0 & 17 \end{vmatrix}$

5. $\begin{vmatrix} 0 & 0 & 1 & 0 & 0 \\ 2 & 0 & 0 & 0 & 0 \\ 0 & 0 & 0 & 3 & 0 \\ 0 & 0 & 0 & 0 & 4 \\ 0 & 5 & 0 & 0 & 0 \end{vmatrix}$

6. $\begin{vmatrix} 3 & 0 & 11 & -5 & 0 \\ -2 & 4 & 13 & 6 & 5 \\ 0 & 0 & 5 & 0 & 0 \\ 7 & 6 & -9 & 17 & 7 \\ 0 & 0 & 8 & 2 & 0 \end{vmatrix}$

In Problems 7–12, evaluate each given determinant after first simplifying the computation (as in Example 6) by adding an appropriate multiple of some row or column to another.

7. $\begin{vmatrix} 1 & 1 & 1 \\ 2 & 2 & 2 \\ 3 & 3 & 3 \end{vmatrix}$

8. $\begin{vmatrix} 2 & 3 & 4 \\ -2 & -3 & 1 \\ 3 & 2 & 7 \end{vmatrix}$

9. $\begin{vmatrix} 3 & -2 & 5 \\ 0 & 5 & 17 \\ 6 & -4 & 12 \end{vmatrix}$

10. $\begin{vmatrix} -3 & 6 & 5 \\ 1 & -2 & -4 \\ 2 & -5 & 12 \end{vmatrix}$

11. $\begin{vmatrix} 1 & 2 & 3 & 4 \\ 0 & 5 & 6 & 7 \\ 0 & 0 & 8 & 9 \\ 2 & 4 & 6 & 9 \end{vmatrix}$

12. $\begin{vmatrix} 2 & 0 & 0 & -3 \\ 0 & 1 & 11 & 12 \\ 0 & 0 & 5 & 13 \\ -4 & 0 & 0 & 7 \end{vmatrix}$

Use the method of elimination to evaluate the determinants in Problems 13–20.

13. $\begin{vmatrix} -4 & 4 & -1 \\ -1 & -2 & 2 \\ 1 & 4 & 3 \end{vmatrix}$

14. $\begin{vmatrix} 4 & 2 & -2 \\ 3 & 1 & -5 \\ -5 & -4 & 3 \end{vmatrix}$

15. $\begin{vmatrix} -2 & 5 & 4 \\ 5 & 3 & 1 \\ 1 & 4 & 5 \end{vmatrix}$

16. $\begin{vmatrix} 2 & 4 & -2 \\ -5 & -4 & -1 \\ -4 & 2 & 1 \end{vmatrix}$

17. $\begin{vmatrix} 2 & 3 & 3 & 1 \\ 0 & 4 & 3 & -3 \\ 2 & -1 & -1 & -3 \\ 0 & -4 & -3 & 2 \end{vmatrix}$

18. $\begin{vmatrix} 1 & 4 & 4 & 1 \\ 0 & 1 & -2 & 2 \\ 3 & 3 & 1 & 4 \\ 0 & 1 & -3 & -2 \end{vmatrix}$

19. $\begin{vmatrix} 1 & 0 & 0 & 3 \\ 0 & 1 & -2 & 0 \\ -2 & 3 & -2 & 3 \\ 0 & -3 & 3 & 3 \end{vmatrix}$

20. $\begin{vmatrix} 1 & 2 & 1 & -1 \\ 2 & 1 & 3 & 3 \\ 0 & 1 & -2 & 3 \\ -1 & 4 & -2 & 4 \end{vmatrix}$

Use Cramer's rule to solve the systems in Problems 21–32.

21. $3x + 4y = 2$
$5x + 7y = 1$

22. $5x + 8y = 3$
$8x + 13y = 5$

23. $17x + 7y = 6$
$12x + 5y = 4$

24. $11x + 15y = 10$
$8x + 11y = 7$

25. $5x + 6y = 12$
$3x + 4y = 6$

26. $6x + 7y = 3$
$8x + 9y = 4$

27. $5x_1 + 2x_2 - 2x_3 = 1$
$x_1 + 5x_2 - 3x_3 = -2$
$5x_1 - 3x_2 + 5x_3 = 2$

28. $5x_1 + 4x_2 - 2x_3 = 4$
$2x_1 \qquad + 3x_3 = 2$
$2x_1 - x_2 + x_3 = 1$

29. $3x_1 - x_2 - 5x_3 = 3$
$4x_1 - 4x_2 - 3x_3 = -4$
$x_1 \qquad - 5x_3 = 2$

30. $x_1 + 4x_2 + 2x_3 = 3$
$4x_1 + 2x_2 + x_3 = 1$
$2x_1 - 2x_2 - 5x_3 = -3$

31. $2x_1 \qquad - 5x_3 = -3$
$4x_1 - 5x_2 + 3x_3 = 3$
$-2x_1 + x_2 + x_3 = 1$

32. $3x_1 + 4x_2 - 3x_3 = 5$
$3x_1 - 2x_2 + 4x_3 = 7$
$3x_1 + 2x_2 - x_3 = 3$

Apply Theorem 5 to find the inverse $\mathbf{A}^{-1}$ of each matrix $\mathbf{A}$ given in Problems 33–40.

33. $\begin{bmatrix} -5 & -2 & 2 \\ 1 & 5 & -3 \\ 5 & -3 & 1 \end{bmatrix}$

34. $\begin{bmatrix} 2 & 0 & 3 \\ -5 & -4 & 2 \\ 2 & -1 & 1 \end{bmatrix}$

35. $\begin{bmatrix} 3 & 5 & 2 \\ -2 & 3 & -4 \\ -5 & 0 & -5 \end{bmatrix}$

36. $\begin{bmatrix} -4 & 4 & 3 \\ 3 & -1 & -5 \\ 1 & 0 & -5 \end{bmatrix}$

37. $\begin{bmatrix} -4 & 1 & 5 \\ -2 & 4 & 5 \\ -3 & -3 & -1 \end{bmatrix}$

38. $\begin{bmatrix} 3 & 4 & -3 \\ 3 & 2 & -1 \\ -3 & 2 & -4 \end{bmatrix}$

39. $\begin{bmatrix} -3 & -2 & 3 \\ 0 & 3 & 2 \\ 2 & 3 & -5 \end{bmatrix}$

40. $\begin{bmatrix} 2 & 4 & -3 \\ 2 & -3 & -1 \\ -5 & 0 & -3 \end{bmatrix}$

41. Show that $(\mathbf{AB})^T = \mathbf{B}^T\mathbf{A}^T$ if $\mathbf{A}$ and $\mathbf{B}$ are arbitrary 2×2 matrices.

42. Consider the 2×2 matrices

$$\mathbf{A} = \begin{bmatrix} a & b \\ c & d \end{bmatrix} \quad \text{and} \quad \mathbf{B} = \begin{bmatrix} \mathbf{x} \\ \mathbf{y} \end{bmatrix},$$

where $\mathbf{x}$ and $\mathbf{y}$ denote the row vectors of $\mathbf{B}$. Then the product $\mathbf{AB}$ can be written in the form

$$\mathbf{AB} = \begin{bmatrix} a\mathbf{x} + b\mathbf{y} \\ c\mathbf{x} + d\mathbf{y} \end{bmatrix}.$$

Use this expression and the properties of determinants to show that

$$\det \mathbf{AB} = (ad - bc) \begin{vmatrix} \mathbf{x} \\ \mathbf{y} \end{vmatrix} = (\det \mathbf{A})(\det \mathbf{B}).$$

Thus the determinant of a product of 2×2 matrices is equal to the product of their determinants.

Each of Problems 43–46 lists a special case of one of Property 1 through Property 5. Verify it by expanding the determinant on the left-hand side along an appropriate row or column.

43. $\begin{vmatrix} ka_{11} & a_{12} & a_{13} \\ ka_{21} & a_{22} & a_{23} \\ ka_{31} & a_{32} & a_{33} \end{vmatrix} = k \begin{vmatrix} a_{11} & a_{12} & a_{13} \\ a_{21} & a_{22} & a_{23} \\ a_{31} & a_{32} & a_{33} \end{vmatrix}$

44. $\begin{vmatrix} a_{21} & a_{22} & a_{23} \\ a_{11} & a_{12} & a_{13} \\ a_{31} & a_{32} & a_{33} \end{vmatrix} = - \begin{vmatrix} a_{11} & a_{12} & a_{13} \\ a_{21} & a_{22} & a_{23} \\ a_{31} & a_{32} & a_{33} \end{vmatrix}$

45. $\begin{vmatrix} a_1 & b_1 & c_1+d_1 \\ a_2 & b_2 & c_2+d_2 \\ a_3 & b_3 & c_3+d_3 \end{vmatrix} = \begin{vmatrix} a_1 & b_1 & c_1 \\ a_2 & b_2 & c_2 \\ a_3 & b_3 & c_3 \end{vmatrix} + \begin{vmatrix} a_1 & b_1 & d_1 \\ a_2 & b_2 & d_2 \\ a_3 & b_3 & d_3 \end{vmatrix}$

46. $\begin{vmatrix} a_{11}+ka_{12} & a_{12} & a_{13} \\ a_{21}+ka_{22} & a_{22} & a_{23} \\ a_{31}+ka_{32} & a_{32} & a_{33} \end{vmatrix} = \begin{vmatrix} a_{11} & a_{12} & a_{13} \\ a_{21} & a_{22} & a_{23} \\ a_{31} & a_{32} & a_{33} \end{vmatrix}$

47. Suppose that $\mathbf{A}$ and $\mathbf{B}$ are matrices of the same size. Show that: (a) $(\mathbf{A}^T)^T = \mathbf{A}$; (b) $(c\mathbf{A})^T = c\mathbf{A}^T$; and (c) $(\mathbf{A} + \mathbf{B})^T = \mathbf{A}^T + \mathbf{B}^T$.

48. Let $\mathbf{A}$ and $\mathbf{B}$ be matrices such that $\mathbf{AB}$ is defined. Show that $(\mathbf{AB})^T = \mathbf{B}^T\mathbf{A}^T$. Begin by recalling that the ijth element of $\mathbf{AB}$ is obtained by multiplying elements in the ith row of $\mathbf{A}$ with those in the jth column of $\mathbf{B}$. What is the ijth element of $\mathbf{B}^T\mathbf{A}^T$?

49. Let $\mathbf{A} = \begin{bmatrix} a_{ij} \end{bmatrix}$ be a 3×3 matrix. Show that $\det(\mathbf{A}^T) = \det \mathbf{A}$ by expanding $\det \mathbf{A}$ along its first row and $\det(\mathbf{A}^T)$ along its first column.

50. Suppose that $\mathbf{A}^2 = \mathbf{A}$. Prove that $|\mathbf{A}| = 0$ or $|\mathbf{A}| = 1$.

51. Suppose that $\mathbf{A}^n = \mathbf{0}$ (the zero matrix) for some positive integer n. Prove that $|\mathbf{A}| = 0$.

52. The square matrix $\mathbf{A}$ is called **orthogonal** provided that $\mathbf{A}^T = \mathbf{A}^{-1}$. Show that the determinant of such a matrix must be either $+1$ or -1.

53. The matrices $\mathbf{A}$ and $\mathbf{B}$ are said to be **similar** provided that $\mathbf{A} = \mathbf{P}^{-1}\mathbf{B}\mathbf{P}$ for some invertible matrix $\mathbf{P}$. Show that if $\mathbf{A}$ and $\mathbf{B}$ are similar, then $|\mathbf{A}| = |\mathbf{B}|$.

54. Deduce from Theorems 2 and 3 that if $\mathbf{A}$ and $\mathbf{B}$ are $n \times n$ invertible matrices, then $\mathbf{AB}$ is invertible if and only if both $\mathbf{A}$ and $\mathbf{B}$ are invertible.

55. Let $\mathbf{A}$ and $\mathbf{B}$ be $n \times n$ matrices. Suppose it is known that *either* $\mathbf{AB} = \mathbf{I}$ *or* $\mathbf{BA} = \mathbf{I}$. Use the result of Problem 54 to conclude that $\mathbf{B} = \mathbf{A}^{-1}$.

56. Let $\mathbf{A}$ be an $n \times n$ matrix with $\det \mathbf{A} = 1$ and with all elements of $\mathbf{A}$ integers.
  (a) Show that $\mathbf{A}^{-1}$ has only integer entries.
  (b) Suppose that $\mathbf{b}$ is an n-vector with only integer entries. Show that the solution vector $\mathbf{x}$ of $\mathbf{Ax} = \mathbf{b}$ has only integer entries.

57. Let $\mathbf{A}$ be a 3×3 upper triangular matrix with nonzero determinant. Show by explicit computation that $\mathbf{A}^{-1}$ is also upper triangular.

58. Figure 3.6.2 shows an acute triangle with angles A, B, and C and opposite sides a, b, and c. By dropping a perpendicular from each vertex to the opposite side, derive the equations

$$c \cos B + b \cos C = a$$
$$c \cos A + a \cos C = b$$
$$a \cos B + b \cos A = c.$$

Regarding these as linear equations in the unknowns $\cos A$, $\cos B$, and $\cos C$, use Cramer's rule to derive the **law of cosines** by solving for

$$\cos A = \frac{b^2 + c^2 - a^2}{2bc}.$$

Thus

$$a^2 = b^2 + c^2 - 2bc \cos A.$$

Note that the case $A = \pi/2$ ($90°$) reduces to the Pythagorean theorem.

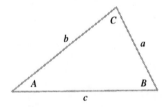

FIGURE 3.6.2. The triangle of Problem 58.

59. Show that

$$\begin{vmatrix} 2 & 1 \\ 1 & 2 \end{vmatrix} = 3 \quad \text{and} \quad \begin{vmatrix} 2 & 1 & 0 \\ 1 & 2 & 1 \\ 0 & 1 & 2 \end{vmatrix} = 4.$$

60. Consider the $n \times n$ determinant

$$B_n = \begin{vmatrix} 2 & 1 & 0 & 0 & \cdots & 0 & 0 \\ 1 & 2 & 1 & 0 & \cdots & 0 & 0 \\ 0 & 1 & 2 & 1 & \cdots & 0 & 0 \\ \vdots & \vdots & \vdots & \vdots & \ddots & \vdots & \vdots \\ 0 & 0 & 0 & 0 & \cdots & 2 & 1 \\ 0 & 0 & 0 & 0 & \cdots & 1 & 2 \end{vmatrix}$$

in which each entry on the main diagonal is a 2, each entry on the two adjacent diagonals is a 1, and every other entry is zero.

(a) Expand along the first row to show that

$$B_n = 2B_{n-1} - B_{n-2}.$$

(b) Prove by induction on n that $B_n = n + 1$ for $n \geq 2$.

*Problems 61–64 deal with the **Vandermonde determinant***

$$V(x_1, x_2, \ldots, x_n) = \begin{vmatrix} 1 & x_1 & x_1^2 & \cdots & x_1^{n-1} \\ 1 & x_2 & x_2^2 & \cdots & x_2^{n-1} \\ \vdots & \vdots & \vdots & \ddots & \vdots \\ 1 & x_n & x_n^2 & \cdots & x_n^{n-1} \end{vmatrix}.$$

61. Show by direct computation that $V(a, b) = b - a$ and that

$$V(a, b, c) = \begin{vmatrix} 1 & a & a^2 \\ 1 & b & b^2 \\ 1 & c & c^2 \end{vmatrix} = (b - a)(c - a)(c - b).$$

62. The formulas in Problem 61 are the cases $n = 2$ and $n = 3$ of the general formula

$$V(x_1, x_2, \ldots, x_n) = \prod_{\substack{i, j = 1 \\ i > j}}^{n} (x_i - x_j). \qquad (25)$$

The case $n = 4$ is

$$V(x_1, x_2, x_3, x_4) = (x_2 - x_1)(x_3 - x_1)(x_3 - x_2)$$
$$\times (x_4 - x_1)(x_4 - x_2)(x_4 - x_3).$$

Prove this as follows. Given x_1, x_2, and x_3, define the cubic polynomial $P(y)$ to be

$$P(y) = \begin{vmatrix} 1 & x_1 & x_1^2 & x_1^3 \\ 1 & x_2 & x_2^2 & x_2^3 \\ 1 & x_3 & x_3^2 & x_3^3 \\ 1 & y & y^2 & y^3 \end{vmatrix}. \qquad (26)$$

Because $P(x_1) = P(x_2) = P(x_3) = 0$ (why?), the roots of $P(y)$ are x_1, x_2, and x_3. It follows that

$$P(y) = k(y - x_1)(y - x_2)(y - x_3),$$

where k is the coefficient of y^3 in $P(y)$. Finally, observe that expansion of the 4×4 determinant in (26) along its last row gives $k = V(x_1, x_2, x_3)$ and that $V(x_1, x_2, x_3, x_4) = P(x_4)$.

63. Generalize the argument in Problem 62 to prove the formula in (25) by induction on n. Begin with the $(n-1)$st-degree polynomial

$$P(y) = \begin{vmatrix} 1 & x_1 & x_1^2 & \cdots & x_1^{n-1} \\ 1 & x_2 & x_2^2 & \cdots & x_2^{n-1} \\ \vdots & \vdots & \vdots & \ddots & \vdots \\ 1 & x_{n-1} & x_{n-1}^2 & \cdots & x_{n-1}^{n-1} \\ 1 & y & y^2 & \cdots & y^{n-1} \end{vmatrix}.$$

64. Use the formula in (25) to evaluate the two determinants given next.

(a) $\begin{vmatrix} 1 & 1 & 1 & 1 \\ 1 & 2 & 4 & 8 \\ 1 & 3 & 9 & 27 \\ 1 & 4 & 16 & 64 \end{vmatrix}$

(b) $\begin{vmatrix} 1 & -1 & 1 & -1 \\ 1 & 2 & 4 & 8 \\ 1 & -2 & 4 & -8 \\ 1 & 3 & 9 & 27 \end{vmatrix}$

3.7 Linear Equations and Curve Fitting

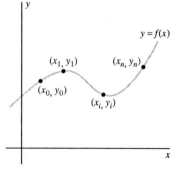

FIGURE 3.7.1. A curve $y = f(x)$ interpolating given data points.

Linear algebra has important applications to the common scientific problem of representing empirical data by means of equations or functions of specified types. We give here only a brief introduction to this extensive subject.

Typically, we begin with a collection of given *data points* $(x_0, y_0), (x_1, y_1)$, $\ldots, (x_n, y_n)$ that are to be represented by a specific type of function $y = f(x)$. For instance, y might be the volume of a sample of gas when its temperature is x. Thus the given data points are the results of experiment or measurement, and we want to determine the curve $y = f(x)$ in the xy-plane so that it passes through each of these points; see Figure 3.7.1. Thus we speak of "fitting" the curve to the data points.

We will confine our attention largely to polynomial curves. A **polynomial of degree** n is a function of the form

$$f(x) = a_0 + a_1 x + a_2 x^2 + \cdots + a_n x^n, \qquad (1)$$

where the coefficients $a_0, a_1, a_2, \ldots, a_n$ are constants. The data point (x_i, y_i) lies on the curve $y = f(x)$ provided that $f(x_i) = y_i$. The condition that this be so for each $i = 0, 1, 2, \ldots, n$ yields the $n + 1$ equations

$$
\begin{aligned}
a_0 + a_1 x_0 + a_2 (x_0)^2 + \cdots + a_n (x_0)^n &= y_0 \\
a_0 + a_1 x_1 + a_2 (x_1)^2 + \cdots + a_n (x_1)^n &= y_1 \\
a_0 + a_1 x_2 + a_2 (x_2)^2 + \cdots + a_n (x_2)^n &= y_2 \\
&\vdots \\
a_0 + a_1 x_n + a_2 (x_n)^2 + \cdots + a_n (x_n)^n &= y_n.
\end{aligned}
\tag{2}
$$

Because the numbers x_i and y_i are given, this is a system of $n+1$ *linear* equations in the $n + 1$ unknowns $a_0, a_1, a_2, \ldots, a_n$ (the coefficients that determine the polynomial in (1)).

The $(n+1) \times (n+1)$ coefficient matrix of the system in (1) is the Vandermonde matrix

$$
\mathbf{A} = \begin{bmatrix}
1 & x_0 & (x_0)^2 & \cdots & (x_0)^n \\
1 & x_1 & (x_1)^2 & \cdots & (x_1)^n \\
1 & x_2 & (x_2)^2 & \cdots & (x_2)^n \\
\vdots & \vdots & \vdots & \ddots & \vdots \\
1 & x_n & (x_n)^2 & \cdots & (x_n)^n
\end{bmatrix}
\tag{3}
$$

that is discussed in Problems 61–63 of Section 3.6. There, it is shown that, if the x-coordinates $x_0, x_1, x_2, \ldots, x_n$ are distinct, then the matrix $\mathbf{A}$ is nonsingular. (See Eq. (25) there.) Hence Theorem 7 in Section 3.5 implies that the system in (2) has a unique solution for the coefficients $a_0, a_1, a_2, \ldots, a_n$ in (1). Thus there is a unique nth degree polynomial that fits the $n + 1$ given data points. We call it an **interpolating polynomial**, and say that it **interpolates** the given points.

Example 1 Find a cubic polynomial of the form

$$
y = A + Bx + Cx^2 + Dx^3
$$

that interpolates the data points $(-1, 4)$, $(1, 2)$, $(2, 1)$, and $(3, 16)$.

Solution In a particular problem, it generally is simpler to use distinct capital letters rather than subscripted symbols to denote the coefficients. Here we want to find the values of A, B, C, and D so that $y(-1) = 4$, $y(1) = 2$, $y(2) = 1$, and $y(3) = 16$. These conditions yield the four linear equations

$$
\begin{aligned}
A - B + C - D &= 4 \\
A + B + C + D &= 2 \\
A + 2B + 4C + 8D &= 1 \\
A + 3B + 9C + 27D &= 16.
\end{aligned}
$$

We readily reduce this system to the echelon form

$$
\begin{aligned}
A - B + C - D &= 4 \\
B + D &= -1 \\
C + 2D &= 0 \\
D &= 2,
\end{aligned}
$$

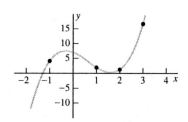

FIGURE 3.7.2. Cubic curve through the four data points of Example 1.

and then back substitution yields $A = 7$, $B = -3$, $C = -4$, and $D = 2$. Thus the desired cubic polynomial is

$$y = 7 - 3x - 4x^2 + 2x^3.$$

The graph of this cubic is shown ion Fig. 3.7.2, along with the four original data points. ∎

Modeling World Population Growth

As a concrete example of interpolation, we consider the growth of the world's human population. The table in Fig. 3.7.3 shows the total world population (in billions) at 5-year intervals. Actual populations are shown for the years 1960–1995. The figures listed for the years 2000–2025 are future populations predicted by the United Nations on the basis of detailed demographic analysis of population trends on a country-by-country basis throughout the world. Each entry in the final column of this table gives the average annual percentage growth rate during the preceding 5-year period. For instance, $3.039(1.0194)^5 \approx 3.345$ for the growth during the 5-year period 1960–1965, so the average annual growth during this period is about 1.94%.

Year	World Population (billions)	Percent Growth
1960	3.039	
1965	3.345	1.94%
1970	3.707	2.08%
1975	4.086	1.97%
1980	4.454	1.74%
1985	4.851	1.72%
1990	5.279	1.71%
1995	5.688	1.50%
2000	6.083	1.35%
2005	6.468	1.23%
2010	6.849	1.15%
2015	7.227	1.08%
2020	7.585	0.97%
2025	7.923	0.88%

FIGURE 3.7.3. World population data.

We see that the world population grew at an annual rate of about 2% during the 1960s, but the rate of growth has slowed since then, and it is expected to slow even more during the early decades of the 21st century. In particular, the growth of the world population at the present time in history is *not* natural or exponential in character—that characterization would imply a constant percentage rate of growth. We explore the possibility of interpolating world population data with polynomial models that might be usable to predict future populations. It seems natural to expect better results with higher-degree interpolating polynomials. Let's see if this is so.

Example 2

First, we fit a linear polynomial $P_1(t) = a + bt$ (with $t = 0$ in 1900) to the 1980 and 1990 world population values. We need only solve the equations

$$a + 80b = 4.454$$
$$a + 90b = 5.279$$

for $a = -2.146$, $b = 0.0825$. Thus our linear interpolating polynomial is

$$P_1(t) = -2.146 + 0.0825t. \tag{4}$$

∎

Example 3

FIGURE 3.7.4. TI-92 calculator solution of the 3×3 system in Example 3.

Now let's fit a quadratic polynomial $P_2(t) = a + bt + ct^2$ (with $t = 0$ in 1900) to the 1980, 1985, and 1990 world population values. With the three data points $(80, 4.454)$, $(85, 4.851)$ and $(90, 5.279)$, the system in (3) yields the equations

$$a + 80b + 80^2c = 4.454$$
$$a + 85b + 85^2c = 4.851$$
$$a + 90b + 90^2c = 5.279$$

having the calculator solution $a = 2.318$, $b = -0.0229$, $c = 0.00062$ (Fig. 3.7.4). Thus our quadratic interpolating polynomial is

$$P_2(t) = 2.318 - 0.0229t + 0.00062t^2. \tag{5}$$

∎

Example 4

Next we fit a cubic polynomial $P_3(t) = a + bt + ct^2 + dt^3$ (with $t = 0$ in 1900) to the 1980, 1985, 1990, and 1995 world population values. With the four data points $(80, 4.454)$, $(85, 4.851)$, $(90, 5.279)$, and $(95, 5.688)$, the system in (3) yields the four equations

$$4.454 = a + 80b + 80^2c + 80^3d$$
$$4.851 = a + 85b + 85^2c + 85^3d$$
$$5.279 = a + 90b + 90^2c + 90^3d$$
$$5.688 = a + 95b + 95^2c + 95^3d.$$

As in the 3.5 Application, a calculator or computer yields the solution

$$\begin{bmatrix} a \\ b \\ c \\ d \end{bmatrix} = \begin{bmatrix} 1 & 80 & 80^2 & 80^3 \\ 1 & 85 & 85^2 & 85^3 \\ 1 & 90 & 90^2 & 90^3 \\ 1 & 95 & 95^2 & 95^3 \end{bmatrix}^{-1} \begin{bmatrix} 4.454 \\ 4.851 \\ 5.279 \\ 5.688 \end{bmatrix} = \begin{bmatrix} 43.118 \\ -1.46623 \\ 0.01762 \\ -0.000066667 \end{bmatrix}.$$

Thus our cubic interpolating polynomial is

$$P_3(t) = 43.118 - 1.46623t + 0.01762t^2 - 0.000066667t^3. \tag{6}$$

∎

Example 5   In order to fit a fourth-degree population model of the form

$$P_4(t) = a + bt + ct^2 + dt^3 + et^4$$

to the 1975-1980-1985-1990-1995 world population data, we need to solve the linear system

$$\begin{bmatrix} 1 & 75 & 75^2 & 75^3 & 75^4 \\ 1 & 80 & 80^2 & 80^3 & 80^4 \\ 1 & 85 & 85^2 & 85^3 & 85^4 \\ 1 & 90 & 90^2 & 90^3 & 90^4 \\ 1 & 95 & 95^2 & 95^3 & 95^4 \end{bmatrix} \begin{bmatrix} a \\ b \\ c \\ d \\ e \end{bmatrix} = \begin{bmatrix} 4.086 \\ 4.454 \\ 4.851 \\ 5.279 \\ 5.688 \end{bmatrix}$$

to find the values of the coefficients a, b, c, d, and e. The result is

$$P_4(t) = -158.434 + 7.78543t - 0.141413t^2$$
$$+ 0.00114667t^3 - 0.00000346667t^4. \tag{7}$$

∎

The table in Fig. 3.7.5 compares our linear, quadratic, cubic, and quartic predictions with the "correct" United Nations prediction for the year 2000. Each "error" in the third column of this table is the amount by which the corresponding prediction undershoots (positive error) or overshoots (negative error) the U.N. prediction. We see that the cubic prediction is better than the quartic but worse than the linear prediction. The quadratic prediction is even worse. Thus there apparently is no correlation between the degree of the polynomial model and the accuracy of its predictions.

Figure 3.7.6 shows the U.N. world population data points for the years 1960 through 2025, together with the plots of the linear, quadratic, cubic, and quartic population functions of Examples 2 through 5. It looks as though, the more work we do to find a polynomial fitting selected data points, the less we get for our effort. It certainly is true in this figure that—outside the interval from 1975 to 1995—the higher the degree of the polynomial is, the worse it appears to fit the given data points. The issue here is the difference between

- *interpolating* data points *within* the interval of given points being fitted and
- *extrapolating* data points *outside* this interval.

	Year 2000	
	Prediction	**Error**
Linear	6.104	−0.021
Quadratic	6.228	−0.145
Cubic	6.028	+0.055
Quartic	5.976	+0.107
United Nations	6.083	

FIGURE 3.7.5. Predictions of the 2000 world population.

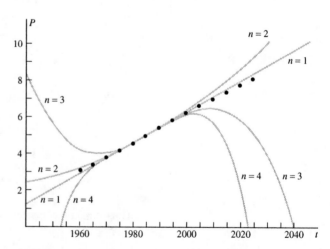

FIGURE 3.7.6. Comparison of world population data and the interpolating polynomials $P_n(t)$ for $t = 1, 2, 3, 4$.

All four of our polynomials appear to do a good job of interpolating but, somewhat paradoxically, the higher the degree is, the worse is the apparent accuracy of extrapolation. The highly questionable accuracy of data extrapolation outside the interval of interpolation has significant implications. For instance, consider a news report that when a certain alleged carcinogen was fed to mice in sufficient amounts to kill an elephant, the mice got cancer. It is then argued that moderate amounts of this carcinogen may cause cancer in humans; or that if 1 part per billion of this carcinogen in the environment kills 1 person, then 1 part per million (a thousand times as much) will kill 1000 people. Such arguments are common, but they may well be cases of extrapolation beyond the range of accuracy. The bottom line is that interpolation is fairly safe—though hardly fail-safe— but extrapolation is risky.

Geometric Applications

In contrast with population prediction, there are interesting situations where curve fitting is exact. For instance, the fact that "two points determine a line" in the plane means that, when we fit the linear function $y = a + bx$ to a given pair of points, we get precisely the one and only straight line in the plane that passes through these points. Similarly, "three points determine a circle", meaning that there is one and only one circle in the plane that passes through three given noncollinear points. In order to find this particular circle, we recall that the equation of a circle with center (h, k) and radius r is

$$(x - h)^2 + (y - k)^2 = r^2 \quad \text{(Fig. 3.7.7)}. \tag{8}$$

Simplification gives

$$(x^2 - 2hx + h^2) + (y^2 - 2ky + k^2) = r^2,$$

that is,

$$x^2 + y^2 + Ax + By + C = 0 \tag{9}$$

(where $A = -2h$, $B = -2k$, and $C = h^2 + k^2 - r^2$) as the general equation of a circle in the plane.

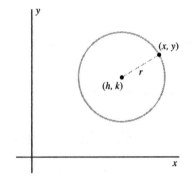

FIGURE 3.7.7. The circle with center (h, k) and radius r.

Example 6

Find the equation of the circle that is determined by the points $P(-1, 5)$, $Q(5, -3)$, and $R(6, 4)$.

Solution

Substitution of the xy-coordinates of each of the three points P, Q, and R into (9) gives the three equations

$$-A + 5B + C = -26$$
$$5A - 3B + C = -34$$
$$6A + 4B + C = -52.$$

Reduction of the corresponding augmented coefficient matrix to reduced row-echelon form (Fig. 3.7.8) yields $A = -4$, $B = -2$, and $C = -20$. Thus the equation of the desired circle is

$$x^2 + y^2 - 4x - 2y - 20 = 0.$$

To find its center and radius, we complete the squares in x and y and get

$$(x - 2)^2 + (y - 1)^2 = 25.$$

Thus the circle has center $(2, 1)$ and radius 5 (Fig. 3.7.9). ∎

FIGURE 3.7.8. TI-92 calculator solution of the 3×3 system in Example 6.

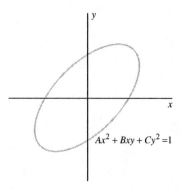

FIGURE 3.7.9. The circle of
Example 6.

FIGURE 3.7.10. A rotated
central ellipse.

Three appropriate points in the plane also determine a **central conic** with
equation of the form

$$Ax^2 + Bxy + Cy^2 = 1. \tag{10}$$

This is a rotated conic section—an ellipse, parabola, or hyperbola—centered at the
origin of the xy-coordinate system. Figure 3.7.10 shows a typical rotated ellipse in
the plane.

Example 7

Find the equation of the central conic that passes through the same three points
$P(-1, 5)$, $Q(5, -3)$, and $R(6, 4)$ of Example 6.

Solution

Substitution of the xy-coordinates of each of the three points P, Q, and R into (10)
gives the linear system of three equations

$$
\begin{aligned}
A - \ 5B + 25C &= 1 \\
25A - 15B + \ 9C &= 1 \\
36A + 24B + 16C &= 1
\end{aligned}
\tag{11}
$$

in the three unknowns A, B, and C. Reduction of the corresponding augmented
coefficient matrix to reduced row-echelon form (Fig. 3.7.11) yields the values

$$A = \frac{277}{14212}, \quad B = -\frac{172}{14212}, \quad \text{and} \quad C = \frac{523}{14212}.$$

FIGURE 3.7.11. TI-92
calculator solution of the
reduced row-echelon form of
the augmented coefficient
matrix in (11).

If we substitute these coefficient values in (10) and multiply the result by the common denominator 14212, we get the desired equation

$$277x^2 - 172xy + 523y^2 = 14212 \tag{12}$$

of our central conic. The computer plot in Fig. 3.7.12 verifies that this rotated ellipse
does, indeed pass through all three points P, Q, and R. ∎

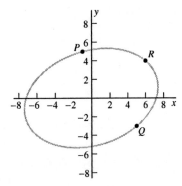

FIGURE 3.7.12. Central ellipse passing through the points P, Q, and R of Example 7.

3.7 Problems

In each of Problems 1–10, $n + 1$ data points are given. Find the nth degree polynomial $y = f(x)$ that fits these points.

1. $(1, 1)$ and $(3, 7)$
2. $(-1, 11)$ and $(2, -10)$
3. $(0, 3)$, $(1, 1)$, and $(2, -5)$
4. $(-1, 1)$, $(1, 5)$, and $(2, 16)$
5. $(1, 3)$, $(2, 3)$, and $(3, 5)$
6. $(-1, -1)$, $(3, -13)$, and $(5, 5)$
7. $(-1, 1)$, $(0, 0)$, $(1, 1)$, and $(2, -4)$
8. $(-1, 3)$, $(0, 5)$, $(1, 7)$, and $(2, 3)$
9. $(-2, -2)$, $(-1, 2)$, $(1, 10)$, and $(2, 26)$
10. $(-1, 27)$, $(1, 13)$, $(2, 3)$, and $(3, -25)$

Three points are given in each of Problems 11–14. Find the equation of the circle determined by these points, as well as its center and radius.

11. $(-1, -1)$, $(6, 6)$, and $(7, 5)$
12. $(3, -4)$, $(5, 10)$, and $(-9, 12)$
13. $(1, 0)$, $(0, -5)$, and $(-5, -4)$
14. $(0, 0)$, $(10, 0)$, and $(-7, 7)$

In Problems 15–18, find an equation of the central ellipse that passes through the three given points.

15. $(0, 5)$, $(5, 0)$, and $(5, 5)$
16. $(0, 5)$, $(5, 0)$, and $(10, 10)$
17. $(0, 1)$, $(1, 0)$, and $(10, 10)$

18. $(0, 4)$, $(3, 0)$, and $(5, 5)$
19. Find a curve of the form $y = A + (B/x)$ that passes through the points $(1, 5)$ and $(2, 4)$.
20. Find a curve of the form $y = Ax + (B/x) + (C/x^2)$ that passes through the points $(1, 2)$, $(2, 20)$, and $(4, 41)$.

*A sphere in space with **center** (h, k, l) and **radius** r has equation*

$$(x - h)^2 + (y - k)^2 + (z - l)^2 = r^2.$$

Four given points in space suffice to determine the values of h, k, l, and r. In Problems 21 and 22, find the center and radius of the sphere that passes through the four given points P, Q, R, and S. Hint: Substitute each given triple of coordinates into the sphere equation above to obtain four equations that h, k, l, and r must satisfy. To solve these equations, first subtract the first one from each of the other three. How many unknowns are left in the three equations that result?

21. $P(4, 6, 15)$, $Q(13, 5, 7)$, $R(5, 14, 6)$, $S(5, 5, -9)$
22. $P(11, 17, 17)$, $Q(29, 1, 15)$, $R(13, -1, 33)$, $S(-19, -13, 1)$

*Problems 23–34 are intended as calculator or computer problems and are based on the U.S. census data in the table of Fig. 3.7.13, listed by national region in millions for the census years 1950–1990. See **www.census.gov/population/ www/censusdata** for further details.*

	1950	1960	1970	1980	1990
Northeast	39.478	44.678	49.061	49.137	50.809
Midwest	44.461	51.619	56.590	58.867	59.669
South	47.197	54.973	62.813	75.367	85.446
West	20.190	28.053	34.838	43.171	52.786
U.S.	151.326	179.323	203.302	226.542	248.710

FIGURE 3.7.13. Regional population data (in millions) for Problems 23–34.

In Problems 23–26, fit a quadratic function to the 1970, 1980, *and* 1990 *population values for the indicated region.*

23. The Northeast   **24.** The Midwest

25. The South   **26.** The West

27–30. The same as Problems 23–26, except fit a cubic polynomial to the 1960, 1970, 1980, and 1990 population data for the indicated region.

31–34. The same as Problems 23–26, except fit a quartic polynomial to the 1950, 1960, 1970, 1980, and 1990 population data for the indicated region.

35. Explain why the determinant equation

$$\begin{vmatrix} y & x^2 & x & 1 \\ y_1 & x_1^2 & x_1 & 1 \\ y_2 & x_2^2 & x_2 & 1 \\ y_3 & x_3^2 & x_3 & 1 \end{vmatrix} = 0$$

fits a quadratic polynomial of the form $y = Ax^2 + Bx + C$ to the three given points (x_1, y_1), (x_2, y_2), and (x_3, y_3).

36. Expand the determinant in Problem 35 to find a parabola that interpolates the points $(1, 3)$, $(2, 3)$, and $(3, 7)$.

37. Explain why the determinant equation

$$\begin{vmatrix} x^2 + y^2 & x & y & 1 \\ x_1^2 + y_1^2 & x_1 & y_1 & 1 \\ x_2^2 + y_2^2 & x_2 & y_2 & 1 \\ x_3^2 + y_3^2 & x_3 & y_3 & 1 \end{vmatrix} = 0$$

fits a circle of the form $x^2 + y^2 + Ax + By + C = 0$ to the three given points (x_1, y_1), (x_2, y_2), and (x_3, y_3).

38. Expand the determinant in Problem 37 to find the equation of a circle passing through the three points $(3, -4)$, $(5, 10)$, and $(-9, 12)$. Then find its center and radius.

39. Explain why the determinant equation

$$\begin{vmatrix} x^2 & xy & y^2 & 1 \\ x_1^2 & x_1y_1 & y_1^2 & 1 \\ x_2^2 & x_2y_2 & y_2^2 & 1 \\ x_3^2 & x_3y_3 & y_3^2 & 1 \end{vmatrix} = 0$$

fits a central conic equation of the form $Ax^2 + Bxy + Cy^2 = 1$ to the three given points (x_1, y_1), (x_2, y_2), and (x_3, y_3).

40. Expand the determinant in Problem 39 to find the equation of the ellipse passing through the three points $(0, 4)$, $(3, 0)$, and $(5, 5)$.

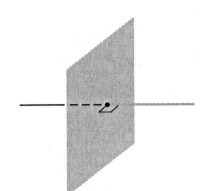

C H A P T E R

Vector Spaces

4.1 The Vector Space $\mathbf{R}^3$

Here we take a fresh look—from the viewpoint of linear algebra—at the familiar 3-dimensional space of the physical world around us (and of multivariable calculus). This review, combining old and new ideas, will provide an introduction to basic concepts that are explored further in subsequent sections of the chapter.

We define **three-dimensional coordinate space** $\mathbf{R}^3$ to be the set of all ordered triples (a, b, c) of real numbers. In ordinary language, the elements of $\mathbf{R}^3$ are called **points.** The numbers a, b, and c are called the **coordinates** of the point $P(a, b, c)$ and can be regarded as specifying the location of P in a fixed xyz-coordinate system.

The location of the point P can also be specified by means of the *arrow* or *directed line segment* (Fig. 4.1.1) that points from the origin (its *initial point*) to P (its *terminal point*). Arrows are often used in physics to represent *vector quantities*, such as force and velocity, that possess both magnitude and direction. For instance, the *velocity vector* **v** of a point moving in space may be represented by an arrow that points in the direction of its motion, with the length of the arrow being equal

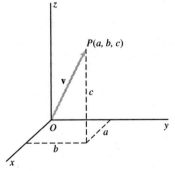

FIGURE 4.1.1. The arrow $\overrightarrow{OP}$ representing the vector $\mathbf{v} = (a, b, c)$.

225

to the speed of the moving point. If we locate this arrow with its initial point at the origin O, then its direction and length are determined by its terminal point (a, b, c). But the arrow is merely a pictorial object; the mathematical object associated with the vector $\mathbf{v}$ is simply the point (a, b, c). For this reason, it is customary to use the words point and vector interchangeably for elements of 3-space $\mathbf{R}^3$ and thus to refer either to the *point* (a, b, c) or to the *vector* (a, b, c).

Definition: Vector

A **vector** $\mathbf{v}$ in 3-space $\mathbf{R}^3$ is simply an ordered triple (a, b, c) of real numbers. We write $\mathbf{v} = (a, b, c)$ and call the numbers a, b, and c the **components** of the vector $\mathbf{v}$.

Thus "a vector is a point is a vector," but vector terminology often aids us in visualizing geometric relationships between different points. The point $P(a, b, c)$ determines the vector $\mathbf{v} = (a, b, c)$ in $\mathbf{R}^3$, and $\mathbf{v}$ is represented geometrically (as in Fig. 4.1.1) by the *position vector* $\overrightarrow{OP}$ from the origin $O(0, 0, 0)$ to P—or equally well by any parallel translate of this arrow. What is important about an arrow usually is not where it is, but how long it is and which way it points.

As in Section 3.4, we adopt the convention that the vector $\mathbf{v}$ with components v_1, v_2, and v_3 may be written interchangeably as either

$$\mathbf{v} = (v_1, v_2, v_3) \quad \text{or} \quad \mathbf{v} = \begin{bmatrix} v_1 \\ v_2 \\ v_3 \end{bmatrix}$$

with the column matrix regarded as just another symbol representing one and the same ordered triple of real numbers. Then the following definitions of addition of vectors and of multiplication of vectors by scalars are consistent with the matrix operations defined in Section 3.4.

Definition: Addition of Vectors

The **sum** $\mathbf{u} + \mathbf{v}$ of the two vectors $\mathbf{u} = (u_1, u_2, u_3)$ and $\mathbf{v} = (v_1, v_2, v_3)$ is the vector

$$\mathbf{u} + \mathbf{v} = (u_1 + v_1, u_2 + v_2, u_3 + v_3) \tag{1}$$

that is obtained upon addition of respective components of $\mathbf{u}$ and $\mathbf{v}$.

Thus we add vectors by adding corresponding components—that is, by *componentwise addition* (just as we add matrices). For instance, the sum of the vectors $\mathbf{u} = (4, 3, -5)$ and $\mathbf{v} = (-5, 2, 15)$ is the vector

$$\mathbf{u} + \mathbf{v} = (4, 3, -5) + (-5, 2, 15) = (4 - 5, 3 + 2, -5 + 15) = (-1, 5, 10).$$

The geometric representation of vectors as arrows often converts an algebraic relation into a picture that is readily understood and remembered. Addition of vectors is defined algebraically by Eq. (1). The geometric interpretation of vector addition is the *triangle law of addition* illustrated in Fig. 4.1.2 (for the case of 2-dimensional vectors in the plane), where the labeled lengths indicate why this interpretation is valid. An equivalent interpretation is the *parallelogram law of addition*, illustrated in Fig. 4.1.3.

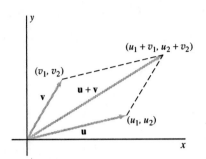

FIGURE 4.1.2. The triangle law of vector addition.

FIGURE 4.1.3. The parallelogram law of vector addition.

Multiplication of a vector by a scalar (a real number) is also defined in a componentwise manner.

Definition: Multiplication of a Vector by a Scalar

If $\mathbf{v} = (v_1, v_2, v_3)$ is a vector and c is a real number, then the **scalar multiple** $c\mathbf{v}$ is the vector

$$c\mathbf{v} = (cv_1, cv_2, cv_3) \tag{2}$$

that is obtained upon multiplying each component of $\mathbf{v}$ by c.

The **length** $|\mathbf{v}|$ of the vector $\mathbf{v} = (a, b, c)$ is defined to be the distance of the point $P(a, b, c)$ from the origin,

$$|\mathbf{v}| = \sqrt{a^2 + b^2 + c^2}. \tag{3}$$

The length of $c\mathbf{v}$ is $|c|$ times the length of $\mathbf{v}$. For instance, if $\mathbf{v} = (4, 3, -12)$, then

$$(-7)\mathbf{v} = (-7 \cdot 4, -7 \cdot 3, -7 \cdot (-12)) = (-28, -21, 84),$$
$$|\mathbf{v}| = \sqrt{(4)^2 + (3)^2 + (-12)^2} = \sqrt{169} = 13, \quad \text{and}$$
$$|-7\mathbf{v}| = |-7| \cdot |\mathbf{v}| = 7 \cdot 13 = 91.$$

FIGURE 4.1.4. The vector $c\mathbf{u}$ may have the same direction as $\mathbf{u}$ or the opposite direction.

The geometric interpretation of scalar multiplication is that $c\mathbf{v}$ is a vector of length $|c| \cdot |\mathbf{v}|$, with the same direction as $\mathbf{v}$ if $c > 0$ but the opposite direction if $c < 0$ (Fig. 4.1.4).

With vector addition and multiplication by scalars defined as in (1) and (2), $\mathbf{R}^3$ is a **vector space**. That is, these operations satisfy the conditions in (a)–(h) of the following theorem.

THEOREM 1: R³ as a Vector Space

If $\mathbf{u}$, $\mathbf{v}$, and $\mathbf{w}$ are vectors in $\mathbf{R}^3$, and r and s are real numbers, then

(a) $\mathbf{u} + \mathbf{v} = \mathbf{v} + \mathbf{u}$ (commutativity)

(b) $\mathbf{u} + (\mathbf{v} + \mathbf{w}) = (\mathbf{u} + \mathbf{v}) + \mathbf{w}$ (associativity)

(c) $\mathbf{u} + \mathbf{0} = \mathbf{0} + \mathbf{u} = \mathbf{u}$ (zero element)

(d) $\mathbf{u} + (-\mathbf{u}) = (-\mathbf{u}) + \mathbf{u} = \mathbf{0}$ (additive inverse)

(e) $r(\mathbf{u} + \mathbf{v}) = r\mathbf{u} + r\mathbf{v}$ (distributivity)

(f) $(r + s)\mathbf{u} = r\mathbf{u} + s\mathbf{u}$

(g) $r(s\mathbf{u}) = (rs)\mathbf{u}$

(h) $1(\mathbf{u}) = \mathbf{u}$ (multiplicative identity).   ▲

Of course, $\mathbf{0} = (0,0,0)$ denotes the **zero vector** in (c) and (d), and $-\mathbf{u} = (-1)\mathbf{u}$ in (d). Each of properties (a)–(h) in Theorem 1 is readily verified in a component-wise manner. For instance, if $\mathbf{u} = (u_1, u_2, u_3)$ and $\mathbf{v} = (v_1, v_2, v_3)$ then

$$
\begin{aligned}
r(\mathbf{u} + \mathbf{v}) &= r(u_1 + v_1, u_2 + v_2, u_3 + v_3) \\
&= (r(u_1 + v_1), r(u_2 + v_2), r(u_3 + v_3)) \\
&= (ru_1 + rv_1, ru_2 + rv_2, ru_3 + rv_3) \\
&= (ru_1, ru_2, ru_3) + (rv_1, rv_2, rv_3) \\
&= r(u_1, u_2, u_3) + r(v_1, v_2, v_3) = r\mathbf{u} + r\mathbf{v},
\end{aligned}
$$

so we have verified property (e).

The Vector Space R²

The familiar coordinate plane $\mathbf{R}^2$ is the set of all ordered pairs (a, b) of real numbers. We may regard $\mathbf{R}^2$ as the xy-plane in $\mathbf{R}^3$ by identifying (a, b) with the vector $(a, b, 0)$ in $\mathbf{R}^3$. Then $\mathbf{R}^2$ is simply the set of all 3-dimensional vectors that have third component 0.

Clearly, the sum of any two vectors in $\mathbf{R}^2$ is again a vector in $\mathbf{R}^2$, as is any scalar multiple of a vector in $\mathbf{R}^2$. Indeed, vectors in $\mathbf{R}^2$ satisfy all the properties of a vector space enumerated in Theorem 1. Consequently, the plane $\mathbf{R}^2$ is a vector space in its own right.

The two vectors $\mathbf{u}$ and $\mathbf{v}$ are collinear—they lie on the same line through the origin and hence point either in the same direction (Fig. 4.1.5) or in opposite directions—if and only if one is a scalar multiple of the other; that is, either

$$\mathbf{u} = c\mathbf{v} \quad \text{or} \quad \mathbf{v} = c\mathbf{u}, \tag{4}$$

for some scalar c. The scalar c merely adjusts the length and direction of one vector to fit the other. If $\mathbf{u}$ and $\mathbf{v}$ are nonzero vectors, $c = \pm|\mathbf{u}|/|\mathbf{v}|$ in the first relation, with c being positive if the two vectors point in the same direction, negative otherwise.

If one of the relations in (4) holds for some scalar c, then we say that the two vectors are **linearly dependent**. Note that if $\mathbf{u} = \mathbf{0}$ while $\mathbf{v} \neq \mathbf{0}$, then $\mathbf{u} = 0\mathbf{v}$ but $\mathbf{v}$ is not a scalar multiple of $\mathbf{u}$. (Why?) Thus, if precisely one of the two vectors $\mathbf{u}$ and $\mathbf{v}$ is the zero vector, then $\mathbf{u}$ and $\mathbf{v}$ are linearly dependent, but only one of the two relations in (4) holds.

If $\mathbf{u}$ and $\mathbf{v}$ are linearly dependent vectors with $\mathbf{u} = c\mathbf{v}$ (for instance), then $1 \cdot \mathbf{u} + (-c) \cdot \mathbf{v} = \mathbf{0}$. Thus there exist scalars a and b *not both zero* such that

$$a\mathbf{u} + b\mathbf{v} = \mathbf{0}. \tag{5}$$

Conversely, suppose that Eq. (5) holds with a and b not both zero. If $a \neq 0$ (for instance) then we can solve for

$$\mathbf{u} = -\frac{b}{a}\mathbf{v} = c\mathbf{v}$$

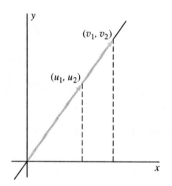

FIGURE 4.1.5. Two linearly dependent vectors $\mathbf{u}$ and $\mathbf{v}$.

with $c = -b/a$, so it follows that $\mathbf{u}$ and $\mathbf{v}$ are linearly dependent. Therefore we have proved the following theorem.

THEOREM 2: Two Linearly Dependent Vectors

The two vectors $\mathbf{u}$ and $\mathbf{v}$ are linearly dependent if and only if there exist scalars a and b *not both zero* such that

$$a\mathbf{u} + b\mathbf{v} = \mathbf{0}. \tag{5}$$

▲

The most interesting pairs of vectors are those that are not linearly dependent. The two vectors $\mathbf{u}$ and $\mathbf{v}$ are said to be **linearly independent** provided that they are *not* linearly dependent. Thus $\mathbf{u}$ and $\mathbf{v}$ are linearly independent if and only if neither is a scalar multiple of the other. By Theorem 2 this is equivalent to the following statement:

> The two vectors $\mathbf{u}$ and $\mathbf{v}$ are linearly independent if and only if the relation
>
> $$a\mathbf{u} + b\mathbf{v} = \mathbf{0} \tag{5}$$
>
> implies that $a = b = 0$.

Thus the vectors $\mathbf{u}$ and $\mathbf{v}$ are linearly independent provided that no *nontrivial* linear combination of them is equal to the zero vector.

Example 1

If $\mathbf{u} = (3, -2)$, $\mathbf{v} = (-6, 4)$, and $\mathbf{w} = (5, -7)$, then $\mathbf{u}$ and $\mathbf{v}$ are linearly dependent, because $\mathbf{v} = -2\mathbf{u}$. On the other hand, $\mathbf{u}$ and $\mathbf{w}$ are linearly independent. Here is an argument to establish this fact: Suppose that there were scalars a and b such that

$$a\mathbf{u} + b\mathbf{w} = \mathbf{0}.$$

Then

$$a(3, -2) + b(5, -7) = \mathbf{0},$$

and thus we get the simultaneous equations

$$3a + 5b = 0$$
$$-2a - 7b = 0.$$

It is now easy to show that $a = b = 0$ is the (unique) solution of this system. This shows that whenever

$$a\mathbf{u} + b\mathbf{w} = \mathbf{0},$$

it follows that $a = b = 0$. Therefore, $\mathbf{u}$ and $\mathbf{w}$ are linearly independent.

Alternatively, we could prove that $\mathbf{u}$ and $\mathbf{w}$ are linearly independent by showing that neither is a scalar multiple of the other (because $\frac{5}{3} \neq \frac{7}{2}$). ■

The most important property of linearly independent pairs of plane vectors is this: If $\mathbf{u}$ and $\mathbf{v}$ are linearly independent vectors in the plane, then any third vector $\mathbf{w}$ in $\mathbf{R}^2$ can be expressed as a *linear combination* of $\mathbf{u}$ and $\mathbf{v}$. That is, there exist scalars a and b such that $\mathbf{w} = a\mathbf{u} + b\mathbf{v}$ (Fig. 4.1.6). This is a statement that the two linearly independent vectors $\mathbf{u}$ and $\mathbf{v}$ suffice (in an obvious sense) to "generate" the whole plane $\mathbf{R}^2$. This general fact—which Section 4.3 discusses in a broader context—is illustrated computationally by the following example.

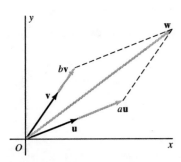

FIGURE 4.1.6. The vector $\mathbf{w}$ as a linear combination of the two vectors $\mathbf{u}$ and $\mathbf{v}$.

| Example 2 | Express the vector $\mathbf{w} = (11, 4)$ as a linear combination of the vectors $\mathbf{u} = (3, -2)$ and $\mathbf{v} = (-2, 7)$. |

Solution We want to find numbers a and b such that

$$a\mathbf{u} + b\mathbf{v} = \mathbf{w};$$

$$a \begin{bmatrix} 3 \\ -2 \end{bmatrix} + b \begin{bmatrix} -2 \\ 7 \end{bmatrix} = \begin{bmatrix} 11 \\ 4 \end{bmatrix};$$

$$\begin{bmatrix} 3 & -2 \\ -2 & 7 \end{bmatrix} \begin{bmatrix} a \\ b \end{bmatrix} = \begin{bmatrix} 11 \\ 4 \end{bmatrix}.$$

Using either Gaussian elimination or Cramer's rule, we readily solve this 2×2 system for $a = 5$, $b = 2$. Thus $\mathbf{w} = 5\mathbf{u} + 2\mathbf{v}$. ∎

Linear Independence in $\mathbf{R}^3$

We have said that the two vectors are linearly dependent provided that they lie on the same line through the origin. For *three* vectors $\mathbf{u} = (u_1, u_2, u_3)$, $\mathbf{v} = (v_1, v_2, v_3)$, and $\mathbf{w} = (w_1, w_2, w_3)$ in space, the analogous condition is that the three points (u_1, u_2, u_3), (v_1, v_2, v_3), and (w_1, w_2, w_3) lie in the same *plane* through the origin in $\mathbf{R}^3$. Given $\mathbf{u}$, $\mathbf{v}$, and $\mathbf{w}$, how can we determine whether the vectors $\mathbf{u}$, $\mathbf{v}$, and $\mathbf{w}$ are *coplanar*? The key to the answer is the following observation: If r and s are scalars, then the parallelogram law of addition implies that the vectors $\mathbf{u}$, $\mathbf{v}$, and $r\mathbf{u} + s\mathbf{v}$ are coplanar; specifically, they lie in the plane through the origin that's determined by the parallelogram with vertices $\mathbf{0}$, $r\mathbf{u}$, $s\mathbf{v}$, and $r\mathbf{u} + s\mathbf{v}$. Thus any linear combination of $\mathbf{u}$ and $\mathbf{v}$ is coplanar with $\mathbf{u}$ and $\mathbf{v}$. This is the motivation for our next definition.

Definition: Linearly Dependent Vectors in $\mathbf{R}^3$

The three vectors $\mathbf{u}$, $\mathbf{v}$, and $\mathbf{w}$ in $\mathbf{R}^3$ are said to be **linearly dependent** provided that one of them is a linear combination of the other two—that is, either

$$\begin{array}{lll} \mathbf{w} = r\mathbf{u} + s\mathbf{v} & \quad \text{or} & \\ \mathbf{u} = r\mathbf{v} + s\mathbf{w} & \quad \text{or} & \qquad (6) \\ \mathbf{v} = r\mathbf{u} + s\mathbf{w} & & \end{array}$$

for appropriate scalars r and s.

Note that each of the three equations in (6) implies that there exist three scalars a, b, and c *not all zero* such that

$$a\mathbf{u} + b\mathbf{v} + c\mathbf{w} = \mathbf{0}. \qquad (7)$$

For if $\mathbf{w} = r\mathbf{u} + s\mathbf{v}$ (for instance) then

$$r\mathbf{u} + s\mathbf{v} + (-1)\mathbf{w} = \mathbf{0},$$

so we can take $a = r$, $b = s$, and $c = -1 \neq 0$. Conversely, suppose that (7) holds with a, b, and c not all zero. If $c \neq 0$ (for instance) then we can solve for

$$\mathbf{w} = -\frac{a}{c}\mathbf{u} - \frac{b}{c}\mathbf{v} = r\mathbf{u} + s\mathbf{v}$$

with $r = -a/c$ and $s = -b/c$, so it follows that the three vectors $\mathbf{u}$, $\mathbf{v}$, and $\mathbf{w}$ are linearly dependent. Therefore we have proved the following theorem.

THEOREM 3: Three Linearly Dependent Vectors

The three vectors $\mathbf{u}$, $\mathbf{v}$, and $\mathbf{w}$ in $\mathbf{R}^3$ are linearly dependent if and only if there exist scalars a, b, and c *not all zero* such that

$$a\mathbf{u} + b\mathbf{v} + c\mathbf{w} = \mathbf{0}. \tag{7}$$

▲

The three vectors $\mathbf{u}$, $\mathbf{v}$, and $\mathbf{w}$ are called **linearly independent** provided that they are *not* linearly dependent. Thus $\mathbf{u}$, $\mathbf{v}$, and $\mathbf{w}$ are linearly independent if and only if neither of them is a linear combination of the other two. As a consequence of Theorem 3, this is equivalent to the following statement:

> The vectors $\mathbf{u}$, $\mathbf{v}$, and $\mathbf{w}$ are linearly independent if and only if the relation
>
> $$a\mathbf{u} + b\mathbf{v} + c\mathbf{w} = \mathbf{0} \tag{7}$$
>
> implies that $a = b = c = 0$.

Thus the three vectors $\mathbf{u}$, $\mathbf{v}$, and $\mathbf{w}$ are linearly independent provided that no *nontrivial* linear combination of them is equal to the zero vector.

Given two vectors, we can see at a glance whether either is a scalar multiple of the other. By contrast, it is not evident at a glance whether or not three given vectors in $\mathbf{R}^3$ are linearly independent. The following theorem provides one way to resolve this question.

THEOREM 4: Three Linearly Independent Vectors

The vectors $\mathbf{u} = (u_1, u_2, u_3)$, $\mathbf{v} = (v_1, v_2, v_3)$, and $\mathbf{w} = (w_1, w_2, w_3)$ are linearly independent if and only if

$$\begin{vmatrix} u_1 & v_1 & w_1 \\ u_2 & v_2 & w_2 \\ u_3 & v_3 & w_3 \end{vmatrix} \neq 0. \tag{8}$$

Proof: We want to show that $\mathbf{u}$, $\mathbf{v}$, and $\mathbf{w}$ are linearly independent if and only if the matrix

$$\mathbf{A} = \begin{bmatrix} u_1 & v_1 & w_1 \\ u_2 & v_2 & w_2 \\ u_3 & v_3 & w_3 \end{bmatrix}$$

—with column vectors $\mathbf{u}$, $\mathbf{v}$, and $\mathbf{w}$—has nonzero determinant. By Theorem 3, the vectors $\mathbf{u}$, $\mathbf{v}$, and $\mathbf{w}$ are linearly independent if and only if the equation

$$a \begin{bmatrix} u_1 \\ u_2 \\ u_3 \end{bmatrix} + b \begin{bmatrix} v_1 \\ v_2 \\ v_3 \end{bmatrix} + c \begin{bmatrix} w_1 \\ w_2 \\ w_3 \end{bmatrix} = \mathbf{0}$$

implies that $a = b = c = 0$—that is, if and only if the system

$$\begin{bmatrix} u_1 & v_1 & w_1 \\ u_2 & v_2 & w_2 \\ u_3 & v_3 & w_3 \end{bmatrix} \begin{bmatrix} a \\ b \\ c \end{bmatrix} = \begin{bmatrix} 0 \\ 0 \\ 0 \end{bmatrix} \qquad (9)$$

with unknowns a, b, and c has only the trivial solution. But Theorem 7 in Section 3.5 implies that this is so if and only if the coefficient matrix **A** is invertible, and Theorem 2 in Section 3.6 implies that **A** is invertible if and only if $|A| \neq 0$. Therefore, **u**, **v**, and **w** are linearly independent if and only if $|A| \neq 0$.   ▲

Hence, in order to determine whether or not three given vectors **u**, **v**, and **w** are linearly independent, we can calculate the determinant in (8). In practice, however, it is usually more efficient to set up an solve the linear system in (9). If we obtain only the trivial solution $a = b = c = 0$, then the three given vectors are linearly independent. But if we find a nontrivial solution, we then can express one of the vectors as a linear combination of the other two and thus see *how* the three vectors are linearly dependent.

Example 3   To determine whether the three vectors $\mathbf{u} = (1, 2, -3)$, $\mathbf{v} = (3, 1, -2)$, and $\mathbf{w} = (5, -5, 6)$ are linearly independent or dependent, we need to solve the system

$$a\mathbf{u} + b\mathbf{v} + c\mathbf{w} = \begin{bmatrix} 1 & 3 & 5 \\ 2 & 1 & -5 \\ -3 & -2 & 6 \end{bmatrix} \begin{bmatrix} a \\ b \\ c \end{bmatrix} = \begin{bmatrix} 0 \\ 0 \\ 0 \end{bmatrix}.$$

By Gaussian elimination, we readily reduce this system to the echelon form

$$\begin{bmatrix} 1 & 3 & 5 \\ 0 & 1 & 3 \\ 0 & 0 & 0 \end{bmatrix} \begin{bmatrix} a \\ b \\ c \end{bmatrix} = \begin{bmatrix} 0 \\ 0 \\ 0 \end{bmatrix}.$$

Therefore, we can choose $c = 1$, and it follows that $b = -3c = -3$ and $a = -3b - 5c = 4$. Therefore,

$$4\mathbf{u} + (-3)\mathbf{v} + \mathbf{w} = \mathbf{0},$$

and hence **u**, **v**, and **w** are linearly dependent, with $\mathbf{w} = -4\mathbf{u} + 3\mathbf{v}$.   ■

Basis Vectors in $\mathbf{R}^3$

Perhaps the most familiar triple of linearly independent vectors in $\mathbf{R}^3$ consists of the **basic unit vectors**

$$\mathbf{i} = (1, 0, 0), \quad \mathbf{j} = (0, 1, 0), \quad \text{and} \quad \mathbf{k} = (0, 0, 1). \qquad (10)$$

When represented by arrows with the initial points at the origin, these three vectors point in the positive directions along the three coordinate axes (Fig. 4.1.7). The expression

$$\mathbf{v} = a\mathbf{i} + b\mathbf{j} + c\mathbf{k} = (a, b, c)$$

shows both that the three vectors **i**, **j**, and **k** are linearly independent (because $\mathbf{v} = \mathbf{0}$ here immediately implies $a = b = c = 0$) and that any vector in $\mathbf{R}^3$ can be expressed as a linear combination of them.

FIGURE 4.1.7. The basic unit vectors **i**, **j**, and **k**.

A **basis** for $\mathbf{R}^3$ is a triple $\mathbf{u}$, $\mathbf{v}$, $\mathbf{w}$ of vectors such that every vector $\mathbf{t}$ in $\mathbf{R}^3$ can be expressed as a linear combination

$$\mathbf{t} = a\mathbf{u} + b\mathbf{v} + c\mathbf{w} \tag{11}$$

of them. That is, given any vector $\mathbf{t}$ in $\mathbf{R}^3$, there exist scalars a, b, c such that Eq. (11) holds. Thus the unit vectors $\mathbf{i}$, $\mathbf{j}$, and $\mathbf{k}$ constitute a basis for $\mathbf{R}^3$. The following theorem says that any three *linearly independent* vectors constitute a basis for $\mathbf{R}^3$.

THEOREM 5: Basis for R³

If the vectors $\mathbf{u}$, $\mathbf{v}$, and $\mathbf{w}$ in $\mathbf{R}^3$ are linearly independent, then they constitute a basis for $\mathbf{R}^3$.

Proof: Let $\mathbf{u} = (u_1, u_2, u_3)$, $\mathbf{v} = (v_1, v_2, v_3)$, and $\mathbf{w} = (w_1, w_2, w_3)$. Given any fourth vector $\mathbf{t} = (t_1, t_2, t_3)$, we must show that there exist scalars a, b, and c such that

$$\mathbf{t} = a\mathbf{u} + b\mathbf{v} + c\mathbf{w} \tag{11}$$

—that is, such that the system

$$\begin{bmatrix} u_1 & v_1 & w_1 \\ u_2 & v_2 & w_2 \\ u_3 & v_3 & w_3 \end{bmatrix} \begin{bmatrix} a \\ b \\ c \end{bmatrix} = \begin{bmatrix} t_1 \\ t_2 \\ t_3 \end{bmatrix} \tag{12}$$

has a solution (a, b, c). But by Theorem 4 the fact that $\mathbf{u}$, $\mathbf{v}$, and $\mathbf{w}$ are linearly independent implies that the coefficient matrix $\mathbf{A}$ in (12) has nonzero determinant and is therefore invertible. Hence, there is a (unique) solution, which may be obtained by multiplying both sides in (12) by $\mathbf{A}^{-1}$.   ▲

Example 4

In order to express the vector $\mathbf{t} = (4, 20, 23)$ as a combination of the linearly independent vectors $\mathbf{u} = (1, 3, 2)$, $\mathbf{v} = (2, 8, 7)$, and $\mathbf{w} = (1, 7, 9)$, we need to solve the system

$$\begin{bmatrix} 1 & 2 & 1 \\ 3 & 8 & 7 \\ 2 & 7 & 9 \end{bmatrix} \begin{bmatrix} a \\ b \\ c \end{bmatrix} = \begin{bmatrix} 4 \\ 20 \\ 23 \end{bmatrix}$$

that we obtain by substitution in Eq. (12). The echelon form found by Gaussian elimination is

$$\begin{bmatrix} 1 & 2 & 1 \\ 0 & 1 & 2 \\ 0 & 0 & 1 \end{bmatrix} \begin{bmatrix} a \\ b \\ c \end{bmatrix} = \begin{bmatrix} 4 \\ 4 \\ 3 \end{bmatrix},$$

so $c = 3$, $b = 4 - 2c = -2$, and $a = 4 - 2b - c = 5$. Thus

$$\mathbf{t} = 5\mathbf{u} - 2\mathbf{v} + 3\mathbf{w}. \qquad \blacksquare$$

Subspaces of $\mathbf{R}^3$

Up until this point, we have used the words *line* and *plane* only in an informal or intuitive way. It is now time for us to say precisely what is meant by a line or plane *through the origin* in $\mathbf{R}^3$. Each is an example of a *subspace* of $\mathbf{R}^3$.

The nonempty subset V of $\mathbf{R}^3$ is called a **subspace** of $\mathbf{R}^3$ provided that V itself is a vector space under the operations of vector addition and multiplication of vectors by scalars. Suppose that the nonempty subset V of $\mathbf{R}^3$ is **closed** under these operations—that is, that the sum of any two vectors in V is also in V and that every scalar multiple of a vector in V is also in V. Then the vectors in V automatically satisfy properties (a) through (h) of Theorem 1, because these properties are "inherited" from $\mathbf{R}^3$; they hold for *all* vectors in $\mathbf{R}^3$, including those in V. Consequently, we see that a nonempty subset V of $\mathbf{R}^3$ is a **subspace** of $\mathbf{R}^3$ if and only if it satisfies the following two conditions:

(i) If $\mathbf{u}$ and $\mathbf{v}$ are vectors in V, then $\mathbf{u} + \mathbf{v}$ is also in V (closure under addition).

(ii) If $\mathbf{u}$ is a vector in V and c is a scalar, then $c\mathbf{u}$ is in V (closure under multiplication by scalars).

It is immediate that $V = \mathbf{R}^3$ is a subspace: $\mathbf{R}^3$ is a subspace of itself. At the opposite extreme, the subset $V = \{\mathbf{0}\}$, containing only the zero vector, is also a subspace of $\mathbf{R}^3$, because $\mathbf{0} + \mathbf{0} = \mathbf{0}$ and $c\mathbf{0} = \mathbf{0}$ for every scalar c. Thus $V = \{\mathbf{0}\}$ satisfies conditions (i) and (ii). The subspaces $\{\mathbf{0}\}$ and $\mathbf{R}^3$ are sometimes called the *trivial* subspaces of $\mathbf{R}^3$ (because the verification that they *are* subspaces is quite trivial). All subspaces other than $\{\mathbf{0}\}$ and $\mathbf{R}^3$ itself are called **proper subspaces** of $\mathbf{R}^3$.

Now we want to show that the proper subspaces of $\mathbf{R}^3$ are what we customarily call lines and planes through the origin. Let V be a subspace of $\mathbf{R}^3$ that is neither $\{\mathbf{0}\}$ nor $\mathbf{R}^3$ itself. There are two cases to consider, depending on whether or not V contains two linearly independent vectors.

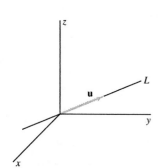

FIGURE 4.1.8. The line L spanned by the vector $\mathbf{u}$.

CASE 1: Suppose that V does *not* contain two linearly independent vectors. If $\mathbf{u}$ is a fixed nonzero vector in V then, by condition (ii) above, every scalar multiple $c\mathbf{u}$ is also in V. Conversely, if $\mathbf{v}$ is any other vector in V, then $\mathbf{u}$ and $\mathbf{v}$ are linearly dependent, so it follows that $\mathbf{v} = c\mathbf{u}$ for some scalar c. Thus the subspace V is the set of all scalar multiples of the fixed nonzero vector $\mathbf{u}$ and is therefore what we call a **line** through the origin in $\mathbf{R}^3$. (See Fig. 4.1.8.)

CASE 2: Suppose that V contains two linearly independent vectors $\mathbf{u}$ and $\mathbf{v}$. It then follows from conditions (i) and (ii) that V contains every linear combination $a\mathbf{u} + b\mathbf{v}$ of $\mathbf{u}$ and $\mathbf{v}$. (See Problem 38.) Conversely, let $\mathbf{w}$ be any other vector in V. If $\mathbf{u}$, $\mathbf{v}$, $\mathbf{w}$ were linearly independent then, by Theorem 4, V would be all of $\mathbf{R}^3$. Therefore, $\mathbf{u}$, $\mathbf{v}$, $\mathbf{w}$ are linearly dependent, so it follows that there exist scalars a and b such that $\mathbf{w} = a\mathbf{u} + b\mathbf{v}$. (See Problem 40.) Thus the subspace V is the set of all linear combinations $a\mathbf{u} + b\mathbf{v}$ of the two linearly independent vectors $\mathbf{u}$ and $\mathbf{v}$ and is therefore what we call a **plane** through the origin in $\mathbf{R}^3$. (See Fig. 4.1.9.)

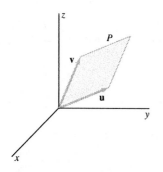

FIGURE 4.1.9. The plane P spanned by the vectors $\mathbf{u}$ and $\mathbf{v}$.

Subspaces of the coordinate plane $\mathbf{R}^2$ are defined similarly—they are the nonempty subsets of $\mathbf{R}^2$ that are closed under addition and multiplication by scalars. In Problem 39 we ask you to show that every proper subspace of $\mathbf{R}^2$ is a line through the origin.

Example 5 Let V be the set of all vectors (x, y) in $\mathbf{R}^2$ such that $y = x$. Given $\mathbf{u}$ and $\mathbf{v}$ in V, we may write $\mathbf{u} = (u, u)$ and $\mathbf{v} = (v, v)$. Then $\mathbf{u} + \mathbf{v} = (u + v, u + v)$ and $c\mathbf{u} = (cu, cu)$ are in V. It follows that V is a subspace of $\mathbf{R}^2$. ∎

| Example 6 | Let V be the set of all vectors (x, y) in $\mathbf{R}^2$ such that $x + y = 1$. Then $\mathbf{u} = (1, 0)$ and $\mathbf{v} = (0, 1)$ are in V, but the vector $\mathbf{u} + \mathbf{v} = (1, 1)$ is not. It follows that V is not a subspace of $\mathbf{R}^2$. ∎ |

Example 6 illustrates the fact that lines that do not pass through the origin are not subspaces of $\mathbf{R}^2$. Because every subspace must contain the zero vector (per Problem 37), only lines and planes that pass through the origin are subspaces of $\mathbf{R}^3$.

4.1 Problems

In Problems 1–4, find $|\mathbf{a} - \mathbf{b}|$, $2\mathbf{a} + \mathbf{b}$, *and* $3\mathbf{a} - 4\mathbf{b}$.

1. $\mathbf{a} = (2, 5, -4)$, $\mathbf{b} = (1, -2, -3)$
2. $\mathbf{a} = (-1, 0, 2)$, $\mathbf{b} = (3, 4, -5)$
3. $\mathbf{a} = 2\mathbf{i} - 3\mathbf{j} + 5\mathbf{k}$, $\mathbf{b} = 5\mathbf{i} + 3\mathbf{j} - 7\mathbf{k}$
4. $\mathbf{a} = 2\mathbf{i} - \mathbf{j}$, $\mathbf{b} = \mathbf{j} - 3\mathbf{k}$

In Problems 5–8, determine whether the given vectors $\mathbf{u}$ and $\mathbf{v}$ are linearly dependent or linearly independent.

5. $\mathbf{u} = (0, 2)$, $\mathbf{v} = (0, 3)$
6. $\mathbf{u} = (0, 2)$, $\mathbf{v} = (3, 0)$
7. $\mathbf{u} = (2, 2)$, $\mathbf{v} = (2, -2)$
8. $\mathbf{u} = (2, -2)$, $\mathbf{v} = (-2, 2)$

In Problems 9–14, express $\mathbf{w}$ as a linear combination of $\mathbf{u}$ and $\mathbf{v}$.

9. $\mathbf{u} = (1, -2)$, $\mathbf{v} = (-1, 3)$, $\mathbf{w} = (1, 0)$
10. $\mathbf{u} = (3, 4)$, $\mathbf{v} = (2, 3)$, $\mathbf{w} = (0, -1)$
11. $\mathbf{u} = (5, 7)$, $\mathbf{v} = (2, 3)$, $\mathbf{w} = (1, 1)$
12. $\mathbf{u} = (4, 1)$, $\mathbf{v} = (-2, -1)$, $\mathbf{w} = (2, -2)$
13. $\mathbf{u} = (7, 5)$, $\mathbf{v} = (3, 4)$, $\mathbf{w} = (5, -2)$
14. $\mathbf{u} = (5, -2)$, $\mathbf{v} = (-6, 4)$, $\mathbf{w} = (5, 6)$

In Problems 15–18, apply Theorem 3 (that is, calculate a determinant) to determine whether the given vectors $\mathbf{u}$, $\mathbf{v}$, and $\mathbf{w}$ are linearly dependent or independent.

15. $\mathbf{u} = (3, -1, 2)$, $\mathbf{v} = (5, 4, -6)$, $\mathbf{w} = (8, 3, -4)$
16. $\mathbf{u} = (5, -2, 4)$, $\mathbf{v} = (2, -3, 5)$, $\mathbf{w} = (4, 5, -7)$
17. $\mathbf{u} = (1, -1, 2)$, $\mathbf{v} = (3, 0, 1)$, $\mathbf{w} = (1, -2, 2)$
18. $\mathbf{u} = (1, 1, 0)$, $\mathbf{v} = (4, 3, 1)$, $\mathbf{w} = (3, -2, -4)$

In Problems 19–24, use the method of Example 3 to determine whether the given vectors $\mathbf{u}$, $\mathbf{v}$, and $\mathbf{w}$ are linearly independent or dependent. If they are linearly dependent, find scalars a, b, and c not all zero such that $a\mathbf{u} + b\mathbf{v} + c\mathbf{w} = \mathbf{0}$.

19. $\mathbf{u} = (2, 0, 1)$, $\mathbf{v} = (-3, 1, -1)$, $\mathbf{w} = (0, -2, -1)$
20. $\mathbf{u} = (5, 5, 4)$, $\mathbf{v} = (2, 3, 1)$, $\mathbf{w} = (4, 1, 5)$
21. $\mathbf{u} = (1, 1, -2)$, $\mathbf{v} = (-2, -1, 6)$, $\mathbf{w} = (3, 7, 2)$
22. $\mathbf{u} = (1, 1, 0)$, $\mathbf{v} = (5, 1, 3)$, $\mathbf{w} = (0, 1, 2)$
23. $\mathbf{u} = (2, 0, 3)$, $\mathbf{v} = (5, 4, -2)$, $\mathbf{w} = (2, -1, 1)$
24. $\mathbf{u} = (1, 4, 5)$, $\mathbf{v} = (4, 2, 5)$, $\mathbf{w} = (-3, 3, -1)$

In Problems 25–28, express the vector $\mathbf{t}$ as a linear combination of the vectors $\mathbf{u}$, $\mathbf{v}$, and $\mathbf{w}$.

25. $\mathbf{t} = (2, -7, 9)$, $\mathbf{u} = (1, -2, 2)$, $\mathbf{v} = (3, 0, 1)$, $\mathbf{w} = (1, -1, 2)$
26. $\mathbf{t} = (5, 30, -21)$, $\mathbf{u} = (5, 2, -2)$, $\mathbf{v} = (1, 5, -3)$, $\mathbf{w} = (5, -3, 4)$
27. $\mathbf{t} = (0, 0, 19)$, $\mathbf{u} = (1, 4, 3)$, $\mathbf{v} = (-1, -2, 2)$, $\mathbf{w} = (4, 4, 1)$
28. $\mathbf{t} = (7, 7, 7)$, $\mathbf{u} = (2, 5, 3)$, $\mathbf{v} = (4, 1, -1)$, $\mathbf{w} = (1, 1, 5)$

In Problems 29–32, show that the given set V is closed under addition and under multiplication by scalars and is therefore a subspace of $\mathbf{R}^3$.

29. V is the set of all (x, y, z) such that $x = 0$.
30. V is the set of all (x, y, z) such that $x + y + z = 0$.
31. V is the set of all (x, y, z) such that $2x = 3y$.
32. V is the set of all (x, y, z) such that $z = 2x + 3y$.

In Problems 33–36, show that the given set V is not a subspace of $\mathbf{R}^3$.

33. V is the set of all (x, y, z) such that $y = 1$.
34. V is the set of all (x, y, z) such that $x + y + z = 3$.
35. V is the set of all (x, y, z) such that $z \geq 0$.
36. V is the set of all (x, y, z) such that $xyz = 1$.
37. Show that every subspace V of $\mathbf{R}^3$ contains the zero vector $\mathbf{0}$.
38. Suppose that V is a subspace of $\mathbf{R}^3$. Show that V is closed under the operation of taking linear combinations of pairs of vectors. That is, show that if $\mathbf{u}$ and $\mathbf{v}$ are in V and a and b are scalars, then $a\mathbf{u} + b\mathbf{v}$ is in V.
39. Suppose that V is a proper subspace of $\mathbf{R}^2$ and that $\mathbf{u}$ is a nonzero vector in V. Show that V is the set of all scalar multiples of $\mathbf{u}$ and therefore that V is a line through the origin.
40. Suppose that $\mathbf{u}$, $\mathbf{v}$, and $\mathbf{w}$ are vectors in $\mathbf{R}^3$ such that $\mathbf{u}$ and $\mathbf{v}$ are linearly independent but $\mathbf{u}$, $\mathbf{v}$, and $\mathbf{w}$ are linearly dependent. Show that there exist scalars a and b such that $\mathbf{w} = a\mathbf{u} + b\mathbf{v}$.
41. Let V_1 and V_2 be subspaces of $\mathbf{R}^3$. Their *intersection* $V = V_1 \cap V_2$ is the set of all vectors that lie both in V_1 and in V_2. Show that V is a subspace of $\mathbf{R}^3$.

4.2 The Vector Space $\mathbf{R}^n$ and Subspaces

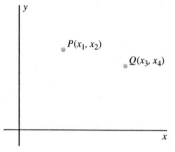

FIGURE 4.2.1. Two points $P(x_1, x_2)$ and $Q(x_3, x_4)$ in $\mathbf{R}^4$.

In Section 4.1 we defined 3-dimensional space $\mathbf{R}^3$ to be the set of all triples (x, y, z) of real numbers. This definition provides a *mathematical model* of the physical space in which we live, because geometric intuition and experience require that the location of every point be specified uniquely by *three* coordinates.

In science fiction, the fourth dimension often plays a rather exotic role. But there are common and ordinary situations where it is convenient to use four (or even more) coordinates rather than just two or three. For example, suppose we want to describe the motion of two points P and Q that are moving in the plane $\mathbf{R}^2$ under the action of some given physical law. (See Fig. 4.2.1.) In order to tell where P and Q are at a given instant, we need to give two coordinates for P and two coordinates for Q. So let us write $P(x_1, x_2)$ and $Q(x_3, x_4)$ to indicate these *four* coordinates. Then the two points P and Q determine a quadruple or 4-tuple (x_1, x_2, x_3, x_4) of real numbers, and any such 4-tuple determines a possible pair of locations of P and Q. In this way the set of all pairs of points P and Q in the plane corresponds to the set of all 4-tuples of real numbers. By analogy with our definition of $\mathbf{R}^3$, we may define *4-dimensional space* $\mathbf{R}^4$ to be the set of all such 4-tuples (x_1, x_2, x_3, x_4). Then we can specify a pair of points P and Q in $\mathbf{R}^2$ by specifying a single *point* (x_1, x_2, x_3, x_4) in $\mathbf{R}^4$, and this viewpoint may simplify our analysis of the motions of the original points P and Q. For instance, it may turn out that their coordinates satisfy some single equation such as

$$3x_1 - 4x_2 + 2x_3 - 5x_4 = 0$$

that is better understood in terms of a single point in $\mathbf{R}^4$ than in terms of the separate points P and Q in $\mathbf{R}^2$. Finally, note that in this example the fourth dimension is quite tangible—it refers simply to the second coordinate x_4 of the point Q.

But the number 4 is no more special in this context than the numbers 2 and 3. To describe similarly the motion of three points in $\mathbf{R}^3$, we would need 9 coordinates rather than 4. For instance, we might be studying the sun-earth-moon system in 3-dimensional space, with (x_1, x_2, x_3) denoting the coordinates of the sun, (x_4, x_5, x_6) the coordinates of the earth, and (x_7, x_8, x_9) the coordinates of the moon at a given instant. Then the single list $(x_1, x_2, x_3, x_4, x_5, x_6, x_7, x_8, x_9)$ of 9 coordinates could be used to specify simultaneously the locations of the sun, earth, and moon. Application of Newton's second law of motion to each of these three bodies would then lead to a system of differential equations involving the dependent variables $x_i(t)$, $i = 1, 2, \ldots, 9$ as functions of time t. (We will discuss this very situation in Section 7.6.)

An efficient description of another situation might require fifty, a hundred, or even a thousand coordinates. For instance, an investor's stock portfolio might contain 50 different high-tech stocks. If x_i denotes the value of the ith stock on a particular day, then the state of the whole portfolio is described by the single list $(x_1, x_2, x_3, \ldots, x_{49}, x_{50})$ of 50 separate numbers. And the evolution of this portfolio with time could then be described by the motion of a single point in 50-dimensional space!

An ***n*-tuple** of real numbers is an (ordered) list $(x_1, x_2, x_3, \ldots, x_n)$ of n real numbers. Thus $(1, 3, 4, 2)$ is a 4-tuple and $(0, -3, 7, 5, 2, -1)$ is a 6-tuple. A 2-tuple is an ordered pair and a 3-tuple is an ordered triple of real numbers, so the following definition generalizes our earlier definitions of the plane $\mathbf{R}^2$ and 3-space $\mathbf{R}^3$.

Definition: *n*-Space $\mathbf{R}^n$

The *n*-**dimensional space** $\mathbf{R}^n$ is the set of all *n*-tuples $(x_1, x_2, x_3, \ldots, x_n)$ of real numbers.

The elements of *n*-space $\mathbf{R}^n$ are called **points** or **vectors**, and we ordinarily use boldface letters to denote vectors. The *i*th entry of the vector $\mathbf{x} = (x_1, x_2, x_3, \ldots, x_n)$ is called its *i*th **coordinate** or its *i*th **component**. For consistency with matrix operations, we agree that

$$\mathbf{x} = (x_1, x_2, x_3, \ldots, x_n) = \begin{bmatrix} x_1 \\ x_2 \\ \vdots \\ x_n \end{bmatrix},$$

so that the $n \times 1$ matrix, or *column* vector, is simply another notation for the same ordered list of *n* real numbers.

If $n > 3$, we cannot visualize vectors in $\mathbf{R}^n$ in the concrete way that we can "see" vectors in $\mathbf{R}^2$ and $\mathbf{R}^3$. Nevertheless, we saw in Section 4.1 that the geometric properties of $\mathbf{R}^2$ and $\mathbf{R}^3$ stem ultimately from algebraic operations with vectors, and these algebraic operations can be defined for vectors in $\mathbf{R}^n$ by analogy with their definitions in dimensions 2 and 3.

If $\mathbf{u} = (u_1, u_2, \ldots, u_n)$ and $\mathbf{v} = (v_1, v_2, \ldots, v_n)$ are vectors in $\mathbf{R}^n$, then their **sum** is the vector $\mathbf{u} + \mathbf{v}$ given by

$$\mathbf{u} + \mathbf{v} = (u_1 + v_1, u_2 + v_2, \ldots, u_n + v_n). \tag{1}$$

Thus addition of vectors in $\mathbf{R}^n$ is defined in a componentwise manner, just as in $\mathbf{R}^2$ and $\mathbf{R}^3$, and we can visualize $\mathbf{u} + \mathbf{v}$ as a diagonal vector in a parallelogram determined by $\mathbf{u}$ and $\mathbf{v}$, as in Fig. 4.2.2. If c is a scalar—a real number—then the **scalar multiple** $c\mathbf{u}$ is also defined in componentwise fashion:

$$c\mathbf{u} = (cu_1, cu_2, \ldots, cu_n). \tag{2}$$

We can visualize $c\mathbf{u}$ as a vector collinear with $\mathbf{u}$, with only its length (and possibly its direction along the same line) altered by multiplication by the scalar c. See Fig. 4.2.3.

FIGURE 4.2.2. The parallelogram law for addition of vectors, in $\mathbf{R}^n$ just as in $\mathbf{R}^2$ or $\mathbf{R}^3$.

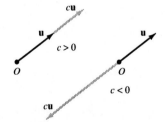

FIGURE 4.2.3. Multiplication of the vector $\mathbf{u}$ by the scalar c, in $\mathbf{R}^n$ just as in $\mathbf{R}^2$ or $\mathbf{R}^3$.

In Section 4.1 we saw that, for vectors in $\mathbf{R}^2$ and $\mathbf{R}^3$, the operations in (1) and (2) satisfy a list of properties that constitute the definition of a *vector space*; the same is true for vectors in $\mathbf{R}^n$.

Definition of a Vector Space

Let V be a set of elements called *vectors*, in which the operations of addition of vectors and multiplication of vectors by scalars are defined. That is, given vectors $\mathbf{u}$ and $\mathbf{v}$ in V and a scalar c, the vectors $\mathbf{u}+\mathbf{v}$ and $c\mathbf{u}$ are also in V (so that V is *closed* under vector addition and multiplication by scalars). Then, with these operations, V is called a **vector space** provided that—given any vectors $\mathbf{u}$, $\mathbf{v}$, and $\mathbf{w}$ in V and any scalars a and b—the following properties hold true:

(a) $\mathbf{u}+\mathbf{v} = \mathbf{v}+\mathbf{u}$ (commutativity)

(b) $\mathbf{u}+(\mathbf{v}+\mathbf{w}) = (\mathbf{u}+\mathbf{v})+\mathbf{w}$ (associativity)

(c) $\mathbf{u}+\mathbf{0} = \mathbf{0}+\mathbf{u} = \mathbf{u}$ (zero element)

(d) $\mathbf{u}+(-\mathbf{u}) = (-\mathbf{u})+\mathbf{u} = \mathbf{0}$ (additive inverse)

(e) $a(\mathbf{u}+\mathbf{v}) = a\mathbf{u}+a\mathbf{v}$ (distributivity)

(f) $(a+b)\mathbf{u} = a\mathbf{u}+b\mathbf{u}$

(g) $a(b\mathbf{u}) = (ab)\mathbf{u}$

(h) $(1)\mathbf{u} = \mathbf{u}$

In property (c), it is meant that there exists a **zero vector 0** in V such that $\mathbf{u}+\mathbf{0} = \mathbf{u}$. The zero vector in $\mathbf{R}^n$ is

$$\mathbf{0} = (0, 0, \ldots, 0).$$

Similarly, property (d) actually means that, given the vector $\mathbf{u}$ in V, there exists a vector $-\mathbf{u}$ in V such that $\mathbf{u}+(-\mathbf{u}) = \mathbf{0}$. In $\mathbf{R}^n$, we clearly have

$$-\mathbf{u} = (-u_1, -u_2, \ldots, -u_n).$$

The fact that $\mathbf{R} = \mathbf{R}^1$ satisfies properties (a)–(h), with the real numbers playing the dual roles of scalars *and* vectors, means that the real line may be regarded as a vector space. If $n > 1$, then each of properties (a)–(h) may be readily verified for $\mathbf{R}^n$ by working with components and applying the corresponding properties of real numbers. For example, to verify the commutativity of vector addition in (a), we begin with Eq. (1) and write

$$\begin{aligned}
\mathbf{u}+\mathbf{v} &= (u_1+v_1, u_2+v_2, \ldots, u_n+v_n) \\
&= (v_1+u_1, v_2+u_2, \ldots, v_n+u_n) \\
&= \mathbf{v}+\mathbf{u}.
\end{aligned}$$

Thus n-space $\mathbf{R}^n$ *is a vector space* with the operations defined in Eqs. (1) and (2). We will understand throughout that our scalars are the *real numbers*, though in more advanced treatments of linear algebra other scalars (such as the complex numbers) are sometimes used.

Observe that, in the definition of a vector space, nothing is said about the elements of V (the "vectors") being n-tuples. They can be any objects for which addition and multiplication by scalars are defined and which satisfy properties (a)–(h). Although many of the vectors you will see in this text actually are n-tuples of real numbers, an example in which they are not may help to clarify the definition of a vector space.

Example 1

Let $\mathcal{F}$ be the set of all real-valued functions defined on the real number line **R**. Then each vector in $\mathcal{F}$ is a function **f** such that the real number **f**(x) is defined for all x in **R**. Given **f** and **g** in $\mathcal{F}$ and a real number c, the functions **f** + **g** and c**f** are defined in the natural way,

$$(\mathbf{f} + \mathbf{g})(x) = \mathbf{f}(x) + \mathbf{g}(x)$$

and

$$(c\mathbf{f})(x) = c(\mathbf{f}(x)).$$

Then each of properties (a)–(h) of a vector space follows readily from the corresponding property of the real numbers. For instance, if a is a scalar, then

$$\begin{aligned}
\{a(\mathbf{f} + \mathbf{g})\}(x) &= a\{(\mathbf{f} + \mathbf{g})(x)\} \\
&= a\{\mathbf{f}(x) + \mathbf{g}(x)\} \\
&= a\mathbf{f}(x) + a\mathbf{g}(x) \\
&= (a\mathbf{f} + a\mathbf{g})(x).
\end{aligned}$$

Thus $a(\mathbf{f} + \mathbf{g}) = a\mathbf{f} + a\mathbf{g}$, so $\mathcal{F}$ enjoys property (e). ∎

After verification of the other seven properties, we conclude that $\mathcal{F}$ is, indeed, a vector space—one that differs in a fundamental way from each of the vector spaces **R**^{n}. We naturally call **R**^{n} an n-dimensional vector space, and in Section 4.4 we will define the word *dimension* in such a way that the dimension of **R**^{n} actually *is* n. But the vector space $\mathcal{F}$ of functions turns out not to have dimension n for any integer n; it is an example of an infinite-dimensional vector space. (See Section 4.5.)

Subspaces

Let $W = \{\mathbf{0}\}$ be the subset of **R**^{n} that contains only the zero vector **0**. Then W satisfies properties (a)–(h) of a vector space, because each reduces trivially to the equation $\mathbf{0} = \mathbf{0}$. Thus W is a subset of the vector space $V = \mathbf{R}^n$ that is itself a vector space.

Definition: Subspace

Let W be a nonempty subset of the vector space V. Then W is a **subspace** of V provided that W itself is a vector space with the operations of addition and multiplication by scalars as defined in V.

In order for the subset W to be a subspace of the vector space V, it first must be closed under the operations of vector addition and multiplication by scalars. Then it must satisfy properties (a)–(h) of a vector space. But W "inherits" all these properties from V, because the vectors in W all are vectors in V, and the vectors in V all satisfy properties (a)–(h). Hence, in order to determine whether the subset W is a vector space, we need check only the two closure conditions.

THEOREM 1: Conditions for a Subspace

The nonempty subset W of the vector space V is a subspace of V if and only if it satisfies the following two conditions:

(i) If **u** and **v** are vectors in W, then **u** + **v** is also in W.

(ii) If **u** is in W and c is a scalar, then the vector c**u** is also in W.   ▲

In Section 4.1 we saw that lines through the origin in $\mathbf{R}^2$ form subspaces of $\mathbf{R}^2$ and that lines and planes through the origin are subspaces of $\mathbf{R}^3$. The subspace W of the following example may be regarded as a higher-dimensional "plane" (or "hyperplane") through the origin in $\mathbf{R}^n$.

Example 2 Let W be the subset of $\mathbf{R}^n$ consisting of all those vectors $(x_1, x_2, \ldots, x_n)$ whose coordinates satisfy the single homogeneous linear equation

$$a_1 x_1 + a_2 x_2 + \cdots + a_n x_n = 0,$$

where the given coefficients $a_1, a_2, \ldots, a_n$ are not all zero. If $\mathbf{u} = (u_1, u_2, \ldots, u_n)$ and $\mathbf{v} = (v_1, v_2, \ldots, v_n)$ are vectors in W, then

$$a_1(u_1 + v_1) + a_2(u_2 + v_2) + \cdots + a_n(u_n + v_n)$$
$$= (a_1 u_1 + a_2 u_2 + \cdots + a_n u_n) + (a_1 v_1 + a_2 v_2 + \cdots + a_n v_n)$$
$$= 0 + 0 = 0,$$

so $\mathbf{u} + \mathbf{v} = (u_1 + v_1, \ldots, u_n + v_n)$ is also in W. If c is a scalar, then

$$a_1(cu_1) + a_2(cu_2) + \cdots + a_n(cu_n) = c(a_1 u_1 + a_2 u_2 + \cdots + a_n u_n)$$
$$= (c)(0) = 0,$$

so $c\mathbf{u} = (cu_1, cu_2, \ldots, cu_n)$ is in W. Thus we have shown that W satisfies conditions (i) and (ii) of Theorem 1 and is therefore a subspace of $\mathbf{R}^n$. ∎

In order to apply Theorem 1 to show that W *is* a subspace of the vector space V, we must show that W satisfies *both* conditions in the theorem. But to apply Theorem 1 to show that W is *not* a subspace of V, we need only show *either* that condition (i) fails *or* that condition (ii) fails.

Example 3 Let W be the set of all those vectors (x_1, x_2, x_3, x_4) in $\mathbf{R}^4$ whose four coordinates are all nonnegative: $x_i \geq 0$ for $i = 1, 2, 3, 4$. Then it should be clear that the sum of two vectors in W is also a vector in W, because the sum of two nonnegative numbers is nonnegative. Thus W satisfies condition (i) of Theorem 1. But if we take $\mathbf{u} = (1, 1, 1, 1)$ in W and $c = -1$, then we find that the scalar multiple

$$c\mathbf{u} = (-1)(1, 1, 1, 1) = (-1, -1, -1, -1)$$

is *not* in W. Thus W fails to satisfy condition (ii) and therefore is *not* a subspace of $\mathbf{R}^4$. ∎

Example 4 Let W be the set of all those vectors (x_1, x_2, x_3, x_4) in $\mathbf{R}^4$ such that $x_1 x_4 = 0$. Now W satisfies condition (ii) of Theorem 1, because $x_1 x_4 = 0$ implies that $(cx_1)(cx_4) = 0$ for any scalar c. But if we take the vectors $\mathbf{u} = (1, 1, 0, 0)$ and $\mathbf{v} = (0, 0, 1, 1)$ in W, we see that their sum $\mathbf{u} + \mathbf{v} = (1, 1, 1, 1)$ is *not* in W. Thus W does not satisfy condition (i) and therefore is *not* a subspace of $\mathbf{R}^4$. ∎

Example 2 implies that the solution set of a homogeneous linear equation

$$a_1 x_1 + a_2 x_2 + \cdots + a_n x_n = 0$$

in n variables is always a *subspace* of $\mathbf{R}^n$. Theorem 2 further implies that the same is true of a *homogeneous* system of linear equations. Recall that any such system of m equations in n unknowns can be written in the form $\mathbf{Ax} = \mathbf{0}$, where $\mathbf{A}$ is the $m \times n$ coefficient matrix and $\mathbf{x} = (x_1, x_2, \ldots, x_n)$ is regarded as a column vector. The solution set of $\mathbf{Ax} = \mathbf{0}$ is then the set of all vectors $\mathbf{x}$ in $\mathbf{R}^n$ that satisfy this equation—that is, the set of all its solution vectors.

THEOREM 2: Solution Subspaces

If $\mathbf{A}$ is a (constant) $m \times n$ matrix, then the solution set of the homogeneous linear system

$$\mathbf{Ax} = \mathbf{0} \tag{3}$$

is a subspace of $\mathbf{R}^n$.

Proof: Let W denote the solution set of Eq. (3). If $\mathbf{u}$ and $\mathbf{v}$ are vectors in W, then $\mathbf{Au} = \mathbf{Av} = \mathbf{0}$. Hence

$$\mathbf{A}(\mathbf{u} + \mathbf{v}) = \mathbf{Au} + \mathbf{Av} = \mathbf{0} + \mathbf{0} = \mathbf{0}.$$

Thus the sum $\mathbf{u} + \mathbf{v}$ is also in W, and hence W satisfies condition (i) of Theorem 1. If c is a scalar, then

$$\mathbf{A}(c\mathbf{u}) = c(\mathbf{Au}) = c\mathbf{0} = \mathbf{0},$$

so $c\mathbf{u}$ is in W if $\mathbf{u}$ is in W. Thus W also satisfies condition (ii) of Theorem 1. It therefore follows that W is a subspace of $\mathbf{R}^n$. ▲

Note that, in order to conclude by Theorem 2 that the solution set of a linear system is a subspace, it is necessary for the system to be *homogeneous*. Indeed, the solution set of a nonhomogeneous linear system

$$\mathbf{Ax} = \mathbf{b} \tag{4}$$

with $\mathbf{b} \neq \mathbf{0}$ is *never* a subspace. For if $\mathbf{u}$ were a solution vector of the system in (4), then

$$\mathbf{A}(2\mathbf{u}) = 2(\mathbf{Au}) = 2\mathbf{b} \neq \mathbf{b}$$

because $\mathbf{b} \neq \mathbf{0}$. Thus the scalar multiple $2\mathbf{u}$ of the solution vector $\mathbf{u}$ is *not* a solution vector. Therefore Theorem 1 implies that the solution set of (4) is *not* a subspace.

Because the solution set of a *homogeneous* linear system is a subspace, we often call it the **solution space** of the system. The subspaces of $\mathbf{R}^n$ are the possible solution spaces of a homogeneous linear system with n unknowns, and this is one of the principal reasons for our interest in subspaces of $\mathbf{R}^n$.

At opposite extremes as subspaces of $\mathbf{R}^n$ lie the **zero subspace** $\{\mathbf{0}\}$ and $\mathbf{R}^n$ itself. Every other subspace of $\mathbf{R}^n$, each one that is neither $\{\mathbf{0}\}$ nor $\mathbf{R}^n$, is called a **proper subspace** of $\mathbf{R}^n$. The proper subspaces of $\mathbf{R}^n$ play the same role in $\mathbf{R}^n$ that lines and planes through the origin play in $\mathbf{R}^3$. In the following two sections we develop the tools that are needed to analyze the structure of a given proper subspace of $\mathbf{R}^n$. In particular, given the homogeneous system $\mathbf{Ax} = \mathbf{0}$, we ask how we can describe its solution space in a concise and illuminating way, beyond the mere statement that it is the set of all solution vectors of the system. Example 5 illustrates one possible way of doing this.

Example 5 In Example 4 of Section 3.4 we considered the homogeneous system

$$x_1 + 3x_2 - 15x_3 + 7x_4 = 0$$
$$x_1 + 4x_2 - 19x_3 + 10x_4 = 0 \tag{5}$$
$$2x_1 + 5x_2 - 26x_3 + 11x_4 = 0.$$

The reduced echelon form of the coefficient matrix of this system is

$$\begin{bmatrix} 1 & 0 & -3 & -2 \\ 0 & 1 & -4 & 3 \\ 0 & 0 & 0 & 0 \end{bmatrix}.$$

Hence x_1 and x_2 are the leading variables and x_3 and x_4 are free variables. Back substitution yields the general solution

$$x_3 = s, \quad x_4 = t, \quad x_2 = 4s - 3t, \quad x_1 = 3s + 2t$$

in terms of arbitrary parameters s and t. Thus a typical solution vector of the system in (5) has the form

$$\mathbf{x} = \begin{bmatrix} x_1 \\ x_2 \\ x_3 \\ x_4 \end{bmatrix} = \begin{bmatrix} 3s + 2t \\ 4s - 3t \\ s \\ t \end{bmatrix} = s \begin{bmatrix} 3 \\ 4 \\ 1 \\ 0 \end{bmatrix} + t \begin{bmatrix} 2 \\ -3 \\ 0 \\ 1 \end{bmatrix}.$$

It follows that the solution space of the system in (5) can be described as the set of all linear combinations of the form

$$\mathbf{x} \stackrel{\triangle}{=} s\mathbf{u} + t\mathbf{v}, \tag{6}$$

where $\mathbf{u} = (3, 4, 1, 0)$ and $\mathbf{v} = (2, -3, 0, 1)$. Thus we have found the two particular solution vectors $\mathbf{u}$ and $\mathbf{v}$ of our system that completely determine its solution space [by the formula in (6)]. ∎

4.2 Problems

In Problems 1–14, a subset W of some n-space $\mathbf{R}^n$ is defined by means of a given condition imposed on the typical vector $(x_1, x_2, \ldots, x_n)$. Apply Theorem 1 to determine whether or not W is a subspace of $\mathbf{R}^n$.

1. W is the set of all vectors in $\mathbf{R}^3$ such that $x_3 = 0$.
2. W is the set of all vectors in $\mathbf{R}^3$ such that $x_1 = 5x_2$.
3. W is the set of all vectors in $\mathbf{R}^3$ such that $x_2 = 1$.
4. W is the set of all vectors in $\mathbf{R}^3$ such that $x_1 + x_2 + x_3 = 1$.
5. W is the set of all vectors in $\mathbf{R}^4$ such that $x_1 + 2x_2 + 3x_3 + 4x_4 = 0$.
6. W is the set of all vectors in $\mathbf{R}^4$ such that $x_1 = 3x_3$ and $x_2 = 4x_4$.
7. W is the set of all vectors in $\mathbf{R}^2$ such that $|x_1| = |x_2|$.
8. W is the set of all vectors in $\mathbf{R}^2$ such that $(x_1)^2 + (x_2)^2 = 0$.
9. W is the set of all vectors in $\mathbf{R}^2$ such that $(x_1)^2 + (x_2)^2 = 1$.

10. W is the set of all vectors in $\mathbf{R}^2$ such that $|x_1| + |x_2| = 1$.
11. W is the set of all vectors in $\mathbf{R}^4$ such that $x_1 + x_2 = x_3 + x_4$.
12. W is the set of all vectors in $\mathbf{R}^4$ such that $x_1 x_2 = x_3 x_4$.
13. W is the set of all vectors in $\mathbf{R}^4$ such that $x_1 x_2 x_3 x_4 = 0$.
14. W is the set of all those vectors in $\mathbf{R}^4$ whose components are all nonzero.

In Problems 15–18, apply the method of Example 5 to find two solution vectors $\mathbf{u}$ and $\mathbf{v}$ such that the solution space is the set of all linear combinations of the form $s\mathbf{u} + t\mathbf{v}$.

15. $x_1 - 4x_2 + x_3 - 4x_4 = 0$
    $x_1 + 2x_2 + x_3 + 8x_4 = 0$
    $x_1 + x_2 + x_3 + 6x_4 = 0$
16. $x_1 - 4x_2 - 3x_3 - 7x_4 = 0$
    $2x_1 - x_2 + x_3 + 7x_4 = 0$
    $x_1 + 2x_2 + 3x_3 + 11x_4 = 0$

17. $x_1 + 3x_2 + 8x_3 - x_4 = 0$
$x_1 - 3x_2 - 10x_3 + 5x_5 = 0$
$x_1 + 4x_2 + 11x_3 - 2x_4 = 0$

18. $x_1 + 3x_2 + 2x_3 + 5x_4 - x_5 = 0$
$2x_1 + 7x_2 + 4x_3 + 11x_4 + 2x_5 = 0$
$2x_1 + 6x_2 + 5x_3 + 12x_4 - 7x_5 = 0$

In Problems 19–22, reduce the given system to echelon form to find a single solution vector **u** *such that the solution space is the set of all scalar multiples of* **u.**

19. $x_1 - 3x_2 - 5x_3 - 6x_4 = 0$
$2x_1 + x_2 + 4x_3 - 4x_4 = 0$
$x_1 + 3x_2 + 7x_3 + x_4 = 0$

20. $x_1 + 5x_2 + x_3 - 8x_4 = 0$
$2x_1 + 5x_2 - 5x_4 = 0$
$2x_1 + 7x_2 + x_3 - 9x_4 = 0$

21. $x_1 + 7x_2 + 2x_3 - 3x_4 = 0$
$2x_1 + 7x_2 + x_3 - 4x_4 = 0$
$3x_1 + 5x_2 - x_3 - 5x_4 = 0$

22. $x_1 + 3x_2 + 3x_3 + 3x_4 = 0$
$2x_1 + 7x_2 + 5x_3 - x_4 = 0$
$2x_1 + 7x_2 + 4x_3 - 4x_4 = 0$

23. Show that every subspace W of a vector space V contains the zero vector **0.**

24. Apply the properties of a vector space V to show each of the following.

  (a) $0\mathbf{u} = \mathbf{0}$ for every **u** in V.
  (b) $c\mathbf{0} = \mathbf{0}$ for every scalar c.
  (c) $(-1)\mathbf{u} = -\mathbf{u}$ for every **u** in V.

Do *not* assume that the vectors in V are n-tuples of real numbers.

25. Show that the nonempty subset W of a vector space V is a subspace of V if and only if for every pair of vectors **u** and **v** in W and every pair of scalars a and b, $a\mathbf{u} + b\mathbf{v}$ is also in W.

26. *Prove*: If **u** is a (fixed) vector in the vector space V, then the set W of all scalar multiples $c\mathbf{u}$ of **u** is a subspace of V.

27. Let **u** and **v** be (fixed) vectors in the vector space V. Show that the set W of all linear combinations $a\mathbf{u} + b\mathbf{v}$ of **u** and **v** is a subspace of V.

28. Suppose that **A** is an $n \times n$ matrix and that k is a (constant) scalar. Show that the set of all vectors **x** such that $\mathbf{Ax} = k\mathbf{x}$ is a subspace of $\mathbf{R}^n$.

29. Let **A** be an $n \times n$ matrix, **b** be a nonzero vector, and $\mathbf{x}_0$ be a solution vector of the system $\mathbf{Ax} = \mathbf{b}$. Show that **x** is a solution of the nonhomogeneous system $\mathbf{Ax} = \mathbf{b}$ if and only if $\mathbf{y} = \mathbf{x} - \mathbf{x}_0$ is a solution of the homogeneous system $\mathbf{Ay} = \mathbf{0}$.

30. Let U and V be subspaces of the vector space W. Their **intersection** $U \cap V$ is the set of all vectors that are both in U and in V. Show that $U \cap V$ is a subspace of W. If U and V are two planes through the origin in $\mathbf{R}^3$, what is $U \cap V$?

31. Let U and V be subspaces of the vector space W. Their **sum** $U + V$ is the set of all vectors **w** of the form

$$\mathbf{w} = \mathbf{u} + \mathbf{v},$$

where **u** is in U and **v** is in V. Show that $U + V$ is a subspace of W. If U and V are lines through the origin in $\mathbf{R}^3$, what is $U + V$?

4.3 Linear Combinations and Independence of Vectors

In Example 5 of Section 4.2 we solved the homogeneous linear system

$$x_1 + 3x_2 - 15x_3 + 7x_4 = 0$$
$$x_1 + 4x_2 - 19x_3 + 10x_4 = 0 \tag{1}$$
$$2x_1 + 5x_2 - 26x_3 + 11x_4 = 0.$$

We found that its solution space W consists of all those vectors **x** in $\mathbf{R}^4$ that have the form

$$\mathbf{x} = s(3, 4, 1, 0) + t(2, -3, 0, 1). \tag{2}$$

We therefore can visualize W as the plane in $\mathbf{R}^4$ determined by the vectors $\mathbf{v}_1 = (3, 4, 1, 0)$ and $\mathbf{v}_2 = (2, -3, 0, 1)$. The fact that every solution vector is a combination [as in (2)] of the particular solution vectors $\mathbf{v}_1$ and $\mathbf{v}_2$ gives us a tangible understanding of the solution space W of the system in (1).

More generally, we know from Theorem 2 in Section 4.2 that the solution set V of any $m \times n$ homogeneous linear system $\mathbf{Ax} = \mathbf{0}$ is a subspace of $\mathbf{R}^n$. In order to understand such a vector space V better, we would like to find a minimal set of vectors $v_1, v_2, \ldots, v_k$ in V such that *every* vector in V is a sum of scalar multiples of these particular vectors.

The vector w is called a **linear combination** of the vectors $v_1, v_2, \ldots, v_k$ provided that there exist scalars $c_1, c_2, \ldots, c_k$ such that

$$w = c_1 v_1 + c_2 v_2 + \cdots + c_k v_k. \tag{3}$$

Given a vector w in $\mathbf{R}^n$, the problem of determining whether or not w is a linear combination of the vectors $v_1, v_2, \ldots, v_k$ amounts to solving a linear system to see whether we can find scalars $c_1, c_2, \ldots, c_k$ so that (3) holds.

Example 1

To determine whether the vector $w = (2, -6, 3)$ in $\mathbf{R}^3$ is a linear combination of the vectors $v_1 = (1, -2, -1)$ and $v_2 = (3, -5, 4)$, we write the equation $c_1 v_1 + c_2 v_2 = w$ in matrix form:

$$c_1 \begin{bmatrix} 1 \\ -2 \\ -1 \end{bmatrix} + c_2 \begin{bmatrix} 3 \\ -5 \\ 4 \end{bmatrix} = \begin{bmatrix} 2 \\ -6 \\ 3 \end{bmatrix}$$

—that is,

$$\begin{aligned} c_1 + 3c_2 &= 2 \\ -2c_1 - 5c_2 &= -6 \\ -c_1 + 4c_2 &= 3. \end{aligned}$$

The augmented coefficient matrix

$$\begin{bmatrix} 1 & 3 & 2 \\ -2 & -5 & -6 \\ -1 & 4 & 3 \end{bmatrix}$$

can be reduced by elementary row operations to echelon form:

$$\begin{bmatrix} 1 & 3 & 2 \\ 0 & 1 & -2 \\ 0 & 0 & 19 \end{bmatrix}.$$

We see now, from the third row, that our system is inconsistent, so the desired scalars c_1 and c_2 do not exist. Thus w is *not* a linear combination of v_1 and v_2. ∎

Example 2

To express the vector $w = (-7, 7, 11)$ as a linear combination of the vectors $v_1 = (1, 2, 1)$, $v_2 = (-4, -1, 2)$, and $v_3 = (-3, 1, 3)$, we write the equation $c_1 v_1 + c_2 v_2 + c_3 v_3 = w$ in the form

$$c_1 \begin{bmatrix} 1 \\ 2 \\ 1 \end{bmatrix} + c_2 \begin{bmatrix} -4 \\ -1 \\ 2 \end{bmatrix} + c_3 \begin{bmatrix} -3 \\ 1 \\ 3 \end{bmatrix} = \begin{bmatrix} -7 \\ 7 \\ 11 \end{bmatrix}$$

—that is,

$$\begin{aligned} c_1 - 4c_2 - 3c_3 &= -7 \\ 2c_1 - c_2 + c_3 &= 7 \\ c_1 + 2c_2 + 3c_3 &= 11. \end{aligned}$$

The reduced echelon form of the augmented coefficient matrix of this system is

$$\begin{bmatrix} 1 & 0 & 1 & 5 \\ 0 & 1 & 1 & 3 \\ 0 & 0 & 0 & 0 \end{bmatrix}.$$

Thus c_3 is a free variable. With $c_3 = t$, back substitution yields $c_1 = 5 - t$ and $c_2 = 3 - t$. For instance, $t = 1$ gives $c_1 = 4$, $c_2 = 2$, and $c_3 = 1$, so

$$\mathbf{w} = 4\mathbf{v}_1 + 2\mathbf{v}_2 + \mathbf{v}_3.$$

But $t = -2$ yields $c_1 = 7$, $c_2 = 5$, and $c_3 = -2$, so $\mathbf{w}$ can also be expressed as

$$\mathbf{w} = 7\mathbf{v}_1 + 5\mathbf{v}_2 - 2\mathbf{v}_3.$$

We have found not only that $\mathbf{w}$ can be expressed as a linear combination of the vectors $\mathbf{v}_1$, $\mathbf{v}_2$, $\mathbf{v}_3$ but also that this can be done in many different ways (one for each choice of the parameter t). ∎

We began this section with the observation that every solution vector of the linear system in (1) is a linear combination of the vectors $\mathbf{v}_1$ and $\mathbf{v}_2$ that appear in the right-hand side of Eq. (2). A brief way of saying this is that the vectors $\mathbf{v}_1$ and $\mathbf{v}_2$ *span* the solution space. More generally, suppose that $\mathbf{v}_1, \mathbf{v}_2, \ldots, \mathbf{v}_k$ are vectors in a vector space V. Then we say that the vectors $\mathbf{v}_1, \mathbf{v}_2, \ldots, \mathbf{v}_k$ **span** the vector space V provided that *every* vector in V is a linear combination of these k vectors. We may also say that the set $S = \{\mathbf{v}_1, \mathbf{v}_2, \ldots, \mathbf{v}_k\}$ of vectors is a **spanning set** for V.

Example 3

The familiar unit vectors $\mathbf{i} = (1, 0, 0)$, $\mathbf{j} = (0, 1, 0)$, and $\mathbf{k} = (0, 0, 1)$ span $\mathbf{R}^3$, because every vector $\mathbf{x} = (x_1, x_2, x_3)$ in $\mathbf{R}^3$ can be expressed as the linear combination

$$\mathbf{x} = x_1\mathbf{i} + x_2\mathbf{j} + x_3\mathbf{k}$$

of these three vectors $\mathbf{i}$, $\mathbf{j}$, and $\mathbf{k}$. ∎

If the vectors $\mathbf{v}_1, \mathbf{v}_2, \ldots, \mathbf{v}_k$ in the vector space V do not span V, we can ask about the subset of V consisting of all those vectors that are linear combinations of $\mathbf{v}_1, \mathbf{v}_2, \ldots, \mathbf{v}_k$. The following theorem implies that this subset is always a *subspace* of V.

THEOREM 1: The Span of a Set of Vectors

Let $\mathbf{v}_1, \mathbf{v}_2, \ldots, \mathbf{v}_k$ be vectors in the vector space V. Then the set W of all linear combinations of $\mathbf{v}_1, \mathbf{v}_2, \ldots, \mathbf{v}_k$ is a subspace of V.

Proof: We must show that W is closed under addition of vectors and multiplication by scalars. If

$$\mathbf{u} = a_1\mathbf{v}_1 + a_2\mathbf{v}_2 + \cdots + a_k\mathbf{v}_k$$

and

$$\mathbf{v} = b_1\mathbf{v}_1 + b_2\mathbf{v}_2 + \cdots + b_k\mathbf{v}_k$$

are vectors in W, then

$$\mathbf{u} + \mathbf{v} = (a_1 + b_1)\mathbf{v}_1 + (a_2 + b_2)\mathbf{v}_2 + \cdots + (a_k + b_k)\mathbf{v}_k$$

and

$$c\mathbf{u} = (ca_1)\mathbf{v}_1 + (ca_2)\mathbf{v}_2 + \cdots + (ca_k)\mathbf{v}_k$$

for any scalar c. Thus $\mathbf{u} + \mathbf{v}$ and $c\mathbf{u}$ are linear combinations of $\mathbf{v}_1, \mathbf{v}_2, \ldots, \mathbf{v}_k$ and therefore are vectors in W. It is clear that W is nonempty, and hence W is a subspace of V. ▲

We say that the subspace W of Theorem 1 is the space **spanned** by the vectors $\mathbf{v}_1, \mathbf{v}_2, \ldots, \mathbf{v}_k$, (or is the **span** of the set $S = \{\mathbf{v}_1, \mathbf{v}_2, \ldots, \mathbf{v}_k\}$ of vectors). We sometimes write

$$W = \mathrm{span}(S) = \mathrm{span}\{\mathbf{v}_1, \mathbf{v}_2, \ldots, \mathbf{v}_k\}.$$

Thus Example 3 implies that $\mathbf{R}^3 = \mathrm{span}\{\mathbf{i}, \mathbf{j}, \mathbf{k}\}$. The question as to whether a given vector $\mathbf{w}$ in $\mathbf{R}^n$ lies in the subspace $\mathrm{span}\{\mathbf{v}_1, \mathbf{v}_2, \ldots, \mathbf{v}_k\}$ reduces to solving a linear system, as illustrated by Examples 1 and 2.

It is easy to verify that the space $W = \mathrm{span}\{\mathbf{v}_1, \mathbf{v}_2, \ldots, \mathbf{v}_k\}$ of Theorem 1 is the smallest subspace of V that contains all the vectors $\mathbf{v}_1, \mathbf{v}_2, \ldots, \mathbf{v}_k$—meaning that every other subspace of V that contains these k vectors must also contain W (Problem 30).

Linear Independence

Henceforth, when we solve a homogeneous system of linear equations, we generally will seek a set $\mathbf{v}_1, \mathbf{v}_2, \ldots, \mathbf{v}_k$ of solution vectors that span the solution space W of the system. Perhaps the most concrete way to describe a subspace W of a vector space V is to give explicitly a set $\mathbf{v}_1, \mathbf{v}_2, \ldots, \mathbf{v}_k$ of vectors that span W. And this type of representation is most useful and desirable (as well as most aesthetically pleasing) when each vector $\mathbf{w}$ in W is expressible in a *unique* way as a linear combination of $\mathbf{v}_1, \mathbf{v}_2, \ldots, \mathbf{v}_k$. (For instance, each vector in $\mathbf{R}^3$ is a unique linear combination of the vectors $\mathbf{i}$, $\mathbf{j}$, and $\mathbf{k}$ of Example 3.) But Example 2 demonstrates that a vector $\mathbf{w}$ may well be expressed in many different ways as a linear combination of given vectors $\mathbf{v}_1, \mathbf{v}_2, \ldots, \mathbf{v}_k$.

Thus not all spanning sets enjoy the uniqueness property that we desire. Two questions arise: Given a subspace W of a vector space V, does there necessarily exist a spanning set with the uniqueness property that we desire? If so, how do we find one that does? The following definition provides the key to both answers.

Definition: Linear Independence

The vectors $\mathbf{v}_1, \mathbf{v}_2, \ldots, \mathbf{v}_k$ in a vector space V are said to be **linearly independent** provided that the equation

$$c_1\mathbf{v}_1 + c_2\mathbf{v}_2 + \cdots + c_k\mathbf{v}_k = \mathbf{0} \tag{4}$$

has only the trivial solution $c_1 = c_2 = \cdots = c_k = 0$. That is, the only linear combination of $\mathbf{v}_1, \mathbf{v}_2, \ldots, \mathbf{v}_k$ that represents the zero vector $\mathbf{0}$ is the trivial combination $0\mathbf{v}_1 + 0\mathbf{v}_2 + \cdots + 0\mathbf{v}_k$.

Example 4 The **standard unit vectors**

$$\mathbf{e}_1 = (1, 0, 0, \ldots, 0),$$
$$\mathbf{e}_2 = (0, 1, 0, \ldots, 0),$$
$$\vdots$$
$$\mathbf{e}_n = (0, 0, 0, \ldots, 1)$$

in $\mathbf{R}^n$ are linearly independent. The reason is that the equation

$$c_1\mathbf{e}_1 + c_2\mathbf{e}_2 + \cdots + c_n\mathbf{e}_n = \mathbf{0}$$

evidently reduces to

$$(c_1, c_2, \ldots, c_n) = (0, 0, \ldots, 0)$$

and thus has only the trivial solution $c_1 = c_2 = \cdots = c_n = 0$. ∎

Example 5 To determine whether the vectors $\mathbf{v}_1 = (1, 2, 2, 1)$, $\mathbf{v}_2 = (2, 3, 4, 1)$, and $\mathbf{v}_3 = (3, 8, 7, 5)$ in $\mathbf{R}^4$ are linearly independent, we write the equation $c_1\mathbf{v}_1 + c_2\mathbf{v}_2 + c_3\mathbf{v}_3 = \mathbf{0}$ as the linear system

$$c_1 + 2c_2 + 3c_3 = 0$$
$$2c_1 + 3c_2 + 8c_3 = 0$$
$$2c_1 + 4c_2 + 7c_3 = 0$$
$$c_1 + c_2 + 5c_3 = 0$$

and then solve for c_1, c_2, and c_3. The augmented coefficient matrix of this system reduces to the echelon form

$$\begin{bmatrix} 1 & 2 & 3 & 0 \\ 0 & 1 & -2 & 0 \\ 0 & 0 & 1 & 0 \\ 0 & 0 & 0 & 0 \end{bmatrix},$$

so we see that the only solution is $c_1 = c_2 = c_3 = 0$. Thus the vectors $\mathbf{v}_1$, $\mathbf{v}_2$, and $\mathbf{v}_3$ are linearly independent. ∎

Observe that linear independence of the vectors $\mathbf{v}_1, \mathbf{v}_2, \ldots, \mathbf{v}_k$ actually is a property of the *set* $S = \{\mathbf{v}_1, \mathbf{v}_2, \ldots, \mathbf{v}_k\}$ whose elements are these vectors. Occasionally the phraseology "the set $S = \{\mathbf{v}_1, \mathbf{v}_2, \ldots, \mathbf{v}_k\}$ is linearly independent" is more convenient. For instance, *any subset of a linearly independent set $S = \{\mathbf{v}_1, \mathbf{v}_2, \ldots, \mathbf{v}_k\}$ is a linearly independent set of vectors* (Problem 29).

Now we show that *the coefficients in a linear combination of the linearly independent vectors $\mathbf{v}_1, \mathbf{v}_2, \ldots, \mathbf{v}_k$ are unique.* If both

$$\mathbf{w} = a_1\mathbf{v}_1 + a_2\mathbf{v}_2 + \cdots + a_k\mathbf{v}_k \tag{5}$$

and

$$\mathbf{w} = b_1\mathbf{v}_1 + b_2\mathbf{v}_2 + \cdots + b_k\mathbf{v}_k, \tag{6}$$

then

$$a_1\mathbf{v}_1 + a_2\mathbf{v}_2 + \cdots + a_k\mathbf{v}_k = b_1\mathbf{v}_1 + b_2\mathbf{v}_2 + \cdots + b_k\mathbf{v}_k,$$

so it follows that

$$(a_1 - b_1)\mathbf{v}_1 + (a_2 - b_2)\mathbf{v}_2 + \cdots + (a_k - b_k)\mathbf{v}_k = \mathbf{0}. \tag{7}$$

Because the vectors $\mathbf{v}_1, \mathbf{v}_2, \ldots, \mathbf{v}_k$ are linearly independent, each of the coefficients in (7) must vanish. Therefore, $a_1 = b_1, a_2 = b_2, \ldots, a_k = b_k$, so we have shown that the linear combinations in (5) and (6) actually are identical. Hence, if a vector $\mathbf{w}$ is in the set span$\{\mathbf{v}_1, \mathbf{v}_2, \ldots, \mathbf{v}_k\}$, then it can be expressed in only one way as a linear combination of these linearly independent vectors.

A set of vectors is called **linearly dependent** provided it is not linearly independent. Hence the vectors $\mathbf{v}_1, \mathbf{v}_2, \ldots, \mathbf{v}_k$ are linearly dependent if and only if there exist scalars $c_1, c_2, \ldots, c_k$ *not all zero* such that

$$c_1\mathbf{v}_1 + c_2\mathbf{v}_2 + \cdots + c_k\mathbf{v}_k = \mathbf{0}. \tag{8}$$

In short, a (finite) set of vectors is linearly dependent provided that some *nontrivial* linear combination of them equals the zero vector.

Example 6   Let $\mathbf{v}_1 = (2, 1, 3)$, $\mathbf{v}_2 = (5, -2, 4)$, $\mathbf{v}_3 = (3, 8, -6)$, and $\mathbf{v}_4 = (2, 7, -4)$. Then the equation $c_1\mathbf{v}_1 + c_2\mathbf{v}_2 + c_3\mathbf{v}_3 + c_4\mathbf{v}_4 = \mathbf{0}$ is equivalent to the linear system

$$2c_1 + 5c_2 + 3c_3 + 2c_4 = 0$$
$$c_1 - 2c_2 + 8c_3 + 7c_4 = 0$$
$$3c_1 + 4c_2 - 6c_3 - 4c_4 = 0$$

of three equations in four unknowns. Because this homogeneous system has more unknowns than equations, Theorem 3 in Section 3.3 implies that it has a nontrivial solution. Therefore we may conclude—without even solving explicitly for c_1, c_2, c_3, and c_4—that the vectors $\mathbf{v}_1$, $\mathbf{v}_2$, $\mathbf{v}_3$, and $\mathbf{v}_4$ are linearly dependent. (It happens that

$$2\mathbf{v}_1 - \mathbf{v}_2 + 3\mathbf{v}_3 - 4\mathbf{v}_4 = \mathbf{0},$$

as you can verify easily.)   ∎

The argument in Example 6 may be generalized in an obvious way to prove that *any set of more than n vectors in $\mathbf{R}^n$ is linearly dependent.* For if $k > n$, then Eq. (8) is equivalent to a homogeneous linear system with more unknowns (k) than equations (n), so Theorem 3 in Section 3.3 yields a nontrivial solution.

We now look at the way in which the elements of a linearly dependent set of vectors $\mathbf{v}_1, \mathbf{v}_2, \ldots, \mathbf{v}_k$ "depend" on one another. We know that there exist scalars $c_1, c_2, \ldots, c_k$ not all zero such that

$$c_1\mathbf{v}_1 + c_2\mathbf{v}_2 + \cdots + c_k\mathbf{v}_k = \mathbf{0}. \tag{9}$$

Suppose that the pth coefficient is nonzero: $c_p \neq 0$. Then we can solve Eq. (9) for $c_p\mathbf{v}_p$ and next divide by c_p to get

$$\mathbf{v}_p = a_1\mathbf{v}_1 + \cdots + a_{p-1}\mathbf{v}_{p-1} + a_{p+1}\mathbf{v}_{p+1} + \cdots + a_k\mathbf{v}_k, \tag{10}$$

where $a_i = -c_i/c_p$ for $i \neq p$. Thus at least one of the linearly dependent vectors is a linear combination of the other $k - 1$. Conversely, suppose we are given a set of vectors $\mathbf{v}_1, \mathbf{v}_2, \ldots, \mathbf{v}_k$ with one of them dependent on the others as in Eq. (10). Then we can transpose all the terms to the left-hand side to get an equation of the form in (9) with $c_p = 1 \neq 0$. This shows that the vectors are linearly dependent. Therefore, we have proved that *the vectors* $\mathbf{v}_1, \mathbf{v}_2, \ldots, \mathbf{v}_k$ *are linearly dependent if and only if at least one of them is a linear combination of the others.*

For instance (as we saw in Section 4.1), two vectors are linearly dependent if and only if one of them is a scalar multiple of the other, in which case the two vectors are collinear. Three vectors are linearly dependent if and only if one of them is a linear combination of the other two, in which case the three vectors are coplanar.

In Theorem 4 of Section 4.1 we saw that the *determinant* provides a criterion for deciding whether three vectors in $\mathbf{R}^3$ are linearly independent: The vectors $\mathbf{v}_1$, $\mathbf{v}_2$, $\mathbf{v}_3$ in $\mathbf{R}^3$ are linearly independent if and only if the determinant of the 3×3 matrix

$$\mathbf{A} = \begin{bmatrix} \mathbf{v}_1 & \mathbf{v}_2 & \mathbf{v}_3 \end{bmatrix}$$

is nonzero. The proof given there in the three-dimensional case generalizes readily to the *n*-dimensional case. Given *n* vectors $\mathbf{v}_1, \mathbf{v}_2, \ldots, \mathbf{v}_n$ in $\mathbf{R}^n$, we consider the $n \times n$ matrix

$$\mathbf{A} = \begin{bmatrix} \mathbf{v}_1 & \mathbf{v}_2 & \cdots & \mathbf{v}_n \end{bmatrix}$$

having these vectors as its column vectors. Then, by Theorem 2 in Section 3.6, $\det \mathbf{A} \neq 0$ if and only if $\mathbf{A}$ is invertible, in which case the system $\mathbf{Ac} = \mathbf{0}$ has only the trivial solution $c_1 = c_2 = \cdots = c_n = 0$, so the vectors $\mathbf{v}_1, \mathbf{v}_2, \ldots, \mathbf{v}_n$ must be linearly independent.

THEOREM 2: Independence of *n* Vectors in R^n

The *n* vectors $\mathbf{v}_1, \mathbf{v}_2, \ldots, \mathbf{v}_n$ in R^n are linearly independent if and only if the $n \times n$ matrix

$$\mathbf{A} = \begin{bmatrix} \mathbf{v}_1 & \mathbf{v}_2 & \cdots & \mathbf{v}_n \end{bmatrix}$$

having them as its column vectors has nonzero determinant.　　　　　▲

We saw earlier that a set of *more* than *n* vectors in $\mathbf{R}^n$ is always linearly dependent. The following theorem shows us how the determinant provides a criterion in the case of *fewer* than *n* vectors in $\mathbf{R}^n$.　　　　■

THEOREM 3: Fewer Than *n* Vectors in R^n

Consider *k* vectors $\mathbf{v}_1, \mathbf{v}_2, \ldots, \mathbf{v}_k$ in $\mathbf{R}^n$, with $k < n$. Let

$$\mathbf{A} = \begin{bmatrix} \mathbf{v}_1 & \mathbf{v}_2 & \cdots & \mathbf{v}_k \end{bmatrix}$$

be the $n \times k$ matrix having them as its column vectors. Then the vectors $\mathbf{v}_1, \mathbf{v}_2, \ldots, \mathbf{v}_k$ are linearly independent if and only if some $k \times k$ submatrix of $\mathbf{A}$ has nonzero determinant.　　　　　▲

Rather than including a complete proof, we will simply illustrate the "if" part of Theorem 3 in the case $n = 5$, $k = 3$. Let $\mathbf{v}_1 = (a_1, a_2, a_3, a_4, a_5)$, $\mathbf{v}_2 = (b_1, b_2, b_3, b_4, b_5)$, and $\mathbf{v}_3 = (c_1, c_2, c_3, c_4, c_5)$ be three vectors in $\mathbf{R}^5$ such that the 5×3 matrix

$$\mathbf{A} = \begin{bmatrix} a_1 & b_1 & c_1 \\ a_2 & b_2 & c_2 \\ a_3 & b_3 & c_3 \\ a_4 & b_4 & c_4 \\ a_5 & b_5 & c_5 \end{bmatrix}$$

has a 3×3 submatrix with nonzero determinant. Suppose, for instance, that

$$\begin{vmatrix} a_1 & b_1 & c_1 \\ a_3 & b_3 & c_3 \\ a_5 & b_5 & c_5 \end{vmatrix} \neq 0.$$

Then Theorem 2 implies that the three vectors $\mathbf{u}_1 = (a_1, a_3, a_5)$, $\mathbf{u}_2 = (b_1, b_3, b_5)$, and $\mathbf{u}_3 = (c_1, c_3, c_5)$ in $\mathbf{R}^3$ are linearly independent. Now suppose that $c_1\mathbf{v}_1 + c_2\mathbf{v}_2 + c_3\mathbf{v}_3 = \mathbf{0}$. Then by deleting the second and fourth components of each vector in this equation, we find that $c_1\mathbf{u}_1 + c_2\mathbf{u}_2 + c_3\mathbf{u}_3 = \mathbf{0}$. But the fact that $\mathbf{u}_1, \mathbf{u}_2, \mathbf{u}_3$ are linearly independent implies that $c_1 = c_2 = c_3 = 0$, and it now follows that $\mathbf{v}_1, \mathbf{v}_2, \mathbf{v}_3$ are linearly independent.

4.3 Problems

In Problems 1–8, determine whether the given vectors $\mathbf{v}_1, \mathbf{v}_2, \ldots, \mathbf{v}_n$ are linearly independent or linearly dependent. Do this essentially by inspection—that is, without solving a linear system of equations.

1. $\mathbf{v}_1 = (4, -2, 6, -4)$, $\mathbf{v}_2 = (6, -3, 9, -6)$
2. $\mathbf{v}_1 = (3, 9, -3, 6)$, $\mathbf{v}_2 = (2, 6, -1, 4)$
3. $\mathbf{v}_1 = (3, 4)$, $\mathbf{v}_2 = (6, -1)$, $\mathbf{v}_3 = (7, 5)$
4. $\mathbf{v}_1 = (4, -2, 2)$, $\mathbf{v}_2 = (5, 4, -3)$, $\mathbf{v}_3 = (4, 6, 5)$, $\mathbf{v}_4 = (-7, 9, 3)$
5. $\mathbf{v}_1 = (1, 0, 0)$, $\mathbf{v}_2 = (0, -2, 0)$, $\mathbf{v}_3 = (0, 0, 3)$
6. $\mathbf{v}_1 = (1, 0, 0)$, $\mathbf{v}_2 = (1, 1, 0)$, $\mathbf{v}_3 = (1, 1, 1)$
7. $\mathbf{v}_1 = (2, 1, 0, 0)$, $\mathbf{v}_2 = (3, 0, 1, 0)$, $\mathbf{v}_3 = (4, 0, 0, 1)$
8. $\mathbf{v}_1 = (1, 0, 3, 0)$, $\mathbf{v}_2 = (0, 2, 0, 4)$, $\mathbf{v}_3 = (1, 2, 3, 4)$

In Problems 9–16, express the indicated vector $\mathbf{w}$ as a linear combination of the given vectors $\mathbf{v}_1, \mathbf{v}_2, \ldots, \mathbf{v}_k$ if this is possible. If not, show that it is impossible.

9. $\mathbf{w} = (1, 0, -7)$; $\mathbf{v}_1 = (5, 3, 4)$, $\mathbf{v}_2 = (3, 2, 5)$
10. $\mathbf{w} = (3, -1, -2)$; $\mathbf{v}_1 = (-3, 1, -2)$, $\mathbf{v}_2 = (6, -2, 3)$
11. $\mathbf{w} = (1, 0, 0, -1)$; $\mathbf{v}_1 = (7, -6, 4, 5)$, $\mathbf{v}_2 = (3, -3, 2, 3)$
12. $\mathbf{w} = (4, -4, 3, 3)$; $\mathbf{v}_1 = (7, 3, -1, 9)$, $\mathbf{v}_2 = (-2, -2, 1, -3)$
13. $\mathbf{w} = (5, 2, -2)$; $\mathbf{v}_1 = (1, 5, -3)$, $\mathbf{v}_2 = (5, -3, 4)$
14. $\mathbf{w} = (2, -3, 2, -3)$; $\mathbf{v}_1 = (1, 0, 0, 3)$, $\mathbf{v}_2 = (0, 1, -2, 0)$, $\mathbf{v}_3 = (0, -1, 1, 1)$
15. $\mathbf{w} = (4, 5, 6)$; $\mathbf{v}_1 = (2, -1, 4)$, $\mathbf{v}_2 = (3, 0, 1)$, $\mathbf{v}_3 = (1, 2, -1)$
16. $\mathbf{w} = (7, 7, 9, 11)$; $\mathbf{v}_1 = (2, 0, 3, 1)$, $\mathbf{v}_2 = (4, 1, 3, 2)$, $\mathbf{v}_3 = (1, 3, -1, 3)$

In Problems 17–22, three vectors $\mathbf{v}_1, \mathbf{v}_2$, and $\mathbf{v}_3$ are given. If they are linearly independent, show this; otherwise find a nontrivial linear combination of them that is equal to the zero vector.

17. $\mathbf{v}_1 = (1, 0, 1)$, $\mathbf{v}_2 = (2, -3, 4)$, $\mathbf{v}_3 = (3, 5, 2)$
18. $\mathbf{v}_1 = (2, 0, -3)$, $\mathbf{v}_2 = (4, -5, -6)$, $\mathbf{v}_3 = (-2, 1, 3)$
19. $\mathbf{v}_1 = (2, 0, 3, 0)$, $\mathbf{v}_2 = (5, 4, -2, 1)$, $\mathbf{v}_3 = (2, -1, 1, -1)$
20. $\mathbf{v}_1 = (1, 1, -1, 1)$, $\mathbf{v}_2 = (2, 1, 1, 1)$, $\mathbf{v}_3 = (3, 1, 4, 1)$

21. $\mathbf{v}_1 = (3, 0, 1, 2)$, $\mathbf{v}_2 = (1, -1, 0, 1)$, $\mathbf{v}_3 = (1, 2, 1, 0)$
22. $\mathbf{v}_1 = (3, 9, 0, 5)$, $\mathbf{v}_2 = (3, 0, 9, -7)$, $\mathbf{v}_3 = (4, 7, 5, 0)$

In Problems 23–26, the vectors $\{\mathbf{v}_i\}$ are known to be linearly independent. Apply the definition of linear independence to show that the vectors $\{\mathbf{u}_i\}$ are also linearly independent.

23. $\mathbf{u}_1 = \mathbf{v}_1 + \mathbf{v}_2$, $\mathbf{u}_2 = \mathbf{v}_1 - \mathbf{v}_2$
24. $\mathbf{u}_1 = \mathbf{v}_1 + \mathbf{v}_2$, $\mathbf{u}_2 = 2\mathbf{v}_1 + 3\mathbf{v}_2$
25. $\mathbf{u}_1 = \mathbf{v}_1$, $\mathbf{u}_2 = \mathbf{v}_1 + 2\mathbf{v}_2$, $\mathbf{u}_3 = \mathbf{v}_1 + 2\mathbf{v}_2 + 3\mathbf{v}_3$
26. $\mathbf{u}_1 = \mathbf{v}_2 + \mathbf{v}_3$, $\mathbf{u}_2 = \mathbf{v}_1 + \mathbf{v}_3$, $\mathbf{u}_3 = \mathbf{v}_1 + \mathbf{v}_2$
27. *Prove*: If the (finite) set S of vectors contains the zero vector, then S is linearly dependent.
28. *Prove*: If the set S of vectors is linearly dependent and the (finite) set T contains S, then T is also linearly dependent. You may assume that $S = \{\mathbf{v}_1, \mathbf{v}_2, \ldots, \mathbf{v}_k\}$ and that $T = \{\mathbf{v}_1, \mathbf{v}_2, \ldots, \mathbf{v}_m\}$ with $m > k$.
29. Show that if the (finite) set S of vectors is linearly independent, then any subset T of S is also linearly independent.
30. Suppose that the subspace U of the vector space V contains the vectors $\mathbf{v}_1, \mathbf{v}_2, \ldots, \mathbf{v}_k$. Show that U contains the subspace spanned by these vectors.
31. Let S and T be sets of vectors in a vector space such that S is a subset of span(T). Show that span(S) is also a subset of span(T).
32. Let $\mathbf{v}_1, \mathbf{v}_2, \ldots, \mathbf{v}_k$ be linearly independent vectors in the set S of vectors. *Prove*: If no set of more than k vectors in S is linearly independent, then every vector in S is a linear combination of $\mathbf{v}_1, \mathbf{v}_2, \ldots, \mathbf{v}_k$.

In Problems 33–35, let $\mathbf{v}_1, \mathbf{v}_2, \ldots, \mathbf{v}_k$ be vectors in $\mathbf{R}^n$ and let

$$\mathbf{A} = \begin{bmatrix} \mathbf{v}_1 & \mathbf{v}_2 & \cdots & \mathbf{v}_k \end{bmatrix}$$

be the $n \times k$ matrix with these vectors as its column vectors.

33. *Prove*: If some $k \times k$ submatrix of $\mathbf{A}$ is the $k \times k$ identity matrix, then $\mathbf{v}_1, \mathbf{v}_2, \ldots, \mathbf{v}_k$ are linearly independent.
34. Suppose that $k = n$, that the vectors $\mathbf{v}_1, \mathbf{v}_2, \ldots, \mathbf{v}_k$ are linearly independent, and that $\mathbf{B}$ is a nonsingular $n \times n$ matrix. Prove that the column vectors of the matrix $\mathbf{AB}$ are linearly independent.

35. Suppose that $k < n$, that the vectors $\mathbf{v}_1, \mathbf{v}_2, \ldots, \mathbf{v}_k$ are linearly independent, and that $\mathbf{B}$ is a nonsingular $k \times k$ matrix. Use Theorem 3 to show that the column vectors of $\mathbf{AB}$ are linearly independent.

4.4 Bases and Dimension for Vector Spaces

An especially useful way of describing the solution space of a homogeneous linear system is to list explicitly a set S of solution vectors such that *every* solution vector is a unique linear combination of these particular ones. The following definition specifies the properties of such a set S of "basic" solution vectors, and the concept is equally important for vector spaces other than solution spaces.

> **Definition: Basis**
>
> A finite set S of vectors in a vector space V is called a **basis** for V provided that
>
> **(a)** the vectors in S are linearly independent, and
> **(b)** the vectors in S span V.

In short, a basis for the vector space V is a linearly independent spanning set of vectors in V. Thus, if $S = \{\mathbf{v}_1, \mathbf{v}_2, \ldots, \mathbf{v}_n\}$ is a basis for V, then any vector $\mathbf{w}$ in V can be expressed as a linear combination

$$\mathbf{w} = c_1 \mathbf{v}_1 + c_2 \mathbf{v}_2 + \cdots + c_n \mathbf{v}_n \tag{1}$$

of the vectors in S, and we saw in Section 4.3 that the linear independence of S implies that the coefficients $c_1, c_2, \ldots, c_n$ in (1) are *unique*. That is, $\mathbf{w}$ cannot be expressed differently as a linear combination of the basis vectors $\mathbf{v}_1, \mathbf{v}_2, \ldots, \mathbf{v}_n$.

Example 1 The **standard basis** for $\mathbf{R}^n$ consists of the unit vectors

$$\mathbf{e}_1 = (1, 0, 0, \ldots, 0), \quad \mathbf{e}_2 = (0, 1, 0, \ldots, 0), \quad \ldots, \quad \mathbf{e}_n = (0, 0, 0, \ldots, 1).$$

If $\mathbf{x} = (x_1, x_2, \ldots, x_n)$ is a vector in $\mathbf{R}^n$, then

$$\mathbf{x} = x_1 \mathbf{e}_1 + x_2 \mathbf{e}_2 + \cdots + x_n \mathbf{e}_n.$$

Thus the vectors $\mathbf{e}_1, \mathbf{e}_2, \ldots, \mathbf{e}_n$ span $\mathbf{R}^n$, and we noted in Example 4 of Section 4.3 that these *standard unit vectors* are linearly independent. ∎

Example 2 Let $\mathbf{v}_1, \mathbf{v}_2, \ldots, \mathbf{v}_n$ be n linearly independent vectors in $\mathbf{R}^n$. We saw in Section 4.3 that any set of more than n vectors in $\mathbf{R}^n$ is linearly dependent. Hence, given a vector $\mathbf{w}$ in $\mathbf{R}^n$, there exist scalars $c, c_1, c_2, \ldots, c_n$ not all zero such that

$$c\mathbf{w} + c_1 \mathbf{v}_1 + c_2 \mathbf{v}_2 + \cdots + c_n \mathbf{v}_n = \mathbf{0}. \tag{2}$$

If c were zero, then (2) would imply that the vectors $\mathbf{v}_1, \mathbf{v}_2, \ldots, \mathbf{v}_n$ are linearly dependent. Hence $c \neq 0$, so Eq. (2) can be solved for $\mathbf{w}$ as a linear combination of $\mathbf{v}_1, \mathbf{v}_2, \ldots, \mathbf{v}_n$. Thus the linearly independent vectors $\mathbf{v}_1, \mathbf{v}_2, \ldots, \mathbf{v}_n$ *also* span $\mathbf{R}^n$ and therefore constitute a basis for $\mathbf{R}^n$. ∎

Example 2 shows that *any set of n linearly independent vectors in $\mathbf{R}^n$ is a basis for $\mathbf{R}^n$*. By Theorem 2 in Section 4.3, we can therefore determine whether n given vectors $\mathbf{v}_1, \mathbf{v}_2, \ldots, \mathbf{v}_n$ form a basis for $\mathbf{R}^n$ by calculating the determinant of the $n \times n$ matrix

$$\mathbf{A} = \begin{bmatrix} \mathbf{v}_1 & \mathbf{v}_2 & \cdots & \mathbf{v}_n \end{bmatrix}$$

with these vectors as its column vectors. They constitute a basis for $\mathbf{R}^n$ if and only if $\det \mathbf{A} \neq 0$.

Example 3   Let $\mathbf{v}_1 = (1, -1, -2, -3)$, $\mathbf{v}_2 = (1, -1, 2, 3)$, $\mathbf{v}_3 = (1, -1, -3, -2)$, and $\mathbf{v}_4 = (0, 3, -1, 2)$. Then we find that

$$\begin{vmatrix} 1 & 1 & 1 & 0 \\ -1 & -1 & -1 & 3 \\ -2 & 2 & -3 & -1 \\ -3 & 3 & -2 & 2 \end{vmatrix} = 30 \neq 0,$$

so it follows that $\{\mathbf{v}_1, \mathbf{v}_2, \mathbf{v}_3, \mathbf{v}_4\}$ is a basis for $\mathbf{R}^4$. ■

Theorem 1 has the following import: Just as in $\mathbf{R}^n$, a basis for *any* vector space V contains the largest possible number of linearly independent vectors in V.

THEOREM 1: Bases as Maximal Linearly Independent Sets

Let $S = \{\mathbf{v}_1, \mathbf{v}_2, \ldots, \mathbf{v}_n\}$ be a basis for the vector space V. Then any set of more than n vectors in V is linearly dependent.

Proof: We need to show that if $m > n$, then any set $T = \{\mathbf{w}_1, \mathbf{w}_2, \ldots, \mathbf{w}_m\}$ of m vectors in V is linearly dependent. Because the basis S spans V, each vector $\mathbf{w}_j$ in T can be expressed as a linear combination of $\mathbf{v}_1, \mathbf{v}_2, \ldots, \mathbf{v}_n$:

$$\begin{aligned} \mathbf{w}_1 &= a_{11}\mathbf{v}_1 + a_{21}\mathbf{v}_2 + \cdots + a_{n1}\mathbf{v}_n \\ \mathbf{w}_2 &= a_{12}\mathbf{v}_1 + a_{22}\mathbf{v}_2 + \cdots + a_{n2}\mathbf{v}_n \\ &\vdots \\ \mathbf{w}_m &= a_{1m}\mathbf{v}_1 + a_{2m}\mathbf{v}_2 + \cdots + a_{nm}\mathbf{v}_n. \end{aligned} \tag{3}$$

Now we need to find scalars $c_1, c_2, \ldots, c_m$ not all zero such that

$$c_1\mathbf{w}_1 + c_2\mathbf{w}_2 + \cdots + c_m\mathbf{w}_m = \mathbf{0}. \tag{4}$$

Substituting in (4) the expressions in (3) for each $\mathbf{w}_j$, we get

$$\begin{aligned} &c_1(a_{11}\mathbf{v}_1 + a_{21}\mathbf{v}_2 + \cdots + a_{n1}\mathbf{v}_n) \\ &+ c_2(a_{12}\mathbf{v}_1 + a_{22}\mathbf{v}_2 + \cdots + a_{n2}\mathbf{v}_n) + \cdots \\ &+ c_m(a_{1m}\mathbf{v}_1 + a_{2m}\mathbf{v}_2 + \cdots + a_{nm}\mathbf{v}_n) = \mathbf{0}. \end{aligned} \tag{5}$$

Because the vectors $\mathbf{v}_1, \mathbf{v}_2, \ldots, \mathbf{v}_n$ are linearly independent, the coefficient in (5) of each $\mathbf{v}_i$ must vanish:

$$\begin{aligned} a_{11}c_1 + a_{12}c_2 + \cdots + a_{1m}c_m &= 0 \\ a_{21}c_1 + a_{22}c_2 + \cdots + a_{2m}c_m &= 0 \\ &\vdots \\ a_{n1}c_1 + a_{n2}c_2 + \cdots + a_{nm}c_m &= 0. \end{aligned} \tag{6}$$

But because $m > n$, this is a homogeneous linear system with more unknowns than equations, and therefore has a nontrivial solution $(c_1, c_2, \ldots, c_m)$. Then $c_1, c_2, \ldots, c_m$ are scalars not all zero such that (4) holds, so we have shown that the set T of more than n vectors in linearly dependent. ▲

Now let $S = \{\mathbf{v}_1, \mathbf{v}_2, \ldots, \mathbf{v}_n\}$ and $T = \{\mathbf{w}_1, \mathbf{w}_2, \ldots, \mathbf{w}_m\}$ be two different bases for the same vector space V. Because S is a basis and T is linearly independent, Theorem 1 implies that $m \leq n$. Next, reverse the roles of S and T; the fact that T is a basis and S is linearly independent implies similarly that $n \leq m$. Hence $m = n$, so we have proved the following theorem for any vector space with a finite basis.

THEOREM 2: The Dimension of a Vector Space

Any two bases for a vector space consist of the same number of vectors. ▲

A nonzero vector space V is called **finite dimensional** provided that there exists a basis for V consisting of a finite number of vectors from V. In this case the number n of vectors in each basis for V is called the **dimension** of V, denoted by $n = \dim V$. Then V is an *n-dimensional* vector space. The standard basis of Example 1 shows that $\mathbf{R}^n$ is, indeed, an n-dimensional vector space.

Note that the zero vector space $\{\mathbf{0}\}$ has no basis because it contains *no* linearly independent set of vectors. (Sometimes it is convenient to adopt the convention that the null set is a basis for $\{\mathbf{0}\}$.) Here we define $\dim\{\mathbf{0}\}$ to be zero. A nonzero vector space that has no finite basis is called **infinite dimensional**. Infinite-dimensional vector spaces are discussed in Section 4.5, but we include an illustrative example of one here.

Example 4 Let $\mathcal{P}$ be the set of all polynomials of the form

$$p(x) = a_0 + a_1 x + a_2 x^2 + \cdots + a_n x^n,$$

where the largest exponent $n \geq 0$ that appears is the *degree* of the polynomial $p(x)$, and the coefficients $a_0, a_1, a_2, \ldots, a_n$ are real numbers. We add polynomials in $\mathcal{P}$ and multiply them by scalars in the usual way—that is, by collecting coefficients of like powers of x. For instance, if

$$p(x) = 3 + 2x + 5x^3 \quad \text{and} \quad q(x) = 7 + 4x + 3x^2 + 9x^4,$$

then

$$(p + q)(x) = (3 + 7) + (2 + 4)x + (0 + 3)x^2 + (5 + 0)x^3 + (0 + 9)x^4$$
$$= 10 + 6x + 3x^2 + 5x^3 + 9x^4$$

and

$$(7p)(x) = 7(3 + 2x + 5x^3) = 21 + 14x + 35x^3.$$

It is readily verified that, with these operations, $\mathcal{P}$ is a vector space. But $\mathcal{P}$ has no finite basis. For if $p_1, p_2, \ldots, p_n$ are elements of $\mathcal{P}$, then the degree of any linear combination of them is at most the maximum of *their* degrees. Hence no polynomial in $\mathcal{P}$ of higher degree lies in $\mathrm{span}\{p_1, p_2, \ldots, p_n\}$. Thus no finite subset of $\mathcal{P}$ spans $\mathcal{P}$, and therefore $\mathcal{P}$ is an infinite-dimensional vector space. ■

Here, our concern is with finite-dimensional vector spaces, and we note first that any proper subspace W of a finite-dimensional vector space V is itself finite dimensional, with $\dim W < \dim V$. For if $\dim V = n$, let $k \le n$ be the largest integer such that W contains k linearly independent vectors $\mathbf{v}_1, \mathbf{v}_2, \ldots, \mathbf{v}_k$. Then, by the same argument as in Example 2, we see that $\{\mathbf{v}_1, \mathbf{v}_2, \ldots, \mathbf{v}_k\}$ is a basis for W, so W is finite dimensional with $\dim W = k$, and $k < n$ because W is a proper subspace.

Moreover, an n-dimensional vector space V contains proper subspaces of each dimension $k = 1, 2, \ldots, n - 1$. For instance, if $\{\mathbf{v}_1, \mathbf{v}_2, \ldots, \mathbf{v}_n\}$ is a basis for V and $k < n$, then $W = \text{span}\{\mathbf{v}_1, \mathbf{v}_2, \ldots, \mathbf{v}_k\}$ is a subspace of dimension k. Thus $\mathbf{R}^4$ contains proper subspaces of dimensions 1, 2, and 3; $\mathbf{R}^5$ contains proper subspaces of dimensions 1, 2, 3, and 4; and so on. The proper subspaces of $\mathbf{R}^n$ of dimensions $1, 2, \ldots, n - 1$ are the higher-dimensional analogues of lines and planes through the origin in $\mathbf{R}^3$.

Suppose that V is an n-dimensional vector space and that $S = \{\mathbf{v}_1, \mathbf{v}_2, \ldots, \mathbf{v}_n\}$ is a set of n vectors in V. Then, in order to show that S is a basis for V, it is not necessary to prove *both* that S is linearly independent *and* that S spans V, because it turns out (for n vectors in an n-dimensional vector space) that either property of S implies the other. For instance, if $S = \{\mathbf{v}_1, \mathbf{v}_2, \ldots, \mathbf{v}_n\}$ is a set of n linearly independent vectors in V, then Theorem 1 and the argument of Example 2 (once again) imply that S spans V and, hence, is a basis for V. This proves part (a) of Theorem 3. The remaining parts are left to the problems. (See Problems 27–32.)

THEOREM 3: Independent Sets, Spanning Sets, and Bases

Let V be an n-dimensional vector space and let S be a subset of V. Then

(a) If S is linearly independent and consists of n vectors, then S is a basis for V;

(b) If S spans V and consists of n vectors, then S is a basis for V;

(c) If S is linearly independent, then S is contained in a basis for V;

(d) If S spans V, then S contains a basis for V. ▲

Part (c) of Theorem 3 is often applied in the following form: If W is a k-dimensional subspace of the n-dimensional vector space V, then any basis $\{\mathbf{v}_1, \mathbf{v}_2, \ldots, \mathbf{v}_k\}$ for W can be "extended" to a basis $\{\mathbf{v}_1, \mathbf{v}_2, \ldots, \mathbf{v}_n\}$ for V, consisting of the original basis vectors for W together with $n - k$ additional vectors $\mathbf{v}_{k+1}, \mathbf{v}_{k+2}, \ldots, \mathbf{v}_n$.

Bases for Solution Spaces

We consider now the homogeneous linear system

$$\mathbf{Ax} = \mathbf{0}, \tag{7}$$

in which $\mathbf{A}$ is an $m \times n$ matrix, so the system consists of m equations in the n variables $x_1, x_2, \ldots, x_n$. Its solution space W is then a subspace of $\mathbf{R}^n$. We want to determine the dimension of W and, moreover, to find an explicit basis for W. Thus we seek a maximal set of linearly independent solution vectors of (7).

Recall the Gaussian elimination method of Section 3.2. We use elementary row operations to reduce the coefficient matrix $\mathbf{A}$ to an echelon matrix $\mathbf{E}$ and note the (nonzero) *leading entries* in the rows of $\mathbf{E}$. The *leading variables* are those that correspond to the columns of $\mathbf{E}$ containing the leading entries. The remaining variables (if any) are the *free variables*. If there are no free variables, then our system has only the trivial solution, so $W = \{\mathbf{0}\}$. If there are free variables, we set each of them (separately) equal to a parameter and solve (by back substitution) for the leading variables as linear combinations of these parameters. The solution space W is then the set of all solution vectors obtained in this manner (for all possible values of the parameters).

To illustrate the general situation, let us suppose that the leading variables are the first r variables $x_1, x_2, \ldots, x_r$, so the $k = n - r$ variables $x_{r+1}, x_{r+2}, \ldots, x_n$ are free variables. The reduced system $\mathbf{Ex} = \mathbf{0}$ then takes the form

$$
\begin{aligned}
b_{11}x_1 + b_{12}x_2 + \cdots + b_{1r}x_r + \cdots + b_{1n}x_n &= 0 \\
b_{22}x_2 + \cdots + b_{2r}x_r + \cdots + b_{2n}x_n &= 0 \\
&\;\;\vdots \\
b_{rr}x_r + \cdots + b_{rn}x_n &= 0
\end{aligned}
\tag{8}
$$

(plus k trivial equations of the form $0 = 0$). We set

$$
x_{r+1} = t_1, \quad x_{r+2} = t_2, \ldots, \quad x_n = t_k
\tag{9}
$$

and then solve (by back substitution) the equations in (8) for the leading variables

$$
\begin{aligned}
x_1 &= c_{11}t_1 + c_{12}t_2 + \cdots + c_{1k}t_k \\
x_2 &= c_{21}t_1 + c_{22}t_2 + \cdots + c_{2k}t_k \\
&\;\;\vdots \\
x_r &= c_{r1}t_1 + c_{r2}t_2 + \cdots + c_{rk}t_k.
\end{aligned}
\tag{10}
$$

The typical solution vector $(x_1, x_2, \ldots, x_n)$ is given in terms of the k parameters $t_1, t_2, \ldots, t_k$ by the equations in (9) and (10).

We now choose k particular solution vectors $\mathbf{v}_1, \mathbf{v}_2, \ldots, \mathbf{v}_k$ as follows: To get $\mathbf{v}_j$ we set the jth parameter t_j equal to 1 and set all other parameters equal to zero. Then

$$
\mathbf{v}_j = (c_{1j}, c_{2j}, \ldots, c_{rj}, 0, \ldots, 1, \ldots, 0),
\tag{11}
$$

with the 1 appearing as the $(r+j)$th entry. The vectors $\mathbf{v}_1, \mathbf{v}_2, \ldots, \mathbf{v}_k$ are the column vectors of the $n \times k$ matrix

$$
\begin{bmatrix}
c_{11} & c_{12} & \cdots & c_{1k} \\
c_{21} & c_{22} & \cdots & c_{2k} \\
\vdots & \vdots & \ddots & \vdots \\
c_{r1} & c_{r2} & \cdots & c_{rk} \\
1 & 0 & \cdots & 0 \\
0 & 1 & \cdots & 0 \\
\vdots & \vdots & \ddots & \vdots \\
0 & 0 & \cdots & 1
\end{bmatrix}.
\tag{12}
$$

Because of the presence of the lower $k \times k$ identity matrix, it is clear that the vectors $\mathbf{v}_1, \mathbf{v}_2, \ldots, \mathbf{v}_k$ are linearly independent. (See Problem 36.) But Eqs. (9) and (10) show that the typical solution vector $\mathbf{x}$ is a linear combination

$$
\mathbf{x} = t_1\mathbf{v}_1 + t_2\mathbf{v}_2 + \cdots + t_k\mathbf{v}_k.
\tag{13}
$$

Therefore the vectors $\mathbf{v}_1, \mathbf{v}_2, \ldots, \mathbf{v}_k$ defined in (11) form a basis for the solution space W of the original system in (7).

The following algorithm summarizes the steps in this procedure.

ALGORITHM: A Basis for the Solution Space

To find a basis for the solution space W of the homogeneous linear system $\mathbf{Ax} = \mathbf{0}$, carry out the following steps.

1. Reduce the coefficient matrix $\mathbf{A}$ to echelon form.
2. Identify the r leading variables and the $k = n - r$ free variables. If $k = 0$ then $W = \{\mathbf{0}\}$.
3. Set the free variables equal to parameters $t_1, t_2, \ldots, t_k$, and then solve by back substitution for the leading variables in terms of these parameters.
4. Let $\mathbf{v}_j$ be the solution vector obtained by setting t_j equal to 1 and the other parameters equal to zero. Then $\{\mathbf{v}_1, \mathbf{v}_2, \ldots, \mathbf{v}_k\}$ is a basis for W. ▲

Example 5 Find a basis for the solution space of the homogeneous linear system

$$
\begin{aligned}
3x_1 + 6x_2 - x_3 - 5x_4 + 5x_5 &= 0 \\
2x_1 + 4x_2 - x_3 - 3x_4 + 2x_5 &= 0 \\
3x_1 + 6x_2 - 2x_3 - 4x_4 + x_5 &= 0.
\end{aligned}
\tag{14}
$$

Solution We readily reduce the coefficient matrix $\mathbf{A}$ to the echelon form

$$
\mathbf{E} = \begin{bmatrix} 1 & 2 & 0 & -2 & 3 \\ 0 & 0 & 1 & -1 & 4 \\ 0 & 0 & 0 & 0 & 0 \end{bmatrix}.
$$

The leading entries are in the first and third columns, so the leading variables are x_1 and x_3; the free variables are x_2, x_4, and x_5. To avoid subscripts, we use r, s, and t rather than t_1, t_2, and t_3 to denote the three parameters. Thus we set

$$
x_2 = r, \quad x_4 = s, \quad \text{and} \quad x_5 = t.
\tag{15}
$$

Then back substitution in the reduced system

$$
\begin{aligned}
x_1 + 2x_2 \phantom{{}- 2x_4} - 2x_4 + 3x_5 &= 0 \\
x_3 - x_4 + 4x_5 &= 0
\end{aligned}
$$

yields

$$
x_1 = -2r + 2s - 3t \quad \text{and} \quad x_3 = s - 4t.
\tag{16}
$$

The equations in (15) and (16) give the typical solution vector $(x_1, x_2, x_3, x_4, x_5)$ in terms of the parameters r, s, and t.

With $r = 1$ and $s = t = 0$,

$$
\text{we obtain} \quad \mathbf{v}_1 = (-2, 1, 0, 0, 0).
$$

With $s = 1$ and $r = t = 0$,

we obtain $\quad \mathbf{v}_2 = (2, 0, 1, 1, 0)$.

With $t = 1$ and $r = s = 0$,

we obtain $\quad \mathbf{v}_3 = (-3, 0, -4, 0, 1)$.

Thus the solution space of the system in (14) is a 3-dimensional subspace of $\mathbf{R}^5$ with basis $\{\mathbf{v}_1, \mathbf{v}_2, \mathbf{v}_3\}$. ■

4.4 Problems

In Problems 1–8, determine whether or not the given vectors in $\mathbf{R}^n$ form a basis for $\mathbf{R}^n$.

1. $\mathbf{v}_1 = (4, 7), \ \mathbf{v}_2 = (5, 6)$

2. $\mathbf{v}_1 = (3, -1, 2), \ \mathbf{v}_2 = (6, -2, 4), \ \mathbf{v}_3 = (5, 3, -1)$

3. $\mathbf{v}_1 = (1, 7, -3), \ \mathbf{v}_2 = (2, 1, 4), \ \mathbf{v}_3 = (6, 5, 1), \ \mathbf{v}_4 = (0, 7, 13)$

4. $\mathbf{v}_1 = (3, -7, 5, 2), \ \mathbf{v}_2 = (1, -1, 3, 4), \ \mathbf{v}_3 = (7, 11, 3, 13)$

5. $\mathbf{v}_1 = (0, 7, -3), \ \mathbf{v}_2 = (0, 5, 4), \ \mathbf{v}_3 = (0, 5, 10)$

6. $\mathbf{v}_1 = (0, 0, 1), \ \mathbf{v}_2 = (0, 1, 2), \ \mathbf{v}_3 = (1, 2, 3)$

7. $\mathbf{v}_1 = (0, 0, 1), \ \mathbf{v}_2 = (7, 4, 11), \ \mathbf{v}_3 = (5, 3, 13)$

8. $\mathbf{v}_1 = (2, 0, 0, 0), \ \mathbf{v}_2 = (0, 3, 0, 0), \ \mathbf{v}_3 = (0, 0, 7, 6), \ \mathbf{v}_4 = (0, 0, 4, 5)$

In Problems 9–11, find a basis for the indicated subspace of $\mathbf{R}^3$.

9. The plane with equation $x - 2y + 5z = 0$.

10. The plane with equation $y = z$.

11. The line of intersection of the planes described in Problems 9 and 10.

In Problems 12–14, find a basis for the indicated subspace of $\mathbf{R}^4$.

12. The set of all vectors of the form (a, b, c, d) for which $a = b + c + d$.

13. The set of all vectors of the form (a, b, c, d) such that $a = 3c$ and $b = 4d$.

14. The set of all vectors of the form (a, b, c, d) for which $a + 2b = c + 3d = 0$.

In Problems 15–26, find a basis for the solution space of the given homogeneous linear system.

15. $\begin{aligned} x_1 - 2x_2 + 3x_3 &= 0 \\ 2x_1 - 3x_2 - \ x_3 &= 0 \end{aligned}$

16. $\begin{aligned} x_1 + 3x_2 + 4x_3 &= 0 \\ 3x_1 + 8x_2 + 7x_3 &= 0 \end{aligned}$

17. $\begin{aligned} x_1 - 3x_2 + 2x_3 - 4x_4 &= 0 \\ 2x_1 - 5x_2 + 7x_3 - 3x_4 &= 0 \end{aligned}$

18. $\begin{aligned} x_1 + 3x_2 + 4x_3 + 5x_4 &= 0 \\ 2x_1 + 6x_2 + 9x_3 + 5x_4 &= 0 \end{aligned}$

19. $\begin{aligned} x_1 - 3x_2 - 9x_3 - \ 5x_4 &= 0 \\ 2x_1 + \ x_2 - 4x_3 + 11x_4 &= 0 \\ x_1 + 3x_2 + 3x_3 + 13x_4 &= 0 \end{aligned}$

20. $\begin{aligned} x_1 - 3x_2 - 10x_3 + 5x_4 &= 0 \\ x_1 + 4x_2 + 11x_3 - 2x_4 &= 0 \\ x_1 + 3x_2 + \ 8x_3 - \ x_4 &= 0 \end{aligned}$

21. $\begin{aligned} x_1 - 4x_2 - 3x_3 - \ 7x_4 &= 0 \\ 2x_1 - \ x_2 + \ x_3 + \ 7x_4 &= 0 \\ x_1 + 2x_2 + 3x_3 + 11x_4 &= 0 \end{aligned}$

22. $\begin{aligned} x_1 - 2x_2 - 3x_3 - 16x_4 &= 0 \\ 2x_1 - 4x_2 + \ x_3 + 17x_4 &= 0 \\ x_1 - 2x_2 + 3x_3 + 26x_4 &= 0 \end{aligned}$

23. $\begin{aligned} x_1 + 5x_2 + 13x_3 + 14x_4 &= 0 \\ 2x_1 + 5x_2 + 11x_3 + 12x_4 &= 0 \\ 2x_1 + 7x_2 + 17x_3 + 19x_4 &= 0 \end{aligned}$

24. $\begin{aligned} x_1 + 3x_2 - \ 4x_3 - \ 8x_4 + \ 6x_5 &= 0 \\ x_1 \qquad\quad + \ 2x_3 + \ \ x_4 + \ 3x_5 &= 0 \\ 2x_1 + 7x_2 - 10x_3 - 19x_4 + 13x_5 &= 0 \end{aligned}$

25. $\begin{aligned} x_1 + 2x_2 + 7x_3 - \ 9x_4 + 31x_5 &= 0 \\ 2x_1 + 4x_2 + 7x_3 - 11x_4 + 34x_5 &= 0 \\ 3x_1 + 6x_2 + 5x_3 - 11x_4 + 29x_5 &= 0 \end{aligned}$

26. $\begin{aligned} 3x_1 + \ x_2 - 3x_3 + 11x_4 + 10x_5 &= 0 \\ 5x_1 + 8x_2 + 2x_3 - \ 2x_4 + \ 7x_5 &= 0 \\ 2x_1 + 5x_2 \qquad\quad - \ \ x_4 + 14x_5 &= 0 \end{aligned}$

27. Suppose that S is a set of n linearly independent vectors in the n-dimensional vector space V. Prove that S is a basis for V.

28. Suppose that S is a set of n vectors that span the n-dimensional vector space V. Prove that S is a basis for V.

29. Let $\{\mathbf{v}_1, \mathbf{v}_2, \ldots, \mathbf{v}_k\}$ be a basis for the proper subspace W of the vector space V, and suppose that the vector $\mathbf{v}$ of V is not in W. Show that the vectors $\mathbf{v}_1, \mathbf{v}_2, \ldots, \mathbf{v}_k, \mathbf{v}$ are linearly independent.

30. Use the result of Problem 29 to prove that every linearly independent set of vectors in a finite-dimensional vector space V is contained in a basis for V.

31. Suppose that the vectors $\mathbf{v}_1, \mathbf{v}_2, \ldots, \mathbf{v}_k, \mathbf{v}_{k+1}$ span the vector space V and that $\mathbf{v}_{k+1}$ is a linear combination of $\mathbf{v}_1, \mathbf{v}_2, \ldots, \mathbf{v}_k$. Show that the vectors $\mathbf{v}_1, \mathbf{v}_2, \ldots, \mathbf{v}_k$ span V.

32. Use the result of Problem 31 to prove that every spanning set for a finite-dimensional vector space V contains a basis for V.

33. Let S be a linearly independent set of vectors in the finite-dimensional vector space V. Then S is called a **maximal linearly independent set** provided that if any other vector is adjoined to S, then the resulting set is linearly dependent. Prove that every maximal linearly independent set in V is a basis for V.

34. Let S be a finite set of vectors that span the vector space V. Then S is called a **minimal spanning set** provided that no proper subset of S spans V. Prove that every

minimal spanning set in V is a basis for V.

35. Let S be a finite set of vectors that span the vector space V. Then S is called a **uniquely spanning set** provided that each vector in V can be expressed in one and only one way as a linear combination of the vectors in S. Prove that every uniquely spanning set in V is a basis for V.

36. Apply the definition of linear independence to show directly that the column vectors of the matrix in (12) are linearly independent.

4.5 Row and Column Spaces

In numerous examples we have observed the phenomenon of "disappearing equations" that sometimes occurs when we solve a linear system using the method of Gaussian elimination. The appearance in this process of a trivial equation $0 = 0$ means that one of the original equations was redundant. For instance, in the system

$$x - 2y + 2z = 0$$
$$x + 4y + 3z = 0$$
$$2x + 2y + 5z = 0,$$

the third equation provides no additional information about a solution (x, y, z) because it is merely the sum of the first two equations.

Given a homogeneous linear system, it is natural to ask how many of the equations are "irredundant," and which ones they are. We will see that an answer to this question leads to a natural and simple relation between the number of irredundant equations, the number of unknowns, and the number of linearly independent solutions.

Row Space and Row Rank

The individual equations of the homogeneous linear system $\mathbf{Ax} = \mathbf{0}$ correspond to the rows of the coefficient matrix $\mathbf{A}$. Given an $m \times n$ matrix $\mathbf{A} = [a_{ij}]$, the **row vectors** of $\mathbf{A}$ are the m vectors

$$
\begin{aligned}
\mathbf{r}_1 &= (a_{11}, a_{12}, \ldots, a_{1n}) \\
\mathbf{r}_2 &= (a_{21}, a_{22}, \ldots, a_{2n}) \\
&\vdots \\
\mathbf{r}_m &= (a_{m1}, a_{m2}, \ldots, a_{mn})
\end{aligned}
\tag{1}
$$

in $\mathbf{R}^n$. The subspace of $\mathbf{R}^n$ spanned by the m row vectors $\mathbf{r}_1, \mathbf{r}_2, \ldots, \mathbf{r}_m$ is called the **row space** Row($\mathbf{A}$) of the matrix $\mathbf{A}$. The *dimension* of the row space Row($\mathbf{A}$) is called the **row rank** of the matrix $\mathbf{A}$.

Example 1 Consider the 4×5 echelon matrix

$$
\mathbf{A} = \begin{bmatrix}
1 & -3 & 2 & 5 & 3 \\
0 & 0 & 1 & -4 & 2 \\
0 & 0 & 0 & 1 & 7 \\
0 & 0 & 0 & 0 & 0
\end{bmatrix}.
$$

Its row vectors are $\mathbf{r}_1 = (1, -3, 2, 5, 3)$, $\mathbf{r}_2 = (0, 0, 1, -4, 2)$, $\mathbf{r}_3 = (0, 0, 0, 1, 7)$, and $\mathbf{r}_4 = (0, 0, 0, 0, 0)$. We want to show that the row vectors that are not zero are linearly independent. To this end we calculate the linear combination

$$c_1\mathbf{r}_1 + c_2\mathbf{r}_2 + c_3\mathbf{r}_3 = (c_1, -3c_1, 2c_1 + c_2, 5c_1 - 4c_2 + c_3, 3c_1 + 2c_2 + 7c_3).$$

If $c_1\mathbf{r}_1 + c_2\mathbf{r}_2 + c_3\mathbf{r}_3 = \mathbf{0}$, then the first component gives $c_1 = 0$, next the third component $2c_1 + c_2 = 0$ yields $c_2 = 0$, and finally the fourth component $5c_1 - 4c_2 + c_3 = 0$ yields $c_3 = 0$. Thus the vectors $\mathbf{r}_1$, $\mathbf{r}_2$, and $\mathbf{r}_3$ are linearly independent and therefore form a basis for the row space Row($\mathbf{A}$). Hence Row($\mathbf{A}$) is a 3-dimensional subspace of $\mathbf{R}^5$, and the row rank of $\mathbf{A}$ is 3. ∎

It should be apparent that the method used in Example 1 applies to any *echelon* matrix $\mathbf{E} = [e_{ij}]$. If the first column of $\mathbf{E}$ is not all zero, then its *nonzero* row vectors $\mathbf{r}_1$, $\mathbf{r}_2$, ..., $\mathbf{r}_k$ have the forms

$$\mathbf{r}_1 = (e_{11}, \ldots, e_{1p}, \ldots, e_{1q}, \ldots),$$
$$\mathbf{r}_2 = (0, \ldots, 0, e_{2p}, \ldots, e_{2q}, \ldots),$$
$$\mathbf{r}_3 = (0, \ldots, \quad 0, \ldots, \quad e_{3q}, \ldots),$$

and so forth (where e_{11}, e_{2p}, and e_{3q} denote nonzero leading entries). Then the equation

$$c_1\mathbf{r}_1 + c_2\mathbf{r}_2 + \cdots + c_k\mathbf{r}_k = \mathbf{0}$$

implies that

$$c_1 e_{11} = 0, \quad c_1 e_{1p} + c_2 e_{2p} = 0, \quad c_1 e_{1q} + c_2 e_{2q} + c_3 e_{3q} = 0,$$

and so forth. We can therefore conclude in turn that $c_1 = 0$, $c_2 = 0$, ..., $c_k = 0$. Thus the row vectors $\mathbf{r}_1, \mathbf{r}_2, \ldots, \mathbf{r}_k$ are linearly independent, and hence we have the following result.

THEOREM 1: Row Space of an Echelon Matrix

The nonzero row vectors of an echelon matrix are linearly independent and therefore form a basis for its row space. ▲

We investigate the row space of an arbitrary matrix $\mathbf{A}$ by reducing $\mathbf{A}$ to an echelon matrix $\mathbf{E}$. The following theorem then guarantees that $\mathbf{A}$ and $\mathbf{E}$ have the same row space. Recall that two matrices are (row) *equivalent* provided that each can be transformed to the other by elementary row operations.

THEOREM 2: Row Spaces of Equivalent Matrices

If two matrices $\mathbf{A}$ and $\mathbf{B}$ are equivalent, then they have the same row space.

Proof: Because $\mathbf{A}$ can be transformed to $\mathbf{B}$ by elementary row operations, it follows that each row vector of $\mathbf{B}$ is a linear combination of the row vectors of $\mathbf{A}$; the fact that this is obviously true if $\mathbf{A}$ is transformed into $\mathbf{B}$ by a single row operation implies its truth for any (finite) number of row operations. But then each vector in Row($\mathbf{B}$) is a linear combination of linear combinations of row vectors of $\mathbf{A}$ and hence is a linear combination of row vectors of $\mathbf{A}$, which means that it is also a vector in Row($\mathbf{A}$). Therefore the fact that $\mathbf{A}$ can be transformed to $\mathbf{B}$ implies that Row($\mathbf{A}$) contains Row($\mathbf{B}$).

But elementary row operations are "reversible," so **B** can also be transformed to **A** by row operations. Hence the same argument shows that Row(**B**) contains Row(**A**). Finally, the fact that each of the two row spaces Row(**A**) and Row(**B**) contains the other means that they are, indeed, identical. ▲

Theorems 1 and 2 together provide a routine procedure for finding a basis for the row space of a given matrix, thereby determining its row rank.

ALGORITHM 1: A Basis for the Row space

To find a basis for the row space of a matrix **A**, use elementary row operations to reduce **A** to an echelon matrix **E**. Then the nonzero row vectors of **E** form a basis for Row(**A**). ▲

Example 2 To find a basis for the row space of the matrix

$$\mathbf{A} = \begin{bmatrix} 1 & 2 & 1 & 3 & 2 \\ 3 & 4 & 9 & 0 & 7 \\ 2 & 3 & 5 & 1 & 8 \\ 2 & 2 & 8 & -3 & 5 \end{bmatrix}, \tag{2}$$

we reduce it to its echelon form

$$\mathbf{E} = \begin{bmatrix} 1 & 2 & 1 & 3 & 2 \\ 0 & 1 & -3 & 5 & -4 \\ 0 & 0 & 0 & 1 & -7 \\ 0 & 0 & 0 & 0 & 0 \end{bmatrix}. \tag{3}$$

Then the nonzero row vectors $\mathbf{v}_1 = (1, 2, 1, 3, 2)$, $\mathbf{v}_2 = (0, 1, -3, 5, -4)$, and $\mathbf{v}_3 = (0, 0, 0, 1, -7)$ form a basis for the row space of **A**. Thus Row(**A**) is a 3-dimensional subspace of $\mathbf{R}^5$ and the row rank of **A** is 3. ■

In Example 2, note that Algorithm 1 does *not* tell us that the first three row vectors of the matrix **A** itself are linearly independent. We know that *some* three row vectors of **A** span Row(**A**), but without further investigation we do not know *which* three.

Column Space and Column Rank

Now we turn our attention from row vectors to column vectors. Given an $m \times n$ matrix $\mathbf{A} = [a_{ij}]$, the **column vectors** of **A** are the n vectors

$$\mathbf{c}_1 = \begin{bmatrix} a_{11} \\ a_{21} \\ \vdots \\ a_{m1} \end{bmatrix}, \quad \mathbf{c}_2 = \begin{bmatrix} a_{12} \\ a_{22} \\ \vdots \\ a_{m2} \end{bmatrix}, \dots, \mathbf{c}_n = \begin{bmatrix} a_{1n} \\ a_{2n} \\ \vdots \\ a_{mn} \end{bmatrix} \tag{4}$$

in $\mathbf{R}^m$. The subspace of $\mathbf{R}^m$ spanned by the n column vectors $\mathbf{c}_1, \mathbf{c}_2, \dots, \mathbf{c}_n$ is called the **column space** Col(**A**) of the matrix **A**. The *dimension* of the space Col(**A**) is called the **column rank** of the matrix **A**.

Example 3   Consider the 4×5 echelon matrix

$$\mathbf{E} = \begin{bmatrix} 1 & 2 & 1 & 3 & 2 \\ 0 & 1 & -3 & 5 & -4 \\ 0 & 0 & 0 & 1 & -7 \\ 0 & 0 & 0 & 0 & 0 \end{bmatrix}. \tag{5}$$

Its five column vectors $\mathbf{c}_1, \mathbf{c}_2, \mathbf{c}_3, \mathbf{c}_4, \mathbf{c}_5$ all lie in the subspace $\mathbf{R}^3 = \{(x_1, x_2, x_3, 0)\}$ of $\mathbf{R}^4$. The column vectors that contain the leading entries in the nonzero rows of $\mathbf{E}$ are

$$\mathbf{c}_1 = \begin{bmatrix} 1 \\ 0 \\ 0 \\ 0 \end{bmatrix}, \quad \mathbf{c}_2 = \begin{bmatrix} 2 \\ 1 \\ 0 \\ 0 \end{bmatrix}, \quad \text{and} \quad \mathbf{c}_4 = \begin{bmatrix} 3 \\ 5 \\ 1 \\ 0 \end{bmatrix}. \tag{6}$$

Note that

$$a_1\mathbf{c}_1 + a_2\mathbf{c}_2 + a_4\mathbf{c}_4 = (a_1 + 2a_2 + 3a_4, a_2 + 5a_4, a_4, 0).$$

Hence $a_1\mathbf{c}_1 + a_2\mathbf{c}_2 + a_4\mathbf{c}_4 = \mathbf{0}$ readily implies that $a_1 = a_2 = a_4 = 0$. Thus the vectors $\mathbf{c}_1$, $\mathbf{c}_2$, and $\mathbf{c}_4$ are linearly independent and therefore form a basis for $\mathbf{R}^3 = \{(x_1, x_2, x_3, 0)\}$. Hence Col($\mathbf{E}$) is a 3-dimensional subspace of $\mathbf{R}^4$ and the column rank of $\mathbf{E}$ is 3.   ∎

To find the column rank of an arbitrary $m \times n$ matrix $\mathbf{A}$ we begin in the same way as when finding the row rank. First we use elementary row operations to reduce $\mathbf{A}$ to an echelon matrix $\mathbf{E}$. But the relationship between the column spaces of $\mathbf{A}$ and $\mathbf{E}$ is far more subtle than between their row spaces; the reason is that elementary row operations generally do *not* preserve column spaces.

To analyze this situation, let us denote by $\mathbf{c}_1, \mathbf{c}_2, \ldots, \mathbf{c}_n$ the column vectors of the original matrix $\mathbf{A}$, and by $\mathbf{c}_1^*, \mathbf{c}_2^*, \ldots, \mathbf{c}_n^*$ the column vectors of the echelon matrix to which we have reduced $\mathbf{A}$. Suppose that $\mathbf{E}$ has k nonzero rows. Then each column vector of $\mathbf{E}$ has the form $\mathbf{c}_j^* = (*, \ldots, *, 0, \ldots, 0)$ with $m - k$ final zeros. Hence the column space Col($\mathbf{E}$) is contained in $\mathbf{R}^k$ (considered as the subspace of $\mathbf{R}^m$ for which $x_{k+1} = \cdots = x_m = 0$).

We are particularly interested in those columns of $\mathbf{E}$ that contain the nonzero leading entries in the nonzero rows of $\mathbf{E}$. These k columns are called the **pivot columns** of $\mathbf{E}$. The echelon matrix $\mathbf{E}$ has the general form

$$\mathbf{E} = \begin{bmatrix} d_1 & * & * & * & \cdots & * & * & * \\ 0 & d_2 & * & * & \cdots & * & * & * \\ 0 & 0 & 0 & d_3 & \cdots & * & * & * \\ \vdots & \vdots & \vdots & \vdots & \ddots & \vdots & \vdots & \vdots \\ 0 & 0 & 0 & 0 & \cdots & d_k & * & * \\ 0 & 0 & 0 & 0 & \cdots & 0 & 0 & 0 \\ \vdots & \vdots & \vdots & \vdots & \ddots & \vdots & \vdots & \vdots \\ 0 & 0 & 0 & 0 & \cdots & 0 & 0 & 0 \end{bmatrix}, \tag{7}$$

where $d_1, d_2, \ldots, d_k$ are the nonzero leading entries. Hence the k pivot column vectors of $\mathbf{E}$ look like

$$\begin{bmatrix} d_1 \\ 0 \\ 0 \\ \vdots \\ 0 \\ 0 \\ \vdots \\ 0 \end{bmatrix}, \begin{bmatrix} * \\ d_2 \\ 0 \\ \vdots \\ 0 \\ 0 \\ \vdots \\ 0 \end{bmatrix}, \begin{bmatrix} * \\ * \\ d_3 \\ \vdots \\ 0 \\ 0 \\ \vdots \\ 0 \end{bmatrix}, \ldots, \begin{bmatrix} * \\ * \\ * \\ \vdots \\ d_k \\ 0 \\ \vdots \\ 0 \end{bmatrix}. \tag{8}$$

Because of the upper triangular pattern visible here, it should be apparent that the argument in Example 3 can be used to show that these k pivot vectors form a basis for Col($\mathbf{E}$). Thus *the column rank of the echelon matrix* $\mathbf{E}$ *is equal to the number k of its nonzero rows, and hence is equal to its row rank.*

Now comes the subtle part. We want to show that the column rank of the original matrix $\mathbf{A}$ also is k. Note first that the homogeneous linear systems

$$\mathbf{Ax} = \mathbf{0} \quad \text{and} \quad \mathbf{Ex} = \mathbf{0} \tag{9}$$

have the same solution set because the matrices $\mathbf{A}$ and $\mathbf{E}$ are equivalent. If $\mathbf{x} = (x_1, x_2, \ldots, x_n)$, then the left-hand sides in (9) are linear combinations of column vectors:

$$\begin{aligned} \mathbf{Ax} &= x_1\mathbf{c}_1 + x_2\mathbf{c}_2 + \cdots + x_n\mathbf{c}_n, \\ \mathbf{Ex} &= x_1\mathbf{c}_1^* + x_2\mathbf{c}_2^* + \cdots + x_n\mathbf{c}_n^*. \end{aligned} \tag{10}$$

Because $\mathbf{x}$ satisfies *either* both *or* neither of the systems in (9), it follows that

$$x_1\mathbf{c}_1 + x_2\mathbf{c}_2 + \cdots + x_n\mathbf{c}_n = \mathbf{0}$$

if and only if

$$x_1\mathbf{c}_1^* + x_2\mathbf{c}_2^* + \cdots + x_n\mathbf{c}_n^* = \mathbf{0}.$$

Hence every linear dependence between column vectors of $\mathbf{E}$ is mirrored in a linear dependence *with the same coefficients* between the corresponding column vectors of $\mathbf{A}$. In particular, because the k pivot column vectors of $\mathbf{E}$ are linearly independent, it follows that the corresponding k column vectors of $\mathbf{A}$ are linearly independent. And because the k pivot column vectors of $\mathbf{E}$ span Col($\mathbf{E}$), it follows that the corresponding k column vectors of $\mathbf{A}$ span Col($\mathbf{A}$). Thus the latter k vectors form a basis for the column space of $\mathbf{A}$, and the column rank of $\mathbf{A}$ is k. Consequently we have established the following method for finding a basis for the column space of a given matrix.

ALGORITHM 2: A Basis for the Column Space

To find a basis for the column space of a matrix $\mathbf{A}$, use elementary row operations to reduce $\mathbf{A}$ to an echelon matrix $\mathbf{E}$. Then the column vectors of $\mathbf{A}$ that correspond to the pivot columns of $\mathbf{E}$ form a basis for Col($\mathbf{A}$). ▲

Example 4

Consider again the 4×5 matrix

$$\mathbf{A} = \begin{bmatrix} 1 & 2 & 1 & 3 & 2 \\ 3 & 4 & 9 & 0 & 7 \\ 2 & 3 & 5 & 1 & 8 \\ 2 & 2 & 8 & -3 & 5 \end{bmatrix}$$

of Example 2, in which we reduced it to the echelon matrix

$$\mathbf{E} = \begin{bmatrix} 1 & 2 & 1 & 3 & 2 \\ 0 & 1 & -3 & 5 & -4 \\ 0 & 0 & 0 & 1 & -7 \\ 0 & 0 & 0 & 0 & 0 \end{bmatrix}.$$

The pivot columns of $\mathbf{E}$ are its first, second, and fourth columns, so the 3-dimensional column space of $\mathbf{A}$ has a basis consisting of its first, second, and fourth column vectors $\mathbf{c}_1 = (1, 3, 2, 2)$, $\mathbf{c}_2 = (2, 4, 3, 2)$, and $\mathbf{c}_4 = (3, 0, 1, -3)$. ∎

The fact that Algorithm 2 provides a basis for Col($\mathbf{A}$) consisting of column vectors of $\mathbf{A}$ itself (rather than the echelon matrix $\mathbf{E}$) enables us to apply it to the problem of extracting a maximal linearly independent subset from a given set of vectors in $\mathbf{R}^n$.

Example 5

Find a subset of the vectors $\mathbf{v}_1 = (1, -1, 2, 2)$, $\mathbf{v}_2 = (-3, 4, 1, -2)$, $\mathbf{v}_3 = (0, 1, 7, 4)$, and $\mathbf{v}_4 = (-5, 7, 4, -2)$ that forms a basis for the subspace W of $\mathbf{R}^4$ spanned by these four vectors.

Solution

It is not clear at the outset whether W is 2-dimensional, 3-dimensional, or 4-dimen-sional. To apply Algorithm 2, we arrange the given vectors as the *column* vectors of the matrix

$$\mathbf{A} = \begin{bmatrix} 1 & -3 & 0 & -5 \\ -1 & 4 & 1 & 7 \\ 2 & 1 & 7 & 4 \\ 2 & -2 & 4 & -2 \end{bmatrix},$$

which reduces readily to the echelon matrix

$$\mathbf{E} = \begin{bmatrix} 1 & -3 & 0 & -5 \\ 0 & 1 & 1 & 2 \\ 0 & 0 & 0 & 0 \\ 0 & 0 & 0 & 0 \end{bmatrix}.$$

The pivot columns of $\mathbf{E}$ are its first two columns, so the first two column vectors $\mathbf{v}_1 = (1, -1, 2, 2)$ and $\mathbf{v}_2 = (-3, 4, 1, -2)$ of $\mathbf{A}$ form a basis for the column space W. In particular, we see that W is 2-dimensional. ∎

Rank and Dimension

We have seen that the row rank *and* the column rank of an echelon matrix $\mathbf{E}$ *both* equal the number of rows of $\mathbf{E}$ that are not all zeros. But if $\mathbf{A}$ is any matrix that reduces by row operations to the echelon matrix $\mathbf{E}$, then—according to Algorithm 1—the row rank of $\mathbf{A}$ is equal to the row rank of $\mathbf{E}$, while Algorithm 2 implies that the column rank of $\mathbf{A}$ is equal to the column rank of $\mathbf{E}$. We therefore have the following fundamental result.

THEOREM 3: Equality of Row Rank and Column Rank

The row rank and column rank of any matrix are equal. ▲

For instance, if A is a 5×7 matrix and Row(A) is a 3-dimensional subspace of $\mathbf{R}^7$, then Theorem 3 tells us that Col(A) must be a 3-dimensional subspace of $\mathbf{R}^5$.

To see what an extraordinary theorem this is, think of a random 11×17 matrix A, possibly printed by a computer that uses a random number generator to produce independently the 187 entries in A. If it turns out that precisely 9 (no more) of the 11 row vectors of A are linearly independent, then Theorem 3 implies that precisely 9 (no more) of the 17 column vectors of A are linearly independent.

The common value of the row rank and the column rank of the matrix A is simply called the **rank** of A and is denoted by rank(A). The rank of A provides a meaning for the number of irredundant equations in the homogeneous linear system

$$Ax = 0. \tag{11}$$

Indeed, the individual scalar equations in (11) correspond to the column vectors of the transpose matrix A^T, whose rank r equals that of A (Why?). Then the r columns vectors of A^T that form a basis for Col(A^T) correspond to the r equations in (11) that are irredundant; the remaining equations are linear combinations of these irredundant ones and hence are redundant.

The solution space of the homogeneous system $Ax = 0$ is sometimes called the **null space** of A, denoted by Null(A). Note that if A is an $m \times n$ matrix, then Null(A) and Row(A) are subspaces of $\mathbf{R}^n$, whereas Col(A) is a subspace of $\mathbf{R}^m$. If $r = \text{rank}(A)$, then the r column vectors of A that form a basis for Col(A) correspond to the r leading variables in a solution of $Ax = 0$ by Gaussian elimination. Moreover, we know from the algorithm in Section 4.4 that the dimension of the solution space Null(A) is equal to the number $n - r$ of free variables. We therefore obtain the important identity

$$\text{rank}(A) + \dim \text{Null}(A) = n \tag{12}$$

for any $m \times n$ matrix A. For instance, if A is the matrix of Example 4 with rank 3 and $n = 5$, then the dimension of the null space of A is $5 - 3 = 2$.

For another typical application of Equation (12), consider a homogeneous system of five linear equations in seven unknowns. If the 5×7 coefficient matrix of the system has rank 3, so only 3 of the 5 equations are irredundant, then (because $n = 7$) the system has $7 - 3 = 4$ linearly independent solutions.

If A is an $m \times n$ matrix with rank m, then Equation (12) implies that the system $Ax = 0$ has $n - m$ linearly independent solutions. Thus rank(A) $= m$ is the condition under which the "conventional wisdom" about the relation between the numbers of equations, unknowns, and solutions is valid.

Nonhomogeneous Linear Systems

It follows immediately from Equation (10) and the definition of Col(A) that *the nonhomogeneous linear system $Ax = b$ is consistent if and only if the vector b is in the column space of A.* In the problems below we outline some of the applications to nonhomogeneous systems of the results in this section.

If we can find a single particular solution x_0 of the nonhomogeneous system

$$Ax = b, \tag{13}$$

then the determination of its solution set reduces to solving the associated homogeneous system

$$\mathbf{A}\mathbf{x} = \mathbf{0}. \qquad (14)$$

For then Problem 29 in Section 4.2 implies that the solution set of (13) is the set of all vectors $\mathbf{x}$ of the form

➤
$$\mathbf{x} = \mathbf{x}_0 + \mathbf{x}_h$$

where $\mathbf{x}_h$ is a solution of (14). Hence if $\mathbf{x}_1, \mathbf{x}_2, \ldots, \mathbf{x}_r$ is a basis for the solution space of (14), then the solution set of the nonhomogeneous system is the set of all vectors of the form

$$\mathbf{x} = \mathbf{x}_0 + c_1\mathbf{x}_1 + c_2\mathbf{x}_2 + \cdots + c_r\mathbf{x}_r.$$

We may describe this solution set as the *translate* by the vector $\mathbf{x}_0$ of the r-dimensional solution space of the corresponding homogeneous system.

4.5 Problems

In Problems 1–12, find both a basis for the row space and abasis for the column space of the given matrix $\mathbf{A}$.

1.
$$\begin{bmatrix} 1 & 2 & 3 \\ 1 & 5 & -9 \\ 2 & 5 & 2 \end{bmatrix}$$

2.
$$\begin{bmatrix} 5 & 2 & 4 \\ 2 & 1 & 1 \\ 4 & 1 & 5 \end{bmatrix}$$

3.
$$\begin{bmatrix} 1 & -4 & -3 & -7 \\ 2 & -1 & 1 & 7 \\ 1 & 2 & 3 & 11 \end{bmatrix}$$

4.
$$\begin{bmatrix} 1 & -3 & -9 & -5 \\ 2 & 1 & 4 & 11 \\ 1 & 3 & 3 & 13 \end{bmatrix}$$

5.
$$\begin{bmatrix} 1 & 1 & 1 & 1 \\ 3 & 1 & -3 & 4 \\ 2 & 5 & 11 & 12 \end{bmatrix}$$

6.
$$\begin{bmatrix} 1 & 4 & 9 & 2 \\ 2 & 2 & 6 & -3 \\ 2 & 7 & 16 & 3 \end{bmatrix}$$

7.
$$\begin{bmatrix} 1 & 1 & -1 & 7 \\ 1 & 4 & 5 & 16 \\ 1 & 3 & 3 & 13 \\ 2 & 5 & 4 & 23 \end{bmatrix}$$

8.
$$\begin{bmatrix} 1 & -2 & -3 & -5 \\ 1 & 4 & 9 & 2 \\ 1 & 3 & 7 & 1 \\ 2 & 2 & 6 & -3 \end{bmatrix}$$

9.
$$\begin{bmatrix} 1 & 3 & 3 & 9 \\ 2 & 7 & 4 & 8 \\ 2 & 7 & 5 & 12 \\ 2 & 8 & 3 & 2 \end{bmatrix}$$

10.
$$\begin{bmatrix} 1 & 2 & 3 & 1 & 3 \\ 1 & 3 & 4 & 3 & 6 \\ 2 & 2 & 4 & 3 & 5 \\ 2 & 1 & 3 & 2 & 3 \end{bmatrix}$$

11.
$$\begin{bmatrix} 1 & 1 & 3 & 3 & 1 \\ 2 & 3 & 7 & 8 & 2 \\ 2 & 3 & 7 & 8 & 3 \\ 3 & 1 & 7 & 5 & 4 \end{bmatrix}$$

12.
$$\begin{bmatrix} 1 & 1 & 3 & 3 & 0 \\ -1 & 0 & -2 & -1 & 1 \\ 2 & 3 & 7 & 8 & 1 \\ -2 & 4 & 0 & 6 & 7 \end{bmatrix}$$

In Problems 13–16, a set S of vectors in $\mathbf{R}^4$ is given. Find a subset of S that forms a basis for the subspace of $\mathbf{R}^4$ spanned by S.

13. $\mathbf{v}_1 = (1, 3, -2, 4)$, $\mathbf{v}_2 = (2, -1, 3, 2)$, $\mathbf{v}_3 = (5, 1, 4, 8)$

14. $\mathbf{v}_1 = (1, -1, 2, 3)$, $\mathbf{v}_2 = (2, 3, 4, 1)$, $\mathbf{v}_3 = (1, 1, 2, 1)$, $\mathbf{v}_4 = (4, 1, 8, 7)$

15. $\mathbf{v}_1 = (3, 2, 2, 2)$, $\mathbf{v}_2 = (2, 1, 2, 1)$, $\mathbf{v}_3 = (4, 3, 2, 3)$, $\mathbf{v}_4 = (1, 2, 3, 4)$

16. $\mathbf{v}_1 = (5, 4, 2, 2)$, $\mathbf{v}_2 = (3, 1, 2, 3)$, $\mathbf{v}_3 = (7, 7, 2, 1)$, $\mathbf{v}_4 = (1, -1, 2, 4)$, $\mathbf{v}_5 = (5, 4, 6, 7)$

Let $S = \{\mathbf{v}_1, \mathbf{v}_2, \ldots, \mathbf{v}_k\}$ be a basis for the subspace W of $\mathbf{R}^n$. Then a basis T for $\mathbf{R}^n$ that contains S can be found by applying the method of Example 5 to the vectors

$$\mathbf{v}_1, \mathbf{v}_2, \ldots, \mathbf{v}_k, \mathbf{e}_1, \mathbf{e}_2, \ldots, \mathbf{e}_n.$$

Do this in Problems 17–20.

17. Find a basis T for $\mathbf{R}^3$ that contains the vectors $\mathbf{v}_1 = (1, 2, 2)$ and $\mathbf{v}_2 = (2, 3, 3)$.

18. Find a basis T for $\mathbf{R}^3$ that contains the vectors $\mathbf{v}_1 = (3, 2, -1)$ and $\mathbf{v}_2 = (2, -2, 1)$.

19. Find a basis T for $\mathbf{R}^4$ that contains the vectors $\mathbf{v}_1 = (1, 1, 1, 1)$ and $\mathbf{v}_2 = (2, 3, 3, 3)$.

20. Find a basis T for $\mathbf{R}^4$ that contains the vectors $\mathbf{v}_1 = (3, 2, 3, 3)$ and $\mathbf{v}_2 = (5, 4, 5, 5)$.

Given a homogeneous system $\mathbf{A}\mathbf{x} = \mathbf{0}$ of (scalar) linear equations, we say that a subset of these equations is irredundant *provided that the corresponding column vectors of the transpose $\mathbf{A}^T$ are linearly independent. In Problems 21–24, extract from each given system a maximal subset of irredundant equations.*

21.
$$x_1 - 3x_2 + 2x_3 = 0$$
$$2x_1 + 3x_2 + 2x_3 = 0$$
$$4x_1 - 3x_2 + 6x_3 = 0$$

22. $3x_1 + 2x_2 + 2x_3 + 2x_4 = 0$
    $2x_1 + 3x_2 + 3x_3 + 3x_4 = 0$
    $8x_1 + 7x_2 + 7x_3 + 7x_4 = 0$
23. $x_1 + 2x_2 - x_3 + 2x_4 = 0$
    $3x_1 - x_2 + 3x_3 + x_4 = 0$
    $5x_1 + 3x_2 + x_3 + 5x_4 = 0$
    $2x_1 + 5x_3 + 4x_4 = 0$
24. $3x_1 + 2x_2 + 2x_3 = 0$
    $2x_1 + 3x_2 + 3x_3 = 0$
    $7x_1 + 8x_2 + 8x_3 = 0$
    $8x_1 + 7x_2 + 7x_3 = 0$
    $5x_1 + 6x_2 + 5x_3 = 0$
25. Explain why the rank of a matrix A is equal to the rank of its transpose A^T.
26. Explain why the $n \times n$ matrix A is invertible if and only if its rank is n.
27. Let A be a 3×5 matrix whose three row vectors are linearly independent. Prove that, for each b in R^3, the nonhomogeneous system $Ax = b$ has a solution.
28. Let A be a 5×3 matrix that has three linearly independent row vectors. Suppose that b is a vector in R^5 such that the nonhomogeneous system $Ax = b$ has a solution. Prove that this solution is unique.

29. Let A be an $m \times n$ matrix with $m < n$. Given b in R^m, note that any solution of $Ax = b$ expresses b as a linear combination of the column vectors of A. Then prove that no such solution is unique.
30. Given the $m \times n$ matrix A with $m > n$, show that there exists a vector b in R^m such that the system $Ax = b$ has no solution.
31. (Existence of Solutions) Let A be an $m \times n$ matrix. Prove that the system $Ax = b$ is consistent for every b in R^m if and only if the rank of A is equal to m.
32. (Uniqueness of Solutions) Let A be an $m \times n$ matrix and suppose that the system $Ax = b$ is consistent. Prove that its solution is unique if and only if the rank of A is equal to n.
33. Prove that the pivot column vectors in (8) are linearly independent.
34. Let A be a matrix with rank r, and suppose that A can be reduced to echelon form *without row interchanges*. Show that the first r row vectors of A are linearly independent.
35. Deduce from Theorem 3 in Section 4.3 that the rank of the matrix A is the largest integer r such that A has a nonsingular $r \times r$ submatrix.

4.6 Orthogonal Vectors in R^n

In this section we show that the geometrical concepts of *distance* and *angle* in n-dimensional space can be based on the definition of the *dot product* of two vectors in R^n. Recall from elementary calculus that the dot product $u \cdot v$ of two 3-dimensional vectors $u = (u_1, u_2, u_3)$ and $v = (v_1, v_2, v_3)$ is (by definition) the sum

$$u \cdot v = u_1 v_1 + u_2 v_2 + u_3 v_3$$

of the products of corresponding scalar components of the two vectors.

Similarly, the **dot product** $u \cdot v$ of two n-dimensional vectors $u = (u_1, u_2, \ldots, u_n)$ and $v = (v_1, v_2, \ldots, v_n)$ is defined by

$$u \cdot v = u_1 v_1 + u_2 v_2 + \cdots + u_n v_n \tag{1}$$

(with one additional scalar product term for each additional dimension). And just as in R^3, it follows readily from the formula in (1) that if u, v, and w are vectors in R^n and c is a scalar, then

$$u \cdot v = v \cdot u \qquad \text{(symmetry)} \tag{2}$$
$$u \cdot (v + w) = u \cdot v + u \cdot w \qquad \text{(distributivity)} \tag{3}$$
$$(cu) \cdot v = c(u \cdot v) \qquad \text{(homogeneity)} \tag{4}$$
$$u \cdot u \geq 0;$$
$$u \cdot u = 0 \quad \text{if and only if}$$
$$u = 0. \qquad \text{(positivity)} \tag{5}$$

Therefore the dot product in R^n is an example of an *inner product*.

Definition: Inner Product

An **inner product** on a vector space V is a function that associates with each pair of vectors $\mathbf{u}$ and $\mathbf{v}$ in V a scalar $\langle \mathbf{u}, \mathbf{v} \rangle$ such that, if $\mathbf{u}$, $\mathbf{v}$, and $\mathbf{w}$ are vectors and c is a scalar, then

(i) $\langle \mathbf{u}, \mathbf{v} \rangle = \langle \mathbf{v}, \mathbf{u} \rangle$;

(ii) $\langle \mathbf{u}, \mathbf{v} + \mathbf{w} \rangle = \langle \mathbf{u}, \mathbf{v} \rangle + \langle \mathbf{u}, \mathbf{w} \rangle$;

(iii) $\langle c\mathbf{u}, \mathbf{v} \rangle = c\langle \mathbf{u}, \mathbf{v} \rangle$;

(iv) $\langle \mathbf{u}, \mathbf{u} \rangle \geqq 0$; $\langle \mathbf{u}, \mathbf{u} \rangle = 0$ if and only if $\mathbf{u} = \mathbf{0}$.

The dot product on $\mathbf{R}^n$ is sometimes called the **Euclidean inner product**, and with this inner product $\mathbf{R}^n$ is sometimes called **Euclidean n-dimensional space**. We can use any of the notations in

$$\mathbf{u} \cdot \mathbf{v} = \langle \mathbf{u}, \mathbf{v} \rangle = \mathbf{u}^T \mathbf{v}$$

for the dot product (recall in the last expression that $\mathbf{u}^T = (u_1, u_2, \ldots, u_n)$ represents the *column* vector with the indicated entries). Here we will use the notation $\mathbf{u} \cdot \mathbf{v}$.

The **length** $|\mathbf{u}|$ of the vector $\mathbf{u} = (u_1, u_2, \ldots, u_n)$ is defined as follows:

➤
$$|\mathbf{u}| = \sqrt{(\mathbf{u} \cdot \mathbf{u})} = \left(u_1^2 + u_2^2 + \cdots + u_n^2 \right)^{1/2}. \tag{6}$$

Note that the case $n = 2$ is a consequence of the familiar Pythagorean formula in the plane.

Theorem 1 gives one of the most important inequalities in mathematics. Many proofs are known, but none of them seems direct and well motivated.

THEOREM 1: The Cauchy-Schwarz Inequality

If $\mathbf{u}$ and $\mathbf{v}$ are vectors in $\mathbf{R}^n$ then

$$|\mathbf{u} \cdot \mathbf{v}| \leqq |\mathbf{u}||\mathbf{v}|. \tag{7}$$

Proof: If $\mathbf{u} = \mathbf{0}$, then $|\mathbf{u} \cdot \mathbf{v}| = |\mathbf{u}| = 0$, so the inequality is satisfied trivially. If $\mathbf{u} \neq \mathbf{0}$, then we let $a = \mathbf{u} \cdot \mathbf{u}$, $b = 2\mathbf{u} \cdot \mathbf{v}$, and $c = \mathbf{v} \cdot \mathbf{v}$. For any real number x, the positivity property of the dot product then yields

$$0 \leqq (x\mathbf{u} + \mathbf{v}) \cdot (x\mathbf{u} + \mathbf{v})$$
$$= (\mathbf{u} \cdot \mathbf{u})x^2 + 2(\mathbf{u} \cdot \mathbf{v})x + (\mathbf{v} \cdot \mathbf{v}),$$

so that

$$0 \leqq ax^2 + bx + c.$$

Thus the quadratic equation $ax^2 + bx + c = 0$ either has no real roots or has a repeated real root. Hence the quadratic formula

$$x = \frac{-b \pm \sqrt{b^2 - 4ac}}{2a}$$

implies that the discriminant $b^2 - 4ac$ cannot be positive; that is, $b^2 \leqq 4ac$, so

$$4(\mathbf{u} \cdot \mathbf{v})^2 \leqq 4(\mathbf{u} \cdot \mathbf{u})(\mathbf{v} \cdot \mathbf{v}).$$

We get the Cauchy-Schwarz inequality in (7) when we take square roots, remembering that the numbers $|\mathbf{u}| = (\mathbf{u} \cdot \mathbf{u})^{1/2}$ and $|\mathbf{v}| = (\mathbf{v} \cdot \mathbf{v})^{1/2}$ are nonnegative.   ▲

The Cauchy-Schwarz inequality enables us to *define* the angle θ between the nonzero vectors $\mathbf{u}$ and $\mathbf{v}$. (See Figure 4.6.1.) Division by the positive number $|\mathbf{u}||\mathbf{v}|$ in (7) yields $|\mathbf{u} \cdot \mathbf{v}|/(|\mathbf{u}||\mathbf{v}|) \leqq 1$, so

$$-1 \leqq \frac{\mathbf{u} \cdot \mathbf{v}}{|\mathbf{u}||\mathbf{v}|} \leqq +1. \tag{8}$$

FIGURE 4.6.1. The angle θ between the vectors $\mathbf{u}$ and $\mathbf{v}$.

Hence there is a unique angle θ between 0 and π radians, inclusive (that is, between $0°$ and $180°$), such that

$$\cos\theta = \frac{\mathbf{u} \cdot \mathbf{v}}{|\mathbf{u}||\mathbf{v}|}. \tag{9}$$

Thus we obtain the same geometric interpretation

➤ $$\mathbf{u} \cdot \mathbf{v} = |\mathbf{u}||\mathbf{v}|\cos\theta \tag{10}$$

of the dot product in $\mathbf{R}^n$ as one sees (for 3-dimensional vectors) in elementary calculus textbooks—for instance, see Section 12.2 of Edwards and Penney, *Calculus*, 6th edition (Prentice Hall) 2002.

On the basis of (10) we call the vectors $\mathbf{u}$ and $\mathbf{v}$ **orthogonal** provided that

➤ $$\mathbf{u} \cdot \mathbf{v} = 0. \tag{11}$$

If $\mathbf{u}$ and $\mathbf{v}$ are nonzero vectors this means that $\cos\theta = 0$, so $\theta = \pi/2$ ($90°$). Note that $\mathbf{u} = \mathbf{0}$ satisfies (11) for all $\mathbf{v}$, so the zero vector is orthogonal to *every* vector.

Example 1   Find the angle θ_n in $\mathbf{R}^n$ between the x_1-axis and the line through the origin and the point $(1, 1, \ldots, 1)$.

Solution   We take $\mathbf{u} = (1, 0, 0, \ldots, 0)$ on the x_1-axis and $\mathbf{v} = (1, 1, \ldots, 1)$. Then $|\mathbf{u}| = 1$, $|\mathbf{v}| = \sqrt{n}$, and $\mathbf{u} \cdot \mathbf{v} = 1$, so the formula in (9) gives

$$\cos\theta_n = \frac{\mathbf{u} \cdot \mathbf{v}}{|\mathbf{u}||\mathbf{v}|} = \frac{1}{\sqrt{n}}.$$

For instance, if

$$n = 3, \quad \text{then} \quad \theta_3 = \cos^{-1}\left(\frac{1}{\sqrt{3}}\right) \approx 0.9553 \quad (55°);$$

$$n = 4, \quad \text{then} \quad \theta_4 = \cos^{-1}\left(\frac{1}{\sqrt{4}}\right) \approx 1.0472 \quad (60°);$$

$$n = 5, \quad \text{then} \quad \theta_5 = \cos^{-1}\left(\frac{1}{\sqrt{5}}\right) \approx 1.1071 \quad (63°);$$

$$n = 100, \quad \text{then} \quad \theta_{100} = \cos^{-1}\left(\frac{1}{10}\right) \approx 1.4706 \quad (84°).$$

It is interesting to note that θ_n increases as n increases. Indeed, θ_n approaches $\cos^{-1}(0) = \pi/2$ ($90°$) as n increases without bound (so that $1/\sqrt{n}$ approaches zero).   ■

In addition to angles, the dot product provides a definition of distance in $\mathbf{R}^n$. The **distance** $d(\mathbf{u}, \mathbf{v})$ between the points (vectors) $\mathbf{u} = (u_1, u_2, \ldots, u_n)$ and $\mathbf{v} = (v_1, v_2, \ldots, v_n)$ is defined to be

$$
d(\mathbf{u}, \mathbf{v}) = |\mathbf{u} - \mathbf{v}| \tag{12}
$$
$$
= \left[(u_1 - v_1)^2 + (u_2 - v_2)^2 + \cdots + (u_n - v_n)^2\right]^{1/2}.
$$

Example 2

The distance between the points $\mathbf{u} = (1, -1, -2, 3, 5)$ and $\mathbf{v} = (4, 3, 4, 5, 9)$ in $\mathbf{R}^5$ is

$$
|\mathbf{u} - \mathbf{v}| = \sqrt{3^2 + 4^2 + 6^2 + 2^2 + 4^2} = \sqrt{81} = 0. \quad \blacksquare
$$

The *triangle inequality* of Theorem 2 relates the three sides of the triangle shown in Figure 4.6.2.

THEOREM 2: The Triangle Inequality

If $\mathbf{u}$ and $\mathbf{v}$ are vectors in $\mathbf{R}^n$, then

$$
|\mathbf{u} + \mathbf{v}| \leqq |\mathbf{u}| + |\mathbf{v}|. \tag{13}
$$

Proof: We apply the Cauchy-Schwarz inequality to find that

$$
\begin{aligned}
|\mathbf{u} + \mathbf{v}|^2 &= (\mathbf{u} + \mathbf{v}) \cdot (\mathbf{u} + \mathbf{v}) \\
&= \mathbf{u} \cdot \mathbf{u} + 2\mathbf{u} \cdot \mathbf{v} + \mathbf{v} \cdot \mathbf{v} \\
&\leqq \mathbf{u} \cdot \mathbf{u} + 2|\mathbf{u}||\mathbf{v}| + \mathbf{v} \cdot \mathbf{v} \\
&= |\mathbf{u}|^2 + 2|\mathbf{u}||\mathbf{v}| + |\mathbf{v}|^2,
\end{aligned} \tag{14}
$$

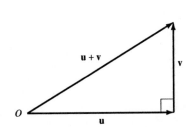

FIGURE 4.6.2. The triangle of the triangle inequality.

and therefore

$$
|\mathbf{u} + \mathbf{v}| \leqq (|\mathbf{u}| + |\mathbf{v}|)^2.
$$

We now get (13) when we take square roots. $\blacktriangle$

If the vectors $\mathbf{u}$ and $\mathbf{v}$ are orthogonal, then $\mathbf{u} \cdot \mathbf{v} = 0$, so line (14) in the proof of the triangle inequality yields the **Pythagorean formula**

$$
|\mathbf{u} + \mathbf{v}|^2 = |\mathbf{u}|^2 + |\mathbf{v}|^2 \tag{15}
$$

for a *right* triangle in $\mathbf{R}^n$ (see Figure 4.6.3).

The following theorem states a simple relationship between orthogonality and linear independence.

FIGURE 4.6.3. A right triangle in $\mathbf{R}^n$.

THEOREM 3: Orthogonality and Linear Independence

If the nonzero vectors $\mathbf{v}_1, \mathbf{v}_2, \ldots, \mathbf{v}_k$ are mutually orthogonal—that is, each two of them are orthogonal—then they are linearly independent.

Proof: Suppose that

$$
c_1 \mathbf{v}_1 + c_2 \mathbf{v}_2 + \cdots + c_k \mathbf{v}_k = \mathbf{0}
$$

where, as usual, $c_1, c_2, \ldots, c_k$ are scalars. When we take the dot product of each side of this equation with $\mathbf{v}_i$, we find that

$$c_i \mathbf{v}_i \cdot \mathbf{v}_i = c_i |\mathbf{v}_i|^2 = 0.$$

Now $|\mathbf{v}_i| \neq 0$ because $\mathbf{v}_i$ is a nonzero vector. It follows that $c_i = 0$. Thus $c_1 = c_2 = \cdots = c_k = 0$, and therefore the mutually orthogonal nonzero vectors $\mathbf{v}_1, \mathbf{v}_2, \ldots, \mathbf{v}_k$ are linearly independent.   ▲

In particular, any set of n mutually orthogonal nonzero vectors in $\mathbf{R}^n$ constitutes a basis for $\mathbf{R}^n$. Such a basis is called an **orthogonal basis**. For instance, the standard unit vectors $\mathbf{e}_1, \mathbf{e}_2, \ldots, \mathbf{e}_n$ form an orthogonal basis for $\mathbf{R}^n$.

Orthogonal Complements

Now we want to relate orthogonality to the solution of systems of linear equations. Consider the homogeneous linear system

$$\mathbf{Ax} = \mathbf{0} \tag{16}$$

of m equations in n unknowns. If $\mathbf{v}_1, \mathbf{v}_2, \ldots, \mathbf{v}_m$ are the row vectors of the $m \times n$ coefficient matrix $\mathbf{A}$, then the system looks like

$$\begin{bmatrix} \text{———} \mathbf{v}_1 \text{———} \\ \text{———} \mathbf{v}_2 \text{———} \\ \vdots \\ \text{———} \mathbf{v}_m \text{———} \end{bmatrix} \begin{bmatrix} | \\ \mathbf{x} \\ | \end{bmatrix} = \begin{bmatrix} \mathbf{v}_1 \cdot \mathbf{x} \\ \mathbf{v}_2 \cdot \mathbf{x} \\ \vdots \\ \mathbf{v}_m \cdot \mathbf{x} \end{bmatrix} = \begin{bmatrix} 0 \\ 0 \\ \vdots \\ 0 \end{bmatrix}.$$

Consequently it is clear that $\mathbf{x}$ is a solution vector of $\mathbf{Ax} = \mathbf{0}$ if and only if $\mathbf{x}$ is orthogonal to each row vector of $\mathbf{A}$. But in the latter event $\mathbf{x}$ is orthogonal to every linear combination of row vectors of $\mathbf{A}$ because

$$\begin{aligned} \mathbf{x} \cdot (c_1 \mathbf{v}_1 + c_2 \mathbf{v}_2 + \cdots + c_k \mathbf{v}_k) \\ = c_1 \mathbf{x}_1 \cdot \mathbf{v}_1 + c_2 \mathbf{x}_2 \cdot \mathbf{v}_2 + \cdots + c_k \mathbf{x}_k \cdot \mathbf{v}_k \\ = (c_1)(0) + (c_2)(0) + \cdots + (c_k)(0) = 0. \end{aligned}$$

Thus we have shown that *the vector $\mathbf{x}$ in $\mathbf{R}^n$ is a solution vector of $\mathbf{Ax} = \mathbf{0}$ if and only if $\mathbf{x}$ is orthogonal to each vector in the row space* Row(A) *of the matrix* $\mathbf{A}$. This situation motivates the following definition.

Definition: The Orthogonal Complement of a Subspace

The vector $\mathbf{u}$ is **orthogonal** to the subspace V of $\mathbf{R}^n$ provided that $\mathbf{u}$ is orthogonal to every vector in V. The **orthogonal complement** $V^\perp$ (read "V perp") of V is the set of all those vectors in $\mathbf{R}^n$ that are orthogonal to the subspace V.

If $\mathbf{u}_1$ and $\mathbf{u}_2$ are vectors in $V^\perp$, $\mathbf{v}$ is in V, and c_1 and c_2 are scalars, then

$$\begin{aligned} (c_1 \mathbf{u}_1 + c_2 \mathbf{u}_2) \cdot \mathbf{v} = c_1 \mathbf{u}_1 \cdot \mathbf{v} + c_2 \mathbf{u}_2 \cdot \mathbf{v} \\ = (c_1)(0) + (c_2)(0) = 0. \end{aligned}$$

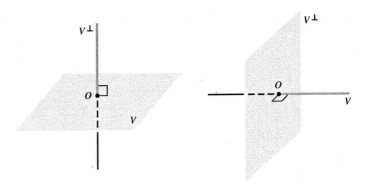

FIGURE 4.6.4. Orthogonal complements.

Thus any linear combination of vectors in $V^\perp$ is orthogonal to every vector in V and hence is a vector in $V^\perp$. Therefore *the orthogonal complement $V^\perp$ of a subspace V is itself a subspace of $\mathbf{R}^n$*. The standard picture of two complementary subspaces V and $V^\perp$ consists of an orthogonal line and plane through the origin in $\mathbf{R}^3$ (see Figure 4.6.4). The proofs of the remaining parts of Theorem 4 are left to the problems.

THEOREM 4: Properties of Orthogonal Complements

Let V be a subspace of $\mathbf{R}^n$. Then

1. Its orthogonal complement $V^\perp$ is also a subspace of $\mathbf{R}^n$;
2. The only vector that lies in both V and $V^\perp$ is the zero vector;
3. The orthogonal complement of $V^\perp$ is V—that is, $(V^\perp)^\perp = V$;
4. If S is a spanning set for V, then the vector $\mathbf{u}$ is in $V^\perp$ if and only if $\mathbf{u}$ is orthogonal to every vector in S. ▲

In our discussion of the homogeneous linear system $\mathbf{Ax} = \mathbf{0}$ in (16), we showed that a vector space lies in the **null space** Null(A) of A—that is, in the solution space of $\mathbf{Ax} = \mathbf{0}$—if and only if it is orthogonal to each vector in the row space of A. In the language of orthogonal complements, this proves Theorem 5.

THEOREM 5: The Row Space and the Null Space

Let A be an $m \times n$ matrix. Then the row space Row(A) and the null space Null(A) are orthogonal complements in $\mathbf{R}^n$. That is,

➤ $$\text{If } V = \text{Row}(\mathbf{A}), \text{ then } V^\perp = \text{Null}(\mathbf{A}). \qquad (17)$$
▲

Now suppose that a subspace V of $\mathbf{R}^n$ is given, with $\mathbf{v}_1, \mathbf{v}_2, \ldots, \mathbf{v}_m$ a set of vectors that span V. For instance, these vectors may form a given basis for V. Then the implication in (17) provides the following algorithm for finding a basis for the orthogonal complement $V^\perp$ of V.

1. Let A be the $m \times n$ matrix with row vectors $\mathbf{v}_1, \mathbf{v}_2, \ldots, \mathbf{v}_m$.
2. Reduce A to echelon form and use the algorithm of Section 4.4 to find a basis $\{\mathbf{u}_1, \mathbf{u}_2, \ldots, \mathbf{u}_k\}$ for the solution space Null(A) of $\mathbf{Ax} = \mathbf{0}$. Because $V^\perp = \text{Null}(\mathbf{A})$, this will be a basis for the orthogonal complement of V.

Example 3 Let V be the 1-dimensional subspace of $\mathbf{R}^3$ spanned by the vector $\mathbf{v}_1 = (1, -3, 5)$. Then

$$A = \begin{bmatrix} 1 & -3 & 5 \end{bmatrix}$$

and our linear system $\mathbf{Ax} = \mathbf{0}$ consists of the single equation

$$x_1 - 3x_2 + 5x_3 = 0.$$

If $x_2 = s$ and $x_3 = t$, then $x_1 = 3s - 5t$. With $s = 1$ and $t = 0$ we get the solution vector $\mathbf{u}_1 = (3, 1, 0)$, whereas with $s = 0$ and $t = 1$ we get the solution vector $\mathbf{u}_2 = (-5, 0, 1)$. Thus the orthogonal complement $V^{\perp}$ is the 2-dimensional subspace of $\mathbf{R}^3$ having $\mathbf{u}_1 = (3, 1, 0)$ and $\mathbf{u}_2 = (-5, 0, 1)$ as basis vectors. ∎

Example 4 Let V be the 2-dimensional subspace of $\mathbf{R}^5$ that has $\mathbf{v}_1 = (1, 2, 1, -3, -3)$ and $\mathbf{v}_2 = (2, 5, 6, -10, -12)$ as basis vectors. The matrix

$$A = \begin{bmatrix} 1 & 2 & 1 & -3 & -3 \\ 2 & 5 & 6 & -10 & -12 \end{bmatrix}$$

with row vectors $\mathbf{v}_1$ and $\mathbf{v}_2$ has reduced echelon form

$$E = \begin{bmatrix} 1 & 0 & -7 & 5 & 9 \\ 0 & 1 & 4 & -4 & -6 \end{bmatrix}.$$

Hence the solution space of $\mathbf{Ax} = \mathbf{0}$ is described parametrically by

$$x_3 = r, \quad x_4 = s, \quad x_5 = t,$$
$$x_2 = -4r + 4s + 6t$$
$$x_1 = 7r - 5s - 9t.$$

Then the choice

$$r = 1, \quad s = 0, \quad t = 0 \quad \text{yields} \quad \mathbf{u}_1 = (7, -4, 1, 0, 0);$$
$$r = 0, \quad s = 1, \quad t = 0 \quad \text{yields} \quad \mathbf{u}_2 = (-5, 4, 0, 1, 0);$$
$$r = 0, \quad s = 0, \quad t = 1 \quad \text{yields} \quad \mathbf{u}_3 = (-9, 6, 0, 0, 1).$$

Thus the orthogonal complement $V^{\perp}$ is the 3-dimensional subspace of $\mathbf{R}^5$ with basis $\{\mathbf{u}_1, \mathbf{u}_2, \mathbf{u}_3\}$. ∎

Observe that $\dim V + \dim V^{\perp} = 3$ in Example 3, but $\dim V + \dim V^{\perp} = 5$ in Example 4. It is no coincidence that in each case the dimensions of V and $V^{\perp}$ add up to the dimension n of the Euclidean space containing them. To see why, suppose that V is a subspace of $\mathbf{R}^n$ and let $\mathbf{A}$ be an $m \times n$ matrix whose row vectors span V. Then Equation (12) in Section 4.5 implies that

$$\text{rank}(\mathbf{A}) + \dim \text{Null}(\mathbf{A}) = n.$$

But

$$\dim V = \dim \text{Row}(\mathbf{A}) = \text{rank}(\mathbf{A})$$

and

$$\dim V^{\perp} = \dim \text{Null}(\mathbf{A})$$

by Theorem 5, so it follows that

$$\dim V + \dim V^\perp = n. \tag{18}$$

Moreover, it should be apparent intuitively that if

$$\{\mathbf{v}_1, \mathbf{v}_2, \ldots, \mathbf{v}_m\} \text{ is a basis for } V$$

and

$$\{\mathbf{u}_1, \mathbf{u}_2, \ldots, \mathbf{u}_k\} \text{ is a basis for } V^\perp,$$

then

$$\{\mathbf{v}_1, \mathbf{v}_2, \ldots, \mathbf{v}_m, \mathbf{u}_1, \mathbf{u}_2, \ldots, \mathbf{u}_k\} \text{ is a basis for } \mathbf{R}^n.$$

That is, *the union of a basis for V and a basis for $V^\perp$ is a basis for $\mathbf{R}^n$*. In Problem 34 of this section we ask you to prove that this is so.

4.6 Problems

In Problems 1–4, determine whether the given vectors are mutually orthogonal.

1. $\mathbf{v}_1 = (2, 1, 2, 1)$, $\mathbf{v}_2 = (3, -6, 1, -2)$,
   $\mathbf{v}_3 = (3, -1, -5, 5)$
2. $\mathbf{v}_1 = (3, -2, 3, -4)$, $\mathbf{v}_2 = (6, 3, 4, 6)$,
   $\mathbf{v}_3 = (17, -12, -21, 3)$
3. $\mathbf{v}_1 = (5, 2, -4, -1)$, $\mathbf{v}_2 = (3, -5, 1, 1)$,
   $\mathbf{v}_3 = (3, 0, 8, -17)$
4. $\mathbf{v}_1 = (1, 2, 3, -2, 1)$, $\mathbf{v}_2 = (3, 2, 3, 6, -4)$,
   $\mathbf{v}_3 = (6, 2, -4, 1, 4)$

In Problems 5–8, the three vertices A, B, and C of a triangle are given. Prove that each triangle is a right triangle by showing that its sides a, b, and c satisfy the Pythagorean relation $a^2 + b^2 = c^2$.

5. $A(6, 6, 5, 8)$, $B(6, 8, 6, 5)$, $C(5, 7, 4, 6)$
6. $A(3, 5, 1, 3)$, $B(4, 2, 6, 4)$, $C(1, 3, 4, 2)$
7. $A(4, 5, 3, 5, -1)$, $B(3, 4, -1, 4, 4)$, $C(1, 3, 1, 3, 1)$
8. $A(2, 8, -3, -1, 2)$, $B(-2, 5, 6, 2, 12)$, $C(-5, 3, 2, -3, 5)$
9–12. Find the acute angles (in degrees) of each of the right triangles of Problems 5–8, respectively.

In Problems 13–22, the given vectors span a subspace V of the indicated Euclidean space. Find a basis for the orthogonal complement $V^\perp$ of V.

13. $\mathbf{v}_1 = (1, -2, 3)$
14. $\mathbf{v}_1 = (1, 5, -3)$
15. $\mathbf{v}_1 = (1, -2, -3, 5)$
16. $\mathbf{v}_1 = (1, 7, -6, -9)$
17. $\mathbf{v}_1 = (1, 3, 2, 4)$, $\mathbf{v}_2 = (2, 7, 7, 3)$
18. $\mathbf{v}_1 = (1, -3, 3, 5)$, $\mathbf{v}_2 = (2, -5, 9, 3)$
19. $\mathbf{v}_1 = (1, 2, 5, 2, 3)$, $\mathbf{v}_2 = (3, 7, 11, 9, 5)$
20. $\mathbf{v}_1 = (2, 5, 5, 4, 3)$, $\mathbf{v}_2 = (3, 7, 8, 8, 8)$
21. $\mathbf{v}_1 = (1, 2, 3, 1, 3)$, $\mathbf{v}_2 = (1, 3, 4, 3, 6)$,
    $\mathbf{v}_3 = (2, 2, 4, 3, 5)$
22. $\mathbf{v}_1 = (1, 1, 1, 1, 3)$, $\mathbf{v}_2 = (2, 3, 1, 4, 7)$,
    $\mathbf{v}_3 = (5, 3, 7, 1, 5)$

23. Prove: For arbitrary vectors $\mathbf{u}$ and $\mathbf{v}$,
    (a) $|\mathbf{u} + \mathbf{v}|^2 + |\mathbf{u} - \mathbf{v}|^2 = 2|\mathbf{u}|^2 + 2|\mathbf{v}|^2$;
    (b) $|\mathbf{u} + \mathbf{v}|^2 - |\mathbf{u} - \mathbf{v}|^2 = 4\mathbf{u} \cdot \mathbf{v}$.

24. Given mutually orthogonal vectors $\mathbf{v}_1, \mathbf{v}_2, \ldots, \mathbf{v}_k$, show that

$$|\mathbf{v}_1 + \mathbf{v}_2 + \cdots + \mathbf{v}_k|^2 = |\mathbf{v}_1|^2 + |\mathbf{v}_2|^2 + \cdots + |\mathbf{v}_k|^2.$$

25. Suppose that A, B, and C are the unit points on distinct coordinate axes in $\mathbf{R}^n$ (for example, perhaps $A = \mathbf{e}_1$, $B = \mathbf{e}_2$, and $C = \mathbf{e}_3$). Show that ABC is an equilateral triangle.

26. Prove that $|\mathbf{u} \cdot \mathbf{v}| = |\mathbf{u}||\mathbf{v}|$ if and only if the vectors $\mathbf{u}$ and $\mathbf{v}$ are linearly dependent.

In Problems 27–29, V denotes a subspace of $\mathbf{R}^n$.

27. Show that the only vector that lies in both V and $V^\perp$ is the zero vector.

28. Prove that if $W = V^\perp$ then $W^\perp = V$.

29. Let S be a spanning set for V. Show that the vector $\mathbf{u}$ is in $V^\perp$ if and only if $\mathbf{u}$ is orthogonal to every vector in S.

30. Suppose that the vectors $\mathbf{u}$ and $\mathbf{v}$ are orthogonal and that $\mathbf{u} + \mathbf{v} = \mathbf{0}$. Show that $\mathbf{u} = \mathbf{v} = \mathbf{0}$.

31. Let S and T be two sets of vectors in $\mathbf{R}^n$ such that each vector in S is orthogonal to every vector in T. Prove that each vector in span(S) is orthogonal to every vector in span(T).

32. Let $S = \{\mathbf{u}_1, \mathbf{u}_2\}$ and $T = \{\mathbf{v}_1, \mathbf{v}_2\}$ be linearly independent sets of vectors such that each $\mathbf{u}_i$ in S is orthogonal to every vector $\mathbf{v}_j$ in T. Then use the results of Problems 30 and 31 to show that the four vectors $\mathbf{u}_1$, $\mathbf{u}_2$, $\mathbf{v}_1$, $\mathbf{v}_2$ are linearly independent.

33. Let $S = \{\mathbf{u}_1, \mathbf{u}_2, \ldots, \mathbf{u}_k\}$ and $T = \{\mathbf{v}_1, \mathbf{v}_2, \ldots, \mathbf{v}_m\}$ be linearly independent sets of vectors such that each $\mathbf{u}_i$ in S is orthogonal to every vector $\mathbf{v}_j$ in T. Then generalize Problem 32 to show that the $k + m$ vectors $\mathbf{u}_1, \mathbf{u}_2, \ldots, \mathbf{u}_k, \mathbf{v}_1, \mathbf{v}_2, \ldots, \mathbf{v}_m$ are linearly independent.

34. Deduce from the result of Problem 33 that if V is a subspace of $\mathbf{R}^n$, then the union of a basis for V and a basis for $V^\perp$ is a basis for $\mathbf{R}^n$.

35. Let $\mathbf{A}$ be an $m \times n$ matrix and $\mathbf{b}$ a vector in $\mathbf{R}^m$. Combine the observations listed below to prove that *the nonhomogeneous linear system* $\mathbf{Ax} = \mathbf{b}$ *is consistent if and only if* $\mathbf{b}$ *is orthogonal to the solution space of the homogeneous system* $\mathbf{A}^T\mathbf{y} = \mathbf{0}$.

(a) $\mathbf{Ax} = \mathbf{b}$ is consistent if and only if $\mathbf{b}$ is in Col($\mathbf{A}$).

(b) $\mathbf{b}$ is in Col($\mathbf{A}$) if and only if $\mathbf{b}$ is orthogonal to $\{\text{Col}(\mathbf{A})\}^\perp = \{\text{Row}(\mathbf{A}^T)\}^\perp$.

(c) $\{\text{Row}(\mathbf{A}^T)\}^\perp = \text{Null}(\mathbf{A}^T)$.

4.7 General Vector Spaces

In the previous six sections of this chapter, almost all the specific vector spaces appearing in our examples and problems have been vector spaces of n-tuples of real numbers. We have thus confined our attention largely to Euclidean spaces and their subspaces. In this section we discuss examples of some other types of vector spaces that play important roles in various branches of mathematics and their applications.

Example 1 Given fixed positive integers m and n, let M_{mn} denote the set of all $m \times n$ matrices with real number entries. Then M_{mn} is a vector space with the usual operations of addition of matrices and multiplication of matrices by scalars (real numbers). That is, these operations satisfy properties (a)–(h) in the definition of a vector space (Section 4.2). In particular, the zero element in M_{mn} is the $m \times n$ matrix $\mathbf{0}$ matrix whose elements are all zeros, and the negative $-\mathbf{A}$ of the matrix $\mathbf{A}$ is (as usual) the matrix whose elements are the negatives of the corresponding entries of $\mathbf{A}$.

Given positive integers i and j with $1 \le i \le m$ and $1 \le j \le n$, let $\mathbf{E}_{ij}$ denote the $m \times n$ matrix whose only nonzero entry is the number 1 in the ith row and the jth column. Then it should be clear that the mn elements $\{\mathbf{E}_{ij}\}$ of M_{mn} form a basis for M_{mn}, and so M_{mn} is a finite-dimensional vector space of dimension mn.

For instance, in the case of the vector space M_{22} of all 2×2 matrices, these alleged basis elements are the four matrices

$$\mathbf{E}_{11} = \begin{bmatrix} 1 & 0 \\ 0 & 0 \end{bmatrix}, \quad \mathbf{E}_{12} = \begin{bmatrix} 0 & 1 \\ 0 & 0 \end{bmatrix},$$

$$\mathbf{E}_{21} = \begin{bmatrix} 0 & 0 \\ 1 & 0 \end{bmatrix}, \quad \text{and} \quad \mathbf{E}_{22} = \begin{bmatrix} 0 & 0 \\ 0 & 1 \end{bmatrix}.$$

Then any matrix $\mathbf{A}$ in M_{22} can be expressed as

$$\mathbf{A} = \begin{bmatrix} a & b \\ c & d \end{bmatrix} = a\mathbf{E}_{11} + b\mathbf{E}_{12} + c\mathbf{E}_{21} + d\mathbf{E}_{22},$$

so the set $\{\mathbf{E}_{11}, \mathbf{E}_{12}, \mathbf{E}_{21}, \mathbf{E}_{22}\}$ spans M_{22}. Moreover,

$$a\mathbf{E}_{11} + b\mathbf{E}_{12} + c\mathbf{E}_{21} + d\mathbf{E}_{22} = \begin{bmatrix} a & b \\ c & d \end{bmatrix} = \begin{bmatrix} 0 & 0 \\ 0 & 0 \end{bmatrix}$$

implies immediately that $a = b = c = d = 0$, so the set $\{\mathbf{E}_{11}, \mathbf{E}_{12}, \mathbf{E}_{21}, \mathbf{E}_{22}\}$ is also linearly independent and therefore forms a basis for M_{22}. Thus, we have shown that M_{22} is a 4-dimensional vector space. ∎

Example 2 Let C denote the subset of M_{22} consisting of all 2×2 matrices of the form

$$\begin{bmatrix} a & -b \\ b & a \end{bmatrix}. \tag{1}$$

Obviously the sum of any two such matrices is such a matrix, as is any scalar multiple of such a matrix. Thus C is closed under the operations of addition of matrices and multiplication by scalars and is therefore a *subspace* of M_{22}.

To determine the *dimension* of the subspace C, we consider the two special matrices

$$\mathbf{Re} = \begin{bmatrix} 1 & 0 \\ 0 & 1 \end{bmatrix} \quad \text{and} \quad \mathbf{Im} = \begin{bmatrix} 0 & -1 \\ 1 & 0 \end{bmatrix} \tag{2}$$

in C. Here $\mathbf{Re}$ is another notation for the 2×2 identity matrix $\mathbf{I}$, whereas the matrix $\mathbf{Im}$ is not so familiar. The matrices $\mathbf{Re}$ and $\mathbf{Im}$ are linearly independent—obviously neither is a scalar multiple of the other—and

$$\begin{bmatrix} a & -b \\ b & a \end{bmatrix} = a\mathbf{Re} + b\mathbf{Im}, \tag{3}$$

so these two matrices span C. Thus $\{\mathbf{Re}, \mathbf{Im}\}$ is a basis for C, and so C is a 2-dimensional subspace of the 4-dimensional vector space M_{22} of 2×2 matrices.

Now observe that

$$(\mathbf{Im})^2 = \begin{bmatrix} 0 & -1 \\ 1 & 0 \end{bmatrix} \begin{bmatrix} 0 & -1 \\ 1 & 0 \end{bmatrix} = \begin{bmatrix} -1 & 0 \\ 0 & -1 \end{bmatrix} = -\mathbf{Re}. \tag{4}$$

It follows that the matrix product of any two elements $a\mathbf{Re} + b\mathbf{Im}$ and $c\mathbf{Re} + d\mathbf{Im}$ of C is given by

$$(a\mathbf{Re} + b\mathbf{Im})(c\mathbf{Re} + d\mathbf{Im}) = ac(\mathbf{Re})^2 + bc\,\mathbf{Im}\,\mathbf{Re} + ad\,\mathbf{Re}\,\mathbf{Im} + bd(\mathbf{Im})^2$$
$$= (ac - bd)\mathbf{Re} + (ad + bc)\mathbf{Im}. \tag{5}$$

This explicit formula for the product of two matrices in C shows that, in addition to being closed under matrix addition and multiplication by scalars, the subspace C of M_{22} also is *closed under matrix multiplication*. ∎

If you feel that the idea of a space of matrices being closed under matrix multiplication is a rather complex one, you are correct! Indeed, the vector space C of Example 2 can be taken as a "model" for the set of all *complex numbers* of the form $a + bi$, where a and b are real numbers and $i = \sqrt{-1}$ denotes the "imaginary" square root of -1 (so that $i^2 = -1$). Because $(\mathbf{Im})^2 = -\mathbf{Re}$, the matrix $\mathbf{Im}$ plays the role of i and the matrix

$$\begin{bmatrix} a & -b \\ b & a \end{bmatrix} = a\mathbf{Re} + b\mathbf{Im}$$

corresponds to the complex number $a + bi$. And the matrix multiplication formula in (5) is then analogous to the formula

$$(a + bi)(c + di) = (ac - bd) + (ad + bc)i$$

for the multiplication of complex numbers. In addition to providing a concrete interpretation of complex numbers in terms of real numbers, the matrix model C provides a convenient way to manipulate complex numbers in computer programming languages in which matrix operations are "built in" but complex operations are not.

Function Spaces

In Example 1 of Section 4.2 we introduced the vector space $\mathcal{F}$ of all real-valued functions defined on the real line $\mathbf{R}$. If $\mathbf{f}$ and $\mathbf{g}$ are elements of $\mathcal{F}$ and c is a scalar, then

$$(\mathbf{f} + \mathbf{g})(x) = \mathbf{f}(x) + \mathbf{g}(x)$$

and   (6)

$$(c\mathbf{f})(x) = c(\mathbf{f}(x))$$

for all x in $\mathbf{R}$. The zero element in $\mathcal{F}$ is the function $\mathbf{0}$ such that $\mathbf{0}(x) = 0$ for all x. We frequently refer to a function in $\mathcal{F}$ by simply specifying its formula. For instance, by "the function x^2" we mean that function whose value at each x in $\mathbf{R}$ is x^2.

The functions $\mathbf{f}_1, \mathbf{f}_2, \ldots, \mathbf{f}_k$ in $\mathcal{F}$ are linearly dependent provided that there exist scalars $c_1, c_2, \ldots, c_k$, not all zero, such that

$$c_1\mathbf{f}_1(x) + c_2\mathbf{f}_2(x) + \cdots + c_k\mathbf{f}_k(x) = 0$$

for all x in $\mathbf{R}$. We often can determine whether two given functions are linearly dependent simply by observing whether one is a scalar multiple of the other.

Example 3   The functions e^x and e^{-2x} are linearly independent because either of the equations $e^x = ae^{-2x}$ or $e^{-2x} = be^x$ would imply that e^{3x} is a constant, which obviously is not so. By contrast, the functions $\sin 2x$ and $\sin x \cos x$ are linearly dependent, because of the trigonometric identity $\sin 2x = 2 \sin x \cos x$. The three functions 1, $\cos^2 x$, and $\sin^2 x$ are linearly dependent, because the fundamental identity $\cos^2 x + \sin^2 x = 1$ can be written in the form

$$(-1)(1) + (1)(\cos^2 x) + (1)(\sin^2 x) = 0. \qquad \blacksquare$$

A subspace of $\mathcal{F}$ is called a **function space**. An example of a function space is the vector space $\mathcal{P}$ of all polynomials in $\mathcal{F}$ (Example 4 in Section 4.4). A function $\mathbf{p}(x)$ in $\mathcal{F}$ is called a **polynomial of degree** $n \geq 0$ if it can be expressed in the form

$$\mathbf{p}(x) = a_0 + a_1 x + a_2 x^2 + \cdots + a_n x^n \qquad (7)$$

with $a_n \neq 0$. Polynomials are added and multiplied by scalars in the usual manner—by collecting coefficients of like powers of x. Clearly any linear combination of polynomials is a polynomial, so $\mathcal{P}$ is, indeed, a subspace of $\mathcal{F}$.

Example 4   Given $n \geq 0$, denote by $\mathcal{P}_n$ the set of all polynomials of degree at most n. That is, $\mathcal{P}_n$ consists of all polynomials of degrees $0, 1, 2, \ldots, n$. Any linear combination of two polynomials of degree at most n is again a polynomial of degree at most n, so $\mathcal{P}_n$ is a subspace of $\mathcal{P}$ (and of $\mathcal{F}$). The formula in (7) shows that the $n + 1$ polynomials

$$1, x, x^2, x^3, \ldots, x^n \qquad (8)$$

span $\mathcal{P}_n$. To show that these "monomials" are linearly independent, suppose that

$$c_0 + c_1 x + c_2 x^2 + \cdots + c_n x^n = 0 \qquad (9)$$

for all x in $\mathbf{R}$. If $a_0, a_1, \ldots, a_n$ are fixed *distinct* real numbers, then each a_i satisfies Eq. (9). In matrix notation this means that

$$\begin{bmatrix} 1 & a_0 & a_0^2 & \cdots & a_0^n \\ 1 & a_1 & a_1^2 & \cdots & a_1^n \\ 1 & a_2 & a_2^2 & \cdots & a_2^n \\ \vdots & \vdots & \vdots & \ddots & \vdots \\ 1 & a_n & a_n^2 & \cdots & a_n^n \end{bmatrix} \begin{bmatrix} c_0 \\ c_1 \\ c_2 \\ \vdots \\ c_n \end{bmatrix} = \begin{bmatrix} 0 \\ 0 \\ 0 \\ \vdots \\ 0 \end{bmatrix}. \qquad (10)$$

The coefficient matrix in (10) is a Vandermonde matrix $\mathbf{V}$, and Problems 61–63 in Section 3.6 imply that any Vandermonde matrix is nonsingular. Therefore the system $\mathbf{Vc} = \mathbf{0}$ has only the trivial solution $\mathbf{c} = \mathbf{0}$, so it follows from (10) that $c_0 = c_1 = c_2 = \cdots = c_n = 0$. Thus we have proved that the $n + 1$ monomials $1, x, x^2, \ldots, x^n$ are linearly independent and hence constitute a basis for $\mathcal{P}_n$. Consequently $\mathcal{P}_n$ is an $(n + 1)$-dimensional vector space. ∎

The fact that the monomials in (8) are linearly independent implies that the coefficients in a polynomial are unique. That is, if

$$a_0 + a_1 x + \cdots + a_n x^n = b_0 + b_1 x + \cdots + b_n x^n$$

for all x, then $a_0 = b_0$, $a_1 = b_1$, $\ldots$, and $a_n = b_n$. This *identity principle* for polynomials is often used without proof in elementary algebra. A typical application is the method of *partial-fraction decomposition* illustrated in Example 5.

Example 5 Find constants A, B, and C such that

$$\frac{6x}{(x-1)(x+1)(x+2)} = \frac{A}{x-1} + \frac{B}{x+1} + \frac{C}{x+2} \qquad (11)$$

for all x (other than $x = 1$, -1, or -2).

Solution Multiplication of each side of the equation in (11) by the denominator on the left-hand side yields

$$6x = A(x+1)(x+2) + B(x-1)(x+2) + C(x-1)(x+1);$$
$$6x = (2A - 2B - C) + (3A + B)x + (A + B + C)x^2.$$

Then the identity principle for polynomials yields the linear equations

$$2A - 2B - C = 0$$
$$3A + B = 6$$
$$A + B + C = 0,$$

which we readily solve for $A = 1$, $B = 3$, and $C = -4$. Therefore

$$\frac{6x}{(x-1)(x+1)(x+2)} = \frac{1}{x-1} + \frac{3}{x+1} - \frac{4}{x+2}$$

if $x \neq 1$, -1, -2. ∎

Example 6   Show that the four polynomials

$$1, \quad x, \quad 3x^2 - 1, \quad \text{and} \quad 5x^3 - 3x \tag{12}$$

form a basis for $\mathcal{P}_3$.

Solution   In order to show simultaneously that these four polynomials span $\mathcal{P}_3$ and are linearly independent, it suffices to see that every polynomial

$$p(x) = b_0 + b_1 x + b_2 x^2 + b_3 x^3 \tag{13}$$

in $\mathcal{P}_3$ can be expressed uniquely as a linear combination

$$\begin{aligned}
c_0(1) + c_1(x) &+ c_2(3x^2 - 1) + c_3(5x^3 - 3x) \\
&= (c_0 - c_2) + (c_1 - 3c_3)x + (3c_2)x^2 + (5c_3)x^3
\end{aligned} \tag{14}$$

of the polynomials in (12). But upon comparing the coefficients in (13) and (14), we see that we need only observe that the linear system

$$\begin{bmatrix} 1 & 0 & -1 & 0 \\ 0 & 1 & 0 & -3 \\ 0 & 0 & 3 & 0 \\ 0 & 0 & 0 & 5 \end{bmatrix} \begin{bmatrix} c_0 \\ c_1 \\ c_2 \\ c_3 \end{bmatrix} = \begin{bmatrix} b_0 \\ b_1 \\ b_2 \\ b_3 \end{bmatrix}$$

obviously has a unique solution for c_0, c_1, c_2, c_3 in terms of b_0, b_1, b_2, b_3. ∎

Because the vector space $\mathcal{P}$ of all polynomials contains $n + 1$ linearly independent functions for every integer $n \geq 0$, it follows that $\mathcal{P}$ is an infinite-dimensional vector space. So too is any function space, such as $\mathcal{F}$ itself, that contains $\mathcal{P}$. Another important function space is the set $\mathcal{C}^{(0)}$ of all continuous functions on **R**; $\mathcal{C}^{(0)}$ is a subspace of $\mathcal{F}$ because every linear combination of continuous functions is again a continuous function. Every polynomial is a continuous function, so $\mathcal{C}^{(0)}$ contains $\mathcal{P}$ and is therefore an infinite-dimensional vector space. Similarly, the set $\mathcal{C}^{(k)}$ of all functions in $\mathcal{F}$ that have continuous kth-order derivatives is an infinite-dimensional function space.

Solution Spaces of Differential Equations

In Section 1.5 we saw that the (now familiar) first-order differential equation

$$y' = ky \quad (k \text{ constant}) \tag{15}$$

has the general solution $y(x) = Ce^{kx}$. Thus the "solution space" of (15) is the set of all constant multiples of the single function e^{kx}, and it is therefore the 1-dimensional function space with basis $\{e^{kx}\}$.

In Section 5.1 we will see that the set of all solutions $y(x)$ of a linear second-order differential equation of the form

$$ay'' + by' + cy = 0 \tag{16}$$

(with constant coefficients a, b, and c) is a 2-dimensional function space $\mathcal{S}$, called the **solution space** of the differential equation. Here we will illustrate this general fact with three simple examples of second-order equations that can be solved in an elementary manner.

Example 7

With $a = 1$ and $b = c = 0$ in (16), we get the differential equation

$$y'' = 0. \tag{17}$$

If $y(x)$ is any solution of this equation, so $y''(x) = 0$, then two integrations give first

$$y'(x) = \int y''(x)\, dx = \int (0)\, dx = A$$

and then

$$y(x) = \int y'(x)\, dx = \int A\, dx = Ax + B,$$

where A and B are arbitrary constants of integration. Thus every solution of (17) is of the form $y(x) = Ax + B$, and clearly every such function is a solution of the differential equation. Thus the solution space of (17) is simply the 2-dimensional space $\mathcal{P}_1$ of linear polynomials generated by the basis $\{1, x\}$. ∎

Example 8

With $a = 1$, $b = -2$, and $c = 0$ in (16), we get the differential equation

$$y'' - 2y' = 0. \tag{18}$$

If $y(x)$ is any solution of this equation and if $v(x) = y'(x)$, then (18) says that

$$v'(x) = 2v(x).$$

But this is a familiar first-order differential equation with general solution $v(x) = Ce^{2x}$. Then integration gives

$$y(x) = \int y'(x)\, dx = \int v(x)\, dx = \int Ce^{2x}\, dx = \tfrac{1}{2}Ce^{2x} + A.$$

Thus every solution of (18) is of the form $y(x) = A + Be^{2x}$ (where $B = \tfrac{1}{2}C$), and you should show by substitution in (18) that every function of this form is a solution of the differential equation. Therefore the solution space of (18) is the 2-dimensional function space that is generated by the basis $\{1, e^{2x}\}$. ∎

Example 9

With $a = 1$, $b = 0$, and $c = -1$ in (16), we get the differential equation

$$y'' - y = 0. \tag{19}$$

If $y(x)$ is any solution of this equation and if $v(x) = y'(x)$, then (19) says that

$$y'' = \frac{dv}{dx} = \frac{dv}{dy}\frac{dy}{dx} = v\frac{dv}{dy} = y;$$

so $v\, dv = y\, dy$. Integration therefore gives

$$\tfrac{1}{2}v^2 = \tfrac{1}{2}y^2 + C, \quad \text{so} \quad v^2 = y^2 \pm a^2, \tag{20}$$

where the final sign depends on the sign of C. The final result is independent of this choice (Problem 27); we'll take the negative sign for the sake of illustration. Since $v = dy/dx$, it then follows from (20) that

$$x = \pm \int \frac{dy}{\sqrt{y^2 - a^2}}. \tag{21}$$

Here again the final result is independent of the choice of sign; this time we'll take the positive sign. Then the substitution $y = au$ and the standard integral

$$\int \frac{du}{\sqrt{u^2 - 1}} = \cosh^{-1} u + C$$

(see Section 7.6 of Edwards and Penney, *Calculus*, 6th edition, Prentice Hall, 2002) yield

$$x = \cosh^{-1} \frac{y}{a} + b,$$

so finally,

$$y = a \cosh(x - b) = a(\cosh x \sinh b - \sinh x \cosh b),$$

which can be written as

$$y(x) = A \cosh x + B \sinh x, \tag{22}$$

with $A = a \sinh b$ and $B = -a \cosh b$. Thus every solution of the differential equation $y'' - y = 0$ in (19) is of the form $y(x) = A \cosh x + B \sinh x$, and you should show by substitution in (19) that every function of this form is a solution of the differential equation. Therefore the solution space $\mathscr{S}$ of (19) is the 2-dimensional function space that is generated by the basis $\{\cosh x, \sinh x\}$. If we substitute into (22) the relations

$$\cosh x = \frac{e^x + e^{-x}}{2}, \quad \sinh x = \frac{e^x - e^{-x}}{2}$$

that define the hyperbolic cosine and sine functions in terms of exponentials, we see that every solution of $y'' - y = 0$ can also be written in the form of the linear combination

$$y(x) = Ce^x + De^{-x}.$$

Consequently $\{e^x, e^{-x}\}$ is a second basis for the 2-dimensional solution space $\mathscr{S}$. ∎

4.7 Problems

In Problems 1–4, determine whether or not the indicated set of 3×3 matrices is a subspace of M_{33}.

1. The set of all diagonal 3×3 matrices.
2. The set of all symmetric 3×3 matrices (that is, matrices $\mathbf{A} = \begin{bmatrix} a_{ij} \end{bmatrix}$ such that $a_{ij} = a_{ji}$ for $1 \leq i \leq 3$, $1 \leq j \leq 3$).
3. The set of all nonsingular 3×3 matrices.
4. The set of all singular 3×3 matrices.

*In Problems 5–8, determine whether or not each indicated set of functions is a subspace of the space $\mathscr{F}$ of all real-valued functions on **R**.*

5. The set of all f such that $f(0) = 0$.
6. The set of all f such that $f(x) \neq 0$ for all x.
7. The set of all f such that $f(0) = 0$ and $f(1) = 1$.
8. The set of all f such that $f(-x) = -f(x)$ for all x.

In Problems 9–12, a condition on the coefficients of a polynomial $a_0 + a_1 x + a_2 x^2 + a_3 x^3$ is given. Determine whether or not the set of all such polynomials satisfying this condition is a subspace of the space $\mathscr{P}$ of all polynomials.

9. $a_3 \neq 0$
10. $a_0 = a_1 = 0$
11. $a_0 + a_1 + a_2 + a_3 = 0$
12. $a_0, a_1, a_2,$ and a_3 are all integers

In Problems 13–18, determine whether the given functions are linearly independent.

13. $\sin x$ and $\cos x$
14. e^x and xe^x
15. $1 + x,\ 1 - x,$ and $1 - x^2$
16. $1 + x,\ x + x^2,$ and $1 - x^2$

17. $\cos 2x$, $\sin^2 x$, and $\cos^2 x$

18. $2\cos x + 3\sin x$ and $4\cos x + 5\sin x$

In Problems 19–22, use the method of Example 5 to find the constants A, B, and C in the indicated partial-fraction decompositions.

19. $\dfrac{x-5}{(x-2)(x-3)} = \dfrac{A}{x-2} + \dfrac{B}{x-3}$

20. $\dfrac{2}{x(x^2-1)} = \dfrac{A}{x} + \dfrac{B}{x-1} + \dfrac{C}{x+1}$

21. $\dfrac{8}{x(x^2+4)} = \dfrac{A}{x} + \dfrac{Bx+C}{x^2+4}$

22. $\dfrac{2x}{(x+1)(x+2)(x+3)} = \dfrac{A}{x+1} + \dfrac{B}{x+2} + \dfrac{C}{x+3}$

In Problems 23 and 24, use the method of Example 7 to find a basis for the solution space of the given differential equation. (It's 3-dimensional in Problem 23 and 4-dimensional in Problem 24.)

23. $y''' = 0$ **24.** $y^{(4)} = 0$

In Problems 25 and 26, use the method of Example 8 to find a basis for the 2-dimensional solution space of the given differential equation.

25. $y'' - 5y' = 0$ **26.** $y'' + 10y' = 0$

27. Take the positive sign in Eq. (20), and then use the standard integral

$$\int \frac{du}{\sqrt{u^2+1}} = \sinh^{-1} u + C$$

to derive the same general solution $y(x) = A\cosh x + B\sinh x$ given in Eq. (22).

28. Use the method of Example 9 and the standard integral

$$\int \frac{du}{\sqrt{1-u^2}} = \sin^{-1} u + C$$

to derive the general solution $y(x) = A\cos x + B\sin x$ of the second-order differential equation $y'' + y = 0$. Thus its solution space has basis $\{\cos x, \sin x\}$.

29. Let V be the set of all infinite sequences $\{x_n\} = \{x_1, x_2, x_3, \dots\}$ of real numbers. Let addition of elements of V and multiplication by scalars be defined as follows:

$$\{x_n\} + \{y_n\} = \{x_n + y_n\}$$

and

$$c\{x_n\} = \{cx_n\}.$$

 (a) Show that V is a vector space with these operations.

 (b) Prove that V is infinite dimensional.

30. Let V be the vector space of Problem 29 and let the subset W consist of those elements $\{x_n\}$ of V such that $x_n = x_{n-1} + x_{n-2}$ for $n \geq 2$. Thus a typical element of W is the *Fibonacci sequence*

$$\{1, 1, 2, 3, 5, 8, 13, 21, 34, 55, \dots\}.$$

 (a) Show that W is a subspace of V.

 (b) Prove that W is 2-dimensional.

31. Motivated by Example 2, let us define a function or transformation T from the set of all complex numbers to the space of all 2×2 matrices of the form in (1) as follows. Given a complex number $z = a + bi$, let

$$T(z) = \begin{bmatrix} a & -b \\ b & a \end{bmatrix}.$$

 (a) Suppose that z_1 and z_2 are complex numbers and c_1 and c_2 are real numbers. Show that

$$T(c_1 z_1 + c_2 z_2) = c_1 T(z_1) + c_2 T(z_2).$$

 (b) Show that

$$T(z_1 z_2) = T(z_1) T(z_2)$$

for all complex numbers z_1 and z_2. Note the complex multiplication on the left in contrast with the matrix multiplication on the right.

 (c) Prove that if z is an arbitrary nonzero complex number, then

$$T(z^{-1}) = \{T(z)\}^{-1},$$

where $z^{-1} = 1/z$ and $\{T(z)\}^{-1}$ is the inverse of the matrix $T(z)$.

32. Let $\mathbf{A}$ and $\mathbf{B}$ be 4×4 (real) matrices partitioned into 2×2 submatrices or "blocks":

$$\mathbf{A} = \begin{bmatrix} \mathbf{A}_{11} & \mathbf{A}_{12} \\ \mathbf{A}_{21} & \mathbf{A}_{22} \end{bmatrix}, \quad \mathbf{B} = \begin{bmatrix} \mathbf{B}_{11} & \mathbf{B}_{12} \\ \mathbf{B}_{21} & \mathbf{B}_{22} \end{bmatrix}.$$

Then verify that $\mathbf{AB}$ can be calculated in "blockwise" fashion:

$$\mathbf{AB} = \begin{bmatrix} \mathbf{A}_{11}\mathbf{B}_{11} + \mathbf{A}_{12}\mathbf{B}_{21} & \mathbf{A}_{11}\mathbf{B}_{12} + \mathbf{A}_{12}\mathbf{B}_{22} \\ \mathbf{A}_{21}\mathbf{B}_{11} + \mathbf{A}_{22}\mathbf{B}_{21} & \mathbf{A}_{21}\mathbf{B}_{12} + \mathbf{A}_{22}\mathbf{B}_{22} \end{bmatrix}.$$

33. Given a 2×2 matrix $\mathbf{M} = \begin{bmatrix} z_{ij} \end{bmatrix}$ whose entries are complex numbers, let $T(\mathbf{M})$ denote the 4×4 matrix of real numbers given in block form by

$$T(\mathbf{M}) = \begin{bmatrix} T(z_{11}) & T(z_{12}) \\ T(z_{21}) & T(z_{22}) \end{bmatrix}.$$

The transformation T on the right-hand side is the one we defined in Problem 31. Suppose that $\mathbf{M}$ and $\mathbf{N}$ are 2×2 complex matrices. Use Problems 31(b) and 32 to show that

$$T(\mathbf{MN}) = T(\mathbf{M})T(\mathbf{N}).$$

Hence one can find the product of the 2×2 complex matrices $\mathbf{M}$ and $\mathbf{N}$ by calculating the product of the 4×4 real matrices $T(\mathbf{M})$ and $T(\mathbf{N})$. For instance, if

$$\mathbf{M} = \begin{bmatrix} 1+i & 2+i \\ 1+2i & 1+3i \end{bmatrix}$$

and

$$N = \begin{bmatrix} 3-i & 1-2i \\ 2-i & 3-2i \end{bmatrix},$$

then

$$T(M)T(N)$$

$$= \begin{bmatrix} 1 & -1 & \vdots & 2 & -1 \\ 1 & 1 & \vdots & 1 & 2 \\ \hdashline 1 & -2 & \vdots & 1 & -3 \\ 2 & 1 & \vdots & 3 & 1 \end{bmatrix} \times \begin{bmatrix} 3 & 1 & \vdots & 1 & 2 \\ -1 & 3 & \vdots & -2 & 1 \\ \hdashline 2 & 1 & \vdots & 3 & 2 \\ -1 & 2 & \vdots & -2 & 3 \end{bmatrix}$$

$$= \begin{bmatrix} 9 & -2 & \vdots & 11 & 2 \\ 2 & 9 & \vdots & -2 & 11 \\ \hdashline 10 & -10 & \vdots & 14 & -7 \\ 10 & 10 & \vdots & 7 & 14 \end{bmatrix}.$$

Therefore

$$MN = \begin{bmatrix} 9+2i & 11-2i \\ 10+10i & 14+7i \end{bmatrix}.$$

If M is a nonsingular 2×2 complex matrix, it can be shown that $T(M^{-1}) = \{T(M)\}^{-1}$. The $n \times n$ versions of these results are sometimes used to carry out complex matrix operations in computer languages that support only real arithmetic.

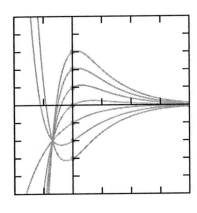

CHAPTER 5

Higher-Order Linear Differential Equations

5.1 Introduction: Second-Order Linear Equations

In Chapters 1 and 2 we investigated first-order differential equations. We now turn to equations of higher order $n \geq 2$, beginning in this chapter with equations that are linear. The general theory of linear differential equations parallels the second-order case ($n = 2$), which we outline in this initial section.

Recall that a second-order differential equation in the (unknown) function $y(x)$ is one of the form

$$G(x, y, y', y'') = 0. \tag{1}$$

This differential equation is said to be **linear** provided that G is linear in the dependent variable y and its derivatives y' and y''. Thus a linear second-order equation takes (or can be written in) the form

$$\blacktriangleright \qquad A(x)y'' + B(x)y' + C(x)y = F(x). \tag{2}$$

Unless otherwise noted, we will always assume that the (known) coefficient functions $A(x)$, $B(x)$, $C(x)$, and $F(x)$ are continuous on some open interval I (perhaps unbounded) on which we wish to solve this differential equation, but we do *not* require that they be linear functions. Thus the differential equation

$$e^x y'' + (\cos x)y' + (1 + \sqrt{x})y = \tan^{-1} x$$

is linear because the dependent variable y and its derivatives y' and y'' appear linearly. By contrast, the equations

$$y'' = yy' \quad \text{and} \quad y'' + 3(y')^2 + 4y^3 = 0$$

are not linear because products and powers of y or its derivatives appear.

283

If the function $F(x)$ on the right-hand side of Eq. (2) vanishes identically on I, then we call Eq. (2) a **homogeneous** linear equation; otherwise, it is **nonhomogeneous**. For example, the second-order equation

$$x^2 y'' + 2xy' + 3y = \cos x$$

is nonhomogeneous; its *associated* homogeneous equation is

$$x^2 y'' + 2xy' + 3y = 0.$$

In general, the homogeneous linear equation **associated** with Eq. (2) is

$$A(x)y'' + B(x)y' + C(x)y = 0. \tag{3}$$

In case the differential equation in (2) models a physical system, the nonhomogeneous term $F(x)$ frequently corresponds to some *external* influence on the system.

A Typical Application

Spring   Mass   Dashpot

$x(t)$

$x = 0$ $x > 0$

Equilibrium
position

FIGURE 5.1.1. A mass-spring-dashpot system.

$F_S \longleftarrow \boxed{m} \longleftarrow F_R$

$x, v > 0$

FIGURE 5.1.2. Directions of the forces acting on m.

Linear differential equations frequently appear as mathematical models of mechanical systems and electrical circuits. For example, suppose that a mass m is attached both to a spring that exerts on it a force F_S and to a dashpot (shock absorber) that exerts a force F_R on the mass (Fig. 5.1.1). Assume that the restoring force F_S of the spring is proportional to the displacement x (positive to the right, negative to the left) of the mass from equilibrium, and that the dashpot force F_R is proportional to the velocity $v = dx/dt$ of the mass. With the aid of Fig. 5.1.2 we also get the appropriate directions of action of these two forces:

$$F_S = -kx \quad \text{and} \quad F_R = -cv \quad (k, c > 0).$$

The minus signs are correct—F_S is negative when x is positive, F_R is negative when v is positive. Newton's law $F = ma$ now gives

$$mx'' = F_S + F_R; \tag{4}$$

that is,

$$m\frac{d^2 x}{dt^2} + c\frac{dx}{dt} + kx = 0. \tag{5}$$

Thus we have a differential equation satisfied by the position function $x(t)$ of the mass m. This homogeneous second-order linear equation governs the *free vibrations* of the mass; we will return to this problem in detail in Section 5.4.

If, in addition to F_S and F_R, the mass m is acted on by an external force $F(t)$—which must then be added to the right-hand side in Eq. (4)—the resulting equation is

$$m\frac{d^2 x}{dt^2} + c\frac{dx}{dt} + kx = F(t). \tag{6}$$

This nonhomogeneous linear differential equation governs the *forced vibrations* of the mass under the influence of the external force $F(t)$.

Homogeneous Second-Order Linear Equations

Consider the general second-order linear equation

$$A(x)y'' + B(x)y' + C(x)y = F(x), \tag{7}$$

where the coefficient functions A, B, C, and F are continuous on the open interval I. Here we assume in addition that $A(x) \neq 0$ at each point of I, so we can divide each term in Eq. (7) by $A(x)$ and write it in the form

➤ $$y'' + p(x)y' + q(x)y = f(x). \tag{8}$$

We will discuss first the associated homogeneous equation

➤ $$y'' + p(x)y' + q(x)y = 0. \tag{9}$$

A particularly useful property of this *homogeneous* linear equation is the fact that the sum of any two solutions of Eq. (9) is again a solution, as is any constant multiple of a solution. This is the central idea of the following theorem.

THEOREM 1: Principle of Superposition for Homogeneous Equations

Let y_1 and y_2 be two solutions of the homogeneous linear equation in (9) on the interval I. If c_1 and c_2 are constants, then the linear combination

$$y = c_1 y_1 + c_2 y_2 \tag{10}$$

is also a solution of Eq. (9) on I.

Proof: The conclusion follows almost immediately from the linearity of the operation of differentiation, which gives

$$y' = c_1 y_1' + c_2 y_2' \quad \text{and} \quad y'' = c_1 y_1'' + c_2 y_2''.$$

Then

$$\begin{aligned}
y'' + py' + qy &= (c_1 y_1 + c_2 y_2)'' + p(c_1 y_1 + c_2 y_2)' + q(c_1 y_1 + c_2 y_2) \\
&= (c_1 y_1'' + c_2 y_2'') + p(c_1 y_1' + c_2 y_2') + q(c_1 y_1 + c_2 y_2) \\
&= c_1 (y_1'' + py_1' + qy_1) + c_2 (y_2'' + py_2' + qy_2) \\
&= c_1 \cdot 0 + c_2 \cdot 0 = 0
\end{aligned}$$

because y_1 and y_2 are solutions. Thus $y = c_1 y_1 + c_2 y_2$ is also a solution. ▲

Remark: According to Theorem 1 in Section 4.2, Theorem 1 here implies that the set $\mathcal{S}$ of all solutions of the homogeneous linear second-order equation (9) is a subspace of the vector space of all functions on the real line **R**—and hence is itself a vector space. We therefore call S the **solution space** of the differential equation.

> **Example 1** We can see by inspection that
>
> $$y_1(x) = \cos x \quad \text{and} \quad y_2(x) = \sin x$$
>
> are two solutions of the equation
>
> $$y'' + y = 0.$$
>
> Theorem 1 tells us that any linear combination of these solutions, such as
>
> $$y(x) = 3y_1(x) - 2y_2(x) = 3\cos x - 2\sin x,$$
>
> is also a solution. Conversely, Problem 28 in Section 4.5 says that *every* solution of $y'' + y = 0$ is a linear combination of these two particular solutions y_1 and y_2. Thus, a general solution of $y'' + y = 0$ is given by
>
> $$y(x) = c_1 \cos x + c_2 \sin x.$$
>
> It is important to understand that this single formula for the general solution encompasses a "twofold infinity" of particular solutions. Indeed, the pair $\{\cos x, \sin x\}$ constitutes a basis of the 2-dimensional solution space $\mathcal{S}$ of the differential equation $y'' + y = 0$. Figures 5.1.3 through 5.1.5 illustrate some of the solutions obtained either with one of the coefficients c_1 and c_2 set equal to zero, or with both nonzero. ∎

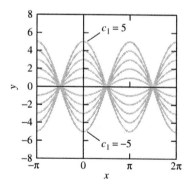

FIGURE 5.1.3. Solutions $y(x) = c_1 \cos x$ of $y'' + y = 0$.

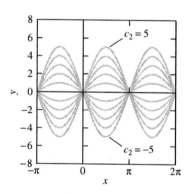

FIGURE 5.1.4. Solutions $y(x) = c_2 \sin x$ of $y'' + y = 0$.

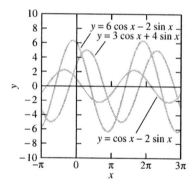

FIGURE 5.1.5. Solutions of $y'' + y = 0$ with c_1 and c_2 both nonzero.

Earlier in this section we gave the linear equation $mx'' + cx' + kx = F(t)$ as a mathematical model of the motion of the mass shown in Fig. 5.1.1. Physical considerations suggest that the motion of the mass should be determined by its initial position and initial velocity. Hence, given any preassigned values of $x(0)$ and $x'(0)$, Eq. (6) ought to have a *unique* solution satisfying these initial conditions. More generally, in order to be a "good" mathematical model of a deterministic physical situation, a differential equation must have unique solutions satisfying any appropriate initial conditions. The following existence and uniqueness theorem (proved in Appendix A) gives us this assurance for the general second-order equation.

THEOREM 2: Existence and Uniqueness for Linear Equations

Suppose that the functions p, q, and f are continuous on the open interval I containing the point a. Then, given any two numbers b_0 and b_1, the equation

$$y'' + p(x)y' + q(x)y = f(x) \tag{8}$$

has a unique (that is, one and only one) solution on the entire interval I that satisfies the initial conditions

$$y(a) = b_0, \quad y'(a) = b_1. \tag{11}$$

▲

Remark 1: Equation (8) and the conditions in (11) constitute a second-order linear **initial value problem.** Theorem 2 tells us that any such initial value problem has a unique solution on the *whole* interval I where the coefficient functions in (8) are continuous. Recall from Section 1.3 that a *nonlinear* differential equation generally has a unique solution on only a smaller interval.

Remark 2: Whereas a *first-order* differential equation $dy/dx = F(x, y)$ generally admits only a single solution curve $y = y(x)$ passing through a given initial point (a, b), Theorem 2 implies that the *second-order* equation in (8) has infinitely many solution curves passing through the point (a, b_0)—namely, one for each (real number) value of the initial slope $y'(a) = b_1$. That is, instead of there being only one line through (a, b_0) tangent to a solution curve, *every* nonvertical straight line through (a, b_0) is tangent to some solution curve of Eq. (8). Figure 5.1.6 shows a number of solution curves of the equation $y'' + 3y' + 2y = 0$ all having the same initial value $y(0) = 1$, while Fig. 5.1.7 shows a number of solution curves all having the same initial slope $y'(0) = 1$. The application at the end of this section suggests how to construct such families of solution curves for a given homogeneous second-order linear differential equation. ∎

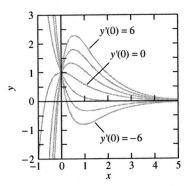

FIGURE 5.1.6. Solutions of $y'' + 3y' + 2y = 0$ with the same initial value $y(0) = 1$ but different initial slopes.

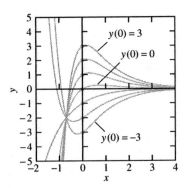

FIGURE 5.1.7. Solutions of $y'' + 3y' + 2y = 0$ with the same initial slope $y'(0) = 1$ but different initial values.

Example 1

Continued

We saw in the first part of Example 1 that $y(x) = 3\cos x - 2\sin x$ is a solution (on the entire real line) of $y'' + y = 0$. It has the initial values $y(0) = 3$, $y'(0) = -2$. Theorem 2 tells us that this is the *only* solution with these initial values. More generally, the solution

$$y(x) = b_0 \cos x + b_1 \sin x$$

satisfies the *arbitrary* initial conditions $y(0) = b_0$, $y'(0) = b_1$; this illustrates the *existence* of such a solution, also as guaranteed by Theorem 2. ∎

Example 1 suggests how, given a *homogeneous* second-order linear equation, we might actually find the solution $y(x)$ whose existence is assured by Theorem 2. First, we find two "essentially different" solutions y_1 and y_2; second, we attempt to impose on the general solution

$$y = c_1 y_1 + c_2 y_2 \tag{12}$$

the initial conditions $y(a) = b_0$, $y'(a) = b_1$. That is, we attempt to solve the simultaneous equations

$$\begin{aligned} c_1 y_1(a) + c_2 y_2(a) &= b_0, \\ c_1 y_1'(a) + c_2 y_2'(a) &= b_1 \end{aligned} \tag{13}$$

for the coefficients c_1 and c_2.

Example 2   Verify that the functions

$$y_1(x) = e^x \quad \text{and} \quad y_2(x) = xe^x$$

are solutions of the differential equation

$$y'' - 2y' + y = 0,$$

and then find a solution satisfying the initial conditions $y(0) = 3$, $y'(0) = 1$.

Solution   The verification is routine; we omit it. We impose the given initial conditions on the general solution

$$y(x) = c_1 e^x + c_2 x e^x,$$

for which

$$y'(x) = (c_1 + c_2)e^x + c_2 x e^x,$$

to obtain the simultaneous equations

$$\begin{aligned} y(0) &= c_1 &&= 3, \\ y'(0) &= c_1 + c_2 &&= 1. \end{aligned}$$

The resulting solution is $c_1 = 3$, $c_2 = -2$. Hence the solution of the original initial value problem is

$$y(x) = 3e^x - 2xe^x.$$

Figure 5.1.8 shows several additional solutions of $y'' - 2y' + y = 0$, all having the same initial value $y(0) = 3$. ∎

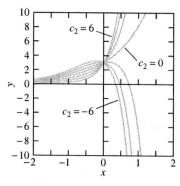

FIGURE 5.1.8. Different solutions $y(x) = 3e^x + c_2 x e^x$ of $y'' - 2y' + y = 0$ with the same initial value $y(0) = 3$.

Linearly Independent Solutions

In order for the procedure of Example 2 to succeed, the two solutions y_1 and y_2 must have the property that the equations in (13) can always be solved for c_1 and c_2, no matter what the initial values $y(a) = b_0$ and $y'(a) = b_1$ might be. This is so, provided that the two functions y_1 and y_2 are linearly independent. According to the following definition, linear independence of functions defined on an interval I is analogous to linear independence of ordinary vectors.

Definition: Linear Independence of Two Functions

Two functions defined on an open interval I are said to be **linearly independent** on I provided that neither is a constant multiple of the other.

Two functions are said to be **linearly dependent** on an open interval provided that they are not linearly independent there; that is, one of them is a constant multiple of the other. We can always determine whether two given functions f and g are linearly dependent on an interval I by noting at a glance whether either of the two quotients f/g or g/f is a constant-valued function on I.

Example 3   Thus it is clear that the following pairs of functions are linearly independent on the entire real line:

$$\sin x \quad \text{and} \quad \cos x;$$
$$e^x \quad \text{and} \quad e^{-2x};$$
$$e^x \quad \text{and} \quad xe^x;$$
$$x + 1 \quad \text{and} \quad x^2;$$
$$x \quad \text{and} \quad |x|.$$

That is, neither $\sin x / \cos x = \tan x$ nor $\cos x / \sin x = \cot x$ is a constant-valued function; neither $e^x / e^{-2x} = e^{3x}$ nor e^{-2x} / e^x is a constant-valued function; and so forth. But the identically zero function $f(x) \equiv 0$ and any other function g are linearly dependent on every interval, because $0 \cdot g(x) = 0 = f(x)$. Also, the functions

$$f(x) = \sin 2x \quad \text{and} \quad g(x) = \sin x \cos x$$

are linearly dependent on any interval because $f(x) = 2g(x)$ is the familiar trigonometric identity $\sin 2x = 2 \sin x \cos x$.   ■

General Solutions

But does the homogeneous equation $y'' + py' + qy = 0$ always have two linearly independent solutions? Theorem 2 says yes! We need only choose y_1 and y_2 so that

$$y_1(a) = 1, \ y_1'(a) = 0 \quad \text{and} \quad y_2(a) = 0, \ y_2'(a) = 1.$$

It is then impossible that either $y_1 = ky_2$ or $y_2 = ky_1$ because $k \cdot 0 \neq 1$ for any constant k. Theorem 2 tells us that two such linearly independent solutions *exist*; actually finding them is a crucial matter that we will discuss briefly at the end of this section, and in greater detail beginning in Section 5.3.

We want to show, finally, that given *any* two linearly independent solutions y_1 and y_2 of the homogeneous equation

$$y''(x) + p(x)y'(x) + q(x)y(x) = 0, \tag{9}$$

every solution y of Eq. (9) can be expressed as a linear combination

$$y = c_1 y_1 + c_2 y_2 \tag{12}$$

of y_1 and y_2. This means that the function in (12) is a *general solution* of Eq. (9)—it provides all possible solutions of the differential equation.

As suggested by the equations in (13), the determination of the constants c_1 and c_2 in (12) depends on a certain 2×2 determinant of values of y_1, y_2, and their derivatives. Given two functions f and g, the **Wronskian** of f and g is the determinant

➤
$$W = \begin{vmatrix} f & g \\ f' & g' \end{vmatrix} = fg' - f'g.$$

We write either $W(f, g)$ or $W(x)$, depending on whether we wish to emphasize the two functions or the point x at which the Wronskian is to be evaluated. For example,

$$W(\cos x, \sin x) = \begin{vmatrix} \cos x & \sin x \\ -\sin x & \cos x \end{vmatrix} = \cos^2 x + \sin^2 x = 1$$

and

$$W(e^x, xe^x) = \begin{vmatrix} e^x & xe^x \\ e^x & e^x + xe^x \end{vmatrix} = e^{2x}.$$

These are examples of linearly *independent* pairs of solutions of differential equations (see Examples 1 and 2). Note that in both cases the Wronskian is everywhere *nonzero*.

On the other hand, if the functions f and g are linearly dependent, with $f = kg$ (for example), then

$$W(f, g) = \begin{vmatrix} kg & g \\ kg' & g' \end{vmatrix} = kgg' - kg'g \equiv 0.$$

Thus the Wronskian of two linearly *dependent* functions is identically zero. In Section 5.2 we will prove that, if the two functions y_1 and y_2 are solutions of a homogeneous second-order linear equation, then the strong converse stated in part (b) of Theorem 3 holds.

THEOREM 3: Wronskians of Solutions

Suppose that y_1 and y_2 are two solutions of the homogeneous second-order linear equation [Eq. (9)]

$$y'' + p(x)y' + q(x)y = 0$$

on an open interval I on which p and q are continuous.

(a) If y_1 and y_2 are linearly dependent, then $W(y_1, y_2) \equiv 0$ on I.

(b) If y_1 and y_2 are linearly independent, then $W(y_1, y_2) \neq 0$ at each point of I.▲

Thus, given two solutions of Eq. (9), there are just two possibilities: The Wronskian W is identically zero if the solutions are linearly dependent; the Wronskian is never zero if the solutions are linearly independent. The latter fact is what we need to show that $y = c_1 y_1 + c_2 y_2$ is the general solution of Eq. (9) if y_1 and y_2 are linearly independent solutions.

THEOREM 4: General Solutions of Homogeneous Equations

Let y_1 and y_2 be two linearly independent solutions of the homogeneous equation [Eq. (9)]

$$y'' + p(x)y' + q(x)y = 0$$

with p and q continuous on the open interval I. If Y is any solution whatsoever of Eq. (9) on I, then there exist numbers c_1 and c_2 such that

$$Y(x) = c_1 y_1(x) + c_2 y_2(x)$$

for all x in I. ▲

Remark: In essence, Theorem 4 tells us that, when we have found *two* linearly independent solutions y_1 and y_2 of the homogeneous equation in (9), we have then found *all* of its solutions. Specifically, $\{y_1, y_2\}$ is then a basis for the solution space of the differential equation. We therefore call the linear combination $Y = c_1 y_1 + c_2 y_2$ a *general solution* of the differential equation.

Proof of Theorem 4: Choose a point a of I, and consider the simultaneous equations

$$\begin{align} c_1 y_1(a) + c_2 y_2(a) = Y(a), \\ c_1 y_1'(a) + c_2 y_2'(a) = Y'(a). \end{align} \tag{14}$$

The determinant of the coefficients in this system of linear equations in the unknowns c_1 and c_2 is simply the Wronskian $W(y_1, y_2)$ evaluated at $x = a$. By Theorem 3, this determinant is nonzero, so by elementary algebra it follows that the equations in (14) can be solved for c_1 and c_2. With these values of c_1 and c_2, we define the solution

$$G(x) = c_1 y_1(x) + c_2 y_2(x)$$

of Eq. (9); then

$$G(a) = c_1 y_1(a) + c_2 y_2(a) = Y(a)$$

and

$$G'(a) = c_1 y_1'(a) + c_2 y_2'(a) = Y'(a).$$

Thus the two solutions Y and G have the same initial values at a, as do Y' and G'. By the uniqueness of a solution determined by such initial values (Theorem 2), it follows that Y and G agree on I. Thus we see that

$$Y(x) \equiv G(x) = c_1 y_1(x) + c_2 y_2(x),$$

as desired. ▲

Example 4   If $y_1(x) = e^{2x}$ and $y_2(x) = e^{-2x}$, then

$$y_1'' = (2)(2)e^{2x} = 4e^{2x} = 4y_1 \quad \text{and} \quad y_2'' = (-2)(-2)e^{-2x} = 4e^{-2x} = 4y_2.$$

Therefore, y_1 and y_2 are linearly independent solutions of

$$y'' - 4y = 0. \tag{15}$$

But $y_3(x) = \cosh 2x$ and $y_4(x) = \sinh 2x$ are also solutions of Eq. (15), because

$$\frac{d^2}{dx^2}(\cosh 2x) = \frac{d}{dx}(2 \sinh 2x) = 4 \cosh 2x$$

and, similarly, $(\sinh 2x)'' = 4 \sinh 2x$. It therefore follows from Theorem 4 that the functions $\cosh 2x$ and $\sinh 2x$ can be expressed as linear combinations of $y_1(x) = e^{2x}$ and $y_2(x) = e^{-2x}$. Of course, this is no surprise, because

$$\cosh 2x = \tfrac{1}{2}e^{2x} + \tfrac{1}{2}e^{-2x} \quad \text{and} \quad \sinh 2x = \tfrac{1}{2}e^{2x} - \tfrac{1}{2}e^{-2x}$$

by the definitions of the hyperbolic cosine and hyperbolic sine functions. Thus the solution space of the differential equation $y'' - 4y = 0$ has the two different bases $\{e^{2x}, e^{-2x}\}$ and $\{\cosh 2x, \sinh 2x\}$. ■

    Remark: Because e^{2x}, e^{-2x} and $\cosh 2x$, $\sinh 2x$ are two different pairs of linearly independent solutions of the equation $y'' - 4y = 0$ in (15), Theorem 4 implies that every particular solution $Y(x)$ of this equation can be written both in the form

$$Y(x) = c_1 e^{2x} + c_2 e^{-2x}$$

and in the form

$$Y(x) = a \cosh 2x + b \sinh 2x.$$

Thus these two different linear combinations (with arbitrary constant coefficients) provide two different descriptions of the set of all solutions of the same differential equation $y'' - 4y = 0$. Hence each of these two linear combinations is a general solution of the equation. Indeed, this is why it is accurate to refer to a specific such linear combination as "*a* general solution" rather than as "*the* general solution." ■

Linear Second-Order Equations with Constant Coefficients

As an illustration of the general theory introduced in this section, we discuss the homogeneous second-order linear differential equation

$$ay'' + by' + cy = 0 \tag{16}$$

with *constant* coefficients a, b, and c. We first look for a *single* solution of Eq. (16) and begin with the observation that

$$(e^{rx})' = re^{rx} \quad \text{and} \quad (e^{rx})'' = r^2 e^{rx}, \tag{17}$$

so any derivative of e^{rx} is a constant multiple of e^{rx}. Hence, if we substituted $y = e^{rx}$ in Eq. (16), then each term would be a constant multiple of e^{rx}, with the constant coefficients dependent on r and the coefficients a, b, and c. This suggests that we try to find a value of r so that these multiples of e^{rx} will have sum zero. If we succeed, then $y = e^{rx}$ will be a solution of Eq. (16).

For example, if we substitute $y = e^{rx}$ in the equation

$$y'' - 5y' + 6y = 0,$$

we obtain

$$r^2 e^{rx} - 5re^{rx} + 6e^{rx} = 0.$$

Thus

$$(r^2 - 5r + 6)e^{rx} = 0; \quad (r-2)(r-3)e^{rx} = 0.$$

Hence $y = e^{rx}$ will be a solution if either $r = 2$ or $r = 3$. So, in searching for a single solution, we actually have found two solutions: $y_1(x) = e^{2x}$ and $y_2(x) = e^{3x}$.

To carry out this procedure in the general case, we substitute $y = e^{rx}$ in Eq. (16). With the aid of the equations in (17), we find the result to be

$$ar^2 e^{rx} + bre^{rx} + ce^{rx} = 0.$$

Because e^{rx} is never zero, we conclude that $y(x) = e^{rx}$ will satisfy the differential equation in (16) precisely when r is a root of the *algebraic* equation

$$ar^2 + br + c = 0. \tag{18}$$

This quadratic equation is called the **characteristic equation** of the homogeneous linear differential equation

$$ay'' + by' + cy = 0. \tag{16}$$

If Eq. (18) has two *distinct* (unequal) real roots r_1 and r_2, then the corresponding solutions $y_1(x) = e^{r_1 x}$ and $y_2(x) = e^{r_2 x}$ of (16) are linearly independent. (Why?) This gives the following result.

THEOREM 5: Distinct Real Roots

If the roots r_1 and r_2 of the characteristic equation in (18) are real and distinct, then

$$y(x) = c_1 e^{r_1 x} + c_2 e^{r_2 x} \tag{19}$$

is a general solution of Eq. (16). Thus the solution space of the equation $ay'' + by' + cy = 0$ has basis $\{e^{r_1 x}, e^{r_2 x}\}$.   ▲

Example 5   Find the general solution of

$$2y'' - 7y' + 3y = 0.$$

Solution   We can solve the characteristic equation

$$2r^2 - 7r + 3 = 0$$

by factoring:

$$(2r - 1)(r - 3) = 0.$$

The roots $r_1 = \frac{1}{2}$ and $r_2 = 3$ are real and distinct, so Theorem 5 yields the general solution

$$y(x) = c_1 e^{x/2} + c_2 e^{3x}. \qquad \blacksquare$$

Example 6   The differential equation $y'' + 2y' = 0$ has characteristic equation

$$r^2 + 2r = r(r + 2) = 0$$

with distinct real roots $r_1 = 0$ and $r_2 = -2$. Because $e^{0 \cdot x} \equiv 1$, we get the general solution

$$y(x) = c_1 + c_2 e^{-2x}.$$

Figure 5.1.9 shows several different solution curves with $c_1 = 1$, all appearing to approach the solution curve $y(x) \equiv 1$ (with $c_2 = 0$) as $x \to +\infty$. $\blacksquare$

Remark: Note that Theorem 5 changes a problem involving a differential equation into one involving only the solution of an *algebraic* equation. $\blacksquare$

If the characteristic equation in (18) has equal roots $r_1 = r_2$, we get (at first) only the single solution $y_1(x) = e^{r_1 x}$ of Eq. (16). The problem in this case is to produce the "missing" second solution of the differential equation.

A double root $r = r_1$ will occur precisely when the characteristic equation is a constant multiple of the equation

$$(r - r_1)^2 = r^2 - 2r_1 r + r_1^2 = 0.$$

Any differential equation with this characteristic equation is equivalent to

$$y'' - 2r_1 y' + r_1^2 y = 0. \qquad (20)$$

But it is easy to verify by direct substitution that $y = x e^{r_1 x}$ is a second solution of Eq. (20). It is clear (but you should verify) that

$$y_1(x) = e^{r_1 x} \quad \text{and} \quad y_2(x) = x e^{r_1 x}$$

are linearly independent functions, so the general solution of the differential equation in (20) is

$$y(x) = c_1 e^{r_1 x} + c_2 x e^{r_1 x}.$$

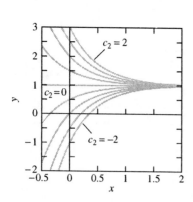

FIGURE 5.1.9. Solutions $y(x) = 1 + c_2 e^{-2x}$ of $y'' + 2y' = 0$ with different values of c_2.

THEOREM 6: Repeated Roots

If the characteristic equation in (18) has equal (necessarily real) roots $r_1 = r_2$, then

$$y(x) = (c_1 + c_2x)e^{r_1x} \tag{21}$$

is a general solution of Eq. (16). In this case the solution space of the equation $ay'' + by' + cy = 0$ has basis $\{e^{r_1x}, xe^{r_1x}\}$. ▲

Example 7

To solve the initial value problem

$$y'' + 2y' + y = 0;$$
$$y(0) = 5, \quad y'(0) = -3,$$

we note first that the characteristic equation

$$r^2 + 2r + 1 = (r+1)^2 = 0$$

has equal roots $r_1 = r_2 = -1$. Hence the general solution provided by Theorem 6 is

$$y(x) = c_1e^{-x} + c_2xe^{-x}.$$

Differentiation yields

$$y'(x) = -c_1e^{-x} + c_2e^{-x} - c_2xe^{-x},$$

so the initial conditions yield the equations

$$\begin{aligned} y(0) &= c_1 &&= 5, \\ y'(0) &= -c_1 + c_2 &&= -3, \end{aligned}$$

which imply that $c_1 = 5$ and $c_2 = 2$. Thus the desired particular solution of the initial value problem is

$$y(x) = 5e^{-x} + 2xe^{-x}.$$

This particular solution, together with several others of the form $y(x) = c_1e^{-x} + 2xe^{-x}$, is illustrated in Fig. 5.1.10. ∎

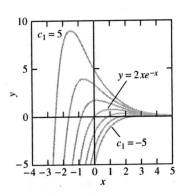

FIGURE 5.1.10. Solutions $y(x) = c_1e^{-x} + 2xe^{-x}$ of $y'' + 2y' + y = 0$ with different values of c_1.

The characteristic equation in (18) may have either real or complex roots. The case of complex roots will be discussed in Section 5.3.

5.1 Problems

In Problems 1 through 16, a homogeneous second-order linear differential equation, two functions y_1 and y_2, and a pair of initial conditions are given. First verify that y_1 and y_2 are solutions of the differential equation. Then find a particular solution of the form $y = c_1 y_1 + c_2 y_2$ that satisfies the given initial conditions. Primes denote derivatives with respect to x.

1. $y'' - y = 0$; $y_1 = e^x$, $y_2 = e^{-x}$; $y(0) = 0$, $y'(0) = 5$

2. $y'' - 9y = 0$; $y_1 = e^{3x}$, $y_2 = e^{-3x}$; $y(0) = -1$, $y'(0) = 15$

3. $y'' + 4y = 0$; $y_1 = \cos 2x$, $y_2 = \sin 2x$; $y(0) = 3$, $y'(0) = 8$

4. $y'' + 25y = 0$; $y_1 = \cos 5x$, $y_2 = \sin 5x$; $y(0) = 10$, $y'(0) = -10$

5. $y'' - 3y' + 2y = 0$; $y_1 = e^x$, $y_2 = e^{2x}$; $y(0) = 1$, $y'(0) = 0$

6. $y'' + y' - 6y = 0$; $y_1 = e^{2x}$, $y_2 = e^{-3x}$; $y(0) = 7$, $y'(0) = -1$

7. $y'' + y' = 0$; $y_1 = 1$, $y_2 = e^{-x}$; $y(0) = -2$, $y'(0) = 8$

8. $y'' - 3y' = 0$; $y_1 = 1$, $y_2 = e^{3x}$; $y(0) = 4$, $y'(0) = -2$

9. $y'' + 2y' + y = 0$; $y_1 = e^{-x}$, $y_2 = xe^{-x}$; $y(0) = 2$, $y'(0) = -1$

10. $y'' - 10y' + 25y = 0$; $y_1 = e^{5x}$, $y_2 = xe^{5x}$; $y(0) = 3$, $y'(0) = 13$

11. $y'' - 2y' + 2y = 0$; $y_1 = e^x \cos x$, $y_2 = e^x \sin x$; $y(0) = 0$, $y'(0) = 5$

12. $y'' + 6y' + 13y = 0$; $y_1 = e^{-3x} \cos 2x$, $y_2 = e^{-3x} \sin 2x$; $y(0) = 2$, $y'(0) = 0$

13. $x^2 y'' - 2xy' + 2y = 0$; $y_1 = x$, $y_2 = x^2$; $y(1) = 3$, $y'(1) = 1$

14. $x^2 y'' + 2xy' - 6y = 0$; $y_1 = x^2$, $y_2 = x^{-3}$; $y(2) = 10$, $y'(2) = 15$

15. $x^2 y'' - xy' + y = 0$; $y_1 = x$, $y_2 = x \ln x$; $y(1) = 7$, $y'(1) = 2$

16. $x^2 y'' + xy' + y = 0$; $y_1 = \cos(\ln x)$, $y_2 = \sin(\ln x)$; $y(1) = 2$, $y'(1) = 3$

The following three problems illustrate the fact that the superposition principle does not generally hold for nonlinear equations.

17. Show that $y = 1/x$ is a solution of $y' + y^2 = 0$, but that if $c \neq 0$ and $c \neq 1$, then $y = c/x$ is not a solution.

18. Show that $y = x^3$ is a solution of $yy'' = 6x^4$, but that if $c^2 \neq 1$, then $y = cx^3$ is not a solution.

19. Show that $y_1 \equiv 1$ and $y_2 = \sqrt{x}$ are solutions of $yy'' + (y')^2 = 0$, but that their sum $y = y_1 + y_2$ is not a solution.

Determine whether the pairs of functions in Problems 20 through 26 are linearly independent or linearly dependent on the real line.

20. $f(x) = \pi$, $g(x) = \cos^2 x + \sin^2 x$

21. $f(x) = x^3$, $g(x) = x^2 |x|$

22. $f(x) = 1 + x$, $g(x) = 1 + |x|$

23. $f(x) = xe^x$, $g(x) = |x| e^x$

24. $f(x) = \sin^2 x$, $g(x) = 1 - \cos 2x$

25. $f(x) = e^x \sin x$, $g(x) = e^x \cos x$

26. $f(x) = 2 \cos x + 3 \sin x$, $g(x) = 3 \cos x - 2 \sin x$

27. Let y_p be a particular solution of the nonhomogeneous equation $y'' + py' + qy = f(x)$ and let y_c be a solution of its associated homogeneous equation. Show that $y = y_c + y_p$ is a solution of the given nonhomogeneous equation.

28. With $y_p = 1$ and $y_c = c_1 \cos x + c_2 \sin x$ in the notation of Problem 27, find a solution of $y'' + y = 1$ satisfying the initial conditions $y(0) = -1 = y'(0)$.

29. Show that $y_1 = x^2$ and $y_2 = x^3$ are two different solutions of $x^2 y'' - 4xy' + 6y = 0$, both satisfying the initial conditions $y(0) = 0 = y'(0)$. Explain why these facts do not contradict Theorem 2 (with respect to the guaranteed uniqueness).

30. (a) Show that $y_1 = x^3$ and $y_2 = |x^3|$ are linearly independent solutions on the real line of the equation $x^2 y'' - 3xy' + 3y = 0$. (b) Verify that $W(y_1, y_2)$ is identically zero. Why do these facts not contradict Theorem 3?

31. Show that $y_1 = \sin x^2$ and $y_2 = \cos x^2$ are linearly independent functions, but that their Wronskian vanishes at $x = 0$. Why does this imply that there is *no* differential equation of the form $y'' + p(x)y' + q(x)y = 0$, with both p and q continuous everywhere, having both y_1 and y_2 as solutions?

32. Let y_1 and y_2 be two solutions of $A(x)y'' + B(x)y' + C(x)y = 0$ on an open interval I where A, B, and C are continuous and $A(x)$ is never zero. (a) Let $W = W(y_1, y_2)$. Show that

$$A(x)\frac{dW}{dx} = (y_1)(Ay_2'') - (y_2)(Ay_1'').$$

Then substitute for Ay_2'' and Ay_1'' from the original differential equation to show that

$$A(x)\frac{dW}{dx} = -B(x)W(x).$$

(b) Solve this first-order equation to deduce **Abel's formula**

$$W(x) = K \exp\left(-\int \frac{B(x)}{A(x)}\, dx\right),$$

where K is a constant. (c) Why does Abel's formula imply that the Wronskian $W(y_1, y_2)$ is either zero everywhere or nonzero everywhere (as stated in Theorem 3)?

Apply Theorems 5 and 6 to find general solutions of the differential equations given in Problems 33 through 42. Primes denote derivatives with respect to x.

33. $y'' - 3y' + 2y = 0$

34. $y'' + 2y' - 15y = 0$

35. $y'' + 5y' = 0$

36. $2y'' + 3y' = 0$

37. $2y'' - y' - y = 0$

38. $4y'' + 8y' + 3y = 0$

39. $4y'' + 4y' + y = 0$

40. $9y'' - 12y' + 4y = 0$

41. $6y'' - 7y' - 20y = 0$

42. $35y'' - y' - 12y = 0$

Each of Problems 43 through 48 gives a general solution $y(x)$ of a homogeneous second-order differential equation $ay'' + by' + cy = 0$ with constant coefficients. Find this equation.

43. $y(x) = c_1 + c_2 e^{-10x}$ **44.** $y(x) = c_1 e^{10x} + c_2 e^{-10x}$
45. $y(x) = c_1 e^{-10x} + c_2 x e^{-10x}$
46. $y(x) = c_1 e^{10x} + c_2 e^{100x}$ **47.** $y(x) = c_1 + c_2 x$
48. $y(x) = e^x \left(c_1 e^{x\sqrt{2}} + c_2 e^{-x\sqrt{2}} \right)$

Problems 49 and 50 deal with the solution curves of $y'' + 3y' + 2y = 0$ shown in Figs. 5.1.6 and 5.1.7.

49. Find the highest point on the solution curve with $y(0) = 1$ and $y'(0) = 6$ in Fig. 5.1.6.
50. Find the third-quadrant point of intersection of the solution curves shown in Fig. 5.1.7.
51. A second-order **Euler equation** is one of the form

$$ax^2 y'' + bxy' + cy = 0, \tag{22}$$

where a, b, c are constants. **(a)** Show that if $x > 0$, then the substitution $v = \ln x$ transforms Eq. (22) into the constant-coefficient linear equation

$$a\frac{d^2 y}{dv^2} + (b - a)\frac{dy}{dv} + cy = 0 \tag{23}$$

with independent variable v. **(b)** If the roots r_1 and r_2 of the characteristic equation of Eq. (23) are real and distinct, conclude that a general solution of the Euler equation in (22) is $y(x) = c_1 x^{r_1} + c_2 x^{r_2}$.

Make the substitution $v = \ln x$ of Problem 51 to find general solutions (for $x > 0$) of the Euler equations in Problems 52–56.

52. $x^2 y'' + xy' - y = 0$ **53.** $x^2 y'' + 2xy' - 12y = 0$
54. $4x^2 y'' + 8xy' - 3y = 0$ **55.** $x^2 y'' + xy' = 0$
56. $x^2 y'' - 3xy' + 4y = 0$

5.1 Application: Plotting Second-Order Solution Families

This application deals with the plotting by computer of families of solutions such as those illustrated in Figs. 5.1.6 and 5.1.7. Show first that the general solution of the differential equation

$$y'' + 3y' + 2y = 0 \tag{1}$$

is

$$y(x) = c_1 e^{-x} + c_2 e^{-2x}. \tag{2}$$

For Fig. 5.1.6, show that the particular solution of Eq. (1) satisfying the initial conditions $y(0) = 1$, $y'(0) = b$ is given by

$$y(x) = (b + 2)e^{-x} - (b + 1)e^{-2x}. \tag{3}$$

The MATLAB loop

```
x = - 1 : 0.02 : 5        % x-vector from x = - 1 to x = 5
for b = -6 : 2 : 6        % for b = -6 to 6 with db = 2 do
    y = (b + 2)*exp(-x) - (b + 1)*exp(-2*x);
    plot(x,y)
end
```

was used to generate Fig. 5.1.6.

For Fig. 5.1.7, show that the particular solution of Eq. (1) satisfying the initial conditions $y(0) = a$, $y'(0) = 1$ is given by

$$y(x) = (2a + 1)e^{-x} - (a + 1)e^{-2x}. \tag{4}$$

The MATLAB loop

```
x = -2 : 0.02 : 4         % x-vector from x = -2 to x = 4
```

```
for a = -3 : 1 : 3        % for a = -3 to 3 with da = 1 do
    y = (2*a + 1)*exp(-x) - (a + 1)*exp(-2*x);
    plot(x,y)
end
```

was used to generate Fig. 5.1.7.

Computer algebra systems such as *Maple* and *Mathematica*, as well as graphing calculators, have commands to carry out for-loops such as the two shown here. Begin by reproducing Figs. 5.1.6 and 5.1.7. Then, for each of the following differential equations, construct both a family of solution curves satisfying $y(0) = 1$ and a family of solution curves satisfying the initial condition $y'(0) = 1$.

1. $y'' - y = 0$

2. $y'' - 3y' + 2y = 0$

3. $2y'' + 3y' + y = 0$

4. $y'' + y = 0$ (see Example 1)

5. $y'' + 2y' + 2y = 0$, which has general solution $y(x) = e^{-x}(c_1 \cos x + c_2 \sin x)$.

5.2 General Solutions of Linear Equations

We now show that our discussion in Section 5.1 of second-order linear equations generalizes in a very natural way to the general *n*th-order linear differential equation of the form

$$P_0(x)y^{(n)} + P_1(x)y^{(n-1)} + \cdots + P_{n-1}(x)y' + P_n(x)y = F(x). \tag{1}$$

Unless otherwise noted, we will always assume that the coefficient functions $P_i(x)$ and $F(x)$ are continuous on some open interval I (perhaps unbounded), where we wish to solve the equation. Under the additional assumption that $P_0(x) \neq 0$ at each point of I, we can divide each term in Eq. (1) by $P_0(x)$ to obtain an equation with leading coefficient 1, of the form

➤ $$y^{(n)} + p_1(x)y^{(n-1)} + \cdots + p_{n-1}(x)y' + p_n(x)y = f(x). \tag{2}$$

The **homogeneous** linear equation **associated with** Eq. (2) is

➤ $$y^{(n)} + p_1(x)y^{(n-1)} + \cdots + p_{n-1}(x)y' + p_n(x)y = 0. \tag{3}$$

Just as in the second-order case, a *homogeneous* nth-order linear differential equation has the valuable property that any superposition, or *linear combination*, of solutions of the equation is again a solution. The proof of the following theorem is essentially the same—a routine verification—as that of Theorem 1 of Section 5.1.

THEOREM 1: Principle of Superposition for Homogeneous Equations

Let $y_1, y_2, \ldots, y_n$ be n solutions of the homogeneous linear equation in (3) on the interval I. If $c_1, c_2, \ldots, c_n$ are constants, then the linear combination

➤ $$y = c_1 y_1 + c_2 y_2 + \cdots + c_n y_n \tag{4}$$

is also a solution of Eq. (3) on I. ▲

Example 1 It is easy to verify that the three functions

$$y_1(x) = e^{-3x}, \quad y_2(x) = \cos 2x, \quad \text{and} \quad y_3(x) = \sin 2x$$

are all solutions of the homogeneous third-order equation

$$y^{(3)} + 3y'' + 4y' + 12y = 0$$

on the entire real line. Theorem 1 tells us that any linear combination of these solutions, such as

$$y(x) = -3y_1(x) + 3y_2(x) - 2y_3(x) = -3e^{-3x} + 3\cos 2x - 2\sin 2x,$$

is also a solution on the entire real line. We will see that, conversely, every solution of the differential equation of this example is a linear combination of the three particular solutions y_1, y_2, and y_3. Thus a general solution is given by

$$y(x) = c_1 e^{-3x} + c_2 \cos 2x + c_3 \sin 2x. \qquad \blacksquare$$

Existence and Uniqueness of Solutions

We saw in Section 5.1 that a particular solution of a *second-order* linear differential equation is determined by *two* initial conditions. Similarly, a particular solution of an nth-order linear differential equation is determined by n initial conditions. The following theorem, proved in the Appendix, is the natural generalization of Theorem 2 of Section 5.1.

THEOREM 2: Existence and Uniqueness for Linear Equations

Suppose that the functions p_1, p_2, ..., p_n, and f are continuous on the open interval I containing the point a. Then, given n numbers b_0, b_1, ..., b_{n-1}, the nth-order linear equation [Eq. (2)]

$$y^{(n)} + p_1(x)y^{(n-1)} + \cdots + p_{n-1}(x)y' + p_n(x)y = f(x)$$

has a unique (that is, one and only one) solution on the entire interval I that satisfies the n initial conditions

$$y(a) = b_0, \quad y'(a) = b_1, \quad \ldots, \quad y^{(n-1)}(a) = b_{n-1}. \qquad (5)$$

▲

Equation (2) and the conditions in (5) constitute an nth-order **initial value problem**. Theorem 2 tells us that any such initial value problem has a unique solution on the *whole* interval I where the coefficient functions in (2) are continuous. It tells us nothing, however, about how to find this solution. In Section 5.3 we will see how to construct explicit solutions of initial value problems in the *constant* coefficient case that occurs often in applications.

Example 1
Continued

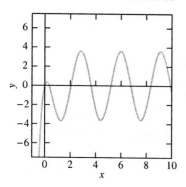

FIGURE 5.2.1. The particular solution $y(x) = -3e^{-3x} + 3\cos 2x - 2\sin 2x$.

We saw earlier that

$$y(x) = -3e^{-3x} + 3\cos 2x - 2\sin 2x$$

is a solution of

$$y^{(3)} + 3y'' + 4y' + 12y = 0$$

on the entire real line. This particular solution has initial values $y(0) = 0$, $y'(0) = 5$, and $y''(0) = -39$, and Theorem 2 implies that there is no other solution with these same initial values. Note that its graph (in Fig. 5.2.1) looks periodic on the right. Indeed, because of the negative exponent, we see that $y(x) \approx 3\cos 2x - 2\sin 2x$ for large positive x. ∎

Remark: Because its general solution involves the three arbitrary constants c_1, c_2, and c_3, the third-order equation in Example 1 has a "threefold infinity" of solutions, including three families of especially simple solutions:

- $y(x) = c_1 e^{-3x}$ (obtained from the general solution with $c_2 = c_3 = 0$),
- $y(x) = c_2 \cos 2x$ (with $c_1 = c_3 = 0$), and
- $y(x) = c_3 \sin 2x$ (with $c_1 = c_2 = 0$).

Alternatively, Theorem 2 suggests a threefold infinity of particular solutions corresponding to independent choices of the three initial values $y(0) = b_0$, $y'(0) = b_1$, and $y''(0) = b_2$. Figures 5.2.2 through 5.2.4 illustrate three corresponding families of solutions—for each of which, two of these three initial values are zero. ∎

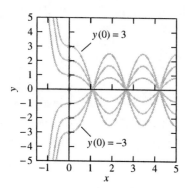

FIGURE 5.2.2. Solutions of $y^{(3)} + 3y'' + 4y' + 12y = 0$ with $y'(0) = y''(0) = 0$ but with different values for $y(0)$.

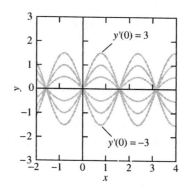

FIGURE 5.2.3. Solutions of $y^{(3)} + 3y'' + 4y' + 12y = 0$ with $y(0) = y''(0) = 0$ but with different values for $y'(0)$.

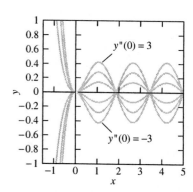

FIGURE 5.2.4. Solutions of $y^{(3)} + 3y'' + 4y' + 12y = 0$ with $y(0) = y'(0) = 0$ but with different values for $y''(0)$.

Note that Theorem 2 implies that the *trivial* solution $y(x) \equiv 0$ is the only solution of the *homogeneous* equation

$$y^{(n)} + p_1(x)y^{(n-1)} + \cdots + p_{n-1}(x)y' + p_n(x)y = 0 \qquad (3)$$

that satisfies the *trivial* initial conditions

$$y(a) = y'(a) = \cdots = y^{(n-1)}(a) = 0.$$

Example 2 It is easy to verify that

$$y_1(x) = x^2 \quad \text{and} \quad y_2(x) = x^3$$

are two different solutions of

$$x^2 y'' - 4xy' + 6y = 0,$$

and that both satisfy the initial conditions $y(0) = y'(0) = 0$. Why does this not contradict the uniqueness part of Theorem 2? It is because the leading coefficient in this differential equation vanishes at $x = 0$, so this equation cannot be written in the form of Eq. (3) with coefficient functions *continuous* on an open interval containing the point $x = 0$. ∎

Linearly Independent Solutions

On the basis of our knowledge of general solutions of second-order linear equations, we anticipate that a general solution of the *homogeneous* nth-order linear equation

➤ $$y^{(n)} + p_1(x)y^{(n-1)} + \cdots + p_{n-1}(x)y' + p_n(x)y = 0 \qquad (3)$$

will be a linear combination

➤ $$y = c_1 y_1 + c_2 y_2 + \cdots + c_n y_n, \qquad (4)$$

where $y_1, y_2, \ldots, y_n$ are particular solutions of Eq. (3). But these n particular solutions must be "sufficiently independent" that we can always choose the coefficients $c_1, c_2, \ldots, c_n$ in (4) to satisfy arbitrary initial conditions of the form in (5). The question is this: What should be meant by *independence* of three or more functions?

Recall that *two* functions f_1 and f_2 are linearly *dependent* if one is a constant multiple of the other; that is, if either $f_1 = k f_2$ or $f_2 = k f_1$ for some constant k. If we write these equations as

$$(1)f_1 + (-k)f_2 = 0 \quad \text{or} \quad (k)f_1 + (-1)f_2 = 0,$$

we see that the linear dependence of f_1 and f_2 implies that there exist two constants c_1 and c_2 *not both zero* such that

$$c_1 f_1 + c_2 f_2 = 0. \qquad (6)$$

Conversely, if c_1 and c_2 are not both zero, then Eq. (6) certainly implies that f_1 and f_2 are linearly dependent.

In analogy with Eq. (6), we say that n functions $f_1, f_2, \ldots, f_n$ are *linearly dependent* provided that some *nontrivial* linear combination

$$c_1 f_1 + c_2 f_2 + \cdots + c_n f_n$$

of them vanishes identically; *nontrivial* means that *not all* of the coefficients $c_1, c_2, \ldots, c_n$ are zero (although some of them may be zero).

> **Definition: Linear Dependence of Functions**
>
> The n functions $f_1, f_2, \ldots, f_n$ are said to be **linearly dependent** on the interval I provided that there exist constants $c_1, c_2, \ldots, c_n$ not all zero such that
>
> $$c_1 f_1 + c_2 f_2 + \cdots + c_n f_n = 0 \qquad (7)$$
>
> on I; that is,
>
> $$c_1 f_1(x) + c_2 f_2(x) + \cdots + c_n f_n(x) = 0$$
>
> for all x in I.

Thus linear dependence of functions on an interval I is precisely analogous to linear dependence of ordinary vectors (Section 4.3).

If not all the coefficients in Eq. (7) are zero, then, clearly, we can solve for at least one of the functions as a linear combination of the others, and conversely. Thus the functions $f_1, f_2, \ldots, f_n$ are linearly dependent if and only if at least one of them is a linear combination of the others.

Example 3 The functions

$$f_1(x) = \sin 2x, \quad f_2(x) = \sin x \cos x, \quad \text{and} \quad f_3(x) = e^x$$

are linearly dependent on the real line because

$$(1)f_1 + (-2)f_2 + (0)f_3 = 0$$

(by the familiar trigonometric identity $\sin 2x = 2 \sin x \cos x$). ∎

The n functions $f_1, f_2, \ldots, f_n$ are called **linearly independent** on the interval I provided that they are not linearly dependent there. Equivalently, they are linearly independent on I provided that the identity

$$c_1 f_1 + c_2 f_2 + \cdots + c_n f_n = 0 \qquad (7)$$

holds on I only in the trivial case

$$c_1 = c_2 = \cdots = c_n = 0;$$

that is, *no* nontrivial linear combination of these functions vanishes on I. Put yet another way, the functions $f_1, f_2, \ldots, f_n$ are linearly independent if no one of them is a linear combination of the others. (Why?)

Sometimes one can show that n given functions are linearly dependent by finding, as in Example 3, nontrivial values of the coefficients so that Eq. (7) holds. But in order to show that n given functions are linearly independent, we must prove that nontrivial values of the coefficients *cannot* be found, and this is seldom easy to do in any direct or obvious manner.

Fortunately, in the case of n solutions of a homogeneous nth-order linear equation, there is a tool that makes the determination of their linear dependence or independence a routine matter in many examples. This tool is the Wronskian determinant, which we introduced (for the case $n = 2$) in Section 5.1. Suppose that the n

functions f_1, f_2, ..., f_n are each $n-1$ times differentiable. Then their **Wronskian** is the $n \times n$ determinant

$$W = \begin{vmatrix} f_1 & f_2 & \cdots & f_n \\ f_1' & f_2' & \cdots & f_n' \\ \vdots & \vdots & & \vdots \\ f_1^{(n-1)} & f_2^{(n-1)} & \cdots & f_n^{(n-1)} \end{vmatrix}. \tag{8}$$

We write $W(f_1, f_2, \ldots, f_n)$ or $W(x)$, depending on whether we wish to emphasize the functions or the point x at which their Wronskian is to be evaluated. The Wronskian is named after the Polish mathematician J. M. H. Wronski (1778–1853).

We saw in Section 5.1 that the Wronskian of two linearly dependent functions vanishes identically. More generally, *the Wronskian of n linearly dependent functions f_1, f_2, ..., f_n is identically zero.* To prove this, assume that Eq. (7) holds on the interval I for some choice of the constants c_1, c_2, ..., c_n not all zero. We then differentiate this equation $n-1$ times in succession, obtaining the n equations

$$\begin{aligned} c_1 f_1(x) + c_2 f_2(x) &+ \cdots + & c_n f_n(x) = 0, \\ c_1 f_1'(x) + c_2 f_2'(x) &+ \cdots + & c_n f_n'(x) = 0, \\ &\vdots \\ c_1 f_1^{(n-1)}(x) + c_2 f_2^{(n-1)}(x) &+ \cdots + c_n f_n^{(n-1)}(x) = 0, \end{aligned} \tag{9}$$

which hold for all x in I. We recall from Theorem 7 in Section 3.5 that a *homogeneous* $n \times n$ linear system of equations has a nontrivial solution if and only if its coefficient matrix is *not* invertible, which by Theorem 2 in Section 3.6 is so if and only if the coefficient determinant vanishes. In Eq. (9) the unknowns are the constants c_1, c_2, ..., c_n and the determinant of coefficients is simply the Wronskian $W(f_1, f_2, \ldots, f_n)$ evaluated at the typical point x of I. Because we know that the c_i are not all zero, it follows that $W(x) \equiv 0$, as we wanted to prove.

Therefore, to show that the functions f_1, f_2,..., f_n are *linearly independent* on the interval I, it suffices to show that their Wronskian is nonzero at just one point of I.

Example 4

Show that the functions $y_1(x) = e^{-3x}$, $y_2(x) = \cos 2x$, and $y_3(x) = \sin 2x$ (of Example 1) are linearly independent.

Solution   Their Wronskian is

$$W = \begin{vmatrix} e^{-3x} & \cos 2x & \sin 2x \\ -3e^{-3x} & -2\sin 2x & 2\cos 2x \\ 9e^{-3x} & -4\cos 2x & -4\sin 2x \end{vmatrix}$$

$$= e^{-3x} \begin{vmatrix} -2\sin 2x & 2\cos 2x \\ -4\cos 2x & -4\sin 2x \end{vmatrix} + 3e^{-3x} \begin{vmatrix} \cos 2x & \sin 2x \\ -4\cos 2x & -4\sin 2x \end{vmatrix}$$

$$+ 9e^{-3x} \begin{vmatrix} \cos 2x & \sin 2x \\ -2\sin 2x & 2\cos 2x \end{vmatrix} = 26e^{-3x} \neq 0.$$

Because $W \neq 0$ everywhere, it follows that y_1, y_2, and y_3 are linearly independent on any open interval (including the entire real line). ∎

Example 5 Show first that the three solutions

$$y_1(x) = x, \quad y_2(x) = x \ln x, \quad \text{and} \quad y_3(x) = x^2$$

of the third-order equation

$$x^3 y^{(3)} - x^2 y'' + 2xy' - 2y = 0 \tag{10}$$

are linearly independent on the open interval $x > 0$. Then find a particular solution of Eq. (10) that satisfies the initial conditions

$$y(1) = 3, \quad y'(1) = 2, \quad y''(1) = 1. \tag{11}$$

Solution Note that for $x > 0$, we could divide each term in (10) by x^3 to obtain a homogeneous linear equation of the standard form in (3). When we compute the Wronskian of the three given solutions, we find that

$$W = \begin{vmatrix} x & x \ln x & x^2 \\ 1 & 1 + \ln x & 2x \\ 0 & \dfrac{1}{x} & 2 \end{vmatrix} = x.$$

Thus $W(x) \neq 0$ for $x > 0$, so y_1, y_2, and y_3 are linearly independent on the interval $x > 0$. To find the desired particular solution, we impose the initial conditions in (11) on

$$y(x) = c_1 x + c_2 x \ln x + c_3 x^2,$$
$$y'(x) = c_1 + c_2 (1 + \ln x) + 2c_3 x,$$
$$y''(x) = 0 + \frac{c_2}{x} + 2c_3.$$

This yields the simultaneous equations

$$y(1) = c_1 \qquad + c_3 = 3,$$
$$y'(1) = c_1 + c_2 + 2c_3 = 2,$$
$$y''(1) = \qquad c_2 + 2c_3 = 1;$$

we solve to find $c_1 = 1$, $c_2 = -3$, and $c_3 = 2$. Thus the particular solution in question is

$$y(x) = x - 3x \ln x + 2x^2. \qquad ∎$$

Provided that $W(y_1, y_2, \ldots, y_n) \neq 0$, it turns out (Theorem 4) that we can always find values of the coefficients in the linear combination

$$y = c_1 y_1 + c_2 y_2 + \cdots + c_n y_n$$

that satisfy any given initial conditions of the form in (5). Theorem 3 provides the necessary nonvanishing of W in the case of linearly independent solutions.

THEOREM 3: Wronskians of Solutions

Suppose that y_1, y_2, ..., y_n are n solutions of the homogeneous nth-order linear equation

$$y^{(n)} + p_1(x)y^{(n-1)} + \cdots + p_{n-1}(x)y' + p_n(x)y = 0 \tag{3}$$

on an open interval I where each p_i is continuous. Let

$$W = W(y_1, y_2, \ldots, y_n).$$

(a) If y_1, y_2, ..., y_n are linearly dependent, then $W \equiv 0$ on I.

(b) If y_1, y_2, ..., y_n are linearly independent, then $W \neq 0$ at each point of I.

Thus there are just two possibilities: Either $W = 0$ everywhere on I, or $W \neq 0$ everywhere on I.

Proof: We have already proven part (a). To prove part (b), it is sufficient to assume that $W(a) = 0$ at some point of I and show this implies that the solutions y_1, y_2, ..., y_n are linearly dependent. But $W(a)$ is simply the determinant of coefficients of the system of n homogeneous linear equations

$$
\begin{aligned}
c_1 y_1(a) + \quad c_2 y_2(a) + \cdots + \quad c_n y_n(a) &= 0, \\
c_1 y_1'(a) + \quad c_2 y_2'(a) + \cdots + \quad c_n y_n'(a) &= 0, \\
&\ \ \vdots \\
c_1 y_1^{(n-1)}(a) + c_2 y_2^{(n-1)}(a) + \cdots + c_n y_n^{(n-1)}(a) &= 0
\end{aligned}
\tag{12}
$$

in the n unknowns c_1, c_2, ..., c_n. Because $W(a) = 0$, the basic fact from linear algebra quoted just after (9) implies that the equations in (12) have a nontrivial solution. That is, the numbers c_1, c_2, ..., c_n are not all zero.

We now use these values to define the particular solution

$$Y(x) = c_1 y_1(x) + c_2 y_2(x) + \cdots + c_n y_n(x) \tag{13}$$

of Eq. (3). The equations in (12) then imply that Y satisfies the trivial initial conditions

$$Y(a) = Y'(a) = \cdots = Y^{(n-1)}(a) = 0.$$

Theorem 2 (uniqueness) therefore implies that $Y(x) \equiv 0$ on I. In view of (13) and the fact that c_1, c_2, ..., c_n are not all zero, this is the desired conclusion that the solutions y_1, y_2, ..., y_n are linearly dependent. This completes the proof of Theorem 3. ▲

General Solutions

We can now show that every solution of a *homogeneous* nth-order equation is a linear combination of n given linearly independent solutions. Using the fact from Theorem 3 that the Wronskian of n linearly independent solutions is nonzero, the proof of the following theorem is essentially the same as the proof of Theorem 4 of Section 5.1 (the case $n = 2$).

THEOREM 4: General Solutions of Homogeneous Equations

Let $y_1, y_2, \ldots, y_n$ be n linearly independent solutions of the homogeneous equation

$$y^{(n)} + p_1(x)y^{(n-1)} + \cdots + p_{n-1}(x)y' + p_n(x)y = 0 \tag{3}$$

on an open interval I where the p_i are continuous. If Y is any solution whatsoever of Eq. (3), then there exist numbers $c_1, c_2, \ldots, c_n$ such that

$$Y(x) = c_1 y_1(x) + c_2 y_2(x) + \cdots + c_n y_n(x)$$

for all x in I. ▲

> **Remark:** Theorem 4 tells us that, once we have found n linearly independent solutions $y_1, y_2, \ldots, y_n$ of the nth order homogeneous linear equation in (3), we really have found *all* of its solutions. For then the solution space $\mathscr{S}$ of the equation is an n-dimensional vector space with basis $\{y_1, y_2, \ldots, y_n\}$. Because *every* solution of (3) can be expressed as a linear combination of the form

$$y = c_1 y_1 + c_2 y_2 + \cdots + c_n y_n,$$

we call such a linear combination of n linearly independent particular solutions a **general solution** of the homogeneous linear differential equation.

Example 6

According to Example 4, the particular solutions $y_1(x) = e^{-3x}$, $y_2(x) = \cos 2x$, and $y_3(x) = \sin 2x$ of the linear differential equation $y^{(3)} + 3y'' + 4y' + 12y = 0$ are linearly independent. Now Theorem 2 says that—given b_0, b_1, and b_2—there exists a particular solution $y(x)$ satisfying the initial conditions $y(0) = b_0$, $y'(0) = b_1$, and $y''(0) = b_2$. Hence Theorem 4 implies that *this* particular solution is a linear combination of y_1, y_2, and y_3. That is, there exist coefficients c_1, c_2, and c_3 such that

$$y(x) = c_1 e^{-3x} + c_2 \cos 2x + c_3 \sin 2x.$$

Upon successive differentiation and substitution of $x = 0$, we discover that to find these coefficients, we need only solve the three linear equations

$$
\begin{aligned}
c_1 + c_2 \quad\;\;\; &= b_0, \\
-3c_1 \quad\;\; + 2c_3 &= b_1, \\
9c_1 - 4c_2 \quad\;\;\; &= b_2.
\end{aligned}
$$

(See the application for this section.) ■

Nonhomogeneous Equations

We now consider the *nonhomogeneous* nth-order linear differential equation

$$\blacktriangleright \qquad Ly = y^{(n)} + p_1(x)y^{(n-1)} + \cdots + p_{n-1}(x)y' + p_n(x)y = f(x) \qquad (2)$$

with associated homogeneous equation

$$\blacktriangleright \qquad Ly = y^{(n)} + p_1(x)y^{(n-1)} + \cdots + p_{n-1}(x)y' + p_n(x)y = 0. \qquad (3)$$

FIGURE 5.2.5. The idea of L "operating" on the function y.

Here we introduce the symbol L to represent an **operator**; given an n times differentiable function y, L *operates* on y (as suggested in Fig. 5.2.5) to produce the linear combination

$$Ly = y^{(n)} + p_1(x)y^{(n-1)} + \cdots + p_{n-1}(x)y' + p_n(x)y \qquad (16)$$

of y and its first n derivatives. The principle of superposition (Theorem 1) means simply that the operator L is linear; that is,

$$\blacktriangleright \qquad L(c_1 y_1 + c_2 y_2) = c_1 L y_1 + c_2 L y_2 \qquad (17)$$

if c_1 and c_2 are constants.

Suppose that a single particular solution y_p of the nonhomogeneous equation in (2) is known and that Y is any other solution of Eq. (2). Then Eq. (15) implies that

$$L(Y - y_p) = LY - Ly_p = f - f = 0.$$

Thus $y_c = Y - y_p$ is a solution of the associated homogeneous equation in (3). Then

$$\blacktriangleright \qquad Y = y_c + y_p, \qquad (18)$$

and it follows from Theorem 4 that

$$\blacktriangleright \qquad y_c = c_1 y_1 + c_2 y_2 + \cdots + c_n y_n, \qquad (19)$$

where $y_1, y_2, \ldots, y_n$ are linearly independent solutions of the associated *homogeneous* equation. We call y_c a **complementary function** of the nonhomogeneous equation and have thus proved that a *general solution* of the nonhomogeneous equation in (2) is the sum of its complementary function y_c and a single particular solution y_p of Eq. (2).

> **THEOREM 5:** Solutions of Nonhomogeneous Equations
>
> Let y_p be a particular solution of the nonhomogeneous equation in (2) on an open interval I where the functions p_i and f are continuous. Let $y_1, y_2, \ldots, y_n$ be linearly independent solutions of the associated homogeneous equation in (3). If Y is any solution whatsoever of Eq. (2) on I, then there exist numbers $c_1, c_2, \ldots, c_n$ such that
>
> $$Y(x) = c_1 y_1(x) + c_2 y_2(x) + \cdots + c_n y_n(x) + y_p(x) \tag{20}$$
>
> for all x in I.   ▲

Example 7   It is evident that $y_p = 3x$ is a particular solution of the equation

$$y'' + 4y = 12x \tag{21}$$

and that $y_c(x) = c_1 \cos 2x + c_2 \sin 2x$ is its complementary solution. Find a solution of Eq. (19) that satisfies the initial conditions $y(0) = 5$, $y'(0) = 7$.

Solution   The general solution of Eq. (19) is

$$y(x) = c_1 \cos 2x + c_2 \sin 2x + 3x.$$

Now

$$y'(x) = -2c_1 \sin 2x + 2c_2 \cos 2x + 3.$$

Hence the initial conditions give

$$y(0) = c_1 = 5,$$
$$y'(0) = 2c_2 + 3 = 7.$$

We find that $c_1 = 5$ and $c_2 = 2$. Thus the desired solution is

$$y(x) = 5 \cos 2x + 2 \sin 2x + 3x.$$ ■

5.2 Problems

In Problems 1 through 6, show directly that the given functions are linearly dependent on the real line. That is, find a nontrivial linear combination of the given functions that vanishes identically.

1. $f(x) = 2x$, $g(x) = 3x^2$, $h(x) = 5x - 8x^2$
2. $f(x) = 5$, $g(x) = 2 - 3x^2$, $h(x) = 10 + 15x^2$
3. $f(x) = 0$, $g(x) = \sin x$, $h(x) = e^x$
4. $f(x) = 17$, $g(x) = 2 \sin^2 x$, $h(x) = 3 \cos^2 x$
5. $f(x) = 17$, $g(x) = \cos^2 x$, $h(x) = \cos 2x$
6. $f(x) = e^x$, $g(x) = \cosh x$, $h(x) = \sinh x$

In Problems 7 through 12, use the Wronskian to prove that the given functions are linearly independent on the indicated interval.

7. $f(x) = 1$, $g(x) = x$, $h(x) = x^2$; the real line
8. $f(x) = e^x$, $g(x) = e^{2x}$, $h(x) = e^{3x}$; the real line
9. $f(x) = e^x$, $g(x) = \cos x$, $h(x) = \sin x$; the real line
10. $f(x) = e^x$, $g(x) = x^{-2}$, $h(x) = x^{-2} \ln x$; $x > 0$
11. $f(x) = x$, $g(x) = xe^x$, $h(x) = x^2 e^x$; the real line
12. $f(x) = x$, $g(x) = \cos(\ln x)$, $h(x) = \sin(\ln x)$; $x > 0$

In Problems 13 through 20, a third-order homogeneous linear equation and three linearly independent solutions are given. Find a particular solution satisfying the given initial conditions.

13. $y^{(3)} + 2y'' - y' - 2y = 0$; $y(0) = 1$, $y'(0) = 2$, $y''(0) = 0$;
$y_1 = e^x$, $y_2 = e^{-x}$, $y_3 = e^{-2x}$

14. $y^{(3)} - 6y'' + 11y' - 6y = 0$; $y(0) = 0$, $y'(0) = 0$, $y''(0) = 3$; $y_1 = e^x$, $y_2 = e^{2x}$, $y_3 = e^{3x}$

15. $y^{(3)} - 3y'' + 3y' - y = 0$; $y(0) = 2$, $y'(0) = 0$, $y''(0) = 0$; $y_1 = e^x$, $y_2 = xe^x$, $y_3 = x^2 e^x$

16. $y^{(3)} - 5y'' + 8y' - 4y = 0$; $y(0) = 1$, $y'(0) = 4$, $y''(0) = 0$; $y_1 = e^x$, $y_2 = e^{2x}$, $y_3 = xe^{2x}$

17. $y^{(3)} + 9y' = 0$; $y(0) = 3$, $y'(0) = -1$, $y''(0) = 2$; $y_1 = 1$, $y_2 = \cos 3x$, $y_3 = \sin 3x$

18. $y^{(3)} - 3y'' + 4y' - 2y = 0$; $y(0) = 1$, $y'(0) = 0$, $y''(0) = 0$; $y_1 = e^x$, $y_2 = e^x \cos x$, $y_3 = e^x \sin x$

19. $x^3 y^{(3)} - 3x^2 y'' + 6xy' - 6y = 0$; $y(1) = 6$, $y'(1) = 14$, $y''(1) = 22$; $y_1 = x$, $y_2 = x^2$, $y_3 = x^3$

20. $x^3 y^{(3)} + 6x^2 y'' + 4xy' - 4y = 0$; $y(1) = 1$, $y'(1) = 5$, $y''(1) = -11$; $y_1 = x$, $y_2 = x^{-2}$, $y_3 = x^{-2} \ln x$

In Problems 21 through 24, a nonhomogeneous differential equation, a complementary solution y_c, and a particular solution y_p are given. Find a solution satisfying the given initial conditions.

21. $y'' + y = 3x$; $y(0) = 2$, $y'(0) = -2$; $y_c = c_1 \cos x + c_2 \sin x$; $y_p = 3x$

22. $y'' - 4y = 12$; $y(0) = 0$, $y'(0) = 10$; $y_c = c_1 e^{2x} + c_2 e^{-2x}$; $y_p = -3$

23. $y'' - 2y' - 3y = 6$; $y(0) = 3$, $y'(0) = 11$; $y_c = c_1 e^{-x} + c_2 e^{3x}$; $y_p = -2$

24. $y'' - 2y' + 2y = 2x$; $y(0) = 4$, $y'(0) = 8$; $y_c = c_1 e^x \cos x + c_2 e^x \sin x$; $y_p = x + 1$

25. Let $Ly = y'' + py' + qy$. Suppose that y_1 and y_2 are two functions such that

$$Ly_1 = f(x) \quad \text{and} \quad Ly_2 = g(x).$$

Show that their sum $y = y_1 + y_2$ satisfies the nonhomogeneous equation $Ly = f(x) + g(x)$.

26. **(a)** Find by inspection particular solutions of the two nonhomogeneous equations

$$y'' + 2y = 4 \quad \text{and} \quad y'' + 2y = 6x.$$

(b) Use the method of Problem 25 to find a particular solution of the differential equation $y'' + 2y = 6x + 4$.

27. Prove directly that the functions

$$f_1(x) \equiv 1, \quad f_2(x) = x, \quad \text{and} \quad f_3(x) = x^2$$

are linearly independent on the whole real line. (*Suggestion:* Assume that $c_1 + c_2 x + c_3 x^2 = 0$. Differentiate this equation twice. You now have three equations that must be satisfied by every real number x, including $x = 0$. Conclude that $c_1 = c_2 = c_3 = 0$.)

28. Generalize the method of Problem 27 to prove directly that the functions

$$f_0(x) \equiv 1, \quad f_1(x) = x, \quad f_2(x) = x^2, \dots, \quad f_n(x) = x^n$$

are linearly independent on the real line.

29. Use the result of Problem 28 and the definition of linear independence to prove directly that, for any constant r, the functions

$$f_0(x) = e^{rx}, \quad f_1(x) = xe^{rx}, \dots, \quad f_n(x) = x^n e^{rx}$$

are linearly independent on the whole real line.

30. Verify that $y_1 = x$ and $y_2 = x^2$ are linearly independent solutions on the entire real line of the equation

$$x^2 y'' - 2xy' + 2y = 0,$$

but that $W(x, x^2)$ vanishes at $x = 0$. Why do these observations not contradict part (b) of Theorem 3?

31. This problem indicates why we can impose *only n* initial conditions on a solution of an nth-order linear differential equation. **(a)** Given the equation

$$y'' + py' + qy = 0,$$

explain why the value of $y''(a)$ is determined by the values of $y(a)$ and $y'(a)$. **(b)** Prove that the equation

$$y'' - 2y' - 5y = 0$$

has a solution satisfying the conditions

$$y(0) = 1, \quad y'(0) = 0, \quad \text{and} \quad y''(0) = C$$

if and only if $C = 5$.

32. Prove that an nth-order homogeneous linear differential equation satisfying the hypotheses of Theorem 2 has n linearly independent solutions $y_1, y_2, \dots, y_n$. [*Suggestion:* Let y_i be the unique solution such that

$$y_i^{(i-1)}(a) = 1 \quad \text{and} \quad y_i^{(k)}(a) = 0 \quad \text{if } k \neq i - 1.]$$

33. Suppose that the three numbers r_1, r_2, and r_3 are distinct. Show that the three functions $\exp(r_1 x)$, $\exp(r_2 x)$, and $\exp(r_3 x)$ are linearly independent by showing that their Wronskian

$$W = \exp([r_1 + r_2 + r_3]x) \cdot \begin{vmatrix} 1 & 1 & 1 \\ r_1 & r_2 & r_3 \\ r_1^2 & r_2^2 & r_3^2 \end{vmatrix}$$

is nonzero for all x.

34. Assume as known that the **Vandermonde determinant**

$$V = \begin{vmatrix} 1 & 1 & \cdots & 1 \\ r_1 & r_2 & \cdots & r_n \\ r_1^2 & r_2^2 & \cdots & r_n^2 \\ \vdots & \vdots & & \vdots \\ r_1^{n-1} & r_2^{n-1} & \cdots & r_n^{n-1} \end{vmatrix}$$

is nonzero if the numbers $r_1, r_2, \dots, r_n$ are distinct. Prove by the method of Problem 33 that the functions

$$f_i(x) = \exp(r_i x), \quad 1 \leq i \leq n$$

are linearly independent.

35. According to Problem 32 of Section 5.1, the Wronskian $W(y_1, y_2)$ of two solutions of the second-order equation

$$y'' + p_1(x)y' + p_2(x)y = 0$$

is given by Abel's's formula

$$W(x) = K \exp\left(-\int p_1(x)\, dx\right)$$

for some constant K. It can be shown that the Wronskian of n solutions $y_1, y_2, \ldots, y_n$ of the nth-order equation

$$y^{(n)} + p_1(x)y^{(n-1)} + \cdots + p_{n-1}(x)y' + p_n(x)y = 0$$

satisfies the same identity. Prove this for the case $n = 3$ as follows: **(a)** The derivative of a determinant of functions is the sum of the determinants obtained by separately differentiating the rows of the original determinant. Conclude that

$$W' = \begin{vmatrix} y_1 & y_2 & y_3 \\ y_1' & y_2' & y_3' \\ y_1^{(3)} & y_2^{(3)} & y_3^{(3)} \end{vmatrix}.$$

(b) Substitute for $y_1^{(3)}$, $y_2^{(3)}$, and $y_3^{(3)}$ from the equation

$$y^{(3)} + p_1 y'' + p_2 y' + p_3 y = 0,$$

and then show that $W' = -p_1 W$. Integration now gives Abel's formula.

36. Suppose that one solution $y_1(x)$ of the homogeneous second-order linear differential equation

$$y'' + p(x)y' + q(x)y = 0 \tag{22}$$

is known (on an interval I where p and q are continuous functions). The method of **reduction of order** consists of substituting $y_2(x) = v(x)y_1(x)$ in (20) and attempting to determine the function $v(x)$ so that $y_2(x)$ is a second linearly independent solution of (20). After substituting $y = v(x)y_1(x)$ in Eq. (20), use the fact that $y_1(x)$ is a solution to deduce that

$$y_1 v'' + (2y_1' + py_1)v' = 0. \tag{23}$$

If $y_1(x)$ is known, then (21) is a separable equation that is readily solved for the derivative $v'(x)$ of $v(x)$. Integration of $v'(x)$ then gives the desired (nonconstant) function $v(x)$.

37. Before applying Eq. (21) with a given homogeneous second-order linear differential equation and a known solution $y_1(x)$, the equation must first be written in the form of (20) with leading coefficient 1 in order to correctly determine the coefficient function $p(x)$. Frequently it is more convenient to simply substitute $y = v(x)y_1(x)$ in the given differential equation and then proceed directly to find $v(x)$. Thus, starting with the readily verified solution $y_1(x) = x^3$ of the equation

$$x^2 y'' - 5xy' + 9y = 0 \quad (x > 0),$$

substitute $y = vx^3$ and deduce that $xv'' + v' = 0$. Then solve for $v(x) = C \ln x$, and thereby obtain (with $C = 1$) the second solution $y_2(x) = x^3 \ln x$.

In each of Problems 38 through 42, a differential equation and one solution y_1 are given. Use the method of reduction of order as in Problem 37 to find a second linearly independent solution y_2.

38. $x^2 y'' + xy' - 9y = 0 \quad (x > 0); \quad y_1(x) = x^3$

39. $4y'' - 4y' + y = 0; \quad y_1(x) = e^{x/2}$

40. $x^2 y'' - x(x+2)y' + (x+2)y = 0 \quad (x > 0); \quad y_1(x) = x$

41. $(x+1)y'' - (x+2)y' + y = 0 \quad (x > -1); \quad y_1(x) = e^x$

42. $(1 - x^2)y'' + 2xy' - 2y = 0 \quad (-1 < x < 1); \quad y_1(x) = x$

43. First note that $y_1(x) = x$ is one solution of Legendre's equation of order 1,

$$(1 - x^2)y'' - 2xy' + 2y = 0.$$

Then use the method of reduction of order to derive the second solution

$$y_2(x) = 1 - \frac{x}{2} \ln \frac{1+x}{1-x} \quad \text{(for } -1 < x < 1\text{)}.$$

44. First verify by substitution that $y_1(x) = x^{-1/2} \cos x$ is one solution (for $x > 0$) of Bessel's equation of order $\frac{1}{2}$,

$$x^2 y'' + xy' + (x^2 - \tfrac{1}{4})y = 0.$$

Then derive by reduction of order the second solution $y_2(x) = x^{-1/2} \sin x$.

5.2 Application: Plotting Third-Order Solution Families

This application deals with the plotting by computer of families of solutions such as those illustrated in Figs. 5.2.2 through 5.2.4. We know from Example 6 that the general solution of

$$y^{(3)} + 3y'' + 4y' + 12y = 0 \tag{1}$$

is

$$y(x) = c_1 e^{-3x} + c_2 \cos 2x + c_3 \sin 2x. \tag{2}$$

For Fig. 5.2.2, use the method of Example 6 to show that the particular solution of Eq. (1) satisfying the initial conditions $y(0) = a$, $y'(0) = 0$, and $y''(0) = 0$ is given by

$$y(x) = \frac{a}{13} \left(4e^{-3x} + 9 \cos 2x + 6 \sin 2x \right). \tag{3}$$

The MATLAB loop

```
x = -1.5 : 0.02 : 5        % x-vector from x = -1.5 to x = 5
for a = -3 : 1 : 3         % for a = -3 to 3 with da = 1 do
    c1 = 4*a/13;
    c2 = 9*a/13;
    c3 = 6*a/13;
    y = c1*exp(-3*x) + c2*cos(2*x) + c3*sin(2*x);
    plot(x,y)
end
```

was used to generate Fig. 5.2.2.

For Fig. 5.2.3, show that the particular solution of Eq. (1) satisfying the initial conditions $y(0) = 0$, $y'(0) = b$, and $y''(0) = 0$ is given by

$$y(x) = \frac{b}{2} \sin 2x, \tag{4}$$

and alter the preceding for-loop accordingly.

For Fig. 5.2.3, show that the particular solution of Eq. (1) satisfying the initial conditions $y(0) = 0$, $y'(0) = 0$, and $y''(0) = c$ is given by

$$y(x) = \frac{c}{26} \left(2e^{-3x} - 2 \cos 2x + 3 \sin 2x \right). \tag{5}$$

Computer algebra systems such as *Maple* and *Mathematica*, as well as graphing calculators, have commands to carry out for-loops such as the one shown here. Begin by reproducing Figs. 5.2.2 through 5.2.4. Then plot similar families of solution curves for the differential equations in Problems 13 through 20.

5.3 Homogeneous Equations with Constant Coefficients

In Section 5.2 we saw that a general solution of an nth-order homogeneous linear equation is a linear combination of n linearly independent particular solutions, but we said little about how actually to find even a single solution. The solution of a linear differential equation with *variable* coefficients ordinarily requires numerical methods (Chapter 2) or infinite series methods (Chapter 11). But we can now show how to find, explicitly and in a rather straightforward way, n linearly independent solutions of a given nth-order linear equation if it has *constant* coefficients. The general such equation may be written in the form

$$\blacktriangleright \qquad a_n y^{(n)} + a_{n-1} y^{(n-1)} + \cdots + a_2 y'' + a_1 y' + a_0 y = 0, \tag{1}$$

where the coefficients a_0, a_1, a_2, ..., a_n are real constants with $a_n \neq 0$.

The Characteristic Equation

We first look for a *single* solution of Eq. (1) and begin with the observation that

$$\frac{d^k}{dx^k}(e^{rx}) = r^k e^{rx}, \tag{2}$$

so any derivative of e^{rx} is a constant multiple of e^{rx}. Hence, if we substituted $y = e^{rx}$ in Eq. (1), each term would be a constant multiple of e^{rx}, with the constant coefficients depending on r and the coefficients a_i. This suggests that we try to find r so that all these multiples of e^{rx} will have sum zero, in which case $y = e^{rx}$ will be a solution of Eq. (1).

For example, in Section 5.1 we substituted $y = e^{rx}$ in the second-order equation

$$ay'' + by' + cy = 0$$

to derive the characteristic equation

$$ar^2 + br + c = 0$$

that r must satisfy.

To carry out this technique in the general case, we substitute $y = e^{rx}$ in Eq. (1), and with the aid of Eq. (2) we find the result to be

$$a_n r^n e^{rx} + a_{n-1} r^{n-1} e^{rx} + \cdots + a_2 r^2 e^{rx} + a_1 r e^{rx} + a_0 e^{rx} = 0;$$

that is,

$$e^{rx}\left(a_n r^n + a_{n-1} r^{n-1} + \cdots + a_2 r^2 + a_1 r + a_0\right) = 0.$$

Because e^{rx} is never zero, we see that $y = e^{rx}$ will be a solution of Eq. (1) precisely when r is a root of the equation

$$a_n r^n + a_{n-1} r^{n-1} + \cdots + a_2 r^2 + a_1 r + a_0 = 0. \tag{3}$$

This equation is called the **characteristic equation** or **auxiliary equation** of the differential equation in (1). Our problem, then, is reduced to the solution of this purely algebraic equation.

According to the fundamental theorem of algebra, every nth-degree polynomial—such as the one in Eq. (3)—has n zeros, though not necessarily distinct and not necessarily real. Finding the exact values of these zeros may be difficult or even impossible; the quadratic formula is sufficient for second-degree equations, but for equations of higher degree we may need either to spot a fortuitous factorization or to apply a numerical technique such as Newton's method (or use a calculator/computer **solve** command).

Distinct Real Roots

Whatever the method we use, let us suppose that we have solved the characteristic equation. Then we can always write a general solution of the differential equation. The situation is slightly more complicated in the case of repeated roots or complex roots of Eq. (3), so let us first examine the simplest case—in which the characteristic equation has n distinct (no two equal) *real* roots $r_1, r_2, \ldots, r_n$. Then the functions

$$e^{r_1 x}, e^{r_2 x} \ldots, e^{r_n x}$$

are all solutions of Eq. (1), and (by Problem 34 of Section 5.2) these n solutions are linearly independent on the entire real line. In summary, we have proved Theorem 1.

THEOREM 1: Distinct Real Roots

If the roots $r_1, r_2, \ldots, r_n$ of the characteristic equation in (3) are real and distinct, then

➤
$$y(x) = c_1 e^{r_1 x} + c_2 e^{r_2 x} + \cdots + c_n e^{r_n x} \tag{4}$$

is a general solution of Eq. (1). Thus the n linearly independent functions $\{e^{r_1 x}, e^{r_2 x}, \ldots, e^{r_n x}\}$ constitute a basis for the n-dimensional solution space of Eq. (1). ▲

Example 1   Solve the initial value problem

$$y^{(3)} + 3y'' - 10y' = 0;$$
$$y(0) = 7, \quad y'(0) = 0, \quad y''(0) = 70.$$

Solution   The characteristic equation of the given differential equation is

$$r^3 + 3r^2 - 10r = 0.$$

We solve by factoring:

$$r(r^2 + 3r - 10) = r(r + 5)(r - 2) = 0,$$

and so the characteristic equation has the three distinct real roots $r = 0$, $r = -5$, and $r = 2$. Because $e^0 = 1$, Theorem 1 gives the general solution

$$y(x) = c_1 + c_2 e^{-5x} + c_3 e^{2x}.$$

Then the given initial conditions yield the linear equations

$$\begin{aligned}
y(0) = c_1 + {} & c_2 + c_3 = 7, \\
y'(0) = {} & -5c_2 + 2c_3 = 0, \\
y''(0) = {} & 25c_2 + 4c_3 = 70
\end{aligned}$$

in the coefficients c_1, c_2, and c_3. The last two equations give $y''(0) - 2y'(0) = 35c_2 = 70$, so $c_2 = 2$. Then the second equation gives $c_3 = 5$, and finally the first equation gives $c_1 = 0$. Thus the desired particular solution is

$$y(x) = 2e^{-5x} + 5e^{2x}. \qquad \blacksquare$$

Polynomial Operators

If the roots of the characteristic equation in (3) are *not* distinct—there are repeated roots—then we cannot produce n linearly independent solutions of Eq. (1) by the method of Theorem 1. For example, if the roots are 1, 2, 2, and 2, we obtain only the *two* functions e^x and e^{2x}. The problem, then, is to produce the missing linearly independent solutions. For this purpose it is convenient to adopt the operator notation introduced near the conclusion of Section 5.2. Equation (1) corresponds to the operator equation $Ly = 0$, where L is the operator

$$L = a_n \frac{d^n}{dx^n} + a_{n-1} \frac{d^{n-1}}{dx^{n-1}} + \cdots + a_2 \frac{d^2}{dx^2} + a_1 \frac{d}{dx} + a_0. \tag{5}$$

We also denote by $D = d/dx$ the operation of differentiation with respect to x, so that

$$Dy = y', \quad D^2 y = y'', \quad D^3 y = y^{(3)},$$

and so on. In terms of D, the operator L in (5) may be written

$$L = a_n D^n + a_{n-1} D^{n-1} + \cdots + a_2 D^2 + a_1 D + a_0, \tag{6}$$

and we will find it useful to think of the right-hand side in Eq. (6) as a (formal) nth-degree polynomial in the "variable" D; it is a **polynomial operator**.

A first-degree polynomial operator has the form $D - a$ where a is a real number. It operates on the function $y = y(x)$ to produce

$$(D - a)y = Dy - ay = y' - ay.$$

The important fact about such operators is that any two of them *commute*:

$$(D - a)(D - b)y = (D - b)(D - a)y \tag{7}$$

for any twice differentiable function $y = y(x)$. The proof of the formula in (7) is the following computation:

$$\begin{aligned}
(D - a)(D - b)y &= (D - a)(y' - by) \\
&= D(y' - by) - a(y' - by) \\
&= y'' - (b + a)y' + aby = y'' - (a + b)y' + bay \\
&= D(y' - ay) - b(y' - ay) \\
&= (D - b)(y' - ay) = (D - b)(D - a)y.
\end{aligned}$$

Repeated Roots

Let us now consider the possibility that the characteristic equation

$$a_n r^n + a_{n-1} r^{n-1} + \cdots + a_2 r^2 + a_1 r + a_0 = 0 \tag{3}$$

has *repeated* roots. For example, suppose that Eq. (3) has only two distinct roots, r_0 of multiplicity 1 and r_1 of multiplicity $k > 1$. Then (after dividing by a_n) Eq. (3) can be rewritten in the form

$$(r - r_1)^k (r - r_0) = (r - r_0)(r - r_1)^k = 0. \tag{8}$$

Similarly, the corresponding operator L in (6) can be written as

$$L = (D - r_1)^k (D - r_0) = (D - r_0)(D - r_1)^k, \tag{9}$$

the order of the factors making no difference because of the formula in (7).

Two solutions of the differential equation $Ly = 0$ are certainly $y_0 = e^{r_0 x}$ and $y_1 = e^{r_1 x}$. This is, however, not sufficient; we need $k + 1$ linearly independent solutions in order to construct a general solution, because the equation is of order $k + 1$. To find the missing $k - 1$ solutions, we note that

$$Ly = (D - r_0)[(D - r_1)^k y] = 0.$$

Consequently, *every* solution of the kth-order equation

$$(D - r_1)^k y = 0 \tag{10}$$

will also be a solution of the original equation $Ly = 0$. Hence our problem is reduced to that of finding a general solution of the differential equation in (10).

The fact that $y_1 = e^{r_1 x}$ is one solution of Eq. (10) suggests that we try the substitution

$$y(x) = u(x)y_1(x) = u(x)e^{r_1 x}, \tag{11}$$

where $u(x)$ is a function yet to be determined. Observe that

$$(D - r_1)\left[u e^{r_1 x}\right] = (Du)e^{r_1 x} + u(r_1 e^{r_1 x}) - r_1(u e^{r_1 x}) = (Du)e^{r_1 x}. \tag{12}$$

Upon k applications of this fact, it follows that

$$(D - r_1)^k \left[u e^{r_1 x}\right] = (D^k u)e^{r_1 x} \tag{13}$$

for any sufficiently differentiable function $u(x)$. Hence $y = u e^{r_1 x}$ will be a solution of Eq. (10) if and only if $D^k u = u^{(k)} = 0$. But this is so if and only if

$$u(x) = c_1 + c_2 x + c_3 x^2 + \cdots + c_k x^{k-1},$$

a polynomial of degree at most $k - 1$. Hence our desired solution of Eq. (10) is

$$y(x) = u e^{r_1 x} = (c_1 + c_2 x + c_3 x^2 + \cdots + c_k x^{k-1})e^{r_1 x}.$$

In particular, we see here the additional solutions $xe^{r_1 x}$, $x^2 e^{r_1 x}$, ..., $x^{k-1}e^{r_1 x}$ of the original differential equation $Ly = 0$.

The preceding analysis can be carried out with the operator $D - r_1$ replaced with an arbitrary polynomial operator. When this is done, the result is a proof of the following theorem.

THEOREM 2: Repeated Roots

If the characteristic equation in (3) has a repeated root r of multiplicity k, then the part of a general solution of the differential equation in (1) corresponding to r is of the form

$$(c_1 + c_2 x + c_3 x^2 + \cdots + c_k x^{k-1})e^{rx}. \tag{14}$$

▲

Remark: According to Problem 29 of Section 5.2, the k functions e^{rx}, xe^{rx}, x^2e^{rx}, ..., $x^{k-1}e^{rx}$ involved in (14) are linearly independent. Thus a root of multiplicity $k \geq 1$ corresponds to k linearly independent "basis solutions" that generate a k-dimensional subspace of the n-dimensional solution space $\mathcal{S}$ of the nth-order homogeneous linear differential equation. Because the sum of the multiplicities of the separate roots of the nth-degree characteristic equation is n, we get a basis $\{y_1, y_2, \ldots, y_n\}$ for $\mathcal{S}$ when we assemble all the basis solutions corresponding to these separate roots. We can then write a general solution $y = c_1 y_1 + c_2 y_2 + \cdots + c_n y_n$ of the differential equation. In effect, we thereby construct a general solution by combining different "parts" corresponding to the separate roots of the characteristic equation.

Example 2   Find a general solution of the fifth-order differential equation

$$9y^{(5)} - 6y^{(4)} + y^{(3)} = 0.$$

Solution   The characteristic equation is

$$9r^5 - 6r^4 + r^3 = r^3(9r^2 - 6r + 1) = r^3(3r - 1)^2 = 0.$$

It has the triple root $r = 0$ and the double root $r = \frac{1}{3}$. The triple root $r = 0$ contributes

$$c_1 e^{0 \cdot x} + c_2 x e^{0 \cdot x} + c_3 x^2 e^{0 \cdot x} = c_1 + c_2 x + c_3 x^2$$

to the solution, while the double root $r = \frac{1}{3}$ contributes $c_4 e^{x/3} + c_5 x e^{x/3}$. Hence a general solution of the given differential equation is

$$y(x) = c_1 + c_2 x + c_3 x^2 + c_4 e^{x/3} + c_5 x e^{x/3}. \qquad \blacksquare$$

Complex-Valued Functions and Euler's Formula

Because we have assumed that the coefficients of the differential equation and its characteristic equation are real, any complex (nonreal) roots will occur in complex conjugate pairs $a \pm bi$ where a and b are real and $i = \sqrt{-1}$. This raises the question as to what might be meant by an exponential such as $\exp([a + bi]x)$.

To answer this question, we recall from elementary calculus the Taylor series for the exponential function

$$e^t = \sum_{n=0}^{\infty} \frac{t^n}{n!} = 1 + t + \frac{t^2}{2!} + \frac{t^3}{3!} + \frac{t^4}{4!} + \cdots.$$

If we substitute $t = ix$ in this series and recall that $i^2 = -1$, $i^3 = -i$, $i^4 = 1$, and so on, we get

$$e^{ix} = \sum_{n=0}^{\infty} \frac{(ix)^n}{n!}$$

$$= 1 + ix - \frac{x^2}{2!} - \frac{ix^3}{3!} + \frac{x^4}{4!} + \frac{ix^5}{5!} - \cdots$$

$$= \left(1 - \frac{x^2}{2!} + \frac{x^4}{4!} - \cdots\right) + i\left(x - \frac{x^3}{3!} + \frac{x^5}{5!} - \cdots\right).$$

Because the two real series in the last line are the Taylor series for $\cos x$ and $\sin x$, respectively, this implies that

$$e^{ix} = \cos x + i \sin x. \tag{15}$$

This result is known as **Euler's formula**. Because of it, we *define* the exponential function e^z, for $z = x + iy$ an arbitrary complex number, to be

$$e^z = e^{x+iy} = e^x e^{iy} = e^x(\cos y + i \sin y). \tag{16}$$

Thus it appears that complex roots of the characteristic equation will lead to complex-valued solutions of the differential equation. A **complex-valued function** F of the real variable x associates with each real number x (in its domain of definition) the complex number

$$F(x) = f(x) + ig(x). \tag{17}$$

The real-valued functions f and g are called the **real** and **imaginary** parts, respectively, of F. If they are differentiable, we define the **derivative** F' of F by

$$F'(x) = f'(x) + ig'(x). \tag{18}$$

Thus we simply differentiate the real and imaginary parts of F separately.

We say that the complex-valued function $F(x)$ satisfies the homogeneous linear differential equation $L[F(x)] = 0$ provided that its real and imaginary parts in (17) separately satisfy this equation—so $L[F(x)] = L[f(x)] + iL[g(x)] = 0$.

The particular complex-valued functions of interest here are of the form $F(x) = e^{rx}$, where $r = a \pm bi$. We note from Euler's formula that

$$e^{(a+bi)x} = e^{ax}e^{ibx} = e^{ax}(\cos bx + i \sin bx) \tag{19a}$$

and

$$e^{(a-bi)x} = e^{ax}e^{-ibx} = e^{ax}(\cos bx - i \sin bx). \tag{19b}$$

The most important property of e^{rx} is that

$$D_x(e^{rx}) = re^{rx}, \tag{20}$$

if r is a complex number. The proof of this assertion is a straightforward computation based on the definitions and formulas given earlier:

$$\begin{aligned}
D_x(e^{rx}) &= D_x(e^{ax}\cos bx) + iD_x(e^{ax}\sin bx) \\
&= (ae^{ax}\cos bx - be^{ax}\sin bx) + i(ae^{ax}\sin bx + be^{ax}\cos bx) \\
&= (a + bi)(e^{ax}\cos bx + ie^{ax}\sin bx) = re^{rx}.
\end{aligned}$$

Complex Roots

It follows from Eq. (20) that when r is complex (just as when r is real), e^{rx} will be a solution of the differential equation in (1) if and only if r is a root of its characteristic equation. If the complex conjugate pair of roots $r_1 = a + bi$ and $r_2 = a - bi$ are simple (nonrepeated), then the corresponding part of a general solution of Eq. (1) is

$$y(x) = C_1 e^{r_1 x} + C_2 e^{r_2 x} = C_1 e^{(a+bi)x} + C_2 e^{(a-bi)x}$$
$$= C_1 e^{ax}(\cos bx + i \sin bx) + C_2 e^{ax}(\cos bx - i \sin bx)$$
$$y(x) = (C_1 + C_2)e^{ax} \cos bx + i(C_1 - C_2)e^{ax} \sin bx,$$

where the arbitrary constants C_1 and C_2 can be complex. For instance, the choice $C_1 = C_2 = \frac{1}{2}$ gives the real-valued solution $y_1(x) = e^{ax} \cos bx$, while the choice $C_1 = -\frac{1}{2}i$, $C_2 = \frac{1}{2}i$ gives the independent real-valued solution $y_2(x) = e^{ax} \sin bx$. This yields the following result.

THEOREM 3: Complex Roots

If the characteristic equation in (3) has an unrepeated pair of complex conjugate roots $a \pm bi$ (with $b \neq 0$), then the corresponding part of a general solution of Eq. (1) has the form

➤
$$e^{ax}(c_1 \cos bx + c_2 \sin bx). \tag{21}$$

Thus the linearly independent solutions $e^{ax} \cos bx$ and $e^{ax} \sin bx$ (corresponding to the complex conjugate characteristic roots $a \pm bi$) generate a 2-dimensional subspace of the solution space of the differential equation.   ▲

Example 3   The characteristic equation of

$$y'' + b^2 y = 0 \quad (b > 0)$$

is $r^2 + b^2 = 0$, with roots $r = \pm bi$. So Theorem 3 (with $a = 0$) gives the general solution

$$y(x) = c_1 \cos bx + c_2 \sin bx. \quad ■$$

Example 4   Find the particular solution of

$$y'' - 4y' + 5y = 0$$

for which $y(0) = 1$ and $y'(0) = 5$.

Solution   The characteristic equation is

$$r^2 - 4r + 5 = (r - 2)^2 + 1 = 0,$$

with roots $2 + i$ and $2 - i$. Hence a general solution is

$$y(x) = e^{2x}(c_1 \cos x + c_2 \sin x).$$

Then

$$y'(x) = 2e^{2x}(c_1 \cos x + c_2 \sin x) + e^{2x}(-c_1 \sin x + c_2 \cos x),$$

so the initial conditions give

$$y(0) = c_1 = 1 \quad \text{and} \quad y'(0) = 2c_1 + c_2 = 5.$$

It follows that $c_2 = 3$, and so the desired particular solution is

$$y(x) = e^{2x}(\cos x + 3 \sin x).$$ ■

Example 5   Find a general solution of $y^{(4)} + 4y = 0$.

Solution   The characteristic equation is

$$r^4 + 4 = (r^2 + 2i)(r^2 - 2i) = 0,$$

and its four roots are $\pm\sqrt{\pm 2i}$. Now $i = e^{i\pi/2}$ and $-i = e^{3i\pi/2}$, so

$$\sqrt{i} = \left(e^{i\pi/2}\right)^{1/2} = e^{i\pi/4} = \frac{1+i}{\sqrt{2}}$$

and

$$\sqrt{-i} = \left(e^{3i\pi/2}\right)^{1/2} = e^{3i\pi/4} = \frac{-1+i}{\sqrt{2}}.$$

Thus the four (distinct) roots of the characteristic equation are $r = \pm(1 \pm i)$. These two pairs of complex conjugate roots, $1 \pm i$ and $-1 \pm i$, give a general solution

$$y(x) = e^x(c_1 \cos x + c_2 \sin x) + e^{-x}(c_3 \cos x + c_4 \sin x)$$

of the differential equation $y^{(4)} + 4y = 0$.   ■

In Example 5 we employed the polar form

$$x + iy = re^{i\theta} \tag{22}$$

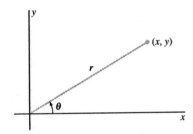

FIGURE 5.3.1. Modulus and argument of the complex number $x + iy$.

of a complex number. The relations between the real and imaginary parts x and y and the **modulus** r and **argument** θ are indicated in Fig. 5.3.1. One consequence of Eq. (22) is that the nonzero complex number $x + iy$ has the two square roots

$$\pm(x + iy)^{1/2} = \pm(re^{i\theta})^{1/2} = \pm r^{1/2}e^{i\theta/2}. \tag{23}$$

Repeated Complex Roots

Theorem 2 holds for repeated complex roots. If the conjugate pair $a \pm bi$ has multiplicity k, then the corresponding part of the general solution has the form

$$(A_1 + A_2 x + \cdots + A_k x^{k-1})e^{(a+bi)x} + (B_1 + B_2 x + \cdots + B_k x^{k-1})e^{(a-bi)x}$$

$$= \sum_{p=0}^{k-1} x^p e^{ax}(c_i \cos bx + d_i \sin bx). \tag{24}$$

It can be shown that the $2k$ functions

$$x^p e^{ax} \cos bx, \quad x^p e^{ax} \sin bx, \quad 0 \le p \le k - 1$$

that appear in Eq. (24) are linearly independent, and therefore generate a $2k$- dimensional subspace of the solution space of the differential equation.

Example 6   Find a general solution of $(D^2 + 6D + 13)^2 y = 0$.

Solution   By completing the square, we see that the characteristic equation

$$(r^2 + 6r + 13)^2 = [(r + 3)^2 + 4]^2 = 0$$

has as its roots the conjugate pair $-3 \pm 2i$ of multiplicity $k = 2$. Hence Eq. (24) gives the general solution

$$y(x) = e^{-3x}(c_1 \cos 2x + d_1 \sin 2x) + xe^{-3x}(c_2 \cos 2x + d_2 \sin 2x). \qquad \blacksquare$$

In applications we are seldom presented in advance with a factorization as convenient as the one in Example 6. Often the most difficult part of solving a homogeneous linear equation is finding the roots of its characteristic equation. Example 7 illustrates an approach that may succeed when a root of the characteristic equation can be found by inspection. The application material for this section illustrates other possibilities.

Example 7   The characteristic equation of the differential equation

$$y^{(3)} + y' - 10y = 0$$

is the cubic equation

$$r^3 + r - 10 = 0.$$

By a standard theorem of elementary algebra, the only possible rational roots are the factors ± 1, ± 2, ± 5, and ± 10 of the constant term 10. By trial and error (if not by inspection) we discover the root 2. The factor theorem of elementary algebra implies that $r - 2$ is a factor of $r^3 + r - 10$, and division of the former into the latter produces as quotient the quadratic polynomial

$$r^2 + 2r + 5 = (r + 1)^2 + 4.$$

The roots of this quotient are the complex conjugates $-1 \pm 2i$. The three roots we have found now yield the general solution

$$y(x) = c_1 e^{2x} + e^{-x}(c_2 \cos 2x + c_3 \sin 2x). \qquad \blacksquare$$

Example 8   The roots of the characteristic equation of a certain differential equation are 3, -5, 0, 0, 0, 0, -5, $2 \pm 3i$, and $2 \pm 3i$. Write a general solution of this homogeneous differential equation.

Solution   The solution can be read directly from the list of roots. It is

$$y(x) = c_1 + c_2 x + c_3 x^2 + c_4 x^3 + c_5 e^{3x} + c_6 e^{-5x} + c_7 x e^{-5x}$$
$$+ e^{2x}(c_8 \cos 3x + c_9 \sin 3x) + xe^{2x}(c_{10} \cos 3x + c_{11} \sin 3x). \qquad \blacksquare$$

5.3 Problems

Find the general solutions of the differential equations in Problems 1 through 20.

1. $y'' - 4y = 0$

2. $2y'' - 3y' = 0$

3. $y'' + 3y' - 10y = 0$

4. $2y'' - 7y' + 3y = 0$

5. $y'' + 6y' + 9y = 0$

6. $y'' + 5y' + 5y = 0$

7. $4y'' - 12y' + 9y = 0$

8. $y'' - 6y' + 13y = 0$

9. $y'' + 8y' + 25y = 0$

10. $5y^{(4)} + 3y^{(3)} = 0$

11. $y^{(4)} - 8y^{(3)} + 16y'' = 0$

12. $y^{(4)} - 3y^{(3)} + 3y'' - y' = 0$

13. $9y^{(3)} + 12y'' + 4y' = 0$

14. $y^{(4)} + 3y'' - 4y = 0$

15. $y^{(4)} - 8y'' + 16y = 0$

16. $y^{(4)} + 18y'' + 81y = 0$

17. $6y^{(4)} + 11y'' + 4y = 0$

18. $y^{(4)} = 16y$

19. $y^{(3)} + y'' - y' - y = 0$

20. $y^{(4)} + 2y^{(3)} + 3y'' + 2y' + y = 0$ [*Suggestion*: Expand $(r^2 + r + 1)^2$.]

Solve the initial value problems given in Problems 21 through 26.

21. $y'' - 4y' + 3y = 0$; $y(0) = 7$, $y'(0) = 11$

22. $9y'' + 6y' + 4y = 0$; $y(0) = 3$, $y'(0) = 4$

23. $y'' - 6y' + 25y = 0$; $y(0) = 3$, $y'(0) = 1$

24. $2y^{(3)} - 3y'' - 2y' = 0$; $y(0) = 1$, $y'(0) = -1$, $y''(0) = 3$

25. $3y^{(3)} + 2y'' = 0$; $y(0) = -1$, $y'(0) = 0$, $y''(0) = 1$

26. $y^{(3)} + 10y'' + 25y' = 0$; $y(0) = 3$, $y'(0) = 4$, $y''(0) = 5$

Find general solutions of the equations in Problems 27 through 32. First find a small integral root of the characteristic equation by inspection; then factor by division.

27. $y^{(3)} + 3y'' - 4y = 0$

28. $2y^{(3)} - y'' - 5y' - 2y = 0$

29. $y^{(3)} + 27y = 0$

30. $y^{(4)} - y^{(3)} + y'' - 3y' - 6y = 0$

31. $y^{(3)} + 3y'' + 4y' - 8y = 0$

32. $y^{(4)} + y^{(3)} - 3y'' - 5y' - 2y = 0$

In Problems 33 through 36, one solution of the differential equation is given. Find the general solution.

33. $y^{(3)} + 3y'' - 54y = 0$; $y = e^{3x}$

34. $3y^{(3)} - 2y'' + 12y' - 8y = 0$; $y = e^{2x/3}$

35. $6y^{(4)} + 5y^{(3)} + 25y'' + 20y' + 4y = 0$; $y = \cos 2x$

36. $9y^{(3)} + 11y'' + 4y' - 14y = 0$; $y = e^{-x} \sin x$

37. Find a function $y(x)$ such that $y^{(4)}(x) = y^{(3)}(x)$ for all x and $y(0) = 18$, $y'(0) = 12$, $y''(0) = 13$, and $y^{(3)}(0) = 7$.

38. Solve the initial value problem

$$y^{(3)} - 5y'' + 100y' - 500y = 0;$$

$$y(0) = 0, \quad y'(0) = 10, \quad y''(0) = 250$$

given that $y_1(x) = e^{5x}$ is one particular solution of the differential equation.

In Problems 39 through 42, find a linear homogeneous constant-coefficient equation with the given general solution.

39. $y(x) = (A + Bx + Cx^2)e^{2x}$

40. $y(x) = Ae^{2x} + B\cos 2x + C\sin 2x$

41. $y(x) = A\cos 2x + B\sin 2x + C\cosh 2x + D\sinh 2x$

42. $y(x) = (A + Bx + Cx^2)\cos 2x + (D + Ex + Fx^2)\sin 2x$

Problems 43 through 47 pertain to the solution of differential equations with complex coefficients.

43. (a) Use Euler's formula to show that every complex number can be written in the form $re^{i\theta}$, where $r \geq 0$ and $-\pi < \theta \leq \pi$. **(b)** Express the numbers 4, -2, $3i$, $1 + i$, and $-1 + i\sqrt{3}$ in the form $re^{i\theta}$. **(c)** The two square roots of $re^{i\theta}$ are $\pm e^{i\theta/2}\sqrt{r}$. Find the square roots of the numbers $2 - 2i\sqrt{3}$ and $-2 + 2i\sqrt{3}$.

44. Use the quadratic formula to solve the following equations. Note in each case that the roots are not complex conjugates.

(a) $x^2 + ix + 2 = 0$ **(b)** $x^2 - 2ix + 3 = 0$

45. Find a general solution of $y'' - 2iy' + 3y = 0$.

46. Find a general solution of $y'' - iy' + 6y = 0$.

47. Find a general solution of $y'' = \left(-2 + 2i\sqrt{3}\right)y$.

48. Solve the initial value problem

$$y^{(3)} = y; \quad y(0) = 1, \quad y'(0) = y''(0) = 0.$$

[*Suggestion*: Impose the given initial conditions on the general solution

$$y(x) = Ae^x + Be^{\alpha x} + Ce^{\beta x},$$

where α and β are the complex conjugate roots of $r^3 - 1 = 0$, to discover that

$$y(x) = \frac{1}{3}\left(e^x + 2e^{-x/2}\cos\frac{x\sqrt{3}}{2}\right)$$

is a solution.]

49. Solve the initial value problem

$$y^{(4)} = y^{(3)} + y'' + y' + 2y;$$

$$y(0) = y'(0) = y''(0) = 0, y^{(3)}(0) = 30.$$

50. The differential equation

$$y'' + (\text{sgn } x)y = 0 \qquad (25)$$

has the discontinuous coefficient function

$$\text{sgn } x = \begin{cases} +1 & \text{if } x > 0, \\ -1 & \text{if } x < 0. \end{cases}$$

Show that Eq. (25) nevertheless has two linearly independent solutions $y_1(x)$ and $y_2(x)$ defined for all x such that

- Each satisfies Eq. (25) at each point $x \neq 0$;
- Each has a continuous derivative at $x = 0$;
- $y_1(0) = y_2'(0) = 1$ and $y_2(0) = y_1'(0) = 0$.

[*Suggestion*: Each $y_i(x)$ will be defined by one formula for $x < 0$ and by another for $x \geq 0$.] The graphs of these two solutions are shown in Fig. 5.3.2.

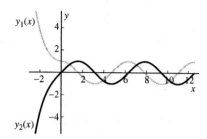

FIGURE 5.3.2. Graphs of $y_1(x)$ and $y_2(x)$ in Problem 50.

51. According to Problem 51 in Section 5.1, the substitution $v = \ln x$ $(x > 0)$ transforms the second-order Euler equation $ax^2y'' + bxy' + cy = 0$ to a constant-coefficient homogeneous linear equation. Show similarly that this same

substitution transforms the third-order Euler equation

$$ax^3y''' + bx^2y'' + cxy' + dy = 0$$

(where a, b, c, d are constants) into the constant-coefficient equation

$$a\frac{d^3y}{dv^3} + (b - 3a)\frac{d^2y}{dv^2} + (c - b + 2a)\frac{dy}{dv} + dy = 0.$$

Make the substitution $v = \ln x$ of Problem 51 to find general solutions (for $x > 0$) of the Euler equations in Problems 52 through 58.

52. $x^2y'' + xy' + 9y = 0$
53. $x^2y'' + 7xy' + 25y = 0$
54. $x^3y''' + 6x^2y'' + 4xy' = 0$
55. $x^3y''' - x^2y'' + xy' = 0$
56. $x^3y''' + 3x^2y'' + xy' = 0$
57. $x^3y''' - 3x^2y'' + xy' = 0$
58. $x^3y''' + 6x^2y'' + 7xy' + y = 0$

5.3 Application: Approximate Solutions of Linear Equations

To meet the needs of applications such as those of this section, polynomial-solving utilities are now a common feature of calculator and computer systems and can be used to solve a characteristic equation numerically even when no simple factorization is evident or even possible. For instance, suppose that we want to solve the homogeneous linear differential equation

$$y^{(3)} - 3y'' + y = 0 \tag{1}$$

with characteristic equation

$$r^3 - 3r^2 + 1 = 0. \tag{2}$$

A typical graphing calculator has a **solve** command that can be used to find the approximate roots of a polynomial equation. As indicated in Figs. 5.3.3 and 5.3.4, we find that the roots of Eq. (2) are given by $r \approx -0.5321$, 0.6527, and 2.8794. Some analogous computer algebra system commands are

```
solve(R^3-3R^2+1,
R,-1)
              -.5321
solve(R^3-3R^2+1,
R,1)
              .6527
solve(R^3-3R^2+1,
R,3)
```

FIGURE 5.3.3. Solving the equation $r^3 - 3r^2 + 1 = 0$ with a TI-83 calculator that requires an estimate of each root.

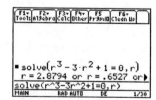

FIGURE 5.3.4. Solving the characteristic equation with a TI-89 calculator having a more sophisticated **solve** facility.

```
fsolve(r^3 - 3*r^2 + 1 = 0, r);        (Maple)
NSolve[r^3 - 3*r^2 + 1 == 0, r]        (Mathematica)
```

$$\texttt{roots([1 -3 0 1])} \qquad \qquad \text{(MATLAB)}$$

(In the MATLAB command, one enters the polynomial's vector **[1 -3 0 1]** of coefficients, listed in descending order.) However we find these approximate roots, it follows that a general solution of the differential equation in (1) is given (approximately) by

$$y(x) = c_1 e^{-(0.5321)x} + c_2 e^{(0.6527)x} + c_3 e^{(2.8794)x}. \tag{3}$$

Use calculator or computer methods like those indicated here to find general solutions (in approximate numerical form) of the following differential equations.

1. $y^{(3)} - 3y' + y = 0$
2. $y^{(3)} + 3y'' - 3y = 0$
3. $y^{(3)} + y' + y = 0$
4. $y^{(3)} + 3y' + 5y = 0$
5. $y^{(4)} + 2y^{(3)} - 3y = 0$
6. $y^{(4)} + 3y' - 4y = 0$

5.4 Mechanical Vibrations

FIGURE 5.4.1. A mass-spring-dashpot system.

The motion of a mass attached to a spring serves as a relatively simple example of the vibrations that occur in more complex mechanical systems. For many such systems, the analysis of these vibrations is a problem in the solution of linear differential equations with constant coefficients.

We consider a body of mass m attached to one end of an ordinary spring that resists compression as well as stretching; the other end of the spring is attached to a fixed wall, as shown in Fig. 5.4.1. Assume that the body rests on a frictionless horizontal plane, so that it can move only back and forth as the spring compresses and stretches. Denote by x the distance of the body from its **equilibrium position**—its position when the spring is unstretched. We take $x > 0$ when the spring is stretched, and thus $x < 0$ when it is compressed.

According to Hooke's law, the restorative force F_S that the spring exerts on the mass is proportional to the distance x that the spring has been stretched or compressed. Because this is the same as the displacement x of the mass m from its equilibrium position, it follows that

$$F_S = -kx. \tag{1}$$

The positive constant of proportionality k is called the **spring constant.** Note that F_S and x have opposite signs: $F_S < 0$ when $x > 0$, $F_S > 0$ when $x < 0$.

Figure 5.4.1 shows the mass attached to a dashpot—a device, like a shock absorber, that provides a force directed opposite to the instantaneous direction of motion of the mass m. We assume the dashpot is so designed that this force F_R is proportional to the velocity $v = dx/dt$ of the mass; that is,

$$F_R = -cv = -c\frac{dx}{dt}. \tag{2}$$

The positive constant c is the **damping constant** of the dashpot. More generally, we may regard Eq. (2) as specifying frictional forces in our system (including air resistance to the motion of m).

If, in addition to the forces F_S and F_R, the mass is subjected to a given **external force** $F_E = F(t)$, then the total force acting on the mass is $F = F_S + F_R + F_E$. Using Newton's law,

$$F = ma = m\frac{d^2x}{dt^2} = mx'',$$

we obtain the second-order linear differential equation

➤ $$mx'' + cx' + kx = F(t) \qquad (3)$$

that governs the motion of the mass.

If there is no dashpot (and we ignore all frictional forces), then we set $c = 0$ in Eq. (3) and call the motion **undamped**; it is **damped** motion if $c > 0$. If there is no external force, we replace $F(t)$ with 0 in Eq. (3). We refer to the motion as **free** in this case and **forced** in the case $F(t) \neq 0$. Thus the homogeneous equation

➤ $$mx'' + cx' + kx = 0 \qquad (4)$$

describes free motion of a mass on a spring with dashpot but with no external forces applied. We will defer discussion of forced motion until Section 5.6.

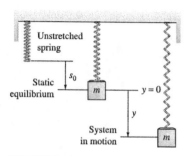

For an alternative example, we might attach the mass to the lower end of a spring that is suspended vertically from a fixed support, as in Fig. 5.4.2. In this case the weight $W = mg$ of the mass would stretch the spring a distance s_0 determined by Eq. (1) with $F_S = -W$ and $x = s_0$. That is, $mg = ks_0$, so that $s_0 = mg/k$. This gives the **static** equilibrium position of the mass. If y denotes the displacement of the mass in motion, measured downward from its static equilibrium position, then we ask you to show in Problem 9 that y satisfies Eq. (3); specifically, that

FIGURE 5.4.2. A mass suspended vertically from a spring.

$$my'' + cy' + ky = F(t) \qquad (5)$$

if we include damping and external forces.

The Simple Pendulum

The importance of the differential equation that appears in Eqs. (3) and (5) stems from the fact that it describes the motion of many other simple mechanical systems. For example, a **simple pendulum** consists of a mass m swinging back and forth on the end of a string (or better, a *massless rod*) of length L, as shown in Fig. 5.4.3. We may specify the position of the mass at time t by giving the counterclockwise angle $\theta = \theta(t)$ that the string or rod makes with the vertical at time t. To analyze the motion of the mass m, we will apply the law of the *conservation of mechanical energy*, according to which the sum of the kinetic energy and the potential energy of m remains constant.

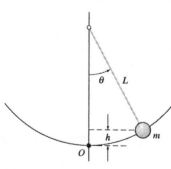

The distance along the circular arc from 0 to m is $s = L\theta$, so the velocity of the mass is $v = ds/dt = L(d\theta/dt)$, and therefore its kinetic energy is

FIGURE 5.4.3. The simple pendulum.

$$T = \frac{1}{2}mv^2 = \frac{1}{2}m\left(\frac{ds}{dt}\right)^2 = \frac{1}{2}mL^2\left(\frac{d\theta}{dt}\right)^2.$$

We next choose as reference point the lowest point O reached by the mass (see Fig. 5.4.3). Then its potential energy V is the product of its weight mg and its vertical height $h = L(1 - \cos\theta)$ above O, so

$$V = mgL(1 - \cos\theta).$$

The fact that the sum of T and V is a constant C therefore gives

$$\frac{1}{2}mL^2\left(\frac{d\theta}{dt}\right)^2 + mgL(1 - \cos\theta) = C.$$

We differentiate both sides of this identity with respect to t to obtain

$$mL^2\left(\frac{d\theta}{dt}\right)\left(\frac{d^2\theta}{dt^2}\right) + mgL(\sin\theta)\frac{d\theta}{dt} = 0,$$

so

$$\frac{d^2\theta}{dt^2} + \frac{g}{L}\sin\theta = 0 \tag{6}$$

after removal of the common factor $mL^2(d\theta/dt)$.

Now recall that $\sin\theta \approx \theta$ when θ is small; in fact, $\sin\theta$ and θ agree to two decimal places when $|\theta|$ is at most $\pi/12$ (that is, 15°). In a typical pendulum clock, for example, θ would never exceed 15°. It therefore seems reasonable to simplify our mathematical model of the simple pendulum by replacing $\sin\theta$ with θ in Eq. (6). If we also insert a term $c\theta'$ to account for the frictional resistance of the surrounding medium, the result is an equation in the form of Eq. (4):

$$\theta'' + c\theta' + k\theta = 0, \tag{7}$$

where $k = g/L$. Note that this equation is independent of the mass m on the end of the rod. We might, however, expect the effects of the discrepancy between θ and $\sin\theta$ to accumulate over a period of time, so that Eq. (7) will probably not describe accurately the actual motion of the pendulum over a long period of time.

In the remainder of this section, we first analyze free undamped motion and then free damped motion.

Free Undamped Motion

If we have only a mass on a spring, with neither damping nor external force, then Eq. (3) takes the simpler form

$$mx'' + kx = 0. \tag{8}$$

It is convenient to define

$$\omega_0 = \sqrt{\frac{k}{m}} \tag{9}$$

and rewrite Eq. (8) as

$$x'' + \omega_0^2 x = 0. \tag{8'}$$

The general solution of Eq. (8′) is

$$x(t) = A\cos\omega_0 t + B\sin\omega_0 t. \tag{10}$$

To analyze the motion described by this solution, we choose constants C and α so that

$$C = \sqrt{A^2 + B^2}, \quad \cos \alpha = \frac{A}{C}, \quad \text{and} \quad \sin \alpha = \frac{B}{C}, \tag{11}$$

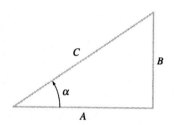

as indicated in Fig. 5.4.4. Note that, although $\tan \alpha = B/A$, the angle α is *not* given by the principal branch of the inverse tangent function (which gives values only in the interval $-\pi/2 < x < \pi/2$). Instead, α is the angle between 0 and 2π whose cosine and sine have the signs given in (11), where either A or B or both may be negative. Thus

$$\alpha = \begin{cases} \tan^{-1}(B/A) & \text{if } A > 0, B > 0 \text{ (first quadrant)}, \\ \pi + \tan^{-1}(B/A) & \text{if } A < 0 \text{ (second or third quadrant)}, \\ 2\pi + \tan^{-1}(B/A) & \text{if } A > 0, B < 0 \text{ (fourth quadrant)}, \end{cases}$$

FIGURE 5.4.4. The angle α.

where $\tan^{-1}(B/A)$ is the angle in $(-\pi/2, \pi/2)$ given by a calculator or computer.

In any event, from (10) and (11) we get

$$x(t) = C\left(\frac{A}{C}\cos \omega_0 t + \frac{B}{C}\sin \omega_0 t\right) = C(\cos \alpha \cos \omega_0 t + \sin \alpha \sin \omega_0 t).$$

With the aid of the cosine addition formula, we find that

$$x(t) = C\cos(\omega_0 t - \alpha). \tag{12}$$

Thus the mass oscillates to and fro about its equilibrium position with

1. **Amplitude** C,
2. **Circular frequency** ω_0, and
3. **Phase angle** α.

Such motion is called **simple harmonic motion**.

If time t is measured in seconds, the circular frequency ω_0 has dimensions of radians per second (rad/s). The **period** of the motion is the time required for the system to complete one full oscillation, so is given by

$$T = \frac{2\pi}{\omega_0} \tag{13}$$

seconds; its **frequency** is

$$\nu = \frac{1}{T} = \frac{\omega_0}{2\pi} \tag{14}$$

in hertz (Hz), which measures the number of complete cycles per second. Note that frequency is measured in cycles per second, whereas circular frequency has the dimensions of radians per second.

A typical graph of a simple harmonic position function

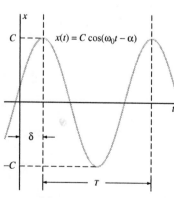

FIGURE 5.4.5. Simple harmonic motion.

$$x(t) = C\cos(\omega_0 t - \alpha) = C\cos\left(\omega_0\left(t - \frac{\alpha}{\omega_0}\right)\right) = C\cos(\omega_0(t - \delta))$$

is shown in Fig. 5.4.5, where the geometric significance of the amplitude C, the period T, and the **time lag**

$$\delta = \frac{\alpha}{\omega_0}$$

are indicated.

If the initial position $x(0) = x_0$ and initial velocity $x'(0) = v_0$ of the mass are given, we first determine the values of the coefficients A and B in Eq. (10), then find the amplitude C and phase angle α by carrying out the transformation of $x(t)$ to the form in Eq. (12), as indicated previously.

Example 1 A body with mass $m = \frac{1}{2}$ kilogram (kg) is attached to the end of a spring that is stretched 2 meters (m) by a force of 100 newtons (N). It is set in motion with initial position $x_0 = 1$ (m) and initial velocity $v_0 = -5$ (m/s). (Note that these initial conditions indicate that the body is displaced to the right and is moving to the left at time $t = 0$.) Find the position function of the body as well as the amplitude, frequency, period of oscillation, and time lag of its motion.

Solution The spring constant is $k = (100 \text{ N})/(2 \text{ m}) = 50$ (N/m), so Eq. (8) yields $\frac{1}{2}x'' + 50x = 0$; that is,

$$x'' + 100x = 0.$$

Consequently, the circular frequency of the resulting simple harmonic motion of the body will be $\omega_0 = \sqrt{100} = 10$ (rad/s). Hence it will oscillate with period

$$T = \frac{2\pi}{\omega_0} = \frac{2\pi}{10} \approx 0.6283 \text{ s}$$

and with frequency

$$\nu = \frac{1}{T} = \frac{\omega_0}{2\pi} = \frac{10}{2\pi} \approx 1.5915 \text{ Hz.}$$

We now impose the initial conditions $x(0) = 1$ and $x'(0) = -5$ on the position function

$$x(t) = A\cos 10t + B\sin 10t \quad \text{with} \quad x'(t) = -10A\sin 10t + 10B\cos 10t.$$

It follows readily that $A = 1$ and $B = -\frac{1}{2}$, so the position function of the body is

$$x(t) = \cos 10t - \frac{1}{2}\sin 10t.$$

Hence its amplitude of motion is

$$C = \sqrt{(1)^2 + (-\tfrac{1}{2})^2} = \tfrac{1}{2}\sqrt{5} \text{ m.}$$

To find the time lag, we write

$$x(t) = \frac{\sqrt{5}}{2}\left(\frac{2}{\sqrt{5}}\cos 10t - \frac{1}{\sqrt{5}}\sin 10t \right) = \frac{\sqrt{5}}{2}\cos(10t - \alpha),$$

where the phase angle α satisfies

$$\cos\alpha = \frac{2}{\sqrt{5}} > 0 \quad \text{and} \quad \sin\alpha = -\frac{1}{\sqrt{5}} < 0.$$

Hence α is the fourth-quadrant angle

$$\alpha = 2\pi + \tan^{-1}\left(\frac{-1/\sqrt{5}}{2/\sqrt{5}}\right) = 2\pi - \tan^{-1}(\tfrac{1}{2}) \approx 5.8195,$$

and the time lag of the motion is

$$\delta = \frac{\alpha}{\omega_0} \approx 0.5820 \text{ s.}$$

With the amplitude and approximate phase angle shown explicitly, the position function of the body takes the form

$$x(t) \approx \tfrac{1}{2}\sqrt{5}\cos(10t - 5.8195),$$

and its graph is shown in Fig. 5.4.6. ∎

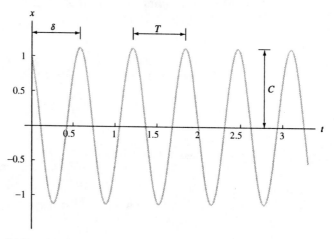

FIGURE 5.4.6. Graph of the position function $x(t) = C\cos(\omega_0 t - \alpha)$ in Example 1, with amplitude $C \approx 1.118$, period $T \approx 0.628$, and time lag $\delta \approx 0.582$.

Free Damped Motion

With damping but no external force, the differential equation we have been studying takes the form $mx'' + cx' + kx = 0$; alternatively,

$$x'' + 2px' + \omega_0^2 x = 0, \tag{15}$$

where $\omega_0 = \sqrt{k/m}$ is the corresponding *undamped* circular frequency and

$$p = \frac{c}{2m} > 0. \tag{16}$$

The characteristic equation $r^2 + 2pr + \omega_0^2 = 0$ of Eq. (15) has roots

$$r_1,\ r_2 = -p \pm (p^2 - \omega_0^2)^{1/2} \tag{17}$$

that depend on the sign of

$$p^2 - \omega_0^2 = \frac{c^2}{4m^2} - \frac{k}{m} = \frac{c^2 - 4km}{4m^2}. \tag{18}$$

The **critical damping** c_{cr} is given by $c_{cr} = \sqrt{4km}$, and we distinguish three cases, according as $c > c_{cr}$, $c = c_{cr}$, or $c < c_{cr}$.

OVERDAMPED CASE: $c > c_{cr}(c^2 > 4km)$. Because c is relatively large in this case, we are dealing with a strong resistance in comparison with a relatively weak spring or a small mass. Then (17) gives distinct real roots r_1 and r_2, both of which are negative. The position function has the form

$$x(t) = c_1 e^{r_1 t} + c_2 e^{r_2 t}. \tag{19}$$

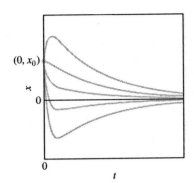

FIGURE 5.4.7. Overdamped motion: $x(t) = c_1 e^{r_1 t} + c_2 e^{r_2 t}$ with $r_1 < 0$ and $r_2 < 0$. Solution curves are graphed with the same initial position x_0 and different initial velocities.

It is easy to see that $x(t) \to 0$ as $t \to +\infty$ and that the body settles to its equilibrium position without any oscillations (Problem 29). Figure 5.4.7 shows some typical graphs of the position function for the overdamped case; we chose x_0 a fixed positive number and illustrated the effects of changing the initial velocity v_0. In every case the would-be oscillations are damped out.

CRITICALLY DAMPED CASE: $c = c_{cr}(c^2 = 4km)$. In this case, (17) gives equal roots $r_1 = r_2 = -p$ of the characteristic equation, so the general solution is

$$x(t) = e^{-pt}(c_1 + c_2 t). \tag{20}$$

Because $e^{-pt} > 0$ and $c_1 + c_2 t$ has at most one positive zero, the body passes through its equilibrium position at most once, and it is clear that $x(t) \to 0$ as $t \to +\infty$. Some graphs of the motion in the critically damped case appear in Fig. 5.4.8, and they resemble those of the overdamped case (Fig. 5.4.7). In the critically damped case, the resistance of the dashpot is just large enough to damp out any oscillations, but even a slight reduction in resistance will bring us to the remaining case, the one that shows the most dramatic behavior.

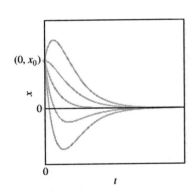

FIGURE 5.4.8. Critically damped motion: $x(t) = (c_1 + c_2 t)e^{-pt}$ with $p > 0$. Solution curves are graphed with the same initial position x_0 and different initial velocities.

UNDERDAMPED CASE: $c < c_{cr}(c^2 < 4km)$. The characteristic equation now has two complex conjugate roots $-p \pm i\sqrt{\omega_0^2 - p^2}$, and the general solution is

➤
$$x(t) = e^{-pt}(A \cos \omega_1 t + B \sin \omega_1 t), \tag{21}$$

where

$$\omega_1 = \sqrt{\omega_0^2 - p^2} = \frac{\sqrt{4km - c^2}}{2m}. \tag{22}$$

Using the cosine addition formula as in the derivation of Eq. (12), we may rewrite Eq. (20) as

$$x(t) = Ce^{-pt}\left(\frac{A}{C}\cos \omega_1 t + \frac{B}{C}\sin \omega_1 t\right),$$

so

➤
$$x(t) = Ce^{-pt}\cos(\omega_1 t - \alpha), \tag{23}$$

where

$$C = \sqrt{A^2 + B^2}, \quad \cos\alpha = \frac{A}{C}, \quad \text{and} \quad \sin\alpha = \frac{B}{C}.$$

The solution in (22) represents exponentially damped oscillations of the body around its equilibrium position. The graph of $x(t)$ lies between the "amplitude envelope" curves $x = -Ce^{-pt}$ and $x = Ce^{-pt}$ and touches them when $\omega_1 t - \alpha$ is an integral multiple of π. The motion is not actually periodic, but it is nevertheless useful to call ω_1 its **circular frequency** (more properly, its **pseudofrequency**), $T_1 = 2\pi/\omega_1$ its **pseudoperiod** of oscillation, and Ce^{-pt} its **time-varying amplitude**. Most of these quantities are shown in the typical graph of underdamped motion shown in Fig. 5.4.9. Note from Eq. (21) that in this case ω_1 is less than the undamped circular frequency ω_0, so T_1 is larger than the period T of oscillation of the same mass without damping on the same spring. Thus the action of the dashpot has at least two effects:

1. It exponentially damps the oscillations, in accord with the time-varying amplitude.

2. It slows the motion; that is, the dashpot decreases the frequency of the motion.

As the following example illustrates, damping typically also delays the motion further—that is, increases the time lag—as compared with undamped motion with the same initial conditions.

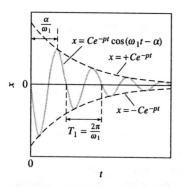

FIGURE 5.4.9. Underdamped oscillations:
$x(t) = Ce^{-pt}\cos(\omega_1 t - \alpha)$.

Example 2   The mass and spring of Example 1 are now attached also to a dashpot that provides 1 N of resistance for each meter per second of velocity. The mass is set in motion with the same initial position $x(0) = 1$ and initial velocity $x'(0) = -5$ as in Example 1. Now find the position function of the mass, its new frequency and pseudoperiod of motion, its new time lag, and the times of its first four passages through the initial position $x = 0$.

Solution   Rather than memorizing the various formulas given in the preceding discussion, it is better practice in a particular case to set up the differential equation and then solve it directly. Recall that $m = \frac{1}{2}$ and $k = 50$; we are now given $c = 1$ in mks units. Hence Eq. (4) is $\frac{1}{2}x'' + x' + 50x = 0$; that is,

$$x'' + 2x' + 100x = 0.$$

The characteristic equation $r^2 + 2r + 100 = (r+1)^2 + 99 = 0$ has roots $r_1, r_2 = -1 \pm \sqrt{99}\,i$, so the general solution is

$$x(t) = e^{-t}(A\cos\sqrt{99}\,t + B\sin\sqrt{99}\,t). \tag{24}$$

Consequently, the new circular (pseudo)frequency is $\omega_1 = \sqrt{99} \approx 9.9499$ (as compared with $\omega_0 = 10$ in Example 1). The new (pseudo)period and frequency are

$$T_1 = \frac{2\pi}{\omega_1} = \frac{2\pi}{\sqrt{99}} \approx 0.6315 \text{ s}$$

and

$$\nu_1 = \frac{1}{T_1} = \frac{\omega_1}{2\pi} = \frac{\sqrt{99}}{2\pi} \approx 1.5836 \text{ Hz}$$

(as compared with $T \approx 0.6283 < T_1$ and $v \approx 1.5915 > v_1$ in Example 1).

We now impose the initial conditions $x(0) = 1$ and $x'(0) = -5$ on the position function in (23) and the resulting velocity function

$$x'(t) = -e^{-t}(A \cos \sqrt{99}\, t + B \sin \sqrt{99}\, t) + \sqrt{99}\, e^{-t}(-A \sin \sqrt{99}\, t + B \cos \sqrt{99}\, t).$$

It follows that

$$x(0) = A = 1 \quad \text{and} \quad x'(0) = -A + B\sqrt{99} = -5,$$

whence we find that $A = 1$ and $B = -4/\sqrt{99}$. Thus the new position function of the body is

$$x(t) = e^{-t}\left(\cos \sqrt{99}\, t - \frac{4}{\sqrt{99}} \sin \sqrt{99}\, t \right).$$

Hence its time-varying amplitude of motion is

$$C_1 e^{-t} = \sqrt{(1)^2 + \left(-\frac{4}{\sqrt{99}}\right)^2}\, e^{-t} = \sqrt{\frac{115}{99}}\, e^{-t}.$$

We therefore write

$$x(t) = \frac{\sqrt{115}}{\sqrt{99}} e^{-t} \left(\frac{\sqrt{99}}{\sqrt{115}} \cos \sqrt{99}\, t - \frac{4}{\sqrt{115}} \sin \sqrt{99}\, t \right)$$

$$= \sqrt{\frac{115}{99}} e^{-t} \cos(\sqrt{99}\, t - \alpha_1),$$

where the phase angle α_1 satisfies

$$\cos \alpha_1 = \frac{\sqrt{99}}{\sqrt{115}} > 0 \quad \text{and} \quad \sin \alpha_1 = -\frac{4}{\sqrt{115}} < 0.$$

Hence α_1 is the fourth-quadrant angle

$$\alpha_1 = 2\pi + \tan^{-1}\left(\frac{-4/\sqrt{115}}{\sqrt{99}/\sqrt{115}} \right) = 2\pi - \tan^{-1}\left(\frac{4}{\sqrt{99}} \right) \approx 5.9009,$$

and the time lag of the motion is

$$\delta_1 = \frac{\alpha_1}{\omega_1} \approx 0.5931 \text{ s}$$

(as compared with $\delta \approx 0.5820 < \delta_1$ in Example 1). With the time-varying amplitude and approximate phase angle shown explicitly, the position function of the mass takes the form

$$x(t) \approx \sqrt{\frac{115}{99}} e^{-t} \cos(\sqrt{99}\, t - 5.9009), \tag{25}$$

and its graph is the damped exponential that is shown in Fig. 5.4.10 (in comparison with the undamped oscillations of Example 1.

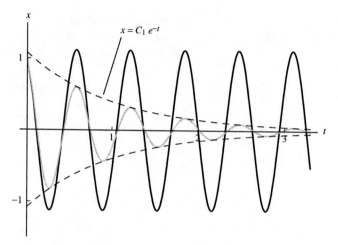

FIGURE 5.4.10. Graphs of the position function $x(t) = C_1 e^{-t} \cos(\omega_1 t - \alpha_1)$ of Example 2 (damped oscillations), the position function $x(t) = C \cos(\omega_0 t - \alpha)$ of Example 1 (undamped oscillations), and the envelope curves $x(t) = \pm C_1 e^{-t}$.

From (24) we see that the mass passes through its equilibrium position $x = 0$ when $\cos(\omega_1 t - \alpha_1) = 0$, and thus when

$$\omega_1 t - \alpha_1 = -\frac{3\pi}{2}, \ -\frac{\pi}{2}, \frac{\pi}{2}, \frac{3\pi}{2}, \ \dots, \quad \text{that is, when}$$

$$t = \delta_1 - \frac{3\pi}{2\omega_1}, \delta_1 - \frac{\pi}{2\omega_1}, \delta_1 + \frac{\pi}{2\omega_1}, \delta_1 + \frac{3\pi}{2\omega_1}, \ \dots.$$

We see similarly that the undamped mass of Example 1 passes through equilibrium when

$$t = \delta_0 - \frac{3\pi}{2\omega_0}, \delta_0 - \frac{\pi}{2\omega_0}, \delta_0 + \frac{\pi}{2\omega_0}, \delta_0 + \frac{3\pi}{2\omega_0}, \ \dots.$$

The following table compares the first four values t_1, t_2, t_3, t_4 we calculate for the undamped and damped cases, respectively.

n	1	2	3	4
t_n (undamped)	0.1107	0.4249	0.7390	1.0532
t_n (damped)	0.1195	0.4352	0.7509	1.0667

Accordingly, in Fig. 5.4.11 (where only the first three equilibrium passages are shown) we see the damped oscillations lagging slightly behind the undamped ones.

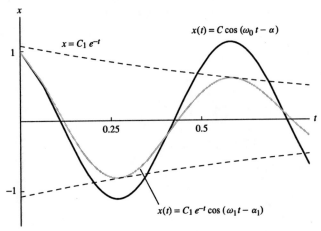

FIGURE 5.4.11. Graphs on the interval $0 \le t \le 0.8$ illustrating the additional delay associated with damping.

5.4 Problems

1. Determine the period and frequency of the simple harmonic motion of a 4-kg mass on the end of a spring with spring constant 16 N/m.

2. Determine the period and frequency of the simple harmonic motion of a body of mass 0.75 kg on the end of a spring with spring constant 48 N/m.

3. A mass of 3 kg is attached to the end of a spring that is stretched 20 cm by a force of 15 N. It is set in motion with initial position $x_0 = 0$ and initial velocity $v_0 = -10$ m/s. Find the amplitude, period, and frequency of the resulting motion.

4. A body with mass 250 g is attached to the end of a spring that is stretched 25 cm by a force of 9 N. At time $t = 0$ the body is pulled 1 m to the right, stretching the spring, and set in motion with an initial velocity of 5 m/s to the left. **(a)** Find $x(t)$ in the form $C \cos(\omega_0 t - \alpha)$. **(b)** Find the amplitude and period of motion of the body.

In Problems 5 through 8, assume that the differential equation of a simple pendulum of length L is $L\theta'' + g\theta = 0$, where $g = GM/R^2$ is the gravitational acceleration at the location of the pendulum (at distance R from the center of the earth; M denotes the mass of the earth).

5. Two pendulums are of lengths L_1 and L_2 and—when located at the respective distances R_1 and R_2 from the center of the earth—have periods p_1 and p_2. Show that

$$\frac{p_1}{p_2} = \frac{R_1 \sqrt{L_1}}{R_2 \sqrt{L_2}}.$$

6. A certain pendulum keeps perfect time in Paris, where the radius of the earth is $R = 3956$ (mi). But this clock loses

2 min 40 s per day at a location on the equator. Use the result of Problem 5 to find the amount of the equatorial bulge of the earth.

7. A pendulum of length 100.10 in., located at a point at sea level where the radius of the earth is $R = 3960$ (mi), has the same period as does a pendulum of length 100.00 in. atop a nearby mountain. Use the result of Problem 5 to find the height of the mountain.

8. Most grandfather clocks have pendulums with adjustable lengths. One such clock loses 10 min per day when the length of its pendulum is 30 in. With what length pendulum will this clock keep perfect time?

9. Derive Eq. (5) describing the motion of a mass attached to the bottom of a vertically suspended spring. [*Suggestion:* First denote by $x(t)$ the displacement of the mass below the unstretched position of the spring; set up the differential equation for x. Then substitute $y = x - x_0$ in this differential equation.]

10. Consider a floating cylindrical buoy with radius r, height h, and uniform density $\rho \le 0.5$ (recall that the density of water is 1 g/cm³). The buoy is initially suspended at rest with its bottom at the top surface of the water and is released at time $t = 0$. Thereafter it is acted on by two forces: a downward gravitational force equal to its weight $mg = \rho \pi r^2 hg$ and an upward force of buoyancy equal to the weight $\pi r^2 xg$ of water displaced, where $x = x(t)$ is the depth of the bottom of the buoy beneath the surface at time t (Fig. 5.4.12). Conclude that the buoy undergoes simple harmonic motion around its equilibrium position $x_e = \rho h$ with period $p = 2\pi \sqrt{\rho h/g}$. Compute p and the

amplitude of the motion if $\rho = 0.5$ g/cm^3, $h = 200$ cm, and $g = 980$ cm/s^2.

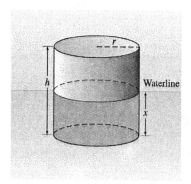

FIGURE 5.4.12.   The buoy of Problem 10.

11. A cylindrical buoy weighing 100 lb (thus of mass $m = 3.125$ slugs in ft-lb-s (fps) units) floats in water with its axis vertical (as in Problem 10). When depressed slightly and released, it oscillates up and down four times every 10 s. Assume that friction is negligible. Find the radius of the buoy.

12. Assume that the earth is a solid sphere of uniform density, with mass M and radius $R = 3960$ (mi). For a particle of mass m *within* the earth at distance r from the center of the earth, the gravitational force attracting m toward the center is $F_r = -GM_r m/r^2$, where M_r is the mass of the part of the earth within a sphere of radius r. (a) Show that $F_r = -GMmr/R^3$. (b) Now suppose that a small hole is drilled straight through the center of the earth, thus connecting two antipodal points on its surface. Let a particle of mass m be dropped at time $t = 0$ into this hole with initial speed zero, and let $r(t)$ be its distance from the center of the earth at time t (Fig. 5.4.13). Conclude from Newton's second law and part (a) that $r''(t) = -k^2 r(t)$, where $k^2 = GM/R^3 = g/R$.

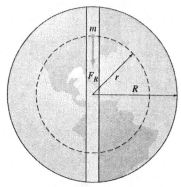

FIGURE 5.4.13.   A mass m falling down a hole through the center of the earth (Problem 12).

(c) Take $g = 32.2$ ft/s^2, and conclude from part (b) that the particle undergoes simple harmonic motion back and forth between the ends of the hole, with a period of about 84 min. (d) Look up (or derive) the period of a satellite that just skims the surface of the earth; compare with the result in part (c). How do you explain the coincidence? Or *is* it a coincidence? (e) With what speed (in miles per hour) does the particle pass through the center of the earth? (f) Look up (or derive) the orbital velocity of a satellite that just skims the surface of the earth; compare with the result in part (e). How do you explain the coincidence? Or *is* it a coincidence?

13. Suppose that the mass in a mass-spring-dashpot system with $m = 10$, $c = 9$, and $k = 2$ is set in motion with $x(0) = 0$ and $x'(0) = 5$. (a) Find the position function $x(t)$ and show that its graph looks as indicated in Fig. 5.4.14. (b) Find how far the mass moves to the right before starting back toward the origin.

FIGURE 5.4.14.   The position function $x(t)$ of Problem 13.

14. Suppose that the mass in a mass-spring-dashpot system with $m = 25$, $c = 10$, and $k = 226$ is set in motion with $x(0) = 20$ and $x'(0) = 41$. (a) Find the position function $x(t)$ and show that its graph looks as indicated in Fig. 5.4.15. (b) Find the pseudoperiod of the oscillations and the equations of the "envelope curves" that are dashed in the figure.

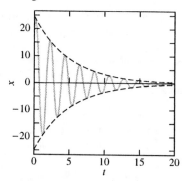

FIGURE 5.4.15.   The position function $x(t)$ of Problem 14.

The remaining problems in this section deal with free damped motion. In Problems 15 through 21, a mass m is attached to both a spring (with given spring constant k) and a dashpot (with given damping constant c). The mass is set in motion with initial position x_0 and initial velocity v_0. Find the position function x(t) and determine whether the motion is overdamped, critically damped, or underdamped. If it is underdamped, write the position function in the form $x(t) = C_1 e^{-pt} \cos(\omega_1 t - \alpha_1)$. Also, find the undamped position function $u(t) = C_0 \cos(\omega_0 t - \alpha_0)$ that would result if the mass on the spring were set in motion with the same initial position and velocity, but with the dashpot disconnected (so $c = 0$). Finally, construct a figure that illustrates the effect of damping by comparing the graphs of $x(t)$ and $u(t)$.

15. $m = \frac{1}{2}$, $c = 3$, $k = 4$; $x_0 = 2$, $v_0 = 0$
16. $m = 3$, $c = 30$, $k = 63$; $x_0 = 2$, $v_0 = 2$
17. $m = 1$, $c = 8$, $k = 16$; $x_0 = 5$, $v_0 = -10$
18. $m = 2$, $c = 12$, $k = 50$; $x_0 = 0$, $v_0 = -8$
19. $m = 4$, $c = 20$, $k = 169$; $x_0 = 4$, $v_0 = 16$
20. $m = 2$, $c = 16$, $k = 40$; $x_0 = 5$, $v_0 = 4$
21. $m = 1$, $c = 10$, $k = 125$; $x_0 = 6$, $v_0 = 50$
22. A 12-lb weight (mass $m = 0.375$ slugs in fps units) is attached both to a vertically suspended spring that it stretches 6 in. and to a dashpot that provides 3 lb of resistance for every foot per second of velocity. **(a)** If the weight is pulled down 1 ft below its static equilibrium position and then released from rest at time $t = 0$, find its position function $x(t)$. **(b)** Find the frequency, time-varying amplitude, and phase angle of the motion.
23. This problem deals with a highly simplified model of a car of weight 3200 lb (mass $m = 100$ slugs in fps units). Assume that the suspension system acts like a single spring and its shock absorbers like a single dashpot, so that its vertical vibrations satisfy Eq. (4) with appropriate values of the coefficients. **(a)** Find the stiffness coefficient k of the spring if the car undergoes free vibrations at 80 cycles per minute (cycles/min) when its shock absorbers are disconnected. **(b)** With the shock absorbers connected the car is set into vibration by driving it over a bump, and the resulting damped vibrations have a frequency of 78 cycles/min. After how long will the time-varying amplitude be 1% of its initial value?

Problems 24 through 34 deal with a mass-spring-dashpot system having position function $x(t)$ satisfying Eq. (4). We write $x_0 = x(0)$ and $v_0 = x'(0)$ and recall that $p = c/(2m)$, $\omega_0^2 = k/m$, and $\omega_1^2 = \omega_0^2 - p^2$. The system is critically damped, overdamped, or underdamped, as specified in each problem.

24. (Critically damped) Show in this case that
$$x(t) = (x_0 + v_0 t + p x_0 t)e^{-pt}.$$

25. (Critically damped) Deduce from Problem 24 that the mass passes through $x = 0$ at some instant $t > 0$ if and only if x_0 and $v_0 + px_0$ have opposite signs.
26. (Critically damped) Deduce from Problem 24 that $x(t)$ has a local maximum or minimum at some instant $t > 0$ if and only if v_0 and $v_0 + px_0$ have the same sign.
27. (Overdamped) Show in this case that
$$x(t) = \frac{1}{2\gamma}\left[(v_0 - r_2 x_0)e^{r_1 t} - (v_0 - r_1 x_0)e^{r_2 t}\right],$$
where $r_1, r_2 = -p \pm \sqrt{p^2 - \omega_0^2}$ and $\gamma = (r_1 - r_2)/2 > 0$.

28. (Overdamped) If $x_0 = 0$, deduce from Problem 27 that
$$x(t) = \frac{v_0}{\gamma}e^{-pt}\sinh\gamma t.$$

29. (Overdamped) Prove that in this case the mass can pass through its equilibrium position $x = 0$ at most once.
30. (Underdamped) Show that in this case
$$x(t) = e^{-pt}\left(x_0 \cos\omega_1 t + \frac{v_0 + px_0}{\omega_1}\sin\omega_1 t\right).$$

31. (Underdamped) If the damping constant c is small in comparison with $\sqrt{8mk}$, apply the binomial series to show that
$$\omega_1 \approx \omega_0\left(1 - \frac{c^2}{8mk}\right).$$

32. (Underdamped) Show that the local maximum and minima of
$$x(t) = Ce^{-pt}\cos(\omega_1 t - \alpha)$$
occur where
$$\tan(\omega_1 t - \alpha) = -\frac{p}{\omega_1}.$$
Conclude that $t_2 - t_1 = 2\pi/\omega_1$ if two consecutive maxima occur at times t_1 and t_2.
33. (Underdamped) Let x_1 and x_2 be two consecutive local maximum values of $x(t)$. Deduce from the result of Problem 32 that
$$\ln\frac{x_1}{x_2} = \frac{2\pi p}{\omega_1}.$$
The constant $\Delta = 2\pi p/\omega_1$ is called the **logarithmic decrement** of the oscillation. Note also that $c = m\omega_1 \Delta/\pi$ because $p = c/(2m)$.

Note: *The result of Problem 33 provides an accurate method for measuring the viscosity of a fluid, which is an important parameter in fluid dynamics but which is not easy to measure directly. According to Stokes's drag law, a spherical body of radius a moving at a (relatively slow) speed through a fluid of viscosity μ experiences a resistive force $F_R = 6\pi a\mu v$. Thus if a spherical mass on a spring is immersed in the fluid and set in motion, this drag resistance damps its oscillations with damping constant $c = 6\pi a\mu$. The frequency ω_1 and logarithmic decrement Δ of the oscillations can be measured by direct observation. The final formula in Problem 33 then gives c and hence the viscosity of the fluid.*

34. (Underdamped) A body weighing 100 lb (mass $m = 3.125$ slugs in fps units) is oscillating attached to a spring and a dashpot. Its first two maximum displacements of 6.73 in. and 1.46 in. are observed to occur at times 0.34 s and 1.17 s, respectively. Compute the damping constant (in pound-seconds per foot) and spring constant (in pounds per foot).

Differential Equations and Determinism

Given a mass m, a dashpot constant c, and a spring constant k, Theorem 2 of Section 5.1 implies that the equation

$$mx'' + cx' + kx = 0 \qquad (26)$$

has a unique *solution for $t \geq 0$ satisfying given initial conditions $x(0) = x_0$, $x'(0) = v_0$. Thus the future motion of an ideal mass-spring-dashpot system is completely determined by the differential equation and the initial conditions. Of course in a real physical system it is impossible to measure the parameters m, c, and k precisely. Problems 35 through 38 explore the resulting uncertainty in predicting the future behavior of a physical system.*

35. Suppose that $m = 1$, $c = 2$, and $k = 1$ in Eq. (25). Show that the solution with $x(0) = 0$ and $x'(0) = 1$ is

$$x_1(t) = te^{-t}.$$

36. Suppose that $m = 1$ and $c = 2$ but $k = 1 - 10^{-2n}$. Show that the solution of Eq. (25) with $x(0) = 0$ and $x'(0) = 1$

is

$$x_2(t) = 10^n e^{-t} \sinh 10^{-n} t.$$

37. Suppose that $m = 1$ and $c = 2$ but that $k = 1 + 10^{-2n}$. Show that the solution of Eq. (25) with $x(0) = 0$ and $x'(0) = 1$ is

$$x_3(t) = 10^n e^{-t} \sin 10^{-n} t.$$

38. Whereas the graphs of $x_1(t)$ and $x_2(t)$ resemble those shown in Figs. 5.4.7 and 5.4.8, the graph of $x_3(t)$ exhibits damped oscillations like those illustrated in Fig. 5.4.9, but with a very long pseudoperiod. Nevertheless, show that for each fixed $t > 0$ it is true that

$$\lim_{n \to \infty} x_2(t) = \lim_{n \to \infty} x_3(t) = x_1(t).$$

Conclude that *on a given finite time interval* the three solutions are in "practical" agreement if n is sufficiently large.

5.5 Nonhomogeneous Equations and Undetermined Coefficients

We learned in Section 5.3 how to solve homogeneous linear equations with constant coefficients, but we saw in Section 5.4 that an external force in a simple mechanical system contributes a nonhomogeneous term to its differential equation. The general nonhomogeneous nth-order linear equation with constant coefficients has the form

$$a_n y^{(n)} + a_{n-1} y^{(n-1)} + \cdots + a_1 y' + a_0 y = f(x). \qquad (1)$$

By Theorem 5 of Section 5.2, a general solution of Eq. (1) has the form

$$y = y_c + y_p, \qquad (2)$$

where the complementary function $y_c(x)$ is a general solution of the associated homogeneous equation

$$a_n y^{(n)} + a_{n-1} y^{(n-1)} + \cdots + a_1 y' + a_0 y = 0, \qquad (3)$$

and $y_p(x)$ is a particular solution of Eq. (1). Thus our remaining task is to find y_p.

The **method of undetermined coefficients** is a straightforward way of doing this when the given function $f(x)$ in Eq. (1) is sufficiently simple that we can make an intelligent guess as to the general form of y_p. For example, suppose that $f(x)$ is a polynomial of degree m. Then, because the derivatives of a polynomial are themselves polynomials of lower degree, it is reasonable to suspect a particular solution

$$y_p(x) = A_m x^m + A_{m-1} x^{m-1} + \cdots + A_1 x + A_0$$

that is also a polynomial of degree m, but with as yet undetermined coefficients. We may, therefore, substitute this expression for y_p into Eq. (1), and then—by equating coefficients of like powers of x on the two sides of the resulting equation—attempt to determine the coefficients $A_0, A_1, \ldots, A_m$ so that y_p will, indeed, be a particular solution of Eq. (1).

Similarly, suppose that

$$f(x) = a\cos kx + b\sin kx.$$

Then it is reasonable to expect a particular solution of the same form:

$$y_p(x) = A\cos kx + B\sin kx,$$

a linear combination with undetermined coefficients A and B. The reason is that any derivative of such a linear combination of $\cos kx$ and $\sin kx$ has the same form. We may therefore substitute this form of y_p in Eq. (1), and then—by equating coefficients of $\cos kx$ and $\sin kx$ on both sides of the resulting equation—attempt to determine the coefficients A and B so that y_p will, indeed, be a particular solution.

It turns out that this approach does succeed whenever all the derivatives of $f(x)$ have the same form as $f(x)$ itself. Before describing the method in full generality, we illustrate it with several preliminary examples.

Example 1   Find a particular solution of $y'' + 3y' + 4y = 3x + 2$.

Solution   Here $f(x) = 3x + 2$ is a polynomial of degree 1, so our guess is that

$$y_p(x) = Ax + B.$$

Then $y'_p = A$ and $y''_p = 0$, so y_p will satisfy the differential equation provided that

$$(0) + 3(A) + 4(Ax + B) = 3x + 2.$$

This is so if and only if $4A = 3$ and $3A + 4B = 2$. These two equations yield $A = \frac{3}{4}$ and $B = -\frac{1}{16}$, so we have found the particular solution

$$y_p(x) = \tfrac{3}{4}x - \tfrac{1}{16}. \qquad\blacksquare$$

Example 2   Find a particular solution of $y'' - 4y = 2e^{3x}$.

Solution   Any derivative of e^{3x} is a constant multiple of e^{3x}, so it is reasonable to try

$$y_p(x) = Ae^{3x}.$$

Then $y''_p = 9Ae^{3x}$, so the given differential equation will be satisfied provided that

$$9Ae^{3x} - 4(Ae^{3x}) = 2e^{3x};$$

that is, $5A = 2$, so that $A = \frac{2}{5}$. Thus our particular solution is $y_p(x) = \frac{2}{5}e^{3x}$. $\blacksquare$

Example 3   Find a particular solution of $3y'' + y' - 2y = 2\cos x$.

Solution A first guess might be $y_p(x) = A\cos x$, but the presence of y' on the left-hand side signals that we probably need a term involving $\sin x$ as well. So we try

$$
\begin{aligned}
y_p(x) &= A\cos x + B\sin x;\\
y_p'(x) &= -A\sin x + B\cos x,\\
y_p''(x) &= -A\cos x - B\sin x.
\end{aligned}
$$

Then substitution of y_p and its derivatives into the given differential equation yields

$$3(-A\cos x - B\sin x) + (-A\sin x + B\cos x) - 2(A\cos x + B\sin x) = 2\cos x.$$

We equate the coefficient of $\cos x$ on the left-hand side with that of $\cos x$ on the right and do the same with $\sin x$ to get the equations

$$
\begin{aligned}
-5A + B &= 2,\\
-A - 5B &= 0,
\end{aligned}
$$

with solution $A = -\frac{5}{13}$, $B = \frac{1}{13}$. Hence a particular solution is

$$y_p(x) = -\tfrac{5}{13}\cos x + \tfrac{1}{13}\sin x. \qquad \blacksquare$$

The following example, which superficially resembles Example 2, indicates that the method of undetermined coefficients is not always quite so simple as we have made it appear.

Example 4 Find a particular solution of $y'' - 4y = 2e^{2x}$.

Solution If we try $y_p(x) = Ae^{2x}$, we find that

$$y_p'' - 4y_p = 4Ae^{2x} - 4Ae^{2x} = 0 \neq 2e^{2x}.$$

Thus, no matter how A is chosen, Ae^{2x} cannot satisfy the given nonhomogeneous equation. In fact, the preceding computation shows that Ae^{2x} satisfies instead the associated *homogeneous* equation. Therefore, we should begin with a trial function $y_p(x)$ whose derivative involves both e^{2x} *and something else* that can cancel upon substitution into the differential equation to leave the e^{2x} term that we need. A reasonable guess is

$$y_p(x) = Axe^{2x},$$

for which

$$y_p'(x) = Ae^{2x} + 2Axe^{2x} \quad \text{and} \quad y_p''(x) = 4Ae^{2x} + 4Axe^{2x}.$$

Substitution into the original differential equation yields

$$(4Ae^{2x} + 4Axe^{2x}) - 4(Axe^{2x}) = 2e^{2x}.$$

The terms involving xe^{2x} obligingly cancel, leaving only $4Ae^{2x} = 2e^{2x}$, so that $A = \frac{1}{2}$. Consequently, a particular solution is

$$y_p(x) = \tfrac{1}{2}xe^{2x}. \qquad \blacksquare$$

The General Approach

Our initial difficulty in Example 4 resulted from the fact that $f(x) = 2e^{2x}$ satisfies the associated homogeneous equation. Rule 1, given shortly, tells what to do when we do not have this difficulty, and Rule 2 tells what to do when we do have it.

The method of undetermined coefficients applies whenever the function $f(x)$ in Eq. (1) is a linear combination of (finite) products of functions of the following three types:

1. A polynomial in x;
2. An exponential function e^{rx}; (4)
3. $\cos kx$ or $\sin kx$.

Any such function, for example

$$f(x) = (3 - 4x^2)e^{5x} - 4x^3 \cos 10x,$$

has the crucial property that only *finitely* many linearly independent functions appear as terms (summands) in $f(x)$ and its derivatives of all orders. In Rules 1 and 2 we assume that $Ly = f(x)$ is a nonhomogeneous linear equation with constant coefficients and that $f(x)$ is a function of this kind.

RULE 1: Method of Undetermined Coefficients

Suppose that no term appearing either in $f(x)$ or in any of its derivatives satisfies the associated homogeneous equation $Ly = 0$. Then take as a trial solution for y_p a linear combination of all linearly independent such terms and their derivatives. Then determine the coefficients by substitution of this trial solution into the nonhomogeneous equation $Ly = f(x)$. ▲

Note that this rule is not a theorem requiring proof; it is merely a procedure to be followed in searching for a particular solution y_p. If we succeed in finding y_p, then nothing more need be said. (It can be proved, however, that this procedure will always succeed under the conditions specified here.)

In practice we check the supposition made in Rule 1 by first using the characteristic equation to find the complementary function y_c, and then write a list of all the terms appearing in $f(x)$ and its successive derivatives. If none of the terms in this list duplicates a term in y_c, then we proceed with Rule 1.

Example 5 Find a particular solution of

$$y'' + 4y = 3x^3. \tag{5}$$

Solution The (familiar) complementary solution of Eq. (5) is

$$y_c(x) = c_1 \cos 2x + c_2 \sin 2x.$$

The function $f(x) = 3x^3$ and its derivatives are constant multiples of the linearly independent functions x^3, x^2, x, and 1. Because none of these appears in y_c, we try

$$y_p = Ax^3 + Bx^2 + Cx + D,$$
$$y_p' = 3Ax^2 + 2Bx + C,$$
$$y_p'' = 6Ax + 2B.$$

Substitution in Eq. (5) gives

$$y_p'' + 4y_p = (6Ax + 2B) + 4(Ax^3 + Bx^2 + Cx + D)$$
$$= 4Ax^3 + 4Bx^2 + (6A + 4C)x + (2B + D) = 3x^3.$$

We equate coefficients of like powers of x in the last equation to get

$$4A = 3, \qquad 4B = 0,$$
$$6A + 4C = 0, \qquad 2B + D = 0$$

with solution $A = \frac{3}{4}$, $B = 0$, $C = -\frac{9}{8}$, and $D = 0$. Hence a particular solution of Eq. (5) is

$$y_p(x) = \tfrac{3}{4}x^3 - \tfrac{9}{8}x. \qquad \blacksquare$$

Example 6   Solve the initial value problem

$$y'' - 3y' + 2y = 3e^{-x} - 10\cos 3x;$$
$$y(0) = 1, \quad y'(0) = 2. \tag{6}$$

Solution   The characteristic equation $r^2 - 3r + 2 = 0$ has roots $r = 1$ and $r = 2$, so the complementary function is

$$y_c(x) = c_1 e^x + c_2 e^{2x}.$$

The terms involved in $f(x) = 3e^{-x} - 10\cos 3x$ and its derivatives are e^{-x}, $\cos 3x$, and $\sin 3x$. Because none of these appears in y_c, we try

$$y_p = \quad Ae^{-x} + \quad B\cos 3x + \quad C\sin 3x,$$
$$y_p' = -Ae^{-x} - 3B\sin 3x + 3C\cos 3x,$$
$$y_p'' = \quad Ae^{-x} - 9B\cos 3x - 9C\sin 3x.$$

After we substitute these expressions into the differential equation in (6) and collect coefficients, we get

$$y_p'' - 3y_p' + 2y_p = 6Ae^{-x} + (-7B - 9C)\cos 3x + (9B - 7C)\sin 3x$$
$$= 3e^{-x} - 10\cos 3x.$$

We equate the coefficients of the terms involving e^{-x}, those involving $\cos 3x$, and those involving $\sin 3x$. The result is the system

$$6A = \quad 3,$$
$$-7B - 9C = -10,$$
$$9B - 7C = \quad 0$$

with solution $A = \frac{1}{2}$, $B = \frac{7}{13}$, and $C = \frac{9}{13}$. This gives the particular solution

$$y_p(x) = \tfrac{1}{2}e^{-x} + \tfrac{7}{13}\cos 3x + \tfrac{9}{13}\sin 3x,$$

which, however, does not have the required initial values in (6).

To satisfy those initial conditions, we begin with the *general* solution

$$y(x) = y_c(x) + y_p(x)$$
$$= c_1 e^x + c_2 e^{2x} + \tfrac{1}{2} e^{-x} + \tfrac{7}{13} \cos 3x + \tfrac{9}{13} \sin 3x,$$

with derivative

$$y'(x) = c_1 e^x + 2c_2 e^{2x} - \tfrac{1}{2} e^{-x} - \tfrac{21}{13} \sin 3x + \tfrac{27}{13} \cos 3x.$$

The initial conditions in (6) lead to the equations

$$y(0) = c_1 + c_2 + \tfrac{1}{2} + \tfrac{7}{13} = 1,$$
$$y'(0) = c_1 + 2c_2 - \tfrac{1}{2} + \tfrac{27}{13} = 2$$

with solution $c_1 = -\tfrac{1}{2}$, $c_2 = \tfrac{6}{13}$. The desired particular solution is therefore

$$y(x) = -\tfrac{1}{2} e^x + \tfrac{6}{13} e^{2x} + \tfrac{1}{2} e^{-x} + \tfrac{7}{13} \cos 3x + \tfrac{9}{13} \sin 3x. \qquad \blacksquare$$

Example 7 Find the general form of a particular solution of

$$y^{(3)} + 9y' = x \sin x + x^2 e^{2x}. \tag{7}$$

Solution The characteristic equation $r^3 + 9r = 0$ has roots $r = 0$, $r = -3i$, and $r = 3i$. So the complementary function is

$$y_c(x) = c_1 + c_2 \cos 3x + c_3 \sin 3x.$$

The derivatives of the right-hand side in Eq. (7) involve the terms

$$\cos x, \quad \sin x, \quad x \cos x, \quad x \sin x,$$
$$e^{2x}, \quad xe^{2x}, \quad \text{and} \quad x^2 e^{2x}.$$

Because there is no duplication with the terms of the complementary function, the trial solution takes the form

$$y_p(x) = A \cos x + B \sin x + Cx \cos x + Dx \sin x + Ee^{2x} + Fxe^{2x} + Gx^2 e^{2x}.$$

Upon substituting y_p in Eq. (7) and equating coefficients of like terms, we get seven equations determining the seven coefficients A, B, C, D, E, F, and G. $\qquad \blacksquare$

The Case of Duplication

Now we turn our attention to the situation in which Rule 1 does not apply: Some of the terms involved in $f(x)$ and its derivatives satisfy the associated homogeneous equation. For instance, suppose that we want to find a particular solution of the differential equation

$$(D - r)^3 y = (2x - 3)e^{rx}. \tag{8}$$

Proceeding as in Rule 1, our first guess would be

$$y_p(x) = Ae^{rx} + Bxe^{rx}. \tag{9}$$

This form of $y_p(x)$ will not be adequate because the complementary function of Eq. (8) is

$$y_c(x) = c_1 e^{rx} + c_2 x e^{rx} + c_3 x^2 e^{rx}, \tag{10}$$

so substitution of (9) in the left-hand side of (8) would yield zero rather than $(2x - 3)e^{rx}$.

To see how to amend our first guess, we observe that

$$(D - r)^2 [(2x - 3)e^{rx}] = [D^2 (2x - 3)]e^{rx} = 0$$

by Eq. (13) of Section 5.3. If $y(x)$ is *any* solution of Eq. (8) and we apply the operator $(D - r)^2$ to both sides, we see that $y(x)$ is also a solution of the equation $(D - r)^5 y = 0$. The general solution of this *homogeneous* equation can be written as

$$y(x) = \underbrace{c_1 e^{rx} + c_2 x e^{rx} + c_3 x^2 e^{rx}}_{y_c} + \underbrace{Ax^3 e^{rx} + Bx^4 e^{rx}}_{y_p}.$$

Thus *every* solution of our original equation in (8) is the sum of a complementary function and a *particular solution* of the form

$$y_p(x) = Ax^3 e^{rx} + Bx^4 e^{rx}. \tag{11}$$

Note that the right-hand side in Eq. (11) can be obtained by multiplying each term of our first guess in (9) by the least positive integral power of x (in this case, x^3) that suffices to eliminate duplication between the terms of the resulting trial solution $y_p(x)$ and the complementary function $y_c(x)$ given in (10). This procedure succeeds in the general case.

To simplify the general statement of Rule 2, we observe that to find a particular solution of the nonhomogeneous linear differential equation

$$Ly = f_1(x) + f_2(x), \tag{12}$$

it suffices to find *separately* particular solutions $Y_1(x)$ and $Y_2(x)$ of the two equations

$$Ly = f_1(x) \quad \text{and} \quad Ly = f_2(x), \tag{13}$$

respectively. For linearity then gives

$$L[Y_1 + Y_2] = LY_1 + LY_2 = f_1(x) + f_2(x),$$

and therefore $y_p = Y_1 + Y_2$ is a particular solution of Eq. (12). (This is a type of "superposition principle" for nonhomogeneous linear equations.)

Now our problem is to find a particular solution of the equation $Ly = f(x)$, where $f(x)$ is a linear combination of products of the elementary functions listed in (4). Thus $f(x)$ can be written as a sum of terms each of the form

$$P_m(x)e^{rx} \cos kx \quad \text{or} \quad P_m(x)e^{rx} \sin kx, \tag{14}$$

where $P_m(x)$ is a polynomial in x of degree m. Note that any derivative of such a term is of the same form but with *both* sines and cosines appearing. The procedure by which we arrived earlier at the particular solution in (11) of Eq. (8) can be generalized to show that the following procedure is always successful.

RULE 2: Method of Undetermined Coefficients

If the function $f(x)$ is of either form in (14), take as the trial solution

$$\begin{aligned} y_p(x) = x^s[(A_0 + A_1 x + A_2 x^2 + \cdots + A_m x^m)e^{rx} \cos kx \\ + (B_0 + B_1 x + B_2 x^2 + \cdots + B_m x^m)e^{rx} \sin kx], \end{aligned} \tag{15}$$

where s is the smallest nonnegative integer such that such that no term in y_p duplicates a term in the complementary function y_c. Then determine the coefficients in Eq. (15) by substituting y_p into the nonhomogeneous equation. ▲

In practice we seldom need to deal with a function $f(x)$ exhibiting the full generality in (14). The table in Fig. 5.5.1 lists the form of y_p in various common cases, corresponding to the possibilities $m = 0$, $r = 0$, and $k = 0$.

On the other hand, it is common to have

$$f(x) = f_1(x) + f_2(x),$$

where $f_1(x)$ and $f_2(x)$ are different functions of the sort listed in the table in Fig. 5.5.1. In this event we take as y_p the sum of the trial solutions for $f_1(x)$ and $f_2(x)$, choosing s *separately* for each part to eliminate duplication with the complementary function. This procedure is illustrated in Examples 8 through 10.

$f(x)$	y_p
$P_m = b_0 + b_1 x + b_2 x^2 + \cdots + b_m x^m$	$x^s(A_0 + A_1 x + A_2 x^2 + \cdots + A_m x^m)$
$a \cos kx + b \sin kx$	$x^s(A \cos kx + B \sin kx)$
$e^{rx}(a \cos kx + b \sin kx)$	$x^s e^{rx}(A \cos kx + B \sin kx)$
$P_m(x)e^{rx}$	$x^s(A_0 + A_1 x + A_2 x^2 + \cdots + A_m x^m)e^{rx}$
$P_m(x)(a \cos kx + b \sin kx)$	$x^s[(A_0 + A_1 x + \cdots + A_m x^m) \cos kx$ $+ (B_0 + B_1 x + \cdots + B_m x^m) \sin kx]$

FIGURE 5.5.1. Substitutions in the method of undetermined coefficients.

Example 8

Find a particular solution of

$$y^{(3)} + y'' = 3e^x + 4x^2. \tag{16}$$

Solution The characteristic equation $r^3 + r^2 = 0$ has roots $r_1 = r_2 = 0$ and $r_3 = -1$, so the complementary function is

$$y_c(x) = c_1 + c_2 x + c_3 e^{-x}.$$

As a first step toward our particular solution, we form the sum

$$(Ae^x) + (B + Cx + Dx^2).$$

The part Ae^x corresponding to $3e^x$ does not duplicate any part of the complementary function, but the part $B+Cx+Dx^2$ must be multiplied by x^2 to eliminate duplication. Hence we take

$$y_p = Ae^x + Bx^2 + Cx^3 + Dx^4,$$

$$y_p' = Ae^x + 2Bx + 3Cx^2 + 4Dx^3,$$

$$y_p'' = Ae^x + 2B + 6Cx + 12Dx^2, \quad \text{and}$$

$$y_p^{(3)} = Ae^x + 6C + 24Dx.$$

Substitution of these derivatives in Eq. (16) yields

$$2Ae^x + (2B + 6C) + (6C + 24D)x + 12Dx^2 = 3e^x + 4x^2.$$

The system of equations

$$2A = 3, \qquad 2B + 6C = 0,$$
$$6C + 24D = 0, \qquad 12D = 4$$

has the solution $A = \frac{3}{2}$, $B = 4$, $C = -\frac{4}{3}$, and $D = \frac{1}{3}$. Hence the desired particular solution is

$$y_p(x) = \frac{3}{2}e^x + 4x^2 - \frac{4}{3}x^3 + \frac{1}{3}x^4. \qquad \blacksquare$$

Example 9 Determine the appropriate form for a particular solution of

$$y'' + 6y' + 13y = e^{-3x}\cos 2x.$$

Solution The characteristic equation $r^2 + 6r + 13 = 0$ has roots $-3 \pm 2i$, so the complementary function is

$$y_c(x) = e^{-3x}(c_1 \cos 2x + c_2 \sin 2x).$$

This is the same form as a first attempt $e^{-3x}(A\cos 2x + B\sin 2x)$ at a particular solution, so we must multiply by x to eliminate duplication. Hence we would take

$$y_p(x) = e^{-3x}(Ax\cos 2x + Bx\sin 2x). \qquad \blacksquare$$

Example 10 Determine the appropriate form for a particular solution of the fifth-order equation

$$(D - 2)^3(D^2 + 9)y = x^2 e^{2x} + x\sin 3x.$$

Solution The characteristic equation $(r-2)^3(r^2+9)=0$ has roots $r=2, 2, 2, 3i$, and $-3i$, so the complementary function is

$$y_c(x) = c_1 e^{2x} + c_2 x e^{2x} + c_3 x^2 e^{2x} + c_4 \cos 3x + c_5 \sin 3x.$$

As a first step toward the form of a particular solution, we examine the sum

$$[(A + Bx + Cx^2)e^{2x}] + [(D + Ex)\cos 3x + (F + Gx)\sin 3x].$$

To eliminate duplication with terms of $y_c(x)$, the first part—corresponding to $x^2 e^{2x}$—must be multiplied by x^3, and the second part—corresponding to $x \sin 3x$—must be multiplied by x. Hence we would take

$$y_p(x) = (Ax^3 + Bx^4 + Cx^5)e^{2x} + (Dx + Ex^2)\cos 3x + (Fx + Gx^2)\sin 3x. \quad ∎$$

Variation of Parameters

Finally, let us point out the kind of situation in which the method of undetermined coefficients cannot be used. Consider, for example, the equation

$$y'' + y = \tan x, \tag{17}$$

which at first glance may appear similar to those considered in the preceding examples. Not so; the function $f(x) = \tan x$ has *infinitely many* linearly independent derivatives

$$\sec^2 x, \quad 2\sec^2 x \tan x, \quad 4\sec^2 x \tan^2 x + 2\sec^4 x, \quad \ldots.$$

Therefore, we do not have available a *finite* linear combination to use as a trial solution.

We discuss here the method of **variation of parameters**, which—in principle (that is, if the integrals that appear can be evaluated)—can always be used to find a particular solution of the nonhomogeneous linear differential equation

$$y^{(n)} + p_{n-1}(x)y^{(n-1)} + \cdots + p_1(x)y' + p_0(x)y = f(x), \tag{18}$$

provided that we already know the general solution

$$y_c = c_1 y_1 + c_2 y_2 + \cdots + c_n y_n \tag{19}$$

of the associated homogeneous equation

$$y^{(n)} + p_{n-1}(x)y^{(n-1)} + \cdots + p_1(x)y' + p_0(x)y = 0. \tag{20}$$

Here, in brief, is the basic idea of the method of variation of parameters. Suppose that we replace the constants, or *parameters*, $c_1, c_2, \ldots, c_n$ in the complementary function in Eq. (19) with *variables*: functions $u_1, u_2, \ldots, u_n$ of x. We ask whether it is possible to choose these functions in such a way that the combination

$$y_p(x) = u_1(x)y_1(x) + u_2(x)y_2(x) + \cdots + u_n(x)y_n(x) \tag{21}$$

is a particular solution of the nonhomogeneous equation in (18). It turns out that this *is* always possible.

The method is essentially the same for all orders $n \geq 2$, but we will describe it in detail only for the case $n = 2$. So we begin with the second-order nonhomogeneous equation

➤
$$L[y] = y'' + P(x)y' + Q(x)y = f(x) \qquad (22)$$

with complementary function

$$y_c(x) = c_1 y_1(x) + c_2 y_2(x) \qquad (23)$$

on some open interval I where the functions P and Q are continuous. We want to find functions u_1 and u_2 such that

➤
$$y_p(x) = u_1(x)y_1(x) + u_2(x)y_2(x) \qquad (24)$$

is a particular solution of Eq. (22).

One condition on the two functions u_1 and u_2 is that $L[y_p] = f(x)$. Because two conditions are required to determine two functions, we are free to impose an additional condition of our choice. We will do so in a way that simplifies the computations as much as possible. But first, to impose the condition $L[y_p] = f(x)$, we must compute the derivatives y'_p and y''_p. The product rule gives

$$y'_p = (u_1 y'_1 + u_2 y'_2) + (u'_1 y_1 + u'_2 y_2).$$

To avoid the appearance of the second derivatives u''_1 and u''_2, the additional condition that we now impose is that the second sum here must vanish:

$$u'_1 y_1 + u'_2 y_2 = 0. \qquad (25)$$

Then

$$y'_p = u_1 y'_1 + u_2 y'_2, \qquad (26)$$

and the product rule gives

$$y''_p = (u_1 y''_1 + u_2 y''_2) + (u'_1 y'_1 + u'_2 y'_2). \qquad (27)$$

But both y_1 and y_2 satisfy the homogeneous equation

$$y'' + Py' + Qy = 0$$

associated with the nonhomogeneous equation in (22), so

$$y''_i = -Py'_i - Qy_i \qquad (28)$$

for $i = 1, 2$. It therefore follows from Eq. (27) that

$$y''_p = (u'_1 y'_1 + u'_2 y'_2) - P \cdot (u_1 y'_1 + u_2 y'_2) - Q \cdot (u_1 y_1 + u_2 y_2).$$

In view of Eqs. (24) and (26), this means that

$$y''_p = (u'_1 y'_1 + u'_2 y'_2) - Py'_p - Qy_p;$$

hence

$$L[y_p] = u_1' y_1' + u_2' y_2'. \tag{29}$$

The requirement that y_p satisfy the nonhomogeneous equation in (22)—that is, that $L[y_p] = f(x)$—therefore implies that

$$u_1' y_1' + u_2' y_2' = f(x). \tag{30}$$

Finally, Eqs. (25) and (30) determine the functions u_1 and u_2 that we need. Collecting these equations, we obtain a system

$$\begin{aligned} u_1' y_1 + u_2' y_2 &= 0, \\ u_1' y_1' + u_2' y_2' &= f(x) \end{aligned} \tag{31}$$

of two linear equations in the two *derivatives* u_1' and u_2'. Note that the determinant of coefficients in (31) is simply the Wronskian $W(y_1, y_2)$. Once we have solved the equations in (31) for the derivatives u_1' and u_2', we integrate each to obtain the functions u_1 and u_2 such that

$$y_p = u_1 y_1 + u_2 y_2 \tag{32}$$

is the desired particular solution of Eq. (22). In Problem 63 we ask you to carry out this process explicitly and thereby verify the formula for $y_p(x)$ in the following theorem.

THEOREM 1: Variation of Parameters

If the nonhomogeneous equation $y'' + P(x)y' + Q(x)y = f(x)$ has complementary function $y_c(x) = c_1 y_1(x) + c_2 y_2(x)$, then a particular solution is given by

$$y_p(x) = -y_1(x) \int \frac{y_2(x) f(x)}{W(x)} \, dx + y_2(x) \int \frac{y_1(x) f(x)}{W(x)} \, dx, \tag{33}$$

where $W = W(y_1, y_2)$ is the Wronskian of the two independent solutions y_1 and y_2 of the associated homogeneous equation. ▲

Example 11   Find a particular solution of the equation $y'' + y = \tan x$.

Solution   The complementary function is $y_c(x) = c_1 \cos x + c_2 \sin x$, and we could simply substitute directly in Eq. (33). But it is more instructive to set up the equations in (31) and solve for u_1' and u_2', so we begin with

$$\begin{aligned} y_1 &= \cos x, & y_2 &= \sin x, \\ y_1' &= -\sin x, & y_2' &= \cos x. \end{aligned}$$

Hence the equations in (31) are

$$(u_1')(\cos x) + (u_2')(\sin x) = 0,$$
$$(u_1')(-\sin x) + (u_2')(\cos x) = \tan x.$$

We easily solve these equations for

$$u'_1 = -\sin x \tan x = -\frac{\sin^2 x}{\cos x} = \cos x - \sec x,$$

$$u'_2 = \cos x \tan x = \sin x.$$

Hence we take

$$u_1 = \int (\cos x - \sec x)\, dx = \sin x - \ln|\sec x + \tan x|$$

and

$$u_2 = \int \sin x\, dx = -\cos x.$$

(Do you see why we choose the constants of integration to be zero?) Thus our particular solution is

$$y_p(x) = u_1(x)y_1(x) + u_2(x)y_2(x)$$
$$= (\sin x - \ln|\sec x + \tan x|)\cos x + (-\cos x)(\sin x);$$

that is,

$$y_p(x) = -(\cos x)\ln|\sec x + \tan x|. \qquad \blacksquare$$

5.5 Problems

In Problems 1 through 20, find a particular solution y_p of the given equation. In all these problems, primes denote derivatives with respect to x.

1. $y'' + 16y = e^{3x}$

2. $y'' - y' - 2y = 3x + 4$

3. $y'' - y' - 6y = 2\sin 3x$

4. $4y'' + 4y' + y = 3xe^x$

5. $y'' + y' + y = \sin^2 x$

6. $2y'' + 4y' + 7y = x^2$

7. $y'' - 4y = \sinh x$

8. $y'' - 4y = \cosh 2x$

9. $y'' + 2y' - 3y = 1 + xe^x$

10. $y'' + 9y = 2\cos 3x + 3\sin 3x$

11. $y^{(3)} + 4y' = 3x - 1$

12. $y^{(3)} + y' = 2 - \sin x$

13. $y'' + 2y' + 5y = e^x \sin x$

14. $y^{(4)} - 2y'' + y = xe^x$

15. $y^{(5)} + 5y^{(4)} - y = 17$

16. $y'' + 9y = 2x^2 e^{3x} + 5$

17. $y'' + y = \sin x + x\cos x$

18. $y^{(4)} - 5y'' + 4y = e^x - xe^{2x}$

19. $y^{(5)} + 2y^{(3)} + 2y'' = 3x^2 - 1$

20. $y^{(3)} - y = e^x + 7$

In Problems 21 through 30, set up the appropriate form of a particular solution y_p, but do not determine the values of the coefficients.

21. $y'' - 2y' + 2y = e^x \sin x$

22. $y^{(5)} - y^{(3)} = e^x + 2x^2 - 5$

23. $y'' + 4y = 3x\cos 2x$

24. $y^{(3)} - y'' - 12y' = x - 2xe^{-3x}$

25. $y'' + 3y' + 2y = x(e^{-x} - e^{-2x})$

26. $y'' - 6y' + 13y = xe^{3x}\sin 2x$

27. $y^{(4)} + 5y'' + 4y = \sin x + \cos 2x$

28. $y^{(4)} + 9y'' = (x^2 + 1)\sin 3x$

29. $(D-1)^3(D^2 - 4)y = xe^x + e^{2x} + e^{-2x}$

30. $y^{(4)} - 2y'' + y = x^2 \cos x$

Solve the initial value problems in Problems 31 through 40.

31. $y'' + 4y = 2x;\ y(0) = 1,\ y'(0) = 2$

32. $y'' + 3y' + 2y = e^x;\ y(0) = 0,\ y'(0) = 3$

33. $y'' + 9y = \sin 2x;\ y(0) = 1,\ y'(0) = 0$

34. $y'' + y = \cos x;\ y(0) = 1,\ y'(0) = -1$

35. $y'' - 2y' + 2y = x + 1;\ y(0) = 3,\ y'(0) = 0$

36. $y^{(4)} - 4y'' = x^2;\ y(0) = y'(0) = 1,\ y''(0) = y^{(3)}(0) = -1$

37. $y^{(3)} - 2y'' + y' = 1 + xe^x;\ y(0) = y'(0) = 0,\ y''(0) = 1$

38. $y'' + 2y' + 2y = \sin 3x;\ y(0) = 2,\ y'(0) = 0$

39. $y^{(3)} + y'' = x + e^{-x};\ y(0) = 1,\ y'(0) = 0,\ y''(0) = 1$

40. $y^{(4)} - y = 5;\ y(0) = y'(0) = y''(0) = y^{(3)}(0) = 0$

41. Find a particular solution of the equation

$$y^{(4)} - y^{(3)} - y'' - y' - 2y = 8x^5.$$

42. Find the solution of the initial value problem consisting of the differential equation of Problem 41 and the initial conditions

$$y(0) = y'(0) = y''(0) = y^{(3)}(0) = 0.$$

43. (a) Write

$$\cos 3x + i \sin 3x = e^{3ix} = (\cos x + i \sin x)^3$$

by Euler's formula, expand, and equate real and imaginary parts to derive the identities

$$\cos^3 x = \tfrac{3}{4}\cos x + \tfrac{1}{4}\cos 3x,$$
$$\sin^3 x = \tfrac{3}{4}\sin x - \tfrac{1}{4}\sin 3x.$$

(b) Use the result of part (a) to find a general solution of

$$y'' + 4y = \cos^3 x.$$

Use trigonometric identities to find general solutions of the equations in Problems 44 through 46.

44. $y'' + y' + y = \sin x \sin 3x$
45. $y'' + 9y = \sin^4 x$
46. $y'' + y = x \cos^3 x$

In Problems 47 through 56, use the method of variation of parameters to find a particular solution of the given differential equation.

47. $y'' + 3y' + 2y = 4e^x$ **48.** $y'' - 2y' - 8y = 3e^{-2x}$
49. $y'' - 4y' + 4y = 2e^{2x}$ **50.** $y'' - 4y = \sinh 2x$
51. $y'' + 4y = \cos 3x$ **52.** $y'' + 9y = \sin 3x$
53. $y'' + 9y = 2 \sec 3x$ **54.** $y'' + y = \csc^2 x$
55. $y'' + 4y = \sin^2 x$ **56.** $y'' - 4y = xe^x$

57. You can verify by substitution that $y_c = c_1 x + c_2 x^{-1}$ is a complementary function for the nonhomogeneous second-order equation

$$x^2 y'' + xy' - y = 72x^5.$$

But before applying the method of variation of parameters, you must first divide this equation by its leading coefficient x^2 to rewrite it in the standard form

$$y'' + \frac{1}{x}y' - \frac{1}{x^2}y = 72x^3.$$

Thus $f(x) = 72x^3$ in Eq. (22). Now proceed to solve the equations in (31) and thereby derive the particular solution $y_p = 3x^5$.

In Problems 58 through 62, a nonhomogeneous second-order linear equation and a complementary function y_c are given. Apply the method of Problem 57 to find a particular solution of the equation.

58. $x^2 y'' - 4xy' + 6y = x^3;\ y_c = c_1 x^2 + c_2 x^3$
59. $x^2 y'' - 3xy' + 4y = x^4;\ y_c = x^2(c_1 + c_2 \ln x)$
60. $4x^2 y'' - 4xy' + 3y = 8x^{4/3};\ y_c = c_1 x + c_2 x^{3/4}$
61. $x^2 y'' + xy' + y = \ln x;\ y_c = c_1 \cos(\ln x) + c_2 \sin(\ln x)$
62. $(x^2 - 1)y'' - 2xy' + 2y = x^2 - 1;\ y_c = c_1 x + c_2(1 + x^2)$
63. Carry out the solution process indicated in the text to derive the variation of parameters formula in (33) from Eqs. (31) and (32).
64. Apply the variation of parameters formula in (33) to find the particular solution $y_p(x) = -x \cos x$ of the nonhomogeneous equation $y'' + y = 2 \sin x$.

5.5 Application: Automated Variation of Parameters

The variation of parameters formula in (33) is especially amenable to implementation in a computer algebra system when the indicated integrals would be too tedious or inconvenient for manual evaluation. For example, suppose that we want to find a particular solution of the nonhomogeneous equation

$$y'' + y = \tan x$$

of Example 11, with complementary function $y_c(x) = c_1 \cos x + c_2 \sin x$. Then the *Maple* commands

```
y1 := cos(x):
y2 := sin(x):
f := tan(x):
W := y1*diff(y2,x) - y2*diff(y1,x):
W := simplify(W):
yp := -y1*int(y2*f/W,x) + y2*int(y1*f/W,x):
simplify(yp);
```

implement (33) and produce the result

$$y_p(x) = -(\cos x) \ln\left(\frac{1 + \sin x}{\cos x}\right)$$

equivalent to the result $y_p(x) = -(\cos x) \ln(\sec x + \tan x)$ found in Example 11. The analogous *Mathematica* commands

```
y1 = Cos[x];
y2 = Sin[x];
f = Tan[x];
W = y1*D[y2,x] - y2*D[y1,x]  //  Simplify
yp = -y1*Integrate[y2*f/W,x] + y2*Integrate[y1*f/W,x];
Simplify[yp]
```

produce the result

$$y_p(x) = -(\cos x) \ln \left(\frac{\cos(x/2) + \sin(x/2)}{\cos(x/2) - \sin(x/2)} \right),$$

which (by the usual difference-of-squares technique) also is equivalent to the result found in Example 11.

To solve similarly a second-order linear equation $y'' + P(x)y' + Q(x)y = f(x)$ whose complementary function $y_c(x) = c_1 y_1(x) + c_2 y_2(x)$ is known, we need only insert the corresponding definitions of $y_1(x)$, $y_2(x)$, and $f(x)$ in the initial lines shown here. Find in this way the indicated particular solution $y_p(x)$ of the nonhomogeneous equations in Problems 1 through 6.

1. $y'' + y = 2 \sin x$ $\qquad$ $y_p(x) = -x \cos x$
2. $y'' + y = 4x \sin x$ $\qquad$ $y_p(x) = x \sin x - x^2 \cos x$
3. $y'' + y = 12x^2 \sin x$ $\qquad$ $y_p(x) = 3x^2 \sin x + (3x - 2x^3) \cos x$
4. $y'' - 2y' + 2y = 2e^x \sin x$ $\qquad$ $y_p(x) = -xe^x \cos x$
5. $y'' - 2y' + 2y = 4xe^x \sin x$ $\qquad$ $y_p(x) = e^x(x \sin x - x^2 \cos x)$
6. $y'' - 2y' + 2y = 12x^2 e^x \sin x$ $\qquad$ $y_p(x) = e^x \left[3x^2 \sin x + (3x - 2x^3) \cos x \right]$

5.6 Forced Oscillations and Resonance

In Section 5.4 we derived the differential equation

$$mx'' + cx' + kx = F(t) \tag{1}$$

that governs the one-dimensional motion of a mass m that is attached to a spring (with constant k) and a dashpot (with constant c) and is also acted on by an external force $F(t)$. Machines with rotating components commonly involve mass-spring systems (or their equivalents) in which the external force is simple harmonic:

$$F(t) = F_0 \cos \omega t \quad \text{or} \quad F(t) = F_0 \sin \omega t, \tag{2}$$

where the constant F_0 is the amplitude of the periodic force and ω is its circular frequency.

FIGURE 5.6.1. The cart-with-flywheel system.

For an example of how a rotating machine component can provide a simple harmonic force, consider the cart with a rotating vertical flywheel shown in Fig. 5.6.1. The cart has mass $m - m_0$, not including the flywheel of mass m_0. The centroid of the flywheel is off center at a distance a from its center, and its angular speed is ω radians per second. The cart is attached to a spring (with constant k) as shown. Assume that the centroid of the cart itself is directly beneath the center of the flywheel, and denote by $x(t)$ its displacement from its equilibrium position (where the spring is unstretched). Figure 5.6.1 helps us to see that the displacement $\bar{x}$ of the centroid of the combined cart plus flywheel is given by

$$\bar{x} = \frac{(m - m_0)x + m_0(x + a\cos\omega t)}{m} = x + \frac{m_0 a}{m}\cos\omega t.$$

Let us ignore friction and apply Newton's second law $m\bar{x}'' = -kx$, because the force exerted by the spring is $-kx$. We substitute for $\bar{x}$ in the last equation to obtain

$$mx'' - m_0 a\omega^2\cos\omega t = -kx;$$

that is,

$$mx'' + kx = m_0 a\omega^2\cos\omega t. \tag{3}$$

Thus the cart with its rotating flywheel acts like a mass on a spring under the influence of a simple harmonic external force with amplitude $F_0 = m_0 a\omega^2$. Such a system is a reasonable model of a front-loading washing machine with the clothes being washed loaded off center. This illustrates the practical importance of analyzing solutions of Eq. (1) with external forces as in (2).

Undamped Forced Oscillations

To study undamped oscillations under the influence of the external force $F(t) = F_0\cos\omega t$, we set $c = 0$ in Eq. (1) and thereby begin with the equation

$$\blacktriangleright \qquad\qquad mx'' + kx = F_0\cos\omega t \tag{4}$$

whose complementary function is $x_c = c_1\cos\omega_0 t + c_2\sin\omega_0 t$. Here,

$$\blacktriangleright \qquad\qquad \omega_0 = \sqrt{\frac{k}{m}}$$

is the (circular) **natural frequency** of the mass-spring system. Let us assume initially that the external and natural frequencies are *unequal*: $\omega \neq \omega_0$. We substitute $x_p = A\cos\omega t$ in Eq. (4) to find a particular solution. [No sine term is needed in x_p because there is no term involving x' on the left-hand side in Eq. (4).] This gives

$$-m\omega^2 A\cos\omega t + kA\cos\omega t = F_0\cos\omega t,$$

so

$$A = \frac{F_0}{k - m\omega^2} = \frac{F_0/m}{\omega_0^2 - \omega^2}, \tag{5}$$

and thus

$$x_p(t) = \frac{F_0/m}{\omega_0^2 - \omega^2}\cos\omega t. \tag{6}$$

Therefore, the general solution $x = x_c + x_p$ is given by

$$x(t) = c_1\cos\omega_0 t + c_2\sin\omega_0 t + \frac{F_0/m}{\omega_0^2 - \omega^2}\cos\omega t, \tag{7}$$

where the constants c_1 and c_2 are determined by the initial values $x(0)$ and $x'(0)$. Equivalently, as in Eq. (12) of Section 5.4, we can rewrite Eq. (7) as

$$x(t) = C\cos(\omega_0 t - \alpha) + \frac{F_0/m}{\omega_0^2 - \omega^2}\cos\omega t, \tag{8}$$

so we see that the resulting motion is a superposition of two oscillations, one with natural circular frequency ω_0, the other with the frequency ω of the external force.

Example 1 Suppose that $m = 1, k = 9, F_0 = 80$, and $\omega = 5$, so the differential equation in (4) is

$$x'' + 9x = 80\cos 5t.$$

Find $x(t)$ if $x(0) = x'(0) = 0$.

Solution Here the natural frequency $\omega_0 = 3$ and the frequency $\omega = 5$ of the external force are unequal, as in the preceding discussion. First we substitute $x_p = A\cos 5t$ in the differential equation and find that $-25A + 9A = 80$, so that $A = -5$. Thus a particular solution is

$$x_p(t) = -5\cos 5t.$$

The complementary function is $x_c = c_1\cos 3t + c_2\sin 3t$, so the general solution of the given nonhomogeneous equation is

$$x(t) = c_1\cos 3t + c_2\sin 3t - 5\cos 5t,$$

with derivative

$$x'(t) = -3c_1\sin 3t + 3c_2\cos 3t + 25\sin 5t.$$

The initial conditions $x(0) = 0$ and $x'(0) = 0$ now yield $c_1 = 5$ and $c_2 = 0$, so the desired particular solution is

$$x(t) = 5\cos 3t - 5\cos 5t.$$

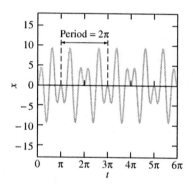

FIGURE 5.6.2. The response $x(t) = 5\cos 3t - 5\cos 5t$ in Example 1.

As indicated in Fig. 5.6.2, the period of $x(t)$ is the least common multiple 2π of the periods $2\pi/3$ and $2\pi/5$ of the two cosine terms. ∎

Beats

If we impose the initial conditions $x(0) = x'(0) = 0$ on the solution in (7), we find that

$$c_1 = -\frac{F_0}{m(\omega_0^2 - \omega^2)} \quad \text{and} \quad c_2 = 0,$$

so the particular solution is

$$x(t) = \frac{F_0}{m(\omega_0^2 - \omega^2)}(\cos\omega t - \cos\omega_0 t). \tag{9}$$

The trigonometric identity $2\sin A\sin B = \cos(A - B) - \cos(A + B)$, applied with $A = \frac{1}{2}(\omega_0 + \omega)t$ and $B = \frac{1}{2}(\omega_0 - \omega)t$, enables us to rewrite Eq. (9) in the form

$$x(t) = \frac{2F_0}{m(\omega_0^2 - \omega^2)}\sin\tfrac{1}{2}(\omega_0 - \omega)t\sin\tfrac{1}{2}(\omega_0 + \omega)t. \tag{10}$$

Suppose now that $\omega \approx \omega_0$, so that $\omega_0 + \omega$ is very large in comparison with $|\omega_0 - \omega|$. Then $\sin \frac{1}{2}(\omega_0 + \omega)t$ is a *rapidly* varying function, whereas $\sin \frac{1}{2}(\omega_0 - \omega)t$ is a *slowly* varying function. We may therefore interpret Eq. (10) as a rapid oscillation with circular frequency $\frac{1}{2}(\omega_0 + \omega)$,

$$x(t) = A(t) \sin \tfrac{1}{2}(\omega_0 + \omega)t,$$

but with a slowly varying amplitude

$$A(t) = \frac{2F_0}{m(\omega_0^2 - \omega^2)} \sin \tfrac{1}{2}(\omega_0 - \omega)t.$$

| Example 2 | With $m = 0.1$, $F_0 = 50$, $\omega_0 = 55$, and $\omega = 45$, Eq. (10) gives |

$$x(t) = \sin 5t \sin 50t.$$

Figure 5.6.3 shows the corresponding oscillation of frequency $\frac{1}{2}(\omega_0 + \omega) = 50$ that is "modulated" by the amplitude function $A(t) = \sin 5t$ of frequency $\frac{1}{2}(\omega_0 - \omega) = 5$. ∎

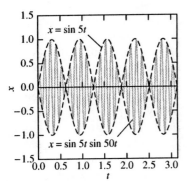

FIGURE 5.6.3. The phenomenon of beats.

A rapid oscillation with a (comparatively) slowly varying periodic amplitude exhibits the phenomenon of *beats*. For example, if two horns not exactly attuned to one another simultaneously play their middle C, one at $\omega_0/(2\pi) = 258$ Hz and the other at $\omega/(2\pi) = 254$ Hz, then one hears a beat—an audible variation in the *amplitude* of the combined sound—with a frequency of

$$\frac{(\omega_0 - \omega)/2}{2\pi} = \frac{258 - 254}{2} = 2 \text{ (Hz)}.$$

Resonance

Looking at Eq. (6), we see that the amplitude A of x_p is large when the natural and external frequencies ω_0 and ω are approximately equal. It is sometimes useful to rewrite Eq. (5) in the form

$$A = \frac{F_0}{k - m\omega^2} = \frac{F_0/k}{1 - (\omega/\omega_0)^2} = \pm\frac{\rho F_0}{k}, \tag{11}$$

where F_0/k is the **static displacement** of a spring with constant k due to a *constant* force F_0, and the **amplification factor** ρ is defined to be

$$\rho = \frac{1}{|1 - (\omega/\omega_0)^2|}. \tag{12}$$

It is clear that $\rho \to +\infty$ as $\omega \to \omega_0$. This is the phenomenon of **resonance**—the increase without bound (as $\omega \to \omega_0$) in the amplitude of oscillations of an undamped system with natural frequency ω_0 in response to an external force with frequency $\omega \approx \omega_0$.

We have been assuming that $\omega \neq \omega_0$. What sort of catastrophe should one expect if ω and ω_0 are precisely equal? Then Eq. (4), upon division of each term by m, becomes

$$x'' + \omega_0^2 x = \frac{F_0}{m} \cos \omega_0 t. \tag{13}$$

Because $\cos \omega_0 t$ is a term of the complementary function, the method of undetermined coefficients calls for us to try

$$x_p(t) = t(A \cos \omega_0 t + B \sin \omega_0 t).$$

We substitute this in Eq. (13) and thereby find that $A = 0$ and $B = F_0/(2m\omega_0)$. Hence the particular solution is

$$x_p(t) = \frac{F_0}{2m\omega_0} t \sin \omega_0 t. \tag{14}$$

The graph of $x_p(t)$ in Fig. 5.6.4 (in which $m = 1$, $F_0 = 100$, and $\omega_0 = 50$) shows vividly how the amplitude of the oscillation theoretically would increase without bound in this case of *pure resonance*, $\omega = \omega_0$. We may interpret this phenomenon as reinforcement of the natural vibrations of the system by externally impressed vibrations at the same frequency.

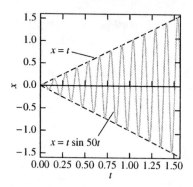

FIGURE 5.6.4. The phenomenon of resonance.

Example 3 Suppose that $m = 5$ kg and that $k = 500$ N/m in the cart with the flywheel of Fig. 5.6.1. Then the natural frequency is $\omega_0 = \sqrt{k/m} = 10$ rad/s; that is, $10/(2\pi)$ ≈ 1.59 Hz. We would therefore expect oscillations of very large amplitude to occur if the flywheel revolves at about $(1.59)(60) \approx 95$ revolutions per minute (rpm). ■

In practice, a mechanical system with very little damping can be destroyed by resonance vibrations. A spectacular example can occur when a column of soldiers marches in step over a bridge. Any complicated structure such as a bridge has many natural frequencies of vibration. If the frequency of the soldiers' cadence is approximately equal to one of the natural frequencies of the structure, then—just as in our simple example of a mass on a spring—resonance will occur. Indeed, the resulting resonance vibrations can be of such large amplitude that the bridge will collapse. This has actually happened—for example, the collapse of Broughton Bridge near Manchester, England, in 1831—and it is the reason for the now-standard practice of breaking cadence when crossing a bridge. Resonance may have been involved in the 1981 Kansas City disaster in which a hotel balcony (called a *skywalk*) collapsed with dancers on it. The collapse of a building in an earthquake is sometimes due to resonance vibrations caused by the ground oscillating at one of the natural frequencies of the structure; this happened to many buildings in the Mexico City earthquake of September 19, 1985. On occasion an airplane has crashed because of resonant wing oscillations caused by vibrations of the engines. It is reported that for some of the first commercial jet aircraft, the natural frequency of the vertical vibrations of the airplane during turbulence was almost exactly that of the mass-spring system consisting of the pilot's head (mass) and spine (spring). Resonance occurred, causing pilots to have difficulty in reading the instruments. Large modern commercial jets have different natural frequencies, so that this resonance problem no longer occurs.

Modeling Mechanical Systems

The avoidance of destructive resonance vibrations is an ever-present consideration in the design of mechanical structures and systems of all types. Often the most important step in determining the natural frequency of vibration of a system is the formulation of its differential equation. In addition to Newton's law $F = ma$, the principle of conservation of energy is sometimes useful for this purpose (as in the derivation of the pendulum equation in Section 5.4). The following kinetic and potential energy formulas are often useful.

1. *Kinetic energy:* $T = \frac{1}{2}mv^2$ for translation of a mass m with velocity v;
2. *Kinetic energy:* $T = \frac{1}{2}I\omega^2$ for rotation of a body of a moment of inertia I with angular velocity ω;
3. *Potential energy:* $V = \frac{1}{2}kx^2$ for a spring with constant k stretched or compressed a distance x;
4. *Potential energy:* $V = mgh$ for the gravitational potential energy of a mass m at height h above the reference level (the level at which $V = 0$), provided that g may be regarded as essentially constant.

Example 4

Find the natural frequency of a mass m on a spring with constant k if, instead of sliding without friction, it is a uniform disk of radius a that rolls without slipping, as shown in Fig 5.6.5.

Solution

With the preceding notation, the principle of conservation of energy gives

$$\tfrac{1}{2}mv^2 + \tfrac{1}{2}I\omega^2 + \tfrac{1}{2}kx^2 = E,$$

where E is a constant (the total mechanical energy of the system). We note that $v = a\omega$ and recall that $I = ma^2/2$ for a uniform circular disk. Then we may simplify the last equation to

$$\tfrac{3}{4}mv^2 + \tfrac{1}{2}kx^2 = E.$$

Differentiation ($v = x'$, $v' = x''$) now gives

$$\tfrac{3}{2}mx'x'' + kxx' = 0.$$

We divide each term by $\tfrac{3}{2}mx'$ to obtain

$$x'' + \frac{2k}{3m}x = 0.$$

Thus the natural circular frequency is $\omega_0 = \sqrt{2k/(3m)}$, which is $\sqrt{2/3} \approx 0.8165$ times the frequency in the previous situation of sliding without friction. ∎

Equilibrium position

a

x

$x = 0$

FIGURE 5.6.5. The rolling disk.

Example 5

Suppose that a car oscillates vertically as if it were a mass $m = 800$ kg on a single spring (with constant $k = 7 \times 10^4$ N/m), attached to a single dashpot (with constant $c = 3000$ N·s/m). Suppose that this car with the dashpot *disconnected* is driven along a washboard road surface with an amplitude of 5 cm and a wavelength of $L = 10$ m (Fig. 5.6.6). At what car speed will resonance vibrations occur?

Solution

We think of the car as a unicycle, as pictured in Fig. 5.6.7. Let $x(t)$ denote the upward displacement of the mass m from its equilibrium position; we ignore the force of gravity, because it merely displaces the equilibrium position as in Problem 9 of Section 5.4. We write the equation of the road surface as

$$y = a\cos\frac{2\pi s}{L} \quad (a = 0.05 \text{ m}, \ L = 10 \text{ m}). \tag{15}$$

FIGURE 5.6.6. The washboard road surface of Example 5.

FIGURE 5.6.7. The "unicycle model" of a car.

When the car is in motion, the spring is stretched by the amount $x - y$, so Newton's second law, $F = ma$, gives

$$mx'' = -k(x - y);$$

that is,

$$mx'' + kx = ky. \tag{16}$$

If the velocity of the car is v, then $s = vt$ in Eq. (15), so Eq. (16) takes the form

$$mx'' + kx = ka\cos\frac{2\pi vt}{L}. \tag{16'}$$

This is the differential equation that governs the vertical oscillations of the car. In comparing it with Eq. (4), we see that we have forced oscillations with circular frequency $\omega = 2\pi v/L$. Resonance will occur when $\omega = \omega_0 = \sqrt{k/m}$. We use our numerical data to find the speed of the car at resonance:

$$v = \frac{L}{2\pi}\sqrt{\frac{k}{m}} = \frac{10}{2\pi}\sqrt{\frac{7 \times 10^4}{800}} \approx 14.89 \text{ (m/s)};$$

that is, about 33.3 mi/h (using the conversion factor of 2.237 mi/h per m/s). ∎

Damped Forced Oscillations

In real physical systems there is always some damping, from frictional effects if nothing else. The complementary function x_c of the equation

➤ $$mx'' + cx' + kx = F_0 \cos\omega t \tag{17}$$

is given by Eq. (18), (19), or (20) of Section 5.4, depending on whether $c > c_{cr} = \sqrt{4km}$, $c = c_{cr}$, or $c < c_{cr}$. The specific form is not important here. What is important is that, in any case, these formulas show that $x_c(t) \to 0$ as $t \to +\infty$. Thus x_c is a **transient solution** of Eq. (17)—one that dies out with the passage of time, leaving only the particular solution x_p.

The method of undetermined coefficients indicates that we should substitute

$$x(t) = A\cos\omega t + B\sin\omega t$$

in Eq. (17). When we do, collect terms, and equate coefficients of $\cos \omega t$ and $\sin \omega t$, we obtain the two equations

$$(k - m\omega^2)A + c\omega B = F_0, \qquad -c\omega A + (k - m\omega^2)B = 0, \qquad (18)$$

which we solve without difficulty for

$$A = \frac{(k - m\omega^2)F_0}{(k - m\omega^2)^2 + (c\omega)^2}, \qquad B = \frac{c\omega F_0}{(k - m\omega^2)^2 + (c\omega)^2}. \qquad (19)$$

If we write

$$A \cos \omega t + B \sin \omega t = C(\cos \omega t \cos \alpha + \sin \omega t \sin \alpha) = C \cos(\omega t - \alpha)$$

as usual, we see that the resulting steady periodic oscillation

$$x_p(t) = C \cos(\omega t - \alpha) \qquad (20)$$

has amplitude

$$C = \sqrt{A^2 + B^2} = \frac{F_0}{\sqrt{(k - m\omega^2)^2 + (c\omega)^2}}. \qquad (21)$$

Now (19) implies that $\sin \alpha = B/C > 0$, so it follows that the phase angle α lies in the first or second quadrant. Thus

$$\tan \alpha = \frac{B}{A} = \frac{c\omega}{k - m\omega^2} \quad \text{with} \quad 0 < \alpha < \pi, \qquad (22)$$

so

$$\alpha = \begin{cases} \tan^{-1} \dfrac{c\omega}{k - m\omega^2} & \text{if } k > m\omega^2, \\ \pi + \tan^{-1} \dfrac{c\omega}{k - m\omega^2} & \text{if } k < m\omega^2 \end{cases}$$

(whereas $\alpha = \pi/2$ if $k = m\omega^2$).

Note that if $c > 0$, then the "forced amplitude"—defined as a function $C(\omega)$ by (21)—always remains finite, in contrast with the case of resonance in the undamped case when the forcing frequency ω equals the critical frequency $\omega_0 = \sqrt{k/m}$. But the forced amplitude may attain a maximum for some value of ω, in which case we speak of *practical resonance*. To see if and when practical resonance occurs, we need only graph C as a function of ω and look for a global maximum. It can be shown (Problem 27) that C is a steadily decreasing function of ω if $c \geq \sqrt{2km}$. But if $c < \sqrt{2km}$, then the amplitude of C attains a maximum value—and so practical resonance occurs—at some value of ω less than ω_0, and then approaches zero as $\omega \to +\infty$. It follows that an underdamped system typically will undergo forced oscillations whose amplitude is

- Large if ω is close to the critical resonance frequency;
- Close to F_0/k if ω is very small;
- Very small if ω is very large.

Example 6

Find the transient motion and steady periodic oscillations of a damped mass-and-spring system with $m = 1$, $c = 2$, and $k = 26$ under the influence of an external force $F(t) = 82 \cos 4t$ with $x(0) = 6$ and $x'(0) = 0$. Also investigate the possibility of practical resonance for this system.

Solution The resulting motion $x(t) = x_{tr}(t) + x_{sp}(t)$ of the mass satisfies the initial value problem

$$x'' + 2x' + 26x = 82 \cos 4t; \quad x(0) = 6, \ x'(0) = 0. \tag{23}$$

Instead of applying the general formulas derived earlier in this section, it is better in a concrete problem to work it directly. The roots of the characteristic equation

$$r^2 + 2r + 26 = (r + 1)^2 + 25 = 0$$

are $r = -1 \pm 5i$, so the complementary function is

$$x_c(t) = e^{-t}(c_1 \cos 5t + c_2 \sin 5t).$$

When we substitute the trial solution

$$x(t) = A \cos 4t + B \sin 4t$$

in the given equation, collect like terms, and equate coefficients of $\cos 4t$ and $\sin 4t$, we get the equations

$$10A + \ 8B = 82,$$
$$-8A + 10B = \ 0$$

with solution $A = 5$, $B = 4$. Hence the general solution of the equation in (23) is

$$x(t) = e^{-t}(c_1 \cos 5t + c_2 \sin 5t) + 5 \cos 4t + 4 \sin 4t.$$

At this point we impose the initial conditions $x(0) = 6$, $x'(0) = 0$ and find that $c_1 = 1$ and $c_2 = -3$. Therefore, the transient motion and the steady periodic oscillation of the mass are given by

$$x_{tr}(t) = e^{-t}(\cos 5t - 3 \sin 5t)$$

and

$$x_{sp}(t) = 5 \cos 4t + 4 \sin 4t = \sqrt{41} \left(\frac{5}{\sqrt{41}} \cos 4t + \frac{4}{\sqrt{41}} \sin 4t \right)$$
$$= \sqrt{41} \cos(4t - \alpha),$$

where $\alpha = \tan^{-1}\left(\frac{4}{5}\right) \approx 0.6747$.

Figure 5.6.8 shows graphs of the solution $x(t) = x_{tr}(t) + x_{sp}(t)$ of the initial value problem

$$x'' + 2x' + 26x = 82 \cos 4t, \quad x(0) = x_0, \ x'(0) = 0 \tag{24}$$

for the different values $x_0 = -20$, -10, 0, 10, and 20 of the initial position. Here we see clearly what it means for the transient solution $x_{tr}(t)$ to "die out with the passage of time," leaving only the steady periodic motion $x_{sp}(t)$. Indeed, because

FIGURE 5.6.8. Solutions of the initial value problem in (24) with $x_0 = -20, -10, 0, 10,$ and 20.

$x_{tr}(t) \to 0$ exponentially, within a very few cycles the full solution $x(t)$ and the steady periodic solution $x_{sp}(t)$ are virtually indistinguishable.

To investigate the possibility of practical resonance in the given system, we substitute the values $m = 1$, $c = 2$, and $k = 26$ in (21) and find that the forced amplitude at frequency ω is

$$C(\omega) = \frac{82}{\sqrt{676 - 48\omega^2 + \omega^4}}.$$

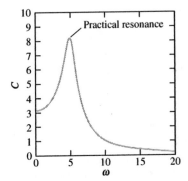

FIGURE 5.6.9. Plot of amplitude C versus external frequency ω.

The graph of $C(\omega)$ is shown in Fig. 5.6.9. The maximum amplitude occurs when

$$C'(\omega) = \frac{-41(4\omega^3 - 96\omega)}{(676 - 48\omega^2 + \omega^4)^{3/2}} = \frac{-164\omega(\omega^2 - 24)}{(676 - 48\omega^2 + \omega^4)^{3/2}} = 0.$$

Thus practical resonance occurs when the external frequency is $\omega = \sqrt{24}$ (a bit less than the mass-and-spring's undamped critical frequency of $\omega_0 = \sqrt{k/m} = \sqrt{26}$). ∎

5.6 Problems

In Problems 1 through 6, express the solution of the given initial value problem as a sum of two oscillations as in Eq. (8). Throughout, primes denote derivatives with respect to time t. In Problems 1 through 4, graph the solution function x(t) in such a way that you can identify and label (as in Fig. 5.6.2) its period.

1. $x'' + 9x = 10 \cos 2t$; $x(0) = x'(0) = 0$

2. $x'' + 4x = 5 \sin 3t$; $x(0) = x'(0) = 0$

3. $x'' + 100x = 225 \cos 5t + 300 \sin 5t$; $x(0) = 375$, $x'(0) = 0$

4. $x'' + 25x = 90 \cos 4t$; $x(0) = 0$, $x'(0) = 90$

5. $mx'' + kx = F_0 \cos \omega t$ with $\omega \neq \omega_0$; $x(0) = x_0$, $x'(0) = 0$

6. $mx'' + kx = F_0 \cos \omega t$ with $\omega = \omega_0$; $x(0) = 0$, $x'(0) = v_0$

In each of Problems 7 through 10, find the steady periodic solution $x_{sp}(t) = C \cos(\omega t - \alpha)$ of the given equation $mx'' + cx' + kx = F(t)$ with periodic forcing function $F(t)$ of frequency ω. Then graph $x_{sp}(t)$ together with (for comparison) the adjusted forcing function $F_1(t) = F(t)/m\omega$.

7. $x'' + 4x' + 4x = 10 \cos 3t$

8. $x'' + 3x' + 5x = -4 \cos 5t$

9. $2x'' + 2x' + x = 3 \sin 10t$

10. $x'' + 3x' + 3x = 8 \cos 10t + 6 \sin 10t$

In each of Problems 11 through 14, find and plot both the steady periodic solution $x_{sp}(t) = C \cos(\omega t - \alpha)$ of the given differential equation and the transient solution $x_{tr}(t)$ that sat-

isfies the given initial conditions.

11. $x'' + 4x' + 5x = 10\cos 3t$; $x(0) = x'(0) = 0$
12. $x'' + 6x' + 13x = 10\sin 5t$; $x(0) = x'(0) = 0$
13. $x'' + 2x' + 26x = 600\cos 10t$; $x(0) = 10$, $x'(0) = 0$
14. $x'' + 8x' + 25x = 200\cos t + 520\sin t$; $x(0) = -30$, $x'(0) = -10$

Each of Problems 15 through 18 gives the parameters for a forced mass-spring-dashpot system with equation $mx'' + cx' + kx = F_0 \cos \omega t$. Investigate the possibility of practical resonance of this system. In particular, find the amplitude $C(\omega)$ of steady periodic forced oscillations with frequency ω. Sketch the graph of $C(\omega)$ and find the practical resonance frequency ω (if any).

15. $m = 1$, $c = 2$, $k = 2$, $F_0 = 2$
16. $m = 1$, $c = 4$, $k = 5$, $F_0 = 10$
17. $m = 1$, $c = 6$, $k = 45$, $F_0 = 50$
18. $m = 1$, $c = 10$, $k = 650$, $F_0 = 100$

19. A mass weighing 100 lb (mass $m = 3.125$ slugs in fps units) is attached to the end of a spring that is stretched 1 in. by a force of 100 lb. A force $F_0 \cos \omega t$ acts on the mass. At what frequency (in hertz) will resonance oscillations occur? Neglect damping.

20. A front-loading washing machine is mounted on a thick rubber pad that acts like a spring; the weight $W = mg$ (with $g = 9.8$ m/s²) of the machine depresses the pad exactly 0.5 cm. When its rotor spins at ω radians per second, the rotor exerts a vertical force $F_0 \cos \omega t$ newtons on the machine. At what speed (in revolutions per minute) will resonance vibrations occur? Neglect friction.

21. Figure 5.6.10 shows a mass m on the end of a pendulum (of length L) also attached to a horizontal spring (with constant k). Assume small oscillations of m so that the spring remains essentially horizontal and neglect damping. Find the natural circular frequency ω_0 of motion of the mass in terms of L, k, m, and the gravitational constant g.

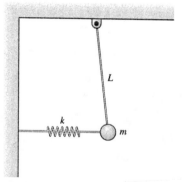

FIGURE 5.6.10. The pendulum-and-spring system of Problem 21.

22. A mass m hangs on the end of a cord around a pulley of radius a and moment of inertia I, as shown in Fig. 5.6.11. The rim of the pulley is attached to a spring (with constant k). Assume small oscillations so that the spring remains essentially horizontal and neglect friction. Find the natural circular frequency of the system in terms of m, a, k, I, and g.

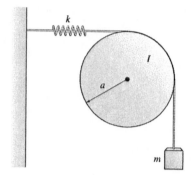

FIGURE 5.6.11. The mass-spring-pulley system of Problem 22.

23. A building consists of two floors. The first floor is attached rigidly to the ground, and the second floor is of mass $m = 1000$ slugs (fps units) and weighs 16 tons (32,000 lb). The elastic frame of the building behaves as a spring that resists horizontal displacements of the second floor; it requires a horizontal force of 5 tons to displace the second floor a distance of 1 ft. Assume that in an earthquake the ground oscillates horizontally with amplitude A_0 and circular frequency ω, resulting in an external horizontal force $F(t) = mA_0\omega^2 \sin \omega t$ on the second floor. **(a)** What is the natural frequency (in hertz) of oscillations of the second floor? **(b)** If the ground undergoes one oscillation every 2.25 s with an amplitude of 3 in., what is the amplitude of the resulting forced oscillations of the second floor?

24. A mass on a spring without damping is acted on by the external force $F(t) = F_0 \cos^3 \omega t$. Show that there are *two* values of ω for which resonance occurs, and find both.

25. Derive the steady periodic solution of

$$mx'' + cx' + kx = F_0 \sin \omega t.$$

In particular, show that it is what one would expect—the same as the formula in (20) with the same values of C and ω, except with $\sin(\omega t - \alpha)$ in place of $\cos(\omega t - \alpha)$.

26. Given the differential equation

$$mx'' + cx' + kx = E_0 \cos \omega t + F_0 \sin \omega t$$

—with both cosine and sine forcing terms—derive the steady periodic solution

$$x_{sp}(t) = \frac{\sqrt{E_0^2 + F_0^2}}{\sqrt{(k - m\omega^2)^2 + (c\omega)^2}} \cos(\omega t - \alpha - \beta),$$

where α is defined in Eq. (22) and $\beta = \tan^{-1}(F_0/E_0)$. [*Suggestion:* Add the steady periodic solutions separately corresponding to $E_0 \cos \omega t$ and $F_0 \sin \omega t$ (see Problem 25).]

27. According to Eq. (21), the amplitude of forced steady periodic oscillations for the system $mx'' + cx' + kx = F_0 \cos \omega t$ is given by

$$C(\omega) = \frac{F_0}{\sqrt{(k - m\omega^2)^2 + (c\omega)^2}}.$$

(a) If $c \geq c_{cr}/\sqrt{2}$, where $c_{cr} = \sqrt{4km}$, show that C steadily decreases as ω increases. **(b)** If $c < c_{cr}/\sqrt{2}$, show that C attains a maximum value (practical resonance) when

$$\omega = \omega_m = \sqrt{\frac{k}{m} - \frac{c^2}{2m^2}} < \omega_0 = \sqrt{\frac{k}{m}}.$$

28. As indicated by the cart-with-flywheel example discussed in this section, an unbalanced rotating machine part typically results in a force having amplitude proportional to the *square* of the frequency ω. **(a)** Show that the amplitude of the steady periodic solution of the differential equation

$$mx'' + cx' + kx = mA\omega^2 \cos \omega t$$

[with a forcing term similar to that in Eq. (17)] is given by

$$C(\omega) = \frac{mA\omega^2}{\sqrt{(k - m\omega^2)^2 + (c\omega)^2}}.$$

(b) Suppose that $c^2 < 2mk$. Show that the maximum amplitude occurs at the frequency ω_m given by

$$\omega_m = \sqrt{\frac{k}{m}\left(\frac{2mk}{2mk - c^2}\right)}.$$

Thus the resonance frequency in this case is *larger* (in contrast with the result of Problem 27) than the natural frequency $\omega_0 = \sqrt{k/m}$. (*Suggestion*: Maximize the *square* of C.)

Automobile Vibrations

Problems 29 and 30 deal further with the car of Example 5. Its upward displacement function satisfies the equation

$mx'' + cx' + kx = cy' + ky$ *when the shock absorber is connected (so that $c > 0$). With $y = a \sin \omega t$ for the road surface, this differential equation becomes*

$$mx'' + cx' + kx = E_0 \cos \omega t + F_0 \sin \omega t,$$

where $E_0 = c\omega a$ and $F_0 = ka$.

29. Apply the result of Problem 26 to show that the amplitude C of the resulting steady periodic oscillation for the car is given by

$$C = \frac{a\sqrt{k^2 + (c\omega)^2}}{\sqrt{(k - m\omega^2)^2 + (c\omega)^2}}.$$

Because $\omega = 2\pi v/L$ when the car is moving with velocity v, this gives C as a function of v.

30. Figure 5.6.12 shows the graph of the amplitude function $C(\omega)$ using the numerical data given in Example 5 (including $c = 3000$ N·s/m). It indicates that, as the car accelerates gradually from rest, it initially oscillates with amplitude slightly over 5 cm. Maximum resonance vibrations with amplitude about 14 cm occur around 32 mi/h, but then subside to more tolerable levels at high speeds. Verify these graphically based conclusions by analyzing the function $C(\omega)$. In particular, find the practical resonance frequency and the corresponding amplitude.

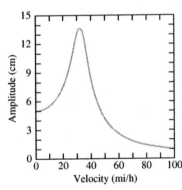

FIGURE 5.6.12. Amplitude of vibrations of the car on a washboard surface.

5.6 Application: Forced Vibrations and Resonance

Here we investigate forced vibrations of the mass-spring-dashpot system with equation

$$mx'' + cx' + kx = F(t). \tag{1}$$

To simplify the notation, let's take $m = p^2$, $c = 2p$, and $k = p^2q^2 + 1$, where $p > 0$ and $q > 0$. Then the complementary function of Eq. (1) is

$$x_c(t) = e^{-t/p}(c_1 \cos qt + c_2 \sin qt). \tag{2}$$

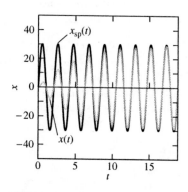

FIGURE 5.6.13. The solution $x(t) = x_{tr}(t) + x_{sp}(t)$ and the steady periodic solution $x(t) = x_{sp}(t)$ with periodic external force $F(t) = 901 \cos 3t$.

We will take $p = 5$, $q = 3$, and thus investigate the transient and steady periodic solutions corresponding to

$$25x'' + 10x' + 226x = F(t), \quad x(0) = 0, \quad x'(0) = 0 \tag{3}$$

with several illustrative possibilities for the external force $F(t)$. For your personal investigations to carry out similarly, you might select integers p and q with $6 \leqq p \leqq 9$ and $2 \leqq q \leqq 5$.

INVESTIGATION 1:   With periodic external force $F(t) = 901 \cos 3t$, the MATLAB commands

```
x = dsolve('25*D2x+10*Dx+226*x=901*cos(3*t)',
      'x(0)=0, Dx(0)=0');
x = simple(x);
syms t, xsp = cos(3*t) + 30*sin(3*t);
ezplot(x, [0  6*pi]),hold on
ezplot(xsp, [0  6*pi])
```

produce the plot shown in Fig. 5.6.13. We see the (transient plus steady periodic) solution

$$x(t) = \cos 3t + 30 \sin 3t + e^{-t/5} \left(-\cos 3t - \tfrac{451}{15} \sin 3t \right)$$

rapidly "building up" to the steady periodic oscillation $x_{sp}(t) = \cos 3t + 30 \sin 3t$.

INVESTIGATION 2:   With damped oscillatory external force

$$F(t) = 900e^{-t/5} \cos 3t,$$

we have duplication with the complementary function in (2). The *Maple* commands

```
de2 := 25*diff(x(t),t,t)+10*diff(x(t),t)+226*x(t) =
      900*exp(-t/5)*cos(3*t);
dsolve({de2,x(0)=0,D(x)(0)=0}, x(t));
x := simplify(combine(rhs(%),trig));
C := 6*t*exp(-t/5);
plot({x,C,-C},t=0..8*Pi);
```

produce the plot shown in Fig. 5.6.14. We see the solution

$$x(t) = 6te^{-t/5} \sin 3t$$

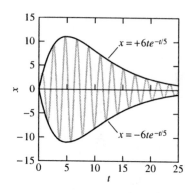

FIGURE 5.6.14. The solution $x(t) = 6te^{-t/5} \sin 3t$ and the envelope curves $x(t) = \pm 6te^{-t/5}$ with damped oscillatory force $F(t) = 900e^{-t/5} \cos 3t$.

oscillating up-and-down between the envelope curves $x = \pm 6te^{-t/5}$. (Note the factor of t that signals a resonance situation.)

INVESTIGATION 3:   With damped oscillatory external force

$$F(t) = 2700te^{-t/5} \cos 3t,$$

we have a still more complicated resonance situation. The *Mathematica* commands

```
de3 = 25 x''[t] + 10 x'[t] + 226 x[t] ==
      2700 t Exp[-t/5] Cos[3t]
soln = DSolve[{de3, x[0] == 0, x'[0] == 0}, x[t], t]
x = First[x[t] /. soln]
```

```
amp = Exp[-t/5] Sqrt[(3t)^2 + (9t^2 - 1)^2]
Plot[{x, amp, -amp}, {t, 0, 10 Pi}];
```

produce the plot shown in Fig. 5.6.15. We see the solution

$$x(t) = e^{-t/5} \left[3t \cos t + (9t^2 - 1) \sin 3t \right]$$

oscillating up-and-down between the envelope curves

$$x = \pm e^{-t/5} \sqrt{(3t)^2 + (9t^2 + 1)^2}.$$

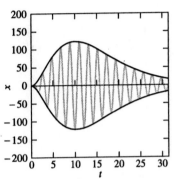

FIGURE 5.6.15. The solution $x(t) = e^{-t/5}[3t \cos t + (9t^2 - 1) \sin 3t]$ and the envelope curves $x(t) = \pm e^{-t/5} \sqrt{(3t)^2 + (9t^2 + 1)^2}$ with external force $F(t) = 2700te^{-t/5} \cos 3t$.

CHAPTER 6

Eigenvalues and Eigenvectors

6.1 Introduction to Eigenvalues

Given a square matrix $\mathbf{A}$, let us pose the following question: Does there exist a nonzero vector $\mathbf{v}$ such that the result $\mathbf{Av}$ of multiplying $\mathbf{v}$ by the matrix $\mathbf{A}$ is simply a scalar multiple of $\mathbf{v}$? Thus we ask whether or not there exist a nonzero vector $\mathbf{v}$ *and* a scalar λ such that

$$\mathbf{Av} = \lambda\mathbf{v}. \tag{1}$$

Section 6.3 and subsequent chapters include interesting applications in which this question arises. The following definition provides the terminology that we use in discussing Eq. (1).

Definition: Eigenvalues and Eigenvectors

The number λ is said to be an **eigenvalue** of the $n \times n$ matrix $\mathbf{A}$ provided there exists a *nonzero* vector $\mathbf{v}$ such that

$$\mathbf{Av} = \lambda\mathbf{v}, \tag{1}$$

in which case the vector $\mathbf{v}$ is called an **eigenvector** of the matrix $\mathbf{A}$. We also say that the eigenvector $\mathbf{v}$ is **associated** with the eigenvalue λ, or that the eigenvalue λ **corresponds** to the eigenvector $\mathbf{v}$.

The prefix *eigen* is a German word that (in some contexts) may be translated as *proper*, so eigenvalues are sometimes called *proper values*. Eigenvalues and eigenvectors are also called *characteristic values* and *characteristic vectors* in some books.

Example 1

Consider the 2×2 matrix

$$\mathbf{A} = \begin{bmatrix} 5 & -6 \\ 2 & -2 \end{bmatrix}.$$

If $\mathbf{v} = (2, 1) = \begin{bmatrix} 2 & 1 \end{bmatrix}^T$, then

$$\mathbf{Av} = \begin{bmatrix} 5 & -6 \\ 2 & -2 \end{bmatrix} \begin{bmatrix} 2 \\ 1 \end{bmatrix} = \begin{bmatrix} 4 \\ 2 \end{bmatrix} = 2\mathbf{v}.$$

Thus, $\mathbf{v} = \begin{bmatrix} 2 & 1 \end{bmatrix}^T$ is an eigenvector of $\mathbf{A}$ that is associated with the eigenvalue $\lambda = 2$. If $\mathbf{v} = \begin{bmatrix} 3 & 2 \end{bmatrix}^T$, then

$$\mathbf{Av} = \begin{bmatrix} 5 & -6 \\ 2 & -2 \end{bmatrix} \begin{bmatrix} 3 \\ 2 \end{bmatrix} = \begin{bmatrix} 3 \\ 2 \end{bmatrix} = 1\mathbf{v},$$

so $\mathbf{v} = \begin{bmatrix} 3 & 2 \end{bmatrix}^T$ is an eigenvector of $\mathbf{A}$ associated with the eigenvalue $\lambda = 1$. In summary, we see that the scalars $\lambda_1 = 2$ and $\lambda_2 = 1$ are both eigenvalues of the matrix $\mathbf{A}$; they correspond to the eigenvectors $\mathbf{v}_1 = \begin{bmatrix} 2 & 1 \end{bmatrix}^T$ and $\mathbf{v}_2 = \begin{bmatrix} 3 & 2 \end{bmatrix}^T$, respectively. ∎

Eigenvalues and eigenvectors have a simple geometric interpretation. Suppose that λ is an eigenvalue of the matrix $\mathbf{A}$ and has the associated eigenvector $\mathbf{v}$, so that $\mathbf{Av} = \lambda\mathbf{v}$. Then the length $|\mathbf{Av}|$ of the vector $\mathbf{Av}$ is $\pm\lambda|\mathbf{v}|$, depending on the sign of λ. Thus, if $\lambda > 0$, then multiplication of $\mathbf{v}$ by the matrix $\mathbf{A}$ expands or contracts the vector $\mathbf{v}$ while preserving its direction; if $\lambda < 0$, then multiplication of $\mathbf{v}$ by $\mathbf{A}$ reverses the direction of $\mathbf{v}$ (see Figure 6.1.1).

Remark 1   If $\mathbf{v} = \mathbf{0}$, then the equation $\mathbf{Av} = \lambda\mathbf{v}$ holds for every scalar λ and hence is of no significance. This is why only *nonzero* vectors qualify as eigenvectors in the definition.

Remark 2   Let λ and $\mathbf{v}$ be an eigenvalue and associated eigenvector of the matrix $\mathbf{A}$. If k is any nonzero scalar and $\mathbf{u} = k\mathbf{v}$, then

$$\mathbf{Au} = \mathbf{A}(k\mathbf{v}) = k(\mathbf{Av})$$
$$= k(\lambda\mathbf{v}) = \lambda(k\mathbf{v}) = \lambda\mathbf{u},$$

so $\mathbf{u} = k\mathbf{v}$ is also an eigenvector associated with λ. Thus, *any nonzero scalar multiple of an eigenvector is also an eigenvector and is associated with the same eigenvalue.* In Example 1, for instance, $\mathbf{u}_1 = -3\mathbf{v}_1 = \begin{bmatrix} -6 & -3 \end{bmatrix}^T$ is an eigenvector associated with $\lambda_1 = 2$, and $\mathbf{u}_2 = 4\mathbf{v}_2 = \begin{bmatrix} 12 & 8 \end{bmatrix}^T$ is an eigenvector associated with $\lambda_2 = 1$.

(a)   (b)

FIGURE 6.1.1. (a) A positive eigenvalue; (b) a negative eigenvalue.

The Characteristic Equation

We now attack the problem of finding the eigenvalues and eigenvectors of a given $n \times n$ square matrix $\mathbf{A}$. According to the definition, the nonzero vector $\mathbf{v}$ is an eigenvector of $\mathbf{A}$ associated with the eigenvalue λ exactly when

$$\mathbf{Av} = \lambda\mathbf{v} = \lambda\mathbf{Iv};$$

that is, when

$$(\mathbf{A} - \lambda\mathbf{I})\mathbf{v} = \mathbf{0}. \tag{2}$$

For a fixed value of λ, Eq. (2) is a homogeneous linear system of n equations in the n components of $\mathbf{v}$. By Theorem 2 in Section 3.6 and Theorem 7 in Section 3.5, this system has a nontrivial solution $\mathbf{v} \neq \mathbf{0}$ if and only if the determinant

$$\det(\mathbf{A} - \lambda\mathbf{I}) = |\mathbf{A} - \lambda\mathbf{I}|$$

of its coefficient matrix is *zero*. The equation $|\mathbf{A} - \lambda\mathbf{I}| = 0$ is called the **characteristic equation** of the square matrix $\mathbf{A}$, and we have proved that there exists an eigenvector $\mathbf{v}$ associated with λ if and only if λ satisfies this equation.

THEOREM 1: The Characteristic Equation

The number λ is an eigenvalue of the $n \times n$ matrix $\mathbf{A}$ if and only if λ satisfies the characteristic equation

$$|\mathbf{A} - \lambda\mathbf{I}| = 0. \tag{3}$$

▲

Now let us see just what sort of equation the characteristic equation in (3) is. Note that the matrix

$$\mathbf{A} - \lambda\mathbf{I} = \begin{bmatrix} a_{11} - \lambda & a_{12} & \cdots & a_{1n} \\ a_{21} & a_{22} - \lambda & \cdots & a_{2n} \\ \vdots & \vdots & \ddots & \vdots \\ a_{n1} & a_{n2} & \cdots & a_{nn} - \lambda \end{bmatrix} \tag{4}$$

is obtained simply by subtracting λ from each diagonal element of $\mathbf{A}$. If we think of expanding the determinant by minors, we see that $|\mathbf{A} - \lambda\mathbf{I}|$ is a *polynomial* in the variable λ, and that the highest power of λ comes from the product of the diagonal elements of the matrix in (4). Therefore, the characteristic equation of the $n \times n$ matrix $\mathbf{A}$ takes the form

$$(-1)^n \lambda^n + c_{n-1}\lambda^{n-1} + \cdots + c_1\lambda + c_0 = 0, \tag{5}$$

an nth-degree polynomial equation in λ.

According to the fundamental theorem of algebra, every nth-degree polynomial equation in one variable has n solutions (counting multiple solutions), but some of them can be complex. Hence, we can say that an $n \times n$ matrix $\mathbf{A}$ *always has n eigenvalues*, though they might not be distinct and might not all be real. In this chapter we confine our attention mainly to real eigenvalues, but in Chapter 7 we will see important applications of complex eigenvalues to the solution of linear systems of differential equations.

ALGORITHM: Eigenvalues and Eigenvectors

To find the eigenvalues and associated eigenvectors of the $n \times n$ matrix $\mathbf{A}$:

1. First solve the characteristic equation

$$|\mathbf{A} - \lambda \mathbf{I}| = 0.$$

2. Then, for *each* eigenvalue λ thereby found, solve the linear system

$$(\mathbf{A} - \lambda \mathbf{I})\mathbf{v} = \mathbf{0}$$

to find the eigenvectors associated with λ.   ▲

Solving the characteristic equation is almost always easier said than done. In the examples that follow and in the problems, we have chosen matrices for which the characteristic polynomial $|\mathbf{A} - \lambda \mathbf{I}|$ readily factors to reveal the eigenvalues.

Example 2   Find the eigenvalues and associated eigenvectors of the matrix

$$\mathbf{A} = \begin{bmatrix} 5 & 7 \\ -2 & -4 \end{bmatrix}.$$

Solution   Here

$$\mathbf{A} - \lambda \mathbf{I} = \begin{bmatrix} 5 - \lambda & 7 \\ -2 & -4 - \lambda \end{bmatrix}, \tag{6}$$

so the characteristic equation of $\mathbf{A}$ is

$$\begin{aligned} 0 &= |\mathbf{A} - \lambda \mathbf{I}| \\ &= \begin{vmatrix} 5 - \lambda & 7 \\ -2 & -4 - \lambda \end{vmatrix} \\ &= (5 - \lambda)(-4 - \lambda) - (-2)(7) \\ &= (\lambda - 5)(\lambda + 4) + 14 = \lambda^2 - \lambda - 6; \end{aligned}$$

that is, $(\lambda + 2)(\lambda - 3) = 0$. Thus, the matrix $\mathbf{A}$ has the two eigenvalues -2 and 3. To distinguish them, we write $\lambda_1 = -2$ and $\lambda_2 = 3$. To find the associated eigenvectors, we must *separately* substitute each eigenvalue in (6) and then solve the resulting system $(\mathbf{A} - \lambda \mathbf{I})\mathbf{v} = \mathbf{0}$.

CASE 1: $\lambda_1 = -2$.   With $\mathbf{v} = \begin{bmatrix} x & y \end{bmatrix}^T$, the system $(\mathbf{A} - \lambda \mathbf{I})\mathbf{v} = \mathbf{0}$ is

$$\begin{bmatrix} 7 & 7 \\ -2 & -2 \end{bmatrix} \begin{bmatrix} x \\ y \end{bmatrix} = \begin{bmatrix} 0 \\ 0 \end{bmatrix}.$$

Each of the two scalar equations here is a multiple of the equation $x + y = 0$, and any nontrivial solution $\mathbf{v} = \begin{bmatrix} x & y \end{bmatrix}^T$ of this equation is a nonzero multiple of $\begin{bmatrix} 1 & -1 \end{bmatrix}^T$. Hence, to within a constant multiple, the only eigenvector associated with $\lambda_1 = -2$ is $\mathbf{v}_1 = \begin{bmatrix} 1 & -1 \end{bmatrix}^T$.

CASE 2: $\lambda_2 = 3$. With $\mathbf{v} = \begin{bmatrix} x & y \end{bmatrix}^T$, the system $(\mathbf{A} - \lambda\mathbf{I})\mathbf{v} = \mathbf{0}$ is

$$\begin{bmatrix} 2 & 7 \\ -2 & -7 \end{bmatrix}\begin{bmatrix} x \\ y \end{bmatrix} = \begin{bmatrix} 0 \\ 0 \end{bmatrix}.$$

Again, we have only a single equation, $2x + 7y = 0$, and any nontrivial solution of this equation will suffice. The choice $y = -2$ yields $x = 7$, so (to within a constant multiple) the only eigenvector associated with $\lambda_2 = 3$ is $\mathbf{v}_2 = \begin{bmatrix} 7 & -2 \end{bmatrix}^T$.

Finally, note that it is not enough to say simply that the given matrix $\mathbf{A}$ has eigenvalues -2 and 3 and has eigenvectors $\begin{bmatrix} 1 & -1 \end{bmatrix}^T$ and $\begin{bmatrix} 7 & -2 \end{bmatrix}^T$. To give complete information, we must say which eigenvector is associated with each eigenvalue. ∎

If the elements of the matrix $\mathbf{A}$ are all real, then so are the coefficients of its characteristic equation $|\mathbf{A} - \lambda\mathbf{I}| = 0$. In this event, it follows that the complex eigenvalues (if any) of $\mathbf{A}$ occur only in conjugate pairs. The next example illustrates the possibility of imaginary or complex eigenvalues and eigenvectors.

Example 3 The characteristic equation of the matrix

$$\mathbf{A} = \begin{bmatrix} 0 & 8 \\ -2 & 0 \end{bmatrix}$$

is

$$|\mathbf{A} - \lambda\mathbf{I}| = \begin{bmatrix} -\lambda & 8 \\ -2 & -\lambda \end{bmatrix} = \lambda^2 + 16 = 0.$$

Hence the matrix $\mathbf{A}$ has the complex conjugate eigenvalues $\lambda = \pm 4i$.

CASE 1: $\lambda_1 = -4i$. With $\mathbf{v} = \begin{bmatrix} x & y \end{bmatrix}^T$, the system $(\mathbf{A} - \lambda\mathbf{I})\mathbf{v} = \mathbf{0}$ is

$$\begin{bmatrix} 4i & 8 \\ -2 & 4i \end{bmatrix}\begin{bmatrix} x \\ y \end{bmatrix} = \begin{bmatrix} 0 \\ 0 \end{bmatrix}.$$

The first equation, here $4ix + 8y = 0$, is $2i$ times the second one and, obviously, is satisfied by $x = 2i$, $y = 1$. Thus $\mathbf{v}_1 = \begin{bmatrix} 2i & 1 \end{bmatrix}^T$ is a complex eigenvector associated with the complex eigenvalue $\lambda_1 = -4i$.

CASE 2: $\lambda_2 = +4i$. In this case, you may verify similarly that the conjugate $\mathbf{v}_2 = \begin{bmatrix} -2i & 1 \end{bmatrix}^T$ of $\mathbf{v}_1$ is an eigenvector associated with the conjugate λ_2 of the eigenvalue λ_1. Thus the complex conjugate eigenvalues $\mp 4i$ of the matrix $\mathbf{A}$ correspond to the complex conjugate eigenvectors $\begin{bmatrix} \pm 2i & 1 \end{bmatrix}^T$ (taking either both upper signs or both lower signs). ∎

Example 4 The 2×2 identity matrix $\mathbf{I}$ has characteristic equation

$$\begin{vmatrix} 1 - \lambda & 0 \\ 0 & 1 - \lambda \end{vmatrix} = (1 - \lambda)^2 = 0,$$

so $\mathbf{I}$ has the single eigenvalue $\lambda = 1$. The equation $(\mathbf{I} - 1\lambda)\mathbf{v} = \mathbf{0}$ is

$$\begin{bmatrix} 0 & 0 \\ 0 & 0 \end{bmatrix}\begin{bmatrix} x \\ y \end{bmatrix} = \begin{bmatrix} 0 \\ 0 \end{bmatrix},$$

so *every* nonzero vector $\mathbf{v} = \begin{bmatrix} x & y \end{bmatrix}^T$ is an eigenvector of $\mathbf{I}$. In particular, the single eigenvalue $\lambda = 1$ corresponds to the *two* linearly independent eigenvectors $\mathbf{v}_1 = \begin{bmatrix} 1 & 0 \end{bmatrix}^T$ and $\mathbf{v}_2 = \begin{bmatrix} 0 & 1 \end{bmatrix}^T$. ∎

Example 5   The characteristic equation of the matrix

$$\mathbf{A} = \begin{bmatrix} 2 & 3 \\ 0 & 2 \end{bmatrix}$$

is $(2 - \lambda)^2 = 0$, so $\mathbf{A}$ has the single eigenvalue $\lambda = 2$. The equation $(\mathbf{A} - 2\mathbf{I})\mathbf{v} = \mathbf{0}$ is

$$\begin{bmatrix} 0 & 3 \\ 0 & 0 \end{bmatrix} \begin{bmatrix} x \\ y \end{bmatrix} = \begin{bmatrix} 0 \\ 0 \end{bmatrix}.$$

Thus x is arbitrary, but $y = 0$, so the eigenvalue $\lambda = 2$ corresponds (to within a constant multiple) to the single eigenvector $\mathbf{v} = \begin{bmatrix} 1 & 0 \end{bmatrix}^T$. ∎

Examples 2–5 illustrate the four possibilities for a 2×2 matrix $\mathbf{A}$. It can have either

- two distinct real eigenvalues, each corresponding to a single eigenvector;
- a single real eigenvalue corresponding to a single eigenvector;
- a single real eigenvalue corresponding to two linearly independent eigenvectors; or
- two complex conjugate eigenvalues corresponding to complex conjugate eigenvectors.

The characteristic equation of a 3×3 matrix is, by Eq. (5), of the form

$$-\lambda^3 + c_2\lambda^2 + c_1\lambda + c_0 = 0. \tag{7}$$

Now the value of the continuous function $-\lambda^3 + \cdots + c_0$ on the left-hand side here approaches $+\infty$ as $\lambda \to -\infty$ and $-\infty$ as $\lambda \to +\infty$. Hence every such cubic equation has at least one real solution, so every 3×3 matrix has (in contrast with 2×2 matrices) at least one real eigenvalue. A 3×3 matrix may have one, two, or three distinct eigenvalues, and a single eigenvalue of a 3×3 matrix may correspond to one, two, or three linearly independent eigenvectors. The remaining two examples of this section illustrate some of the possibilities. The next example shows also that, whereas the zero vector $\mathbf{0}$ cannot be an eigenvector of a matrix, there is nothing to prevent $\lambda = 0$ from being an eigenvalue.

Example 6   Find the eigenvalues and associated eigenvectors of the matrix

$$\mathbf{A} = \begin{bmatrix} 3 & 0 & 0 \\ -4 & 6 & 2 \\ 16 & -15 & -5 \end{bmatrix}.$$

Solution   The matrix $\mathbf{A} - \lambda\mathbf{I}$ is

$$\mathbf{A} - \lambda\mathbf{I} = \begin{bmatrix} 3 - \lambda & 0 & 0 \\ -4 & 6 - \lambda & 2 \\ 16 & -15 & -5 - \lambda \end{bmatrix}. \tag{8}$$

Upon expansion of the determinant along its first row, we find that

$$|\mathbf{A} - \lambda\mathbf{I}| = (3 - \lambda)[(6 - \lambda)(-5 - \lambda) + 30]$$
$$= (3 - \lambda)(\lambda^2 - \lambda) = \lambda(\lambda - 1)(3 - \lambda).$$

Hence the characteristic equation $|\mathbf{A} - \lambda\mathbf{I}| = 0$ yields the three eigenvalues $\lambda_1 = 0$, $\lambda_2 = 1$, and $\lambda_3 = 3$. To find the associated eigenvectors, we must solve the system $(\mathbf{A} - \lambda\mathbf{I})\mathbf{v} = \mathbf{0}$ separately for each of these three eigenvalues.

CASE 1: $\lambda_1 = 0$. We write $\mathbf{v} = \begin{bmatrix} x & y & z \end{bmatrix}^T$ and substitute $\lambda = 0$ in the coefficient matrix in (8) to obtain the system

$$\begin{bmatrix} 3 & 0 & 0 \\ -4 & 6 & 2 \\ 16 & -15 & -5 \end{bmatrix} \begin{bmatrix} x \\ y \\ z \end{bmatrix} = \begin{bmatrix} 0 \\ 0 \\ 0 \end{bmatrix}.$$

From the first of the three equations here, $3x = 0$, we see that $x = 0$. Then each of the remaining two equations is a multiple of the equation $3y + z = 0$. The choice $y = 1$ yields $z = -3$. Thus the eigenvector $\mathbf{v}_1 = \begin{bmatrix} 0 & 1 & -3 \end{bmatrix}^T$ is associated with $\lambda_1 = 0$.

CASE 2: $\lambda_2 = 1$. Substitution of $\lambda = 1$ in the coefficient matrix in (8) yields the system

$$\begin{bmatrix} 2 & 0 & 0 \\ -4 & 5 & 2 \\ 16 & -15 & -6 \end{bmatrix} \begin{bmatrix} x \\ y \\ z \end{bmatrix} = \begin{bmatrix} 0 \\ 0 \\ 0 \end{bmatrix}$$

for $\mathbf{v} = \begin{bmatrix} x & y & z \end{bmatrix}^T$. The first equation $2x = 0$ implies that $x = 0$. Then the third equation is a multiple of the second equation, $5y + 2z = 0$. The choice of $y = 2$ yields $z = -5$, so the eigenvector $\mathbf{v}_2 = \begin{bmatrix} 0 & 2 & -5 \end{bmatrix}^T$ is associated with $\lambda_2 = 1$.

CASE 3: $\lambda_3 = 3$. Substitution of $\lambda = 3$ in the coefficient matrix in (8) yields the system

$$\begin{bmatrix} 0 & 0 & 0 \\ -4 & 3 & 2 \\ 16 & -15 & -8 \end{bmatrix} \begin{bmatrix} x \\ y \\ z \end{bmatrix} = \begin{bmatrix} 0 \\ 0 \\ 0 \end{bmatrix}.$$

In this case, the first equation yields no information, but the result of adding 4 times the second equation to the third equation is $-3y = 0$, so $y = 0$. Consequently, the second and third equations are both multiples of the equation $2x - z = 0$. The choice $x = 1$ yields $z = 2$, so the eigenvector $\mathbf{v}_3 = \begin{bmatrix} 1 & 0 & 2 \end{bmatrix}^T$ is associated with $\lambda_3 = 3$.

In summary, we have found the eigenvectors $\mathbf{v}_1 = \begin{bmatrix} 0 & 1 & -3 \end{bmatrix}^T$, $\mathbf{v}_2 = \begin{bmatrix} 0 & 2 & -5 \end{bmatrix}^T$, and $\mathbf{v}_3 = \begin{bmatrix} 1 & 0 & 2 \end{bmatrix}^T$ associated with the distinct eigenvalues $\lambda_1 = 0$, $\lambda_2 = 1$, and $\lambda_3 = 3$, respectively.   ∎

Remark: Substitution of $\lambda = 0$ in the characteristic equation $|\mathbf{A} - \lambda\mathbf{I}| = 0$ yields $|\mathbf{A}| = 0$. Therefore, $\lambda = 0$ is an eigenvalue of the matrix $\mathbf{A}$ if and only if $\mathbf{A}$ is singular: $|\mathbf{A}| = 0$.

Eigenspaces

Let λ be a fixed eigenvalue of the matrix $\mathbf{A}$. Then the set of all eigenvectors associated with $\mathbf{A}$ is the set of all nonzero solution vectors of the system

$$(\mathbf{A} - \lambda\mathbf{I})\mathbf{v} = \mathbf{0}. \tag{9}$$

The solution space of this system is called the **eigenspace** of $\mathbf{A}$ associated with the eigenvalue λ; it consists of all eigenvectors associated with λ *together with the zero vector*. In Example 6 we found (to within a constant multiple) only a single eigenvector associated with each eigenvalue λ; in this case, the eigenspace of λ is 1-dimensional. In the case of an eigenspace of higher dimension, we generally want to find a basis for the solution space of Eq. (9).

Example 7 Find bases for the eigenspaces of the matrix

$$\mathbf{A} = \begin{bmatrix} 4 & -2 & 1 \\ 2 & 0 & 1 \\ 2 & -2 & 3 \end{bmatrix}.$$

Solution Here we have

$$\mathbf{A} - \lambda\mathbf{I} = \begin{bmatrix} 4-\lambda & -2 & 1 \\ 2 & -\lambda & 1 \\ 2 & -2 & 3-\lambda \end{bmatrix}. \tag{10}$$

We expand along the first row to obtain

$$\begin{aligned} |\mathbf{A} - \lambda\mathbf{I}| &= (4-\lambda)(\lambda^2 - 3\lambda + 2) - (-2)(4 - 2\lambda) + (1)(-4 + 2\lambda) \\ &= -\lambda^3 + 7\lambda^2 - 16\lambda + 12. \end{aligned}$$

Thus, to find the eigenvalues we need to solve the cubic equation

$$\lambda^3 - 7\lambda^2 + 16\lambda - 12 = 0. \tag{11}$$

We look (hopefully) for integer solutions. The factor theorem of algebra implies that if the polynomial equation

$$\lambda^n + c_{n-1}\lambda^{n-1} + \cdots + c_1\lambda + c_0 = 0$$

with integer coefficients and leading coefficient 1 has an integer solution, then that integer is a divisor of the constant c_0. In the case of the cubic equation in (11), the possibilities for such a solution are ± 1, ± 2, ± 3, ± 4, ± 6, and ± 12. We substitute these numbers successively in (11) and thereby find that $+1$ and -1 are not solutions but that $\lambda = +2$ is a solution. Hence $\lambda - 2$ is a factor of the cubic polynomial in (11). Next, the long division

$$
\begin{array}{r}
\lambda^2 - 5\lambda + 6 \\
\lambda - 2 \;\overline{\smash{\big)}\; \lambda^3 - 7\lambda^2 + 16\lambda - 12} \\
\underline{\lambda^3 - 2\lambda^2} \\
-5\lambda^2 + 16\lambda - 12 \\
\underline{-5\lambda^2 + 10\lambda} \\
6\lambda - 12 \\
\underline{6\lambda - 12} \\
0
\end{array}
$$

shows that

$$\lambda^3 - 7\lambda^2 + 16\lambda - 12 = (\lambda - 2)(\lambda^2 - 5\lambda + 6)$$
$$= (\lambda - 2)(\lambda - 2)(\lambda - 3)$$
$$= (\lambda - 2)^2(\lambda - 3).$$

Thus we see finally that the given matrix **A** has the repeated eigenvalue $\lambda = 2$ and the eigenvalue $\lambda = 3$.

CASE 1: $\lambda = 2$.   The system $(\mathbf{A} - \lambda\mathbf{I})\mathbf{v} = \mathbf{0}$ is

$$\begin{bmatrix} 2 & -2 & 1 \\ 2 & -2 & 1 \\ 2 & -2 & 1 \end{bmatrix} \begin{bmatrix} x \\ y \\ z \end{bmatrix} = \begin{bmatrix} 0 \\ 0 \\ 0 \end{bmatrix},$$

which reduces to the single equation $2x - 2y + z = 0$. This equation obviously has a 2-dimensional solution space. With $y = 1$ and $z = 0$, we get $x = 1$ and, hence, obtain the basis eigenvector $\mathbf{v}_1 = \begin{bmatrix} 1 & 1 & 0 \end{bmatrix}^T$. With $y = 0$ and $z = 2$, we get $x = -1$ and, hence, the basis eigenvector $\mathbf{v}_2 = \begin{bmatrix} -1 & 0 & 2 \end{bmatrix}^T$. The 2-dimensional eigenspace of **A** associated with the repeated eigenvalue $\lambda = 2$ has basis $\{\mathbf{v}_1, \mathbf{v}_2\}$.

CASE 2: $\lambda = 3$.   The system $(\mathbf{A} - \lambda\mathbf{I})\mathbf{v} = \mathbf{0}$ is

$$\begin{bmatrix} 1 & -2 & 1 \\ 2 & -3 & 1 \\ 2 & -2 & 0 \end{bmatrix} \begin{bmatrix} x \\ y \\ z \end{bmatrix} = \begin{bmatrix} 0 \\ 0 \\ 0 \end{bmatrix}.$$

The last equation here implies that $x = y$, and then each of the first two equations yields $x = y = z$. It follows that the eigenspace of **A** associated with $\lambda = 3$ is 1-dimensional and has $\mathbf{v}_3 = \begin{bmatrix} 1 & 1 & 1 \end{bmatrix}^T$ as a basis eigenvector.   ■

Remark: The typical higher-degree polynomial is not so easy to factor as the one in Example 7. Hence a numerical technique such as Newton's method is often needed to solve the characteristic equation. Moreover, for an $n \times n$ matrix with n greater than about 4, the amount of labor required to find the characteristic equation by expanding the determinant $|\mathbf{A} - \lambda\mathbf{I}|$ is generally prohibitive; because of the presence of the variable λ, row and column elimination methods do not work as they do with numerical determinants. Consequently, specialized techniques, beyond the scope of the present discussion, are often required to find the eigenvalues and eigenvectors of the large matrices that occur in many applications. Problems 40 and 41 at the end of this section outline a numerical technique that sometimes is useful with matrices of moderate size.

6.1 Problems

In Problems 1–26, find the (real) eigenvalues and associated eigenvectors of the given matrix **A**. Find a basis for each eigenspace of dimension 2 or larger.

1. $\begin{bmatrix} 4 & -2 \\ 1 & 1 \end{bmatrix}$

2. $\begin{bmatrix} 5 & -6 \\ 3 & -4 \end{bmatrix}$

3. $\begin{bmatrix} 8 & -6 \\ 3 & -1 \end{bmatrix}$

4. $\begin{bmatrix} 4 & -3 \\ 2 & -1 \end{bmatrix}$

5. $\begin{bmatrix} 10 & -9 \\ 6 & -5 \end{bmatrix}$

6. $\begin{bmatrix} 6 & -4 \\ 3 & -1 \end{bmatrix}$

7. $\begin{bmatrix} 10 & -8 \\ 6 & -4 \end{bmatrix}$

8. $\begin{bmatrix} 7 & -6 \\ 12 & -10 \end{bmatrix}$

9. $\begin{bmatrix} 8 & -10 \\ 2 & -1 \end{bmatrix}$

10. $\begin{bmatrix} 9 & -10 \\ 2 & 0 \end{bmatrix}$

11. $\begin{bmatrix} 19 & -10 \\ 21 & -10 \end{bmatrix}$

12. $\begin{bmatrix} 13 & -15 \\ 6 & -6 \end{bmatrix}$

13. $\begin{bmatrix} 2 & 0 & 0 \\ 2 & -2 & -1 \\ -2 & 6 & 3 \end{bmatrix}$

14. $\begin{bmatrix} 5 & 0 & 0 \\ 4 & -4 & -2 \\ -2 & 12 & 6 \end{bmatrix}$

15. $\begin{bmatrix} 2 & -2 & 0 \\ 2 & -2 & -1 \\ -2 & 2 & 3 \end{bmatrix}$

16. $\begin{bmatrix} 1 & 0 & -1 \\ -2 & 3 & -1 \\ -6 & 6 & 0 \end{bmatrix}$

17. $\begin{bmatrix} 3 & 5 & -2 \\ 0 & 2 & 0 \\ 0 & 2 & 1 \end{bmatrix}$

18. $\begin{bmatrix} 1 & 0 & 0 \\ -6 & 8 & 2 \\ 12 & -15 & -3 \end{bmatrix}$

19. $\begin{bmatrix} 3 & 6 & -2 \\ 0 & 1 & 0 \\ 0 & 0 & 1 \end{bmatrix}$

20. $\begin{bmatrix} 1 & 0 & 0 \\ -4 & 7 & 2 \\ 10 & -15 & -4 \end{bmatrix}$

21. $\begin{bmatrix} 4 & -3 & 1 \\ 2 & -1 & 1 \\ 0 & 0 & 2 \end{bmatrix}$

22. $\begin{bmatrix} 5 & -6 & 3 \\ 6 & -7 & 3 \\ 6 & -6 & 2 \end{bmatrix}$

23. $\begin{bmatrix} 1 & 2 & 2 & 2 \\ 0 & 2 & 2 & 2 \\ 0 & 0 & 3 & 2 \\ 0 & 0 & 0 & 4 \end{bmatrix}$

24. $\begin{bmatrix} 1 & 0 & 4 & 0 \\ 0 & 1 & 4 & 0 \\ 0 & 0 & 3 & 0 \\ 0 & 0 & 0 & 3 \end{bmatrix}$

25. $\begin{bmatrix} 1 & 0 & 1 & 0 \\ 0 & 1 & 1 & 0 \\ 0 & 0 & 2 & 0 \\ 0 & 0 & 0 & 2 \end{bmatrix}$

26. $\begin{bmatrix} 4 & 0 & 0 & -3 \\ 0 & 2 & 0 & 0 \\ 0 & 0 & -1 & 0 \\ 6 & 0 & 0 & -5 \end{bmatrix}$

Find the complex conjugate eigenvalues and corresponding eigenvectors of the matrices given in Problems 27–32.

27. $A = \begin{bmatrix} 0 & 1 \\ -1 & 0 \end{bmatrix}$

28. $A = \begin{bmatrix} 0 & -6 \\ 6 & 0 \end{bmatrix}$

29. $A = \begin{bmatrix} 0 & -3 \\ 12 & 0 \end{bmatrix}$

30. $A = \begin{bmatrix} 0 & -12 \\ 12 & 0 \end{bmatrix}$

31. $A = \begin{bmatrix} 0 & 24 \\ -6 & 0 \end{bmatrix}$

32. $A = \begin{bmatrix} 0 & -4 \\ 36 & 0 \end{bmatrix}$

33. Suppose that λ is an eigenvalue of the matrix A with associated eigenvector v and that n is a positive integer. Show that λ^n is an eigenvalue of A^n with associated eigenvector v.

34. Show that λ is an eigenvalue of the invertible matrix A if and only if λ^{-1} is an eigenvalue of A^{-1}. Are the associated eigenvectors the same?

35. (a) Suppose that A is a square matrix. Use the characteristic equation to show that A and A^T have the same eigenvalues.

    (b) Give an example of a 2×2 matrix A such that A and A^T do not have the same eigenvectors.

36. Show that the eigenvalues of a triangular $n \times n$ matrix are its diagonal elements.

37. Suppose that the characteristic equation $|A - \lambda I| = 0$ is written as a polynomial equation [Eq. (5)]. Show that the constant term is $c_0 = \det A$. *Suggestion*: Substitute an appropriate value for λ.

38. If $A = \begin{bmatrix} a_{ij} \end{bmatrix}$ is an $n \times n$ matrix, then the **trace** $\operatorname{Tr} A$ of A is defined to be

$$\operatorname{Tr} A = a_{11} + a_{22} + \cdots + a_{nn},$$

the sum of the diagonal elements of A. It can be proved that the coefficient of λ^{n-1} in Eq. (5) is $c_{n-1} = (-1)^{n-1}(\operatorname{Tr} A)$. Show explicitly that this is true in the case of a 2×2 matrix.

39. Suppose that the $n \times n$ matrix A has n (real) eigenvalues $\lambda_1, \lambda_2, \ldots, \lambda_n$. Assuming the general result stated in Problem 38, prove that

$$\lambda_1 + \lambda_2 + \cdots + \lambda_n = \operatorname{Tr} A$$
$$= a_{11} + a_{22} + \cdots + a_{nn}.$$

40. According to the results stated in Problems 37 and 38, the characteristic polynomial

$$p(\lambda) = |A - \lambda I|$$

of a 3×3 matrix A is given by

$$p(\lambda) = -\lambda^3 + (\operatorname{Tr} A)\lambda^2 + c_1 \lambda + (\det A).$$

The remaining coefficient c_1 can be found by substituting $\lambda = 1$ and then calculating the two determinants $|A|$ and $p(1) = |A - I|$. Use this method to find the characteristic equation, eigenvalues, and associated eigenvectors of the matrix

$$A = \begin{bmatrix} 32 & -67 & 47 \\ 7 & -14 & 13 \\ -7 & 15 & -6 \end{bmatrix}.$$

41. According to the results stated in Problems 37 and 38, the characteristic polynomial

$$p(\lambda) = |A - \lambda I|$$

of a 4×4 matrix A is given by

$$p(\lambda) = \lambda^4 - (\operatorname{Tr} A)\lambda^3 + c_2 \lambda^2 + c_1 \lambda + (\det A).$$

The remaining coefficients c_1 and c_2 can be found by substituting $\lambda = \pm 1$ and calculating the three determinants $|A|$, $p(1) = |A - I|$, and $p(-1) = |A + I|$. Use this method to find the characteristic equation, eigenvalues, and associated eigenvectors of the matrix

$$A = \begin{bmatrix} 22 & -9 & -8 & -8 \\ 10 & -7 & -14 & 2 \\ 10 & 0 & 8 & -10 \\ 29 & -9 & -3 & -15 \end{bmatrix}.$$

6.2 Diagonalization of Matrices

Given an $n \times n$ matrix $\mathbf{A}$, we may ask *how many* linearly independent eigenvectors the matrix $\mathbf{A}$ has. In Section 6.1, we saw several examples (with $n = 2$ and $n = 3$) in which the $n \times n$ matrix $\mathbf{A}$ has n linearly independent eigenvectors—the largest possible number. By contrast, in Example 5 of Section 6.1, we saw that the 2×2 matrix

$$\mathbf{A} = \begin{bmatrix} 2 & 3 \\ 0 & 2 \end{bmatrix}$$

has the single eigenvalue $\lambda = 2$ corresponding to the single eigenvector $\mathbf{v} = \begin{bmatrix} 1 & 0 \end{bmatrix}^T$.

Something very nice happens when the $n \times n$ matrix $\mathbf{A}$ does have n linearly independent eigenvectors. Suppose that the eigenvalues $\lambda_1, \lambda_2, \ldots, \lambda_n$ (not necessarily distinct) of $\mathbf{A}$ correspond to the n linearly independent eigenvectors $\mathbf{v}_1, \mathbf{v}_2, \ldots, \mathbf{v}_n$, respectively. Let

$$\mathbf{P} = \begin{bmatrix} | & | & & | \\ \mathbf{v}_1 & \mathbf{v}_2 & \cdots & \mathbf{v}_n \\ | & | & & | \end{bmatrix} \tag{1}$$

be the $n \times n$ matrix having these eigenvectors as its *column* vector. Then

$$\mathbf{AP} = \mathbf{A} \begin{bmatrix} | & | & & | \\ \mathbf{v}_1 & \mathbf{v}_2 & \cdots & \mathbf{v}_n \\ | & | & & | \end{bmatrix}$$

$$= \begin{bmatrix} | & | & & | \\ \mathbf{Av}_1 & \mathbf{Av}_2 & \cdots & \mathbf{Av}_n \\ | & | & & | \end{bmatrix}$$

and hence

$$\mathbf{AP} = \begin{bmatrix} | & | & & | \\ \lambda_1 \mathbf{v}_1 & \lambda_2 \mathbf{v}_2 & \cdots & \lambda_n \mathbf{v}_n \\ | & | & & | \end{bmatrix}, \tag{2}$$

because $\mathbf{Av}_j = \lambda_j \mathbf{v}_j$ for each $j = 1, 2, \ldots, n$. Thus the product matrix $\mathbf{AP}$ has column vectors $\lambda_1 \mathbf{v}_1, \lambda_2 \mathbf{v}_2, \ldots, \lambda_n \mathbf{v}_n$.

Now consider the diagonal matrix

$$\mathbf{D} = \begin{bmatrix} \lambda_1 & 0 & \cdots & 0 \\ 0 & \lambda_2 & \cdots & 0 \\ \vdots & \vdots & \ddots & \vdots \\ 0 & 0 & \cdots & \lambda_n \end{bmatrix}, \tag{3}$$

whose diagonal elements are the eigenvalues corresponding (in the same order) to the eigenvectors forming the columns of $\mathbf{P}$. Then

$$\mathbf{PD} = \begin{bmatrix} | & | & & | \\ \mathbf{v}_1 & \mathbf{v}_2 & \cdots & \mathbf{v}_n \\ | & | & & | \end{bmatrix} \begin{bmatrix} \lambda_1 & 0 & \cdots & 0 \\ 0 & \lambda_2 & \cdots & 0 \\ \vdots & \vdots & \ddots & \vdots \\ 0 & 0 & \cdots & \lambda_n \end{bmatrix}$$

$$= \begin{bmatrix} | & | & & | \\ \lambda_1 \mathbf{v}_1 & \lambda_2 \mathbf{v}_2 & \cdots & \lambda_n \mathbf{v}_n \\ | & | & & | \end{bmatrix}, \tag{4}$$

because the product of the ith row of $\mathbf{P}$ and the jth column of $\mathbf{D}$ is simply the product of λ_j and the ith component of $\mathbf{v}_j$.

Finally, upon comparing the results in (2) and (4), we see that

$$\mathbf{AP} = \mathbf{PD}. \tag{5}$$

But the matrix $\mathbf{P}$ is invertible, because its n column vectors are linearly independent. So we may multiply on the right by $\mathbf{P}^{-1}$ to obtain

$$\mathbf{A} = \mathbf{PDP}^{-1}. \tag{6}$$

Equation (6) expresses the $n \times n$ matrix $\mathbf{A}$ having n linearly independent eigenvectors in terms of the *eigenvector matrix* $\mathbf{P}$ and the diagonal *eigenvalue matrix* $\mathbf{D}$. It can be rewritten as $\mathbf{D} = \mathbf{P}^{-1}\mathbf{AP}$, but the form in (6) is the one that should be memorized.

Example 1

In Example 1 of Section 6.1 we saw that the matrix

$$\mathbf{A} = \begin{bmatrix} 5 & -6 \\ 2 & -2 \end{bmatrix}$$

has eigenvalues $\lambda_1 = 2$ and $\lambda_2 = 1$ corresponding to the linearly independent eigenvectors $\mathbf{v}_1 = \begin{bmatrix} 2 & 1 \end{bmatrix}^T$ and $\mathbf{v}_2 = \begin{bmatrix} 3 & 2 \end{bmatrix}^T$, respectively. Then

$$\mathbf{P} = \begin{bmatrix} 2 & 3 \\ 1 & 2 \end{bmatrix}, \quad \mathbf{D} = \begin{bmatrix} 2 & 0 \\ 0 & 1 \end{bmatrix}, \quad \text{and} \quad \mathbf{P}^{-1} = \begin{bmatrix} 2 & -3 \\ -1 & 2 \end{bmatrix}.$$

So

$$\mathbf{PDP^{-1}} = \begin{bmatrix} 2 & 3 \\ 1 & 2 \end{bmatrix} \begin{bmatrix} 2 & 0 \\ 0 & 1 \end{bmatrix} \begin{bmatrix} 2 & -3 \\ -1 & 2 \end{bmatrix}$$

$$= \begin{bmatrix} 4 & 3 \\ 2 & 2 \end{bmatrix} \begin{bmatrix} 2 & -3 \\ -1 & 2 \end{bmatrix} = \begin{bmatrix} 5 & -6 \\ 2 & -2 \end{bmatrix} = \mathbf{A},$$

in accord with Eq. (6). ∎

Similarity and Diagonalization

The following definition embodies the precise relationship in (6) between the original matrix **A** and the diagonal matrix **D**.

> ### Definition: Similar Matrices
> The $n \times n$ matrices **A** and **B** are called **similar** provided that there exists an invertible matrix **P** such that
> $$\mathbf{B} = \mathbf{P^{-1}AP}. \qquad (7)$$

Note that this relationship between **A** and **B** is symmetric, for if $\mathbf{B} = \mathbf{P^{-1}AP}$, then $\mathbf{A} = \mathbf{Q^{-1}BQ}$ for some invertible matrix **Q**—just take $\mathbf{Q} = \mathbf{P^{-1}}$.

An $n \times n$ matrix **A** is called **diagonalizable** if it is similar to a diagonal matrix **D**; that is, there exist a diagonal matrix **D** and an invertible matrix **P** such that $\mathbf{A} = \mathbf{PDP^{-1}}$, and so

$$\mathbf{P^{-1}AP} = \mathbf{D}. \qquad (8)$$

The process of finding the diagonalizing matrix **P** and the diagonal matrix **D** in (8) is called **diagonalization** of the matrix **A**. In Example 1 we showed that the matrices

$$\mathbf{A} = \begin{bmatrix} 5 & -6 \\ 2 & -2 \end{bmatrix} \quad \text{and} \quad \mathbf{D} = \begin{bmatrix} 2 & 0 \\ 0 & 1 \end{bmatrix}$$

are similar, and hence that the 2×2 matrix **A** is diagonalizable.

Now we ask under what conditions a given square matrix is diagonalizable. In deriving Eq. (6), we showed that *if* the $n \times n$ matrix **A** has n linearly independent eigenvectors, *then* **A** is diagonalizable. The converse of this statement is also true.

THEOREM 1: Criterion for Diagonalizability

The $n \times n$ matrix **A** is diagonalizable if and only if it has n linearly independent eigenvectors.

Proof: It remains only to show that, if the $n \times n$ matrix **A** is diagonalizable, then it has n linearly independent eigenvectors. Suppose that **A** is similar to the diagonal matrix **D** with diagonal elements $d_1, d_2, \ldots, d_n$, and let

$$\mathbf{P} = \begin{bmatrix} \mathbf{v}_1 & \mathbf{v}_2 & \cdots & \mathbf{v}_n \end{bmatrix}$$

be an invertible matrix such that $\mathbf{D} = \mathbf{P^{-1}AP}$. Then

$$\mathbf{AP} = \mathbf{A} \begin{bmatrix} \mathbf{v}_1 & \mathbf{v}_2 & \cdots & \mathbf{v}_n \end{bmatrix}$$

$$= \begin{bmatrix} \mathbf{Av}_1 & \mathbf{Av}_2 & \cdots & \mathbf{Av}_n \end{bmatrix}$$

and

$$\mathbf{PD} = \begin{bmatrix} d_1\mathbf{v}_1 & d_2\mathbf{v}_2 & \cdots & d_n\mathbf{v}_n \end{bmatrix},$$

by essentially the same computation as in Eq. (4). But $\mathbf{AP} = \mathbf{PD}$ because $\mathbf{D} = \mathbf{P}^{-1}\mathbf{AP}$, so it follows that

$$\mathbf{Av}_j = d_j\mathbf{v}_j$$

for each $j = 1, 2, \ldots, n$. Thus the vectors $\mathbf{v}_1, \mathbf{v}_2, \ldots, \mathbf{v}_n$ are eigenvectors of $\mathbf{A}$ associated with the eigenvalues $d_1, d_2, \ldots, d_n$, respectively. And it follows from Theorem 2 in Section 3.6 and Theorem 2 in Section 4.3 that these n eigenvectors of the matrix $\mathbf{A}$ are linearly independent, because they are the column vectors of the invertible matrix $\mathbf{P}$. ▲

Remark: It is important to remember not only the fact that an $n \times n$ matrix $\mathbf{A}$ having n linearly independent eigenvectors is diagonalizable, but also the specific diagonalization $\mathbf{A} = \mathbf{PDP}^{-1}$ in Eq. (6), where the matrix $\mathbf{P}$ has the n eigenvectors as its columns, and the corresponding eigenvalues are the diagonal elements of the diagonal matrix $\mathbf{D}$.

Example 2 In Example 5 of Section 6.1 we saw that the matrix

$$\mathbf{A} = \begin{bmatrix} 2 & 3 \\ 0 & 2 \end{bmatrix}$$

has only one eigenvalue, $\lambda = 2$, and that (to within a constant multiple) only the single eigenvector $\mathbf{v} = \begin{bmatrix} 1 & 0 \end{bmatrix}^T$ is associated with this eigenvalue. Thus the 2×2 matrix $\mathbf{A}$ does *not* have $n = 2$ linearly independent eigenvectors. Hence Theorem 1 implies that $\mathbf{A}$ is not diagonalizable. ■

Example 3 In Example 5 of Section 6.1 we saw that the matrix

$$\mathbf{A} = \begin{bmatrix} 3 & 0 & 0 \\ -4 & 6 & 2 \\ 16 & -15 & -5 \end{bmatrix}$$

has the following eigenvalues and associated eigenvectors:

$$\lambda_1 = 3: \quad \mathbf{v}_1 = \begin{bmatrix} 1 & 0 & 2 \end{bmatrix}^T$$
$$\lambda_2 = 1: \quad \mathbf{v}_2 = \begin{bmatrix} 0 & 2 & -5 \end{bmatrix}^T$$
$$\lambda_3 = 0: \quad \mathbf{v}_3 = \begin{bmatrix} 0 & 1 & -3 \end{bmatrix}^T.$$

It is obvious (why?) that the three eigenvectors $\mathbf{v}_1, \mathbf{v}_2, \mathbf{v}_3$ are linearly independent, so Theorem 1 implies that the 3×3 matrix $\mathbf{A}$ is diagonalizable. In particular, the inverse of the eigenvector matrix

$$\mathbf{P} = \begin{bmatrix} \mathbf{v}_1 & \mathbf{v}_2 & \mathbf{v}_3 \end{bmatrix} = \begin{bmatrix} 1 & 0 & 0 \\ 0 & 2 & 1 \\ 2 & -5 & -3 \end{bmatrix}$$

is

$$\mathbf{P}^{-1} = \begin{bmatrix} 1 & 0 & 0 \\ -2 & 3 & 1 \\ 4 & -5 & -2 \end{bmatrix},$$

and the diagonal eigenvalue matrix is

$$\mathbf{D} = \begin{bmatrix} \lambda_1 & 0 & 0 \\ 0 & \lambda_2 & 0 \\ 0 & 0 & \lambda_3 \end{bmatrix} = \begin{bmatrix} 3 & 0 & 0 \\ 0 & 1 & 0 \\ 0 & 0 & 0 \end{bmatrix}.$$

Therefore Eq. (6) in the form $\mathbf{P}^{-1}\mathbf{AP} = \mathbf{D}$ yields the diagonalization

$$\mathbf{P}^{-1}\mathbf{AP} = \begin{bmatrix} 1 & 0 & 0 \\ -2 & 3 & 1 \\ 4 & -5 & -2 \end{bmatrix} \begin{bmatrix} 3 & 0 & 0 \\ -4 & 6 & 2 \\ 16 & -15 & -5 \end{bmatrix} \begin{bmatrix} 1 & 0 & 0 \\ 0 & 2 & 1 \\ 2 & -5 & -3 \end{bmatrix}$$

$$= \begin{bmatrix} 3 & 0 & 0 \\ 0 & 1 & 0 \\ 0 & 0 & 0 \end{bmatrix}$$

of the matrix $\mathbf{A}$. ∎

The following theorem tells us that any set of eigenvectors associated with *distinct* eigenvalues (as in Example 3) is automatically linearly independent.

THEOREM 2: Eigenvectors Associated with Distinct Eigenvalues

Suppose that the eigenvectors $\mathbf{v}_1, \mathbf{v}_2, \ldots, \mathbf{v}_k$ are associated with the distinct eigenvalues $\lambda_1, \lambda_2, \ldots, \lambda_k$ of the matrix $\mathbf{A}$. Then these k eigenvectors are linearly independent.

Proof: Our proof will be by induction on k. The theorem is certainly true in the case $k = 1$, because any single (nonzero) eigenvector constitutes a linearly independent set. Now assume inductively that any set of $k-1$ eigenvectors associated with distinct eigenvalues is linearly independent. Supposing that

$$c_1\mathbf{v}_1 + c_2\mathbf{v}_2 + \cdots + c_k\mathbf{v}_k = \mathbf{0}, \tag{9}$$

we need to show that $c_1 = c_2 = \cdots = c_k = 0$. To do this, we will multiply in Eq. (9) by the matrix $\mathbf{A} - \lambda_1\mathbf{I}$. First note that

$$(\mathbf{A} - \lambda_1\mathbf{I})\mathbf{v}_j = \mathbf{A}\mathbf{v}_j - \lambda_1\mathbf{v}_j = \begin{cases} \mathbf{0} & \text{if } j = 1, \\ (\lambda_j - \lambda_1)\mathbf{v}_j & \text{if } j > 1, \end{cases}$$

because $\mathbf{A}\mathbf{v}_j = \lambda_j\mathbf{v}_j$ for each j. Therefore the result of multiplying Eq. (9) by $\mathbf{A} - \lambda_1\mathbf{I}$ is

$$c_2(\lambda_2 - \lambda_1)\mathbf{v}_2 + \cdots + c_k(\lambda_k - \lambda_1)\mathbf{v}_k = \mathbf{0}. \tag{10}$$

But the $k - 1$ eigenvectors $\mathbf{v}_2, \mathbf{v}_3, \ldots, \mathbf{v}_k$ are linearly independent by the inductive assumption. Because $\lambda_j - \lambda_1 \neq 0$ for each $j > 1$, it therefore follows from Eq. (10) that $c_2 = c_3 = \cdots = c_k = 0$. But then Eq. (9) reduces to $c_1\mathbf{v}_1 = \mathbf{0}$, so it now follows (because $v_1 \neq 0$) that $c_1 = 0$ as well. Thus we have shown that all the coefficients in Eq. (9) must vanish, and hence that the k eigenvectors $v_1, v_2, \ldots, v_k$ are linearly independent. Theorem 2 now follows by induction.   ▲

If the $n \times n$ matrix A has n distinct eigenvalues, then by Theorem 2 the n associated eigenvectors are linearly independent, so Theorem 1 implies that the matrix A is diagonalizable. Thus we have the sufficient condition for diagonalizability given in Theorem 3.

THEOREM 3: An $n \times n$ Matrix with n Distinct Eigenvalues

If the $n \times n$ matrix A has n distinct eigenvalues, then it is diagonalizable.   ▲

In general, however, an $n \times n$ matrix A can be expected to have fewer than n distinct eigenvalues $\lambda_1, \lambda_2, \ldots, \lambda_k$. If $k < n$, then we may *attempt* to diagonalize A by carrying out the following procedure.

Step 1. Find a basis S_i for the eigenspace associated with each eigenvalue λ_i.

Step 2. Form the union S of the bases $S_1, S_2, \ldots, S_k$. According to Theorem 4 in this section, the set S of eigenvectors of A is linearly independent.

Step 3. If S contains n eigenvectors $v_1, v_2, \ldots, v_n$, then the matrix

$$P = \begin{bmatrix} v_1 & v_2 & \cdots & v_n \end{bmatrix}$$

diagonalizes A: that is, $P^{-1}AP = D$, where the diagonal elements of D are the eigenvalues (repeated as necessary) corresponding to the k eigenvectors $v_1, v_2, \ldots, v_n$.

If the set S—obtained by "merging" the bases for all the eigenspaces of A—contains fewer than n eigenvectors, then it can be proved that the matrix A is not diagonalizable.

Example 4	In Example 7 of Section 6.1, we saw that the matrix

$$A = \begin{bmatrix} 4 & -2 & 1 \\ 2 & 0 & 1 \\ 2 & -2 & 3 \end{bmatrix}$$

has only two distinct eigenvalues, $\lambda_1 = 2$ and $\lambda_2 = 3$. We found that the eigenvalue $\lambda_1 = 2$ corresponds to a 2-dimensional eigenspace with basis vectors $v_1 = \begin{bmatrix} 1 & 1 & 0 \end{bmatrix}^T$ and $v_2 = \begin{bmatrix} -1 & 0 & 2 \end{bmatrix}^T$, and that $\lambda_2 = 3$ corresponds to a 1-dimensional eigenspace with basis vector $v_3 = \begin{bmatrix} 1 & 1 & 1 \end{bmatrix}^T$. By Theorem 4 (or by explicit verification), these three eigenvectors are linearly independent, so Theorem 1 implies that the 3×3 matrix A is diagonalizable. The diagonalizing matrix

$$P = \begin{bmatrix} v_1 & v_2 & v_3 \end{bmatrix} = \begin{bmatrix} 1 & -1 & 1 \\ 1 & 0 & 1 \\ 0 & 2 & 1 \end{bmatrix}$$

has inverse matrix

$$P^{-1} = \begin{bmatrix} -2 & 3 & -1 \\ -1 & 1 & 0 \\ 2 & -2 & 1 \end{bmatrix},$$

so we obtain the diagonalization

$$\mathbf{P^{-1}AP} = \begin{bmatrix} -2 & 3 & -1 \\ -1 & 1 & 0 \\ 2 & -2 & 1 \end{bmatrix} \begin{bmatrix} 4 & -2 & 1 \\ 2 & 0 & 1 \\ 2 & -2 & 3 \end{bmatrix} \begin{bmatrix} 1 & -1 & 1 \\ 1 & 0 & 1 \\ 0 & 2 & 1 \end{bmatrix}$$

$$= \begin{bmatrix} 2 & 0 & 0 \\ 0 & 2 & 0 \\ 0 & 0 & 3 \end{bmatrix} = \mathbf{D}$$

of the matrix **A**. ■

THEOREM 4:   Complete Independence of Eigenvectors

Let $\lambda_1, \lambda_2, \ldots, \lambda_k$ be the distinct eigenvalues of the $n \times n$ matrix **A**. For each $i = 1, 2, \ldots, k$, let S_i be a basis for the eigenspace associated with λ_i. Then the union S of the bases $S_1, S_2, \ldots, S_k$ is a linearly independent set of eigenvectors of **A**.

Proof: To simplify the notation, we will illustrate the proof with the typical case $k = 3$, with **A** having three distinct eigenvalues λ_1, λ_2, and λ_3. Let

$$S_1 = \{\mathbf{u}_1, \mathbf{u}_2, \ldots, \mathbf{u}_p\},$$
$$S_2 = \{\mathbf{v}_1, \mathbf{v}_2, \ldots, \mathbf{v}_q\}, \quad \text{and}$$
$$S_3 = \{\mathbf{w}_1, \mathbf{w}_2, \ldots, \mathbf{w}_r\}$$

be bases for the eigenspaces associated with the eigenvalues λ_1, λ_2, and λ_3. Assuming that a linear combination of the vectors in $S = S_1 \cup S_2 \cup S_3$ vanishes—

$$a_1\mathbf{u}_1 + a_2\mathbf{u}_2 + \cdots + a_p\mathbf{u}_p$$
$$+ b_1\mathbf{v}_1 + b_2\mathbf{v}_2 + \cdots + b_q\mathbf{v}_q$$
$$+ c_1\mathbf{w}_1 + c_2\mathbf{w}_2 + \cdots + c_r\mathbf{w}_r = \mathbf{0} \qquad (11)$$

—we need to show that the coefficients are all zero. If we write

$$\mathbf{u} = a_1\mathbf{u}_1 + a_2\mathbf{u}_2 + \cdots + a_p\mathbf{u}_p,$$
$$\mathbf{v} = b_1\mathbf{v}_1 + b_2\mathbf{v}_2 + \cdots + b_q\mathbf{v}_q, \quad \text{and}$$
$$\mathbf{w} = c_1\mathbf{w}_1 + c_2\mathbf{w}_2 + \cdots + c_r\mathbf{w}_r,$$

then Eq. (11) takes the simple form

$$\mathbf{u} + \mathbf{v} + \mathbf{w} = \mathbf{0}. \qquad (12)$$

But the vectors **u**, **v**, and **w** either are zero vectors or are eigenvectors associated with the distinct eigenvalues λ_1, λ_2, and λ_3. In the latter event, Theorem 2 would imply that **u**, **v**, and **w** are linearly independent. Therefore, Eq. (12) implies that $\mathbf{u} = \mathbf{v} = \mathbf{w} = \mathbf{0}$. Finally, the fact that the $\{\mathbf{u}_i\}$ are linearly independent implies that $a_1 = a_2 = \cdots = a_p = 0$; the fact that the $\{\mathbf{v}_i\}$ are linearly independent implies that $b_1 = b_2 = \cdots = b_q = 0$; similarly, $c_1 = c_2 = \cdots = c_r = 0$. Thus we have shown that the coefficients in (11) all vanish, and hence that the vectors in $S = S_1 \cup S_2 \cup S_3$ are linearly independent. ▲

6.2 Problems

In Problems 1–28, determine whether or not the given matrix **A** *is diagonalizable. If it is, find a diagonalizing matrix* **P** *and a diagonal matrix* **D** *such that* $P^{-1}AP = D$.

1. $\begin{bmatrix} 5 & -4 \\ 2 & -1 \end{bmatrix}$ **2.** $\begin{bmatrix} 6 & -6 \\ 4 & -4 \end{bmatrix}$ **3.** $\begin{bmatrix} 5 & -3 \\ 2 & 0 \end{bmatrix}$

4. $\begin{bmatrix} 5 & -4 \\ 3 & -2 \end{bmatrix}$ **5.** $\begin{bmatrix} 9 & -8 \\ 6 & -5 \end{bmatrix}$ **6.** $\begin{bmatrix} 10 & -6 \\ 12 & -7 \end{bmatrix}$

7. $\begin{bmatrix} 6 & -10 \\ 2 & -3 \end{bmatrix}$ **8.** $\begin{bmatrix} 11 & -15 \\ 6 & -8 \end{bmatrix}$ **9.** $\begin{bmatrix} -1 & 4 \\ -1 & 3 \end{bmatrix}$

10. $\begin{bmatrix} 3 & -1 \\ 1 & 1 \end{bmatrix}$ **11.** $\begin{bmatrix} 5 & 1 \\ -9 & -1 \end{bmatrix}$ **12.** $\begin{bmatrix} 11 & 9 \\ -16 & -13 \end{bmatrix}$

13. $\begin{bmatrix} 1 & 3 & 0 \\ 0 & 2 & 0 \\ 0 & 0 & 2 \end{bmatrix}$ **14.** $\begin{bmatrix} 2 & -2 & 1 \\ 2 & -2 & 1 \\ 2 & -2 & 1 \end{bmatrix}$

15. $\begin{bmatrix} 3 & -3 & 1 \\ 2 & -2 & 1 \\ 0 & 0 & 1 \end{bmatrix}$ **16.** $\begin{bmatrix} 3 & -2 & 0 \\ 0 & 1 & 0 \\ -4 & 4 & 1 \end{bmatrix}$

17. $\begin{bmatrix} 7 & -8 & 3 \\ 6 & -7 & 3 \\ 2 & -2 & 2 \end{bmatrix}$ **18.** $\begin{bmatrix} 6 & -5 & 2 \\ 4 & -3 & 2 \\ 2 & -2 & 3 \end{bmatrix}$

19. $\begin{bmatrix} 1 & 1 & -1 \\ -2 & 4 & -1 \\ -4 & 4 & 1 \end{bmatrix}$ **20.** $\begin{bmatrix} 2 & 0 & 0 \\ -6 & 11 & 2 \\ 6 & -15 & 0 \end{bmatrix}$

21. $\begin{bmatrix} 0 & 1 & 0 \\ -1 & 2 & 0 \\ -1 & 1 & 1 \end{bmatrix}$ **22.** $\begin{bmatrix} 2 & -2 & 1 \\ -1 & 2 & 0 \\ -5 & 7 & -1 \end{bmatrix}$

23. $\begin{bmatrix} -2 & 4 & -1 \\ -3 & 5 & -1 \\ -1 & 1 & 1 \end{bmatrix}$ **24.** $\begin{bmatrix} 3 & -2 & 1 \\ 1 & 0 & 1 \\ -1 & 1 & 2 \end{bmatrix}$

25. $\begin{bmatrix} 1 & 0 & -2 & 0 \\ 0 & 1 & -2 & 0 \\ 0 & 0 & -1 & 0 \\ 0 & 0 & 0 & -1 \end{bmatrix}$ **26.** $\begin{bmatrix} 1 & 0 & 0 & 1 \\ 0 & 1 & 0 & 1 \\ 0 & 0 & 1 & 1 \\ 0 & 0 & 0 & 2 \end{bmatrix}$

27. $\begin{bmatrix} 1 & 1 & 0 & 0 \\ 0 & 1 & 1 & 0 \\ 0 & 0 & 1 & 1 \\ 0 & 0 & 0 & 2 \end{bmatrix}$ **28.** $\begin{bmatrix} 1 & 1 & 0 & 1 \\ 0 & 1 & 1 & 1 \\ 0 & 0 & 2 & 1 \\ 0 & 0 & 0 & 2 \end{bmatrix}$

29. Prove: If the matrices **A** and **B** are similar and the matrices **B** and **C** are similar, then the matrices **A** and **C** are similar.

30. Suppose that the matrices **A** and **B** are similar and that n is a positive integer. Prove that the matrices A^n and B^n are similar.

31. Suppose that the invertible matrices **A** and **B** are similar. Prove that their inverses A^{-1} and B^{-1} are also similar.

32. Show that if the $n \times n$ matrices **A** and **B** are similar, then they have the same characteristic equation and therefore have the same eigenvalues.

33. Suppose that the $n \times n$ matrices **A** and **B** are similar and that each has n real eigenvalues. Show that $\det A = \det B$ and that $\operatorname{Tr} A = \operatorname{Tr} B$. See Problems 38 and 39 in Section 6.1.

34. Consider the 2×2 matrix

$$A = \begin{bmatrix} a & b \\ c & d \end{bmatrix}$$

and let $\Delta = (a - d)^2 + 4bc$. Then show that

(a) **A** is diagonalizable if $\Delta > 0$;

(b) **A** is not diagonalizable if $\Delta < 0$;

(c) If $\Delta = 0$, then **A** may be diagonalizable or it may not be.

35. Let **A** be a 3×3 matrix with three distinct eigenvalues. Tell how to construct six different invertible matrices $P_1, P_2, \ldots, P_6$ and six different diagonal matrices $D_1, D_2, \ldots, D_6$ such that $P_i D_i (P_i)^{-1} = A$ for each $i = 1, 2, \ldots, 6$.

36. Prove: If the diagonalizable matrices **A** and **B** have the same eigenvalues (with the same multiplicities), then **A** and **B** are similar.

37. Given: The diagonalizable matrix **A**. Show that the eigenvalues of A^2 are the squares of the eigenvalues of **A** but that **A** and A^2 have the same eigenvectors.

38. Suppose that the $n \times n$ matrix **A** has n linearly independent eigenvectors associated with a single eigenvalue λ. Show that **A** is a diagonal matrix.

39. Let λ_i be an eigenvalue of the $n \times n$ matrix **A**, and assume that the characteristic equation of **A** has only real solutions. The **algebraic multiplicity** of λ_i is the largest positive integer $p(i)$ such that $(\lambda - \lambda_i)^{p(i)}$ is a factor of the characteristic polynomial $|A - \lambda I|$. The **geometric multiplicity** of λ_i is the dimension $q(i)$ of the eigenspace associated with λ_i. It can be shown that $p(i) \geq q(i)$ for every eigenvalue λ_i. Taking this as already established, prove that the given matrix **A** is diagonalizable if and only if the geometric multiplicity of each eigenvalue is equal to its algebraic multiplicity.

6.3 Applications Involving Powers of Matrices

In this section we discuss applications that depend on an ability to compute the matrix A^k for large values of k, given the $n \times n$ matrix **A**. If **A** is diagonalizable, then A^k can be found directly by a method that avoids the labor of calculating the powers $A^2, A^3, A^4, \ldots$ by successive matrix multiplications.

Recall from Section 6.2 that, if the $n \times n$ matrix $\mathbf{A}$ has n linearly independent eigenvectors $\mathbf{v}_1, \mathbf{v}_2, \ldots, \mathbf{v}_n$ associated with the eigenvalues $\lambda_1, \lambda_2, \ldots, \lambda_n$ (not necessarily distinct), then

$$\mathbf{A} = \mathbf{PDP}^{-1}, \tag{1}$$

where

$$\mathbf{P} = \begin{bmatrix} | & | & & | \\ \mathbf{v}_1 & \mathbf{v}_2 & \cdots & \mathbf{v}_n \\ | & | & & | \end{bmatrix}$$

and

$$\mathbf{D} = \begin{bmatrix} \lambda_1 & 0 & \cdots & 0 \\ 0 & \lambda_2 & \cdots & 0 \\ \vdots & \vdots & \ddots & \vdots \\ 0 & 0 & \cdots & \lambda_n \end{bmatrix}.$$

Note that (1) yields

$$\mathbf{A}^2 = (\mathbf{PDP}^{-1})(\mathbf{PDP}^{-1}) = \mathbf{PD}(\mathbf{P}^{-1}\mathbf{P})\mathbf{DP}^{-1} = \mathbf{PD}^2\mathbf{P}^{-1}$$

because $\mathbf{P}^{-1}\mathbf{P} = \mathbf{I}$. More generally, for each positive integer k,

$$\begin{aligned} \mathbf{A}^k &= (\mathbf{PDP}^{-1})^k \\ &= (\mathbf{PDP}^{-1})(\mathbf{PDP}^{-1}) \cdots (\mathbf{PDP}^{-1})(\mathbf{PDP}^{-1}) \\ &= \mathbf{PD}(\mathbf{P}^{-1}\mathbf{P})\mathbf{D} \cdots (\mathbf{P}^{-1}\mathbf{P})\mathbf{DP}^{-1}; \\ \mathbf{A}^k &= \mathbf{PD}^k\mathbf{P}^{-1}. \end{aligned} \tag{2}$$

But the kth power $\mathbf{D}^k$ of the diagonal matrix $\mathbf{D}$ is easily computed:

$$\mathbf{D}^k = \begin{bmatrix} \lambda_1^k & 0 & \cdots & 0 \\ 0 & \lambda_2^k & \cdots & 0 \\ \vdots & \vdots & \ddots & \vdots \\ 0 & 0 & \cdots & \lambda_n^k \end{bmatrix}. \tag{3}$$

Consequently the formula in (2) gives a quick and effective way to calculate any desired power of the diagonalizable matrix $\mathbf{A}$, once its eigenvalues and associated eigenvectors—and hence the matrices $\mathbf{P}$ and $\mathbf{D}$—have been found.

Example 1   Find $\mathbf{A}^5$ if

$$\mathbf{A} = \begin{bmatrix} 4 & -2 & 1 \\ 2 & 0 & 1 \\ 2 & -2 & 3 \end{bmatrix}.$$

Solution In Example 7 of Section 6.1, we found that the 3×3 matrix $\mathbf{A}$ has the eigenvalue $\lambda_1 = 3$ with associated eigenvector $\mathbf{v}_1 = \begin{bmatrix} 1 & 1 & 1 \end{bmatrix}^T$, and the repeated eigenvalue $\lambda_2 = 2$ with associated eigenvectors $\mathbf{v}_2 = \begin{bmatrix} 1 & 1 & 0 \end{bmatrix}^T$ and $\mathbf{v}_3 = \begin{bmatrix} -1 & 0 & 2 \end{bmatrix}^T$. Therefore $\mathbf{A} = \mathbf{PDP}^{-1}$ with

$$\mathbf{P} = \begin{bmatrix} 1 & 1 & -1 \\ 1 & 1 & 0 \\ 1 & 0 & 2 \end{bmatrix} \quad \text{and} \quad \mathbf{D} = \begin{bmatrix} 3 & 0 & 0 \\ 0 & 2 & 0 \\ 0 & 0 & 2 \end{bmatrix}.$$

We first calculate

$$\mathbf{P}^{-1} = \begin{bmatrix} 2 & -2 & 1 \\ -2 & 3 & -1 \\ -1 & 1 & 0 \end{bmatrix}$$

and

$$\mathbf{D}^5 = \begin{bmatrix} 243 & 0 & 0 \\ 0 & 32 & 0 \\ 0 & 0 & 32 \end{bmatrix}.$$

Then the formula in (3) yields

$$
\begin{aligned}
\mathbf{A}^5 &= \begin{bmatrix} 1 & 1 & -1 \\ 1 & 1 & 0 \\ 1 & 0 & 2 \end{bmatrix} \begin{bmatrix} 243 & 0 & 0 \\ 0 & 32 & 0 \\ 0 & 0 & 32 \end{bmatrix} \begin{bmatrix} 2 & -2 & 1 \\ -2 & 3 & -1 \\ -1 & 1 & 0 \end{bmatrix} \\
&= \begin{bmatrix} 243 & 32 & -32 \\ 243 & 32 & 0 \\ 243 & 0 & 64 \end{bmatrix} \begin{bmatrix} 2 & -2 & 1 \\ -2 & 3 & -1 \\ -1 & 1 & 0 \end{bmatrix} \\
&= \begin{bmatrix} 454 & -422 & 211 \\ 422 & -390 & 211 \\ 422 & -422 & 243 \end{bmatrix}.
\end{aligned}
$$

$\blacksquare$

Transition Matrices

We want to apply this method of computing $\mathbf{A}^k$ to the analysis of a certain type of physical system that can be described by means of the following kind of mathematical model. Suppose that the sequence

$$\mathbf{x}_0, \mathbf{x}_1, \mathbf{x}_2, \ldots, \mathbf{x}_k, \ldots \tag{4}$$

of n-vectors is defined by its **initial vector** $\mathbf{x}_0$ and an $n \times n$ **transition matrix** $\mathbf{A}$ in the following manner:

$$\mathbf{x}_{k+1} = \mathbf{A}\mathbf{x}_k \qquad \text{for each } k \geq 0. \tag{5}$$

We envision a physical system—such as a population with n specified subpopulations—that evolve through a sequence of successive *states* described by the vectors in (4). Then our goal is to calculate the kth *state vector* $\mathbf{x}_k$. But using (5) repeatedly, we find that

$$\mathbf{x}_1 = \mathbf{A}\mathbf{x}_0, \quad \mathbf{x}_2 = \mathbf{A}\mathbf{x}_1 = \mathbf{A}^2\mathbf{x}_0, \quad \mathbf{x}_3 = \mathbf{A}\mathbf{x}_2 = \mathbf{A}^3\mathbf{x}_0,$$

and in general that

$$\mathbf{x}_k = \mathbf{A}^k \mathbf{x}_0. \tag{6}$$

Thus our task amounts to calculating the k power $\mathbf{A}^k$ of the transition matrix $\mathbf{A}$.

Example 2   Consider a metropolitan area with a *constant* total population of 1 million individuals. This area consists of a city and its suburbs, and we want to analyze the changing urban and suburban populations. Let C_k denote the city population and S_k the suburban population after k years. Suppose that each year 15% of the people in the city move to the suburbs, whereas 10% of the people in the suburbs move to the city. Then it follows that

$$\begin{aligned} C_{k+1} &= 0.85 C_k + 0.10 S_k \\ S_{k+1} &= 0.15 C_k + 0.90 S_k \end{aligned} \tag{7}$$

for each $k \geq 0$. (For instance, next year's city population C_{k+1} will equal 85% of this year's city population C_k plus 10% of this year's suburban population S_k.) Thus the metropolitan area's *population vector* $\mathbf{x}_k = \begin{bmatrix} C_k & S_k \end{bmatrix}^T$ satisfies

$$\mathbf{x}_{k+1} = \mathbf{A}\mathbf{x}_k \quad \text{and hence} \quad \mathbf{x}_k = \mathbf{A}^k \mathbf{x}_0 \tag{8}$$

(for each $k \geq 0$) with *transition matrix*

$$\mathbf{A} = \begin{bmatrix} 0.85 & 0.10 \\ 0.15 & 0.90 \end{bmatrix}.$$

The characteristic equation of the transition matrix $\mathbf{A}$ is

$$\left(\frac{17}{20} - \lambda \right) \left(\frac{9}{10} - \lambda \right) - \left(\frac{3}{20} \right) \left(\frac{1}{10} \right) = 0;$$
$$(17 - 20\lambda)(9 - 10\lambda) - 3 = 0;$$
$$200\lambda^2 - 350\lambda + 150 = 0;$$
$$4\lambda^2 - 7\lambda + 3 = 0;$$
$$(\lambda - 1)(4\lambda - 3) = 0$$

Thus the eigenvalues of $\mathbf{A}$ are $\lambda_1 = 1$ and $\lambda_2 = 0.75$. For $\lambda_1 = 1$, the system $(\mathbf{A} - \lambda\mathbf{I})\mathbf{v} = \mathbf{0}$ is

$$\begin{bmatrix} -0.15 & 0.10 \\ 0.15 & -0.10 \end{bmatrix} \begin{bmatrix} x \\ y \end{bmatrix} = \begin{bmatrix} 0 \\ 0 \end{bmatrix},$$

so an associated eigenvector is $\mathbf{v}_1 = \begin{bmatrix} 2 & 3 \end{bmatrix}^T$. For $\lambda_2 = 0.75$, the system $(\mathbf{A} - \lambda\mathbf{I})\mathbf{v} = \mathbf{0}$ is

$$\begin{bmatrix} 0.10 & 0.10 \\ 0.15 & 0.15 \end{bmatrix} \begin{bmatrix} x \\ y \end{bmatrix} = \begin{bmatrix} 0 \\ 0 \end{bmatrix},$$

so an associated eigenvector is $\mathbf{v}_2 = \begin{bmatrix} -1 & 1 \end{bmatrix}^T$. It follows that $\mathbf{A} = \mathbf{PDP}^{-1}$, where

$$\mathbf{P} = \begin{bmatrix} 2 & -1 \\ 3 & 1 \end{bmatrix} \quad \text{and} \quad \mathbf{D} = \begin{bmatrix} 1 & 0 \\ 0 & \frac{3}{4} \end{bmatrix},$$

and

$$\mathbf{P}^{-1} = \tfrac{1}{5} \begin{bmatrix} 1 & 1 \\ -3 & 2 \end{bmatrix}.$$

Now suppose that our goal is to determine the long-term distribution of population between the city and its suburbs. Note first that $\left(\tfrac{3}{4}\right)^k$ is "negligible" when k is sufficiently large; for instance, $\left(\tfrac{3}{4}\right)^{40} \approx 0.00001$. It follows that if $k \geq 40$, then the formula $\mathbf{A}^k = \mathbf{P}\mathbf{D}^k\mathbf{P}^{-1}$ yields

$$\begin{aligned}
\mathbf{A}^k &= \begin{bmatrix} 2 & -1 \\ 3 & 1 \end{bmatrix} \begin{bmatrix} 1 & 0 \\ 0 & \left(\tfrac{3}{4}\right)^k \end{bmatrix} \left(\tfrac{1}{5}\right) \begin{bmatrix} 1 & 1 \\ -3 & 2 \end{bmatrix} \\
&\approx \tfrac{1}{5} \begin{bmatrix} 2 & -1 \\ 3 & 1 \end{bmatrix} \begin{bmatrix} 1 & 0 \\ 0 & 0 \end{bmatrix} \begin{bmatrix} 1 & 1 \\ -3 & 2 \end{bmatrix} \\
&= \tfrac{1}{5} \begin{bmatrix} 2 & 0 \\ 3 & 0 \end{bmatrix} \begin{bmatrix} 1 & 1 \\ -3 & 2 \end{bmatrix} = \tfrac{1}{5} \begin{bmatrix} 2 & 2 \\ 3 & 3 \end{bmatrix}.
\end{aligned} \qquad (9)$$

Hence it follows that, if k is sufficiently large, then

$$\begin{aligned}
\mathbf{x}_k = \mathbf{A}^k\mathbf{x}_0 &\approx \tfrac{1}{5} \begin{bmatrix} 2 & 2 \\ 3 & 3 \end{bmatrix} \begin{bmatrix} C_0 \\ S_0 \end{bmatrix} \\
&= (C_0 + S_0) \begin{bmatrix} 0.4 \\ 0.6 \end{bmatrix} = \begin{bmatrix} 0.4 \\ 0.6 \end{bmatrix},
\end{aligned}$$

because $C_0 + S_0 = 1$ (million), the constant total population of the metropolitan area. Thus, our analysis shows that, irrespective of the initial distribution of population between the city and its suburbs, the long-term distribution consists of 40% in the city and 60% in the suburbs. ∎

Remark: The result in Example 2—that the long-term situation is independent of the initial situation—is characteristic of a general class of common problems. Note that the transition matrix $\mathbf{A}$ in (8) has the property that *the sum of the elements in each column is* 1. An $n \times n$ matrix with nonnegative entries having this property is called a **stochastic matrix**. It can be proved that, if $\mathbf{A}$ is a stochastic matrix having only positive entries, then $\lambda_1 = 1$ is one eigenvalue of $\mathbf{A}$ and $|\lambda_i| < 1$ for the others. (See Problems 39 and 40.) Moreover, as $k \to \infty$, the matrix $\mathbf{A}^k$ approaches the constant matrix

$$\begin{bmatrix} \mathbf{v}_1 & \mathbf{v}_1 & \cdots & \mathbf{v}_1 \end{bmatrix},$$

each of whose identical columns is the eigenvector of $\mathbf{A}$ associated with $\lambda_1 = 1$ that has the sum of its elements equal to 1. The 2×2 stochastic matrix $\mathbf{A}$ of Example 1 illustrates this general result, with $\lambda_1 = 1$, $\lambda_2 = \tfrac{3}{4}$, and $\mathbf{v}_1 = \left(\tfrac{2}{5}, \tfrac{3}{5}\right)$. ∎

Predator-Prey Models

Next, we consider a predator-prey population consisting of the foxes and rabbits living in a certain forest. Initially, there are F_0 foxes and R_0 rabbits; after k months, there are F_k foxes and R_k rabbits. We assume that the transition from each month to the next is described by the equations

$$\begin{aligned}
F_{k+1} &= 0.4F_k + 0.3R_k \\
R_{k+1} &= -rF_k + 1.2R_k,
\end{aligned} \qquad (10)$$

where the constant $r > 0$ is the "capture rate" representing the average number of rabbits consumed monthly by each fox. Thus

$$\mathbf{x}_{k+1} = \mathbf{A}\mathbf{x}_k \quad \text{and hence} \quad \mathbf{x}_k = \mathbf{A}^k \mathbf{x}_0, \tag{11}$$

where

$$\mathbf{x}_k = \begin{bmatrix} F_k \\ R_k \end{bmatrix} \quad \text{and} \quad \mathbf{A} = \begin{bmatrix} 0.4 & 0.3 \\ -r & 1.2 \end{bmatrix}. \tag{12}$$

The term $0.4F_k$ in the first equation in (10) indicates that, without rabbits to eat, only 40% of the foxes would survive each month, while the term $0.3R_k$ represents the growth in the fox population due to the available food supply of rabbits. The term $1.2R_k$ in the second equation indicates that, in the absence of any foxes, the rabbit population would increase by 20% each month. We want to investigate the long-term behavior of the fox and rabbit populations for different values of the capture rate r of rabbits by foxes.

The characteristic equation of the transition matrix $\mathbf{A}$ in (12) is

$$(0.4 - \lambda)(1.2 - \lambda) + (0.3)r = 0;$$
$$(4 - 10\lambda)(12 - 10\lambda) + 30r = 0;$$
$$100\lambda^2 - 160\lambda + (48 + 30r) = 0.$$

The quadratic formula then yields the equation

$$\begin{aligned}
\lambda &= \frac{1}{200}\left[160 \pm \sqrt{(160)^2 - (400)(48 + 30r)}\right] \\
&= \frac{1}{10}\left(8 \pm \sqrt{16 - 30r}\right),
\end{aligned} \tag{13}$$

which gives the eigenvalues of $\mathbf{A}$ in terms of the capture rate r. Examples 3, 4, and 5 illustrate three possibilities (for different values of r) for what may happen to the fox and rabbit populations as k increases:

- F_k and R_k may approach constant nonzero values. This is the case of *stable limiting populations* that coexist in equilibrium with one another.
- F_k and R_k may both approach zero. This is the case of *mutual extinction* of the two species.
- F_k and R_k may both increase without bound. This is the case of a *population explosion*.

Example 3

Stable Limiting Population

If $r = 0.4$, then Eq. (13) gives the eigenvalues $\lambda_1 = 1$ and $\lambda_2 = 0.6$. For $\lambda_1 = 1$, the system $(\mathbf{A} - \lambda\mathbf{I})\mathbf{v} = \mathbf{0}$ is

$$\begin{bmatrix} -0.6 & 0.3 \\ -0.4 & 0.2 \end{bmatrix}\begin{bmatrix} x \\ y \end{bmatrix} = \begin{bmatrix} 0 \\ 0 \end{bmatrix},$$

so an associated eigenvector is $\mathbf{v}_1 = \begin{bmatrix} 1 & 2 \end{bmatrix}^T$. For $\lambda_2 = 0.6$, the system $(\mathbf{A} - \lambda\mathbf{I})\mathbf{v} = \mathbf{0}$ is

$$\begin{bmatrix} -0.2 & 0.3 \\ -0.4 & 0.6 \end{bmatrix}\begin{bmatrix} x \\ y \end{bmatrix} = \begin{bmatrix} 0 \\ 0 \end{bmatrix},$$

so an associated eigenvector is $v_2 = \begin{bmatrix} 3 & 2 \end{bmatrix}^T$. It follows that $\mathbf{A} = \mathbf{PDP}^{-1}$, where

$$\mathbf{P} = \begin{bmatrix} 1 & 3 \\ 2 & 2 \end{bmatrix}, \quad \mathbf{D} = \begin{bmatrix} 1 & 0 \\ 0 & 0.6 \end{bmatrix}, \quad \text{and} \quad \mathbf{P}^{-1} = -\tfrac{1}{4} \begin{bmatrix} 2 & -3 \\ -2 & 1 \end{bmatrix}.$$

We are now ready to calculate $\mathbf{A}^k$. If k is sufficiently large that $(0.6)^k \approx 0$ [for instance, $(0.6)^{25} \approx 0.000003$], then the formula $\mathbf{A}^k = \mathbf{PD}^k\mathbf{P}^{-1}$ yields

$$\mathbf{A}^k = \begin{bmatrix} 1 & 3 \\ 2 & 2 \end{bmatrix} \begin{bmatrix} 1 & 0 \\ 0 & (0.6)^k \end{bmatrix} \left(-\tfrac{1}{4}\right) \begin{bmatrix} 2 & -3 \\ -2 & 1 \end{bmatrix}$$

$$\approx -\tfrac{1}{4} \begin{bmatrix} 1 & 3 \\ 2 & 2 \end{bmatrix} \begin{bmatrix} 1 & 0 \\ 0 & 0 \end{bmatrix} \begin{bmatrix} 2 & -3 \\ -2 & 1 \end{bmatrix}$$

$$= -\tfrac{1}{4} \begin{bmatrix} 1 & 0 \\ 2 & 0 \end{bmatrix} \begin{bmatrix} 2 & -3 \\ -2 & 1 \end{bmatrix}$$

$$= \tfrac{1}{4} \begin{bmatrix} -2 & 3 \\ -4 & 6 \end{bmatrix}.$$

Hence it follows that if k is sufficiently large, then

$$\mathbf{x}_k = \mathbf{A}^k \mathbf{x}_0 = \tfrac{1}{4} \begin{bmatrix} -2 & 3 \\ -4 & 6 \end{bmatrix} \begin{bmatrix} F_0 \\ R_0 \end{bmatrix} = \tfrac{1}{4} \begin{bmatrix} 3R_0 - 2F_0 \\ 6R_0 - 4F_0 \end{bmatrix}$$

—that is,

$$\begin{bmatrix} F_k \\ R_k \end{bmatrix} = \alpha \begin{bmatrix} 1 \\ 2 \end{bmatrix}, \quad \text{where} \quad \alpha = \tfrac{1}{4}(3R_0 - 2F_0). \tag{14}$$

Assuming that the initial populations are such that $\alpha > 0$ (that is, $3R_0 > 2F_0$), (14) implies that, as k increases, the fox and rabbit populations approach a stable situation in which there are twice as many rabbits as foxes. For instance, if $F_0 = R_0 = 100$, then when k is sufficiently large, there will be 25 foxes and 50 rabbits. ∎

Example 4

Mutual Extinction

If $r = 0.5$, then Eq. (13) gives the eigenvalues $\lambda_1 = 0.9$ and $\lambda_2 = 0.7$. For $\lambda_1 = 0.9$, the system $(\mathbf{A} - \lambda \mathbf{I})\mathbf{v} = \mathbf{0}$ is

$$\begin{bmatrix} -0.5 & 0.3 \\ -0.5 & 0.3 \end{bmatrix} \begin{bmatrix} x \\ y \end{bmatrix} = \begin{bmatrix} 0 \\ 0 \end{bmatrix},$$

so an associated eigenvector is $v_1 = \begin{bmatrix} 3 & 5 \end{bmatrix}^T$. For $\lambda_2 = 0.7$, the system $(\mathbf{A} - \lambda \mathbf{I})\mathbf{v} = \mathbf{0}$ is

$$\begin{bmatrix} -0.3 & 0.3 \\ -0.5 & 0.5 \end{bmatrix} \begin{bmatrix} x \\ y \end{bmatrix} = \begin{bmatrix} 0 \\ 0 \end{bmatrix},$$

so an associated eigenvector is $v_2 = \begin{bmatrix} 1 & 1 \end{bmatrix}^T$. It follows that $\mathbf{A} = \mathbf{PDP}^{-1}$, with

$$\mathbf{P} = \begin{bmatrix} 3 & 1 \\ 5 & 1 \end{bmatrix}, \quad \mathbf{D} = \begin{bmatrix} 0.9 & 0 \\ 0 & 0.7 \end{bmatrix}, \quad \text{and} \quad \mathbf{P}^{-1} = -\tfrac{1}{2} \begin{bmatrix} 1 & -1 \\ -5 & 3 \end{bmatrix}.$$

Now both $(0.9)^k$ and $(0.7)^k$ approach 0 as k increases without bound ($k \to +\infty$). Hence if k is sufficiently large, then the formula $\mathbf{A}^k = \mathbf{P}\mathbf{D}^k\mathbf{P}^{-1}$ yields

$$\mathbf{A}^k = \begin{bmatrix} 3 & 1 \\ 5 & 1 \end{bmatrix} \begin{bmatrix} (0.9)^k & 0 \\ 0 & (0.7)^k \end{bmatrix} \left(-\tfrac{1}{2}\right) \begin{bmatrix} 1 & -1 \\ -5 & 3 \end{bmatrix}$$

$$\approx -\tfrac{1}{2} \begin{bmatrix} 3 & 1 \\ 5 & 1 \end{bmatrix} \begin{bmatrix} 0 & 0 \\ 0 & 0 \end{bmatrix} \begin{bmatrix} 1 & -1 \\ -5 & 3 \end{bmatrix} = \begin{bmatrix} 0 & 0 \\ 0 & 0 \end{bmatrix},$$

so

$$\begin{bmatrix} F_k \\ R_k \end{bmatrix} = \mathbf{A}^k \begin{bmatrix} F_0 \\ R_0 \end{bmatrix} \approx \begin{bmatrix} 0 & 0 \\ 0 & 0 \end{bmatrix} \begin{bmatrix} F_0 \\ R_0 \end{bmatrix} = \begin{bmatrix} 0 \\ 0 \end{bmatrix}. \tag{15}$$

Thus F_k and R_k both approach zero as $k \to +\infty$, so both the foxes and the rabbits die out—mutual extinction occurs. ∎

Example 5

Population Explosion

If $r = 0.325$, then Eq. (13) gives the eigenvalues $\lambda_1 = 1.05$ and $\lambda_2 = 0.55$. For $\lambda_1 = 1.05$, the system $(\mathbf{A} - \lambda\mathbf{I})\mathbf{v} = \mathbf{0}$ is

$$\begin{bmatrix} -0.650 & 0.30 \\ -0.325 & 0.15 \end{bmatrix} \begin{bmatrix} x \\ y \end{bmatrix} = \begin{bmatrix} 0 \\ 0 \end{bmatrix}.$$

Each equation is a multiple of $-13x + 6y = 0$, so an associated eigenvector is $\mathbf{v}_1 = \begin{bmatrix} 6 & 13 \end{bmatrix}^T$. For $\lambda_2 = 0.55$, the system $(\mathbf{A} - \lambda\mathbf{I})\mathbf{v} = \mathbf{0}$ is

$$\begin{bmatrix} -0.150 & 0.30 \\ -0.325 & 0.65 \end{bmatrix} \begin{bmatrix} x \\ y \end{bmatrix} = \begin{bmatrix} 0 \\ 0 \end{bmatrix},$$

so an associated eigenvector is $\mathbf{v}_2 = \begin{bmatrix} 2 & 1 \end{bmatrix}^T$. It follows that $\mathbf{A} = \mathbf{P}\mathbf{D}\mathbf{P}^{-1}$ with

$$\mathbf{P} = \begin{bmatrix} 6 & 2 \\ 13 & 1 \end{bmatrix}, \quad \mathbf{D} = \begin{bmatrix} 1.05 & 0 \\ 0 & 0.55 \end{bmatrix}, \quad \text{and} \quad \mathbf{P}^{-1} = -\tfrac{1}{20} \begin{bmatrix} 1 & -2 \\ -13 & 6 \end{bmatrix}.$$

Note that $(0.55)^k$ approaches zero but that $(1.05)^k$ increases without bound as $k \to +\infty$. It follows that if k is sufficiently large, then the formula $\mathbf{A}^k = \mathbf{P}\mathbf{D}^k\mathbf{P}^{-1}$ yields

$$\mathbf{A}^k = \begin{bmatrix} 6 & 2 \\ 13 & 1 \end{bmatrix} \begin{bmatrix} (1.05)^k & 0 \\ 0 & (0.55)^k \end{bmatrix} \left(-\tfrac{1}{20}\right) \begin{bmatrix} 1 & -2 \\ -13 & 6 \end{bmatrix}$$

$$\approx -\tfrac{1}{20} \begin{bmatrix} 6 & 2 \\ 13 & 1 \end{bmatrix} \begin{bmatrix} (1.05)^k & 0 \\ 0 & 0 \end{bmatrix} \begin{bmatrix} 1 & -2 \\ -13 & 6 \end{bmatrix}$$

$$= -\tfrac{1}{20} \begin{bmatrix} (6)(1.05)^k & 0 \\ (13)(1.05)^k & 0 \end{bmatrix} \begin{bmatrix} 1 & -2 \\ -13 & 6 \end{bmatrix},$$

and therefore

$$\mathbf{A}^k \approx -\tfrac{1}{20}(1.05)^k \begin{bmatrix} 6 & -12 \\ 13 & -26 \end{bmatrix}. \tag{16}$$

Hence, if k is sufficiently large, then

$$\mathbf{x}_k = \mathbf{A}^k \mathbf{x}_0 \approx -\tfrac{1}{20}(1.05)^k \begin{bmatrix} 6 & -12 \\ 13 & -26 \end{bmatrix} \begin{bmatrix} F_0 \\ R_0 \end{bmatrix}$$

$$= -\tfrac{1}{20}(1.05)^k \begin{bmatrix} 6F_0 - 12R_0 \\ 13F_0 - 26R_0 \end{bmatrix},$$

and so

$$\begin{bmatrix} F_k \\ R_k \end{bmatrix} \approx (1.05)^k \gamma \begin{bmatrix} 6 \\ 13 \end{bmatrix}, \quad \text{where} \quad \gamma = \tfrac{1}{20}(2R_0 - F_0). \tag{17}$$

If $\gamma > 0$ (that is, if $2R_0 > F_0$), then the factor $(1.05)^k$ in (17) implies that the fox and rabbit populations both increase at a rate of 5% per month, and thus each increases without bound as $k \to +\infty$. Moreover, when k is sufficiently large, the two populations maintain a constant ratio of 6 foxes for every 13 rabbits. It is also of interest to note that the monthly "population multiplier" is the larger eigenvalue $\lambda_1 = 1.05$ and that the limiting *ratio* of populations is determined by the associated eigenvector $\mathbf{v}_1 = \begin{bmatrix} 6 & 13 \end{bmatrix}^T$. ∎

In summary, let us compare the results in Examples 3, 4, and 5. The critical capture rate $r = 0.4$ of Example 3 represents a monthly consumption of 0.4 rabbits per fox, resulting in stable limiting populations of both species. But if the foxes are greedier and consume more than 0.4 rabbits per fox monthly, then the result is extinction of both species (as in Example 4). If the rabbits become more skilled at evading foxes, so that less than 0.4 rabbits per fox are consumed each month, then both populations grow without bound, as in Example 5.

The Cayley-Hamilton Theorem

One of the more notable and important theorems in advanced linear algebra says that *every matrix satisfies its own characteristic equation.*

THEOREM 1: Cayley-Hamilton

If the $n \times n$ matrix $\mathbf{A}$ has the characteristic polynomial

$$p(\lambda) = (-1)^n \lambda^n + c_{n-1}\lambda^{n-1} + \cdots + c_2\lambda^2 + c_1\lambda + c_0,$$

then

$$p(\mathbf{A}) = (-1)^n \mathbf{A}^n + c_{n-1}\mathbf{A}^{n-1} + \cdots + c_2\mathbf{A}^2 + c_1\mathbf{A} + c_0\mathbf{I} = \mathbf{0}. \tag{18}$$

Proof: We establish (18) only for the special case in which the matrix $\mathbf{A}$ is *diagonalizable*; the general case will be discussed in Section 7.5. If $\lambda_1, \lambda_2, \ldots, \lambda_n$ are the eigenvalues of $\mathbf{A}$, then

$$\mathbf{A}^k = \mathbf{P}\mathbf{D}^k\mathbf{P}^{-1} \quad \text{where} \quad \mathbf{D}^k = \begin{bmatrix} \lambda_1^k & 0 & \cdots & 0 \\ 0 & \lambda_2^k & \cdots & 0 \\ \vdots & \vdots & \ddots & \vdots \\ 0 & 0 & \cdots & \lambda_n^k \end{bmatrix}$$

as in Eqs. (2) and (3) at the beginning of this section. First, we note that

$$p(\mathbf{D}) = (-1)^n \mathbf{D}^n + c_{n-1}\mathbf{D}^{n-1} + \cdots + c_2\mathbf{D}^2 + c_1\mathbf{D} + c_0\mathbf{I}$$

$$= (-1)^n \begin{bmatrix} \lambda_1^n & 0 & \cdots & 0 \\ 0 & \lambda_2^n & \cdots & 0 \\ \vdots & \vdots & \ddots & \vdots \\ 0 & 0 & \cdots & \lambda_n^n \end{bmatrix} + c_{n-1} \begin{bmatrix} \lambda_1^{n-1} & 0 & \cdots & 0 \\ 0 & \lambda_2^{n-1} & \cdots & 0 \\ \vdots & \vdots & \ddots & \vdots \\ 0 & 0 & \cdots & \lambda_n^{n-1} \end{bmatrix}$$

$$+ \cdots + c_2 \begin{bmatrix} \lambda_1^2 & 0 & \cdots & 0 \\ 0 & \lambda_2^2 & \cdots & 0 \\ \vdots & \vdots & \ddots & \vdots \\ 0 & 0 & \cdots & \lambda_n^2 \end{bmatrix} + c_1 \begin{bmatrix} \lambda_1 & 0 & \cdots & 0 \\ 0 & \lambda_2 & \cdots & 0 \\ \vdots & \vdots & \ddots & \vdots \\ 0 & 0 & \cdots & \lambda_n \end{bmatrix}$$

$$+ c_0 \begin{bmatrix} 1 & 0 & \cdots & 0 \\ 0 & 1 & \cdots & 0 \\ \vdots & \vdots & \ddots & \vdots \\ 0 & 0 & \cdots & 1 \end{bmatrix}$$

$$= \begin{bmatrix} p(\lambda_1) & 0 & \cdots & 0 \\ 0 & p(\lambda_2) & \cdots & 0 \\ \vdots & \vdots & \ddots & \vdots \\ 0 & 0 & \cdots & p(\lambda_n) \end{bmatrix} = \mathbf{0},$$

because $p(\lambda_k) = 0$ for $k = 1, 2, \ldots, n$. Thus the diagonal form $\mathbf{D}$ of the matrix $\mathbf{A}$ satisfies the characteristic equation of $\mathbf{A}$. It therefore follows that

$$p(\mathbf{A}) = (-1)^n \mathbf{PD}^n\mathbf{P}^{-1} + c_{n-1}\mathbf{PD}^{n-1}\mathbf{P}^{-1} + \cdots$$
$$+ c_2\mathbf{PD}^2\mathbf{P}^{-1} + c_1\mathbf{PDP}^{-1} + c_0\mathbf{PIP}^{-1}$$
$$= \mathbf{P}p(\mathbf{D})\mathbf{P}^{-1}$$
$$= \mathbf{P}\,\mathbf{0}\,\mathbf{P}^{-1} = \mathbf{0},$$

as desired. ▲

Example 6 In Example 7 of Section 6.1, we found that the matrix

$$\mathbf{A} = \begin{bmatrix} 4 & -2 & 1 \\ 2 & 0 & 1 \\ 2 & -2 & 3 \end{bmatrix}$$

has the characteristic polynomial

$$p(\lambda) = -\lambda^3 + 7\lambda^2 - 16\lambda + 12,$$

so

$$-\mathbf{A}^3 + 7\mathbf{A}^2 - 16\mathbf{A} + 12\mathbf{I} = \mathbf{0}, \tag{19}$$

by the Cayley-Hamilton theorem. Because

$$\mathbf{A}^2 = \begin{bmatrix} 14 & -10 & 5 \\ 10 & -6 & 5 \\ 10 & -10 & 9 \end{bmatrix},$$

it follows from (19) that

$$\mathbf{A}^3 = 7\mathbf{A}^2 - 16\mathbf{A} + 12\mathbf{I}$$

$$= 7\begin{bmatrix} 14 & -10 & 5 \\ 10 & -6 & 5 \\ 10 & -10 & 9 \end{bmatrix} - 16\begin{bmatrix} 4 & -2 & 1 \\ 2 & 0 & 1 \\ 2 & -2 & 3 \end{bmatrix} + 12\begin{bmatrix} 1 & 0 & 0 \\ 0 & 1 & 0 \\ 0 & 0 & 1 \end{bmatrix}$$

$$= \begin{bmatrix} 46 & -38 & 19 \\ 38 & -30 & 19 \\ 38 & -38 & 27 \end{bmatrix}.$$

Multiplication by **A** now gives

$$\mathbf{A}^4 = 7\mathbf{A}^3 - 16\mathbf{A}^2 + 12\mathbf{A}$$

$$= 7(7\mathbf{A}^2 - 16\mathbf{A} + 12\mathbf{I}) - 16\mathbf{A}^2 + 12\mathbf{A}$$

$$= 33\mathbf{A}^2 - 100\mathbf{A} + 84\mathbf{I}$$

$$= 33\begin{bmatrix} 14 & -10 & 5 \\ 10 & -6 & 5 \\ 10 & -10 & 9 \end{bmatrix} - 100\begin{bmatrix} 4 & -2 & 1 \\ 2 & 0 & 1 \\ 2 & -2 & 3 \end{bmatrix} + 84\begin{bmatrix} 1 & 0 & 0 \\ 0 & 1 & 0 \\ 0 & 0 & 1 \end{bmatrix}$$

$$= \begin{bmatrix} 146 & -130 & 65 \\ 130 & -114 & 65 \\ 130 & -130 & 81 \end{bmatrix}.$$

Thus we can use the Cayley-Hamilton theorem to express (positive integral) powers of the 3×3 matrix **A** in terms of **A** and $\mathbf{A}^2$. We also can use the Cayley-Hamilton theorem to find the inverse matrix $\mathbf{A}^{-1}$. If we multiply Eq. (19) by $\mathbf{A}^{-1}$, we can solve the resulting equation $-\mathbf{A}^2 + 7\mathbf{A} - 16\mathbf{I} + 12\mathbf{A}^{-1} = \mathbf{0}$:

$$\mathbf{A}^{-1} = \frac{1}{12}(\mathbf{A}^2 - 7\mathbf{A} + 16\mathbf{I})$$

$$= \frac{1}{12}\begin{bmatrix} 14 & -10 & 5 \\ 10 & -6 & 5 \\ 10 & -10 & 9 \end{bmatrix} - \frac{7}{12}\begin{bmatrix} 4 & -2 & 1 \\ 2 & 0 & 1 \\ 2 & -2 & 3 \end{bmatrix} + \frac{16}{12}\begin{bmatrix} 1 & 0 & 0 \\ 0 & 1 & 0 \\ 0 & 0 & 1 \end{bmatrix}$$

$$= \frac{1}{6}\begin{bmatrix} 1 & 2 & -1 \\ -2 & 5 & -1 \\ -2 & 2 & 2 \end{bmatrix}.$$

6.3 Problems

In Problems 1–10, a matrix **A** *is given. Use the method of Example 1 to compute* $\mathbf{A}^5$.

1. $\begin{bmatrix} 3 & -2 \\ 1 & 0 \end{bmatrix}$ **2.** $\begin{bmatrix} 5 & -6 \\ 3 & -4 \end{bmatrix}$

3. $\begin{bmatrix} 6 & -6 \\ 4 & -4 \end{bmatrix}$ **4.** $\begin{bmatrix} 4 & -3 \\ 2 & -1 \end{bmatrix}$

5. $\begin{bmatrix} 5 & -4 \\ 3 & -2 \end{bmatrix}$ **6.** $\begin{bmatrix} 6 & -10 \\ 2 & -3 \end{bmatrix}$

7. $\begin{bmatrix} 1 & 3 & 0 \\ 0 & 2 & 0 \\ 0 & 0 & 2 \end{bmatrix}$ **8.** $\begin{bmatrix} 1 & -2 & 1 \\ 0 & 1 & 0 \\ 0 & -2 & 2 \end{bmatrix}$

9. $\begin{bmatrix} 1 & -3 & 1 \\ 0 & 2 & 0 \\ 0 & 0 & 2 \end{bmatrix}$ **10.** $\begin{bmatrix} 4 & -3 & 1 \\ 2 & -1 & 1 \\ 0 & 0 & 2 \end{bmatrix}$

Find $\mathbf{A}^{10}$ *for each matrix* **A** *given in Problems 11–14.*

11. $\begin{bmatrix} 1 & 0 & 0 \\ 6 & 5 & 2 \\ 21 & -15 & -6 \end{bmatrix}$ **12.** $\begin{bmatrix} 11 & -6 & -2 \\ 20 & -11 & -4 \\ 0 & 0 & 1 \end{bmatrix}$

13. $\begin{bmatrix} 1 & -1 & 1 \\ 2 & -2 & 1 \\ 4 & -4 & 1 \end{bmatrix}$ **14.** $\begin{bmatrix} 5 & -5 & -3 \\ 2 & -2 & -1 \\ 4 & -4 & -3 \end{bmatrix}$

15–24. Use the Cayley-Hamilton theorem (as in Example 6) to find $\mathbf{A}^{-1}$, $\mathbf{A}^3$, and $\mathbf{A}^4$ for each matrix **A** given in Problems 5–14 (respectively).

In Problems 25–30, a city-suburban population transition matrix **A** *(as in Example 2) is given. Find the resulting long-term distribution of a constant total population between the city and its suburbs.*

25. $\mathbf{A} = \begin{bmatrix} 0.9 & 0.1 \\ 0.1 & 0.9 \end{bmatrix}$ **26.** $\mathbf{A} = \begin{bmatrix} 0.85 & 0.05 \\ 0.15 & 0.95 \end{bmatrix}$

27. $\mathbf{A} = \begin{bmatrix} 0.75 & 0.15 \\ 0.25 & 0.85 \end{bmatrix}$ **28.** $\mathbf{A} = \begin{bmatrix} 0.8 & 0.1 \\ 0.2 & 0.9 \end{bmatrix}$

29. $\mathbf{A} = \begin{bmatrix} 0.9 & 0.05 \\ 0.1 & 0.95 \end{bmatrix}$ **30.** $\mathbf{A} = \begin{bmatrix} 0.8 & 0.15 \\ 0.2 & 0.85 \end{bmatrix}$

Problems 31–33 deal with a fox-rabbit population as in Examples 3–5, except with the transition matrix

$$\mathbf{A} = \begin{bmatrix} 0.6 & 0.5 \\ -r & 1.2 \end{bmatrix}.$$

in place of the one used in the text.

31. If $r = 0.16$, show that in the long term the populations of foxes and rabbits are stable, with 5 foxes for each 4 rabbits.

32. If $r = 0.175$, show that in the long term the populations of foxes and rabbits both die out.

33. If $r = 0.135$, show that in the long term the fox and rabbit populations both increase at the rate of 5% per month, maintaining a constant ratio of 10 foxes for each 9 rabbits.

34. Suppose that the 2×2 matrix **A** has eigenvalues $\lambda_1 = 1$ and $\lambda_2 = -1$ with eigenvectors $\mathbf{v}_1 = (3, 4)$ and $\mathbf{v}_2 = (5, 7)$, respectively. Find the matrix **A** and the powers $\mathbf{A}^{99}$ and $\mathbf{A}^{100}$.

35. Suppose that $|\lambda| = 1$ for each eigenvalue λ of the diagonalizable matrix **A**. Show that $\mathbf{A}^n = \mathbf{I}$ for every even positive integer n.

36. Suppose that

$$\mathbf{A} = \begin{bmatrix} 0 & 1 \\ 1 & 0 \end{bmatrix}.$$

Show that $\mathbf{A}^{2n} = \mathbf{I}$ and that $\mathbf{A}^{2n+1} = \mathbf{A}$ for every positive integer n.

37. Suppose that

$$\mathbf{A} = \begin{bmatrix} 0 & 1 \\ -1 & 0 \end{bmatrix}.$$

Show that $\mathbf{A}^{4n} = \mathbf{I}$, $\mathbf{A}^{4n+1} = \mathbf{A}$, $\mathbf{A}^{4n+2} = -\mathbf{I}$, and $\mathbf{A}^{4n+3} = -\mathbf{A}$ for every positive integer n.

38. The matrix

$$\mathbf{A} = \begin{bmatrix} 1 & 1 \\ 0 & 1 \end{bmatrix}$$

is not diagonalizable. (Why not?) Write $\mathbf{A} = \mathbf{I} + \mathbf{B}$. Show that $\mathbf{B}^2 = \mathbf{0}$ and thence that

$$\mathbf{A}^n = \begin{bmatrix} 1 & n \\ 0 & 1 \end{bmatrix}.$$

39. Consider the stochastic matrix

$$\mathbf{A} = \begin{bmatrix} p & 1-q \\ 1-p & q \end{bmatrix}$$

where $0 < p < 1$ and $0 < q < 1$. Show that the eigenvalues of **A** are $\lambda_1 = 1$ and $\lambda_2 = p + q - 1$, so that $|\lambda_2| < 1$.

40. Suppose that **A** is an $n \times n$ stochastic matrix—the sum of the elements of each column vector is 1. If $\mathbf{v} = (1, 1, \ldots, 1)$, show that $\mathbf{A}^T \mathbf{v} = \mathbf{v}$. Why does it follow that $\lambda = 1$ is an eigenvalue of **A**?

41. In his *Liber abaci* published in 1202, Leonardo Fibonacci* asked the following question: How many pairs of rabbits are produced from a single original pair in one year, if every month each pair begets a new pair, which is similarly productive beginning in the second succeeding month? The answer is provided by the **Fibonacci sequence**

$$1, 1, 2, 3, 5, 8, 13, 21, 34, 55, \ldots$$

in which each term is the sum of its two immediate predecessors. That is, the sequence is defined recursively as follows:

$$s_0 = 1 = s_1, \quad s_{n+1} = s_n + s_{n-1} \quad \text{for } n \geq 1.$$

* "Leonardo, son of Bonacci," 1175–1250?, one of the outstanding mathematicians of the middle ages. He is also known as Leonardo of Pisa (Leonardo Pisano).

Then s_n is the number of rabbit pairs present after n months. Note that if

$$\mathbf{x}_n = \begin{bmatrix} s_{n+1} \\ s_n \end{bmatrix} \quad \text{and} \quad \mathbf{A} = \begin{bmatrix} 1 & 1 \\ 1 & 0 \end{bmatrix},$$

then

$$\mathbf{x}_n = \mathbf{A}\mathbf{x}_{n-1} \quad \text{and so} \quad \mathbf{x}_n = \mathbf{A}^n\mathbf{x}_0,$$

where $\mathbf{x}_0 = (1, 1)$.

(a) Show that $\mathbf{A}$ has eigenvalues $\lambda_1 = \frac{1}{2}(1 + \sqrt{5})$ and $\lambda_2 = \frac{1}{2}(1 - \sqrt{5})$ with associated eigenvectors $\mathbf{v}_1 = (1 + \sqrt{5}, 2)$ and $\mathbf{v}_2 = (1 - \sqrt{5}, 2)$, respectively.

(b) Compute

$$\begin{bmatrix} s_{n+1} \\ s_n \end{bmatrix} = \mathbf{A}^n\mathbf{x}_0 = \mathbf{P}\mathbf{D}^n\mathbf{P}^{-1} \begin{bmatrix} 1 \\ 1 \end{bmatrix}$$

to derive the amazing formula

$$s_n = \frac{1}{\sqrt{5}} \left[\left(\frac{1 + \sqrt{5}}{2} \right)^{n+1} - \left(\frac{1 - \sqrt{5}}{2} \right)^{n+1} \right].$$

Thus after 1 year the number of rabbit pairs is

$$s_{12} = \frac{1}{\sqrt{5}} \left[\left(\frac{1 + \sqrt{5}}{2} \right)^{13} - \left(\frac{1 - \sqrt{5}}{2} \right)^{13} \right] = 233.$$

Show that there are 75,025 rabbit pairs after 2 years and over 2.5 trillion rabbit pairs after 5 years.

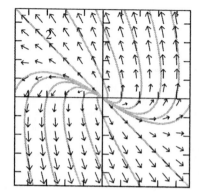

CHAPTER 7

Linear Systems of Differential Equations

7.1 First-Order Systems and Applications

In Chapters 1 and 5 we discussed methods for solving an ordinary differential equation that involves only one dependent variable. Many applications, however, require the use of two or more dependent variables, each a function of a single independent variable (typically time). Such a problem leads naturally to a *system* of simultaneous ordinary differential equations. We will usually denote the independent variable by t and the dependent variables (the unknown functions of t) by x_1, x_2, x_3, ..., or by x, y, z, ... Primes will indicate derivatives with respect to t.

We will restrict our attention to systems in which the number of equations is the same as the number of dependent variables (unknown functions). For instance, a system of two first-order equations in the dependent variables x and y has the general form

$$f(t, x, y, x', y') = 0,$$
$$g(t, x, y, x', y') = 0,$$
(1)

where the functions f and g are given. A **solution** of this system is a pair $x(t)$, $y(t)$ of functions of t that satisfy both equations identically over some interval of values of t.

For an example of a second-order system, consider a particle of mass m that moves in space under the influence of a force field $\mathbf{F}$ that depends on time t, the position $(x(t), y(t), z(t))$ of the particle, and its velocity $(x'(t), y'(t), z'(t))$. Writing Newton's law $m\mathbf{a} = \mathbf{F}$ componentwise, we get the system

$$mx'' = F_1(t, x, y, z, x', y', z'),$$
$$my'' = F_2(t, x, y, z, x', y', z'),$$
$$mz'' = F_3(t, x, y, z, x', y', z')$$
(2)

of three second-order equations with independent variable t and dependent variables x, y, z; the three right-hand side functions F_1, F_2, F_3 are the components of the vector-valued function **F**.

Initial Applications

Examples 1 and 2 further illustrate how systems of differential equations arise naturally in scientific problems.

Example 1

FIGURE 7.1.1. The mass-and- spring system of Example 1.

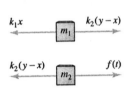

FIGURE 7.1.2. The free body diagrams for the system of Example 1.

Consider the system of two masses and two springs shown in Fig. 7.1.1, with a given external force $f(t)$ acting on the right-hand mass m_2. We denote by $x(t)$ the displacement (to the right) of the mass m_1 from its static equilibrium position [when the system is motionless and in equilibrium and $f(t) = 0$] and by $y(t)$ the displacement of the mass m_2 from its static position. Thus the two springs are neither stretched nor compressed when x and y are zero.

In the configuration in Fig. 7.1.1, the first spring is stretched x units and the second by $y - x$ units. We apply Newton's law of motion to the two "free body diagrams" shown in Fig. 7.1.2; we thereby obtain the system

$$m_1 x'' = -k_1 x + k_2(y - x),$$
$$m_2 y'' = -k_2(y - x) + f(t) \tag{3}$$

of differential equations that the position functions $x(t)$ and $y(t)$ must satisfy. For instance, if $m_1 = 2$, $m_2 = 1$, $k_1 = 4$, $k_2 = 2$, and $f(t) = 40 \sin 3t$ in appropriate physical units, then the system in (3) reduces to

$$2x'' = -6x + 2y,$$
$$y'' = 2x - 2y + 40 \sin 3t. \tag{4}$$

■

Example 2

FIGURE 7.1.3. The two brine tanks of Example 2.

Consider two brine tanks connected as shown in Fig. 7.1.3. Tank 1 contains $x(t)$ pounds of salt in 100 gal of brine and tank 2 contains $y(t)$ pounds of salt in 200 gal of brine. The brine in each tank is kept uniform by stirring, and brine is pumped from each tank to the other at the rates indicated in Fig. 7.1.3. In addition, fresh water flows into tank 1 at 20gal/min, and the brine in tank 2 flows out at 20 gal/min (so the total volume of brine in the two tanks remains constant). The salt concentrations in the two tanks are $x/100$ pounds per gallon and $y/200$ pounds per gallon, respectively. When we compute the rates of change of the amount of salt in the two tanks, we therefore get the system of differential equations that $x(t)$ and $y(t)$ must satisfy:

$$x' = -30 \cdot \frac{x}{100} + 10 \cdot \frac{y}{200} = -\frac{3}{10}x + \frac{1}{20}y,$$
$$y' = 30 \cdot \frac{x}{100} - 10 \cdot \frac{y}{200} - 20 \cdot \frac{y}{200} = \frac{3}{10}x - \frac{3}{20}y$$

—that is,

$$20x' = -6x + y,$$
$$20y' = 6x - 3y. \tag{5}$$

■

First-Order Systems

Consider a system of differential equations that can be solved for the highest-order derivatives of the dependent variables that appear, as explicit functions of t and lower-order derivatives of the dependent variables. For instance, in the case of a system of two second-order equations, our assumption is that it can be written in the form

$$x_1'' = f_1(t, x_1, x_2, x_1', x_2'),$$
$$x_2'' = f_2(t, x_1, x_2, x_1', x_2'). \tag{6}$$

It is of both practical and theoretical importance that any such higher-order system can be transformed into a equivalent system of *first-order* equations.

To describe how such a transformation is accomplished, we consider first the "system" consisting of the single nth-order equation

➤
$$x^{(n)} = f(t, x, x', \ldots, x^{(n-1)}). \tag{7}$$

We introduce the dependent variables $x_1, x_2, \ldots, x_n$ defined as follows:

$$x_1 = x, \quad x_2 = x', \quad x_3 = x'', \quad \ldots, \quad x_n = x^{(n-1)}. \tag{8}$$

Note that $x_1' = x' = x_2$, $x_2' = x'' = x_3$, and so on. Hence the substitution of (8) in Eq. (7) yields the system

$$x_1' = x_2,$$
$$x_2' = x_3,$$

➤
$$\vdots \tag{9}$$

$$x_{n-1}' = x_n,$$
$$x_n' = f(t, x_1, x_2, \ldots, x_n)$$

of n *first-order* equations. Evidently, this system is equivalent to the original nth-order equation in (7), in the sense that $x(t)$ is a solution of Eq. (7) if and only if the functions $x_1(t)$, $x_2(t)$, $\ldots$, $x_n(t)$ defined in (8) satisfy the system of equations in (9).

Example 3   The third-order equation

$$x^{(3)} + 3x'' + 2x' - 5x = \sin 2t$$

is of the form in (7) with

$$f(t, x, x', x'') = 5x - 2x' - 3x'' + \sin 2t.$$

Hence the substitutions

$$x_1 = x, \quad x_2 = x' = x_1', \quad x_3 = x'' = x_2'$$

yield the system

$$x_1' = x_2,$$
$$x_2' = x_3,$$
$$x_3' = 5x_1 - 2x_2 - 3x_3 + \sin 2t$$

of three first-order equations.   ■

It may appear that the first-order system obtained in Example 3 offers little advantage, because we could use the methods of Chapter 5 to solve the original (linear) third-order equation. But suppose that we were confronted with the nonlinear equation

$$x'' = x^3 + (x')^3,$$

to which none of our earlier methods can be applied. The corresponding first-order system is

$$x_1' = x_2,$$
$$x_2' = (x_1)^3 + (x_2)^3, \tag{10}$$

and we will see in Section 7.6 that there exist effective numerical techniques for approximating the solution of essentially any first-order system. So, in this case, the transformation to a first-order system *is* advantageous. From a practical viewpoint, large systems of higher-order differential equations typically are solved numerically with the aid of the computer, and the first step is to transform such a system into a first-order system for which a standard computer program is available.

Example 4   The system

$$2x'' = -6x + 2y,$$
$$y'' = 2x - 2y + 40\sin 3t \tag{4}$$

of second-order equations was derived in Example 1. Transform this system into an equivalent first-order system.

Solution   Motivated by the equations in (8), we define

$$x_1 = x, \quad x_2 = x' = x_1', \quad y_1 = y, \quad y_2 = y' = y_1'.$$

Then the system in (4) yields the system

$$x_1' = x_2,$$
$$2x_2' = -6x_1 + 2y_1,$$
$$y_1' = y_2, \tag{11}$$
$$y_2' = 2x_1 - 2y_1 + 40\sin 3t$$

of four first-order equations in the dependent variables x_1, x_2, y_1, and y_2.   ■

Simple Two-Dimensional Systems

The linear second-order differential equation

$$x'' + px' + qx = 0 \tag{12}$$

(with constant coefficients and independent variable t) transforms via the substitutions $x' = y$, $x'' = y'$ into the two-dimensional linear system

$$x' = y,$$
$$y' = -qx - py. \tag{13}$$

Conversely, we can solve this system in (13) by solving the familiar single equation in (12).

Example 5   To solve the two-dimensional system

$$x' = -2y,$$
$$y' = \tfrac{1}{2}x, \tag{14}$$

we begin with the observation that

$$x'' = -2y' = -2\left(\tfrac{1}{2}x\right) = -x.$$

This gives the single second-order equation $x'' + x = 0$ having general solution

$$x(t) = A\cos t + B\sin t = C\cos(t - \alpha),$$

where $A = C\cos\alpha$ and $B = C\sin\alpha$. Then

$$y(t) = -\tfrac{1}{2}x'(t) = -\tfrac{1}{2}(-A\sin t + B\cos t)$$
$$= \tfrac{1}{2}C\sin(t - \alpha).$$

The identity $\cos^2\theta + \sin^2\theta = 1$ therefore implies that, for each value of t, the point $(x(t), y(t))$ lies on the ellipse

$$\frac{x^2}{C^2} + \frac{y^2}{(C/2)^2} = 1$$

with semiaxes C and $C/2$. Figure 7.1.4 shows several such ellipses in the xy-plane. ∎

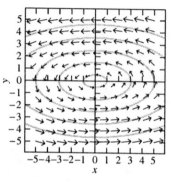

FIGURE 7.1.4. Direction field and solution curves for the system $x' = -2y$, $y' = \tfrac{1}{2}x$ of Example 5.

A solution $(x(t), y(t))$ of a two-dimensional system

$$x' = f(t, x, y),$$
$$y' = g(t, x, y)$$

can be regarded as a parametrization of a **solution curve** or **trajectory** of the system in the xy-plane. Thus the trajectories of the system in (14) are the ellipses of Fig. 7.1.4. The choice of an initial point $(x(0), y(0))$ determines which one of these trajectories a particular solution parametrizes.

The picture showing a system's trajectories in the xy-plane—its so-called *phase plane portrait*—fails to reveal precisely how the point $(x(t), y(t))$ moves along its trajectory. If the functions f and g do not involve the independent variable t, then a direction field—showing typical arrows representing vectors with components (proportional to) the derivatives $x' = f(x, y)$ and $y' = g(x, y)$—can be plotted. Because the moving point $(x(t), y(t))$ has velocity vector $(x'(t), y'(t))$, this direction field indicates the point's direction of motion along its trajectory. For instance, the direction field plotted in Fig. 7.1.4 indicates that each such point moves counterclockwise around its elliptical trajectory. Additional information can be shown in the separate graphs of $x(t)$ and $y(t)$ as functions of t.

Example 5

Continued

With initial values $x(0) = 2$, $y(0) = 0$, the general solution in Example 5 yields

$$x(0) = A = 2, \quad y(0) = -\tfrac{1}{2}B = 0.$$

The resulting particular solution is given by

$$x(t) = 2\cos t, \quad y(t) = \sin t.$$

The graphs of the two functions are shown in Fig. 7.1.5. We see that $x(t)$ initially decreases while $y(t)$ increases. It follows that, as t increases, the solution point $(x(t), y(t))$ traverses the trajectory $\frac{1}{4}x^2 + y^2 = 1$ in the counterclockwise direction, as indicated by the direction field vectors in Fig. 7.1.4. ∎

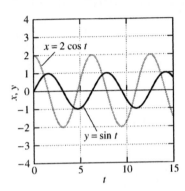

FIGURE 7.1.5. x- and y-solution curves for the initial value problem $x' = -2y$, $y' = \frac{1}{2}x$, $x(0) = 2$, $y(0) = 0$.

Example 6

To find a general solution of the system

$$\begin{aligned} x' &= y, \\ y' &= 2x + y, \end{aligned} \tag{15}$$

we begin with the observation that

$$x'' = y' = 2x + y = x' + 2x.$$

This gives the single linear second-order equation

$$x'' - x' - 2x = 0$$

having the characteristic equation

$$r^2 - r - 2 = (r + 1)(r - 2) = 0$$

and the general solution

$$x(t) = Ae^{-t} + Be^{2t}. \tag{16}$$

Therefore,

$$y(t) = x'(t) = -Ae^{-t} + 2Be^{2t}. \tag{17}$$

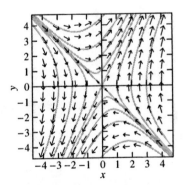

FIGURE 7.1.6. Direction field and solution curves for the system $x' = y$, $y' = 2x + y$ of Example 6.

Typical phase plane trajectories of the system in (15) parametrized by Eqs. (16) and (17) are shown in Fig. 7.1.6. See Problem 23 for further discussion of these trajectories. ∎

Example 7

To solve the initial value problem

$$x' = -y,$$
$$y' = (1.01)x - (0.2)y, \tag{18}$$
$$x(0) = 0, \quad y(0) = -1,$$

we begin with the observation that

$$x'' = -y' = -[(1.01)x - (0.2)y] = (-1.01)x - (0.2)x'.$$

This gives the single linear second-order equation

$$x'' + (0.2)x' + (1.01)x = 0$$

having the characteristic equation

$$r^2 + (0.2)r + 1.01 = (r + 0.1)^2 + 1 = 0,$$

characteristic roots $-0.1 \pm i$, and the general solution

$$x(t) = e^{-t/10}(A \cos t + B \sin t).$$

Then $x(0) = A = 0$, so

$$x(t) = Be^{-t/10} \sin t,$$
$$y(t) = -x'(t) = \tfrac{1}{10} Be^{-t/10} \sin t - Be^{-t/10} \cos t.$$

Finally, $y(0) = -B = -1$, so the desired solution of the system in (18) is

$$x(t) = e^{-t/10} \sin t,$$
$$y(t) = \tfrac{1}{10} e^{-t/10}(\sin t - 10 \cos t). \tag{19}$$

These equations parametrize the spiral trajectory in Fig. 7.1.7; the trajectory approaches the origin as $t \to +\infty$. Figure 7.1.8 shows the x- and y-solution curves given in (19). ∎

When we study linear systems in subsequent sections, we will learn why the superficially similar systems in Examples 5 through 7 have the markedly different trajectories shown in Figs. 7.1.4, 7.1.6, and 7.1.7.

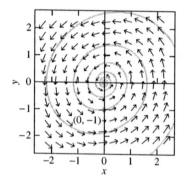

FIGURE 7.1.7. Direction field and solution curve for the system $x' = -y$, $y' = (1.01)x - (0.2)y$ of Example 7.

Linear Systems

In addition to practical advantages for numerical computation, the general theory of systems and systematic solution techniques are more easily and more concisely described for first-order systems than for higher-order systems. For instance, consider a *linear* first-order system of the form

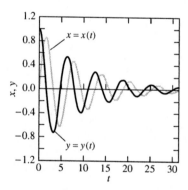

FIGURE 7.1.8. x- and y-solution curves for the initial value problem of Example 7.

$$x_1' = p_{11}(t)x_1 + p_{12}(t)x_2 + \cdots + p_{1n}x_n + f_1(t),$$
$$x_2' = p_{21}(t)x_1 + p_{22}(t)x_2 + \cdots + p_{2n}x_n + f_2(t),$$
$$\vdots \tag{20}$$
$$x_n' = p_{n1}(t)x_1 + p_{n2}(t)x_2 + \cdots + p_{nn}(t)x_n + f_n(t).$$

We say that this system is **homogeneous** if the functions f_1, f_2, ..., f_n are all identically zero; otherwise, it is **nonhomogeneous.** Thus the linear system in (5) is homogeneous, whereas the linear system in (11) is nonhomogeneous. The system in (10) is nonlinear because the right-hand side of the second equation is not a linear function of the dependent variables x_1 and x_2.

A **solution** of the system in (20) is an *n*-tuple of functions $x_1(t)$, $x_2(t)$, ..., $x_n(t)$ that (on some interval) identically satisfy each of the equations in (20). We will see that the general theory of a system of *n* linear first-order equations shares many similarities with the general theory of a single *n*th-order linear differential equation. Theorem 1 (proved in Appendix A) is analogous to Theorem 2 of Section 5.2. It tells us that if the coefficient functions p_{ij} and f_j in (20) are continuous, then the system has a unique solution satisfying given initial conditions.

THEOREM 1: Existence and Uniqueness for Linear Systems

Suppose that the functions p_{11}, p_{12}, ..., p_{nn} and the functions f_1, f_2, ..., f_n are continuous on the open interval I containing the point a. Then, given the n numbers b_1, b_2, ..., b_n, the system in (20) has a unique solution on the entire interval I that satisfies the n initial conditions

$$x_1(a) = b_1, \quad x_2(a) = b_2, \quad ..., \quad x_n(a) = b_n. \tag{21}$$

▲

Thus n initial conditions are needed to determine a solution of a system of n linear first-order equations, and we therefore expect a general solution of such a system to involve n arbitrary constants. For instance, we saw in Example 4 that the second-order linear system

$$2x'' = -6x + 2y,$$
$$y'' = \quad 2x - 2y + 40 \sin 3t,$$

which describes the position functions $x(t)$ and $y(t)$ of Example 1, is equivalent to the system of *four* first-order linear equations in (11). Hence four initial conditions would be needed to determine the subsequent motions of the two masses in Example 1. Typical initial values would be the initial positions $x(0)$ and $y(0)$ and the initial velocities $x'(0)$ and $y'(0)$. On the other hand, we found that the amounts $x(t)$ and $y(t)$ of salt in the two tanks of Example 2 are described by the system

$$20x' = -6x + \quad y,$$
$$20y' = \quad 6x - 3y$$

of *two* first-order linear equations. Hence the two initial values $x(0)$ and $y(0)$ should suffice to determine the solution. Given a higher-order system, we often must transform it into an equivalent first-order system to discover how many initial conditions are needed to determine a unique solution. Theorem 1 tells us that the number of such conditions is precisely the same as the number of equations in the equivalent first-order system.

7.1 Problems

In Problems 1 through 10, transform the given differential equation or system into an equivalent system of first-order differential equations.

1. $x'' + 3x' + 7x = t^2$
2. $x^{(4)} + 6x'' - 3x' + x = \cos 3t$
3. $t^2 x'' + tx' + (t^2 - 1)x = 0$
4. $t^3 x^{(3)} - 2t^2 x'' + 3tx' + 5x = \ln t$
5. $x^{(3)} = (x')^2 + \cos x$
6. $x'' - 5x + 4y = 0, \quad y'' + 4x - 5y = 0$
7. $x'' = -\dfrac{kx}{(x^2 + y^2)^{3/2}}, \quad y'' = -\dfrac{ky}{(x^2 + y^2)^{3/2}}$
8. $x'' + 3x' + 4x - 2y = 0, \quad y'' + 2y' - 3x + y = \cos t$
9. $x'' = 3x - y + 2z, \quad y'' = x + y - 4z, \quad z'' = 5x - y - z$
10. $x'' = (1 - y)x, \quad y'' = (1 - x)y$

Use the method of Examples 5, 6, and 7 to find general solutions of the systems in Problems 11 through 20. If initial conditions are given, find the corresponding particular solution. For each problem, use a computer system or graphing calculator to construct a direction field and typical solution curves for the given system.

11. $x' = y, \quad y' = -x$
12. $x' = y, \quad y' = x$
13. $x' = -2y, \quad y' = 2x; \quad x(0) = 1, \ y(0) = 0$
14. $x' = 10y, \quad y' = -10x; \quad x(0) = 3, \ y(0) = 4$
15. $x' = \frac{1}{2}y, \quad y' = -8x$
16. $x' = 8y, \quad y' = -2x$
17. $x' = y, \quad y' = 6x - y; \quad x(0) = 1, \ y(0) = 2$
18. $x' = -y, \quad y' = 10x - 7y; \quad x(0) = 2, \ y(0) = -7$
19. $x' = -y, \quad y' = 13x + 4y; \quad x(0) = 0, \ y(0) = 3$
20. $x' = y, \quad y' = -9x + 6y$

21. (a) Calculate $[x(t)]^2 + [y(t)]^2$ to show that the trajectories of the system $x' = y, \ y' = -x$ of Problem 11 are circles. (b) Calculate $[x(t)]^2 - [y(t)]^2$ to show that the trajectories of the system $x' = y, \ y' = x$ of Problem 12 are hyperbolas.

22. (a) Beginning with the general solution of the system $x' = -2y, \ y' = 2x$ of Problem 13, calculate $x^2 + y^2$ to show that the trajectories are circles. (b) Show similarly that the trajectories of the system $x' = \frac{1}{2}y, \ y' = -8x$ of Problem 15 are ellipses with equations of the form $16x^2 + y^2 = C^2$.

23. First solve Eqs. (16) and (17) for e^{-t} and e^{2t} in terms of $x(t)$, $y(t)$, and the constants A and B. Then substitute the results in $(e^{2t})(e^{-t})^2 = 1$ to show that the trajectories of the system $x' = y, \ y' = 2x + y$ in Example 6 satisfy an equation of the form

$$4x^3 - 3xy^2 + y^3 = C \quad \text{(constant)}.$$

Then show that $C = 0$ yields the straight lines $y = -x$ and $y = 2x$ that are visible in Fig. 7.1.6.

24. Derive the equations

$$m_1 x_1'' = -(k_1 + k_2)x_1 + k_2 x_2,$$
$$m_2 x_2'' = k_2 x_1 - (k_2 + k_3)x_2$$

for the displacements (from equilibrium) of the two masses shown in Fig. 7.1.9.

FIGURE 7.1.9. The system of Problem 24.

25. Two particles each of mass m are attached to a string under (constant) tension T, as indicated in Fig. 7.1.10. Assume that the particles oscillate vertically (that is, parallel to the y-axis) with amplitudes so small that the sines of the angles shown are accurately approximated by their tangents. Show that the displacements y_1 and y_2 satisfy the equations

$$ky_1'' = -2y_1 + y_2, \quad ky_2'' = y_1 - 2y_2,$$

where $k = mL/T$.

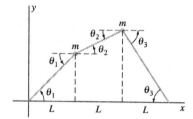

FIGURE 7.1.10. The mechanical system of Problem 25.

26. Three 100-gal fermentation vats are connected as indicated in Fig. 7.1.11, and the mixtures in each tank are kept uniform by stirring. Denote by $x_i(t)$ the amount (in pounds) of alcohol in tank T_i at time t ($i = 1, 2, 3$). Suppose that the mixture circulates between the tanks at the rate of 10 gal/min. Derive the equations

$$10x_1' = -x_1 + x_3$$
$$10x_2' = x_1 - x_2$$
$$10x_3' = x_2 - x_3.$$

FIGURE 7.1.11. The fermentation tanks of Problem 26.

27. A particle of mass m moves in the plane with coordinates $(x(t), y(t))$ under the influence of a force that is directed toward the origin and has magnitude $k/(x^2 + y^2)$—an inverse-square central force field. Show that

$$mx'' = -\frac{kx}{r^3} \quad \text{and} \quad my'' = -\frac{ky}{r^3},$$

where $r = \sqrt{x^2 + y^2}$.

28. Suppose that a projectile of mass m moves in a vertical plane in the atmosphere near the surface of the earth under the influence of two forces: a downward gravitational force of magnitude mg, and a resistive force $\mathbf{F}_R$ that is directed opposite to the velocity vector $\mathbf{v}$ and has magnitude kv^2 (where $v = |\mathbf{v}|$ is the speed of the projectile; see Fig. 7.1.12). Show that the equations of motion of the projectile are

$$mx'' = -kvx', \quad my'' = -kvy' - mg,$$

where $v = \sqrt{(x')^2 + (y')^2}$.

29. Suppose that a particle with mass m and electrical charge q moves in the xy-plane under the influence of the magnetic field $\mathbf{B} = B\mathbf{k}$ (thus a uniform field parallel to the z-axis), so the force on the particle is $\mathbf{F} = q\mathbf{v} \times \mathbf{B}$ if its velocity is $\mathbf{v}$. Show that the equations of motion of the particle are

$$mx'' = +qBy', \quad my'' = -qBx'.$$

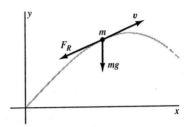

FIGURE 7.1.12. The trajectory of the projectile of Problem 28.

7.1 Application: Gravitation and Kepler's Laws of Planetary Motion

Around the turn of the seventeenth century, Johannes Kepler analyzed a lifetime of planetary observations by the astronomer Tycho Brahe. Kepler concluded that the motion of the planets around the sun is described by the following three propositions, now known as **Kepler's laws of planetary motion:**

1. The orbit of each planet is an ellipse with the sun at one focus.
2. The radius vector from the sun to each planet sweeps out area at a constant rate.
3. The square of the planet's period of revolution is proportional to the cube of the major semiaxis of its elliptical orbit.

In his *Principia Mathematica* (1687) Isaac Newton deduced the inverse-square law of gravitation from Kepler's laws. In this application we lead you through a derivation of Kepler's first two laws from Newton's law of gravitation. The intellectual and historical significance of this computation would be difficult to exaggerate.

Assume that the sun is located at the origin in the plane of motion of a planet, and write the position vector of the planet in the form

$$\mathbf{r}(t) = (x(t), y(t)) = x\mathbf{i} + y\mathbf{j}, \tag{1}$$

where $\mathbf{i} = (1, 0)$ and $\mathbf{j} = (0, 1)$ denote the unit vectors in the positive x- and y-directions. Then the inverse-square law of gravitation implies (Problem 27) that the acceleration vector $\mathbf{r}''(t)$ of the planet is given by

$$\mathbf{r}'' = -\frac{k\mathbf{r}}{r^3}, \tag{2}$$

where $r = \sqrt{x^2 + y^2}$ is the distance from the sun to the planet. If the polar coordinates of the planet at time t are $(r(t), \theta(t))$, then the radial and transverse unit

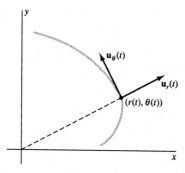

FIGURE 7.1.13. The radial and transverse unit vectors $\mathbf{u}_r$ and $\mathbf{u}_\theta$.

vectors shown in Fig. 7.1.13 are given by

$$\mathbf{u}_r = \mathbf{i}\cos\theta + \mathbf{j}\sin\theta \quad \text{and} \quad \mathbf{u}_\theta = -\mathbf{i}\sin\theta + \mathbf{j}\cos\theta. \tag{3}$$

The radial unit vector $\mathbf{u}_r$ (when located at the planet's position) always points directly away from the origin, and the transverse unit vector $\mathbf{u}_\theta$ is obtained from $\mathbf{u}_r$ by a 90° counterclockwise rotation.

STEP 1: Differentiate the equations in (3) componentwise to show that

$$\frac{d\mathbf{u}_r}{dt} = \mathbf{u}_\theta \frac{d\theta}{dt} \quad \text{and} \quad \frac{d\mathbf{u}_\theta}{dt} = -\mathbf{u}_r \frac{d\theta}{dt}. \tag{4}$$

STEP 2: Use the equations in (4) to differentiate the planet's position vector $\mathbf{r} = r\mathbf{u}_r$ and thereby show that its velocity vector is given by

$$\mathbf{v} = \frac{d\mathbf{r}}{dt} = \mathbf{u}_r \frac{dr}{dt} + r\frac{d\theta}{dt}\mathbf{u}_\theta. \tag{5}$$

STEP 3: Differentiate again to show that the planet's acceleration vector $\mathbf{a} = d\mathbf{v}/dt$ is given by

$$\mathbf{a} = \left[\frac{d^2r}{dt^2} - r\left(\frac{d\theta}{dt}\right)^2\right]\mathbf{u}_r + \left[\frac{1}{r}\frac{d}{dt}\left(r^2\frac{d\theta}{dt}\right)\right]\mathbf{u}_\theta. \tag{6}$$

STEP 4: The radial and transverse components on the right-hand sides in Eqs. (2) and (6) must agree. Equating the transverse components, we get

$$\frac{1}{r}\frac{d}{dt}\left(r^2\frac{d\theta}{dt}\right) = 0, \tag{7}$$

so it follows that

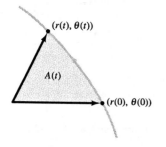

FIGURE 7.1.14. Area swept out by the radius vector.

$$r^2\frac{d\theta}{dt} = h, \tag{8}$$

where h is a constant. Because the polar-coordinate area element—for computation of the area $A(t)$ in Fig. 7.1.14—is given by $dA = \frac{1}{2}r^2\,d\theta$, Eq. (8) implies that the derivative $A'(t)$ is *constant*, which is a statement of Kepler's second law.

STEP 5: Equate radial components in (2) and (6), and then use the result in (8) to show that the planet's radial coordinate function $r(t)$ satisfies the second-order differential equation

$$\frac{d^2r}{dt^2} - \frac{h^2}{r^3} = -\frac{k}{r^2}. \tag{9}$$

STEP 6: Assuming that the orbit can be written in the polar-coordinate form $r = r(\theta)$, use the chain rule and Eq. (8) to show that if $r = 1/z$, then

$$\frac{dr}{dt} = -h\frac{dz}{d\theta}. \tag{}$$

Differentiate again, to deduce from Eq. (9) that the function $z(\theta) = 1/r(\theta)$ satisfies the second-order equation

$$\frac{d^2z}{d\theta^2} + z = \frac{k}{h^2}. \tag{10}$$

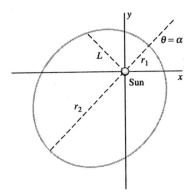

FIGURE 7.1.15. The elliptical orbit

$$r = \frac{L}{1 + e\cos(\theta - \alpha)}$$

with perihelion distance $r_1 = L/(1 + e)$ and aphelion distance $r_2 = L/(1 - e)$.

FIGURE 7.1.16. The shape of the orbit of Halley's comet.

STEP 7: Show that the general solution of Eq. (10) is

$$z(\theta) = A\sin\theta + B\cos\theta + \frac{k}{h^2}. \tag{11}$$

STEP 8: Finally, deduce from Eq. (11) that $r(\theta) = 1/z(\theta)$ is given by

$$r(\theta) = \frac{L}{1 + e\cos(\theta - \alpha)}, \tag{12}$$

with $e = Ch^2/k$, $C\cos\alpha = A$, $C\sin\alpha = B$, and $L = h^2/k$. The polar-coordinate graph of Eq. (12) is a conic section of eccentricity e—an ellipse if $0 \leq e < 1$, a parabola if $e = 1$, and a hyperbola if $e > 1$—with focus at the origin. Planetary orbits are bounded and therefore are ellipses, with eccentricity $e < 1$. As indicated in Fig. 7.1.15, the major axis of the ellipse lies along the radial line $\theta = \alpha$.

STEP 9: Plot some typical elliptical orbits—as described by (12)—having different eccentricities, sizes, and orientations. In rectangular coordinates you can write

$$x(t) = r(t)\cos t, \quad y(t) = r(t)\sin t, \quad 0 \leqq t \leqq 2\pi$$

to plot an elliptical orbit with eccentricity e, semilatus rectum L (Fig. 7.1.15), and rotation angle α. The eccentricity of the earth's orbit is $e \approx 0.0167$, so close to zero that the orbit looks nearly circular (though with the sun off center), and the eccentricities of the other planetary orbits range from 0.0068 for Venus and 0.0933 for Mars to 0.2056 for Mercury and 0.2486 for Pluto. But many comets have highly eccentric orbits—Halley's comet has $e \approx 0.97$ (Fig. 7.1.16).

7.2 Matrices and Linear Systems

A system of differential equations often can be simplified by expressing it as a single differential equation involving a matrix-valued function. A **matrix-valued function**, or simply **matrix function**, is a matrix such as

$$\mathbf{x}(t) = \begin{bmatrix} x_1(t) \\ x_2(t) \\ \vdots \\ x_n(t) \end{bmatrix} \tag{1}$$

or

$$\mathbf{A}(t) = \begin{bmatrix} a_{11}(t) & a_{12}(t) & \cdots & a_{1n}(t) \\ a_{21}(t) & a_{22}(t) & \cdots & a_{2n}(t) \\ \vdots & \vdots & & \vdots \\ a_{m1}(t) & a_{m2}(t) & \cdots & a_{mn}(t) \end{bmatrix}, \tag{2}$$

in which each entry is a function of t. We say that the matrix function $\mathbf{A}(t)$ is **continuous** (or **differentiable**) at a point (or on an interval) if each of its elements has the same property. The **derivative** of a differentiable matrix function is defined by elementwise differentiation; that is,

$$\mathbf{A}'(t) = \frac{d\mathbf{A}}{dt} = \left[\frac{da_{ij}}{dt} \right]. \tag{3}$$

Example 1   If

$$\mathbf{x}(t) = \begin{bmatrix} t \\ t^2 \\ e^{-t} \end{bmatrix} \quad \text{and} \quad \mathbf{A}(t) = \begin{bmatrix} \sin t & 1 \\ t & \cos t \end{bmatrix},$$

then

$$\frac{d\mathbf{x}}{dt} = \begin{bmatrix} 1 \\ 2t \\ -e^{-t} \end{bmatrix} \quad \text{and} \quad \mathbf{A}'(t) = \begin{bmatrix} \cos t & 0 \\ 1 & -\sin t \end{bmatrix}. \quad \blacksquare$$

The differentiation rules

$$\frac{d}{dt}(\mathbf{A} + \mathbf{B}) = \frac{d\mathbf{A}}{dt} + \frac{d\mathbf{B}}{dt} \tag{4}$$

and

$$\frac{d}{dt}(\mathbf{A}\mathbf{B}) = \mathbf{A}\frac{d\mathbf{B}}{dt} + \frac{d\mathbf{A}}{dt}\mathbf{B} \tag{5}$$

follow readily by elementwise application of the analogous differentiation rules of elementary calculus for real-valued functions. If c is a (constant) real number and $\mathbf{C}$ is a constant matrix, then

$$\frac{d}{dt}(c\mathbf{A}) = c\frac{d\mathbf{A}}{dt}, \quad \frac{d}{dt}(\mathbf{C}\mathbf{A}) = \mathbf{C}\frac{d\mathbf{A}}{dt}, \quad \text{and} \quad \frac{d}{dt}(\mathbf{A}\mathbf{C}) = \frac{d\mathbf{A}}{dt}\mathbf{C}. \tag{6}$$

Because of the noncommutativity of matrix multiplication, it is important not to reverse the order of the factors in Eqs. (5) and (6).

First-Order Linear Systems

The notation and terminology of matrices and vectors may seem rather elaborate when first encountered, but it is readily assimilated with practice. Our main use for matrix notation will be the simplification of computations with systems of differential equations, especially those computations that would be burdensome in scalar notation.

We discuss here the general system of n first-order linear equations

$$\begin{aligned}
x_1' &= p_{11}(t)x_1 + p_{12}(t)x_2 + \cdots + p_{1n}(t)x_n + f_1(t), \\
x_2' &= p_{21}(t)x_1 + p_{22}(t)x_2 + \cdots + p_{2n}(t)x_n + f_2(t), \\
x_3' &= p_{31}(t)x_1 + p_{32}(t)x_2 + \cdots + p_{3n}(t)x_n + f_3(t), \\
&\quad \vdots \\
x_n' &= p_{n1}(t)x_1 + p_{n2}(t)x_2 + \cdots + p_{nn}(t)x_n + f_n(t).
\end{aligned} \tag{7}$$

If we introduce the *coefficient matrix*

$$\mathbf{P}(t) = \left[\, p_{ij}(t) \,\right]$$

and the column vectors

$$\mathbf{x} = \left[\, x_i \,\right] \quad \text{and} \quad \mathbf{f}(t) = \left[\, f_i(t) \,\right],$$

then the system in (7) takes the form of a single matrix equation

$$\blacktriangleright \qquad\qquad \frac{d\mathbf{x}}{dt} = \mathbf{P}(t)\mathbf{x} + \mathbf{f}(t). \qquad\qquad (8)$$

We will see that the general theory of the linear system in (7) closely parallels that of a single *n*th-order equation. The matrix notation used in Eq. (8) not only emphasizes this analogy, but also saves a great deal of space.

A **solution** of Eq. (8) on the open interval *I* is a column vector function $\mathbf{x}(t) = \left[x_i(t)\right]$ such that the component functions of $\mathbf{x}$ satisfy the system in (7) identically on *I*. If the functions $p_{ij}(t)$ and $f_i(t)$ are all continuous on *I*, then Theorem 1 of Section 7.1 guarantees the existence on *I* of a unique solution $\mathbf{x}(t)$ satisfying preassigned initial conditions $\mathbf{x}(a) = \mathbf{b}$.

Example 2

The first-order system

$$x_1' = 4x_1 - 3x_2,$$
$$x_2' = 6x_1 - 7x_2$$

can be written as the single matrix equation

$$\frac{d\mathbf{x}}{dt} = \begin{bmatrix} 4 & -3 \\ 6 & -7 \end{bmatrix} \mathbf{x} = \mathbf{P}\mathbf{x}.$$

To verify that the vector functions

$$\mathbf{x}_1(t) = \begin{bmatrix} 3e^{2t} \\ 2e^{2t} \end{bmatrix} \quad \text{and} \quad \mathbf{x}_2(t) = \begin{bmatrix} e^{-5t} \\ 3e^{-5t} \end{bmatrix}$$

are both solutions of the matrix differential equation with coefficient matrix $\mathbf{P}$, we need only calculate

$$\mathbf{P}\mathbf{x}_1 = \begin{bmatrix} 4 & -3 \\ 6 & -7 \end{bmatrix} \begin{bmatrix} 3e^{2t} \\ 2e^{2t} \end{bmatrix} = \begin{bmatrix} 6e^{2t} \\ 4e^{2t} \end{bmatrix} = \mathbf{x}_1'$$

and

$$\mathbf{P}\mathbf{x}_2 = \begin{bmatrix} 4 & -3 \\ 6 & -7 \end{bmatrix} \begin{bmatrix} e^{-5t} \\ 3e^{-5t} \end{bmatrix} = \begin{bmatrix} -5e^{-5t} \\ -15e^{-5t} \end{bmatrix} = \mathbf{x}_2'. \qquad \blacksquare$$

To investigate the general nature of the solutions of Eq. (8), we consider first the **associated homogeneous equation**

$$\frac{d\mathbf{x}}{dt} = \mathbf{P}(t)\mathbf{x}, \tag{9}$$

which has the form shown in Eq. (8), but with $\mathbf{f}(t) \equiv \mathbf{0}$. We expect it to have n solutions $\mathbf{x}_1, \mathbf{x}_2, \ldots, \mathbf{x}_n$ that are independent in some appropriate sense, and that are such that every solution of Eq. (9) is a linear combination of these n particular solutions. Given n solutions $\mathbf{x}_1, \mathbf{x}_2, \ldots, \mathbf{x}_n$ of Eq. (9), let us write

$$\mathbf{x}_j(t) = \begin{bmatrix} x_{1j}(t) \\ \vdots \\ x_{ij}(t) \\ \vdots \\ x_{nj}(t) \end{bmatrix}. \tag{10}$$

Thus $x_{ij}(t)$ denotes the ith component of the vector $\mathbf{x}_j(t)$, so the second subscript refers to the vector function $\mathbf{x}_j(t)$, whereas the first subscript refers to a component of this function. Theorem 1 is analogous to Theorem 1 of Section 5.2.

THEOREM 1: Principle of Superposition

Let $\mathbf{x}_1, \mathbf{x}_2, \ldots, \mathbf{x}_n$ be n solutions of the homogeneous linear equation in (9) on the open interval I. If $c_1, c_2, \ldots, c_n$ are constants, then the linear combination

$$\mathbf{x}(t) = c_1\mathbf{x}_1(t) + c_2\mathbf{x}_2(t) + \cdots + c_n\mathbf{x}_n(t) \tag{11}$$

is also a solution of Eq. (9) on I.

Proof: We know that $\mathbf{x}_i' = \mathbf{P}(t)\mathbf{x}_i$ for each i $(1 \leqq i \leqq n)$, so it follows immediately that

$$\begin{aligned}
\mathbf{x}' &= c_1\mathbf{x}_1' + c_2\mathbf{x}_2' + \cdots + c_n\mathbf{x}_n' \\
&= c_1\mathbf{P}(t)\mathbf{x}_1 + c_2\mathbf{P}(t)\mathbf{x}_2 + \cdots + c_n\mathbf{P}(t)\mathbf{x}_n \\
&= \mathbf{P}(t)(c_1\mathbf{x}_1 + c_2\mathbf{x}_2 + \cdots + c_n\mathbf{x}_n).
\end{aligned}$$

That is, $\mathbf{x}' = \mathbf{P}(t)\mathbf{x}$, as desired. The remarkable simplicity of this proof demonstrates clearly one advantage of matrix notation. ▲

Example 2
Continued

If $\mathbf{x}_1$ and $\mathbf{x}_2$ are the two solutions of

$$\frac{d\mathbf{x}}{dt} = \begin{bmatrix} 4 & -3 \\ 6 & -7 \end{bmatrix} \mathbf{x}$$

discussed in Example 2, then the linear combination

$$\mathbf{x}(t) = c_1\mathbf{x}_1(t) + c_2\mathbf{x}_2(t) = c_1 \begin{bmatrix} 3e^{2t} \\ 2e^{2t} \end{bmatrix} + c_2 \begin{bmatrix} e^{-5t} \\ 3e^{-5t} \end{bmatrix}$$

is also a solution. In scalar form with $\mathbf{x} = [x_1 \quad x_2]^T$, this gives the solution

$$x_1(t) = 3c_1e^{2t} + c_2e^{-5t},$$
$$x_2(t) = 2c_1e^{2t} + 3c_2e^{-5t}.$$

■

Independence and General Solutions

Linear independence is defined in the same way for vector-valued functions as for real-valued functions (Section 5.2). The vector-valued functions $x_1, x_2, \ldots, x_n$ are **linearly dependent** on the interval I provided that there exist constants $c_1, c_2, \ldots, c_n$, *not all zero*, such that

$$c_1 x_1(t) + c_2 x_2(t) + \cdots + c_n x_n(t) = 0 \tag{12}$$

for all t in I. Otherwise, they are **linearly independent.** Equivalently, they are linearly independent provided that no one of them is a linear combination of the others. For instance, the two solutions x_1 and x_2 of Example 2 are linearly independent because, clearly, neither is a scalar multiple of the other.

Just as in the case of a single nth-order equation, there is a Wronskian determinant that tells us whether or not n given solutions of the homogeneous equation in (9) are linearly dependent. If $x_1, x_2, \ldots, x_n$ are such solutions, then their **Wronskian** is the $n \times n$ determinant

$$W(t) = \begin{vmatrix} x_{11}(t) & x_{12}(t) & \cdots & x_{1n}(t) \\ x_{21}(t) & x_{22}(t) & \cdots & x_{2n}(t) \\ \vdots & \vdots & & \vdots \\ x_{n1}(t) & x_{n2}(t) & \cdots & x_{nn}(t) \end{vmatrix}, \tag{13}$$

using the notation in (10) for the components of the solutions. We may write either $W(t)$ or $W(x_1, x_2, \ldots, x_n)$. Note that W is the determinant of the matrix that has as its *column* vectors the solutions $x_1, x_2, \ldots, x_n$. Theorem 2 is analogous to Theorem 3 of Section 5.2. Moreover, its proof is essentially the same, with the definition of $W(x_1, x_2, \ldots, x_n)$ in Eq. (13) substituted for the definition of the Wronskian of n solutions of a single nth-order equation. (See Problems 34 through 36.)

THEOREM 2: Wronskians of Solutions

Suppose that $x_1, x_2, \ldots, x_n$ are n solutions of the homogeneous linear equation $x' = P(t)x$ on an open interval I. Suppose also that $P(t)$ is continuous on I. Let

$$W = W(x_1, x_2, \ldots, x_n).$$

Then

- If $x_1, x_2, \ldots, x_n$ are linearly dependent on I, then $W = 0$ at every point of I.
- If $x_1, x_2, \ldots, x_n$ are linearly independent on I, then $W \neq 0$ at each point of I.

Thus there are only two possibilities for solutions of homogeneous systems: Either $W = 0$ at *every* point of I, or $W = 0$ at *no* point of I. ▲

Example 3   It is readily verified (as in Example 2) that

$$x_1(t) = \begin{bmatrix} 2e^t \\ 2e^t \\ e^t \end{bmatrix}, \quad x_2(t) = \begin{bmatrix} 2e^{3t} \\ 0 \\ -e^{3t} \end{bmatrix}, \quad \text{and} \quad x_3(t) = \begin{bmatrix} 2e^{5t} \\ -2e^{5t} \\ e^{5t} \end{bmatrix}$$

are solutions of the equation

$$\frac{d\mathbf{x}}{dt} = \begin{bmatrix} 3 & -2 & 0 \\ -1 & 3 & -2 \\ 0 & -1 & 3 \end{bmatrix} \mathbf{x}. \tag{14}$$

The Wronskian of these solutions is

$$W = \begin{vmatrix} 2e^t & 2e^{3t} & 2e^{5t} \\ 2e^t & 0 & -2e^{5t} \\ e^t & -e^{3t} & e^{5t} \end{vmatrix} = e^{9t} \begin{vmatrix} 2 & 2 & 2 \\ 2 & 0 & -2 \\ 1 & -1 & 1 \end{vmatrix} = -16e^{9t},$$

which is never zero. Hence Theorem 2 implies that the solutions $\mathbf{x}_1$, $\mathbf{x}_2$, and $\mathbf{x}_3$ are linearly independent (on any open interval). ∎

Theorem 3 is analogous to Theorem 4 of Section 5.2. It says that the **general solution** of the *homogeneous* $n \times n$ system $\mathbf{x}' = \mathbf{P}(t)\mathbf{x}$ is a linear combination

$$\mathbf{x} = c_1\mathbf{x}_1 + c_2\mathbf{x}_2 + \cdots + c_n\mathbf{x}_n \tag{15}$$

of any n given linearly independent solutions $\mathbf{x}_1$, $\mathbf{x}_2$, ..., $\mathbf{x}_n$.

THEOREM 3: General Solutions of Homogeneous Systems

Let $\mathbf{x}_1$, $\mathbf{x}_2$, ..., $\mathbf{x}_n$ be n linearly independent solutions of the homogeneous linear equation $\mathbf{x}' = \mathbf{P}(t)\mathbf{x}$ on an open interval I where $\mathbf{P}(t)$ is continuous. If $\mathbf{x}(t)$ is any solution whatsoever of the equation $\mathbf{x}' = \mathbf{P}(t)\mathbf{x}$ on I, then there exist numbers c_1, c_2, ..., c_n such that

$$\mathbf{x}(t) = c_1\mathbf{x}_1(t) + c_2\mathbf{x}_2(t) + \cdots + c_n\mathbf{x}_n(t) \tag{15}$$

for all t in I.

Proof: Let a be a fixed point of I. We first show that there exist numbers c_1, c_2, ..., c_n such that the solution

$$\mathbf{y}(t) = c_1\mathbf{x}_1(t) + c_2\mathbf{x}_2(t) + \cdots + c_n\mathbf{x}_n(t) \tag{16}$$

has the same initial values at $t = a$ as does the given solution $\mathbf{x}(t)$; that is, such that

$$c_1\mathbf{x}_1(a) + c_2\mathbf{x}_2(a) + \cdots + c_n\mathbf{x}_n(a) = \mathbf{x}(a). \tag{17}$$

Let $\mathbf{X}(t)$ be the $n \times n$ matrix with column vectors $\mathbf{x}_1$, $\mathbf{x}_2$, ..., $\mathbf{x}_n$, and let $\mathbf{c}$ be the column vector with components c_1, c_2, ..., c_n. Then Eq. (17) may be written in the form

$$\mathbf{X}(a)\mathbf{c} = \mathbf{x}(a). \tag{18}$$

The Wronskian determinant $W(a) = |\mathbf{X}(a)|$ is nonzero because the solutions $\mathbf{x}_1$, $\mathbf{x}_2$, ..., $\mathbf{x}_n$ are linearly independent. Hence the matrix $\mathbf{X}(a)$ has an inverse matrix $\mathbf{X}(a)^{-1}$. Therefore the vector $\mathbf{c} = \mathbf{X}(a)^{-1}\mathbf{x}(a)$ satisfies Eq. (18), as desired.

Finally, note that the given solution $\mathbf{x}(t)$ and the solution $\mathbf{y}(t)$ of Eq. (16)—with the values of c_i determined by the equation $\mathbf{c} = \mathbf{X}(a)^{-1}\mathbf{x}(a)$—have the same initial values (at $t = a$). It follows from the existence-uniqueness theorem of Section 7.1 that $\mathbf{x}(t) = \mathbf{y}(t)$ for all t in I. This establishes Eq. (15). ▲

Remark: Every $n \times n$ system $\mathbf{x}' = \mathbf{P}(t)\mathbf{x}$ with continuous coefficient matrix does have a set of n linearly independent solutions $\mathbf{x}_1, \mathbf{x}_2, \ldots, \mathbf{x}_n$ as in the hypotheses of Theorem 3. It suffices to choose for $\mathbf{x}_j(t)$ the unique solution such that

$$\mathbf{x}_j(a) = \begin{bmatrix} 0 \\ 0 \\ 0 \\ \vdots \\ 0 \\ 1 \\ 0 \\ \vdots \\ 0 \end{bmatrix} \longleftarrow \text{position } j$$

—that is, the column vector with all elements zero except for a 1 in row j. (In other words, $\mathbf{x}_j(a)$ is merely the jth column of the identity matrix.) Then

$$W(\mathbf{x}_1, \mathbf{x}_2, \ldots, \mathbf{x}_n)\Big|_{t=a} = |\mathbf{I}| \neq 0,$$

so the solutions $\mathbf{x}_1, \mathbf{x}_2, \ldots, \mathbf{x}_n$ are linearly independent by Theorem 2. How to actually find these solutions explicitly is another matter—one that we address in Section 7.3 (for the case of constant-coefficient matrices).

Initial Value Problems and Elementary Row Operations

The general solution in Eq. (15) of the homogeneous linear system $\mathbf{x}' = \mathbf{P}(t)\mathbf{x}$ can be written in the form

$$\mathbf{x}(t) = \mathbf{X}(t)\mathbf{c}, \tag{19}$$

where

$$\mathbf{X}(t) = \begin{bmatrix} \mathbf{x}_1(t) & \mathbf{x}_2(t) & \cdots & \mathbf{x}_n(t) \end{bmatrix} \tag{20}$$

is the $n \times n$ matrix whose *column vectors* are the linearly independent solutions $\mathbf{x}_1, \mathbf{x}_2, \ldots, \mathbf{x}_n$, and where $\mathbf{c} = \begin{bmatrix} c_1 & c_2 & \cdots & c_n \end{bmatrix}^T$ is the vector of coefficients in the linear combination

$$\mathbf{x}(t) = c_1\mathbf{x}_1(t) + c_2\mathbf{x}_2(t) + \cdots + c_n\mathbf{x}_n(t). \tag{15}$$

Suppose now that we wish to solve the *initial value problem*

$$\frac{d\mathbf{x}}{dt} = \mathbf{P}\mathbf{x}, \quad \mathbf{x}(a) = \mathbf{b}, \tag{21}$$

where the initial vector $\mathbf{b} = \begin{bmatrix} b_1 & b_2 & \cdots & b_n \end{bmatrix}^T$ is given. Then, according to Eq. (19), it suffices to solve the system

$$\mathbf{X}(a)\mathbf{c} = \mathbf{b} \tag{22}$$

to find the coefficients $c_1, c_2, \ldots, c_n$ in Eq. (15). For instance, we can use the row-reduction techniques of Sections 3.2 and 3.3.

Example 4   Use the solution vectors given in Example 3 to solve the initial value problem

$$\frac{d\mathbf{x}}{dt} = \begin{bmatrix} 3 & -2 & 0 \\ -1 & 3 & -2 \\ 0 & -1 & 3 \end{bmatrix} \mathbf{x}, \quad \mathbf{x}(0) = \begin{bmatrix} 0 \\ 2 \\ 6 \end{bmatrix}. \tag{23}$$

Solution   It follows from Theorem 3 that the linear combination

$$\mathbf{x}(t) = c_1\mathbf{x}_1(t) + c_2\mathbf{x}_2(t) + c_3\mathbf{x}_3(t)$$

$$= c_1 \begin{bmatrix} 2e^t \\ 2e^t \\ e^t \end{bmatrix} + c_2 \begin{bmatrix} 2e^{3t} \\ 0 \\ -e^{3t} \end{bmatrix} + c_3 \begin{bmatrix} 2e^{5t} \\ -2e^{5t} \\ e^{5t} \end{bmatrix}$$

is a general solution of the 3×3 linear system in (23). In scalar form, this gives the general solution

$$\begin{aligned}
x_1(t) &= 2c_1 e^t + 2c_2 e^{3t} + 2c_3 e^{5t}, \\
x_2(t) &= 2c_1 e^t \qquad\quad - 2c_3 e^{5t}, \\
x_3(t) &= c_1 e^t - c_2 e^{3t} + c_3 e^{5t}.
\end{aligned}$$

We seek the particular solution satisfying the initial conditions

$$x_1(0) = 0, \quad x_2(0) = 2, \quad x_3(0) = 6.$$

When we substitute these values in the preceding three scalar equations, we get the algebraic linear system

$$\begin{aligned}
2c_1 + 2c_2 + 2c_3 &= 0, \\
2c_1 \qquad\quad - 2c_3 &= 2, \\
c_1 - c_2 + c_3 &= 6
\end{aligned}$$

having the augmented coefficient matrix

$$\begin{bmatrix} 2 & 2 & 2 & \vdots & 0 \\ 2 & 0 & -2 & \vdots & 2 \\ 1 & -1 & 1 & \vdots & 6 \end{bmatrix}.$$

Multiplication of each of the first two rows by $\frac{1}{2}$ gives

$$\begin{bmatrix} 1 & 1 & 1 & \vdots & 0 \\ 1 & 0 & -1 & \vdots & 1 \\ 1 & -1 & 1 & \vdots & 6 \end{bmatrix};$$

then subtraction of the first row both from the second row and from the third row gives the matrix

$$\begin{bmatrix} 1 & 1 & 1 & \vdots & 0 \\ 0 & -1 & -2 & \vdots & 1 \\ 0 & -2 & 0 & \vdots & 6 \end{bmatrix}.$$

The first column of this matrix now has the desired form.

Now, we multiply the second row by -1, then add twice the result to the third row. Thereby, we get the upper triangular augmented coefficient matrix

$$\begin{bmatrix} 1 & 1 & 1 & | & 0 \\ 0 & 1 & 2 & | & -1 \\ 0 & 0 & 4 & | & 4 \end{bmatrix}$$

that corresponds to the transformed system

$$\begin{aligned} c_1 + c_2 + c_3 &= 0, \\ c_2 + 2c_3 &= -1, \\ 4c_3 &= 4. \end{aligned}$$

We finally solve in turn for $c_3 = 1$, $c_2 = -3$, and $c_1 = 2$. Thus the desired particular solution is given by

$$\mathbf{x}(t) = 2\mathbf{x}_1(t) - 3\mathbf{x}_2(t) + \mathbf{x}_3(t) = \begin{bmatrix} 4e^t - 6e^{3t} + 2e^{5t} \\ 4e^t \qquad - 2e^{5t} \\ 2e^t + 3e^{3t} + e^{5t} \end{bmatrix}. \qquad \blacksquare$$

Nonhomogeneous Solutions

We finally turn our attention to a *nonhomogeneous* linear system of the form

$$\frac{d\mathbf{x}}{dt} = \mathbf{P}(t)\mathbf{x} + \mathbf{f}(t). \tag{24}$$

The following theorem is analogous to Theorem 5 of Section 5.2 and is proved in precisely the same way, substituting the preceding theorems in this section for the analogous theorems of Section 5.2. In brief, Theorem 4 means that the general solution of Eq. (24) has the form

$$\mathbf{x}(t) = \mathbf{x}_c(t) + \mathbf{x}_p(t), \tag{25}$$

where $\mathbf{x}_p(t)$ is a single particular solution of Eq. (24) and the **complementary function** $\mathbf{x}_c(t)$ is a general solution of the associated homogeneous equation $\mathbf{x}' = \mathbf{P}(t)\mathbf{x}$.

THEOREM 4: Solutions of Nonhomogeneous Systems

Let $\mathbf{x}_p$ be a particular solution of the nonhomogeneous linear equation in (24) on an open interval I on which the functions $\mathbf{P}(t)$ and $\mathbf{f}(t)$ are continuous. Let $\mathbf{x}_1, \mathbf{x}_2, \ldots,$ $\mathbf{x}_n$ be linearly independent solutions of the associated homogeneous equation on I. If $\mathbf{x}(t)$ is any solution whatsoever of Eq. (24) on I, then there exist numbers $c_1, c_2,$ $\ldots, c_n$ such that

$$\mathbf{x}(t) = c_1\mathbf{x}_1(t) + c_2\mathbf{x}_2(t) + \cdots + c_n\mathbf{x}_n(t) + \mathbf{x}_p(t) \tag{26}$$

for all t in I. $\qquad \blacktriangle$

Thus, finding a general solution of a homogeneous linear system involves two separate steps:

1. Finding the general solution $\mathbf{x}_c(t)$ of the associated homogeneous system;
2. Finding a single particular solution $\mathbf{x}_p(t)$ of the nonhomogeneous system.

The sum $\mathbf{x}(t) = \mathbf{x}_c(t) + \mathbf{x}_p(t)$ will then be a general solution of the nonhomogeneous system.

Example 5 The nonhomogeneous linear system

$$
\begin{aligned}
x_1' &= 3x_1 - 2x_2 && - 9t + 13, \\
x_2' &= -x_1 + 3x_2 - 2x_3 + 7t - 15, \\
x_3' &= - x_2 + 3x_3 - 6t + 7
\end{aligned}
$$

is of the form in (24) with

$$
\mathbf{P}(t) = \begin{bmatrix} 3 & -2 & 0 \\ -1 & 3 & -2 \\ 0 & -1 & 3 \end{bmatrix}, \quad \mathbf{f}(t) = \begin{bmatrix} -9t + 13 \\ 7t - 15 \\ -6t + 7 \end{bmatrix}.
$$

In Example 3 we saw that a general solution of the associated homogeneous linear system

$$
\frac{d\mathbf{x}}{dt} = \begin{bmatrix} 3 & -2 & 0 \\ -1 & 3 & -2 \\ 0 & -1 & 3 \end{bmatrix} \mathbf{x}
$$

is given by

$$
\mathbf{x}_c(t) = \begin{bmatrix} 2c_1 e^t + 2c_2 e^{3t} + 2c_3 e^{5t} \\ 2c_1 e^t \phantom{+ 2c_2 e^{3t}} - 2c_3 e^{5t} \\ c_1 e^t - c_2 e^{3t} + c_2 e^{5t} \end{bmatrix},
$$

and we can verify, by substitution, that the function

$$
\mathbf{x}_p(t) = \begin{bmatrix} 3t \\ 5 \\ 2t \end{bmatrix}
$$

(found by using a computer algebra system) is a particular solution of the original nonhomogeneous system. Consequently, Theorem 4 implies that a general solution of the nonhomogeneous system is given by

$$
\mathbf{x}(t) = \mathbf{x}_c(t) + \mathbf{x}_p(t)
$$

—that is, by

$$
\begin{aligned}
x_1(t) &= 2c_1 e^t + 2c_2 e^{3t} + 2c_3 e^{5t} + 3t, \\
x_2(t) &= 2c_1 e^t \phantom{+ 2c_2 e^{3t}} - 2c_3 e^{5t} + 5, \\
x_3(t) &= c_1 e^t - c_2 e^{3t} + c_3 e^{5t} + 2t.
\end{aligned}
$$

∎

7.2 Problems

In Problems 1 and 2, verify the product law for differentiation,
$(AB)' = A'B + AB'.$

1. $A(t) = \begin{bmatrix} t & 2t-1 \\ t^3 & \dfrac{1}{t} \end{bmatrix}$ and $B(t) = \begin{bmatrix} 1-t & 1+t \\ 3t^2 & 4t^3 \end{bmatrix}.$

2. $A(t) = \begin{bmatrix} e^t & t & t^2 \\ -t & 0 & 2 \\ 8t & -1 & t^3 \end{bmatrix}$ and $B(t) = \begin{bmatrix} 3 \\ 2e^{-t} \\ 3t \end{bmatrix}.$

In Problems 3 through 12, write the given system in the form
$x' = P(t)x + f(t).$

3. $x' = -3y, y' = 3x$
4. $x' = 3x - 2y, y' = 2x + y$
5. $x' = 2x + 4y + 3e^t, y' = 5x - y - t^2$
6. $x' = tx - e^t y + \cos t, y' = e^{-t}x + t^2 y - \sin t$
7. $x' = y + z, y' = z + x, z' = x + y$
8. $x' = 2x - 3y, y' = x + y + 2z, z' = 5y - 7z$
9. $x' = 3x - 4y + z + t, \ y' = x - 3z + t^2, \ z' = 6y - 7z + t^3$
10. $x' = tx - y + e^t z, \ y' = 2x + t^2 y - z, \ z' = e^{-t}x + 3ty + t^3 z$
11. $x_1' = x_2, x_2' = 2x_3, x_3' = 3x_4, x_4' = 4x_1$
12. $x_1' = x_2 + x_3 + 1, \ x_2' = x_3 + x_4 + t,$
$\quad x_3' = x_1 + x_4 + t^2, \ x_4' = x_1 + x_2 + t^3$

In Problems 13 through 22, first verify that the given vectors are solutions of the given system. Then use the Wronskian to show that they are linearly independent. Finally, write the general solution of the system.

13. $x' = \begin{bmatrix} 4 & 2 \\ -3 & -1 \end{bmatrix} x; \ x_1 = \begin{bmatrix} 2e^t \\ -3e^t \end{bmatrix}, \ x_2 = \begin{bmatrix} e^{2t} \\ -e^{2t} \end{bmatrix}$

14. $x' = \begin{bmatrix} -3 & 2 \\ -3 & 4 \end{bmatrix} x; \ x_1 = \begin{bmatrix} e^{3t} \\ 3e^{3t} \end{bmatrix}, \ x_2 = \begin{bmatrix} 2e^{-2t} \\ e^{-2t} \end{bmatrix}$

15. $x' = \begin{bmatrix} 3 & -1 \\ 5 & -3 \end{bmatrix} x; \ x_1 = e^{2t}\begin{bmatrix} 1 \\ 1 \end{bmatrix}, \ x_2 = e^{-2t}\begin{bmatrix} 1 \\ 5 \end{bmatrix}$

16. $x' = \begin{bmatrix} 4 & 1 \\ -2 & 1 \end{bmatrix} x; \ x_1 = e^{3t}\begin{bmatrix} 1 \\ -1 \end{bmatrix}, \ x_2 = e^{2t}\begin{bmatrix} 1 \\ -2 \end{bmatrix}$

17. $x' = \begin{bmatrix} 4 & -3 \\ 6 & -7 \end{bmatrix} x; \ x_1 = \begin{bmatrix} 3e^{2t} \\ 2e^{2t} \end{bmatrix}, \ x_2 = \begin{bmatrix} e^{-5t} \\ 3e^{-5t} \end{bmatrix}$

18. $x' = \begin{bmatrix} 3 & -2 & 0 \\ -1 & 3 & -2 \\ 0 & -1 & 3 \end{bmatrix} x; \ x_1 = e^t\begin{bmatrix} 2 \\ 2 \\ 1 \end{bmatrix},$
$x_2 = e^{3t}\begin{bmatrix} -2 \\ 0 \\ 1 \end{bmatrix}, \ x_3 = e^{5t}\begin{bmatrix} 2 \\ -2 \\ 1 \end{bmatrix}$

19. $x' = \begin{bmatrix} 0 & 1 & 1 \\ 1 & 0 & 1 \\ 1 & 1 & 0 \end{bmatrix} x; \ x_1 = e^{2t}\begin{bmatrix} 1 \\ 1 \\ 1 \end{bmatrix},$
$x_2 = e^{-t}\begin{bmatrix} 1 \\ 0 \\ -1 \end{bmatrix}, \ x_3 = e^{-t}\begin{bmatrix} 0 \\ 1 \\ -1 \end{bmatrix}$

20. $x' = \begin{bmatrix} 1 & 2 & 1 \\ 6 & -1 & 0 \\ -1 & -2 & -1 \end{bmatrix} x; \ x_1 = \begin{bmatrix} 1 \\ 6 \\ -13 \end{bmatrix},$
$x_2 = e^{3t}\begin{bmatrix} 2 \\ 3 \\ -2 \end{bmatrix}, \ x_3 = e^{-4t}\begin{bmatrix} -1 \\ 2 \\ 1 \end{bmatrix}$

21. $x' = \begin{bmatrix} -8 & -11 & -2 \\ 6 & 9 & 2 \\ -6 & -6 & 1 \end{bmatrix} x; \ x_1 = e^{-2t}\begin{bmatrix} 3 \\ -2 \\ 2 \end{bmatrix},$
$x_2 = e^t\begin{bmatrix} 1 \\ -1 \\ 1 \end{bmatrix}, \ x_3 = e^{3t}\begin{bmatrix} 1 \\ -1 \\ 0 \end{bmatrix}$

22. $x' = \begin{bmatrix} 1 & -4 & 0 & -2 \\ 0 & 1 & 0 & 0 \\ 6 & -12 & -1 & -6 \\ 0 & -4 & 0 & -1 \end{bmatrix} x; \ x_1 = e^{-t}\begin{bmatrix} 1 \\ 0 \\ 0 \\ 1 \end{bmatrix},$
$x_2 = e^{-t}\begin{bmatrix} 0 \\ 0 \\ 1 \\ 0 \end{bmatrix}, \ x_3 = e^t\begin{bmatrix} 0 \\ 1 \\ 0 \\ -2 \end{bmatrix}, \ x_4 = e^t\begin{bmatrix} 1 \\ 0 \\ 3 \\ 0 \end{bmatrix}$

In Problems 23 through 32, find a particular solution of the indicated linear system that satisfies the given initial conditions.

23. The system of Problem 14: $x_1(0) = 0, x_2(0) = 5$
24. The system of Problem 15: $x_1(0) = 5, x_2(0) = -3$
25. The system of Problem 16: $x_1(0) = 11, x_2(0) = -7$
26. The system of Problem 17: $x_1(0) = 8, x_2(0) = 0$
27. The system of Problem 18: $x_1(0) = 0, \ x_2(0) = 0, x_3(0) = 4$
28. The system of Problem 19: $x_1(0) = 10, \ x_2(0) = 12, x_3(0) = -1$
29. The system of Problem 21: $x_1(0) = 1, \ x_2(0) = 2, x_3(0) = 3$
30. The system of Problem 21: $x_1(0) = 5, \ x_2(0) = -7, x_3(0) = 11$
31. The system of Problem 22: $x_1(0) = x_2(0) = x_3(0) = x_4(0) = 1$
32. The system of Problem 22: $x_1(0) = 1, \ x_2(0) = 3, x_3(0) = 4, x_4(0) = 7$

33. (a) Show that the vector functions
$$x_1(t) = \begin{bmatrix} t \\ t^2 \end{bmatrix} \quad \text{and} \quad x_2 = \begin{bmatrix} t^2 \\ t^3 \end{bmatrix}$$
are linearly independent on the real line. (b) Why does it follow from Theorem 2 that there is *no* continuous matrix $P(t)$ such that x_1 and x_2 are both solutions of $x' = P(t)x$?

34. Suppose that one of the vector functions
$$x_1(t) = \begin{bmatrix} x_{11}(t) \\ x_{21}(t) \end{bmatrix} \quad \text{and} \quad x_2(t) = \begin{bmatrix} x_{12}(t) \\ x_{22}(t) \end{bmatrix}$$
is a constant multiple of the other on the open interval I. Show that their Wronskian $W(t) = |[x_{ij}(t)]|$ must vanish identically on I. This proves part (a) of Theorem 2 in the case $n = 2$.

35. Suppose that the vectors $x_1(t)$ and $x_2(t)$ of Problem 34 are solutions of the equation $x' = P(t)x$, where the 2×2 matrix $P(t)$ is continuous on the open interval I. Show that if there exists a point a of I at which their Wronskian $W(a)$ is zero, then there exist numbers c_1 and c_2 not both zero such that $c_1 x_1(a) + c_2 x_2(a) = 0$. Then conclude from the uniqueness of solutions of the equation $x' = P(t)x$ that

$$c_1 x_1(t) + c_2 x_2(t) = 0$$

for all t in I; that is, that x_1 and x_2 are linearly dependent. This proves part (b) of Theorem 2 in the case $n = 2$.

36. Generalize Problems 34 and 35 to prove Theorem 2 for n an arbitrary positive integer.

37. Let $x_1(t)$, $x_2(t)$, ..., $x_n(t)$ be vector functions whose ith components (for some fixed i) $x_{i1}(t)$, $x_{i2}(t)$, ..., $x_{in}(t)$ are linearly independent real-valued functions. Conclude that the vector functions are themselves linearly independent.

7.3 The Eigenvalue Method for Linear Systems

We now introduce a powerful method for constructing the general solution of a *homogeneous* first-order system with *constant* coefficients,

$$
\begin{aligned}
x_1' &= a_{11}x_1 + a_{12}x_2 + \cdots + a_{1n}x_n, \\
x_2' &= a_{21}x_1 + a_{22}x_2 + \cdots + a_{2n}x_n, \\
&\;\;\vdots \\
x_n' &= a_{n1}x_1 + a_{n2}x_2 + \cdots + a_{nn}x_n.
\end{aligned}
\tag{1}
$$

By Theorem 3 of Section 7.2, we know that it suffices to find n linearly independent solution vectors $x_1, x_2, \ldots, x_n$; the linear combination

$$\blacktriangleright \qquad\qquad x(t) = c_1 x_1 + c_2 x_2 + \cdots + c_n x_n \tag{2}$$

with arbitrary coefficients will then be a general solution of the system in (1).

To search for the n needed linearly independent solution vectors, we proceed by analogy with the characteristic root method for solving a single homogeneous equation with constant coefficients (Section 5.3). It is reasonable to anticipate solution vectors of the form

$$
x(t) =
\begin{bmatrix}
x_1 \\ x_2 \\ x_3 \\ \vdots \\ x_n
\end{bmatrix}
=
\begin{bmatrix}
v_1 e^{\lambda t} \\ v_2 e^{\lambda t} \\ v_3 e^{\lambda t} \\ \vdots \\ v_n e^{\lambda t}
\end{bmatrix}
=
\begin{bmatrix}
v_1 \\ v_2 \\ v_3 \\ \vdots \\ v_n
\end{bmatrix}
e^{\lambda t} = v e^{\lambda t},
\tag{3}
$$

where λ, v_1, v_2, v_3, ..., v_n are appropriate scalar constants. For, if we substitute

$$x_i = v_i e^{\lambda t}, \qquad x_i' = \lambda v_i e^{\lambda t}$$

($i = 1, 2, \ldots, n$) in (1), then the factor $e^{\lambda t}$ will cancel throughout. This will leave us with n linear equations that—for appropriate values of λ—we can hope to solve for values of the coefficients $v_1, v_2, \ldots, v_n$ in Eq. (3), so that $x(t) = v e^{\lambda t}$ is, indeed, a solution of the system in (1).

To investigate this possibility, it is more efficient to write the system in (1) in the matrix form

$$\blacktriangleright \qquad\qquad x' = Ax, \tag{4}$$

where $\mathbf{A} = \begin{bmatrix} a_{ij} \end{bmatrix}$. When we substitute the trial solution $\mathbf{x} = \mathbf{v}e^{\lambda t}$ (having derivative $\mathbf{x}' = \lambda\mathbf{v}e^{\lambda t}$) in Eq. (4), the result is

$$\lambda\mathbf{v}e^{\lambda t} = \mathbf{A}\mathbf{v}e^{\lambda t}.$$

We cancel the nonzero scalar factor $e^{\lambda t}$ to get

➤ $$\mathbf{A}\mathbf{v} = \lambda\mathbf{v}. \tag{5}$$

Recall, from Section 6.1, that Eq. (5) means that $\mathbf{v} \neq \mathbf{0}$ is an *eigenvector* of the matrix $\mathbf{A}$ associated with the *eigenvalue* λ. Our discussion of Eqs. (3)–(5) therefore provides a proof of the following theorem, which is the basis for the **eigenvalue method** of solving a first-order system with constant coefficients.

THEOREM 1: Eigenvalue Solutions of $\mathbf{x}' = \mathbf{A}\mathbf{x}$

Let λ be an eigenvalue of the [constant] coefficient matrix $\mathbf{A}$ of the first-order linear system

$$\frac{d\mathbf{x}}{dt} = \mathbf{A}\mathbf{x}.$$

If $\mathbf{v}$ is an eigenvector associated with λ, then

$$\mathbf{x}(t) = \mathbf{v}e^{\lambda t}$$

is a nontrivial solution of the system. ▲

Recall that an eigenvalue λ of the matrix $\mathbf{A}$ is a solution of the *characteristic equation*

$$|\mathbf{A} - \lambda\mathbf{I}| = \det(\mathbf{A} - \lambda\mathbf{I}) = 0 \tag{6}$$

and that an eigenvector $\mathbf{v}$ associated with λ is then a solution of the *eigenvector equation*

$$(\mathbf{A} - \lambda\mathbf{I})\mathbf{v} = \mathbf{0}. \tag{7}$$

The Eigenvalue Method

In outline, this method for solving the $n \times n$ homogeneous constant-coefficient system $\mathbf{x}' = \mathbf{A}\mathbf{x}$ proceeds as follows:

1. First, we solve the characteristic equation in (6) for the eigenvalues λ_1, λ_2, ..., λ_n of the matrix $\mathbf{A}$.

2. Next, we attempt to find n *linearly independent* eigenvectors $\mathbf{v}_1$, $\mathbf{v}_2$, ..., $\mathbf{v}_n$ associated with these eigenvalues.

3. Step 2 is not always possible, but, when it is, we get n linearly independent solutions

$$\mathbf{x}_1(t) = \mathbf{v}_1 e^{\lambda_1 t}, \quad \mathbf{x}_2(t) = \mathbf{v}_2 e^{\lambda_2 t}, \quad \ldots, \quad \mathbf{x}_n(t) = \mathbf{v}_n e^{\lambda_n t}. \tag{8}$$

In this case the general solution of $\mathbf{x}' = \mathbf{A}\mathbf{x}$ is a linear combination

$$\mathbf{x}(t) = c_1\mathbf{x}_1(t) + c_2\mathbf{x}_2(t) + \cdots + c_n\mathbf{x}_n(t)$$

of these n solutions.

We will discuss separately the various cases that can occur, depending on whether the eigenvalues are distinct or repeated, real or complex. The case of repeated eigenvalues—multiple roots of the characteristic equation—will be deferred to Section 7.5.

Distinct Real Eigenvalues

If the eigenvalues $\lambda_1, \lambda_2, \ldots, \lambda_n$ are real and distinct, then we substitute each of them in turn in Eq. (7) and solve for the associated eigenvectors $\mathbf{v}_1, \mathbf{v}_2, \ldots, \mathbf{v}_n$. It then follows from Theorem 2 in Section 6.2 that the particular solutions given in (8) are linearly independent. (In any particular example, such linear independence can always be verified by using the Wronskian determinant of Section 7.2.) The following example illustrates the eigenvalue method.

Example 1 Find a general solution of the system

$$\begin{aligned} x_1' &= 4x_1 + 2x_2, \\ x_2' &= 3x_1 - x_2. \end{aligned} \tag{9}$$

Solution The matrix form of the system in (9) is

$$\mathbf{x}' = \begin{bmatrix} 4 & 2 \\ 3 & -1 \end{bmatrix} \mathbf{x}. \tag{10}$$

The characteristic equation of the coefficient matrix is

$$\begin{vmatrix} 4 - \lambda & 2 \\ 3 & -1 - \lambda \end{vmatrix} = (4 - \lambda)(-1 - \lambda) - 6$$

$$= \lambda^2 - 3\lambda - 10 = (\lambda + 2)(\lambda - 5) = 0,$$

so we have the distinct real eigenvalues $\lambda_1 = -2$ and $\lambda_2 = 5$.

For the coefficient matrix $\mathbf{A}$ in Eq. (10), the eigenvector equation $(\mathbf{A} - \lambda \mathbf{I})\mathbf{v} = \mathbf{0}$ takes the form

$$\begin{bmatrix} 4 - \lambda & 2 \\ 3 & -1 - \lambda \end{bmatrix} \begin{bmatrix} a \\ b \end{bmatrix} = \begin{bmatrix} 0 \\ 0 \end{bmatrix} \tag{11}$$

for the associated eigenvector $\mathbf{v} = \begin{bmatrix} a & b \end{bmatrix}^T$.

CASE 1: $\lambda_1 = -2$. Substitution of the first eigenvalue $\lambda_1 = -2$ in Eq. (11) yields the system

$$\begin{bmatrix} 6 & 2 \\ 3 & 1 \end{bmatrix} \begin{bmatrix} a \\ b \end{bmatrix} = \begin{bmatrix} 0 \\ 0 \end{bmatrix}$$

—that is, the two scalar equations

$$\begin{aligned} 6a + 2b &= 0, \\ 3a + b &= 0. \end{aligned} \tag{12}$$

In contrast with the typical nonsingular (algebraic) linear system that has a unique solution, the homogeneous linear system in (12) is *singular*—the two scalar equations obviously are equivalent (each being a multiple of the other). Therefore,

Eq. (12) has infinitely many nonzero solutions—we can choose a arbitrary (but nonzero) and then solve for b.

Substitution of an eigenvalue λ in the eigenvector equation $(\mathbf{A} - \lambda\mathbf{I})\mathbf{v} = \mathbf{0}$ always yields a singular homogeneous linear system, and among its infinity of solutions we generally seek a "simple" solution with small integer values (if possible). Looking at the second equation in (12), the choice $a = 1$ yields $b = -3$, and thus

$$\mathbf{v}_1 = \begin{bmatrix} 1 \\ -3 \end{bmatrix}$$

is an eigenvector associated with $\lambda_1 = -2$ (as is any nonzero constant multiple of $\mathbf{v}_1$).

Remark: If, instead of the "simplest" choice $a = 1$, $b = -3$, we had made another choice $a = c$, $b = -3c$, we would have obtained the eigenvector

$$\mathbf{v}_1 = \begin{bmatrix} c \\ -3c \end{bmatrix} = c \begin{bmatrix} 1 \\ -3 \end{bmatrix}.$$

Because this is a constant multiple of our previous result, any choice we make leads to (a constant multiple of) the same solution

$$\mathbf{x}_1(t) = \begin{bmatrix} 1 \\ -3 \end{bmatrix} e^{-2t}.$$

CASE 2: $\lambda_2 = 5$. Substitution of the second eigenvalue $\lambda = 5$ in (11) yields the pair

$$\begin{aligned} -a + 2b &= 0, \\ 3a - 6b &= 0 \end{aligned} \tag{13}$$

of equivalent scalar equations. With $b = 1$ in the first equation we get $a = 2$, so

$$\mathbf{v}_2 = \begin{bmatrix} 2 \\ 1 \end{bmatrix}$$

is an eigenvector associated with $\lambda_2 = 5$. A different choice: $a = 2c$, $b = c$ would merely give a [constant] multiple of $\mathbf{v}_2$.

These two eigenvalues and their associated eigenvectors yield the two solutions

$$\mathbf{x}_1(t) = \begin{bmatrix} 1 \\ -3 \end{bmatrix} e^{-2t} \quad \text{and} \quad \mathbf{x}_2(t) = \begin{bmatrix} 2 \\ 1 \end{bmatrix} e^{5t}.$$

They are linearly independent, because their Wronskian

$$\begin{vmatrix} e^{-2t} & 2e^{5t} \\ -3e^{-2t} & e^{5t} \end{vmatrix} = 7e^{3t}$$

is nonzero. Hence a general solution of the system in (11) is

$$\mathbf{x}(t) = c_1\mathbf{x}_1(t) + c_2\mathbf{x}_2(t) = c_1 \begin{bmatrix} 1 \\ -3 \end{bmatrix} e^{-2t} + c_2 \begin{bmatrix} 2 \\ 1 \end{bmatrix} e^{5t};$$

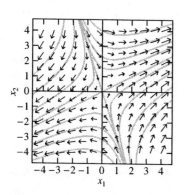

FIGURE 7.3.1. Direction field and solution curves for the linear system $x_1' = 4x_1 + 2x_2$, $x_2' = 3x_1 - x_2$ of Example 1.

in scalar form,

$$x_1(t) = \quad c_1 e^{-2t} + 2c_2 e^{5t},$$
$$x_2(t) = -3c_1 e^{-2t} + \quad c_2 e^{5t}.$$

Figure 7.3.1 shows some typical solution curves of the system in (10). We see two families of hyperbolas sharing the same pair of asymptotes: the line $x_1 = 2x_2$ obtained from the general solution with $c_1 = 0$ and the line $x_2 = -3x_1$ obtained with $c_2 = 0$. Given initial values $x_1(0) = b_1$, $x_2(0) = b_2$, it is apparent from the figure that

- If (b_1, b_2) lies to the right of the line $x_2 = -3x_1$, then $x_1(t)$ and $x_2(t)$ both tend to $+\infty$ as $t \to +\infty$;
- If (b_1, b_2) lies to the left of the line $x_2 = -3x_1$, then $x_1(t)$ and $x_2(t)$ both tend to $-\infty$ as $t \to +\infty$. ∎

Remark: As in Example 1, it is convenient when discussing a linear system $\mathbf{x}' = \mathbf{A}\mathbf{x}$ to use vectors $\mathbf{x}_1, \mathbf{x}_2, \ldots, \mathbf{x}_n$ to denote different vector-valued solutions of the system, whereas the *scalars* $x_1, x_2, \ldots, x_n$ denote the components of a single vector-valued solution $\mathbf{x}$.

Compartmental Analysis

Frequently, a complex process or system can be broken down into simpler subsystems or "compartments" that can be analyzed separately. The whole system can then be modeled by describing the interactions between the various compartments. Thus a chemical plant may consist of a succession of separate stages (or even physical compartments) in which various reactants and products combine or are mixed. It may happen that a single differential equation describes each compartment of the system; then the whole physical system is modeled by a system of differential equations.

As a simple example of a three-stage system, Fig. 7.3.2 shows three brine tanks containing V_1, V_2, and V_3 gallons of brine, respectively. Fresh water flows into tank 1, while mixed brine flows from tank 1 into tank 2, from tank 2 into tank 3, and out of tank 3. Let $x_i(t)$ denote the amount (in pounds) of salt in tank i at time t, for $i = 1, 2$, and 3. If each flow rate is r gallons per minute, then a simple accounting of salt concentrations, as in Example 2 of Section 7.1, yields the first-order system

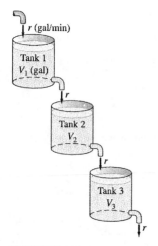

FIGURE 7.3.2. The three brine tanks of Example 2.

$$\begin{aligned} x_1' &= -k_1 x_1, \\ x_2' &= \quad k_1 x_1 - k_2 x_2, \\ x_3' &= \qquad\qquad k_2 x_2 - k_3 x_3, \end{aligned} \tag{14}$$

where

$$k_i = \frac{r}{V_i}, \quad i = 1, 2, 3. \tag{15}$$

Example 2   If $V_1 = 20$, $V_2 = 40$, $V_3 = 50$, $r = 10$ (gal/min), and the initial amounts of salt in the three brine tanks, in pounds, are

$$x_1(0) = 15, \quad x_2(0) = x_3(0) = 0,$$

find the amount of salt in each tank at time $t \geqq 0$.

Solution   Substituting the given numerical values in (14) and (15), we get the initial value problem

$$\mathbf{x}'(t) = \begin{bmatrix} -0.5 & 0.0 & 0.0 \\ 0.5 & -0.25 & 0.0 \\ 0.0 & 0.25 & -0.2 \end{bmatrix} \mathbf{x}, \quad \mathbf{x}(0) = \begin{bmatrix} 15 \\ 0 \\ 0 \end{bmatrix} \tag{16}$$

for the vector $\mathbf{x}(t) = \begin{bmatrix} x_1(t) & x_2(t) & x_3(t) \end{bmatrix}^T$. The simple form of the matrix

$$\mathbf{A} - \lambda\mathbf{I} = \begin{bmatrix} -0.5 - \lambda & 0.0 & 0.0 \\ 0.5 & -0.25 - \lambda & 0.0 \\ 0.0 & 0.25 & -0.2 - \lambda \end{bmatrix} \tag{17}$$

leads readily to the characteristic equation

$$|\mathbf{A} - \lambda\mathbf{I}| = (-0.5 - \lambda)(-0.25 - \lambda)(-0.2 - \lambda) = 0.$$

Thus, the coefficient matrix $\mathbf{A}$ in (16) has the distinct eigenvalues $\lambda_1 = -0.5$, $\lambda_2 = -0.25$, and $\lambda_3 = -0.2$.

CASE 1: $\lambda_1 = -0.5$.   Substituting $\lambda = -0.5$ in (17), we get the equation

$$\begin{bmatrix} \mathbf{A} + (0.5) \cdot \mathbf{I} \end{bmatrix} \mathbf{v} = \begin{bmatrix} 0.0 & 0.0 & 0.0 \\ 0.5 & 0.25 & 0.0 \\ 0.0 & 0.25 & 0.3 \end{bmatrix} \begin{bmatrix} a \\ b \\ c \end{bmatrix} = \begin{bmatrix} 0 \\ 0 \\ 0 \end{bmatrix}$$

for the associated eigenvector $\mathbf{v} = \begin{bmatrix} a & b & c \end{bmatrix}^T$. The last two rows, after division by 0.25 and 0.05, respectively, yield the scalar equations

$$\begin{aligned} 2a + b \quad &= 0, \\ 5b + 6c &= 0. \end{aligned}$$

The second equation is satisfied by $b = -6$ and $c = 5$, and then the first equation gives $a = 3$. Thus the eigenvector

$$\mathbf{v}_1 = \begin{bmatrix} 3 & -6 & 5 \end{bmatrix}^T$$

is associated with the eigenvalue $\lambda_1 = -0.5$.

CASE 2: $\lambda_2 = -0.25$.   Substituting $\lambda = -0.25$ in (17), we get the equation

$$\begin{bmatrix} \mathbf{A} + (0.25) \cdot \mathbf{I} \end{bmatrix} \mathbf{v} = \begin{bmatrix} -0.25 & 0 & 0 \\ 0.5 & 0 & 0 \\ 0 & 0.25 & 0.05 \end{bmatrix} \begin{bmatrix} a \\ b \\ c \end{bmatrix} = \begin{bmatrix} 0 \\ 0 \\ 0 \end{bmatrix}$$

for the associated eigenvector $\mathbf{v} = \begin{bmatrix} a & b & c \end{bmatrix}^T$. Each of the first two rows implies that $a = 0$, and division of the third row by 0.05 gives the equation

$$5b + c = 0,$$

which is satisfied by $b = 1$, $c = -5$. Thus the eigenvector

$$\mathbf{v}_2 = \begin{bmatrix} 0 & 1 & -5 \end{bmatrix}^T$$

is associated with the eigenvalue $\lambda_2 = -0.25$.

CASE 3: $\lambda_3 = -0.2.$ Substituting $\lambda = -0.2$ in (17), we get the equation

$$\left[\mathbf{A} + (0.2) \cdot \mathbf{I} \right] \mathbf{v} = \begin{bmatrix} -0.3 & 0.0 & 0.0 \\ 0.5 & -0.05 & 0.0 \\ 0.0 & 0.25 & 0.0 \end{bmatrix} \begin{bmatrix} a \\ b \\ c \end{bmatrix} = \begin{bmatrix} 0 \\ 0 \\ 0 \end{bmatrix}$$

for the eigenvector $\mathbf{v}$. The first and third rows imply that $a = 0$, and $b = 0$, respectively, but the all-zero third column leaves c arbitrary (but nonzero). Thus

$$\mathbf{v}_3 = \begin{bmatrix} 0 & 0 & 1 \end{bmatrix}^T$$

is an eigenvector associated with $\lambda_3 = -0.2$.
  The general solution

$$\mathbf{x}(t) = c_1 \mathbf{v}_1 e^{\lambda_1 t} + c_2 \mathbf{v}_2 e^{\lambda_2 t} + c_3 \mathbf{v}_3 e^{\lambda_3 t}$$

therefore takes the form

$$\mathbf{x}(t) = c_1 \begin{bmatrix} 3 \\ -6 \\ 5 \end{bmatrix} e^{(-0.5)t} + c_2 \begin{bmatrix} 0 \\ 1 \\ -5 \end{bmatrix} e^{(-0.25)t} + c_3 \begin{bmatrix} 0 \\ 0 \\ 1 \end{bmatrix} e^{(-0.2)t}.$$

The resulting scalar equations are

$$\begin{aligned} x_1(t) &= 3c_1 e^{(-0.5)t}, \\ x_2(t) &= -6c_1 e^{(-0.5)t} + c_2 e^{(-0.25)t}, \\ x_3(t) &= 5c_1 e^{(-0.5)t} - 5c_2 e^{(-0.25)t} + c_3 e^{(-0.2)t}. \end{aligned}$$

When we impose the initial conditions $x_1(0) = 15$, $x_2(0) = x_3(0) = 0$, we get the equations

$$\begin{aligned} 3c_1 & & & = 15, \\ -6c_1 &+ c_2 & & = 0, \\ 5c_1 &- 5c_2 &+ c_3 &= 0 \end{aligned}$$

that are readily solved (in turn) for $c_1 = 5$, $c_2 = 30$, and $c_3 = 125$. Thus, finally, the amounts of salt at time t in the three brine tanks are given by

$$\begin{aligned} x_1(t) &= 15e^{(-0.5)t}, \\ x_2(t) &= -30e^{(-0.5)t} + 30e^{(-0.25)t}, \\ x_3(t) &= 25e^{(-0.5)t} - 150e^{(-0.25)t} + 125e^{(-0.2)t}. \end{aligned}$$

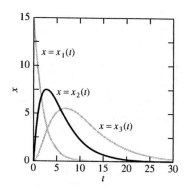

FIGURE 7.3.3. The salt content functions of Example 2.

Figure 7.3.3 shows the graphs of $x_1(t)$, $x_2(t)$, and $x_3(t)$. As we would expect, tank 1 is rapidly "flushed" by the incoming fresh water, and $x_1(t) \to 0$ as $t \to +\infty$. The amounts $x_2(t)$ and $x_3(t)$ of salt in tanks 2 and 3 peak in turn and then approach zero as the whole three-tank system is purged of salt as $t \to +\infty$. ∎

Complex Eigenvalues

Even if some of the eigenvalues are complex, so long as they are distinct the method described previously still yields n linearly independent solutions. The only complication is that the eigenvectors associated with complex eigenvalues are ordinarily complex-valued, so we will have complex-valued solutions.

To obtain real-valued solutions, we note that—because we are assuming that the matrix $\mathbf{A}$ has only real entries—the coefficients in the characteristic equation will all be real. Consequently any complex eigenvalues must appear in complex-conjugate pairs. Suppose, then, that $\lambda = p + qi$ and $\overline{\lambda} = p - qi$ are such a pair of eigenvalues. If $\mathbf{v}$ is an eigenvector associated with λ, so that

$$(\mathbf{A} - \lambda \mathbf{I})\mathbf{v} = \mathbf{0},$$

then taking complex conjugates in this equation yields

$$(\mathbf{A} - \overline{\lambda}\mathbf{I})\overline{\mathbf{v}} = \mathbf{0}.$$

Thus the conjugate $\overline{\mathbf{v}}$ of $\mathbf{v}$ is an eigenvector associated with $\overline{\lambda}$. Of course, the conjugate of a vector is defined componentwise; if

$$\mathbf{v} = \begin{bmatrix} a_1 + b_1 i \\ a_2 + b_2 i \\ \vdots \\ a_n + b_n i \end{bmatrix} = \begin{bmatrix} a_1 \\ a_2 \\ \vdots \\ a_n \end{bmatrix} + \begin{bmatrix} b_1 \\ b_2 \\ \vdots \\ b_n \end{bmatrix} i = \mathbf{a} + \mathbf{b}i, \tag{18}$$

then $\overline{\mathbf{v}} = \mathbf{a} - \mathbf{b}i$. The complex-valued solution associated with λ and $\mathbf{v}$ is then

$$\mathbf{x}(t) = \mathbf{v}e^{\lambda t} = \mathbf{v}e^{(p+qi)t} = (\mathbf{a} + \mathbf{b}i)e^{pt}(\cos qt + i \sin qt)$$

—that is,

$$\mathbf{x}(t) = e^{pt}(\mathbf{a}\cos qt - \mathbf{b}\sin qt) + ie^{pt}(\mathbf{b}\cos qt + \mathbf{a}\sin qt). \tag{19}$$

Because the real and imaginary parts of a complex-valued solution are also solutions, we thus get the two *real-valued* solutions

$$\begin{aligned} \mathbf{x}_1(t) &= \mathrm{Re}(\mathbf{x}(t)) = e^{pt}(\mathbf{a}\cos qt - \mathbf{b}\sin qt), \\ \mathbf{x}_2(t) &= \mathrm{Im}(\mathbf{x}(t)) = e^{pt}(\mathbf{b}\cos qt + \mathbf{a}\sin qt) \end{aligned} \tag{20}$$

associated with the complex conjugate eigenvalues $p \pm qi$. It is easy to check that the same two real-valued solutions result from taking real and imaginary parts of $\overline{\mathbf{v}}e^{\overline{\lambda}t}$. Rather than memorizing the formulas in (20), it is preferable in a specific example to proceed as follows:

- First, find explicitly a single complex-valued solution $\mathbf{x}(t)$ associated with the complex eigenvalue λ;
- Then, find the real and imaginary parts $\mathbf{x}_1(t)$ and $\mathbf{x}_2(t)$, to get two independent real-valued solutions corresponding to the two complex conjugate eigenvalues λ and $\overline{\lambda}$.

Example 3 Find a general solution of the system

$$\frac{dx_1}{dt} = 4x_1 - 3x_2,$$

$$\frac{dx_2}{dt} = 3x_1 + 4x_2. \tag{21}$$

Solution The coefficient matrix

$$\mathbf{A} = \begin{bmatrix} 4 & -3 \\ 3 & 4 \end{bmatrix}$$

has the characteristic equation

$$|\mathbf{A} - \lambda\mathbf{I}| = \begin{vmatrix} 4-\lambda & -3 \\ 3 & 4-\lambda \end{vmatrix} = (4-\lambda)^2 + 9 = 0$$

and hence has the complex conjugate eigenvalues $\lambda = 4 - 3i$ and $\overline{\lambda} = 4 + 3i$.

Substituting $\lambda = 4 - 3i$ in the eigenvector equation $(\mathbf{A} - \lambda\mathbf{I})\mathbf{v} = \mathbf{0}$, we get the equation

$$[\mathbf{A} - (4 - 3i) \cdot \mathbf{I}]\mathbf{v} = \begin{bmatrix} 3i & -3 \\ 3 & 3i \end{bmatrix} \begin{bmatrix} a \\ b \end{bmatrix} = \begin{bmatrix} 0 \\ 0 \end{bmatrix}$$

for an associated eigenvalue $\mathbf{v} = \begin{bmatrix} a & b \end{bmatrix}^T$. Division of each row by 3 yields the two scalar equations

$$ia - b = 0,$$

$$a + ib = 0,$$

each of which is satisfied by $a = 1$ and $b = i$. Thus, $\mathbf{v} = \begin{bmatrix} 1 & i \end{bmatrix}^T$ is a complex eigenvector associated with the complex eigenvalue $\lambda = 4 - 3i$.

The corresponding complex-valued solution $\mathbf{x}(t) = \mathbf{v}e^{\lambda t}$ of $\mathbf{x}' = \mathbf{A}\mathbf{x}$ is then

$$\mathbf{x}(t) = \begin{bmatrix} 1 \\ i \end{bmatrix} e^{(4-3i)t} = \begin{bmatrix} 1 \\ i \end{bmatrix} e^{4t}(\cos 3t - i \sin 3t) = e^{4t} \begin{bmatrix} \cos 3t - i \sin 3t \\ i \cos 3t + \sin 3t \end{bmatrix}.$$

The real and imaginary parts of $\mathbf{x}(t)$ are the real-valued solutions

$$\mathbf{x}_1(t) = e^{4t} \begin{bmatrix} \cos 3t \\ \sin 3t \end{bmatrix} \quad \text{and} \quad \mathbf{x}_2(t) = e^{4t} \begin{bmatrix} -\sin 3t \\ \cos 3t \end{bmatrix}.$$

A real-valued general solution of $\mathbf{x}' = \mathbf{A}\mathbf{x}$ is then given by

$$\mathbf{x}(t) = c_1\mathbf{x}_1(t) + c_2\mathbf{x}_2(t) = e^{4t} \begin{bmatrix} c_1 \cos 3t - c_2 \sin 3t \\ c_1 \sin 3t + c_2 \cos 3t \end{bmatrix}.$$

Finally, a general solution of the system in (21) in scalar form is

$$x_1(t) = e^{4t}(c_1 \cos 3t - c_2 \sin 3t),$$

$$x_2(t) = e^{4t}(c_1 \sin 3t + c_2 \cos 3t).$$

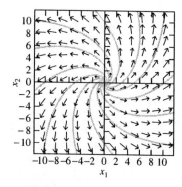

FIGURE 7.3.4. Direction field and solution curves for the linear system $x_1' = 4x_1 - 3x_2$, $x_2' = 3x_1 + 4x_2$ of Example 3.

Figure 7.3.4 shows some typical solution curves of the system in (21). Each appears to spiral counterclockwise as it emanates from the origin in the x_1x_2-plane. Actually, because of the factor e^{4t} in the general solution, we see that

- Along each solution curve, the point $(x_1(t), x_2(t))$ approaches the origin as $t \to -\infty$, whereas
- The absolute values of $x_1(t)$ and $x_2(t)$ both increase without bound as $t \to +\infty$. ∎

Flow rate: r

FIGURE 7.3.5. The three brine tanks of Example 4.

Figure 7.3.5 shows a "closed" system of three brine tanks with volumes V_1, V_2, and V_3. The difference between this system and the "open" system of Fig. 7.3.2 is that now the inflow to tank 1 is the outflow from tank 3. With the same notation as in Example 2, the appropriate modification of Eq. (14) is

$$\frac{dx_1}{dt} = -k_1 x_1 \qquad\qquad + k_3 x_3,$$

$$\frac{dx_2}{dt} = \quad k_1 x_1 - k_2 x_2, \qquad\qquad (22)$$

$$\frac{dx_3}{dt} = \qquad\qquad k_2 x_2 - k_3 x_3,$$

where $k_i = r/V_i$ as in (15).

Example 4

Find the amounts $x_1(t)$, $x_2(t)$, and $x_3(t)$ of salt at time t in the three brine tanks of Fig. 7.3.5 if $V_1 = 50$ gal, $V_2 = 25$ gal, $V_3 = 50$ gal, and $r = 10$ gal/min.

Solution   With the given numerical values, (22) takes the form

$$\frac{d\mathbf{x}}{dt} = \begin{bmatrix} -0.2 & 0 & 0.2 \\ 0.2 & -0.4 & 0 \\ 0 & 0.4 & -0.2 \end{bmatrix} \mathbf{x}, \qquad\qquad (23)$$

where $\mathbf{x} = \begin{bmatrix} x_1 & x_2 & x_3 \end{bmatrix}^T$ as usual. When we expand the determinant of the matrix

$$\mathbf{A} - \lambda \cdot \mathbf{I} = \begin{bmatrix} -0.2 - \lambda & 0.0 & 0.2 \\ 0.2 & -0.4 - \lambda & 0.0 \\ 0.0 & 0.4 & -0.2 - \lambda \end{bmatrix} \qquad\qquad (24)$$

along its first row, we find that the characteristic equation of $\mathbf{A}$ is

$$(-0.2 - \lambda)(-0.4 - \lambda)(-0.2 - \lambda) + (0.2)(0.2)(0.4)$$
$$= -\lambda^3 - (0.8) \cdot \lambda^2 - (0.2) \cdot \lambda$$
$$= -\lambda \left[(\lambda + 0.4)^2 + (0.2)^2 \right] = 0.$$

Thus $\mathbf{A}$ has the zero eigenvalue $\lambda_0 = 0$ and the complex conjugate eigenvalues λ, $\overline{\lambda} = -0.4 \pm (0.2)i$.

CASE 1: $\lambda_0 = 0$.   Substitution of $\lambda = 0$ in Eq. (24) gives the eigenvector equation

$$(\mathbf{A} - 0 \cdot \mathbf{I})\mathbf{v} = \begin{bmatrix} -0.2 & 0.0 & 0.2 \\ 0.2 & -0.4 & 0.0 \\ 0.0 & 0.4 & -0.2 \end{bmatrix} \begin{bmatrix} a \\ b \\ c \end{bmatrix} = \begin{bmatrix} 0 \\ 0 \\ 0 \end{bmatrix} \qquad\qquad (25)$$

for $\mathbf{v} = \begin{bmatrix} a & b & c \end{bmatrix}^T$. The first row gives $a = c$ and the second row gives $a = 2b$, so $\mathbf{v}_0 = \begin{bmatrix} 2 & 1 & 2 \end{bmatrix}^T$ is an eigenvector associated with the eigenvalue $\lambda_0 = 0$. The corresponding solution $\mathbf{x}_0(t) = \mathbf{v}_0 e^{\lambda_0 t}$ of Eq. (23) is the constant solution

$$\mathbf{x}_0(t) = \begin{bmatrix} 2 \\ 1 \\ 2 \end{bmatrix}. \tag{26}$$

CASE 2: $\lambda = -0.4 - (0.2)i$.   Substitution of $\lambda = -0.4 - (0.2)i$ in Eq. (24) gives the eigenvector equation

$$[\mathbf{A} - (-0.4 - (0.2)i)\mathbf{I}]\,\mathbf{v} = \begin{bmatrix} 0.2 + (0.2)i & 0.0 & 0.2 \\ 0.2 & (0.2)i & 0.0 \\ 0.0 & 0.4 & 0.2 + (0.2)i \end{bmatrix} \begin{bmatrix} a \\ b \\ c \end{bmatrix}$$

$$= \begin{bmatrix} 0 \\ 0 \\ 0 \end{bmatrix}.$$

The second equation $(0.2)a + (0.2)ib = 0$ is satisfied by $a = 1$ and $b = i$. Then the first equation

$$[0.2 + (0.2)i]a + (0.2)c = 0$$

gives $c = -1 - i$. Thus, $\mathbf{v} = \begin{bmatrix} 1 & i & (-1 - i) \end{bmatrix}^T$ is a complex eigenvector associated with the complex eigenvalue $\lambda = -0.4 - (0.2)i$.

The corresponding complex-valued solution $\mathbf{x}(t) = \mathbf{v}e^{\lambda t}$ of (23) is

$$\mathbf{x}(t) = \begin{bmatrix} 1 & i & -1 - i \end{bmatrix}^T e^{(-0.4 - 0.2i)t}$$

$$= \begin{bmatrix} 1 & i & -1 - i \end{bmatrix}^T e^{(-0.4)t}(\cos 0.2t - i \sin 0.2t)$$

$$= e^{(-0.4)t} \begin{bmatrix} \cos 0.2t - i \sin 0.2t \\ \sin 0.2t + i \cos 0.2t \\ -\cos 0.2t - \sin 0.2t - i \cos 0.2t + i \sin 0.2t \end{bmatrix}.$$

The real and imaginary parts of $\mathbf{x}(t)$ are the real-valued solutions

$$\mathbf{x}_1(t) = e^{(-0.4)t} \begin{bmatrix} \cos 0.2t \\ \sin 0.2t \\ -\cos 0.2t - \sin 0.2t \end{bmatrix},$$

$$\mathbf{x}_2(t) = e^{(-0.4)t} \begin{bmatrix} -\sin 0.2t \\ \cos 0.2t \\ -\cos 0.2t + \sin 0.2t \end{bmatrix}. \tag{27}$$

The general solution

$$\mathbf{x}(t) = c_0 \mathbf{x}_0(t) + c_1 \mathbf{x}_1(t) + c_2 \mathbf{x}_2(t)$$

has scalar components

$$
\begin{aligned}
x_1(t) &= 2c_0 + e^{(-0.4)t}(c_1 \cos 0.2t - c_2 \sin 0.2t), \\
x_2(t) &= c_0 + e^{(-0.4)t}(c_1 \sin 0.2t + c_2 \cos 0.2t), \\
x_3(t) &= 2c_0 + e^{(-0.4)t}[(-c_1 - c_2)\cos 0.2t + (-c_1 + c_2)\sin 0.2t]
\end{aligned}
\tag{28}
$$

giving the amounts of salt in the three tanks at time t.
Observe that

$$x_1(t) + x_2(t) + x_3(t) \equiv 5c_0. \tag{29}$$

Of course, the total amount of salt in the closed system is constant; the constant c_0 in (29) is one-fifth the total amount of salt. Because of the factors of $e^{(-0.4)t}$ in (28), we see that

$$\lim_{t \to \infty} x_1(t) = 2c_0, \quad \lim_{t \to \infty} x_2(t) = c_0, \quad \text{and} \quad \lim_{t \to \infty} x_3(t) = 2c_0.$$

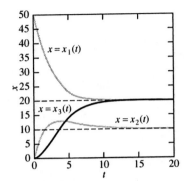

FIGURE 7.3.6. The salt content functions of Example 4.

Thus, as $t \to +\infty$ the salt in the system approaches a *steady-state* distribution with 40% of the salt in each of the two 50-gallon tanks and 20% in the 25-gallon tank. So whatever the initial distribution of salt among the three tanks, the limiting distribution is one of uniform concentration throughout the system. Figure 7.3.6 shows the graphs of the three solution functions with $c_0 = 10$, $c_1 = 30$, and $c_2 = -10$, in which case

$$x_1(0) = 50 \quad \text{and} \quad x_2(0) = x_3(0) = 0. \qquad \blacksquare$$

7.3 Problems

In Problems 1 through 16, apply the eigenvalue method of this section to find a general solution of the given system. If initial values are given, find also the corresponding particular solution. For each problem, use a computer system or graphing calculator to construct a direction field and typical solution curves for the given system.

1. $x_1' = x_1 + 2x_2, \quad x_2' = 2x_1 + x_2$
2. $x_1' = 2x_1 + 3x_2, \quad x_2' = 2x_1 + x_2$
3. $x_1' = 3x_1 + 4x_2, \quad x_2' = 3x_1 + 2x_2; \quad x_1(0) = x_2(0) = 1$
4. $x_1' = 4x_1 + x_2, \quad x_2' = 6x_1 - x_2$
5. $x_1' = 6x_1 - 7x_2, \quad x_2' = x_1 - 2x_2$
6. $x_1' = 9x_1 + 5x_2, \quad x_2' = -6x_1 - 2x_2; \quad x_1(0) = 1, \quad x_2(0) = 0$
7. $x_1' = -3x_1 + 4x_2, \quad x_2' = 6x_1 - 5x_2$
8. $x_1' = x_1 - 5x_2, \quad x_2' = x_1 - x_2$
9. $x_1' = 2x_1 - 5x_2, \quad x_2' = 4x_1 - 2x_2; \quad x_1(0) = 2, \quad x_2(0) = 3$
10. $x_1' = -3x_1 - 2x_2, \quad x_2' = 9x_1 + 3x_2$
11. $x_1' = x_1 - 2x_2, \quad x_2' = 2x_1 + x_2; \quad x_1(0) = 0, \quad x_2(0) = 4$
12. $x_1' = x_1 - 5x_2, \quad x_2' = x_1 + 3x_2$
13. $x_1' = 5x_1 - 9x_2, \quad x_2' = 2x_1 - x_2$
14. $x_1' = 3x_1 - 4x_2, \quad x_2' = 4x_1 + 3x_2$
15. $x_1' = 7x_1 - 5x_2, \quad x_2' = 4x_1 + 3x_2$
16. $x_1' = -50x_1 + 20x_2, \quad x_2' = 100x_1 - 60x_2$

In Problems 17 through 25, the eigenvalues of the coefficient matrix can be found by inspection and factoring. Apply the eigenvalue method to find a general solution of each system.

17. $x_1' = 4x_1 + x_2 + 4x_3, \quad x_2' = x_1 + 7x_2 + x_3,$
    $x_3' = 4x_1 + x_2 + 4x_3$
18. $x_1' = x_1 + 2x_2 + 2x_3, \quad x_2' = 2x_1 + 7x_2 + x_3,$
    $x_3' = 2x_1 + x_2 + 7x_3$
19. $x_1' = 4x_1 + x_2 + x_3, \quad x_2' = x_1 + 4x_2 + x_3, \quad x_3' = x_1 + x_2 + 4x_3$

20. $x_1' = 5x_1 + x_2 + 3x_3, \quad x_2' = x_1 + 7x_2 + x_3,$
    $x_3' = 3x_1 + x_2 + 5x_3$
21. $x_1' = 5x_1 - 6x_3, \quad x_2' = 2x_1 - x_2 - 2x_3, \quad x_3' = 4x_1 - 2x_2 - 4x_3$
22. $x_1' = 3x_1 + 2x_2 + 2x_3, \quad x_2' = -5x_1 - 4x_2 - 2x_3,$
    $x_3' = 5x_1 + 5x_2 + 3x_3$
23. $x_1' = 3x_1 + x_2 + x_3, \quad x_2' = -5x_1 - 3x_2 - x_3,$
    $x_3' = 5x_1 + 5x_2 + 3x_3$
24. $x_1' = 2x_1 + x_2 - x_3, \quad x_2' = -4x_1 - 3x_2 - x_3,$
    $x_3' = 4x_1 + 4x_2 + 2x_3$
25. $x_1' = 5x_1 + 5x_2 + 2x_3, \quad x_2' = -6x_1 - 6x_2 - 5x_3,$
    $x_3' = 6x_1 + 6x_2 + 5x_3$

26. Find the particular solution of the system

$$\frac{dx_1}{dt} = 3x_1 \qquad\quad + x_3,$$

$$\frac{dx_2}{dt} = 9x_1 - x_2 + 2x_3,$$

$$\frac{dx_3}{dt} = -9x_1 + 4x_2 - x_3$$

that satisfies the initial conditions $x_1(0) = 0$, $x_2(0) = 0$, $x_3(0) = 17$.

The amounts $x_1(t)$ and $x_2(t)$ of salt in the two brine tanks of Fig. 7.3.7 satisfy the differential equations

$$\frac{dx_1}{dt} = -k_1 x_1, \quad \frac{dx_2}{dt} = k_1 x_1 - k_2 x_2,$$

where $k_i = r/V_i$ for $i = 1, 2$. In Problems 27 and 28 the volumes V_1 and V_2 are given. First solve for $x_1(t)$ and $x_2(t)$, assuming that $r = 10$ (gal/min), $x_1(0) = 15$ (lb), and $x_2(0) = 0$.

Then find the maximum amount of salt ever in tank 2. Finally, construct a figure showing the graphs of $x_1(t)$ and $x_2(t)$.

Fresh water
Flow rate r

Tank 1
Volume V_1
Salt $x_1(t)$

r

Tank 2
Volume V_2
Salt $x_2(t)$

r

FIGURE 7.3.7. The two brine tanks of Problems 27 and 28.

27. $V_1 = 50$ (gal), $V_2 = 25$ (gal)
28. $V_1 = 25$ (gal), $V_2 = 40$ (gal)

The amounts $x_1(t)$ and $x_2(t)$ of salt in the two brine tanks of Fig. 7.3.8 satisfy the differential equations

$$\frac{dx_1}{dt} = -k_1 x_1 + k_2 x_2, \quad \frac{dx_2}{dt} = k_1 x_1 - k_2 x_2,$$

where $k_i = r/V_i$ as usual. In Problems 29 and 30, solve for $x_1(t)$ and $x_2(t)$, assuming that $r = 10$ (gal/min), $x_1(0) = 15$ (lb), and $x_2(0) = 0$. Then construct a figure showing the graphs of $x_1(t)$ and $x_2(t)$.

Tank 1 — r — Tank 2 — r

FIGURE 7.3.8. The two brine tanks of Problems 29 and 30.

29. $V_1 = 50$ (gal), $V_2 = 25$ (gal)
30. $V_1 = 25$ (gal), $V_2 = 40$ (gal)

Problems 31 through 34 deal with the open three-tank system of Fig. 7.3.2. Fresh water flows into tank 1; mixed brine flows from tank 1 into tank 2, from tank 2 into tank 3, and out of tank 3; all at the given flow rate r gallons per minute. The initial amounts $x_1(0) = x_0$ (lb), $x_2(0) = 0$, and $x_3(0) = 0$ of salt in the three tanks are given, as are their volumes V_1, V_2, and V_3 (in gallons). First solve for the amounts of salt in the three tanks at time t, then determine the maximal amount of salt that tank 3 ever contains. Finally, construct a figure showing the graphs of $x_1(t)$, $x_2(t)$, and $x_3(t)$.

31. $r = 30$, $x_0 = 27$, $V_1 = 30$, $V_2 = 15$, $V_3 = 10$
32. $r = 60$, $x_0 = 45$, $V_1 = 20$, $V_2 = 30$, $V_3 = 60$
33. $r = 60$, $x_0 = 45$, $V_1 = 15$, $V_2 = 10$, $V_3 = 30$

34. $r = 60$, $x_0 = 40$, $V_1 = 20$, $V_2 = 12$, $V_3 = 60$

Problems 35 through 37 deal with the closed three-tank system of Fig. 7.3.5, which is described by the equations in (24). Mixed brine flows from tank 1 into tank 2, from tank 2 into tank 3, and from tank 3 into tank 1, all at the given flow rate r gallons per minute. The initial amounts $x_1(0) = x_0$ (pounds), $x_2(0) = 0$, and $x_3(0) = 0$ of salt in the three tanks are given, as are their volumes V_1, V_2, and V_3 (in gallons). First solve for the amounts of salt in the three tanks at time t, then determine the limiting amount (as $t \to +\infty$) of salt in each tank. Finally, construct a figure showing the graphs of $x_1(t)$, $x_2(t)$, and $x_3(t)$.

35. $r = 120$, $x_0 = 33$, $V_1 = 20$, $V_2 = 6$, $V_3 = 40$
36. $r = 10$, $x_0 = 18$, $V_1 = 20$, $V_2 = 50$, $V_3 = 20$
37. $r = 60$, $x_0 = 55$, $V_1 = 60$, $V_2 = 20$, $V_3 = 30$

For each matrix A given in Problems 38 through 40, the zeros in the matrix make its characteristic polynomial easy to calculate. Find the general solution of $\mathbf{x}' = \mathbf{Ax}$.

38. $\mathbf{A} = \begin{bmatrix} 1 & 0 & 0 & 0 \\ 2 & 2 & 0 & 0 \\ 0 & 3 & 3 & 0 \\ 0 & 0 & 4 & 4 \end{bmatrix}$

39. $\mathbf{A} = \begin{bmatrix} -2 & 0 & 0 & 9 \\ 4 & 2 & 0 & -10 \\ 0 & 0 & -1 & 8 \\ 0 & 0 & 0 & 1 \end{bmatrix}$

40. $\mathbf{A} = \begin{bmatrix} 2 & 0 & 0 & 0 \\ -21 & -5 & -27 & -9 \\ 0 & 0 & 5 & 0 \\ 0 & 0 & -21 & -2 \end{bmatrix}$

41. The coefficient matrix $\mathbf{A}$ of the 4×4 system

$$\begin{aligned} x_1' &= 4x_1 + x_2 + x_3 + 7x_4, \\ x_2' &= x_1 + 4x_2 + 10x_3 + x_4, \\ x_3' &= x_1 + 10x_2 + 4x_3 + x_4, \\ x_4' &= 7x_1 + x_2 + x_3 + 4x_4 \end{aligned}$$

has eigenvalues $\lambda_1 = -3$, $\lambda_2 = -6$, $\lambda_3 = 10$, and $\lambda_4 = 15$. Find the particular solution of this system that satisfies the initial conditions

$$x_1(0) = 3, \quad x_2(0) = x_3(0) = 1, \quad x_4(0) = 3.$$

In Problems 42 through 50, use a calculator or computer system to calculate the eigenvalues and eigenvectors (as illustrated in Application 7.3) in order to find a general solution of the linear system $\mathbf{x}' = \mathbf{Ax}$ with the given coefficient matrix $\mathbf{A}$.

42. $\mathbf{A} = \begin{bmatrix} -40 & -12 & 54 \\ 35 & 13 & -46 \\ -25 & -7 & 34 \end{bmatrix}$

43. $\mathbf{A} = \begin{bmatrix} -20 & 11 & 13 \\ 12 & -1 & -7 \\ -48 & 21 & 31 \end{bmatrix}$

44. $A = \begin{bmatrix} 147 & 23 & -202 \\ -90 & -9 & 129 \\ 90 & 15 & -123 \end{bmatrix}$

45. $A = \begin{bmatrix} 9 & -7 & -5 & 0 \\ -12 & 7 & 11 & 9 \\ 24 & -17 & -19 & -9 \\ -18 & 13 & 17 & 9 \end{bmatrix}$

46. $A = \begin{bmatrix} 13 & -42 & 106 & 139 \\ 2 & -16 & 52 & 70 \\ 1 & 6 & -20 & -31 \\ -1 & -6 & 22 & 33 \end{bmatrix}$

47. $A = \begin{bmatrix} 23 & -18 & -16 & 0 \\ -8 & 6 & 7 & 9 \\ 34 & -27 & -26 & -9 \\ -26 & 21 & 25 & 12 \end{bmatrix}$

48. $A = \begin{bmatrix} 47 & -8 & 5 & -5 \\ -10 & 32 & 18 & -2 \\ 139 & -40 & -167 & -121 \\ -232 & 64 & 360 & 248 \end{bmatrix}$

49. $A = \begin{bmatrix} 139 & -14 & -52 & -14 & 28 \\ -22 & 5 & 7 & 8 & -7 \\ 370 & -38 & -139 & -38 & 76 \\ 152 & -16 & -59 & -13 & 35 \\ 95 & -10 & -38 & -7 & 23 \end{bmatrix}$

50. $A = \begin{bmatrix} 9 & 13 & 0 & 0 & 0 & -13 \\ -14 & 19 & -10 & -20 & 10 & 4 \\ -30 & 12 & -7 & -30 & 12 & 18 \\ -12 & 10 & -10 & -9 & 10 & 2 \\ 6 & 9 & 0 & 6 & 5 & -15 \\ -14 & 23 & -10 & -20 & 10 & 0 \end{bmatrix}$

7.3 Application: Automatic Calculation of Eigenvalues and Eigenvectors

Most computational systems offer the capability to find eigenvalues and eigenvectors readily. For instance, Fig. 7.3.9 shows a graphing calculator computation of the eigenvalues and eigenvectors of the matrix

$$A = \begin{bmatrix} -0.5 & 0.0 & 0.0 \\ 0.5 & -0.25 & 0.0 \\ 0.0 & 0.25 & -0.2 \end{bmatrix}$$

of Example 2. We see each eigenvector displayed as a column vector beneath its eigenvalue. Note that with results presented in decimal form, it is up to us to guess (and verify by matrix multiplication) that the exact eigenvector associated with the third eigenvalue $\lambda = -\frac{1}{2}$ is $\mathbf{v} = \begin{bmatrix} 1 & -2 & \frac{5}{3} \end{bmatrix}^T$. The *Maple* commands

```
with(linalg)
A := matrix(3,3,[-0.5,0,0,0.5,-0.25,0,0,0.25,-0.2]);
eigenvects(A);
```

the *Mathematica* commands

```
A = {{-0.5,0,0},{0.5,-0.25,0},{0,0.25,-0.2}}
Eigensystem[A]
```

and the MATLAB commands

```
A = [-0.5,0,0; 0.5,-0.25,0; 0,0.25,-0.2]
[V,D] = eig(A)
```

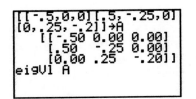

FIGURE 7.3.9. TI-86 calculation of the eigenvalues and eigenvectors of the matrix **A**.

(where **D** will be a diagonal matrix displaying the eigenvalues of **A** and the column vectors of **V** are the corresponding eigenvectors) produce similar results. You can use these commands to find the eigenvalues and eigenvectors needed for any of the problems in this section.

For a more substantial investigation, choose a positive integer $n < 10$ ($n = 5$, for instance) and let $q_1, q_2, \ldots, q_n$ denote the first n nonzero digits in your student ID number. Now consider an open system of brine tanks as in Fig. 7.3.2, except with n rather than three successive tanks having volumes $V_i = 10q_i$ ($i = 1, 2, \ldots, n$)

in gallons. If each flow rate is $r = 10$ gallons per minute, then the salt amounts $x_1(t)$, $x_2(t)$, ..., $x_n(t)$ satisfy the linear system

$$x_1' = -k_1 x_1,$$
$$x_i' = \quad k_{i-1}x_{i-1} - k_i x_i \quad (i = 2, 3, \ldots, n),$$

where $k_i = r/V_i$. Apply the eigenvalue method to solve this system with initial conditions

$$x_1(0) = 10, \quad x_2(0) = x_3(0) = \cdots = x_n(0) = 0.$$

Graph the solution functions and estimate graphically the maximum amount of salt that each tank ever contains.

For an alternative investigation, suppose that the system of n tanks is closed as in Fig. 7.3.5, so that tank 1 receives as inflow the outflow from tank n (rather than fresh water). Then the first equation should be replaced with $x_1' = k_n x_n - k_1 x_1$. Now show that, in this *closed* system, as $t \to +\infty$ the salt originally in tank 1 distributes itself with constant density throughout the various tanks. A plot like Fig. 7.3.6 should make this fairly obvious.

7.4 Second-Order Systems and Mechanical Applications*

In this section we apply the matrix methods of Sections 7.2 and 7.3 to investigate the oscillations of typical mass-and-spring systems having two or more degrees of freedom. Our examples are chosen to illustrate phenomena that are generally characteristic of complex mechanical systems.

Figure 7.4.1 shows three masses connected to each other and to two walls by the four indicated springs. We assume that the masses slide without friction and that each spring obeys Hooke's law—its extension or compression x and force F of reaction are related by the formula $F = -kx$. If the rightward displacements x_1, x_2, and x_3 of the three masses (from their respective equilibrium positions) are all positive, then

FIGURE 7.4.1. Three spring-coupled masses.

- The first spring is stretched the distance x_1;
- The second spring is stretched the distance $x_2 - x_1$;
- The third spring is stretched the distance $x_3 - x_2$;
- The fourth spring is compressed the distance x_3.

Therefore, application of Newton's law $F = ma$ to the three masses (as in Example 1 of Section 7.1) yields their equations of motion:

$$m_1 x_1'' = -k_1 x_1 \qquad + k_2(x_2 - x_1),$$
$$m_2 x_2'' = -k_2(x_2 - x_1) + k_3(x_3 - x_2), \tag{1}$$
$$m_3 x_3'' = -k_3(x_3 - x_2) - k_4 x_3.$$

In terms of the **displacement vector** $\mathbf{x} = \begin{bmatrix} x_1 & x_2 & x_3 \end{bmatrix}^T$, the **mass matrix**

$$\mathbf{M} = \begin{bmatrix} m_1 & 0 & 0 \\ 0 & m_2 & 0 \\ 0 & 0 & m_3 \end{bmatrix}, \tag{2}$$

*This optional section may be omitted without loss of continuity. It provides a sample of the more technical applications of eigenvalues to physics and engineering problems.

and the **stiffness matrix**

$$\mathbf{K} = \begin{bmatrix} -(k_1 + k_2) & k_2 & 0 \\ k_2 & -(k_2 + k_3) & k_3 \\ 0 & k_3 & -(k_3 + k_4) \end{bmatrix}, \tag{3}$$

the system in (1) takes the matrix form

$$\blacktriangleright \qquad\qquad \mathbf{Mx''} = \mathbf{Kx}. \tag{4}$$

The notation in Eqs. (1) through (4) generalizes in a natural way to the system of n spring-coupled masses shown in Fig. 7.4.2. We need only write

FIGURE 7.4.2. A system of n spring-coupled masses.

$$\mathbf{M} = \begin{bmatrix} m_1 & 0 & \cdots & 0 \\ 0 & m_2 & \cdot & 0 \\ \vdots & \vdots & & \vdots \\ 0 & 0 & \cdots & m_n \end{bmatrix} \tag{5}$$

and

$$\mathbf{K} = \begin{bmatrix} -(k_1 + k_2) & k_2 & 0 & \cdots & 0 \\ k_2 & -(k_2 + k_3) & k_3 & \cdots & 0 \\ 0 & k_3 & -(k_3 + k_4) & \cdots & 0 \\ 0 & 0 & k_4 & \cdots & 0 \\ \vdots & \vdots & & & \vdots \\ 0 & 0 & \cdots & -(k_{n-1} + k_n) & k_n \\ 0 & 0 & \cdots & k_n & -(k_n + k_{n+1}) \end{bmatrix} \tag{6}$$

for the mass and stiffness matrices in Eq. (4).

The diagonal matrix $\mathbf{M}$ is obviously nonsingular; to get its inverse $\mathbf{M}^{-1}$ we need only replace each diagonal element with its reciprocal. Hence multiplication of each side in Eq. (4) by $\mathbf{M}^{-1}$ yields the homogeneous **second-order system**

$$\blacktriangleright \qquad\qquad \mathbf{x''} = \mathbf{Ax}, \tag{7}$$

where $\mathbf{A} = \mathbf{M}^{-1}\mathbf{K}$. There is a wide variety of *frictionless* mechanical systems for which a displacement or position vector $\mathbf{x}$, a nonsingular mass matrix $\mathbf{M}$, and a stiffness matrix $\mathbf{K}$ satisfying Eq. (4) can be defined.

Solution of Second-Order Systems

To seek a solution of Eq. (7), we substitute (as in Section 7.3 for a first-order system) a trial solution of the form

$$\mathbf{x}(t) = \mathbf{v}e^{\alpha t}, \tag{8}$$

where $\mathbf{v}$ is a constant vector. Then $\mathbf{x''} = \alpha^2 \mathbf{v}e^{\alpha t}$, so substitution of Eq. (8) in (7) gives

$$\alpha^2 \mathbf{v}e^{\alpha t} = \mathbf{A}\mathbf{v}e^{\alpha t},$$

which implies that

$$\mathbf{A}\mathbf{v} = \alpha^2 \mathbf{v}. \tag{9}$$

Therefore, $\mathbf{x}(t) = \mathbf{v}e^{\alpha t}$ is a solution of $\mathbf{x}'' = \mathbf{A}\mathbf{x}$ if and only if $\alpha^2 = \lambda$, an eigenvalue of the matrix $\mathbf{A}$, and $\mathbf{v}$ is an associated eigenvector.

If $\mathbf{x}'' = \mathbf{A}\mathbf{x}$ models a mechanical system, then it is typical that the eigenvalues of $\mathbf{A}$ are *negative* real numbers. If

$$\alpha^2 = \lambda = -\omega^2 < 0,$$

then $\alpha = \pm\omega i$. In this case the solution given by Eq. (8) is

$$\mathbf{x}(t) = \mathbf{v}e^{i\omega t} = \mathbf{v}(\cos \omega t + i \sin \omega t).$$

The real and imaginary parts

$$\mathbf{x}_1(t) = \mathbf{v}\cos \omega t \quad \text{and} \quad \mathbf{x}_2(t) = \mathbf{v}\sin \omega t \tag{10}$$

of $\mathbf{x}(t)$ are then linearly independent *real-valued* solutions of the system. This analysis leads to the following theorem.

THEOREM 1: Second-Order Homogeneous Linear Systems

If the $n \times n$ matrix $\mathbf{A}$ has distinct negative eigenvalues $-\omega_1^2, -\omega_2^2, \ldots, -\omega_n^2$ with associated [real] eigenvectors $\mathbf{v}_1, \mathbf{v}_2, \ldots, \mathbf{v}_n$, then a general solution of

➤ $$\mathbf{x}'' = \mathbf{A}\mathbf{x}$$

is given by

➤ $$\mathbf{x}(t) = \sum_{i=1}^{n} (a_i \cos \omega_i t + b_i \sin \omega_i t)\mathbf{v}_i \tag{11}$$

with a_i and b_i arbitrary constants. In the special case of a nonrepeated zero eigenvalue λ_0 with associated eigenvector $\mathbf{v}_0$,

$$\mathbf{x}_0(t) = (a_0 + b_0 t)\mathbf{v}_0 \tag{12}$$

is the corresponding part of the general solution. ▲

Remark: The nonzero vector $\mathbf{v}_0$ is an eigenvector corresponding to $\lambda_0 = 0$ provided that $\mathbf{A}\mathbf{v}_0 = \mathbf{0}$. If $\mathbf{x}(t) = (a_0 + b_0 t)\mathbf{v}_0$, then

$$\mathbf{x}'' = 0 \cdot \mathbf{v}_0 = (a_0 + b_0 t) \cdot \mathbf{0} = (a_0 + b_0 t) \cdot (\mathbf{A}\mathbf{v}_0) = \mathbf{A}\mathbf{x},$$

thus verifying the form in Eq. (12). ∎

Example 1

Consider the mass-and-spring system with $n = 2$ shown in Fig. 7.4.3. Because there is no third spring connected to a right-hand wall, we set $k_3 = 0$. If $m_1 = 2$, $m_2 = 1$, $k_1 = 100$, and $k_2 = 50$, then the equation $\mathbf{Mx''} = \mathbf{Kx}$ is

$$\begin{bmatrix} 2 & 0 \\ 0 & 1 \end{bmatrix} \mathbf{x''} = \begin{bmatrix} -150 & 50 \\ 50 & -50 \end{bmatrix} \mathbf{x}, \tag{13}$$

which reduces to $\mathbf{x''} = \mathbf{Ax}$ with

$$\mathbf{A} = \begin{bmatrix} -75 & 25 \\ 50 & -50 \end{bmatrix}.$$

The characteristic equation of $\mathbf{A}$ is

$$(-75 - \lambda)(-50 - \lambda) - 50 \cdot 25 = \lambda^2 + 125\lambda + 2500$$
$$= (\lambda + 25)(\lambda + 100) = 0,$$

so $\mathbf{A}$ has the negative eigenvalues $\lambda_1 = -25$ and $\lambda_2 = -100$. By Theorem 1, the system in (13) therefore has solutions with [circular] frequencies $\omega_1 = 5$ and $\omega_2 = 10$.

CASE 1: $\lambda_1 = -25$. The eigenvector equation $(\mathbf{A} - \lambda\mathbf{I})\mathbf{v} = \mathbf{0}$ is

$$\begin{bmatrix} -50 & 25 \\ 50 & -25 \end{bmatrix} \begin{bmatrix} a \\ b \end{bmatrix} = \begin{bmatrix} 0 \\ 0 \end{bmatrix},$$

so an eigenvector associated with $\lambda_1 = -25$ is $\mathbf{v}_1 = \begin{bmatrix} 1 & 2 \end{bmatrix}^T$.

CASE 2: $\lambda_2 = -100$. The eigenvector equation $(\mathbf{A} - \lambda\mathbf{I})\mathbf{v} = \mathbf{0}$ is

$$\begin{bmatrix} 25 & 25 \\ 50 & 50 \end{bmatrix} \begin{bmatrix} a \\ b \end{bmatrix} = \begin{bmatrix} 0 \\ 0 \end{bmatrix},$$

so an eigenvector associated with $\lambda_2 = -100$ is $\mathbf{v}_2 = \begin{bmatrix} 1 & -1 \end{bmatrix}^T$.

By Eq. (11) it follows that a general solution of the system in (13) is given by

$$\mathbf{x}(t) = (a_1 \cos 5t + b_1 \sin 5t)\mathbf{v}_1 + (a_2 \cos 10t + b_2 \sin 10t)\mathbf{v}_2. \tag{14}$$

The two terms on the right in Eq. (14) represent **free oscillations** of the mass-and-spring system. They describe the physical system's two **natural modes of oscillation** at its two [circular] **natural frequencies** $\omega_1 = 5$ and $\omega_2 = 10$. The natural mode

$$\mathbf{x}_1(t) = (a_1 \cos 5t + b_1 \sin 5t)\mathbf{v}_1 = c_1 \cos(5t - \alpha_1) \begin{bmatrix} 1 \\ 2 \end{bmatrix}$$

(with $c_1 = \sqrt{a_1^2 + b_1^2}$, $\cos \alpha_1 = a_1/c_1$, and $\sin \alpha_1 = b_1/c_1$) has the scalar component equations

$$\begin{aligned} x_1(t) &= c_1 \cos(5t - \alpha_1), \\ x_2(t) &= 2c_1 \cos(5t - \alpha_1) \end{aligned} \tag{15}$$

k_1 k_2
m_1 m_2
$x_1(t)$ $x_2(t)$

Equilibrium positions

FIGURE 7.4.3. The mass-and-spring system of Example 1.

and therefore describes a free oscillation in which the two masses move in synchrony in the same direction and with the same frequency $\omega_1 = 5$, but with the amplitude of motion of m_2 twice that of m_1 (see Fig. 7.4.4). The natural mode

$$\mathbf{x}_2(t) = (a_2 \cos 10t + b_2 \sin 10t)\mathbf{v}_2 = c_2 \cos(10t - \alpha_2) \begin{bmatrix} 1 \\ -1 \end{bmatrix}$$

has the scalar component equations

$$\begin{aligned} x_1(t) &= \ \ c_2 \cos(10t - \alpha_2), \\ x_2(t) &= -c_2 \cos(10t - \alpha_2) \end{aligned} \tag{16}$$

and therefore describes a free oscillation in which the two masses move in synchrony in opposite directions with the same frequency $\omega_2 = 10$ and with equal amplitudes of oscillation (see Fig. 7.4.5). ∎

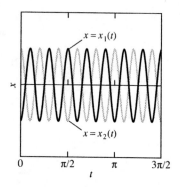

FIGURE 7.4.4. Oscillations in the same direction with frequency $\omega_1 = 5$; the amplitude of motion of mass 2 is twice that of mass 1.

FIGURE 7.4.5. Oscillations in opposite directions with frequency $\omega_2 = 10$; the amplitude of motion of the two masses are the same.

Example 2

Figure 7.4.6 shows three railway cars connected by buffer springs that react when compressed, but disengage instead of stretching. With $n = 3$, $k_2 = k_3 = k$, and $k_1 = k_4 = 0$ in Eqs. (2) through (4), we get the system

$$\begin{bmatrix} m_1 & 0 & 0 \\ 0 & m_2 & 0 \\ 0 & 0 & m_3 \end{bmatrix} \mathbf{x}'' = \begin{bmatrix} -k & k & 0 \\ k & -2k & k \\ 0 & k & -k \end{bmatrix} \mathbf{x}, \tag{17}$$

which is equivalent to

$$\mathbf{x}'' = \begin{bmatrix} -c_1 & c_1 & 0 \\ c_2 & -2c_2 & c_2 \\ 0 & c_3 & -c_3 \end{bmatrix} \mathbf{x} \tag{18}$$

with

$$c_i = \frac{k}{m_i} \quad (i = 1, 2, 3). \tag{19}$$

FIGURE 7.4.6. The three railway cars of Example 2.

If we assume further that $m_1 = m_3$, so that $c_1 = c_3$, then a brief computation gives

$$-\lambda(\lambda + c_1)(\lambda + c_1 + 2c_2) = 0 \tag{20}$$

for the characteristic equation of the coefficient matrix **A** in Eq. (18). Hence the matrix **A** has eigenvalues

$$\lambda_1 = 0, \quad \lambda_2 = -c_1, \quad \lambda_3 = -c_1 - 2c_2 \tag{21a}$$

corresponding to the natural frequencies

$$\omega_1 = 0, \quad \omega_2 = \sqrt{c_1}, \quad \omega_3 = \sqrt{c_1 + 2c_2} \tag{21b}$$

of the physical system.

For a numerical example, suppose that the first and third railway cars weigh 12 tons each, that the middle car weighs 8 tons, and that the spring constant is $k = 1.5$ tons/ft (i.e., $k = 3000$ lb/ft). Then, using fps units with mass measured in slugs (a weight of 32 pounds has a mass of 1 slug), we have

$$m_1 = m_3 = 750, \quad m_2 = 500,$$

and

$$c_1 = \frac{3000}{750} = 4, \quad c_2 = \frac{3000}{500} = 6.$$

Hence the coefficient matrix **A** is

$$\mathbf{A} = \begin{bmatrix} -4 & 4 & 0 \\ 6 & -12 & 6 \\ 0 & 4 & -4 \end{bmatrix}, \tag{22}$$

and the eigenvalue-frequency pairs given by (21a) and (21b) are $\lambda_1 = 0$, $\omega_1 = 0$; $\lambda_2 = -4$, $\omega_2 = 2$; and $\lambda_3 = -16$, $\omega_3 = 4$.

CASE 1: $\lambda_1 = 0$, $\omega_1 = 0$. The eigenvector equation $(\mathbf{A} - \lambda\mathbf{I})\mathbf{v} = \mathbf{0}$ is

$$\mathbf{Av} = \begin{bmatrix} -4 & 4 & 0 \\ 6 & -12 & 6 \\ 0 & 4 & -4 \end{bmatrix} \begin{bmatrix} a \\ b \\ c \end{bmatrix} = \begin{bmatrix} 0 \\ 0 \\ 0 \end{bmatrix},$$

so it is clear that $\mathbf{v}_1 = \begin{bmatrix} 1 & 1 & 1 \end{bmatrix}^T$ is an eigenvector associated with $\lambda_1 = 0$. According to Theorem 1, the corresponding part of a general solution of $\mathbf{x}'' = \mathbf{Ax}$ is

$$\mathbf{x}_1(t) = (a_1 + b_1 t)\mathbf{v}_1.$$

CASE 2: $\lambda_2 = -4$, $\omega_2 = 2$. The eigenvector equation $(\mathbf{A} - \lambda\mathbf{I})\mathbf{v} = \mathbf{0}$ is

$$(\mathbf{A} + 4\mathbf{I})\mathbf{v} = \begin{bmatrix} 0 & 4 & 0 \\ 6 & -8 & 6 \\ 0 & 4 & 0 \end{bmatrix} \begin{bmatrix} a \\ b \\ c \end{bmatrix} = \begin{bmatrix} 0 \\ 0 \\ 0 \end{bmatrix}$$

so it is clear that $\mathbf{v}_2 = \begin{bmatrix} 1 & 0 & -1 \end{bmatrix}^T$ is an eigenvector associated with $\lambda_2 = -4$. According to Theorem 1, the corresponding part of a general solution of $\mathbf{x}'' = \mathbf{Ax}$ is

$$\mathbf{x}_2(t) = (a_2 \cos 2t + b_2 \sin 2t)\mathbf{v}_2.$$

CASE 3: $\lambda_3 = -16$, $\omega_3 = 4$.   The eigenvector equation $(\mathbf{A} - \lambda \mathbf{I})\mathbf{v} = \mathbf{0}$ is

$$(\mathbf{A} + 16\mathbf{I})\mathbf{v} = \begin{bmatrix} 12 & 4 & 0 \\ 6 & 4 & 6 \\ 0 & 4 & 12 \end{bmatrix} \begin{bmatrix} a \\ b \\ c \end{bmatrix} = \begin{bmatrix} 0 \\ 0 \\ 0 \end{bmatrix},$$

so it is clear that $\mathbf{v}_3 = \begin{bmatrix} 1 & -3 & 1 \end{bmatrix}^T$ is an eigenvector associated with $\lambda_3 = -16$. According to Theorem 1, the corresponding part of a general solution of $\mathbf{x}'' = \mathbf{A}\mathbf{x}$ is

$$\mathbf{x}_3(t) = (a_3 \cos 4t + b_3 \sin 4t)\mathbf{v}_3.$$

The general solution $\mathbf{x} = \mathbf{x}_1 + \mathbf{x}_2 + \mathbf{x}_3$ of $\mathbf{x}'' = \mathbf{A}\mathbf{x}$ is therefore given by

$$\mathbf{x}(t) = a_1 \begin{bmatrix} 1 \\ 1 \\ 1 \end{bmatrix} + b_1 t \begin{bmatrix} 1 \\ 1 \\ 1 \end{bmatrix} + a_2 \begin{bmatrix} 1 \\ 0 \\ -1 \end{bmatrix} \cos 2t$$

$$+ b_2 \begin{bmatrix} 1 \\ 0 \\ -1 \end{bmatrix} \sin 2t + a_3 \begin{bmatrix} 1 \\ -3 \\ 1 \end{bmatrix} \cos 4t + b_3 \begin{bmatrix} 1 \\ -3 \\ 1 \end{bmatrix} \sin 4t. \qquad (23)$$

To determine a particular solution, let us suppose that the leftmost car is moving to the right with velocity v_0 and at time $t = 0$ strikes the other two cars, which are together but at rest. The corresponding initial conditions are

$$x_1(0) = x_2(0) = x_3(0) = 0, \qquad (24a)$$
$$x_1'(0) = v_0, \quad x_2'(0) = x_3'(0) = 0. \qquad (24b)$$

Then substitution of (24a) in (23) gives the scalar equations

$$\begin{aligned} a_1 + a_2 + \; a_3 &= 0, \\ a_1 \quad\;\; - 3a_3 &= 0, \\ a_1 - a_2 + \; a_3 &= 0, \end{aligned}$$

which readily yield $a_1 = a_2 = a_3 = 0$. Hence the position functions of the three cars are

$$\begin{aligned} x_1(t) &= b_1 t + b_2 \sin 2t + \; b_3 \sin 4t, \\ x_2(t) &= b_1 t \qquad\quad\; - 3b_3 \sin 4t, \\ x_3(t) &= b_1 t - b_2 \sin 2t + \; b_3 \sin 4t, \end{aligned} \qquad (25)$$

and their velocity functions are

$$\begin{aligned} x_1'(t) &= b_1 + 2b_2 \cos 2t + \; 4b_3 \cos 4t, \\ x_2'(t) &= b_1 \qquad\qquad\; - 12b_3 \cos 4t, \\ x_3'(t) &= b_1 - 2b_2 \cos 2t + \; 4b_3 \cos 4t. \end{aligned} \qquad (26)$$

Substitution of (24b) in (26) gives the equations

$$\begin{aligned} b_1 + 2b_2 + \; 4b_3 &= v_0, \\ b_1 \qquad\quad\; - 12b_3 &= 0, \\ b_1 - 2b_2 + \; 4b_3 &= 0 \end{aligned}$$

that readily yield $b_1 = \frac{3}{8}v_0$, $b_2 = \frac{1}{4}v_0$, and $b_3 = \frac{1}{32}v_0$. Finally, the position functions in (25) are

$$x_1(t) = \tfrac{1}{32}v_0(12t + 8\sin 2t + \sin 4t),$$

$$x_2(t) = \tfrac{1}{32}v_0(12t \qquad\quad - 3\sin 4t), \tag{27}$$

$$x_3(t) = \tfrac{1}{32}v_0(12t - 8\sin 2t + \sin 4t).$$

But these equations hold only so long as the two buffer springs remain compressed; that is, while both

$$x_2 - x_1 < 0 \quad\text{and}\quad x_3 - x_2 < 0.$$

To discover what this implies about t, we compute

$$x_2(t) - x_1(t) = \tfrac{1}{32}v_0(-8\sin 2t - 4\sin 4t)$$

$$= -\tfrac{1}{32}v_0(8\sin 2t + 8\sin 2t \cos 2t)$$

$$= -\tfrac{1}{4}v_0(\sin 2t)(1 + \cos 2t)$$

and, similarly,

$$x_3(t) - x_2(t) = -\tfrac{1}{4}v_0(\sin 2t)(1 - \cos 2t).$$

It follows that $x_2 - x_1 < 0$ and $x_3 - x_2 < 0$ until $t = \pi/2 \approx 1.57$ (seconds), at which time the equations in (26) and (27) give the values

$$x_1\left(\frac{\pi}{2}\right) = x_2\left(\frac{\pi}{2}\right) = x_3\left(\frac{\pi}{2}\right) = \frac{3\pi v_0}{16},$$

$$x_1'\left(\frac{\pi}{2}\right) = x_2'\left(\frac{\pi}{2}\right) = 0, \quad x_3'\left(\frac{\pi}{2}\right) = v_0.$$

We conclude that the three railway cars remain engaged and moving to the right until disengagement occurs at time $t = \pi/2$. Thereafter, cars 1 and 2 remain at rest (!), while car 3 continues to the right with speed v_0. If, for instance, $v_0 = 48$ feet per second (about 33 miles per hour), then the three cars travel a distance of $9\pi \approx 28.27$ (ft) during their 1.57 seconds of engagement, and

$$x_1(t) = x_2(t) = 9\pi, \quad x_3(t) = 48t - 15\pi \tag{27'}$$

for $t > \pi/2$. Figure 7.4.7 illustrates the "before" and "after" situations, and Fig. 7.4.8 shows the graphs of the functions $x_1(t)$, $x_2(t)$, and $x_3(t)$ in Eqs. (27) and (27'). ∎

At rest

(a)

At rest

(b)

FIGURE 7.4.7. (a) Before;   (b) after.

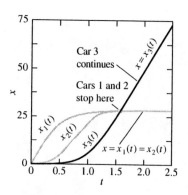

FIGURE 7.4.8. Position functions of the three railway cars of Example 2.

Forced Oscillations and Resonance

Suppose now that the *i*th mass of the mass-and-spring system in Fig. 7.4.2 is subject to an external force F_i ($i = 1, 2, \ldots, n$) in addition to the forces exerted by the springs attached to it. Then the homogeneous equation $\mathbf{Mx}'' = \mathbf{Kx}$ is replaced with the nonhomogeneous equation

$$\mathbf{Mx}'' = \mathbf{Kx} + \mathbf{F}, \tag{28}$$

where $\mathbf{F} = \begin{bmatrix} F_1 & F_2 & \ldots & F_n \end{bmatrix}^T$ is the **external force vector** for the system. Multiplication by $\mathbf{M}^{-1}$ yields

$$\mathbf{x}'' = \mathbf{Ax} + \mathbf{f}, \tag{29}$$

where $\mathbf{f}$ is the external force vector *per unit mass*. We are especially interested in the case of a *periodic external force*

$$\mathbf{f}(t) = \mathbf{F}_0 \cos \omega t \tag{30}$$

(where $\mathbf{F}_0$ is a constant vector). We then anticipate a periodic particular solution

$$\mathbf{x}_p(t) = \mathbf{c} \cos \omega t \tag{31}$$

with the known external frequency ω and with a coefficient vector $\mathbf{c}$ yet to be determined. Because $\mathbf{x}_p'' = -\omega^2 \mathbf{c} \cos \omega t$, substitution of (30) and (31) in (29), followed by cancellation of the common factor $\cos \omega t$, gives the linear system

$$(\mathbf{A} + \omega^2 \mathbf{I})\mathbf{c} = -\mathbf{F}_0 \tag{32}$$

to be solved for $\mathbf{c}$.

Observe that the matrix $\mathbf{A} + \omega^2 \mathbf{I}$ is nonsingular—in which case Eq. (32) can be solved for $\mathbf{c}$—unless $-\omega^2 = \lambda$, an eigenvalue of $\mathbf{A}$. Thus a periodic particular solution of the form in Eq. (31) exists provided that the external forcing frequency does *not* equal one of the natural frequencies $\omega_1, \omega_2, \ldots, \omega_n$ of the system. The case in which ω *is* a natural frequency corresponds to the phenomenon of **resonance** discussed in Section 5.6.

Example 3

Suppose that the second mass in Example 1 is subjected to the external periodic force $50\cos\omega t$. Then with $m_1 = 2$, $m_2 = 1$, $k_1 = 100$, $k_2 = 50$, and $F_0 = 50$ in Fig. 7.4.9, Eq. (29) takes the form

$$\mathbf{x}'' = \begin{bmatrix} -75 & 25 \\ 50 & -50 \end{bmatrix} \mathbf{x} + \begin{bmatrix} 0 \\ 50 \end{bmatrix} \cos\omega t, \tag{33}$$

FIGURE 7.4.9. The forced mass-and-spring system of Example 3.

and the substitution $\mathbf{x} = \mathbf{c}\cos\omega t$ leads to the equation

$$\begin{bmatrix} \omega^2 - 75 & 25 \\ 50 & \omega^2 - 50 \end{bmatrix} \mathbf{c} = \begin{bmatrix} 0 \\ -50 \end{bmatrix} \tag{34}$$

for the coefficient vector $\mathbf{c} = \begin{bmatrix} c_1 & c_2 \end{bmatrix}^T$. This system is readily solved for

$$c_1 = \frac{1250}{(\omega^2 - 25)(\omega^2 - 100)}, \quad c_2 = -\frac{50(\omega^2 - 75)}{(\omega^2 - 25)(\omega^2 - 100)}. \tag{35}$$

For instance, if the external squared frequency is $\omega^2 = 50$, then (35) yields $c_1 = -1$, $c_2 = -1$. The resulting forced periodic oscillation is described by

$$x_1(t) = -\cos\omega t, \quad x_2(t) = -\cos\omega t.$$

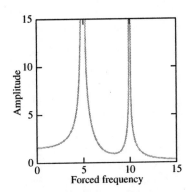

Thus the two masses oscillate in synchrony with equal amplitudes and in the same direction.

If the external squared frequency is $\omega^2 = 125$, then (35) yields $c_1 = \frac{1}{2}$, $c_2 = -1$. The resulting forced periodic oscillation is described by

$$x_1(t) = \tfrac{1}{2}\cos\omega t, \quad x_2(t) = -\cos\omega t,$$

and now the two masses oscillate in synchrony in opposite directions, but with the amplitude of motion of m_2 twice that of m_1.

It is evident from the denominators in (35) that c_1 and c_2 approach $+\infty$ as ω approaches either of the two natural frequencies $\omega_1 = 5$ and $\omega_2 = 10$ (found in Example 1). Figure 7.4.10 shows a plot of the amplitude $\sqrt{c_1^2 + c_2^2}$ of the forced periodic solution $\mathbf{x}(t) = \mathbf{c}\cos\omega t$ as a function of the forced frequency ω. The peaks at $\omega_2 = 5$ and $\omega_2 = 10$ exhibit visually the phenomenon of resonance. ∎

FIGURE 7.4.10. Frequency-amplitude plot for Example 3.

Periodic and Transient Solutions

It follows from Theorem 4 of Section 7.2 that a particular solution of the forced system

$$\mathbf{x}'' = \mathbf{A}\mathbf{x} + \mathbf{F}_0\cos\omega t \tag{36}$$

will be of the form

$$\mathbf{x}(t) = \mathbf{x}_c(t) + \mathbf{x}_p(t), \tag{37}$$

where $\mathbf{x}_p(t)$ is a particular solution of the nonhomogeneous system and $\mathbf{x}_c(t)$ is a solution of the corresponding homogeneous system. It is typical for the effects of frictional resistance in mechanical systems to damp out the complementary function solution $\mathbf{x}_c(t)$, so that

$$\mathbf{x}_c(t) \to \mathbf{0} \quad \text{as} \quad t \to +\infty. \tag{38}$$

Hence $\mathbf{x}_c(t)$ is a **transient solution** that depends only on the initial conditions; it dies out with time, leaving the **steady periodic solution** $\mathbf{x}_p(t)$ resulting from the external driving force:

$$\mathbf{x}(t) \to \mathbf{x}_p(t) \quad \text{as} \quad t \to +\infty. \tag{39}$$

As a practical matter, every physical system includes frictional resistance (however small) that damps out transient solutions in this manner.

7.4 Problems

Problems 1 through 7 deal with the mass-and-spring system shown in Fig. 7.4.11 with stiffness matrix

$$\mathbf{K} = \begin{bmatrix} -(k_1 + k_2) & k_2 \\ k_2 & -(k_2 + k_3) \end{bmatrix}$$

and with the given mks values for the masses and spring constants. Find the two natural frequencies of the system and describe its two natural modes of oscillation.

FIGURE 7.4.11. The mass-and-spring system for Problems 1 through 6.

1. $m_1 = m_2 = 1$; $k_1 = 0, k_2 = 2, k_3 = 0$ (no walls)
2. $m_1 = m_2 = 1$; $k_1 = 1, k_2 = 4, k_3 = 1$
3. $m_1 = 1, m_2 = 2$; $k_1 = 1, k_2 = k_3 = 2$
4. $m_1 = m_2 = 1$; $k_1 = 1, k_2 = 2, k_3 = 1$
5. $m_1 = m_2 = 1$; $k_1 = 2, k_2 = 1, k_3 = 2$
6. $m_1 = 1, m_2 = 2$; $k_1 = 2, k_2 = k_3 = 4$
7. $m_1 = m_2 = 1$; $k_1 = 4, k_2 = 6, k_3 = 4$

In Problems 8 through 10, the indicated mass-and-spring system is set in motion from rest $(x_1'(0) = x_2'(0) = 0)$ in its equilibrium position $(x_1(0) = x_2(0) = 0)$ with the given external forces $F_1(t)$ and $F_2(t)$ acting on the masses m_1 and m_2, respectively. Find the resulting motion of the system and describe it as a superposition of oscillations at three different frequencies.

8. The mass-and-spring system of Problem 2, with $F_1(t) = 96\cos 5t$, $F_2(t) \equiv 0$

9. The mass-and-spring system of Problem 3, with $F_1(t) \equiv 0$, $F_2(t) = 120\cos 3t$

10. The mass-and-spring system of Problem 7, with $F_1(t) = 30\cos t$, $F_2(t) = 60\cos t$

11. Consider a mass-and-spring system containing two masses $m_1 = 1$ and $m_2 = 1$ whose displacement functions $x(t)$ and $y(t)$ satisfy the differential equations

$$x'' = -40x + 8y,$$
$$y'' = 12x - 60y.$$

(a) Describe the two fundamental modes of free oscillation of the system. **(b)** Assume that the two masses start in motion with the initial conditions

$$x(0) = 19, \quad x'(0) = 12$$

and

$$y(0) = 3, \quad y'(0) = 6$$

and are acted on by the same force, $F_1(t) = F_2(t) = -195\cos 7t$. Describe the resulting motion as a superposition of oscillations at three different frequencies.

In Problems 12 and 13, find the natural frequencies of the three-mass system of Fig. 7.4.1, using the given masses and spring constants. For each natural frequency ω, give the ratio $a_1:a_2:a_3$ of amplitudes for a corresponding natural mode $x_1 = a_1\cos\omega t$, $x_2 = a_2\cos\omega t$, $x_3 = a_3\cos\omega t$.

12. $m_1 = m_2 = m_3 = 1$; $k_1 = k_2 = k_3 = k_4 = 1$
13. $m_1 = m_2 = m_3 = 1$; $k_1 = k_2 = k_3 = k_4 = 2$
   (*Hint*: One eigenvalue is $\lambda = -4$.)

14. In the system of Fig. 7.4.12, assume that $m_1 = 1$, $k_1 = 50$, $k_2 = 10$, and $F_0 = 5$ in mks units, and that $\omega = 10$. Then find m_2 so that in the resulting steady periodic oscillations, the mass m_1 will remain at rest(!). Thus the effect of the second mass-and-spring pair will be to neutralize the effect of the force on the first mass. This is an example of a *dynamic damper*. It has an electrical analogy that some cable companies use to prevent your reception of certain cable channels.

FIGURE 7.4.12. The mechanical system of Problem 14.

15. Suppose that $m_1 = 2$, $m_2 = \frac{1}{2}$, $k_1 = 75$, $k_2 = 25$, $F_0 = 100$, and $\omega = 10$ (all in mks units) in the forced mass-and-spring system of Fig. 7.4.9. Find the solution of the system $\mathbf{M}\mathbf{x}'' = \mathbf{K}\mathbf{x} + \mathbf{F}$ that satisfies the initial conditions $\mathbf{x}(0) = \mathbf{x}'(0) = \mathbf{0}$.

16. Figure 7.4.13 shows two railway cars with a buffer spring. We want to investigate the transfer of momentum that occurs after car 1 with initial velocity v_0 impacts car 2 at rest. The analogue of Eq. (18) in the text is

$$\mathbf{x}'' = \begin{bmatrix} -c_1 & c_1 \\ c_2 & -c_2 \end{bmatrix} \mathbf{x}$$

with $c_i = k/m_i$ for $i = 1, 2$. Show that the eigenvalues of the coefficient matrix $\mathbf{A}$ are $\lambda_1 = 0$ and $\lambda_2 = -c_1 - c_2$, with associated eigenvectors $\mathbf{v}_1 = \begin{bmatrix} 1 & 1 \end{bmatrix}^T$ and $\mathbf{v}_2 = \begin{bmatrix} c_1 & -c_2 \end{bmatrix}^T$.

$x_1'(0) = 0 \qquad x_2'(0) = 0$

FIGURE 7.4.13. The two railway cars of Problems 16 through 19.

17. If the two cars of Problem 16 both weigh 16 tons [so that $m_1 = m_2 = 1000$ (slugs)] and $k = 1$ ton/ft (that is, 2000 lb/ft), show that the cars separate after $\pi/2$ seconds and that $x_1'(t) = 0$ and $x_2'(t) = v_0$ thereafter. Thus the original momentum of car 1 is completely transferred to car 2.

18. If cars 1 and 2 weigh 8 and 16 tons, respectively, and $k = 3000$ lb/ft, show that the two cars separate after $\pi/3$ seconds, and that

$$x_1'(t) = -\tfrac{1}{3}v_0 \quad \text{and} \quad x_2'(t) = +\tfrac{2}{3}v_0$$

thereafter. Thus the two cars rebound in opposite directions.

19. If cars 1 and 2 weigh 24 and 8 tons, respectively, and $k = 1500$ lb/ft, show that the cars separate after $\pi/2$ seconds, and that

$$x_1'(t) = +\tfrac{1}{2}v_0 \quad \text{and} \quad x_2'(t) = +\tfrac{3}{2}v_0$$

thereafter. Thus both cars continue in the original direction of motion, but with different velocities.

20. In the three-railway-car system of Fig. 7.4.6, suppose that cars 1 and 3 each weigh 32 tons, that car 2 weighs 8 tons, and that each spring constant is 4 tons/ft. If $x_1'(0) = v_0$ and $x_2'(0) = x_3'(0) = 0$, show that the two springs are compressed until $t = \pi/2$ and that

$$x_1'(t) = -\tfrac{1}{9}v_0 \quad \text{and} \quad x_2'(t) = x_3'(t) = +\tfrac{8}{9}v_0$$

thereafter. Thus car 1 rebounds, but cars 2 and 3 continue with the same velocity.

The Two-Axle Automobile

In Example 4 of Section 5.6 we investigated the vertical oscillations of a one-axle car—actually a unicycle. Now we can analyze a more realistic model: a car with two axles and with separate front and rear suspension systems. Figure 7.4.14 represents the suspension system of such a car. We assume that the car body acts as would a solid bar of mass m and length $L = L_1 + L_2$. It has moment of inertia I about its center of mass C, which is at distance L_1 from the front of the car. The

car has front and back suspension springs with Hooke's constants k_1 and k_2, respectively. When the car is in motion, let $x(t)$ denote the vertical displacement of the center of mass of the car from equilibrium; let $\theta(t)$ denote its angular displacement (in radians) from the horizontal. Then Newton's laws of motion for linear and angular acceleration can be used to derive the equations

$$mx'' = -(k_1 + k_2)x + (k_1 L_1 - k_2 L_2)\theta,$$

$$I\theta'' = (k_1 L_1 - k_2 L_2)x - (k_1 L_1^2 + k_2 L_2^2)\theta. \tag{40}$$

FIGURE 7.4.14. Model of the two-axle automobile.

21. Suppose that $m = 75$ slugs (the car weighs 2400 lb), $L_1 = 7$ ft, $L_2 = 3$ ft (it's a rear-engine car), $k_1 = k_2 = 2000$ lb/ft, and $I = 1000$ ft·lb·s². Then the equations in (40) take the form

$$75x'' + 4000x - \quad 8000\theta = 0,$$

$$1000\theta'' - 8000x + 116{,}000\theta = 0.$$

   (a) Find the two natural frequencies ω_1 and ω_2 of the car.
   (b) Now suppose that the car is driven at a speed of v feet per second along a washboard surface shaped like a sine curve with a wavelength of 40 ft. The result is a periodic force on the car with frequency $\omega = 2\pi v/40 = \pi v/20$. Resonance occurs when with $\omega = \omega_1$ or $\omega = \omega_2$. Find the corresponding two critical speeds of the car (in feet per second and in miles per hour).

22. Suppose that $k_1 = k_2 = k$ and $L_1 = L_2 = \tfrac{1}{2}L$ in Fig. 7.4.14 (the symmetric situation). Then show that every free oscillation is a combination of a vertical oscillation with frequency

$$\omega_1 = \sqrt{2k/m}$$

and an angular oscillation with frequency

$$\omega_2 = \sqrt{kL^2/(2I)}.$$

In Problems 23 through 25, the system of Fig. 7.4.14 is taken as a model for an undamped car with the given parameters in fps units. (a) Find the two natural frequencies of oscillation (in hertz). (b) Assume that this car is driven along a sinusoidal washboard surface with a wavelength of 40 ft. Find the two critical speeds.

23. $m = 100$, $I = 800$, $L_1 = L_2 = 5$, $k_1 = k_2 = 2000$
24. $m = 100$, $I = 1000$, $L_1 = 6$, $L_2 = 4$, $k_1 = k_2 = 2000$
25. $m = 100$, $I = 800$, $L_1 = L_2 = 5$, $k_1 = 1000$, $k_2 = 2000$

7.4 Application: Earthquake-Induced Vibrations of Multistory Buildings

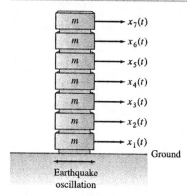

FIGURE 7.4.15. The seven-story building.

FIGURE 7.4.16. Forces on the ith floor.

In this application you are to investigate the response to transverse earthquake ground oscillations of the seven-story building illustrated in Fig. 7.4.15. Suppose that each of the seven (aboveground) floors weighs 16 tons, so the mass of each is $m = 1000$ (slugs). Also assume a horizontal restoring force of $k = 5$ (tons per foot) between adjacent floors. That is, the internal forces in response to horizontal displacements of the individual floors are those shown in Fig. 7.4.16. It follows that the free transverse oscillations indicated in Fig. 7.4.15 satisfy the equation $\mathbf{M}\mathbf{x}'' = \mathbf{K}\mathbf{x}$ with $n = 7$, $m_i = 1000$ (for each i), and $k_i = 10000$ (lb/ft) for $1 \leq i \leq 7$. The system then reduces to the form $\mathbf{x}'' = \mathbf{A}\mathbf{x}$ with

$$\mathbf{A} = \begin{bmatrix} -20 & 10 & 0 & 0 & 0 & 0 & 0 \\ 10 & -20 & 10 & 0 & 0 & 0 & 0 \\ 0 & 10 & -20 & 10 & 0 & 0 & 0 \\ 0 & 0 & 10 & -20 & 10 & 0 & 0 \\ 0 & 0 & 0 & 10 & -20 & 10 & 0 \\ 0 & 0 & 0 & 0 & 10 & -20 & 10 \\ 0 & 0 & 0 & 0 & 0 & 10 & -10 \end{bmatrix}. \tag{1}$$

Once the matrix $\mathbf{A}$ has been entered, the TI-86 command **eigVl A** takes about 15 seconds to calculate the seven eigenvalues shown in the λ-column of the table in Fig. 7.4.17. Alternatively, you can use the *Maple* command **eigenvals(A)**, the MATLAB command **eig(A)**, or the *Mathematica* command **Eigenvalues[A]**. Then calculate the entries in the remaining columns of the table showing the natural frequencies and periods of oscillation of the seven-story building. Note that a typical earthquake producing ground oscillations with a period of 2 seconds is uncomfortably close to the fifth natural frequency (with period 1.9869 seconds) of the building.

A horizontal earthquake oscillation $E \cos \omega t$ of the ground, with amplitude E and acceleration $a = -E\omega^2 \cos \omega t$, produces an opposite inertial force $F = ma = mE\omega^2 \sin \omega t$ on each floor of the building. The resulting nonhomogeneous system is

$$\mathbf{x}'' = \mathbf{A}\mathbf{x} + (E\omega^2 \cos \omega t)\mathbf{b}, \tag{2}$$

i	Eigenvalue λ	Frequency $\omega = \sqrt{-\lambda}$	Period $P = \dfrac{2\pi}{\omega}$ (s)
1	−38.2709	6.1863	1.0157
2	−33.3826	5.7778	1.0875
3	−26.1803	5.1167	1.2280
4	−17.9094	4.2320	1.4847
5	−10.0000	3.1623	1.9869
6	−3.8197	1.9544	3.2149
7	−0.4370	0.6611	9.5042

FIGURE 7.4.17. Frequencies and periods of natural oscillations of the seven-story building.

FIGURE 7.4.18. Resonance vibrations of a seven-story building—maximal amplitude as a function of period.

where $\mathbf{b} = \begin{bmatrix} 1 & 1 & 1 & 1 & 1 & 1 & 1 \end{bmatrix}^T$ and $\mathbf{A}$ is the matrix of Eq. (1). Figure 7.4.18 shows a plot of *maximal amplitude* (for the forced oscillations of any single floor) versus the *period* of the earthquake vibrations. The spikes correspond to the first six of the seven resonant frequencies. We see, for instance, that whereas an earthquake with period 2 (s) likely would produce destructive resonance vibrations in the building, it probably would be unharmed by an earthquake with period 2.5 (s). Different buildings have different natural frequencies of vibration, and so a given earthquake may demolish one building but leave untouched the one next door. This seeming anomaly was observed in Mexico City after the devastating earthquake of September 19, 1985.

For your personal seven-story building to investigate, let the weight (in tons) of each story equal the largest digit of your student ID number and let k (in tons/ft) equal the smallest nonzero digit. Produce numerical and graphical results like those illustrated in Figs. 7.4.17 and 7.4.18. Is your building susceptible to likely damage from an earthquake with period in the 2- to 3-second range?

You might like to begin by working manually the following warm-up problems.

1. Find the periods of the natural vibrations of a building with two above-ground floors, each weighing 16 tons and with each restoring force being $k = 5$ tons/ft.

2. Find the periods of the natural vibrations of a building with three above-ground floors, with each weighing 16 tons and with each restoring force being $k = 5$ tons/ft.

3. Find the natural frequencies and natural modes of vibration of a building with three aboveground floors as in Problem 2, except that the upper two floors weigh 8 tons each instead of 16. Give the ratios of the amplitudes A, B, and C of oscillations of the three floors in the form $A:B:C$ with $A = 1$.

4. Suppose that the building of Problem 3 is subject to an earthquake in which the ground undergoes horizontal sinusoidal oscillations with a period of 3 s and an amplitude of 3 in. Find the amplitudes of the resulting steady periodic oscillations of the three aboveground floors. Assume the fact that a motion $E \sin \omega t$ of the ground, with acceleration $a = -E\omega^2 \sin \omega t$, produces an opposite inertial force $F = -ma = mE\omega^2 \sin \omega t$ on a floor of mass m.

7.5 Multiple Eigenvalue Solutions

In Section 7.3 we saw that if the $n \times n$ matrix $\mathbf{A}$ has n *distinct* (real or complex) eigenvalues $\lambda_1, \lambda_2, \ldots, \lambda_n$ with respective associated eigenvectors $\mathbf{v}_1, \mathbf{v}_2, \ldots, \mathbf{v}_n$, then a general solution of the system

$$\frac{d\mathbf{x}}{dt} = \mathbf{A}\mathbf{x} \tag{1}$$

is given by

$$\mathbf{x}(t) = c_1\mathbf{v}_1 e^{\lambda_1 t} + c_2\mathbf{v}_2 e^{\lambda_2 t} + \cdots + c_n\mathbf{v}_n e^{\lambda_n t} \tag{2}$$

with arbitrary constants $c_1, c_2, \ldots, c_n$. In this section we discuss the situation when the characteristic equation

$$|\mathbf{A} - \lambda\mathbf{I}| = 0 \tag{3}$$

does *not* have n distinct roots, and thus has at least one repeated root.

An eigenvalue is of **multiplicity** k if it is a k-fold root of Eq. (3). For each eigenvalue λ, the eigenvector equation

$$(\mathbf{A} - \lambda\mathbf{I})\mathbf{v} = \mathbf{0} \qquad (4)$$

has at least one nonzero solution $\mathbf{v}$, so there is at least one eigenvector associated with λ. But an eigenvalue of multiplicity $k > 1$ may have *fewer* than k linearly independent associated eigenvectors. In this case we are unable to find a "complete set" of n linearly independent eigenvectors of $\mathbf{A}$, as needed to form the general solution in (2).

Let us call an eigenvalue of multiplicity k **complete** if it has k linearly independent associated eigenvectors. If every eigenvalue of the matrix $\mathbf{A}$ is complete, then—because eigenvectors associated with different eigenvalues are linearly independent (by Theorem 2 in Section 6.2)—it follows that $\mathbf{A}$ does have a complete set of n linearly independent eigenvectors $\mathbf{v}_1, \mathbf{v}_2, \ldots, \mathbf{v}_n$ associated with the eigenvalues $\lambda_1, \lambda_2, \ldots, \lambda_n$ (each repeated with its multiplicity). In this case a general solution of $\mathbf{x}' = \mathbf{A}\mathbf{x}$ is still given by the usual combination in (2).

Example 1

Find a general solution of the system

$$\mathbf{x}' = \begin{bmatrix} 9 & 4 & 0 \\ -6 & -1 & 0 \\ 6 & 4 & 3 \end{bmatrix} \mathbf{x}. \qquad (5)$$

Solution   The characteristic equation of the coefficient matrix $\mathbf{A}$ in Eq. (5) is

$$
|\mathbf{A} - \lambda\mathbf{I}| = \begin{vmatrix} 9 - \lambda & 4 & 0 \\ -6 & -1 - \lambda & 0 \\ 6 & 4 & 3 - \lambda \end{vmatrix}
$$

$$= (3 - \lambda)[(9 - \lambda)(-1 - \lambda) + 24]$$

$$= (3 - \lambda)(15 - 8\lambda + \lambda^2)$$

$$= (5 - \lambda)(3 - \lambda)^2 = 0.$$

Thus $\mathbf{A}$ has the distinct eigenvalue $\lambda_1 = 5$ and the repeated eigenvalue $\lambda_2 = 3$ of multiplicity $k = 2$.

CASE 1: $\lambda_1 = 5$.   The eigenvector equation $(\mathbf{A} - \lambda\mathbf{I})\mathbf{v} = \mathbf{0}$, where $\mathbf{v} = [a \quad b \quad c]^T$, is

$$
(\mathbf{A} - 5\mathbf{I})\mathbf{v} = \begin{bmatrix} 4 & 4 & 0 \\ -6 & -6 & 0 \\ 6 & 4 & -2 \end{bmatrix} \begin{bmatrix} a \\ b \\ c \end{bmatrix} = \begin{bmatrix} 0 \\ 0 \\ 0 \end{bmatrix}.
$$

Each of the first two equations, $4a + 4b = 0$ and $-6a - 6b = 0$, yields $b = -a$. Then the third equation reduces to $2a - 2c = 0$, so that $c = a$. The choice $a = 1$ then yields the eigenvector

$$\mathbf{v}_1 = \begin{bmatrix} 1 & -1 & 1 \end{bmatrix}^T$$

associated with the eigenvalue $\lambda_1 = 5$.

CASE 2: $\lambda_2 = 3$. Now the eigenvector equation is

$$(\mathbf{A} - 3\mathbf{I})\mathbf{v} = \begin{bmatrix} 6 & 4 & 0 \\ -6 & -4 & 0 \\ 6 & 4 & 0 \end{bmatrix} \begin{bmatrix} a \\ b \\ c \end{bmatrix} = \begin{bmatrix} 0 \\ 0 \\ 0 \end{bmatrix},$$

so the nonzero vector $\mathbf{v} = \begin{bmatrix} a & b & c \end{bmatrix}^T$ is an eigenvector if and only if

$$6a + 4b = 0; \tag{6}$$

that is, $b = -\frac{3}{2}a$. The fact that Eq. (6) does not involve c means that c is arbitrary, subject to the condition $\mathbf{v} \neq \mathbf{0}$. If $c = 1$, then we may choose $a = b = 0$; this gives the eigenvector

$$\mathbf{v}_2 = \begin{bmatrix} 0 & 0 & 1 \end{bmatrix}^T$$

associated with $\lambda_2 = 3$. If $c = 0$, then we must choose a to be nonzero. For instance, if $a = 2$ (to avoid fractions), then $b = -3$, so

$$\mathbf{v}_3 = \begin{bmatrix} 2 & -3 & 0 \end{bmatrix}^T$$

is a second linearly independent eigenvector associated with the multiplicity 2 eigenvalue $\lambda_2 = 3$.

Thus we have found a complete set $\mathbf{v}_1$, $\mathbf{v}_2$, $\mathbf{v}_3$ of three eigenvectors associated with the eigenvalues 5, 3, 3. The corresponding general solution of Eq. (5) is

$$\mathbf{x}(t) = c_1 \mathbf{v}_1 e^{5t} + c_2 \mathbf{v}_2 e^{3t} + c_3 \mathbf{v}_3 e^{3t} \tag{7}$$

$$= c_1 \begin{bmatrix} 1 \\ -1 \\ 1 \end{bmatrix} e^{5t} + c_2 \begin{bmatrix} 0 \\ 0 \\ 1 \end{bmatrix} e^{3t} + c_3 \begin{bmatrix} 2 \\ -3 \\ 0 \end{bmatrix} e^{3t},$$

with scalar component functions given by

$$\begin{aligned} x_1(t) &= c_1 e^{5t} + 2c_3 e^{3t}, \\ x_2(t) &= -c_1 e^{5t} - 3c_3 e^{3t}, \\ x_3(t) &= c_1 e^{5t} + c_2 e^{3t}. \end{aligned}$$ ∎

Remark: Our choice in Example 1 of the two eigenvectors

$$\mathbf{v}_2 = \begin{bmatrix} 0 & 0 & 1 \end{bmatrix}^T \quad \text{and} \quad \mathbf{v}_3 = \begin{bmatrix} 2 & -3 & 0 \end{bmatrix}^T$$

associated with the repeated eigenvalue $\lambda_2 = 3$ bears comment. The fact that $b = -\frac{3}{2}a$ for any eigenvector associated with $\lambda_2 = 3$ means that any such eigenvector can be written as

$$\mathbf{v} = \begin{bmatrix} a \\ -\frac{3}{2}a \\ c \end{bmatrix} = c \begin{bmatrix} 0 \\ 0 \\ 1 \end{bmatrix} + \frac{1}{2}a \begin{bmatrix} 2 \\ -3 \\ 0 \end{bmatrix} = c\mathbf{v}_2 + \frac{1}{2}a\mathbf{v}_3,$$

and thus is a linear combination of $\mathbf{v}_2$ and $\mathbf{v}_3$. Therefore, given a and c not both zero, we could choose $\mathbf{v}$ rather than $\mathbf{v}_3$ as our third eigenvector, and the new general solution

$$\mathbf{x}(t) = c_1 \mathbf{v}_1 e^{5t} + c_2 \mathbf{v}_2 e^{3t} + c_3 \mathbf{v} e^{3t}$$

would be equivalent to the one in Eq. (7). Thus we need not worry about making the "right" choice of independent eigenvectors associated with a multiple eigenvalue. Any choice will do; we generally make the simplest one we can. ∎

Defective Eigenvalues

The following example shows that—unfortunately—not all multiple eigenvalues are complete.

Example 2 The matrix

$$A = \begin{bmatrix} 1 & -3 \\ 3 & 7 \end{bmatrix} \tag{8}$$

has characteristic equation

$$|A - \lambda I| = \begin{vmatrix} 1 - \lambda & -3 \\ 3 & 7 - \lambda \end{vmatrix}$$

$$= (1 - \lambda)(7 - \lambda) + 9$$

$$= \lambda^2 - 8\lambda + 16 = (\lambda - 4)^2 = 0.$$

Thus A has the single eigenvalue $\lambda_1 = 4$ of multiplicity 2. The eigenvector equation

$$(A - 4I)v = \begin{bmatrix} -3 & -3 \\ 3 & 3 \end{bmatrix} \begin{bmatrix} a \\ b \end{bmatrix} = \begin{bmatrix} 0 \\ 0 \end{bmatrix}$$

then amounts to the equivalent scalar equations

$$-3a - 3b = 0, \quad 3a + 3b = 0.$$

Hence $b = -a$ if $v = \begin{bmatrix} a & b \end{bmatrix}^T$ is to be an eigenvector of A. Therefore, any eigenvector associated with $\lambda_1 = 4$ is a nonzero multiple of $v = \begin{bmatrix} 1 & -1 \end{bmatrix}^T$. Thus the multiplicity 2 eigenvalue $\lambda_1 = 4$ has only one independent eigenvector and hence is incomplete. ∎

An eigenvalue λ of multiplicity $k > 1$ is called **defective** if it is not complete. If λ has only $p < k$ linearly independent eigenvectors, then the number

$$d = k - p \tag{9}$$

of "missing" eigenvectors is called the **defect** of the defective eigenvalue λ. Thus the defective eigenvalue $\lambda_1 = 4$ in Example 2 has multiplicity $k = 2$ and defect $d = 1$, because we saw that it has only $p = 1$ associated eigenvector.

If the eigenvalues of the $n \times n$ matrix A are not all complete, then the eigenvalue method as yet described will produce *fewer* than the needed n linearly independent solutions of the system $x' = Ax$. We therefore need to discover how to find the "missing solutions" corresponding to a defective eigenvalue λ of multiplicity $k > 1$.

The Case of Defect $k = 2$

Let us begin with the case $k = 2$, and suppose that we have found (as in Example 2) that there is only a single eigenvector v_1 associated with the defective eigenvalue λ. Then at this point we have found only the single solution

$$x_1(t) = v_1 e^{\lambda t} \tag{10}$$

of $\mathbf{x}' = \mathbf{Ax}$. By analogy with the case of a repeated characteristic root for a single linear differential equation (Section 5.3), we might hope to find a second solution of the form

$$\mathbf{x}_2(t) = (\mathbf{v}_2 t)e^{\lambda t} = \mathbf{v}_2 t e^{\lambda t}. \tag{11}$$

When we substitute $\mathbf{x} = \mathbf{v}_2 t e^{\lambda t}$ in $\mathbf{x}' = \mathbf{Ax}$, we get the equation

$$\mathbf{v}_2 e^{\lambda t} + \lambda \mathbf{v}_2 t e^{\lambda t} = \mathbf{A}\mathbf{v}_2 t e^{\lambda t}.$$

But because the coefficients of both $e^{\lambda t}$ and $t e^{\lambda t}$ must balance, it follows that $\mathbf{v}_2 = \mathbf{0}$, and hence that $\mathbf{x}_2(t) \equiv \mathbf{0}$. This means that—contrary to our hope—the system $\mathbf{x}' = \mathbf{Ax}$ does not have a *nontrivial* solution of the form assumed in (11).

Instead of simply giving up on the idea behind Eq. (11), let us extend it slightly and replace $\mathbf{v}_2 t$ with $\mathbf{v}_1 t + \mathbf{v}_2$. Thus we explore the possibility of a second solution of the form

➤ $$\mathbf{x}_2(t) = (\mathbf{v}_1 t + \mathbf{v}_2)e^{\lambda t} = \mathbf{v}_1 t e^{\lambda t} + \mathbf{v}_2 e^{\lambda t}, \tag{12}$$

where $\mathbf{v}_1$ and $\mathbf{v}_2$ are nonzero constant vectors. When we substitute $\mathbf{x} = \mathbf{v}_1 t e^{\lambda t} + \mathbf{v}_2 e^{\lambda t}$ in $\mathbf{x}' = \mathbf{Ax}$, we get the equation

$$\mathbf{v}_1 e^{\lambda t} + \lambda \mathbf{v}_1 t e^{\lambda t} + \lambda \mathbf{v}_2 e^{\lambda t} = \mathbf{A}\mathbf{v}_1 t e^{\lambda t} + \mathbf{A}\mathbf{v}_2 e^{\lambda t}. \tag{13}$$

We equate coefficients of $e^{\lambda t}$ and $t e^{\lambda t}$ here and thereby obtain the two equations

$$(\mathbf{A} - \lambda \mathbf{I})\mathbf{v}_1 = \mathbf{0} \tag{14}$$

and

$$(\mathbf{A} - \lambda \mathbf{I})\mathbf{v}_2 = \mathbf{v}_1 \tag{15}$$

that the vectors $\mathbf{v}_1$ and $\mathbf{v}_2$ must satisfy in order for (12) to give a solution of $\mathbf{x}' = \mathbf{Ax}$.

Note that Eq. (14) merely confirms that $\mathbf{v}_1$ is an eigenvector of $\mathbf{A}$ associated with the eigenvalue λ. Then Eq. (15) says that the vector $\mathbf{v}_2$ satisfies the equation

$$(\mathbf{A} - \lambda \mathbf{I})^2 \mathbf{v}_2 = (\mathbf{A} - \lambda \mathbf{I})[(\mathbf{A} - \lambda \mathbf{I})\mathbf{v}_2] = (\mathbf{A} - \lambda \mathbf{I})\mathbf{v}_1 = \mathbf{0}.$$

It follows that, in order to solve simultaneously the two equations in (14) and (15), it suffices to find a solution $\mathbf{v}_2$ of the single equation $(\mathbf{A} - \lambda \mathbf{I})^2 \mathbf{v}_2 = \mathbf{0}$ such that the resulting vector $\mathbf{v}_1 = (\mathbf{A} - \lambda \mathbf{I})\mathbf{v}_2$ is *nonzero*. It turns out that this is always possible if the defective eigenvalue λ of $\mathbf{A}$ is of multiplicity 2. Consequently, the procedure described in the following algorithm always succeeds in finding two independent solutions associated with such an eigenvalue.

ALGORITHM: Defective Multiplicity 2 Eigenvalues

1. First find a nonzero solution $\mathbf{v}_2$ of the equation

$$(\mathbf{A} - \lambda \mathbf{I})^2 \mathbf{v}_2 = \mathbf{0} \tag{16}$$

such that

$$(\mathbf{A} - \lambda \mathbf{I})\mathbf{v}_2 = \mathbf{v}_1 \tag{17}$$

is nonzero, and therefore is an eigenvector $\mathbf{v}_1$ associated with λ.

2. Then form the two independent solutions

$$\mathbf{x}_1(t) = \mathbf{v}_1 e^{\lambda t} \tag{18}$$

and

$$\mathbf{x}_2(t) = (\mathbf{v}_1 t + \mathbf{v}_2)e^{\lambda t} \tag{19}$$

of $\mathbf{x}' = \mathbf{A}\mathbf{x}$ corresponding to λ.   ▲

Example 3   Find a general solution of the system

$$\mathbf{x}' = \begin{bmatrix} 1 & -3 \\ 3 & 7 \end{bmatrix} \mathbf{x}. \tag{20}$$

Solution   In Example 2 we found that the coefficient matrix $\mathbf{A}$ in Eq. (20) has the defective eigenvalue $\lambda = 4$ of multiplicity 2. We therefore begin by calculating

$$(\mathbf{A} - 4\mathbf{I})^2 = \begin{bmatrix} -3 & -3 \\ 3 & 3 \end{bmatrix} \begin{bmatrix} -3 & -3 \\ 3 & 3 \end{bmatrix} = \begin{bmatrix} 0 & 0 \\ 0 & 0 \end{bmatrix}.$$

Hence Eq. (16) is

$$\begin{bmatrix} 0 & 0 \\ 0 & 0 \end{bmatrix} \mathbf{v}_2 = \mathbf{0},$$

and therefore is satisfied by *any* choice of $\mathbf{v}_2$. In principle, it could happen that $(\mathbf{A} - 4\mathbf{I})\mathbf{v}_2$ is nonzero (as desired) for some choices of $\mathbf{v}_2$ though not for others. If we try $\mathbf{v}_2 = \begin{bmatrix} 1 & 0 \end{bmatrix}^T$ we find that

$$(\mathbf{A} - 4\mathbf{I})\mathbf{v}_2 = \begin{bmatrix} -3 & -3 \\ 3 & 3 \end{bmatrix} \begin{bmatrix} 1 \\ 0 \end{bmatrix} = \begin{bmatrix} -3 \\ 3 \end{bmatrix} = \mathbf{v}_1$$

is nonzero and therefore is an eigenvector associated with $\lambda = 4$. (It is -3 times the eigenvector found in Example 2.) Therefore the two solutions of Eq. (20) given by Eqs. (18) and (19) are

$$\mathbf{x}_1(t) = \mathbf{v}_1 e^{4t} = \begin{bmatrix} -3 \\ 3 \end{bmatrix} e^{4t},$$

$$\mathbf{x}_2(t) = (\mathbf{v}_1 t + \mathbf{v}_2)e^{4t} = \begin{bmatrix} -3t + 1 \\ 3t \end{bmatrix} e^{4t}.$$

The resulting general solution

$$\mathbf{x}(t) = c_1 \mathbf{x}_1(t) + c_2 \mathbf{x}_2(t)$$

has scalar component functions

$$x_1(t) = (-3c_2 t + c_2 - 3c_1)e^{4t},$$
$$x_2(t) = (3c_2 t + 3c_1)e^{4t}.$$

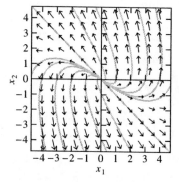

FIGURE 7.5.1. Direction field and solution curves for the linear system $x_1' = x_1 - 3x_2$, $x_2' = 3x_1 + 7x_2$ of Example 3.

With $c_2 = 0$ these solution equations reduce to the equations $x_1(t) = -3c_1 e^{4t}$, $x_2(t) = 3c_1 e^{4t}$, which parametrize the line $x_1 = -x_2$ in the $x_1 x_2$-plane. The point $(x_1(t), x_2(t))$ then recedes along this line away from the origin as $t \to +\infty$, to the northwest if $c_1 > 0$ and to the southeast if $c_1 < 0$. As indicated in Fig. 7.5.1, each solution curve with $c_2 \neq 0$ is tangent to the line $x_1 = -x_2$ at the origin; the point $(x_1(t), x_2(t))$ approaches the origin as $t \to -\infty$ and approaches $+\infty$ along the solution curve as $t \to +\infty$.   ■

Generalized Eigenvectors

The vector $\mathbf{v}_2$ in Eq. (16) is an example of a generalized eigenvector. If λ is an eigenvalue of the matrix $\mathbf{A}$, then a **rank r generalized eigenvector** associated with λ is a vector $\mathbf{v}$ such that

$$
(\mathbf{A} - \lambda\mathbf{I})^r\mathbf{v} = \mathbf{0} \quad \text{but} \quad (\mathbf{A} - \lambda\mathbf{I})^{r-1}\mathbf{v} \neq \mathbf{0}. \tag{21}
$$

If $r = 1$, then (21) simply means that $\mathbf{v}$ is an eigenvector associated with λ. Thus a rank 1 generalized eigenvector is an ordinary eigenvector. The vector $\mathbf{v}_2$ in (16) is a rank 2 generalized eigenvector (and not an ordinary eigenvector).

The multiplicity 2 method described earlier boils down to finding a pair $\{\mathbf{v}_1, \mathbf{v}_2\}$ of generalized eigenvectors, one of rank 1 and one of rank 2, such that $(\mathbf{A} - \lambda\mathbf{I})\mathbf{v}_2 = \mathbf{v}_1$. Higher multiplicity methods involve longer "chains" of generalized eigenvectors. A **length k chain of generalized eigenvectors based on the eigenvector $\mathbf{v}_1$** is a set $\{\mathbf{v}_1, \mathbf{v}_2, \ldots, \mathbf{v}_k\}$ of k generalized eigenvectors such that

$$
\begin{aligned}
(\mathbf{A} - \lambda\mathbf{I})\mathbf{v}_k &= \mathbf{v}_{k-1}, \\
(\mathbf{A} - \lambda\mathbf{I})\mathbf{v}_{k-1} &= \mathbf{v}_{k-2}, \\
&\vdots \\
(\mathbf{A} - \lambda\mathbf{I})\mathbf{v}_2 &= \mathbf{v}_1.
\end{aligned} \tag{22}
$$

Because $\mathbf{v}_1$ is an ordinary eigenvector, $(\mathbf{A} - \lambda\mathbf{I})\mathbf{v}_1 = \mathbf{0}$. Therefore, it follows from (22) that

$$
(\mathbf{A} - \lambda\mathbf{I})^k\mathbf{v}_k = \mathbf{0}. \tag{23}
$$

If $\{\mathbf{v}_1, \mathbf{v}_2, \mathbf{v}_3\}$ is a length 3 chain of generalized eigenvectors associated with the multiple eigenvalue λ of the matrix $\mathbf{A}$, then it is easy to verify that three linearly independent solutions of $\mathbf{x}' = \mathbf{A}\mathbf{x}$ are given by

$$
\begin{aligned}
\mathbf{x}_1(t) &= \mathbf{v}_1 e^{\lambda t}, \\
\mathbf{x}_2(t) &= (\mathbf{v}_1 t + \mathbf{v}_2)e^{\lambda t}, \\
\mathbf{x}_3(t) &= \left(\tfrac{1}{2}\mathbf{v}_1 t^2 + \mathbf{v}_2 t + \mathbf{v}_3\right)e^{\lambda t}.
\end{aligned} \tag{24}
$$

For instance, the equations in (22) give

$$
\mathbf{A}\mathbf{v}_3 = \mathbf{v}_2 + \lambda\mathbf{v}_3, \quad \mathbf{A}\mathbf{v}_2 = \mathbf{v}_1 + \lambda\mathbf{v}_2, \quad \mathbf{A}\mathbf{v}_1 = \lambda\mathbf{v}_1,
$$

so

$$
\begin{aligned}
\mathbf{A}\mathbf{x}_3 &= \left[\tfrac{1}{2}\mathbf{A}\mathbf{v}_1 t^2 + \mathbf{A}\mathbf{v}_2 t + \mathbf{A}\mathbf{v}_3\right]e^{\lambda t} \\
&= \left[\tfrac{1}{2}\lambda\mathbf{v}_1 t^2 + (\mathbf{v}_1 + \lambda\mathbf{v}_2)t + (\mathbf{v}_2 + \lambda\mathbf{v}_3)\right]e^{\lambda t} \\
&= (\mathbf{v}_1 t + \mathbf{v}_2)e^{\lambda t} + \lambda\left(\tfrac{1}{2}\mathbf{v}_1 t^2 + \mathbf{v}_2 t + \mathbf{v}_3\right)e^{\lambda t} \\
&= \mathbf{x}_3'.
\end{aligned}
$$

Therefore, $\mathbf{x}_3(t)$ in (24) does, indeed, define a solution of $\mathbf{x}' = \mathbf{A}\mathbf{x}$.

Consequently, in order to "handle" a multiplicity 3 eigenvalue λ, it suffices to find a length 3 chain $\{v_1, v_2, v_3\}$ of generalized eigenvalues associated with λ. Looking at Eq. (23), we see that we need only find a solution v_3 of

$$(A - \lambda I)^3 v_3 = 0$$

such that the vectors

$$v_2 = (A - \lambda I)v_3 \quad \text{and} \quad v_1 = (A - \lambda I)v_2$$

are both nonzero (although, as we will see, this is not always possible).

Example 4   Find three linearly independent solutions of the system

$$x' = \begin{bmatrix} 0 & 1 & 2 \\ -5 & -3 & -7 \\ 1 & 0 & 0 \end{bmatrix} x. \tag{25}$$

Solution   The characteristic equation of the coefficient matrix in Eq. (25) is

$$|A - \lambda I| = \begin{bmatrix} -\lambda & 1 & 2 \\ -5 & -3-\lambda & -7 \\ 1 & 0 & -\lambda \end{bmatrix}$$

$$= 1 \cdot [-7 - 2 \cdot (-3 - \lambda)] + (-\lambda)[(-\lambda)(-3 - \lambda) + 5]$$

$$= -\lambda^3 - 3\lambda^2 - 3\lambda - 1 = -(\lambda + 1)^3 = 0$$

and thus A has the eigenvalue $\lambda = -1$ of multiplicity 3. The eigenvector equation $(A - \lambda I)v = 0$ for an eigenvector $v = \begin{bmatrix} a & b & c \end{bmatrix}^T$ is

$$(A + I)v = \begin{bmatrix} 1 & 1 & 2 \\ -5 & -2 & -7 \\ 1 & 0 & 1 \end{bmatrix} \begin{bmatrix} a \\ b \\ c \end{bmatrix} = \begin{bmatrix} 0 \\ 0 \\ 0 \end{bmatrix}.$$

The third row $a + c = 0$ gives $c = -a$; then the first row $a + b + 2c = 0$ gives $b = a$. Thus, to within a constant multiple, the eigenvalue $\lambda = -1$ has only the single associated eigenvector $v = \begin{bmatrix} a & a & -a \end{bmatrix}^T$ with $a \neq 0$, and so the defect of $\lambda = -1$ is 2.

To apply the method described here for triple eigenvalues, we first calculate

$$(A + I)^2 = \begin{bmatrix} 1 & 1 & 2 \\ -5 & -2 & -7 \\ 1 & 0 & 1 \end{bmatrix} \begin{bmatrix} 1 & 1 & 2 \\ -5 & -2 & -7 \\ 1 & 0 & 1 \end{bmatrix} = \begin{bmatrix} -2 & -1 & -3 \\ -2 & -1 & -3 \\ 2 & 1 & 3 \end{bmatrix}$$

and

$$(A + I)^3 = \begin{bmatrix} 1 & 1 & 2 \\ -5 & -2 & -7 \\ 1 & 0 & 1 \end{bmatrix} \begin{bmatrix} -2 & -1 & -3 \\ -2 & -1 & -3 \\ 2 & 1 & 3 \end{bmatrix} = \begin{bmatrix} 0 & 0 & 0 \\ 0 & 0 & 0 \\ 0 & 0 & 0 \end{bmatrix}.$$

Thus *any* nonzero vector $\mathbf{v}_3$ will be a solution of the equation $(\mathbf{A} + \mathbf{I})^3 \mathbf{v}_3 = \mathbf{0}$. Beginning with $\mathbf{v}_3 = \begin{bmatrix} 1 & 0 & 0 \end{bmatrix}^T$, for instance, we calculate

$$\mathbf{v}_2 = (\mathbf{A} + \mathbf{I})\mathbf{v}_3 = \begin{bmatrix} 1 & 1 & 2 \\ -5 & -2 & -7 \\ 1 & 0 & 1 \end{bmatrix} \begin{bmatrix} 1 \\ 0 \\ 0 \end{bmatrix} = \begin{bmatrix} 1 \\ -5 \\ 1 \end{bmatrix},$$

$$\mathbf{v}_1 = (\mathbf{A} + \mathbf{I})\mathbf{v}_2 = \begin{bmatrix} 1 & 1 & 2 \\ -5 & -2 & -7 \\ 1 & 0 & 1 \end{bmatrix} \begin{bmatrix} 1 \\ -5 \\ 1 \end{bmatrix} = \begin{bmatrix} -2 \\ -2 \\ 2 \end{bmatrix}.$$

Note that $\mathbf{v}_1$ is the previously found eigenvector $\mathbf{v}$ with $a = -2$; this agreement serves as a check of the accuracy of our matrix computations.

Thus we have found a length 3 chain $\{\mathbf{v}_1, \mathbf{v}_2, \mathbf{v}_3\}$ of generalized eigenvectors associated with the triple eigenvalue $\lambda = -1$. Substitution in (24) now yields the linearly independent solutions

$$\mathbf{x}_1(t) = \mathbf{v}_1 e^{-t} = \begin{bmatrix} -2 \\ -2 \\ 2 \end{bmatrix} e^{-t},$$

$$\mathbf{x}_2(t) = (\mathbf{v}_1 t + \mathbf{v}_2)e^{-t} = \begin{bmatrix} -2t + 1 \\ -2t - 5 \\ 2t + 1 \end{bmatrix} e^{-t},$$

$$\mathbf{x}_3(t) = \left(\tfrac{1}{2}\mathbf{v}_1 t^2 + \mathbf{v}_2 t + \mathbf{v}_3 \right) e^{-t} = \begin{bmatrix} -t^2 + t + 1 \\ -t^2 - 5t \\ t^2 + t \end{bmatrix} e^{-t}$$

of the system $\mathbf{x}' = \mathbf{A}\mathbf{x}$. ∎

The General Case

A fundamental theorem of advanced linear algebra states that every $n \times n$ matrix $\mathbf{A}$ has n linearly independent generalized eigenvectors. These n generalized eigenvectors may be arranged in chains, with the sum of the lengths of the chains associated with a given eigenvalue λ equal to the multiplicity of λ. But the structure of these chains depends on the defect of λ, and can be quite complicated. For instance, a multiplicity 4 eigenvalue can correspond to

- Four length 1 chains (defect 0);
- Two length 1 chains and a length 2 chain (defect 1);
- Two length 2 chains (defect 2);
- A length 1 chain and a length 3 chain (defect 2); or
- A length 4 chain (defect 3).

Note that, in each of these cases, the length of the longest chain is at most $d + 1$, where d is the defect of the eigenvalue. Consequently, once we have found all the ordinary eigenvectors associated with a multiple eigenvalue λ, and therefore know the defect d of λ, we can begin with the equation

$$(\mathbf{A} - \lambda\mathbf{I})^{d+1}\mathbf{u} = \mathbf{0} \tag{26}$$

to start building the chains of generalized eigenvectors associated with λ.

ALGORITHM: Chains of Generalized Eigenvectors

Begin with a nonzero solution $\mathbf{u}_1$ of Eq. (26) and successively multiply by the matrix $\mathbf{A} - \lambda \mathbf{I}$ until the zero vector is obtained. If

$$(\mathbf{A} - \lambda \mathbf{I})\mathbf{u}_1 = \mathbf{u}_2 \neq \mathbf{0},$$

$$\vdots$$

$$(\mathbf{A} - \lambda \mathbf{I})\mathbf{u}_{k-1} = \mathbf{u}_k \neq \mathbf{0},$$

but $(\mathbf{A} - \lambda \mathbf{I})\mathbf{u}_k = \mathbf{0}$, then the vectors

$$\{\mathbf{v}_1, \mathbf{v}_2, \ldots, \mathbf{v}_k\} = \{\mathbf{u}_k, \mathbf{u}_{k-1}, \ldots, \mathbf{u}_2, \mathbf{u}_1\}$$

(listed in reverse order of their appearance) form a length k chain of generalized eigenvectors based on the (ordinary) eigenvector $\mathbf{v}_1$. ▲

Each length k chain $\{\mathbf{v}_1, \mathbf{v}_2, \ldots, \mathbf{v}_k\}$ of generalized eigenvectors (with $\mathbf{v}_1$ an ordinary eigenvector associated with λ) determines a set of k independent solutions of $\mathbf{x}' = \mathbf{A}\mathbf{x}$ corresponding to the eigenvalue λ:

$$\begin{aligned}
\mathbf{x}_1(t) &= \mathbf{v}_1 e^{\lambda t}, \\
\mathbf{x}_2(t) &= (\mathbf{v}_1 t + \mathbf{v}_2)e^{\lambda t}, \\
\mathbf{x}_3(t) &= \left(\tfrac{1}{2}\mathbf{v}_1 t^2 + \mathbf{v}_2 t + \mathbf{v}_3\right) e^{\lambda t}, \\
&\ \vdots \\
\mathbf{x}_k(t) &= \left(\frac{\mathbf{v}_1 t^{k-1}}{(k-1)!} + \cdots + \frac{\mathbf{v}_{k-2} t^2}{2!} + \mathbf{v}_{k-1} t + \mathbf{v}_k\right) e^{\lambda t}.
\end{aligned} \tag{27}$$

Note that (27) reduces to Eqs. (18) through (19) and (24) in the cases $k = 2$ and $k = 3$, respectively.

To ensure that we obtain n generalized eigenvectors of the $n \times n$ matrix $\mathbf{A}$ that are actually linearly independent, and therefore produce a complete set of n linearly independent solutions of $\mathbf{x}' = \mathbf{A}\mathbf{x}$ when we amalgamate all the "chains of solutions" corresponding to different chains of generalized eigenvectors, we may rely on the following two facts:

- Any chain of generalized eigenvectors constitutes a linearly independent set of vectors.

- If two chains of generalized eigenvectors are based on linearly independent eigenvectors, then the union of these two chains is a linearly independent set of vectors (whether the two base eigenvectors are associated with different eigenvalues or with the same eigenvalue).

Example 5 Suppose that the 6×6 matrix $\mathbf{A}$ has two multiplicity 3 eigenvalues $\lambda_1 = -2$ and $\lambda_2 = 3$ with defects 1 and 2, respectively. Then λ_1 must have an associated eigenvector $\mathbf{u}_1$ and a length 2 chain $\{\mathbf{v}_1, \mathbf{v}_2\}$ of generalized eigenvectors (with the eigenvectors $\mathbf{u}_1$ and $\mathbf{v}_1$ being linearly independent), whereas λ_2 must have a length 3 chain $\{\mathbf{w}_1, \mathbf{w}_2, \mathbf{w}_3\}$ of generalized eigenvectors based on its single eigenvector $\mathbf{w}_1$. The six generalized eigenvectors $\mathbf{u}_1$, $\mathbf{v}_1$, $\mathbf{v}_2$, $\mathbf{w}_1$, $\mathbf{w}_2$, and $\mathbf{w}_3$ are then linearly independent and yield the following six independent solutions of $\mathbf{x}' = \mathbf{A}\mathbf{x}$:

$$\mathbf{x}_1(t) = \mathbf{u}_1 e^{-2t},$$
$$\mathbf{x}_2(t) = \mathbf{v}_1 e^{-2t},$$
$$\mathbf{x}_3(t) = (\mathbf{v}_1 t + \mathbf{v}_2) e^{-2t},$$
$$\mathbf{x}_4(t) = \mathbf{w}_1 e^{3t},$$
$$\mathbf{x}_5(t) = (\mathbf{w}_1 t + \mathbf{w}_2) e^{3t},$$
$$\mathbf{x}_6(t) = \left(\tfrac{1}{2}\mathbf{w}_1 t^2 + \mathbf{w}_2 t + \mathbf{w}_3 \right) e^{3t}. \qquad\blacksquare$$

As Example 5 illustrates, the computation of independent solutions corresponding to different eigenvalues and chains of generalized eigenvalues is a routine matter. The determination of the chain structure associated with a given multiple eigenvalue can be more interesting (as in Example 6).

An Application

FIGURE 7.5.2. The railway cars of Example 6.

Figure 7.5.2 shows two railway cars that are connected with a spring (permanently attached to both cars) and with a damper that exerts opposite forces on the two cars, of magnitude $c(x_1' - x_2')$ proportional to their relative velocity. The two cars are also subject to frictional resistance forces $c_1 x_1'$ and $c_2 x_2'$ proportional to their respective velocities. An application of Newton's law $ma = F$ (as in Example 1 of Section 7.1) yields the equations of motion

$$\begin{aligned} m_1 x_1'' &= k(x_2 - x_1) - c_1 x_1' - c(x_1' - x_2'), \\ m_2 x_2'' &= k(x_1 - x_2) - c_2 x_2' - c(x_2' - x_1'). \end{aligned} \qquad (28)$$

In terms of the position vector $\mathbf{x}(t) = \begin{bmatrix} x_1(t) & x_2(t) \end{bmatrix}^T$, these equations can be written in the matrix form

$$\mathbf{M}\mathbf{x}'' = \mathbf{K}\mathbf{x} + \mathbf{R}\mathbf{x}', \qquad (29)$$

where $\mathbf{M}$ and $\mathbf{K}$ are mass and stiffness matrices [as in Eqs. (2) and (3) of Section 7.4], and

$$\mathbf{R} = \begin{bmatrix} -(c + c_1) & c \\ c & -(c + c_2) \end{bmatrix}$$

is the *resistance matrix*. Unfortunately, because of the presence of the term involving $\mathbf{x}'$, the methods of Section 7.4 cannot be used.

Instead, we write (28) as a first-order system in the four unknown functions $x_1(t)$, $x_2(t)$, $x_3(t) = x_1'(t)$, and $x_4(t) = x_2'(t)$. If $m_1 = m_2 = 1$ we get

$$\mathbf{x}' = \mathbf{A}\mathbf{x}, \qquad (30)$$

where now $\mathbf{x} = \begin{bmatrix} x_1 & x_2 & x_3 & x_4 \end{bmatrix}^T$ and

$$\mathbf{A} = \begin{bmatrix} 0 & 0 & 1 & 0 \\ 0 & 0 & 0 & 1 \\ -k & k & -(c + c_1) & c \\ k & -k & c & -(c + c_2) \end{bmatrix}. \qquad (31)$$

Example 6 With $m_1 = m_2 = c = 1$ and $k = c_1 = c_2 = 2$, the system in Eq. (30) is

$$\mathbf{x}' = \begin{bmatrix} 0 & 0 & 1 & 0 \\ 0 & 0 & 0 & 1 \\ -2 & 2 & -3 & 1 \\ 2 & -2 & 1 & -3 \end{bmatrix} \mathbf{x}. \tag{32}$$

It is not too tedious to calculate manually—although a computer algebra system such as *Maple*, *Mathematica*, or MATLAB is useful here—the characteristic equation

$$\lambda^4 + 6\lambda^3 + 12\lambda^2 + 8\lambda = \lambda(\lambda + 2)^3 = 0$$

of the coefficient matrix $\mathbf{A}$ in Eq. (32). Thus $\mathbf{A}$ has the distinct eigenvalue $\lambda_0 = 0$ and the triple eigenvalue $\lambda_1 = -2$.

CASE 1: $\lambda_0 = 0$. The eigenvalue equation $(\mathbf{A} - \lambda\mathbf{I})\mathbf{v} = \mathbf{0}$ for the eigenvector $\mathbf{v} = \begin{bmatrix} a & b & c & d \end{bmatrix}^T$ is

$$\mathbf{Av} = \begin{bmatrix} 0 & 0 & 1 & 0 \\ 0 & 0 & 0 & 1 \\ -2 & 2 & -3 & 1 \\ 2 & -2 & 1 & -3 \end{bmatrix} \begin{bmatrix} a \\ b \\ c \\ d \end{bmatrix} = \begin{bmatrix} 0 \\ 0 \\ 0 \\ 0 \end{bmatrix}.$$

The first two rows give $c = d = 0$, then the last two rows yield $a = b$. Thus

$$\mathbf{v}_0 = \begin{bmatrix} 1 & 1 & 0 & 0 \end{bmatrix}^T$$

is an eigenvector associated with $\lambda_0 = 0$.

CASE 2: $\lambda_1 = -2$. The eigenvalue equation $(\mathbf{A} - \lambda\mathbf{I})\mathbf{v} = \mathbf{0}$ is

$$(\mathbf{A} + 2\mathbf{I})\mathbf{v} = \begin{bmatrix} 2 & 0 & 1 & 0 \\ 0 & 2 & 0 & 1 \\ -2 & 2 & -1 & 1 \\ 2 & -2 & 1 & -1 \end{bmatrix} \begin{bmatrix} a \\ b \\ c \\ d \end{bmatrix} = \begin{bmatrix} 0 \\ 0 \\ 0 \\ 0 \end{bmatrix}.$$

The third and fourth scalar equations here are the differences of the first and second equations and therefore are redundant. Hence $\mathbf{v}$ is determined by the first two equations,

$$2a + c = 0 \quad \text{and} \quad 2b + d = 0.$$

We can choose a and b independently, then solve for c and d. Thereby we obtain *two* eigenvectors associated with the triple eigenvalue $\lambda_1 = -2$. The choice $a = 1$, $b = 0$ yields $c = -2$, $d = 0$ and thereby the eigenvector

$$\mathbf{u}_1 = \begin{bmatrix} 1 & 0 & -2 & 0 \end{bmatrix}^T.$$

The choice $a = 0$, $b = 1$ yields $c = 0$, $d = -2$ and thereby the eigenvector

$$\mathbf{u}_2 = \begin{bmatrix} 0 & 1 & 0 & -2 \end{bmatrix}^T.$$

Because $\lambda_1 = -2$ has defect 1, we need a generalized eigenvector of rank 2, and hence a nonzero solution $\mathbf{v}_2$ of the equation

$$(\mathbf{A} + 2\mathbf{I})^2 \mathbf{v}_2 = \begin{bmatrix} 2 & 2 & 1 & 1 \\ 2 & 2 & 1 & 1 \\ 0 & 0 & 0 & 0 \\ 0 & 0 & 0 & 0 \end{bmatrix} \mathbf{v}_2 = \mathbf{0}.$$

Obviously,

$$\mathbf{v}_2 = \begin{bmatrix} 0 & 0 & 1 & -1 \end{bmatrix}^T$$

is such a vector, and we find that

$$(\mathbf{A} + 2\mathbf{I})\mathbf{v}_2 = \begin{bmatrix} 2 & 0 & 1 & 0 \\ 0 & 2 & 0 & 1 \\ -2 & 2 & -1 & 1 \\ 2 & -2 & 1 & -1 \end{bmatrix} \begin{bmatrix} 0 \\ 0 \\ 1 \\ -1 \end{bmatrix} = \begin{bmatrix} 1 \\ -1 \\ -2 \\ 2 \end{bmatrix} = \mathbf{v}_1$$

is nonzero and therefore is an eigenvector associated with $\lambda_1 = -2$. Then $\{\mathbf{v}_1, \mathbf{v}_2\}$ is the length 2 chain we need.

The eigenvector $\mathbf{v}_1$ just found is neither of the two eigenvectors $\mathbf{u}_1$ and $\mathbf{u}_2$ found previously, but we observe that $\mathbf{v}_1 = \mathbf{u}_1 - \mathbf{u}_2$. For a length 1 chain $\mathbf{w}_1$ to complete the picture we can choose any linear combination of $\mathbf{u}_1$ and $\mathbf{u}_2$ that is independent of $\mathbf{v}_1$. For instance, we could choose either $\mathbf{w}_1 = \mathbf{u}_1$ or $\mathbf{w}_1 = \mathbf{u}_2$. However, we will see momentarily that the particular choice

$$\mathbf{w}_1 = \mathbf{u}_1 + \mathbf{u}_2 = \begin{bmatrix} 1 & 1 & -2 & -2 \end{bmatrix}^T$$

yields a solution of the system that is of physical interest.

Finally, the chains $\{\mathbf{v}_0\}$, $\{\mathbf{w}_1\}$, and $\{\mathbf{v}_1, \mathbf{v}_2\}$ yield the four independent solutions

$$\begin{aligned}
\mathbf{x}_1(t) &= \mathbf{v}_0 e^{0 \cdot t} = \begin{bmatrix} 1 & 1 & 0 & 0 \end{bmatrix}^T, \\
\mathbf{x}_2(t) &= \mathbf{w}_1 e^{-2t} = \begin{bmatrix} 1 & 1 & -2 & -2 \end{bmatrix}^T e^{-2t}, \\
\mathbf{x}_3(t) &= \mathbf{v}_1 e^{-2t} = \begin{bmatrix} 1 & -1 & -2 & 2 \end{bmatrix}^T e^{-2t}, \\
\mathbf{x}_4(t) &= (\mathbf{v}_1 t + \mathbf{v}_2) e^{-2t} \\
&= \begin{bmatrix} t & -t & -2t+1 & 2t-1 \end{bmatrix}^T e^{-2t}
\end{aligned} \qquad (33)$$

of the system $\mathbf{x}' = \mathbf{A}\mathbf{x}$ in (32).

The four scalar components of the general solution

$$\mathbf{x}(t) = c_1 \mathbf{x}_1(t) + c_2 \mathbf{x}_2(t) + c_3 \mathbf{x}_3(t) + c_4 \mathbf{x}_4(t)$$

are described by the equations

$$\begin{aligned}
x_1(t) &= c_1 + e^{-2t}(c_2 + c_3 + c_4 t), \\
x_2(t) &= c_1 + e^{-2t}(c_2 - c_3 - c_4 t), \\
x_3(t) &= e^{-2t}(-2c_2 - 2c_3 + c_4 - 2c_4 t), \\
x_4(t) &= e^{-2t}(-2c_2 + 2c_3 - c_4 + 2c_4 t).
\end{aligned} \qquad (34)$$

Recall that $x_1(t)$ and $x_2(t)$ are the position functions of the two masses, whereas $x_3(t) = x_1'(t)$ and $x_4(t) = x_2'(t)$ are their respective velocity functions.

For instance, suppose that $x_1(0) = x_2(0) = 0$ and that $x_1'(0) = x_2'(0) = v_0$. Then the equations

$$
\begin{aligned}
x_1(0) &= c_1 + c_2 + c_3 && = 0, \\
x_2(0) &= c_1 + c_2 - c_3 && = 0, \\
x_1'(0) &= \quad\;\; -2c_2 - 2c_3 + c_4 &&= v_0, \\
x_2'(0) &= \quad\;\; -2c_2 + 2c_3 - c_4 &&= v_0
\end{aligned}
$$

are readily solved for $c_1 = \frac{1}{2}v_0$, $c_2 = -\frac{1}{2}v_0$, and $c_3 = c_4 = 0$, so

$$
\begin{aligned}
x_1(t) &= x_2(t) = \tfrac{1}{2}v_0\left(1 - e^{-2t}\right), \\
x_1'(t) &= x_2'(t) = v_0 e^{-2t}.
\end{aligned}
$$

In this case the two railway cars continue in the same direction with equal but exponentially damped velocities, approaching the displacements $x_1 = x_2 = \frac{1}{2}v_0$ as $t \to +\infty$.

It is of interest to interpret physically the individual generalized eigenvector solutions given in (33). The degenerate ($\lambda_0 = 0$) solution

$$
\mathbf{x}_1(t) = \begin{bmatrix} 1 & 1 & 0 & 0 \end{bmatrix}^T
$$

describes the two masses at rest with position functions $x_1(t) \equiv 1$ and $x_2(t) \equiv 1$. The solution

$$
\mathbf{x}_2(t) = \begin{bmatrix} 1 & 1 & -2 & -2 \end{bmatrix}^T e^{-2t}
$$

corresponding to the carefully chosen eigenvector $\mathbf{w}_1$ describes damped motions $x_1(t) = e^{-2t}$ and $x_2(t) = e^{-2t}$ of the two masses, with equal velocities in the same direction. Finally, the solutions $\mathbf{x}_3(t)$ and $\mathbf{x}_4(t)$ resulting from the length 2 chain $\{\mathbf{v}_1, \mathbf{v}_2\}$ both describe damped motion with the two masses moving in opposite directions. ∎

The methods of this section apply to complex multiple eigenvalues just as to real multiple eigenvalues (although the necessary computations tend to be somewhat lengthy). Given a complex conjugate pair $\alpha \pm \beta i$ of eigenvalues of multiplicity k, we work with one of them (say, $\alpha - \beta i$) as if it were real to find k independent complex-valued solutions. The real and imaginary parts of these complex-valued solutions then provide $2k$ real-valued solutions associated with the two eigenvalues $\lambda = \alpha - \beta i$ and $\overline{\lambda} = \alpha + \beta i$ each of multiplicity k. See Problems 33 and 34.

The Jordan Normal Form

In Section 6.2 we saw that if the $n \times n$ matrix $\mathbf{A}$ has a complete set $\mathbf{v}_1, \mathbf{v}_2, \ldots, \mathbf{v}_n$ of n linearly independent eigenvectors, then it is similar to a diagonal matrix. In particular,

$$
\mathbf{P}^{-1}\mathbf{A}\mathbf{P} = \mathbf{D}, \tag{35}
$$

where $\mathbf{P} = \begin{bmatrix} \mathbf{v}_1 & \mathbf{v}_2 & \cdots & \mathbf{v}_n \end{bmatrix}$ and the diagonal elements of the diagonal matrix $\mathbf{D}$ are the corresponding eigenvalues $\lambda_1, \lambda_2, \ldots, \lambda_n$ (not necessarily distinct). This result is a special case of the following general theorem, a proof of which can be found in Appendix B of Gilbert Strang, *Linear Algebra and Its Applications* (2nd edition, Academic Press, 1980).

THEOREM 1: Jordan Normal Form

If the $n \times n$ matrix $\mathbf{A}$ has s linearly independent eigenvectors $\mathbf{v}_1, \mathbf{v}_2, \ldots, \mathbf{v}_s$, then it is similar to a block-diagonal matrix of the *Jordan normal form*

$$\mathbf{J} = \begin{bmatrix} \mathbf{J}_1 & \mathbf{0} & \cdots & \mathbf{0} \\ \mathbf{0} & \mathbf{J}_2 & \cdots & \mathbf{0} \\ \vdots & \vdots & \ddots & \vdots \\ \mathbf{0} & \mathbf{0} & \cdots & \mathbf{J}_s \end{bmatrix}, \tag{36}$$

where each submatrix $\mathbf{J}_i$ is a *Jordan block* of the form

$$\mathbf{J}_i = \begin{bmatrix} \lambda_i & 1 & 0 & \cdots & 0 \\ 0 & \lambda_i & 1 & \cdots & 0 \\ \vdots & \vdots & \ddots & \ddots & \vdots \\ 0 & 0 & \cdots & \lambda_i & 1 \\ 0 & 0 & 0 & \cdots & \lambda_i \end{bmatrix}, \tag{37}$$

with λ_i being the eigenvalue of $\mathbf{A}$ corresponding to the eigenvector $\mathbf{v}_i$. ▲

If the Jordan block $\mathbf{J}_i$ in (37) is of size $k \times k$, then it corresponds to a length k chain of generalized eigenvectors based on the (ordinary) eigenvector $\mathbf{v}_i$. If all these generalized eigenvectors are arranged as column vectors in proper order corresponding to the appearance of the Jordan blocks in (36), the result is a nonsingular $n \times n$ matrix $\mathbf{Q}$ such that

$$\mathbf{Q}^{-1}\mathbf{A}\mathbf{Q} = \mathbf{J}. \tag{38}$$

The block-diagonal matrix $\mathbf{J}$ such that $\mathbf{A} = \mathbf{Q}\mathbf{J}\mathbf{Q}^{-1}$ is called the **Jordan normal form** of the matrix $\mathbf{A}$ and is unique [except for the order of appearance of the Jordan blocks in (36)].

Example 7

In Example 3 we saw that the matrix

$$\mathbf{A} = \begin{bmatrix} 1 & -3 \\ 3 & 7 \end{bmatrix}$$

has the single eigenvalue $\lambda = 4$ and the associated length 2 chain of generalized eigenvectors $\{\mathbf{v}_1, \mathbf{v}_2\}$, where $\mathbf{v}_1 = \begin{bmatrix} -3 & 3 \end{bmatrix}^T$ and $\mathbf{v}_2 = \begin{bmatrix} 1 & 0 \end{bmatrix}^T$, based on the eigenvector $\mathbf{v}_1 = \mathbf{A}\mathbf{v}_2$. If we define

$$\mathbf{Q} = \begin{bmatrix} \mathbf{v}_1 & \mathbf{v}_2 \end{bmatrix} = \begin{bmatrix} -3 & 1 \\ 3 & 0 \end{bmatrix},$$

then we find that the Jordan normal form of $\mathbf{A}$ is

$$\mathbf{J} = \mathbf{Q}^{-1}\mathbf{A}\mathbf{Q} = \begin{bmatrix} 4 & 1 \\ 0 & 4 \end{bmatrix}.$$

Here $\mathbf{J} = \mathbf{J}_1$ is a single 2×2 Jordan block corresponding to the single eigenvalue $\lambda = 4$ of $\mathbf{A}$. ∎

Example 8

In Example 6 we saw that the matrix

$$\mathbf{A} = \begin{bmatrix} 0 & 0 & 1 & 0 \\ 0 & 0 & 0 & 1 \\ -2 & 2 & -3 & 1 \\ 2 & -2 & 1 & -3 \end{bmatrix}$$

has the distinct eigenvalue $\lambda_1 = 0$ corresponding to the eigenvector

$$\mathbf{v}_1 = \begin{bmatrix} 1 & 1 & 0 & 0 \end{bmatrix}^T$$

and the triple eigenvalue $\lambda_2 = -2$ corresponding both to the eigenvector $\mathbf{v}_2 = \begin{bmatrix} 1 & 0 & -2 & 0 \end{bmatrix}^T$ and to the length 2 chain of generalized eigenvectors $\{\mathbf{v}_3, \mathbf{v}_4\}$ with $\mathbf{v}_3 = \begin{bmatrix} 1 & -1 & -2 & 2 \end{bmatrix}^T$ and $\mathbf{v}_4 = \begin{bmatrix} 0 & 0 & 1 & -1 \end{bmatrix}^T$, such that $\mathbf{v}_3 = \mathbf{A}\mathbf{v}_4$. If we define

$$\mathbf{Q} = \begin{bmatrix} \mathbf{v}_1 & \mathbf{v}_2 & \mathbf{v}_3 & \mathbf{v}_4 \end{bmatrix} = \begin{bmatrix} 1 & 1 & 1 & 0 \\ 1 & 0 & -1 & 0 \\ 0 & -2 & -2 & 1 \\ 0 & 0 & 2 & -1 \end{bmatrix},$$

then (using a computer algebra system to ease the labor of calculation) we find that the Jordan normal form of $\mathbf{A}$ is

$$\mathbf{J} = \mathbf{Q}^{-1}\mathbf{A}\mathbf{Q} = \begin{bmatrix} 0 & 0 & 0 & 0 \\ 0 & -2 & 0 & 0 \\ 0 & 0 & -2 & 1 \\ 0 & 0 & 0 & -2 \end{bmatrix}.$$

Here we see the 1×1 Jordan block $\mathbf{J}_1 = \begin{bmatrix} 0 \end{bmatrix}$ corresponding to the eigenvalue $\lambda_1 = 0$ of $\mathbf{A}$, as well as the two Jordan blocks $\mathbf{J}_2 = \begin{bmatrix} -2 \end{bmatrix}$ and $\mathbf{J}_3 = \begin{bmatrix} -2 & 1 \\ 0 & -2 \end{bmatrix}$ corresponding to the two linearly independent eigenvectors $\mathbf{v}_2$ and $\mathbf{v}_3$ associated with the eigenvalue $\lambda_2 = -2$. ∎

The General Cayley-Hamilton Theorem

In Section 6.3, we showed that every diagonalizable matrix $\mathbf{A}$ satisfies its characteristic equation $p(\lambda) = |\mathbf{A} - \lambda\mathbf{I}| = 0$, that is, $p(\mathbf{A}) = \mathbf{0}$. We can now use the Jordan normal form to show that this is true whether or not $\mathbf{A}$ is diagonalizable.

If $\mathbf{J} = \mathbf{Q}^{-1}\mathbf{A}\mathbf{Q}$ is the Jordan normal form of the matrix $\mathbf{A}$, then $p(\mathbf{A}) = \mathbf{Q}p(\mathbf{J})\mathbf{Q}^{-1}$, just as in the conclusion to the proof of Theorem 1 in Section 6.3. It therefore suffices to show that $p(\mathbf{J}) = \mathbf{0}$. If the Jordan blocks $\mathbf{J}_1, \mathbf{J}_2, \ldots, \mathbf{J}_s$ in (36) have sizes $m_1, m_2, \ldots, m_s$—that is, $\mathbf{J}_i$ is an $m_i \times m_i$ matrix—and corresponding eigenvalues $\lambda_1, \lambda_2, \ldots, \lambda_s$ (respectively), then

$$p(\lambda) = (\lambda_1 - \lambda)^{m_1}(\lambda_2 - \lambda)^{m_2} \cdots (\lambda_s - \lambda)^{m_s},$$

and so

$$p(\mathbf{J}) = (\lambda_1\mathbf{I} - \mathbf{J})^{m_1}(\lambda_2\mathbf{I} - \mathbf{J})^{m_2} \cdots (\lambda_s\mathbf{I} - \mathbf{J})^{m_s}. \tag{39}$$

Now $p(\mathbf{J})$ has the same block-diagonal structure as $\mathbf{J}$ itself, and we see from (39) that the ith block of $p(\mathbf{J})$ involves the factor

$$(\lambda_i \mathbf{I} - \mathbf{J}_i)^{m_i} = \begin{bmatrix} 0 & -1 & 0 & \cdots & 0 \\ 0 & 0 & -1 & \cdots & 0 \\ \vdots & \vdots & \ddots & \ddots & \vdots \\ 0 & 0 & \cdots & 0 & -1 \\ 0 & 0 & 0 & \cdots & 0 \end{bmatrix}^{m_i},$$

where the $m_i \times m_i$ matrix $\lambda_i \mathbf{I} - \mathbf{J}_i$ has all elements zero except on its first superdiagonal. It is easily seen that $(\lambda_i \mathbf{I} - \mathbf{J}_i)^2$ then has nonzero elements only on its second superdiagonal; $(\lambda_i \mathbf{I} - \mathbf{J}_i)^3$ has nonzero elements only on its third superdiagonal; and so on, in turn, until we see that $(\lambda_i \mathbf{I} - \mathbf{J}_i)^{m_i} = \mathbf{0}$. Hence it follows from (39) that the ith block of $p(\mathbf{J})$ is the $m_i \times m_i$ zero matrix. This being true for each $i = 1, 2, \ldots, s$, we conclude that $p(\mathbf{J}) = \mathbf{0}$, as desired. This completes the proof of the general case of the Cayley-Hamilton theorem.

7.5 Problems

Find general solutions of the systems in Problems 1 through 22. In Problems 1 through 6, use a computer system or graphing calculator to construct a direction field and typical solution curves for the given system.

1. $\mathbf{x}' = \begin{bmatrix} -2 & 1 \\ -1 & -4 \end{bmatrix} \mathbf{x}$

2. $\mathbf{x}' = \begin{bmatrix} 3 & -1 \\ 1 & 1 \end{bmatrix} \mathbf{x}$

3. $\mathbf{x}' = \begin{bmatrix} 1 & -2 \\ 2 & 5 \end{bmatrix} \mathbf{x}$

4. $\mathbf{x}' = \begin{bmatrix} 3 & -1 \\ 1 & 5 \end{bmatrix} \mathbf{x}$

5. $\mathbf{x}' = \begin{bmatrix} 7 & 1 \\ -4 & 3 \end{bmatrix} \mathbf{x}$

6. $\mathbf{x}' = \begin{bmatrix} 1 & -4 \\ 4 & 9 \end{bmatrix} \mathbf{x}$

7. $\mathbf{x}' = \begin{bmatrix} 2 & 0 & 0 \\ -7 & 9 & 7 \\ 0 & 0 & 2 \end{bmatrix} \mathbf{x}$

8. $\mathbf{x}' = \begin{bmatrix} 25 & 12 & 0 \\ -18 & -5 & 0 \\ 6 & 6 & 13 \end{bmatrix} \mathbf{x}$

9. $\mathbf{x}' = \begin{bmatrix} -19 & 12 & 84 \\ 0 & 5 & 0 \\ -8 & 4 & 33 \end{bmatrix} \mathbf{x}$

10. $\mathbf{x}' = \begin{bmatrix} -13 & 40 & -48 \\ -8 & 23 & -24 \\ 0 & 0 & 3 \end{bmatrix} \mathbf{x}$

11. $\mathbf{x}' = \begin{bmatrix} -3 & 0 & -4 \\ -1 & -1 & -1 \\ 1 & 0 & 1 \end{bmatrix} \mathbf{x}$

12. $\mathbf{x}' = \begin{bmatrix} -1 & 0 & 1 \\ 0 & -1 & 1 \\ 1 & -1 & -1 \end{bmatrix} \mathbf{x}$

13. $\mathbf{x}' = \begin{bmatrix} -1 & 0 & 1 \\ 0 & 1 & -4 \\ 0 & 1 & -3 \end{bmatrix} \mathbf{x}$

14. $\mathbf{x}' = \begin{bmatrix} 0 & 0 & 1 \\ -5 & -1 & -5 \\ 4 & 1 & -2 \end{bmatrix} \mathbf{x}$

15. $\mathbf{x}' = \begin{bmatrix} -2 & -9 & 0 \\ 1 & 4 & 0 \\ 1 & 3 & 1 \end{bmatrix} \mathbf{x}$

16. $\mathbf{x}' = \begin{bmatrix} 1 & 0 & 0 \\ -2 & -2 & -3 \\ 2 & 3 & 4 \end{bmatrix} \mathbf{x}$

17. $\mathbf{x}' = \begin{bmatrix} 1 & 0 & 0 \\ 18 & 7 & 4 \\ -27 & -9 & -5 \end{bmatrix} \mathbf{x}$

18. $\mathbf{x}' = \begin{bmatrix} 1 & 0 & 0 \\ 1 & 3 & 1 \\ -2 & -4 & -1 \end{bmatrix} \mathbf{x}$

19. $\mathbf{x}' = \begin{bmatrix} 1 & -4 & 0 & -2 \\ 0 & 1 & 0 & 0 \\ 6 & -12 & -1 & -6 \\ 0 & -4 & 0 & -1 \end{bmatrix} \mathbf{x}$

20. $\mathbf{x}' = \begin{bmatrix} 2 & 1 & 0 & 1 \\ 0 & 2 & 1 & 0 \\ 0 & 0 & 2 & 1 \\ 0 & 0 & 0 & 2 \end{bmatrix} \mathbf{x}$

21. $\mathbf{x}' = \begin{bmatrix} -1 & -4 & 0 & 0 \\ 1 & 3 & 0 & 0 \\ 1 & 2 & 1 & 0 \\ 0 & 1 & 0 & 1 \end{bmatrix} \mathbf{x}$

22. $\mathbf{x}' = \begin{bmatrix} 1 & 3 & 7 & 0 \\ 0 & -1 & -4 & 0 \\ 0 & 1 & 3 & 0 \\ 0 & -6 & -14 & 1 \end{bmatrix} \mathbf{x}$

In Problems 23 through 32, the eigenvalues of the coefficient matrix $\mathbf{A}$ are given. Find a general solution of the indicated system $\mathbf{x}' = \mathbf{Ax}$. Especially in Problems 29 through 32, use of a computer algebra system (as in the application material for this section) may be useful.

23. $\mathbf{x}' = \begin{bmatrix} 39 & 8 & -16 \\ -36 & -5 & 16 \\ 72 & 16 & -29 \end{bmatrix} \mathbf{x}; \quad \lambda = -1, 3, 3$

24. $\mathbf{x}' = \begin{bmatrix} 28 & 50 & 100 \\ 15 & 33 & 60 \\ -15 & -30 & -57 \end{bmatrix} \mathbf{x}; \quad \lambda = -2, 3, 3$

25. $\mathbf{x}' = \begin{bmatrix} -2 & 17 & 4 \\ -1 & 6 & 1 \\ 0 & 1 & 2 \end{bmatrix} \mathbf{x}; \quad \lambda = 2, 2, 2$

26. $\mathbf{x}' = \begin{bmatrix} 5 & -1 & 1 \\ 1 & 3 & 0 \\ -3 & 2 & 1 \end{bmatrix} \mathbf{x}; \quad \lambda = 3, 3, 3$

27. $\mathbf{x}' = \begin{bmatrix} -3 & 5 & -5 \\ 3 & -1 & 3 \\ 8 & -8 & 10 \end{bmatrix} \mathbf{x}; \quad \lambda = 2, 2, 2$

28. $\mathbf{x}' = \begin{bmatrix} -15 & -7 & 4 \\ 34 & 16 & -11 \\ 17 & 7 & 5 \end{bmatrix} \mathbf{x}; \quad \lambda = 2, 2, 2$

29. $\mathbf{x}' = \begin{bmatrix} -1 & 1 & 1 & -2 \\ 7 & -4 & -6 & 11 \\ 5 & -1 & 1 & 3 \\ 6 & -2 & -2 & 6 \end{bmatrix} \mathbf{x}; \quad \lambda = -1, -1, 2, 2$

30. $\mathbf{x}' = \begin{bmatrix} 2 & 1 & -2 & 1 \\ 0 & 3 & -5 & 3 \\ 0 & -13 & 22 & -12 \\ 0 & -27 & 45 & -25 \end{bmatrix} \mathbf{x}; \quad \lambda = -1, -1, 2, 2$

31. $\mathbf{x}' = \begin{bmatrix} 35 & -12 & 4 & 30 \\ 22 & -8 & 3 & 19 \\ -10 & 3 & 0 & -9 \\ -27 & 9 & -3 & -23 \end{bmatrix} \mathbf{x}; \quad \lambda = 1, 1, 1, 1$

32. $\mathbf{x}' = \begin{bmatrix} 11 & -1 & 26 & 6 & -3 \\ 0 & 3 & 0 & 0 & 0 \\ -9 & 0 & -24 & -6 & 3 \\ 3 & 0 & 9 & 5 & -1 \\ -48 & -3 & -138 & -30 & 18 \end{bmatrix} \mathbf{x};$
$\lambda = 2, 2, 3, 3, 3$

33. The characteristic equation of the coefficient matrix $\mathbf{A}$ of the system

$$\mathbf{x}' = \begin{bmatrix} 3 & -4 & 1 & 0 \\ 4 & 3 & 0 & 1 \\ 0 & 0 & 3 & -4 \\ 0 & 0 & 4 & 3 \end{bmatrix} \mathbf{x}$$

is

$$\phi(\lambda) = (\lambda^2 - 6\lambda + 25)^2 = 0.$$

Therefore, $\mathbf{A}$ has the repeated complex conjugate pair $3 \pm 4i$ of eigenvalues. First show that the complex vectors

$$\mathbf{v}_1 = \begin{bmatrix} 1 & i & 0 & 0 \end{bmatrix}^T \quad \text{and} \quad \mathbf{v}_2 = \begin{bmatrix} 9 & 0 & 1 & i \end{bmatrix}^T$$

form a length 2 chain $\{\mathbf{v}_1, \mathbf{v}_2\}$ associated with the eigenvalue $\lambda = 3 - 4i$. Then calculate the real and imaginary parts of the complex-valued solutions

$$\mathbf{v}_1 e^{\lambda t} \quad \text{and} \quad (\mathbf{v}_1 t + \mathbf{v}_2) e^{\lambda t}$$

to find four independent real-valued solutions of $\mathbf{x}' = \mathbf{Ax}$.

34. The characteristic equation of the coefficient matrix $\mathbf{A}$ of the system

$$\mathbf{x}' = \begin{bmatrix} 2 & 0 & -8 & -3 \\ -18 & -1 & 0 & 0 \\ -9 & -3 & -25 & -9 \\ 33 & 10 & 90 & 32 \end{bmatrix} \mathbf{x}$$

is

$$\phi(\lambda) = (\lambda^2 - 4\lambda + 13)^2 = 0.$$

Therefore, $\mathbf{A}$ has the repeated complex conjugate pair $2 \pm 3i$ of eigenvalues. First show that the complex vectors

$$\mathbf{v}_1 = \begin{bmatrix} -i & 3+3i & 0 & -i \end{bmatrix}^T,$$
$$\mathbf{v}_2 = \begin{bmatrix} 3 & -10+9i & -i & 0 \end{bmatrix}^T$$

form a length 2 chain $\{\mathbf{v}_1, \mathbf{v}_2\}$ associated with the eigenvalue $\lambda = 2 + 3i$. Then calculate (as in Problem 33) four independent real-valued solutions of $\mathbf{x}' = \mathbf{Ax}$.

35. Find the position functions $x_1(t)$ and $x_2(t)$ of the railway cars of Fig. 7.5.1 if the physical parameters are given by

$$m_1 = m_2 = c_1 = c_2 = c = k = 1$$

and the initial conditions are

$$x_1(0) = x_2(0) = 0, \quad x_1'(0) = x_2'(0) = v_0.$$

How far do the cars travel before stopping?

36. Repeat Problem 35 under the assumption that car 1 is shielded from air resistance by car 2, so now $c_1 = 0$. Show that, before stopping, the cars travel twice as far as those of Problem 35.

37–46. Use the method of Examples 7 and 8 to find the Jordan normal form $\mathbf{J}$ of each coefficient matrix $\mathbf{A}$ given in Problems 23–32 (respectively).

7.5 Application: Defective Eigenvalues and Generalized Eigenvectors

A typical computer algebra system can calculate both the eigenvalues of a given matrix A and the linearly independent (ordinary) eigenvectors associated with each eigenvalue. For instance, consider the 4×4 matrix

$$A = \begin{bmatrix} 35 & -12 & 4 & 30 \\ 22 & -8 & 3 & 19 \\ -10 & 3 & 0 & -9 \\ -27 & 9 & -3 & -23 \end{bmatrix} \tag{1}$$

of Problem 31 in this section. When the matrix A has been entered, the *Maple* calculation

```
with(linalg): eigenvectors(A);
[1, 4, {[-1, 0, 1, 1], [0, 1, 3, 0]}]
```

or the *Mathematica* calculation

```
Eigensystem[A]
{{1,1,1,1},
{{-3,-1,0,3}, {0,1,3,0}, {0,0,0,0}, {0,0,0,0}}}
```

reveals that the matrix A in Eq. (1) has the single eigenvalue $\lambda = 1$ of multiplicity 4 with only two independent associated eigenvectors v_1 and v_2. The MATLAB command

```
[V, D] = eig(sym(A))
```

provides the same information. The eigenvalue $\lambda = 1$ therefore has defect $d = 2$. If $B = A - (1)I$, you should find that $B^2 \neq 0$ but $B^3 = 0$. If

$$u_1 = \begin{bmatrix} 1 & 0 & 0 & 0 \end{bmatrix}^T, \quad u_2 = Bu_1, \quad u_3 = Bu_2,$$

then $\{u_1, u_2, u_3\}$ should be a length 3 chain of generalized eigenvectors based on the ordinary eigenvector u_3 (which should be a linear combination of the original eigenvectors v_1 and v_2). Use your computer algebra system to carry out this construction, and finally write four linearly independent solutions of the linear system $x' = Ax$.

For a more exotic matrix to investigate, consider the MATLAB's **gallery(5)** example matrix

$$A = \begin{bmatrix} -9 & 11 & -21 & 63 & -252 \\ 70 & -69 & 141 & -421 & 1684 \\ -575 & 575 & -1149 & 3451 & -13801 \\ 3891 & -3891 & 7782 & -23345 & 93365 \\ 1024 & -1024 & 2048 & -6144 & 24572 \end{bmatrix}. \tag{2}$$

Use appropriate commands like those illustrated here to show that A has a single eigenvalue $\lambda = 0$ of multiplicity 5 and defect 4. Noting that $A - (0)I = A$, you should find that $A^4 \neq 0$ but that $A^5 = 0$. Hence calculate the vectors

$$u_1 = \begin{bmatrix} 1 & 0 & 0 & 0 & 0 \end{bmatrix}^T, \quad u_2 = Au_1, \quad u_3 = Au_2, \quad u_4 = Au_3, \quad u_5 = Au_4.$$

You should find that $\mathbf{u}_5$ is a nonzero vector such that $\mathbf{Au}_5 = \mathbf{0}$ and is therefore an (ordinary) eigenvector of $\mathbf{A}$ associated with the eigenvalue $\lambda = 0$. Thus $\{\mathbf{u}_1, \mathbf{u}_2, \mathbf{u}_3, \mathbf{u}_4, \mathbf{u}_5\}$ is a length 5 chain of generalized eigenvectors of the matrix $\mathbf{A}$ in Eq. (2), and you can finally write five linearly independent solutions of the linear system $\mathbf{x}' = \mathbf{Ax}$.

7.6 Numerical Methods for Systems

We now discuss the numerical approximation of solutions of systems of differential equations. Our goal is to apply the methods of Sections 2.4 through 2.6 to the initial value problem

$$\mathbf{x}' = \mathbf{f}(t, \mathbf{x}), \quad \mathbf{x}(t_0) = \mathbf{x}_0 \tag{1}$$

for a system of m first-order differential equations. In (1) the independent variable is the scalar t, and

$$\mathbf{x} = (x_1, x_2, \ldots, x_m) \quad \text{and} \quad \mathbf{f} = (f_1, f_2, \ldots, f_m)$$

are vector-valued functions. If the component functions of $\mathbf{f}$ and their first-order partial derivatives are all continuous in a neighborhood of the point $(t_0, \mathbf{x}_0)$, then Theorems 3 and 4 of Appendix A guarantee the existence and uniqueness of a solution $\mathbf{x} = \mathbf{x}(t)$ of (1) on some subinterval [of the t-axis] containing t_0. With this assurance we can proceed to discuss the numerical approximation of this solution.

Beginning with step size h, we want to approximate the values of $\mathbf{x}(t)$ at the points $t_1, t_2, t_3, \ldots$, where $t_{n+1} = t_n + h$ for $n \geq 0$. Suppose that we have already computed the *approximations*

$$\mathbf{x}_1, \quad \mathbf{x}_2, \quad \mathbf{x}_3, \quad \ldots, \quad \mathbf{x}_n$$

to the *actual values*

$$\mathbf{x}(t_1), \quad \mathbf{x}(t_2), \quad \mathbf{x}(t_3), \quad \ldots, \quad \mathbf{x}(t_n)$$

of the exact solution of the system in (1). We can then make the step from $\mathbf{x}_n$ to the next approximation $\mathbf{x}_{n+1} \approx \mathbf{x}(t_{n+1})$ by any one of the methods of Sections 2.4 through 2.6. Essentially all that is required is to write the iterative formula of the selected method in the vector notation of the present discussion.

Euler Methods for Systems

For example, the iterative formula of Euler's method for systems is

$$\mathbf{x}_{n+1} = \mathbf{x}_n + h\mathbf{f}(t, \mathbf{x}_n). \tag{2}$$

To examine the case $m = 2$ of a pair of first-order differential equations, let us write

$$\mathbf{x} = \begin{bmatrix} x \\ y \end{bmatrix} \quad \text{and} \quad \mathbf{f} = \begin{bmatrix} f \\ g \end{bmatrix}.$$

Then the initial value problem in (1) is

$$x' = f(t, x, y), \quad x(t_0) = x_0,$$
$$y' = g(t, x, y), \quad y(t_0) = y_0, \tag{3}$$

and the scalar components of the vector formula in (2) are

$$x_{n+1} = x_n + hf(t_n, x_n, y_n),$$
$$y_{n+1} = y_n + hg(t_n, x_n, y_n). \tag{4}$$

Note that each iterative formula in (4) has the form of a single Euler iteration, but with y_n inserted like a parameter in the first formula (for x_{n+1}) and with x_n inserted like a parameter in the second formula (for y_{n+1}). The generalization to the system in (3) of each of the other methods in Sections 2.4 through 2.6 follows a similar pattern.

The improved Euler method for systems consists at each step of calculating first the predictor

$$\blacktriangleright \qquad \mathbf{u}_{n+1} = \mathbf{x}_n + h\mathbf{f}(t_n, \mathbf{x}_n) \tag{5}$$

and then the corrector

$$\blacktriangleright \qquad \mathbf{x}_{n+1} = \mathbf{x}_n + \frac{h}{2}[\mathbf{f}(t_n, \mathbf{x}_n) + \mathbf{f}(t_{n+1}, \mathbf{u}_{n+1})]. \tag{6}$$

For the case of the two-dimensional initial value problem in (3), the scalar components of the formulas in (5) and (6) are

$$u_{n+1} = x_n + hf(t_n, x_n, y_n),$$
$$v_{n+1} = y_n + hg(t_n, x_n, y_n) \tag{7}$$

and

$$x_{n+1} = x_n + \frac{h}{2}[f(t_n, x_n, y_n) + f(t_{n+1}, u_{n+1}, v_{n+1})],$$

$$y_{n+1} = y_n + \frac{h}{2}[g(t_n, x_n, y_n) + g(t_{n+1}, u_{n+1}, v_{n+1})]. \tag{8}$$

Example 1 Consider the initial value problem

$$x' = 3x - 2y, \quad x(0) = 3;$$
$$y' = 5x - 4y, \quad y(0) = 6. \tag{9}$$

The exact solution of the system in (9) is

$$x(t) = 2e^{-2t} + e^t, \quad y(t) = 5e^{-2t} + e^t. \tag{10}$$

Here we have $f(x, y) = 3x - 2y$ and $g(x, y) = 5x - 4y$ in (3), so the Euler iterative formulas in (4) are

$$x_{n+1} = x_n + h \cdot (3x_n - 2y_n), \quad y_{n+1} = y_n + h \cdot (5x_n - 4y_n).$$

With step size $h = 0.1$ we calculate

$$x_1 = 3 + (0.1) \cdot [3 \cdot 3 - 2 \cdot 6] = 2.7,$$
$$y_1 = 6 + (0.1) \cdot [5 \cdot 3 - 4 \cdot 6] = 5.1$$

and

$$x_2 = 2.7 + (0.1) \cdot [3 \cdot (2.7) - 2 \cdot (5.1)] = 2.49,$$
$$y_2 = 5.1 + (0.1) \cdot [5 \cdot (2.7) - 4 \cdot (5.1)] = 4.41.$$

The actual values at $t_2 = 0.2$ given by (10) are $x(0.2) \approx 2.562$ and $y(0.2) \approx 4.573$.

To compute the improved Euler approximations to $x(0.2)$ and $y(0.2)$ with a single step of size $h = 0.2$, we first calculate the predictors

$$u_1 = 3 + (0.2) \cdot [3 \cdot 3 - 2 \cdot 6] = 2.4,$$
$$v_1 = 6 + (0.2) \cdot [5 \cdot 3 - 4 \cdot 6] = 4.2.$$

Then the corrector formulas in (8) yield

$$x_1 = 3 + (0.1) \cdot ([3 \cdot 3 - 2 \cdot 6] + [3 \cdot (2.4) - 2 \cdot (4.2)]) = 2.58,$$
$$y_1 = 6 + (0.1) \cdot ([5 \cdot 3 - 4 \cdot 6] + [5 \cdot (2.4) - 4 \cdot (4.2)]) = 4.62.$$

As we would expect, a single improved Euler step gives better accuracy than two ordinary Euler steps. ∎

The Runge-Kutta Method and Second-Order Equations

The vector version of the iterative formula for the Runge-Kutta method is

➤
$$\mathbf{x}_{n+1} = \mathbf{x}_n + \frac{h}{6}(\mathbf{k}_1 + 2\mathbf{k}_2 + 2\mathbf{k}_3 + \mathbf{k}_4), \tag{11}$$

where the vectors $\mathbf{k}_1$, $\mathbf{k}_2$, $\mathbf{k}_3$, and $\mathbf{k}_4$ are defined (by analogy with Eqs. (5a)–(5d) of Section 2.6) as follows:

➤
$$\begin{aligned}
\mathbf{k}_1 &= \mathbf{f}(t_n, \mathbf{x}_n), \\
\mathbf{k}_2 &= \mathbf{f}\left(t_n + \tfrac{1}{2}h, \mathbf{x}_n + \tfrac{1}{2}h\mathbf{k}_1\right), \\
\mathbf{k}_3 &= \mathbf{f}\left(t_n + \tfrac{1}{2}h, \mathbf{x}_n + \tfrac{1}{2}h\mathbf{k}_2\right), \\
\mathbf{k}_4 &= \mathbf{f}(t_n + h, \mathbf{x}_n + h\mathbf{k}_3).
\end{aligned} \tag{12}$$

To describe in scalar notation the Runge-Kutta method for the two-dimensional initial value problem

$$\begin{aligned}
x' &= f(t, x, y), & x(t_0) &= x_0, \\
y' &= g(t, x, y), & y(t_0) &= y_0,
\end{aligned} \tag{3}$$

let us write

$$\mathbf{x} = \begin{bmatrix} x \\ y \end{bmatrix}, \quad \mathbf{f} = \begin{bmatrix} f \\ g \end{bmatrix}, \quad \text{and} \quad \mathbf{k}_i = \begin{bmatrix} F_i \\ G_i \end{bmatrix}.$$

Then the Runge-Kutta iterative formulas for the step from (x_n, y_n) to the next approximation $(x_{n+1}, y_{n+1}) \approx (x(t_{n+1}), y(t_{n+1}))$ are

$$x_{n+1} = x_n + \frac{h}{6}(F_1 + 2F_2 + 2F_3 + F_4),$$
$$y_{n+1} = y_n + \frac{h}{6}(G_1 + 2G_2 + 2G_3 + G_4),$$

(13)

where the values F_1, F_2, F_3, and F_4 of the function f are

$$\begin{aligned} F_1 &= f(t_n, x_n, y_n), \\ F_2 &= f\left(t_n + \tfrac{1}{2}h, x_n + \tfrac{1}{2}hF_1, y_n + \tfrac{1}{2}hG_1\right), \\ F_3 &= f\left(t_n + \tfrac{1}{2}h, x_n + \tfrac{1}{2}hF_2, y_n + \tfrac{1}{2}hG_2\right), \\ F_4 &= f(t_n + h, x_n + hF_3, y_n + hG_3); \end{aligned}$$

(14)

G_1, G_2, G_3, and G_4 are the similarly defined values of the function g.

Perhaps the most common application of the two-dimensional Runge-Kutta method is to the numerical solution of second-order initial value problems of the form

$$x'' = g(t, x, x'),$$
$$x(t_0) = x_0, \quad x'(t_0) = y_0.$$

(15)

If we introduce the auxiliary variable $y = x'$, then the problem in (15) translates into the two-dimensional first-order problem

$$\begin{aligned} x' &= y, & x(t_0) &= x_0, \\ y' &= g(t, x, y), & y(t_0) &= y_0. \end{aligned}$$

(16)

This is a problem of the form in (3) with $f(t, x, y) = y$.

If the functions f and g are not too complicated, then it is feasible to carry out manually a reasonable number of steps of the two-dimensional Runge-Kutta method described here. But the first operating electronic computers were constructed (during World War II) specifically to implement methods similar to the Runge-Kutta method for the numerical computation of trajectories of artillery projectiles. The application material for this section lists TI-89 and BASIC versions of Program RK2DIM that can be used with two-dimensional systems.

t	$x = \sin t$	$y = \cos t$
0.5	+0.47943	+0.87758
1.0	+0.84147	+0.54030
1.5	+0.99749	+0.07074
2.0	+0.90930	−0.41615
2.5	+0.59847	−0.80114
3.0	+0.14112	−0.98999
3.5	−0.35078	−0.93646
4.0	−0.75680	−0.65364
4.5	−0.97753	−0.21080
5.0	−0.95892	+0.28366

FIGURE 7.6.1. Runge-Kutta values (with $h = 0.05$) for the problem in Eq. (18).

Example 2

The exact solution of the initial value problem

$$x'' = -x; \quad x(0) = 0, \quad x'(0) = 1$$

(17)

is $x(t) = \sin t$. The substitution $y = x'$ translates (17) into the two-dimensional problem

$$\begin{aligned} x' &= y, & x(0) &= 0; \\ y' &= -x, & y(0) &= 1, \end{aligned}$$

(18)

which has the form in (3) with $f(t, x, y) = y$ and $g(t, x, y) = -x$. The table in Fig. 7.6.1 shows the results produced for $0 \leq t \leq 5$ (radians) using Program RK2DIM with step size $h = 0.05$. The values shown for $x = \sin t$ and $y = \cos t$ are all accurate to five decimal places. ∎

Example 3

In Example 4 of Section 2.3 we considered a lunar lander that initially is falling freely toward the surface of the moon. Its retrorockets, when fired, provide a deceleration of $T = 4$ m/s^2. We found that a soft touchdown at the lunar surface is achieved by igniting these retrorockets when the lander is at a height of 41,870 meters (just over 26 miles) above the surface and is then descending at the rate of 450 m/s.

Now we want to compute the *descent time* of the lunar lander. Let the distance $x(t)$ of the lander from the center of the moon be measured in meters and measure time t in seconds. According to the analysis in Section 2.3 [where we used $r(t)$ instead of $x(t)$], $x(t)$ satisfies the initial value problem

$$\frac{d^2x}{dt^2} = T - \frac{GM}{x^2} = 4 - \frac{4.9044 \times 10^{12}}{x^2},$$
$$x(0) = R + 41870 = 1781870, \quad x'(0) = -450,$$

(19)

where $G \approx 6.6726 \times 10^{-11}$ N·(m/kg)^2 is the universal gravitational constant and $M = 7.35 \times 10^{22}$ kg and $R = 1.74 \times 10^6$ m are the mass and radius of the moon. We seek the value of t when $x(t) = R = 1740000$.

The problem in (19) is equivalent to the first-order system

$$\frac{dx}{dt} = y, \quad x(0) = 1781870;$$
$$\frac{dy}{dx} = 4 - \frac{4.9044 \times 10^{12}}{x^2}, \quad y(0) = -450.$$

(20)

The table in Fig. 7.6.2 shows the result of a Runge-Kutta approximation with step size $h = 1$ (the indicated data agreeing with those obtained with step size $h = 2$). Evidently, touchdown on the lunar surface ($x = 1740000$) occurs at some time between $t = 180$ and $t = 190$ seconds. The table in Fig. 7.6.3 shows a second Runge-Kutta approximation with $t(0) = 180$, $x(0) = 1740059$, $y(0) = -16.83$, and $h = 0.1$. Now it is apparent that the lander's time of descent to the lunar surface is very close to 187 seconds; that is, 3 min 7 s. (The final velocity terms in these two tables are positive because the lander would begin to ascend if its retrorockets were not turned off at touchdown.) ∎

t (s)	x (m)	v (m/s)
0	1781870	−450.00
20	1773360	−401.04
40	1765826	−352.37
60	1759264	−303.95
80	1753667	−255.74
100	1749033	−207.73
120	1745357	−159.86
140	1742637	−112.11
160	1740872	−64.45
180	1740059	−16.83
200	1740199	30.77

FIGURE 7.6.2. The lander's descent to the lunar surface.

t (s)	x (m)	v (m/s)
180	1740059	−16.83
181	1740044	−14.45
182	1740030	−12.07
183	1740019	−9.69
184	1740011	−7.31
185	1740005	−4.93
186	1740001	−2.55
187	1740000	−0.17
188	1740001	2.21
189	1740004	4.59
190	1740010	6.97

FIGURE 7.6.3. Focusing on the lunar lander's soft touchdown.

Higher-Order Systems

As we saw in Section 7.1, any system of higher-order differential equations can be replaced with an equivalent system of first-order differential equations. For example, consider the system

$$
\begin{aligned}
x'' &= F(t, x, y, x', y'), \\
y'' &= G(t, x, y, x', y')
\end{aligned}
\tag{21}
$$

of second-order equations. If we substitute

$$
x = x_1, \quad y = x_2, \quad x' = x_3 = x_1', \quad y' = x_4 = x_2',
$$

then we get the equivalent system

$$
\begin{aligned}
x_1' &= x_3, \\
x_2' &= x_4, \\
x_3' &= F(t, x_1, x_2, x_3, x_4), \\
x_4' &= G(t, x_1, x_2, x_3, x_4)
\end{aligned}
\tag{22}
$$

of four first-order equations in the unknown functions $x_1(t) = x(t)$, $x_2(t) = y(t)$, $x_3(t)$, and $x_4(t)$. It would be a routine (if slightly tedious) matter to write a four-dimensional version of program RK2DIM for the purpose of solving such a system. But in a programming language that accommodates vectors, an n-dimensional Runge-Kutta program is scarcely more complicated than a one-dimensional program. For instance, the application material for this section lists the n-dimensional MATLAB program **rkn** that closely resembles the one-dimensional program **rk** of Fig. 2.6.11.

Example 4   Suppose that a batted ball starts at $x_0 = 0$, $y_0 = 0$ with initial velocity $v_0 = 160$ ft/s and with initial angle of inclination $\theta = 30°$. If air resistance is ignored, we find by the elementary methods of Section 1.2 that the baseball travels a (horizontal) distance of $400\sqrt{3}$ ft (approximately 693 ft) in 5 s before striking the ground. Now suppose that in addition to a downward gravitational acceleration ($g = 32$ ft/s^2), the baseball experiences an acceleration due to air resistance of $(0.0025)v^2$ feet per second per second, directed opposite to its instantaneous direction of motion. Determine how far the baseball will travel horizontally under these conditions.

Solution   According to Problem 30 of Section 7.1, the equations of motion of the baseball are

$$
\frac{d^2x}{dt^2} = -cv\frac{dx}{dt}, \quad \frac{d^2y}{dt^2} = -cv\frac{dy}{dt} - g,
\tag{23}
$$

where $v = \sqrt{(x')^2 + (y')^2}$ is the speed of the ball and where $c = 0.0025$ and $g = 32$ in fps units. We convert to a first-order system as in (22) and thereby obtain the system

$$
\begin{aligned}
x_1' &= x_3, \\
x_2' &= x_4, \\
x_3' &= -cx_3\sqrt{x_3^2 + x_4^2}, \\
x_4' &= -cx_4\sqrt{x_3^2 + x_4^2} - g
\end{aligned}
\tag{24}
$$

of four first-order differential equations with

$$x_1(0) = x_2(0) = 0,$$
$$x_3(0) = 80\sqrt{3}, \quad x_4(0) = 80. \tag{25}$$

Note that $x_3(t)$ and $x_4(t)$ are simply the x- and y-components of the baseball's velocity vector, so $v = \sqrt{x_3^2 + x_4^2}$.

WITHOUT AIR RESISTANCE: Figure 7.6.4 shows the numerical results obtained when a Runge-Kutta program such as **rkn** is applied with step size $k = 0.1$ and with $c = 0$ (no air resistance). For convenience in interpreting the results, the printed output at each selected step consists of the horizontal and vertical coordinates x and y of the baseball, its velocity v, and the angle of inclination α of its velocity vector (in degrees measured from the horizontal). These results agree with the exact solution when $c = 0$. The ball travels a horizontal distance of $400\sqrt{3} \approx 692.82$ ft in exactly 5 s, having reached a maximum height of 100 ft after 2.5 s. Note also that the ball strikes the ground at the same angle and with the same speed as its initial angle and speed.

t	x	y	v	α
0.0	0.00	0.00	160.00	+30
0.5	69.28	36.00	152.63	+25
1.0	138.56	64.00	146.64	+19
1.5	207.85	84.00	142.21	+13
2.0	277.13	96.00	139.48	+7
2.5	346.41	100.00	138.56	+0
3.0	415.69	96.00	139.48	−7
3.5	484.97	84.00	142.21	−13
4.0	554.26	64.00	146.64	−19
4.5	623.54	36.00	152.63	−25
5.0	692.82	0.00	160.00	−30

FIGURE 7.6.4. The batted baseball with no air resistance ($c = 0$).

t	x	y	v	α
0.0	0.00	0.00	160.00	+30
0.5	63.25	32.74	127.18	+24
1.0	117.11	53.20	104.86	+17
1.5	164.32	63.60	89.72	+8
2.0	206.48	65.30	80.17	−3
2.5	244.61	59.22	75.22	−15
3.0	279.29	46.05	73.99	−27
3.5	310.91	26.41	75.47	−37
4.0	339.67	0.91	78.66	−46

FIGURE 7.6.5. The batted baseball with air resistance ($c = 0.0025$).

WITH AIR RESISTANCE: Figure 7.6.5 shows the results obtained with the fairly realistic value of $c = 0.0025$ for the air resistance for a batted baseball. To within a hundredth of a foot in either direction, the same results are obtained with step sizes $h = 0.05$ and $h = 0.025$. We now see that with air resistance the ball travels a distance well under 400 ft in just over 4 s. The more refined data in Fig. 7.6.6 show that the ball travels horizontally only about 340 ft and that its maximum height is only about 66 ft. As illustrated in Fig. 7.6.7, air resistance has converted a massive home run into a routine fly ball (if hit straightaway to center field). Note also that when the ball strikes the ground, it has slightly under *half* its initial speed (only about 79 ft/s) and is falling at a steeper angle (about 46°). Every baseball fan has observed empirically these aspects of the trajectory of a fly ball.

t	x	y	v	α
1.5	164.32	63.60	89.72	+8
1.6	173.11	64.60	87.40	+5
1.7	181.72	65.26	85.29	+3
1.8	190.15	65.60	83.39	+1 ← Apex
1.9	198.40	65.61	81.68	−1
2.0	206.48	65.30	80.17	−3
⋮	⋮	⋮	⋮	⋮
3.8	328.50	11.77	77.24	−42
3.9	334.14	6.45	77.93	−44
4.0	339.67	0.91	78.66	−46 ← Impact
4.1	345.10	−4.84	79.43	−47
4.2	350.41	−10.79	80.22	−49

FIGURE 7.6.6. The batted ball's apex and its impact with the ground.

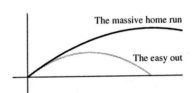

FIGURE 7.6.7. An "easy out" or a home run?

Variable Step Size Methods

The Runge-Kutta method for a large system requires an appreciable amount of computational labor, even when a computer is employed. Therefore, just as the step size h should not be so large that the resulting error in the solution is unacceptable, h ought not to be so small that too many steps are needed, hence requiring an unacceptable amount of computation. Thus the practical numerical solution of differential equations involves a tradeoff between accuracy and efficiency.

To facilitate this tradeoff, modern *variable step size methods* vary the step size h as the solution process proceeds. Large steps are taken in regions where the dependent variables are changing slowly; smaller steps are taken when these variables are changing rapidly, in order to prevent large errors.

An *adaptable* or *variable step size* Runge-Kutta method employs both a preassigned minimum error tolerance *MinTol* and a maximum error tolerance *MaxTol* to attempt to ensure that the error made in the typical step from x_n to x_{n+1} is neither too large (and hence inaccurate) nor too small (and hence inefficient). A fairly simple scheme for doing this may be outlined as follows:

- Having reached x_n with a Runge-Kutta step of length $t_n - t_{n-1} = h$, let $x^{(1)}$ denote the result of a further Runge-Kutta step of length h and let $x^{(2)}$ denote the result of *two* successive Runge-Kutta steps each of length $h/2$.
- On the grounds that $x^{(2)}$ should be a more accurate approximation to $x(t_n + h)$ than is $x^{(1)}$, take

$$Err = |x^{(1)} - x^{(2)}|$$

as an estimate of the error in $x^{(1)}$.

- If $MinTol \leq Err \leq MaxTol$, then let $x_{n+1} = x^{(1)}$, $t_{n+1} = t_n + h$, and proceed to the next step.
- If $Err < MinTol$, then the error is too small! Hence let $x_{n+1} = x^{(1)}$, $t_{n+1} = t_n + h$, but *double* the step size to $2h$ before making the next step.
- If $Err > MaxTol$, then the error is too large. Hence reject $x^{(1)}$ and start afresh at x_n with the *halved* step size $h/2$.

The detailed implementation of such a scheme can be complicated. For a much more complete but readable discussion of adaptive Runge-Kutta methods, see Section 15.2 of William H. Press et al., *Numerical Recipes: The Art of Scientific Computing* (Cambridge University Press, 1986).

Several widely available scientific computing packages (such as *Maple*, *Mathematica*, and MATLAB) include sophisticated variable step size programs that will accommodate an essentially arbitrary number of simultaneous differential equations. Such a general-purpose program might be used, for example, to model numerically the major components of the solar system: the sun and the nine (known) major planets. If m_i denotes the mass and $\mathbf{r}_i = (x_i, y_i, z_i)$ denotes the position vector of the ith one of these 10 bodies, then—by Newton's laws—the equation of motion of m_i is

$$m_i \mathbf{r}_i'' = \sum_{j \neq i} \frac{G m_i m_j}{(r_{ij})^3} (\mathbf{r}_j - \mathbf{r}_i), \qquad (26)$$

where $r_{ij} = |\mathbf{r}_j - \mathbf{r}_i|$ denotes the distance between m_i and m_j. For each $i = 1, 2, \ldots, 10$, the summation in Eq. (26) is over all values of $j \neq i$ from 1 to 10. The 10 vector equations in (26) constitute a system of 30 second-order scalar equations, and the equivalent first-order system consists of 60 differential equations in the coordinates and velocity components of the 10 major bodies in the solar system. Mathematical models that involve this many (or more) differential equations—and that require sophisticated software and hardware for their numerical analysis—are quite common in science, engineering, and applied technology.

Earth-Moon Satellite Orbits

For an example of a program whose efficient solution requires adaptive step size methods, we consider an Apollo satellite in orbit about the Earth E and Moon M. Figure 7.6.8 shows an $x_1 x_2$-coordinate system whose origin lies at the center of mass of the Earth and the Moon and that rotates at the rate of one revolution per "moon month" of approximately $\tau = 27.32$ days, so the Earth and Moon remain fixed in their positions on the x_1-axis. If we take as unit distance the distance (about 384,000 kilometers, assumed constant) between the Earth and Moon centers, then their coordinates are $E(-\mu, 0)$ and $M(1 - \mu, 0)$, where $\mu = m_M / (m_E + m_M)$ in terms of the Earth mass m_E and Moon mass m_M. If we take the total mass $m_E + m_M$ as the unit of mass and $\tau / (2\pi) \approx 4.35$ days as the unit of time, then the gravitational constant is $G = 1$ in Eq. (26), and the equations of motion of the satellite position $S(x_1, x_2)$ are

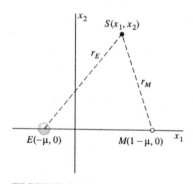

FIGURE 7.6.8. The Earth-Moon center-of-mass coordinate system.

$$x_1'' = x_1 + 2x_2' - \frac{(1 - \mu)(x_1 + \mu)}{(r_E)^3} - \frac{\mu(x_1 - 1 + \mu)}{(r_M)^3},$$

$$x_2'' = x_2 - 2x_1' - \frac{(1 - \mu)x_2}{(r_E)^3} - \frac{\mu x_2}{(r_M)^3}, \qquad (27)$$

where r_E and r_M denote the satellite's distance to the Earth and Moon (indicated in Fig. 7.6.8). The initial two terms on the right-hand side of each equation result from the rotation of the coordinate system. In the system of units described here, the lunar mass is approximately $m_M = 0.012277471$. The second-order system in (27) can be converted to an equivalent first-order system (of four differential equations) by substituting

$$x_1' = x_3, \quad x_2' = x_4, \quad \text{so that} \quad x_1'' = x_3', \quad x_2'' = x_4'.$$

Suppose that the satellite initially is in a clockwise circular orbit of radius about 2400 kilometers about the Moon. At its farthest point from the Earth ($x_1 = 0.994$) it is "launched" into Earth-Moon orbit with initial velocity v_0. The corresponding initial conditions are

$$x_1(0) = 0.994, \quad x_2(0) = 0, \quad x_3(0) = 0, \quad x_4(0) = -v_0.$$

An adaptive step size method (**ode45**) in the MATLAB software system was used to solve numerically the system in (27). The orbits in Figs. 7.6.9 and 7.6.10 were obtained with

$$v_0 = 2.031732629557 \quad \text{and} \quad v_0 = 2.001585106379,$$

respectively. (In the system of units used here, the unit of velocity is approximately 3680 km/h.) In each case a closed but multilooped periodic trajectory about the Earth and the Moon—a so-called bus orbit—is obtained, but a relatively small change in the initial velocity changes the number of loops! For more information, see NASA Contractor Report CR-61139, "Study of the Methods for the Numerical Solution of Ordinary Differential Equations," prepared by O. B. Francis, Jr. et al. for the NASA–George C. Marshall Space Flight Center, June 7, 1966.

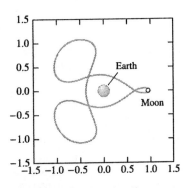

FIGURE 7.6.9. Apollo Moon- Earth bus orbit with insertion velocity $v_0 = 7476$ km/h.

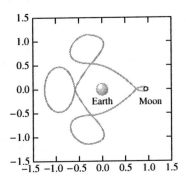

FIGURE 7.6.10. Apollo Moon- Earth bus orbit with insertion velocity $v_0 = 7365$ km/h.

7.6 Problems

A hand-held calculator will suffice for Problems 1 through 8. In each problem an initial value problem and its exact solution are given. Approximate the values of $x(0.2)$ and $y(0.2)$ in three ways: (a) by the Euler method with two steps of size $h = 0.1$; (b) by the improved Euler method with a single step of size $h = 0.2$; and (c) by the Runge-Kutta method with a single step of size $h = 0.2$. Compare the approximate values with the actual values $x(0.2)$ and $y(0.2)$.

1. $x' = x + 2y, \ x(0) = 0,$
$y' = 2x + y, \ y(0) = 2;$
$x(t) = e^{3t} - e^{-t}, \ y(t) = e^{3t} + e^{-t}$

2. $x' = 2x + 3y, \ x(0) = 1,$
$y' = 2x + y, \ y(0) = -1;$

$x(t) = e^{-t}, \ y(t) = -e^{-t}$

3. $x' = 3x + 4y, \ x(0) = 1,$
$y' = 3x + 2y, \ y(0) = 1;$
$x(t) = \frac{1}{7}(8e^{6t} - e^{-t}), \ y(t) = \frac{1}{7}(6e^{6t} + e^{-t})$

4. $x' = 9x + 5y, \ x(0) = 1,$
$y' = -6x - 2y, \ y(0) = 0;$
$x(t) = -5e^{3t} + 6e^{4t}, \ y(t) = 6e^{3t} - 6e^{4t}$

5. $x' = 2x - 5y, \ x(0) = 2,$
$y' = 4x - 2y, \ y(0) = 3;$
$x(t) = 2\cos 4t - \frac{11}{4}\sin 4t, \ y(t) = 3\cos 4t + \frac{1}{2}\sin 4t$

6. $x' = x - 2y, \ x(0) = 0,$
$y' = 2x + y, \ y(0) = 4;$
$x(t) = -4e^t \sin 2t, \ y(t) = 4e^t \cos 2t$

7. $x' = 3x - y$, $x(0) = 2$,
$y' = x + y$, $y(0) = 1$;
$x(t) = (t + 2)e^{2t}$, $y(t) = (t + 1)e^{2t}$
8. $x' = 5x - 9y$, $x(0) = 0$,
$y' = 2x - y$, $y(0) = -1$;
$x(t) = 3e^{2t} \sin 3t$, $y(t) = e^{2t}(\sin 3t - \cos 3t)$

A computer will be required for the remaining problems in this section. In Problems 9 through 12, an initial value problem and its exact solution are given. In each of these four problems, use the Runge-Kutta method with step sizes $h = 0.1$ and $h = 0.05$ to approximate to five decimal places the values $x(1)$ and $y(1)$. Compare the approximations with the actual values.

9. $x' = 2x - y$, $x(0) = 1$,
$y' = x + 2y$, $y(0) = 0$;
$x(t) = e^{2t} \cos t$, $y(t) = e^{2t} \sin t$
10. $x' = x + 2y$, $x(0) = 0$,
$y' = x + e^{-t}$, $y(0) = 0$;
$x(t) = \frac{1}{9}(2e^{2t} - 2e^{-t} + 6te^{-t})$,
$y(t) = \frac{1}{9}(e^{2t} - e^{-t} + 6te^{-t})$
11. $x' = -x - y - (1 + t^3)e^{-t}$, $x(0) = 0$,
$y' = -x - y - (t - 3t^2)e^{-t}$, $y(0) = 1$;
$x(t) = e^{-t}(\sin t - t)$, $y(t) = e^{-t}(\cos t + t^3)$
12. $x'' + x = \sin t$, $x(0) = 0$;
$x(t) = \frac{1}{2}(\sin t - t \cos t)$
13. Suppose that a crossbow bolt is shot straight upward with initial velocity 288 ft/s. If its deceleration due to air resistance is $(0.04)v$, then its height $x(t)$ satisfies the initial value problem

$$x'' = -32 - (0.04)x'; \quad x(0) = 0, \quad x'(0) = 288.$$

Find the maximum height that the bolt attains and the time required for it to reach this height.
14. Repeat Problem 13, but assume instead that the deceleration of the bolt due to air resistance is $(0.0002)v^2$.
15. Suppose that a projectile is fired straight upward with initial velocity v_0 from the surface of the earth. If air resistance is not a factor, then its height $x(t)$ at time t satisfies the initial value problem

$$\frac{d^2x}{dt^2} = -\frac{gR^2}{(x + R)^2}; \quad x(0) = 0, \quad x'(0) = v_0.$$

Use the values $g = 32.15$ ft/s$^2 \approx 0.006089$ mi/s^2 for the gravitational acceleration of the earth at its surface and $R = 3960$ mi as the radius of the earth. If $v_0 = 1$ mi/s, find the maximum height attained by the projectile and its time of ascent to this height.

Problems 16 through 18 deal with the batted baseball of Example 4, having initial velocity 160 ft/s and air resistance coefficient $c = 0.0025$.

16. Find the *range*—the horizontal distance the ball travels before it hits the ground—and its total time of flight with initial inclination angles 40°, 45°, and 50°.
17. Find (to the nearest degree) the initial inclination that maximizes the range. If there were no air resistance it would be exactly 45°, but your answer should be less than 45°.
18. Find (to the nearest half degree) the initial inclination angle greater than 45° for which the range is 300 ft.
19. Find the initial velocity of a baseball hit by Babe Ruth (with $c = 0.0025$ and initial inclination 40°) if it hit the bleachers at a point 50 ft high and 500 horizontal feet from home plate.
20. Consider the crossbow bolt of Problem 14, fired with the same initial velocity of 288 ft/s and with the air resistance deceleration $(0.0002)v^2$ directed opposite its direction of motion. Suppose that this bolt is fired from ground level at an initial angle of 45°. Find how high vertically and how far horizontally it goes, and how long it remains in the air.
21. Suppose that an artillery projectile is fired from ground level with initial velocity 3000 ft/s and initial inclination angle 40°. Assume that its air resistance deceleration is $(0.0001)v^2$. **(a)** What is the range of the projectile and what is its total time of flight? What is its speed at impact with the ground? **(b)** What is the maximum altitude of the projectile, and when is that altitude attained? **(c)** You will find that the projectile is still losing speed at the apex of its trajectory. What is the *minimum* speed that it attains during its descent?

7.6 Application: Comets and Spacecraft

Figure 7.6.11 lists TI-89 and BASIC versions of the two-dimensional Runge-Kutta program RK2DIM. You should note that it closely parallels the one-dimensional Runge-Kutta program listed in Fig. 7.6.11, with a single line there replaced (where appropriate) with two lines here to calculate a *pair* of x- and y-values or slopes. Note also that the notation used is essentially that of Eqs. (13) and (14) in this section. The first several lines define the functions and initial data needed for Example 1.

Figure 7.6.12 exhibits an *n*-dimensional MATLAB implementation of the Runge-Kutta method. The MATLAB function **f** defines the vector of right-hand sides of the differential equations in the system $\mathbf{x}' = \mathbf{f}(t, \mathbf{x})$ to be solved. The **rkn** function then takes as input the initial *t*-value **t**, the column vector **x** of initial

TI-89	BASIC	Comment
:rk2dim()	Program RK2DIM	Program title
:Prgm		
:Define f(t,x,y)=y	DEF FN F(T,X,Y) = Y	Define function f
:Define g(t,x,y)=-x	DEF FN G(T,X,Y) = -X	Define function g
:100→n	N = 100	Number of steps
:0→t	T = 0	Initial t
:0→x	X = 0	Initial x
:1→y	Y = 1	Initial y
:5→t1	T1 = 5	Final t
:(t1-t)/n→h	H = (T1-T)/N	Step size
:For i,1,n,1	FOR I=1 TO N	Begin loop
:t→t0	T0 = T	Save previous t
:x→x0	X0 = X	Save previous x
:y→y0	Y0 = Y	Save previous y
:f(t,x,y)→f1	F1 = FNF(T,X,Y)	First f-slope
:g(t,x,y)→g1	G1 = FNG(T,X,Y)	First g-slope
:t0+h/2→t	T = T0 + H/2	Midpoint t
:x0+h*f1/2→x	X = X0 + H*F1/2	Midpt x-predictor
:y0+h*g1/2→y	Y = Y0 + H*G1/2	Midpt y-predictor
:f(t,x,y)→f2	F2 = FNF(T,X,Y)	Second f-slope
:g(t,x,y)→g2	G2 = FNG(T,X,Y)	Second g-slope
:x0+h*f2/2→x	X = X0 + H*F2/2	Midpt x-predictor
:y0+h*g2/2→y	Y = Y0 + H*G2/2	Midpt y-predictor
:f(t,x,y)→f3	F3 = FNF(T,X,Y)	Third f-slope
:g(t,x,y)→g3	G3 = FNG(T,X,Y)	Third g-slope
:t0+h→t	T = T0 + H	New t
:x0+h*f3→x	X = X0 + H*F3	Endpt x-predictor
:y0+h*g3→y	Y = Y0 + H*G3	Endpt y-predictor
:f(t,x,y)→f4	F4 = FNF(T,X,Y)	Fourth f-slope
:g(t,x,y)→g4	G4 = FNG(T,X,Y)	Fourth g-slope
:(f1+2*f2+2*f3 +f4)/6→fa	FA = (F1+2*F2+2*F3 +F4)/6	Average f-slope
:(g1+2*g2+2*g3 +g4)/6→ga	GA = (G1+2*G2+2*G3 +G4)/6	Average g-slope
:x0+h*fa→x	X = X0 + H*FA	x-corrector
:y0+h*ga→y	Y = Y0 + H*GA	y-corrector
:Disp t,x,y	PRINT T,X,Y	Display results
:EndFor	NEXT I	End loop
:EndPrgm	END	End program

FIGURE 7.6.11. TI-89 and BASIC two-dimensional Runge-Kutta programs.

```
function xp = f(t,x)
xp = x;
xp(1) = x(2);
xp(2) = -x(1);

function [T,Y] = rkn(t,x,t1,n)
h = (t1 - t)/n;                    % step size
T = t;                            % initial t
X = x';                           % initial x-vector
for i = 1:n                       % begin loop
    k1 = f(t,x);                  % first k-vector
    k2 = f(t+h/2,x+h*k1/2);       % second k-vector
    k3 = f(t+h/2,x+h*k2/2);       % third k-vector
    k4 = f(t+h  ,x+h*k3  );       % fourth k-vector
    k  = (k1+2*k2+2*k3+k4)/6;     % average k-vector
    t  = t + h;                   % new t
    x  = x + h*k;                 % new x
    T = [T;t];                    % update t-column
    X = [X;x'];                   % update x-matrix
end                               % end loop
```

FIGURE 7.6.12. MATLAB implementation of the Runge-Kutta method.

x-values, the final t-value **t1**, and the desired number **n** of subintervals. As output it produces the resulting column vector **T** of t-values and the matrix **X** whose rows give the corresponding x-values. For instance, with **f** as indicated in the figure, the MATLAB command

```
[T,X] = rkn(0, [0;1], 5, 50)
```

then generates the data shown in the table of Fig. 7.6.1 (which lists only every fifth value of each variable).

You can use Examples 1 through 3 in this section to test your own implementation of the Runge-Kutta method. Then investigate the comet and space-craft problems described next. Additional application material at the Web site **www.prenhall.com/edwards** describes additional numerical ODE investigations ranging from batted baseballs to the Apollo orbits shown in Figs. 7.6.9 and 7.6.10.

Your Spacecraft Landing

Your spacecraft is traveling at constant velocity V, approaching a distant earthlike planet with mass M and radius R. When activated, your deceleration system provides a constant thrust T until impact with the surface of the planet. During the period of deceleration, your distance $x(t)$ from the center of the planet satisfies the differential equation

$$\frac{d^2x}{dt^2} = T - \frac{GM}{x^2}, \tag{1}$$

where $G \approx 6.6726 \times 10^{-11}$ N·(m/kg)^2 as in Example 3. Your question is this: At what altitude above the surface should your deceleration system be activated in order to achieve a soft touchdown? For a reasonable problem, you can take

$$M = 5.97 \times 10^{24} \text{ (kg)},$$
$$R = 6.38 \times 10^6 \text{ (m)},$$
$$V = p \times 10^4 \text{ (km/h)},$$
$$T = g + q \text{ (m/s}^2),$$

where $g = GM/R^2$ is the surface gravitational acceleration of the planet. Choose p to be the smallest nonzero digit and q the next-to-smallest nonzero digit in your ID number. Find the "ignition altitude" accurate to the nearest meter and the resulting "descent time" accurate to the nearest tenth of a second.

Kepler's Law of Planetary (or Satellite) Motion

Consider a satellite in elliptical orbit around a planet of mass M, and suppose that physical units are so chosen that $GM = 1$ (where G is the gravitational constant). If the planet is located at the origin in the xy-plane, then the equations of motion of the satellite are

$$\frac{d^2x}{dt^2} = -\frac{x}{(x^2 + y^2)^{3/2}}, \quad \frac{d^2y}{dt^2} = -\frac{y}{(x^2 + y^2)^{3/2}}. \tag{2}$$

Let T denote the period of revolution of the satellite. Kepler's third law says that the *square* of T is proportional to the *cube* of the major semiaxis a of its elliptical orbit. In particular, if $GM = 1$, then

$$T^2 = 4\pi^2 a^3. \tag{3}$$

(For details, see Section 12.6 of Edwards and Penney, *Calculus*, 6th ed. [Upper Saddle River, N.J.: Prentice Hall, 2002].) If the satellite's x- and y-components of velocity, $x_3 = x' = x_1'$ and $x_4 = y' = x_2'$, are introduced, then the system in (2) translates into a system of four first-order differential equations having the form of those in Eq. (22) of this section.

(a) Solve this 4×4 system numerically with the initial conditions

$$x(0) = 1, \quad y(0) = 0, \quad x'(0) = 0, \quad y'(0) = 1$$

that correspond theoretically to a circular orbit of radius $a = 1$, so Eq. (3) gives $T = 2\pi$. Is this what you get?

(b) Now solve the system numerically with the initial conditions

$$x(0) = 1, \quad y(0) = 0, \quad x'(0) = 0, \quad y'(0) = \tfrac{1}{2}\sqrt{6}$$

that correspond theoretically to an elliptical orbit with major semiaxis $a = 2$, so Eq. (3) gives $T = 4\pi\sqrt{2}$. Is this what you get?

Halley's Comet

Halley's comet last reached perihelion (its point of closest approach to the sun at the origin) on February 9, 1986. Its position and velocity components at that time were

$$\mathbf{p}_0 = (0.325514, -0.459460, 0.166229) \quad \text{and}$$
$$\mathbf{v}_0 = (-9.096111, -6.916686, -1.305721)$$

(respectively), with position in AU (astronomical units, in which the unit of distance is the major semiaxis of the earth's orbit) and time in years. In this system, the three-dimensional equations of motion of the comet are

$$\frac{d^2x}{dt^2} = -\frac{\mu x}{r^3}, \quad \frac{d^2y}{dt^2} = -\frac{\mu y}{r^3}, \quad \frac{d^2z}{dt^2} = -\frac{\mu z}{r^3} \tag{4}$$

where

$$\mu = 4\pi^2 \quad \text{and} \quad r = \sqrt{x^2 + y^2 + z^2}.$$

FIGURE 7.6.13. yz-projection of the orbit of Halley's comet.

Solve the equations in (4) numerically to verify the appearance of the yz-projection of the orbit of Halley's comet shown in Fig. 7.6.13. Plot the xy- and xz-projections as well.

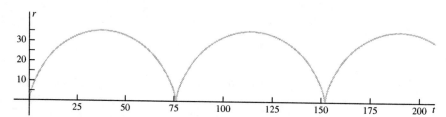

FIGURE 7.6.14. 200-year plot of the distance $r(t)$ of Halley's comet from the sun. Is there a cusp near $t = 75$?

Figure 7.6.14 shows the graph of the distance $r(t)$ of Halley's comet from the sun. Inspection of this graph indicates that Halley's comet reaches a maximum distance (at aphelion) of about 35 AU in a bit less than 40 years and returns to perihelion after about three-quarters of a century. The closer look in Fig. 7.6.15 indicates that the period of revolution of Halley's comet is about 76 years. Use your numerical solution to refine these observations. What is your best estimate of the calendar date of the comet's next perihelion passage?

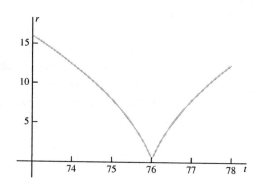

FIGURE 7.6.15. A closer look at Halley's perihelion passage after about 76 years.

Your Own Comet

The night before your birthday in 1997 you set up your telescope on a nearby mountaintop. It was a clear night, and you had a stroke of luck: At 12:30 A.M. you spotted a new comet. After repeating the observation on successive nights, you were able to calculate its solar system coordinates $\mathbf{p}_0 = (x_0, y_0, z_0)$ and its velocity vector $\mathbf{v}_0 = (vx_0, vy_0, vz_0)$ on that first night. Using this information, determine the following:

- the comet's perihelion (point nearest the sun) and aphelion (point farthest from the sun),
- the comet's velocity at perihelion and at aphelion,
- the comet's period of revolution around the sun, and
- the comet's next two dates of perihelion passage.

Using units of length in AU and time in earth years, the equations of motion of your comet are given in (4). For your personal comet, begin with random initial position and velocity vectors with the same order of magnitude as those of Halley's comet. Repeat the random selection of initial position and velocity vectors, if necessary, until you get a plausible eccentric orbit that ranges well outside the earth's orbit (as most real comets do).

APPENDIX A

Existence and Uniqueness of Solutions

In Chapter 1 we saw that an initial value problem of the form

$$\frac{dy}{dx} = f(x, y), \quad y(a) = b \tag{1}$$

can fail (on a given interval containing the point $x = a$) to have a unique solution. For instance, in Example 4 of Section 1.3, we saw that the initial value problem

$$x^2 \frac{dy}{dx} + y^2 = 0, \quad y(0) = b \tag{2}$$

has no solutions at all unless $b = 0$, in which case there are infinitely many solutions. According to Problem 31 of Section 1.3, the initial value problem

$$\frac{dy}{dx} = -\sqrt{1 - y^2}, \quad y(0) = 1 \tag{3}$$

has the two distinct solutions $y_1(x) \equiv 1$ and $y_2(x) = \cos x$ on the interval $0 \leq x \leq \pi$. In this appendix we investigate conditions on the function $f(x, y)$ that suffice to guarantee that the initial value problem in (1) has one and only one solution, and we then proceed to establish appropriate versions of the existence-uniqueness theorems that were stated without proof in Sections 1.3, 5.1, 5.2, and 7.1.

A.1 Existence of Solutions

The approach we employ is the **method of successive approximations**, which was developed by the French mathematician Emile Picard (1856–1941). This method is based on the fact that the function $y(x)$ satisfies the initial value problem in (1) on the open interval I containing $x = a$ if and only if it satisfies the integral equation

$$y(x) = b + \int_a^x f(t, y(t)) \, dt \tag{4}$$

for all x in I. In particular, if $y(x)$ satisfies Eq. (4), then clearly $y(a) = b$, and differentiation of both sides in (4)—using the fundamental theorem of calculus—yields the differential equation $y'(x) = f(x, y(x))$.

To attempt to solve Eq. (4), we begin with the initial function

$$y_0(x) \equiv b \tag{5}$$

and then define iteratively a sequence y_1, y_2, y_3, ... of functions that we hope will converge to the solution. Specifically, we let

$$y_1(x) = b + \int_a^x f(t, y_0(t))\, dt \quad \text{and} \quad y_2(x) = b + \int_a^x f(t, y_1(t))\, dt. \tag{6}$$

In general, y_{n+1} is obtained by substitution of y_n for y in the right-hand side in Eq. (4):

$$y_{n+1}(x) = b + \int_a^x f(t, y_n(t))\, dt. \tag{7}$$

Suppose we know that each of these functions $\{y_n(x)\}_0^\infty$ is defined on some open interval (the same for each n) containing $x = a$ and that the limit

$$y(x) = \lim_{n \to \infty} y_n(x) \tag{8}$$

exists at each point of this interval. Then it will follow that

$$y(x) = \lim_{n \to \infty} y_{n+1}(x) = \lim_{n \to \infty} \left[b + \int_a^x f(t, y_n(t))\, dt \right]$$

$$= b + \lim_{n \to \infty} \int_a^x f(t, y_n(t))\, dt \tag{9}$$

$$= b + \int_a^x f\left(t, \lim_{n \to \infty} y_n(t)\right) dt \tag{10}$$

and, hence, that

$$y(x) = b + \int_a^x f(t, y(t))\, dt,$$

provided that we can validate the interchange of limit operations involved in passing from (9) to (10). It is therefore reasonable to expect that, under favorable conditions, the sequence $\{y_n(x)\}$ defined iteratively in Eqs. (5) and (7) will converge to a solution $y(x)$ of the integral equation in (4), and hence to a solution of the original initial value problem in (1).

Example 1   To apply the method of successive approximations to the initial value problem

$$\frac{dy}{dx} = y, \quad y(0) = 1, \tag{11}$$

we write Eqs. (5) and (7), thereby obtaining

$$y_0(x) \equiv 1, \quad y_{n+1}(x) = 1 + \int_0^x y_n(t)\, dt. \tag{12}$$

The iteration formula in (12) yields

$$y_1(x) = 1 + \int_0^x 1\, dt = 1 + x,$$

$$y_2(x) = 1 + \int_0^x (1 + t)\, dt = 1 + x + \tfrac{1}{2}x^2,$$

$$y_3(x) = 1 + \int_0^x \left(1 + t + \tfrac{1}{2}t^2\right) dt = 1 + x + \tfrac{1}{2}x^2 + \tfrac{1}{6}x^3,$$

and

$$y_4(x) = 1 + \int_0^x \left(1 + t + \tfrac{1}{2}t^2 + \tfrac{1}{6}t^3\right) dt$$

$$= 1 + x + \tfrac{1}{2}x^2 + \tfrac{1}{6}x^3 + \tfrac{1}{24}x^4.$$

It is clear that we are generating the sequence of partial sums of a power series solution; indeed, we immediately recognize the series as that of $y(x) = e^x$. There is no difficulty in demonstrating that the exponential function is indeed the solution of the initial value problem in (11); moreover, a diligent student can verify (by using a proof by induction on n) that $y_n(x)$, obtained in the aforementioned manner, is indeed the nth partial sum for the Taylor series with center zero for $y(x) = e^x$. ■

Example 2   To apply the method of successive approximations to the initial value problem

$$\frac{dy}{dx} = 4xy, \qquad y(0) = 3, \tag{13}$$

we write Eqs. (5) and (7) as in Example 1. Now we obtain

$$y_0(x) \equiv 3, \quad y_{n+1}(x) = 3 + \int_0^x 4t\, y_n(t)\, dt. \tag{14}$$

The iteration formula in (14) yields

$$y_1(x) = 3 + \int_0^x (4t)(3)\, dt = 3 + 6x^2,$$

$$y_2(x) = 3 + \int_0^x (4t)(3 + 6t^2)\, dt = 3 + 6x^2 + 6x^4,$$

$$y_3(x) = 3 + \int_0^x (4t)(3 + 6t^2 + 6t^4)\, dt = 3 + 6x^2 + 6x^4 + 4x^6,$$

and

$$y_4(x) = 3 + \int_0^x (4t)(3 + 6t^2 + 6t^4 + 4t^6)\, dt$$

$$= 3 + 6x^2 + 6x^4 + 4x^6 + 2x^8.$$

It is again clear that we are generating partial sums of a power series solution. It is not quite so obvious what function has such a power series representation, but the initial value problem in (13) is readily solved by separation of variables:

$$y(x) = 3\exp\left(2x^2\right) = 3 \sum_{n=0}^{\infty} \frac{(2x^2)^n}{n!}$$

$$= 3 + 6x^2 + 6x^4 + 4x^6 + 2x^8 + \tfrac{4}{5}x^{10} + \cdots. \qquad ■$$

In some cases, it may be necessary to compute a much larger number of terms, either in order to identify the solution or to use a partial sum of its series with large subscript to approximate the solution accurately for x near its initial value. Fortunately, computer algebra systems such as *Maple* and *Mathematica* can perform the symbolic integrations (as opposed to numerical integrations) of the sort in Examples 1 and 2. If necessary, you could generate the first hundred terms in Example 2 in a matter of minutes.

In general, of course, we apply Picard's method because we cannot find a solution by elementary methods. Suppose that we have produced a large number of terms of what we believe to be the correct power series expansion of the solution. We *must* have conditions under which the sequence $\{y_n(x)\}$ provided by the method of successive approximations is guaranteed in advance to converge to a solution. It is just as convenient to discuss the initial value problem

$$\frac{d\mathbf{x}}{dt} = \mathbf{f}(\mathbf{x}, t), \quad \mathbf{x}(a) = \mathbf{b} \tag{15}$$

for a system of m first-order equations, where

$$\mathbf{x} = \begin{bmatrix} x_1 \\ x_2 \\ x_3 \\ \vdots \\ x_m \end{bmatrix}, \quad \mathbf{f} = \begin{bmatrix} f_1 \\ f_2 \\ f_3 \\ \vdots \\ f_m \end{bmatrix}, \quad \text{and} \quad \mathbf{b} = \begin{bmatrix} b_1 \\ b_2 \\ b_3 \\ \vdots \\ b_m \end{bmatrix}.$$

It turns out that with the aid of this vector notation (which we introduced in Section 7.1), most results concerning a single [scalar] equation $x' = f(x, t)$ can be generalized readily to analogous results for a system of m first-order equations, as abbreviated in (15). Consequently, the effort of using vector notation is amply justified by the generality it provides.

The method of successive approximations for the system in (15) calls for us to compute the sequence $\{\mathbf{x}_n(t)\}_0^\infty$ of vector-valued functions of t,

$$\mathbf{x}_n(t) = \begin{bmatrix} x_{1n}(t) \\ x_{2n}(t) \\ x_{3n}(t) \\ \vdots \\ x_{mn}(t) \end{bmatrix},$$

defined iteratively by

$$\mathbf{x}_0(a) \equiv \mathbf{b}, \quad \mathbf{x}_{n+1}(t) = \mathbf{b} + \int_a^t \mathbf{f}(\mathbf{x}_n(s), s)\, ds. \tag{16}$$

Recall that vector-valued functions are integrated componentwise.

Example 3   Consider the m-dimensional initial value problem

$$\frac{d\mathbf{x}}{dt} = \mathbf{A}\mathbf{x}, \quad \mathbf{x}(0) = \mathbf{b} \tag{17}$$

for a homogeneous linear system with $m \times m$ constant coefficient matrix $\mathbf{A}$. The equations in (16) take the form

$$\mathbf{x}_0(t) = \mathbf{b}, \quad \mathbf{x}_{n+1} = \mathbf{b} + \int_0^x \mathbf{A}\mathbf{x}_n(s)\, ds. \tag{18}$$

Thus

$$\mathbf{x}_1(t) = \mathbf{b} + \int_0^t \mathbf{A}\mathbf{b}\, ds = \mathbf{b} + \mathbf{A}\mathbf{b}t = (\mathbf{I} + \mathbf{A}t)\mathbf{b},$$

$$\mathbf{x}_2(t) = \mathbf{b} + \int_0^t \mathbf{A}(\mathbf{b} + \mathbf{A}\mathbf{b}s)\, ds = \mathbf{b} + \mathbf{A}\mathbf{b}t + \tfrac{1}{2}\mathbf{A}^2\mathbf{b}t^2 = (\mathbf{I} + \mathbf{A}t + \tfrac{1}{2}\mathbf{A}^2t^2)\mathbf{b},$$

and

$$\mathbf{x}_3(t) = \mathbf{b} + \int_0^t \mathbf{A}(\mathbf{b} + \mathbf{A}\mathbf{b}s + \tfrac{1}{2}\mathbf{A}^2\mathbf{b}s^2)\, ds = (\mathbf{I} + \mathbf{A}t + \tfrac{1}{2}\mathbf{A}^2t^2 + \tfrac{1}{6}\mathbf{A}^3t^3)\mathbf{b}.$$

We have therefore obtained the first several partial sums of the exponential series solution

$$\mathbf{x}(t) = e^{\mathbf{A}t}\mathbf{b} = \left(\sum_{n=0}^{\infty} \frac{(\mathbf{A}t)^n}{n!} \right) \mathbf{b} \tag{19}$$

of (17), which was derived earlier in Section 8.1. ∎

The key to establishing convergence in the method of successive approximations is an appropriate condition on the rate at which $\mathbf{f}(\mathbf{x}, t)$ changes when $\mathbf{x}$ varies but t is held fixed. If R is a region in $(m + 1)$-dimensional $(\mathbf{x}, t)$-space, then the function $\mathbf{f}(\mathbf{x}, t)$ is said to be **Lipschitz continuous** on R if there exists a constant $k > 0$ such that

$$|\mathbf{f}(\mathbf{x}_1, t) - \mathbf{f}(\mathbf{x}_2, t)| \leqq k|\mathbf{x}_1 - \mathbf{x}_2| \tag{20}$$

if $(\mathbf{x}_1, t)$ and $(\mathbf{x}_2, t)$ are points of R. Recall that the **norm** of an m-dimensional point or vector $\mathbf{x}$ is defined to be

$$|\mathbf{x}| = \sqrt{x_1^2 + x_2^2 + x_3^2 + \cdots + x_m^2}. \tag{21}$$

Then $|\mathbf{x}_1 - \mathbf{x}_2|$ is simply the Euclidean distance between the points $\mathbf{x}_1$ and $\mathbf{x}_2$.

Example 4   Let $f(x, t) = x^2 \exp\left(-t^2\right) \sin t$ and let R be the strip $0 \leqq x \leqq 2$ in the xy-plane. If (x_1, t) and (x_2, t) are both points of R, then

$$|f(x_1, t) - f(x_2, t)| = |\exp\left(-t^2\right)\sin t| \cdot |x_1 + x_2| \cdot |x_1 - x_2| \leqq 4|x_1 - x_2|,$$

because $\left| \exp\left(-t^2\right)\sin t \right| \leqq 1$ for all t and $|x_1 + x_2| \leqq 4$ if x_1 and x_2 are both in the interval $[0, 2]$. Thus f satisfies the Lipschitz condition in (20) with $k = 4$ and is therefore Lipschitz continuous in the strip R. ∎

Example 5   Let $f(x, t) = t\sqrt{x}$ on the rectangle R consisting of the points (x, t) in the xt-plane for which $0 \leqq x \leqq 1$ and $0 \leqq t \leqq 1$. Then, taking $x_1 = x$, $x_2 = 0$, and $t = 1$, we find that

$$|f(x, 1) - f(0, 1)| = \sqrt{x} = \frac{1}{\sqrt{x}}|x - 0|.$$

Because $x^{-1/2} \to +\infty$ as $x \to 0^+$, we see that the Lipschitz condition in (20) cannot be satisfied by any (finite) constant $k > 0$. Thus the function f, though obviously continuous on R, is *not* Lipschitz continuous on R. ∎

Suppose, however, that the function $f(x,t)$ has a continuous partial derivative $f_x(x,t)$ on the closed rectangle R in the xt-plane, and denote by k the maximum value of $|f_x(x,t)|$ on R. Then the mean-value theorem of differential calculus yields

$$|f(x_1,t) - f(x_2,t)| = |f_x(\overline{x},t) \cdot (x_1 - x_2)|$$

for some $\overline{x}$ in (x_1, x_2), so it follows that

$$|f(x_1,t) - f(x_2,t)| \leqq k|x_1 - x_2|$$

because $|f_x(\overline{x},t)| \leqq k$. Thus a continuously differentiable function $f(x,t)$ defined on a closed rectangle *is* Lipschitz continuous there. More generally, the multivariable mean value theorem of advanced calculus can be used similarly to prove that a *vector-valued function $\mathbf{f}(\mathbf{x},t)$ with continuously differentiable component functions on a closed rectangular region R in $(\mathbf{x},t)$-space is Lipschitz continuous on R.*

Example 6

The function $f(x,t) = x^2$ is Lipschitz continuous on any closed [bounded] region in the xt-plane. But consider this function on the infinite strip R consisting of the points (x,t) for which $0 \leqq t \leqq 1$ and x is arbitrary. Then

$$|f(x_1,t) - f(x_2,t)| = |x_1^2 - x_2^2| = |x_1 + x_2| \cdot |x_1 - x_2|,$$

Because $|x_1 + x_2|$ can be made arbitrarily large, it follows that f is *not* Lipschitz continuous on the infinite strip R. ∎

If I is an interval on the t-axis, then the set of all points $(\mathbf{x},t)$ with t in I is an infinite strip or slab in $(m + 1)$-space (as indicated in Fig. A.1). Example 6 shows that Lipschitz continuity of $\mathbf{f}(\mathbf{x},t)$ on such an infinite slab is a very strong condition. Nevertheless, the existence of a solution of the initial value problem

$$\frac{d\mathbf{x}}{dt} = \mathbf{f}(\mathbf{x},t), \quad \mathbf{x}(a) = \mathbf{b} \tag{15}$$

under the hypothesis of Lipschitz continuity of $\mathbf{f}$ in such a slab is of considerable importance.

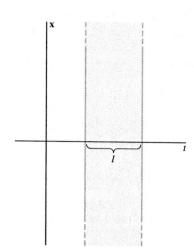

FIGURE A.1. An infinite slab in $(m + 1)$-space.

THEOREM 1: Global Existence of Solutions

Let $\mathbf{f}$ be a vector-valued function (with m components) of $m + 1$ real variables, and let I be a (bounded or unbounded) open interval containing $t = a$. If $\mathbf{f}(\mathbf{x},t)$ is continuous and satisfies the Lipschitz condition in (20) for all t in I and for all $\mathbf{x}_1$ and $\mathbf{x}_2$, then the initial value problem in (15) has a solution on the entire interval I.

Proof: We want to show that the sequence $\{\mathbf{x}_n(t)\}_0^\infty$ of successive approximations determined iteratively by

$$\mathbf{x}_0(a) = \mathbf{b}, \quad \mathbf{x}_{n+1}(t) = \mathbf{b} + \int_0^t \mathbf{f}(\mathbf{x}_n(s), s)\, ds \tag{16}$$

converges to a solution $\mathbf{x}(t)$ of (15). We see that each of these functions in turn is continuous on I, as each is an (indefinite) integral of a continuous function.

We may assume that $a = 0$, because the transformation $t \to t + a$ converts (15) into an equivalent problem with initial point $t = 0$. Also, we will consider only the portion $t \geqq 0$ of the interval I; the details for the case $t \leqq 0$ are very similar.

The main part of the proof consists in showing that if $[0, T]$ is a closed (and bounded) interval contained in I, then the sequence $\{\mathbf{x}_n(t)\}$ converges *uniformly* on

$[0, T]$ to a limit function $\mathbf{x}(t)$. This means that, given $\epsilon > 0$, there exists an integer N such that

$$|\mathbf{x}_n(t) - \mathbf{x}(t)| < \epsilon \tag{22}$$

for all $n \geq N$ and all t in $[0, T]$. For ordinary (perhaps nonuniform) convergence the integer N, for which (22) holds for all $n \geq N$, might depend on t, with no single value of N working for all t in I. Once this uniform convergence of the sequence $\{\mathbf{x}_n(t)\}$ has been established, the following conclusions will follow from standard theorems of advanced calculus [see pages 620–622 of A. E. Taylor and W. R. Mann, *Advanced Calculus*, 3rd ed. (New York: John Wiley, 1983)].

1. The limit function $\mathbf{x}(t)$ is continuous on $[0, T]$.
2. If N is so chosen that the inequality in (22) holds for $n \geq N$, then the Lipschitz continuity of $\mathbf{f}$ implies that

$$|\mathbf{f}(\mathbf{x}_n(t), t) - \mathbf{f}(\mathbf{x}(t), t)| \leq k|\mathbf{x}_n(t) - \mathbf{x}(t)| < k\epsilon$$

for all t in $[0, T]$ and $n \geq N$, so it follows that the sequence $\{\mathbf{f}(\mathbf{x}_n(t), t)\}_0^\infty$ converges uniformly to $\mathbf{f}(\mathbf{x}(t), t)$ on $[0, T]$.
3. But a uniformly convergent sequence or series can be integrated termwise, so it follows that, on taking limits in the iterative formula in (16),

$$\mathbf{x}(t) = \lim_{n \to \infty} \mathbf{x}_{n+1}(t) = \mathbf{b} + \lim_{n \to \infty} \int_0^t \mathbf{f}(\mathbf{x}_n(s), s)\, ds$$

$$= \mathbf{b} + \int_0^t \lim_{n \to \infty} \mathbf{f}(\mathbf{x}_n(s), s)\, ds;$$

thus

$$\mathbf{x}(t) = \mathbf{b} + \int_0^t \mathbf{f}(\mathbf{x}(s), s)\, ds. \tag{23}$$

4. Because the function $\mathbf{x}(t)$ is continuous on $[0, T]$, the integral equation in (23) [analogous to the one-dimensional case in (4)] implies that $\mathbf{x}'(t) = \mathbf{f}(\mathbf{x}(t), t)$ on $[0, T]$. If this is true on every closed subinterval of the open interval I, however, then it is true on the entire interval I as well.

It therefore remains only to prove that the sequence $\{\mathbf{x}_n(t)\}_0^\infty$ converges uniformly on the closed interval $[0, T]$. Let M be the maximum value of $|\mathbf{f}(\mathbf{b}, t)|$ for t in $[0, T]$. Then

$$|\mathbf{x}_1(t) - \mathbf{x}_0(t)| = \left| \int_0^t \mathbf{f}(\mathbf{x}_0(s), s)\, ds \right| \leq \int_0^t |\mathbf{f}(\mathbf{b}, s)|\, ds \leq Mt. \tag{24}$$

Next,

$$|\mathbf{x}_2(t) - \mathbf{x}_1(t)| = \left| \int_0^t [\mathbf{f}(\mathbf{x}_1(s), s) - \mathbf{f}(\mathbf{x}_0(s), s)]\, ds \right| \leq k \int_0^t |\mathbf{x}_1(s) - \mathbf{x}_0(s)|\, ds,$$

and hence

$$|\mathbf{x}_2(t) - \mathbf{x}_1(t)| \leq k \int_0^t Ms\, ds = \tfrac{1}{2}kMt^2. \tag{25}$$

We now proceed by induction. Assume that

$$|\mathbf{x}_n(t) - \mathbf{x}_{n-1}(t)| \leq \frac{M}{k} \cdot \frac{(kt)^n}{n!}. \tag{26}$$

It then follows that

$$|\mathbf{x}_{n+1}(t) - \mathbf{x}_n(t)| = \left| \int_0^t \mathbf{f}(\mathbf{x}_n(s), s) - \mathbf{f}(\mathbf{x}_{n-1}(s), s)] \, ds \right|$$

$$\leq k \int_0^t |\mathbf{x}_n(s) - \mathbf{x}_{n-1}(s)| \, ds;$$

consequently,

$$|\mathbf{x}_{n+1}(t) - \mathbf{x}_n(t)| \leq k \int_0^t \frac{M}{k} \cdot \frac{(ks)^n}{n!} \, ds.$$

It follows, upon evaluation of this integral, this integral that

$$|\mathbf{x}_{n+1}(t) - \mathbf{x}_n(t)| \leq \frac{M}{k} \cdot \frac{(kt)^{n+1}}{(n+1)!}.$$

Thus (26) holds on $[0, T]$ for all $n \geq 1$.

Hence the terms of the infinite series

$$\mathbf{x}_0(t) + \sum_{n=1}^{\infty} [\mathbf{x}_n(t) - \mathbf{x}_{n-1}(t)] \tag{27}$$

are dominated (in magnitude on the interval $[0, T]$) by the terms of the convergent series

$$\sum_{n=1}^{\infty} \frac{M}{k} \cdot \frac{(kT)^{n+1}}{(n+1)!} = \frac{M}{k}(e^{kT} - 1), \tag{28}$$

which is a series of positive constants. It therefore follows (from the Weierstrass M-test on pages 618–619 of Taylor and Mann) that the series in (27) converges uniformly on $[0, T]$. But the sequence of partial sums of this series is, however, simply our original sequence $\{\mathbf{x}_n(t)\}_0^{\infty}$ of successive approximations, so the proof of Theorem 1 is finally complete. ▲

A.2 Linear Systems

An important application of the global existence theorem just given is to the initial value problem

$$\frac{d\mathbf{x}}{dt} = \mathbf{A}(t)\mathbf{x} + \mathbf{g}(t), \quad \mathbf{x}(a) = \mathbf{b} \tag{29}$$

for a linear system, where the $m \times m$ matrix-valued function $\mathbf{A}(t)$ and the vector-valued function $\mathbf{g}(t)$ are continuous on a (bounded or unbounded) open interval I containing the point $t = a$. In order to apply Theorem 1 to the linear system in (29), we note first that the proof of Theorem 1 requires only that, for each closed and bounded subinterval J of I, there exists a Lipschitz constant k such that

$$|\mathbf{f}(\mathbf{x}_1, t) - \mathbf{f}(\mathbf{x}_2, t)| \leq k|\mathbf{x}_1 - \mathbf{x}_2| \tag{20}$$

for all t in J (and all $\mathbf{x}_1$ and $\mathbf{x}_2$). Thus we do not need a single Lipschitz constant for the entire open interval I.

In (29) we have $\mathbf{f}(\mathbf{x}, t) = \mathbf{A}(t)\mathbf{x} + \mathbf{g}$, so

$$\mathbf{f}(\mathbf{x}_1, t) - \mathbf{f}(\mathbf{x}_2, t) = \mathbf{A}(t)(\mathbf{x}_1 - \mathbf{x}_2). \tag{30}$$

It therefore suffices to show that, if $\mathbf{A}(t)$ is continuous on the closed and bounded interval J, then there is a constant k such that

$$|\mathbf{A}(t)\mathbf{x}| \leqq k|\mathbf{x}| \tag{31}$$

for all t in J. But this follows from the fact (Problem 17) that

$$|\mathbf{Ax}| \leqq \|\mathbf{A}\| \cdot |\mathbf{x}|, \tag{32}$$

where the **norm** $\|\mathbf{A}\|$ of the matrix $\mathbf{A}$ is defined to be

$$\|\mathbf{A}\| = \left(\sum_{i,j=1}^{m} (a_{ij})^2 \right)^{1/2}. \tag{33}$$

Because $\mathbf{A}(t)$ is continuous on the closed and bounded interval J, the norm $\|\mathbf{A}\|$ is bounded on J, so Eq. (31) follows, as desired. Thus we have the following global existence theorem for the linear initial value problem in (29).

THEOREM 2: Existence for Linear Systems

Let the $m \times m$ matrix-valued function $\mathbf{A}(t)$ and the vector-valued function $\mathbf{g}(t)$ be continuous on the (bounded or unbounded) open interval I containing the point $t = a$. Then the initial value problem

$$\frac{d\mathbf{x}}{dt} = \mathbf{A}(t)\mathbf{x} + \mathbf{g}(t), \quad \mathbf{x}(a) = \mathbf{b} \tag{29}$$

has a solution on the (entire) interval I. ▲

As we saw in Section 4.1, the mth-order initial value problem

$$x^{(m)} + a_1(t)x^{(m-1)} + \cdots + a_{m-1}(t)x' + a_m(t)x = p(t), \\ x(a) = b_0, \quad x'(a) = b_1, \ldots, x^{(m-1)}(a) = b_{m-1} \tag{34}$$

is readily transformed into an equivalent $m \times m$ system of the form in (29). It therefore follows from Theorem 2 that if the functions $a_1(t)$, $a_2(t)$, ..., $a_m(t)$ and $p(t)$ in (34) are all continuous on the (bounded or unbounded) open interval I containing $t = a$, then the initial value problem in (34) has a solution on the (entire) interval I.

A.3 Local Existence

In the case of a *nonlinear* initial value problem

$$\frac{d\mathbf{x}}{dt} = \mathbf{f}(\mathbf{x}, t), \quad \mathbf{x}(a) = \mathbf{b}, \tag{35}$$

the hypothesis in Theorem 1 that $\mathbf{f}$ satisfies a Lipschitz condition on a slab $(\mathbf{x}, t)$ (t in I, all $\mathbf{x}$) is unrealistic and rarely satisfied. This is illustrated by the following simple example.

Example 1 Consider the initial value problem

$$\frac{dy}{dx} = x^2, \quad x(0) = b > 0. \tag{36}$$

As we saw in Example 6, the equation $x' = x^2$ does not satisfy a "strip Lipschitz condition." When we solve (36) by separation of variables, we get

$$x(t) = \frac{b}{1 - bt}. \tag{37}$$

Because the denominator vanishes for $t = 1/b$, Eq. (37) provides a solution of the initial value problem in (36) only for $t < 1/b$, despite the fact that the differential equation $x' = x^2$ "looks nice" on the entire real line—certainly the function appearing on the right-hand side of the equation is continuous everywhere. In particular, if b is large, then we have a solution only on a very small interval to the right of $t = 0$. ∎

Although Theorem 2 assures us that *linear* equations have global solutions, Example 7 shows that, in general, even a "nice" nonlinear differential equation can be expected to have a solution only on a small interval around the initial point $t = a$, and it also shows that the length of this interval of existence can depend on the initial value $\mathbf{x}(a) = \mathbf{b}$, as well as on the differential equation itself. The reason is this: If $\mathbf{f}(\mathbf{x}, t)$ is continuously differentiable in a neighborhood of the point $(\mathbf{b}, a)$ in $(m + 1)$-dimensional space, then—as indicated in the discussion preceding Example 6—we can conclude that $\mathbf{f}(\mathbf{x}, t)$ satisfies a Lipschitz condition on some rectangular region R centered at $(\mathbf{b}, a)$, of the form

$$|t - a| < A, \quad |x_i - b_i| < B_i \tag{38}$$

($i = 1, 2, \ldots, m$). In the proof of Theorem 1, we need to apply the Lipschitz condition on the function $\mathbf{f}$ in analyzing the iterative formula

$$\mathbf{x}_{n+1}(t) = \mathbf{b} + \int_a^t \mathbf{f}(\mathbf{x}_n(s), s) \, ds. \tag{39}$$

The potential difficulty is that, unless the values of t are suitably restricted, the point $(\mathbf{x}_n(t), t)$ appearing in the integrand in (39) may not lie in the region R where $\mathbf{f}$ is known to satisfy a Lipschitz condition. On the other hand, it can be shown that—on a sufficiently small open interval J containing the point $t = a$—the graphs of the functions $\{\mathbf{x}_n(t)\}$ given iteratively by the formula in (39) remain within the region R, so the proof of convergence can then be carried out as in the proof of Theorem 1. A proof of the following *local* existence theorem can be found in Chapter 6 of G. Birkhoff and G.-C. Rota, *Ordinary Differential Equations*, 2nd ed. (New York: John Wiley, 1969).

THEOREM 3: Local Existence of Solutions

Let $\mathbf{f}$ be a vector-valued function (with m components) of the $m + 1$ real variables $x_1, x_2, \ldots, x_m$, and t. If the first-order partial derivatives of $\mathbf{f}$ all exist and are continuous in some neighborhood of the point $\mathbf{x} = \mathbf{b}$, $t = a$, then the initial value problem

$$\frac{d\mathbf{x}}{dt} = \mathbf{f}(\mathbf{x}, t), \quad \mathbf{x}(a) = \mathbf{b}, \tag{35}$$

has a solution on some open interval containing the point $t = a$. ▲

A.4 Uniqueness of Solutions

It is possible to establish the existence of solutions of the initial value problem in (35) under the much weaker hypothesis that $\mathbf{f}(\mathbf{x}, t)$ is merely continuous; techniques other than those used in this section are required. By contrast, the Lipschitz condition that we used in proving Theorem 1 is the key to *uniqueness* of solutions. In particular, the solution provided by Theorem 3 is unique near the point $t = a$.

THEOREM 4: Uniqueness of Solutions

Suppose that on some region R in $(m+1)$-space, the function $\mathbf{f}$ in (35) is continuous and satisfies the Lipschitz condition

$$|\mathbf{f}(\mathbf{x}_1, t) - \mathbf{f}(\mathbf{x}_2, t)| \leqq k \cdot |\mathbf{x}_1 - \mathbf{x}_2|. \tag{20}$$

If $\mathbf{x}_1(t)$ and $\mathbf{x}_2(t)$ are two solutions of the initial problem in (35) on some open interval I containing $x = a$, such that the solution curves $(\mathbf{x}_1(t), t)$ and $(\mathbf{x}_2(t), t)$ both lie in R for all t in I, then $\mathbf{x}_1(t) = \mathbf{x}_2(t)$ for all t in I. ▲

We will outline the proof of Theorem 4 for the one-dimensional case in which x is a real variable. A generalization of this proof to the multivariable case can be found in Chapter 6 of Birkhoff and Rota.

Let us consider the function

$$\phi(t) = [x_1(t) - x_2(t)]^2 \tag{40}$$

for which $\phi(a) = 0$, because $x_1(a) = x_2(a) = b$. We want to show that $\phi(t) \equiv 0$, so that $x_1(t) \equiv x_2(t)$. We will consider only the case $t \geqq a$; the details are similar for the case $t \leqq a$.

If we differentiate each side in Eq. (40), we find that

$$\begin{aligned}
\left|\phi'(t)\right| &= \left|2[x_1(t) - x_2(t)] \cdot [x_1'(t) - x_2'(t)]\right| \\
&= \left|2[x_1(t) - x_2(t)] \cdot [f(x_1(t), t) - f(x_2(t), t)]\right| \\
&\leqq 2k|x_1(t) - x_2(t)|^2 = 2k\phi(t),
\end{aligned}$$

by using the Lipschitz condition on f. Hence

$$\phi'(t) \leqq 2k\phi(t). \tag{41}$$

Now let us temporarily ignore the fact that $\phi(a) = 0$ and compare $\phi(t)$ with the solution of the differential equation

$$\Phi'(t) = 2k\Phi(t) \tag{42}$$

such that $\Phi(a) = \phi(a)$; clearly

$$\Phi(t) = \Phi(a)e^{2k(t-a)}. \tag{43}$$

In comparing (41) with (42), it seems inevitable that

$$\phi(t) \leqq \Phi(t) \qquad \text{for } t \geqq a, \tag{44}$$

and this is easily proved (Problem 18). Hence

$$0 \leqq [x_1(t) - x_2(t)]^2 \leqq [x_1(a) - x_2(a)]^2 e^{2k(t-a)}.$$

On taking square roots, we get

$$0 \leq |x_1(t) - x_2(t)| \leq |x_1(a) - x_2(a)|e^{k(t-a)}. \tag{45}$$

But $x_1(a) - x_2(a) = 0$, so (45) implies that $x_1(t) \equiv x_2(t)$.

Example 1 The initial value problem

$$\frac{dx}{dt} = 3x^{2/3}, \quad x(0) = 0 \tag{46}$$

has both the obvious solution $x_1(t) \equiv 0$ and the solution $x_2(t) = t^3$ (which is readily found by separation of variables). Hence the function $f(x, t)$ must *fail* to satisfy a Lipschitz condition near $(0, 0)$. Indeed, the mean value theorem yields

$$|f(x, 0) - f(0, 0)| = |f_x(\overline{x}, 0)| \cdot |x - 0|$$

for some $\overline{x}$ between 0 and x. But $f_x(x, 0) = 2x^{-1/3}$ is unbounded as $x \to 0$, so no Lipschitz condition can be satisfied. ∎

A.5 Well-Posed Problems and Mathematical Models

In addition to uniqueness, another consequence of the inequality in (45) is the fact that solutions of the differential equation

$$\frac{dx}{dt} = f(x, t) \tag{47}$$

depend *continuously* on the initial value $x(a)$; that is, if $x_1(t)$ and $x_2(t)$ are two solutions of (47) on the interval $a \leq t \leq T$ such that the initial values $x_1(a)$ and $x_2(a)$ are sufficiently close to one another, then the values of $x_1(t)$ and $x_2(t)$ remain close to one another. In particular, if $|x_1(a) - x_2(a)| \leq \delta$, then (45) implies that

$$|x_1(t) - x_2(t)| \leq \delta e^{k(T-a)} = \epsilon \tag{48}$$

for all t with $a \leq t \leq T$. Obviously, we can make ϵ as small as we wish by choosing δ sufficiently close to zero.

This continuity of solutions of (47) with respect to initial values is important in practical applications where we are unlikely to know the initial value $x_0 = x(a)$ with absolute precision. For example, suppose that the initial value problem

$$\frac{dx}{dt} = f(x, t), \quad x(a) = x_0 \tag{49}$$

models a population for which we know only that the initial population is within $\delta > 0$ of the assumed value x_0. Then even if the function $f(x, t)$ is accurate, the solution $x(t)$ of (49) will be only an approximation to the actual population. But (45) implies that the actual population at time t will be within $\delta e^{k(T-a)}$ of the approximate population $x(t)$. Thus, on a given closed interval $[a, T]$, $x(t)$ will be a close approximation to the actual population provided that $\delta > 0$ is sufficiently small.

An initial value problem is usually considered *well posed* as a mathematical model for a real-world situation only if the differential equation has unique solutions that are continuous with respect to initial values. Otherwise it is unlikely that the initial value problem adequately mirrors the real-world situation.

An even stronger "continuous dependence" of solutions is often desirable. In addition to possible inaccuracy in the initial value, the function $f(x, t)$ may not model precisely the physical situation. For instance, it may involve physical parameters (such as resistance coefficients) whose values cannot be measured with absolute precision. Birkhoff and Rota generalize the proof of Theorem 4 to establish the following result.

THEOREM 5: Continuous Dependence of Solutions

Let $\mathbf{x}(t)$ and $\mathbf{y}(t)$ be solutions of the equations

$$\frac{d\mathbf{x}}{dt} = \mathbf{f}(\mathbf{x}, t) \quad \text{and} \quad \frac{d\mathbf{y}}{dt} = \mathbf{g}(\mathbf{y}, t) \tag{50}$$

on the closed interval $[a, T]$. Let $\mathbf{f}$ and $\mathbf{g}$ be continuous for $a \leqq t \leqq T$ and for $\mathbf{x}$ and $\mathbf{y}$ in a common region D of n-space and assume that $\mathbf{f}$ satisfies the Lipschitz condition in (20) on the region D. If

$$|\mathbf{f}(\mathbf{z}, t) - \mathbf{g}(\mathbf{z}, t)| \leqq \mu \tag{51}$$

for all t in the interval $[a, T]$ and all $\mathbf{z}$ in D, it then follows that

$$|\mathbf{x}(t) - \mathbf{y}(t)| \leqq |\mathbf{x}(a) - \mathbf{y}(a)| \cdot e^{k(t-a)} + \frac{\mu}{k} \left[e^{k(t-a)} - 1 \right] \tag{52}$$

on the interval $[a, T]$. ▲

If $\mu > 0$ is small, then (51) implies that the functions $\mathbf{f}$ and $\mathbf{g}$ appearing in the two differential equations, though different, are "close" to each other. If $\epsilon > 0$ is given, then it is apparent from (52) that

$$|\mathbf{x}(t) - \mathbf{y}(t)| \leqq \epsilon \tag{53}$$

for all t in $[a, T]$ if both $|\mathbf{x}(a) - \mathbf{y}(a)|$ and μ are sufficiently small. Thus Theorem 5 says (roughly) that if both the two initial values and the two differential equations in (50) are close to each other, then the two solutions remain close to each other for $a \leqq t \leqq T$.

For example, suppose that a falling body is subject both to constant gravitational acceleration g and to resistance proportional to some power of its velocity, so (with the positive axis directed downward) its velocity v satisfies the differential equation

$$\frac{dv}{dt} = g - cv^\rho. \tag{54}$$

Assume, however, that only an approximation $\bar{c}$ to the actual resistance c and an approximation $\bar{\rho}$ to the actual exponent ρ are known. Then our mathematical model is based on the differential equation

$$\frac{du}{dt} = g - \bar{c}u^{\bar{\rho}} \tag{55}$$

instead of the actual equation in (54). Thus if we solve Eq. (55), we obtain only an approximation $u(t)$ to the actual velocity $v(t)$. But if the parameters $\bar{c}$ and $\bar{\rho}$ are sufficiently close to the actual values c and ρ, then the right-hand sides in (54) and (55) will be close to each other. If so, then Theorem 5 implies that the actual and approximate velocity functions $v(t)$ and $u(t)$ are close to each other. In this case, the approximation in (55) will be a good model of the actual physical situation.

Appendix A Problems

In Problems 1 through 8, apply the successive approximation formula to compute $y_n(x)$ for $n \leqq 4$. Then write the exponential series for which these approximations are partial sums (perhaps with the first term or two missing; for example,

$$e^x - 1 = x + \tfrac{1}{2}x^2 + \tfrac{1}{6}x^3 + \tfrac{1}{24}x^4 + \cdots).$$

1. $\dfrac{dy}{dx} = y$, $y(0) = 3$

2. $\dfrac{dy}{dx} = -2y$, $y(0) = 4$

3. $\dfrac{dy}{dx} = -2xy$, $y(0) = 1$

4. $\dfrac{dy}{dx} = 3x^2 y$, $y(0) = 2$

5. $\dfrac{dy}{dx} = 2y + 2$, $y(0) = 0$

6. $\dfrac{dy}{dx} = x + y$, $y(0) = 0$

7. $\dfrac{dy}{dx} = 2x(1 + y)$, $y(0) = 0$

8. $\dfrac{dy}{dx} = 4x(y + 2x^2)$, $y(0) = 0$

In Problems 9 through 12, compute the successive approximations $y_n(x)$ for $n \leqq 3$; then compare them with the appropriate partial sums of the Taylor series of the exact solution.

9. $\dfrac{dy}{dx} = x + y$, $y(0) = 1$

10. $\dfrac{dy}{dx} = y + e^x$, $y(0) = 0$

11. $\dfrac{dy}{dx} = y^2$, $y(0) = 1$

12. $\dfrac{dy}{dx} = \tfrac{1}{2}y^3$, $y(0) = 1$

13. Apply the iterative formula in (16) to compute the first three successive approximations to the solution of the initial value problem

$$\frac{dx}{dt} = 2x - y, \qquad x(0) = 1;$$

$$\frac{dy}{dt} = 3x - 2y, \qquad y(0) = -1.$$

14. Apply the matrix exponential series in (19) to solve (in closed form) the initial value problem

$$\mathbf{x}'(t) = \begin{bmatrix} 1 & 1 \\ 0 & 1 \end{bmatrix} \mathbf{x}, \quad \mathbf{x}(0) = \begin{bmatrix} 1 \\ 1 \end{bmatrix}.$$

(*Suggestion*: Show first that

$$\begin{bmatrix} 1 & 1 \\ 0 & 1 \end{bmatrix}^n = \begin{bmatrix} 1 & n \\ 0 & 1 \end{bmatrix}$$

for each positive integer n.)

15. For the initial value problem $dy/dx = 1 + y^3$, $y(1) = 1$, show that the second Picard approximation is

$$y_2(x) = 1 + 2(x - 1) + 3(x - 1)^2 + 4(x - 1)^3 + 2(x - 1)^4.$$

Then compute $y_2(1.1)$ and $y_2(1.2)$. The fourth-order Runge-Kutta method with step size $h = 0.005$ yields $y(1.1) \approx 1.2391$ and $y(1.2) \approx 1.6269$.

16. For the initial value problem $dy/dx = x^2 + y^2$, $y(0) = 0$, show that the third Picard approximation is

$$y_3(x) = \frac{1}{3}x^3 + \frac{1}{63}x^7 + \frac{2}{2079}x^{11} + \frac{1}{59535}x^{15}.$$

Compute $y_3(1)$. The fourth-order Runge-Kutta method yields $y(1) \approx 0.350232$, both with step size $h = 0.05$ and with step size $h = 0.025$.

17. Prove as follows the inequality $|\mathbf{Ax}| \leqq \|\mathbf{A}\| \cdot |\mathbf{x}|$, where $\mathbf{A}$ is an $m \times m$ matrix with row vectors $\mathbf{a}_1, \mathbf{a}_2, \ldots, \mathbf{a}_m$, and $\mathbf{x}$ is an m-dimensional vector. First note that the components of the vector $\mathbf{Ax}$ are $\mathbf{a}_1 \cdot \mathbf{x}, \mathbf{a}_2 \cdot \mathbf{x}, \ldots, \mathbf{a}_m \cdot \mathbf{x}$, so

$$|\mathbf{Ax}| = \left[\sum_{n=1}^{m} (\mathbf{a}_i \cdot \mathbf{x})^2 \right]^{1/2}.$$

Then use the Cauchy-Schwarz inequality $(\mathbf{a} \cdot \mathbf{x})^2 \leqq |\mathbf{a}|^2 |\mathbf{x}|^2$ for the dot product.

18. Suppose that $\phi(t)$ is a differentiable function with

$$\phi'(t) \leqq k\phi(t) \qquad (k > 0)$$

for $t \geqq a$. Multiply both sides by e^{-kt}, then transpose to show that

$$\frac{d}{dt} \left[\phi(t)e^{-kt} \right] \leqq 0$$

for $t \geqq a$. Then apply the mean value theorem to conclude that

$$\phi(t) \leqq \phi(a)e^{k(t-a)}$$

for $t \geqq a$.

APPENDIX B

Theory of Determinants

The proof of the theorem on row and column cofactor expansions (Theorem 1 in Section 3.6) involves an alternative interpretation of determinants that in more advanced treatments is usually taken as the original definition. Consider the following elementary scheme for evaluating a 3×3 determinant:

The first two columns of $\mathbf{A} = \begin{bmatrix} a_{ij} \end{bmatrix}$ are duplicated to its right. It is readily verified that $\det \mathbf{A}$ is equal to the sum of the three products along the indicated diagonals that point down and to the *right*, minus the sum of the products along the three diagonals that point down and to the *left*:

$$\det \mathbf{A} = + a_{11}a_{22}a_{33} + a_{12}a_{23}a_{31} + a_{13}a_{21}a_{32}$$
$$- a_{13}a_{22}a_{31} - a_{11}a_{23}a_{32} - a_{12}a_{21}a_{33}. \tag{1}$$

Remark: This scheme works **only** in dimensions 2 and 3. Neither the analogous scheme nor anything resembling it gives the correct value of an $n \times n$ determinant with $n \geq 4$.

Note that each of the six terms on the right in (1) is of the form $\pm a_{1i}a_{2j}a_{3k}$, where $(i \ j \ k)$ is a **permutation** of $(1 \ 2 \ 3)$. That is, the triple $(i \ j \ k)$ consists of the three distinct numbers 1, 2, and 3 written in some specific order. The six terms in (1) correspond to the six possible permutations of $(1 \ 2 \ 3)$:

$$\begin{matrix} (1 \ 2 \ 3) & (2 \ 1 \ 3) & (3 \ 1 \ 2) \\ (1 \ 3 \ 2) & (2 \ 3 \ 1) & (3 \ 2 \ 1) \end{matrix} \tag{2}$$

The $+$ and $-$ signs in (1) can also be explained in terms of these permutations. A **transposition** of an ordered sequence of objects (such as the numbers 1, 2, 3) is the operation of *interchanging* some single pair of them. For instance, the operation $(1 \ 2 \ 3) \rightarrow (1 \ 3 \ 2)$ is a transposition that consists of interchanging 2 and 3. But it requires two transpositions to change $(1 \ 2 \ 3)$ into the permutation $(3 \ 1 \ 2)$:

$$(1 \ 2 \ 3) \rightarrow (3 \ 2 \ 1) \rightarrow (3 \ 1 \ 2).$$

Given a permutation $P = (i \ j \ k)$ of $(1 \ 2 \ 3)$, we denote by $s(P)$ the *minimum* number of transpositions required to change $(1 \ 2 \ 3)$ into $(i \ j \ k)$. For the six permutations in (2) it is easy to verify that

$$\begin{matrix} s(1 \ 2 \ 3) = 0, & s(2 \ 1 \ 3) = 1, & s(3 \ 1 \ 2) = 2, \\ s(1 \ 3 \ 2) = 1, & s(2 \ 3 \ 1) = 2, & s(3 \ 2 \ 1) = 1. \end{matrix} \tag{3}$$

493

Now for the point to all this: If you check each of the six terms in (1) you will find that the *sign* of the term $a_{1i}a_{2j}a_{3k}$ is $(-1)^{s(P)}$, where $P = (i\ j\ k)$. Therefore, we can rewrite (1) more concisely as

$$\det \mathbf{A} = \sum_P (-1)^{s(P)} a_{1i}a_{2j}a_{3k}, \tag{4}$$

where there is one term on the right for each possible permutation $P = (i\ j\ k)$ of $(1\ 2\ 3)$.

The formula in (4) generalizes to determinants of higher order. If $\mathbf{A}$ is an $n \times n$ matrix, then

$$\det \mathbf{A} = \sum_P (-1)^{s(P)} a_{1i_1}a_{2i_2} \cdots a_{ni_n}, \tag{5}$$

where there is one term on the right for each possible permutation $P = (i_1\ i_2\ \cdots\ i_n)$ of $(1\ 2\ \cdots\ n)$, and $s(P)$ denotes the minimum number of transpositions required to change $(1\ 2\ \cdots\ n)$ into $(i_1\ i_2\ \cdots\ i_n)$. The formula in (5) can be established by induction on n. Assuming its validity for $(n-1) \times (n-1)$ determinants, the formula can be verified for an $n \times n$ matrix $\mathbf{A}$ by expanding along its first row. It is fairly easy to see that this gives terms of the form $\pm a_{1i_1}a_{2i_2} \cdots a_{ni_n}$, but somewhat more difficult to check the signs.

Finally, the proof of the cofactor expansion theorem consists of verifying similarly that the cofactor expansion of $\det \mathbf{A}$ along *any* row *or* column of $\mathbf{A}$ agrees with the formula in (5). The details are more lengthy than instructive, and therefore we omit them.

Determinants and Elementary Row Operations

As we described in Section 3.6, the determinant of any square matrix $\mathbf{A}$ can be evaluated directly by carrying out a cofactor expansion of $\det \mathbf{A}$ along any row or column of $\mathbf{A}$. Because this approach involves so much computational labor, it is more efficient instead to reduce $\mathbf{A}$ to an echelon matrix $\mathbf{R}$. Because any square echelon matrix is (upper) triangular, the determinant of the echelon matrix $\mathbf{R}$ is simply the product of its diagonal elements. But because we have altered the matrix $\mathbf{A}$ by transforming it into $\mathbf{R}$, the question is this: What effects do elementary row operations have on the determinant of $\mathbf{A}$?

The following theorem summarizes Properties 1, 2, and 5 of Section 3.6 and tells us how to keep track of the effect each elementary row operation will have on $\det \mathbf{A}$ as we reduce $\mathbf{A}$ to echelon form. We use here the concise notation

$$|\mathbf{A}| = \det \mathbf{A}$$

for the determinant of the matrix $\mathbf{A}$.

THEOREM 1: Effect of Elementary Row Operations

Let $\mathbf{A}$ be a square matrix and let $\mathbf{B}$ be the matrix obtained by performing one of the three types of elementary row operations on $\mathbf{A}$.

(a) Type 1: If $\mathbf{B}$ is obtained by *dividing* some row of $\mathbf{A}$ by k, then

$$|\mathbf{A}| = k|B|. \tag{6}$$

(b) Type 2: If $\mathbf{B}$ is obtained by interchanging two rows of $\mathbf{A}$, then

$$|\mathbf{A}| = -|\mathbf{B}|. \tag{7}$$

(c) Type 3: If **B** is obtained by adding a multiple of some row of **A** to another row, then

$$|\mathbf{A}| = |\mathbf{B}|. \tag{8}$$

▲

The following example shows how to lay out the computation of det **A** by using row operations to reduce **A** to echelon form.

Example 1

$$\begin{vmatrix} 2 & 2 & -2 & 0 \\ -4 & 2 & 3 & 1 \\ 0 & 4 & -1 & -4 \\ 3 & 1 & 3 & -1 \end{vmatrix} = 2 \begin{vmatrix} 1 & 1 & -1 & 0 \\ -4 & 2 & 3 & 1 \\ 0 & 4 & -1 & -4 \\ 3 & 1 & 3 & -1 \end{vmatrix}$$

We have divided row 1 by 2.

$$= 2 \begin{vmatrix} 1 & 1 & -1 & 0 \\ 0 & 6 & -1 & 1 \\ 0 & 4 & -1 & -4 \\ 0 & -2 & 6 & -1 \end{vmatrix}$$

We have added 4 times row 1 to row 2, and −3 times row 1 to row 4.

$$= +2 \begin{vmatrix} 1 & 1 & -1 & 0 \\ 0 & 0 & 17 & -2 \\ 0 & 0 & 11 & -6 \\ 0 & -2 & 6 & -1 \end{vmatrix}$$

We have added 3 times row 4 to row 2, and 2 times row 4 to row 3.

$$= -2 \begin{vmatrix} 1 & 1 & -1 & 0 \\ 0 & -2 & 6 & -1 \\ 0 & 0 & 11 & -6 \\ 0 & 0 & 17 & -2 \end{vmatrix}$$

We have interchanged rows 2 and 4.

$$= -22 \begin{vmatrix} 1 & 1 & -1 & 0 \\ 0 & -2 & 6 & -1 \\ 0 & 0 & 1 & -\frac{6}{11} \\ 0 & 0 & 17 & -2 \end{vmatrix}$$

We have divided row 3 by 11.

$$= -22 \begin{vmatrix} 1 & 1 & -1 & 0 \\ 0 & -2 & 6 & -1 \\ 0 & 0 & 1 & -\frac{6}{11} \\ 0 & 0 & 0 & \frac{80}{11} \end{vmatrix}$$

We have added −17 times row 3 to row 4.

$$= (-22)(1)(-2)(1)\left(\tfrac{80}{11}\right) = 320.$$ ■

If the square matrix **A** has only *integer* entries, it is always possible to carry out the reduction to echelon form without introducing any fractions. In the computation of determinants (as opposed to the solution of linear systems), we have the additional flexibility of using elementary *column* operations; their effects are precisely analogous to those of elementary row operations, as described in Theorem 1. In Example 2, we illustrate this by finishing differently the evaluation in Example 1.

Example 2

$$\begin{vmatrix} 2 & 2 & -2 & 0 \\ -4 & 2 & 3 & 1 \\ 0 & 4 & -1 & -4 \\ 3 & 1 & 3 & -1 \end{vmatrix} = -2 \begin{vmatrix} 1 & 1 & -1 & 0 \\ 0 & -2 & 6 & -1 \\ 0 & 0 & 11 & -6 \\ 0 & 0 & 17 & -2 \end{vmatrix}$$ (As in Example 1.)

$$= -2 \begin{vmatrix} 1 & 1 & -1 & 0 \\ 0 & -2 & 5 & -1 \\ 0 & 0 & 5 & -6 \\ 0 & 0 & 15 & -2 \end{vmatrix}$$ We have added column 4 to column 3.

$$= -2 \begin{vmatrix} 1 & 1 & -1 & 0 \\ 0 & -2 & 5 & -1 \\ 0 & 0 & 5 & -6 \\ 0 & 0 & 0 & 16 \end{vmatrix}$$ We have added (-3) times row 3 to row 4.

$$= (-2)(1)(-2)(5)(16) = 320.$$

Yet another alternative is to reduce only the first $n - 2$ rows of the $n \times n$ matrix **A**. We then directly calculate the 2×2 determinant that remains in the lower right-hand corner. We get det **A** by multiplying this 2×2 determinant by the preceding factors and diagonal elements. Thus

$$\begin{vmatrix} 2 & 2 & -2 & 0 \\ -4 & 2 & 3 & 1 \\ 0 & 4 & -1 & -4 \\ 3 & 1 & 3 & -1 \end{vmatrix} = -2 \begin{vmatrix} 1 & 1 & -1 & 0 \\ 0 & -2 & 6 & -1 \\ 0 & 0 & 11 & -6 \\ 0 & 0 & 17 & -2 \end{vmatrix}$$

$$= (-2)(1)(-2) \begin{vmatrix} 11 & -6 \\ 17 & -2 \end{vmatrix} = (4)(-22 + 102) = 320. \quad \blacksquare$$

Determinants and Invertibility

We began Section 3.6 with the remark that a 2×2 matrix **A** is invertible if and only if its determinant is nonzero: $|\mathbf{A}| \neq 0$. Now we want to show that this result also holds for $n \times n$ matrices. This connection between determinants and invertibility is closely related to the fact that the determinant function "respects" matrix multiplication in the sense that

$$|\mathbf{AB}| = |\mathbf{A}| \, |\mathbf{B}| \tag{9}$$

if **A** and **B** are $n \times n$ matrices. Our first step is to show that Eq. (9) holds if **A** is an *elementary matrix* obtained from the $n \times n$ identity matrix **I** by performing a single elementary row operation.

LEMMA Multiplication by an Elementary Matrix

If **B** is an $n \times n$ matrix and **E** is an $n \times n$ elementary matrix then

$$|\mathbf{EB}| = |\mathbf{E}| \, |\mathbf{B}|. \tag{10}$$

Proof: This is really just a restatement of Theorem 1. For instance, suppose that **E** is obtained from **I** by multiplying the pth row by c, so that $|\mathbf{E}| = c$. Then

Theorem 5 in Section 3.5 tells us that the product **EB** is the result of multiplying the pth row of **B** by c. Therefore

$$|\mathbf{EB}| = c|\mathbf{B}| = |\mathbf{E}|\,|\mathbf{B}|,$$

and so we have verified Eq. (10) for the first of the three types of elementary matrices. The verifications for the other two types are similar.   ▲

Now, let **A** be an $n \times n$ matrix whose invertibility we want to discuss, and let **R** be the *reduced* echelon form of **A**. If the elementary matrices $\mathbf{F}_1, \mathbf{F}_2, \ldots, \mathbf{F}_k$ correspond to the elementary row operations that reduce **A** to **R**, then

$$\mathbf{F}_k \cdots \mathbf{F}_2 \mathbf{F}_1 \mathbf{A} = \mathbf{R} \tag{11}$$

by Theorem 5 in Section 3.5. Recalling that every elementary matrix is invertible (Section 3.5), we can rewrite Eq. (11) as

$$\mathbf{A} = \mathbf{E}_1 \mathbf{E}_2 \cdots \mathbf{E}_k \mathbf{R}, \tag{12}$$

where each $\mathbf{E}_i = (\mathbf{F}_i)^{-1}$ is an elementary matrix. It now follows, by k applications of the lemma, that

$$\mathbf{A} = |\mathbf{E}_1|\,|\mathbf{E}_2| \cdots |\mathbf{E}_k|\,|\mathbf{R}|. \tag{13}$$

This relation is the key both to the proof of (9) and to the proof of the following theorem.

THEOREM 2: Determinants and Invertibility

The $n \times n$ matrix **A** is invertible if and only if $\det \mathbf{A} \neq 0$.

Proof: If (as previously) **R** is the reduced echelon form of **A**, then Theorem 6 in Section 3.5 implies that

$$\mathbf{A} \text{ is invertible} \quad \text{if and only if} \quad \mathbf{R} = \mathbf{I}. \tag{14}$$

Because **R** is a *square* reduced echelon matrix, we see that *either* **R** is the identity matrix **I** and $|\mathbf{R}| = 1$, *or* **R** has an all-zero row and, consequently, $|\mathbf{R}| = 0$. Therefore

$$\mathbf{R} = \mathbf{I} \quad \text{if and only if} \quad |\mathbf{R}| \neq 0. \tag{15}$$

Finally, because $|\mathbf{E}| \neq 0$ if **E** is an elementary matrix, it follows immediately from Eq. (13) that

$$|\mathbf{R}| \neq 0 \quad \text{if and only if} \quad |\mathbf{A}| \neq 0. \tag{16}$$

Combining the statements in (14), (15), and (16), we see that **A** is invertible if and only if $|\mathbf{A}| \neq 0$.   ▲

So now we can add the statement $\det \mathbf{A} \neq 0$ to the list of equivalent properties of nonsingular matrices stated in Theorem 7 of Section 3.5. Indeed, some texts *define* the square matrix **A** to be nonsingular if and only if $\det \mathbf{A} \neq 0$.

THEOREM 3: Determinants and Matrix Products

If **A** and **B** are $n \times n$ matrices, then

$$|\mathbf{AB}| = |\mathbf{A}|\,|\mathbf{B}|. \tag{9}$$

Proof: If **R** is the reduced echelon form of **A**, then we see that

$$A = E_1 E_2 \cdots E_k R, \tag{12}$$

where $E_1, E_2, \ldots,$ and E_k are elementary matrices. Hence

$$AB = E_1 E_2 \cdots E_k RB.$$

We now take the determinant of both sides, using the lemma stated earlier to "split off" the elementary matrices:

$$|AB| = |E_1| |E_2 E_3 \cdots E_k RB| \qquad \text{(lemma once)}$$
$$= |E_1| |E_2| |E_3 \cdots E_k RB| \qquad \text{(lemma twice)}$$
$$= |E_1 E_2| |E_3 \cdots E_k RB|. \qquad \text{(lemma thrice)}$$

After $2k - 1$ steps, we get

$$|AB| = |E_1 E_2 \cdots E_k| |RB|. \tag{17}$$

The remainder of the proof depends on whether or not **A** is invertible.

If **A** is invertible then $R = I$, so Eq. (12) yields

$$A = E_1 E_2 \cdots E_k$$

and also that $RB = IB = B$. In this case the meaning of Eq. (17) is precisely that $|AB| = |A| |B|$.

If **A** is *not* invertible then $|A| = 0$ by Theorem 2. Also, as we noted previously, the reduced echelon form **R** of **A** has an all-zero row in this case. Hence it follows from the definition of matrix multiplication that the product **RB** has an all-zero row and, therefore, that $|RB| = 0$. In this case Eq. (17) implies that $|AB| = 0$. Because both $|A| = 0$ and $|AB| = 0$, the equation $|AB| = |A| |B|$ holds, and the proof is complete. ▲

Cramer's Rule and Inverse Matrices

Suppose that we need to solve the $n \times n$ linear system

$$Ax = b, \tag{18}$$

where

$$A = \begin{bmatrix} a_{ij} \end{bmatrix}, \quad x = \begin{bmatrix} x_1 \\ x_2 \\ \vdots \\ x_n \end{bmatrix} \quad \text{and} \quad b = \begin{bmatrix} b_1 \\ b_2 \\ \vdots \\ b_n \end{bmatrix}. \tag{19}$$

We assume that the coefficient matrix **A** is invertible, so we know in advance that a unique solution **x** of (18) exists. The question is how to write **x** explicitly in terms of the coefficients a_{ij} and the constants b_i. In the following discussion, we think of **x** as a fixed (though as yet unknown) vector.

If we denote by $a_1, a_2, \ldots, a_n$ the column vectors of the $n \times n$ matrix **A**, then

$$A = \begin{bmatrix} a_1 & a_2 & \cdots & a_n \end{bmatrix}. \tag{20}$$

By Fact 1 in Section 3.5, we can rewrite Eq. (18) as

$$x_1 a_1 + x_2 a_2 + \cdots + x_n a_n = b.$$

Thus the constant vector **b** is expressed in terms of the entries $x_1, x_2, \ldots, x_n$ of the solution vector **x** and the column vectors of **A** by

$$\mathbf{b} = \sum_{j=1}^{n} x_j \mathbf{a}_j. \tag{21}$$

The trick for finding the ith unknown x_i is to compute the determinant of the matrix

$$\begin{bmatrix} \mathbf{a}_1 & \cdots & \mathbf{b} & \cdots & \mathbf{a}_n \end{bmatrix} = \begin{bmatrix} a_{11} & \cdots & b_1 & \cdots & a_{1n} \\ a_{21} & \cdots & b_2 & \cdots & a_{2n} \\ \vdots & \ddots & \vdots & \ddots & \vdots \\ a_{n1} & \cdots & b_n & \cdots & a_{nn} \end{bmatrix} \tag{22}$$

that we obtain by replacing the ith column $\mathbf{a}_i$ of **A** with the constant vector **b**. Using Eq. (21) to substitute for **b**, we find that

$$\begin{vmatrix} \mathbf{a}_1 & \cdots & \mathbf{b} & \cdots & \mathbf{a}_n \end{vmatrix} = \begin{vmatrix} \mathbf{a}_1 & \cdots & \sum_{j=1}^{n} x_j \mathbf{a}_j & \cdots & \mathbf{a}_n \end{vmatrix}$$

$$= \sum_{j=1}^{n} \begin{vmatrix} \mathbf{a}_1 & \cdots & x_j \mathbf{a}_j & \cdots & \mathbf{a}_n \end{vmatrix} \qquad \text{(by Property 4 of determinants)}$$

$$= \sum_{j=1}^{n} x_j \begin{vmatrix} \mathbf{a}_1 & \cdots & \mathbf{a}_j & \cdots & \mathbf{a}_n \end{vmatrix} \qquad \text{(by Property 1 of determinants)}.$$

Note that, in the jth term of this summation, the vector $\mathbf{a}_j$ appears in the ith position. Thus we have found that

$$\begin{vmatrix} \mathbf{a}_1 & \cdots & \mathbf{b} & \cdots & \mathbf{a}_n \end{vmatrix} = x_1 \begin{vmatrix} \mathbf{a}_1 & \mathbf{a}_2 & \cdots & \mathbf{a}_1 & \cdots & \mathbf{a}_n \end{vmatrix}$$

$$+ x_2 \begin{vmatrix} \mathbf{a}_1 & \mathbf{a}_2 & \cdots & \mathbf{a}_2 & \cdots & \mathbf{a}_n \end{vmatrix}$$

$$\vdots$$

$$+ x_i \begin{vmatrix} \mathbf{a}_1 & \mathbf{a}_2 & \cdots & \mathbf{a}_i & \cdots & \mathbf{a}_n \end{vmatrix}$$

$$\vdots$$

$$+ x_n \begin{vmatrix} \mathbf{a}_1 & \mathbf{a}_2 & \cdots & \mathbf{a}_n & \cdots & \mathbf{a}_n \end{vmatrix}.$$

Of the n determinants on the right-hand side here, all but the ith one have two identical columns and therefore are equal to zero. The coefficient of x_i in the ith term is simply

$$|\mathbf{A}| = \begin{vmatrix} \mathbf{a}_1 & \mathbf{a}_2 & \cdots & \mathbf{a}_i & \cdots & \mathbf{a}_n \end{vmatrix}.$$

Consequently, a result of our computation is that

$$\begin{vmatrix} \mathbf{a}_1 & \cdots & \mathbf{b} & \cdots & \mathbf{a}_n \end{vmatrix} = x_i |\mathbf{A}|. \tag{23}$$

We get the desired simple formula for x_i after we divide each side by $|\mathbf{A}| \neq 0$.

THEOREM 4: Cramer's Rule

Consider the $n \times n$ linear system $\mathbf{Ax} = \mathbf{b}$ with

$$\mathbf{A} = \begin{bmatrix} \mathbf{a}_1 & \mathbf{a}_2 & \cdots & \mathbf{a}_n \end{bmatrix}.$$

If $|\mathbf{A}| \neq 0$, then the ith entry of the unique solution $\mathbf{x} = (x_1, x_2, \ldots, x_n)$ is given by

$$x_i = \frac{\begin{vmatrix} \mathbf{a}_1 & \cdots & \mathbf{b} & \cdots & \mathbf{a}_n \end{vmatrix}}{|\mathbf{A}|}$$

$$= \frac{1}{|\mathbf{A}|} \begin{vmatrix} a_{11} & \cdots & b_1 & \cdots & a_{1n} \\ a_{21} & \cdots & b_2 & \cdots & a_{2n} \\ \vdots & \ddots & \vdots & \ddots & \vdots \\ a_{n1} & \cdots & b_n & \cdots & a_{nn} \end{vmatrix}, \tag{24}$$

where (in the last expression) the constant vector $\mathbf{b}$ replaces the ith column vector $\mathbf{a}_i$ of $\mathbf{A}$. ▲

Inverses and the Adjoint Matrix

We now use Cramer's rule to develop an explicit formula for the inverse $\mathbf{A}^{-1}$ of the invertible matrix $\mathbf{A}$. First, we need to rewrite Cramer's rule more concisely. Expansion of the determinant in the numerator in Eq. (24) along its ith column yields

$$x_i = \frac{1}{|\mathbf{A}|} (b_1 A_{1i} + b_2 A_{2i} + \cdots + b_n A_{ni}), \tag{25}$$

because the cofactor of b_p is simply the cofactor A_{pi} of a_{pi} in $|\mathbf{A}|$. The formula in Eq. (25) gives the solution vector

$$\mathbf{x} = \begin{bmatrix} x_1 \\ x_2 \\ \vdots \\ x_n \end{bmatrix} = \frac{1}{|\mathbf{A}|} \begin{bmatrix} b_1 A_{11} + b_2 A_{21} + \ldots + b_n A_{n1} \\ b_1 A_{12} + b_2 A_{22} + \ldots + b_n A_{n2} \\ \vdots \\ b_1 A_{1n} + b_2 A_{2n} + \ldots + b_n A_{nn} \end{bmatrix}.$$

Then the definition of matrix multiplication yields

$$\mathbf{x} = \frac{1}{|\mathbf{A}|} \begin{bmatrix} A_{11} & A_{21} & \cdots & A_{n1} \\ A_{12} & A_{22} & \cdots & A_{n2} \\ \vdots & \vdots & \ddots & \vdots \\ A_{1n} & A_{2n} & \cdots & A_{nn} \end{bmatrix} \begin{bmatrix} b_1 \\ b_2 \\ \vdots \\ b_n \end{bmatrix} \tag{26}$$

for the solution $\mathbf{x}$ of $\mathbf{A}\mathbf{x} = \mathbf{b}$.

Observe that the double subscripts in (26) are reversed from their usual order; the element in the ith row and jth column is A_{ji} (rather than A_{ij}). We therefore see in (26) the *transpose* of the **cofactor matrix** $\begin{bmatrix} A_{ij} \end{bmatrix}$ of the $n \times n$ matrix $\mathbf{A}$. The transpose of the cofactor matrix of $\mathbf{A}$ is called the **adjoint matrix** of $\mathbf{A}$ and is denoted by

$$\operatorname{adj} \mathbf{A} = \begin{bmatrix} A_{ij} \end{bmatrix}^T = \begin{bmatrix} A_{ji} \end{bmatrix}. \tag{27}$$

With the aid of this notation, Cramer's rule as expressed in Eq. (26) can be written in the especially simple form

$$\mathbf{x} = \frac{\begin{bmatrix} A_{ji} \end{bmatrix} \mathbf{b}}{|\mathbf{A}|} = \frac{(\operatorname{adj} \mathbf{A})\mathbf{b}}{|\mathbf{A}|}. \tag{28}$$

The fact that the formula in (28) gives the unique solution $\mathbf{x}$ of $\mathbf{Ax = b}$ implies that

$$\mathbf{A}\frac{(\text{adj }\mathbf{A})\mathbf{b}}{|\mathbf{A}|} = \mathbf{b} \qquad (29)$$

for every n-vector $\mathbf{b}$. If we write

$$\mathbf{C} = \frac{\text{adj }\mathbf{A}}{|\mathbf{A}|} \qquad (30)$$

for brevity, then

$$\mathbf{ACb = b} \qquad (31)$$

for every n-vector $\mathbf{b}$. From this it follows (one column at a time, as we use Fact 2 in Section 3.5) that

$$\mathbf{ACB = B} \qquad (32)$$

for every matrix $\mathbf{B}$ having n rows. In particular, with $\mathbf{B = I}$ (the $n \times n$ identity matrix), we see that

$$\mathbf{AC = I}. \qquad (33)$$

Therefore, we have discovered that the matrix $\mathbf{C}$ as defined in Eq. (30) is the inverse matrix $\mathbf{A}^{-1}$ of $\mathbf{A}$.

THEOREM 5: The Inverse Matrix

The inverse of the invertible matrix $\mathbf{A}$ is given by the formula

$$\mathbf{A}^{-1} = \frac{\text{adj }\mathbf{A}}{|\mathbf{A}|} = \frac{\left[a_{ij} \right]^T}{|\mathbf{A}|}, \qquad (34)$$

where, as usual, A_{ij} is the ijth cofactor of $\mathbf{A}$—that is, A_{ij} is the product of $(-1)^{i+j}$ and the ijth minor of $\mathbf{A}$. ▲

ANSWERS TO SELECTED PROBLEMS

Chapter 1

Section 1.1

11. If $y = y_1 = x^{-2}$, then $y'(x) = -2x^{-3}$ and $y''(x) = 6x^{-4}$, so
$x^2 y'' + 5xy' + 4y = x^2(6x^{-4}) + 5x(-2x^{-3}) + 4(x^{-2}) = 6x^{-2} - 10x^{-2} + 4x^{-2} = 0$. If $y = y_2 = x^{-2} \ln x$, then
$y'(x) = x^{-3} - 2x^{-3} \ln x$ and $y''(x) = -5x^{-4} + 6x^{-4} \ln x$, so
$x^2 y'' + 5xy' + 4y = x^2(-5x^{-4} + 6x^{-4} \ln x) + 5x(x^{-3} - 2x^{-3} \ln x) + 4(x^{-2} \ln x) = 0$.

13. $r = \frac{2}{3}$ **14.** $r = \pm\frac{1}{2}$ **15.** $r = -2, 1$

16. $r = \frac{1}{6}(-3 \pm \sqrt{57})$

17. $C = 2$

18. $C = 3$

19. $C = 6$

20. $C = 11$

21. $C = 7$

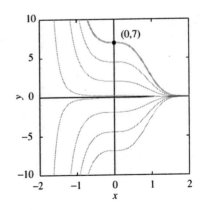

503

22. $C = 1$

23. $C = -56$

24. $C = 17$

25. $C = \pi/4$

26. $C = -\pi$

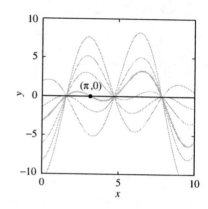

27. $y' = x + y$

28. $y' = 2y/x$

29. $y' = x/(1 - y)$

31. $y' = (y - x)/(y + x)$

32. $dP/dt = k\sqrt{P}$

33. $dv/dt = kv^2$

35. $dN/dt = k(P - N)$

37. $y \equiv 1$ or $y = x$

39. $y = x^2$

41. $y = \frac{1}{2}e^x$

42. $y = \cos x$ or $y = \sin x$

43. (b) The identically zero function $x(0) \equiv 0$

44. (a) The graphs (figure below) of typical solutions with $k = \frac{1}{2}$ suggest that (for each) the value $x(t)$ increases without bound as t increases.

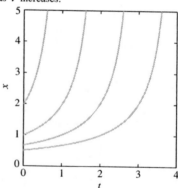

(b) The graphs (figure below) of typical solutions with $k = -\frac{1}{2}$ suggest that now the value $x(t)$ approaches 0 as t increases without bound.

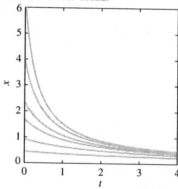

45. $P(t) = 100/(50 - t)$; $P = 100$ when $t = 49$, and $P = 1000$ when $t = 49.9$. Thus it appears that $P(t)$ grows without bound as t approaches 50.

46. $v(t) = 50/(5 + 2t)$; $v = 1$ when $t = 22.5$, and $v = \frac{1}{10}$ when $t = 247.5$. Thus it appears that $v(t)$ approaches 0 as t increases without bound.

47. (a) $C = 10.1$; (b) No such C, but the constant function $y(x) \equiv 0$ satisfies the conditions $y' = y^2$ and $y(0) = 0$.

Section 1.2

1. $y(x) = x^2 + x + 3$

2. $y(x) = \frac{1}{3}(x - 2)^3$

3. $y(x) = \frac{1}{3}(2x^{3/2} - 16)$

4. $y(x) = -1/x + 6$

5. $y(x) = 2\sqrt{x + 2} - 5$

6. $y(x) = \frac{1}{3}[(x^2 + 9)^{3/2} - 125]$

7. $y(x) = 10\tan^{-1} x$

8. $y(x) = \frac{1}{2}\sin 2x + 1$

9. $y(x) = \sin^{-1} x$

10. $y(x) = -(x + 1)e^{-x} + 2$

11. $x(t) = 25t^2 + 10t + 20$

12. $x(t) = -10t^2 - 15t + 5$

13. $x(t) = \frac{1}{2}t^3 + 5t$

14. $x(t) = \frac{1}{3}t^3 + \frac{1}{2}t - 7t + 4$

15. $x(t) = \frac{1}{3}(t + 3)^4 - 37t - 26$

16. $x(t) = \frac{4}{3}(t + 4)^{3/2} - 5t - \frac{29}{3}$

17. $x(t) = \frac{1}{2}\left[(t + 1)^{-1} + t - 1\right]$

19. $x(t) = \begin{cases} 5t & \text{if } 0 \le t \le 5, \\ 10t - \frac{1}{2}t^2 - \frac{25}{2} & \text{if } 5 \le t \le 10 \end{cases}$

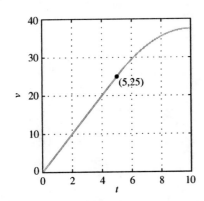

20. $x(t) = \begin{cases} \frac{1}{2}t^2 & \text{if } 0 \le t \le 5, \\ 5t - \frac{25}{2} & \text{if } 5 \le t \le 10 \end{cases}$

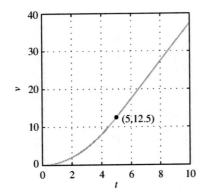

21. $x(t) = \begin{cases} \frac{1}{2}t^2 & \text{if } 0 \le t \le 5, \\ 10t - \frac{1}{2}t^2 - 25 & \text{if } 5 \le t \le 10 \end{cases}$

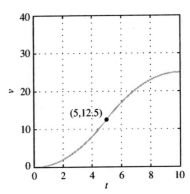

22. $x(t) = \begin{cases} \frac{5}{6}t^2 & \text{if } 0 \le t \le 3, \\ 5t - \frac{15}{2} & \text{if } 3 \le t \le 7, \\ \frac{1}{6}(-5t^2 + 100t - 290) & \text{if } 7 \le t \le 10 \end{cases}$

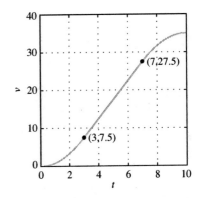

23. $v(t) = -(9.8)t + 49$, so the ball reaches its maximum height ($v = 0$) after $t = 5$ seconds. Its maximum height then is $y(5) = 122.5$ (m).

24. $v(5) = -160$ ft/s

25. The car stops when $t \approx 2.78$ (s), so the distance traveled before stopping is approximately $x(2.78) \approx 38.58$ (m).

26. (a) $y \approx 530$ m (b) $t \approx 20.41$ s (c) $t \approx 20.61$ s

27. $y_0 \approx 178.57$ (m)

28. $v(4.77) \approx -192.64$ ft/s

29. After 10 seconds the car has traveled 200 ft and is traveling at 70 ft/s.

30. $a = 22$ ft/s^2; it skids for 4 seconds.

31. $v_0 = 10\sqrt{30}$ (m/s), about 197.18 km/h

32. 60 m

33. $20\sqrt{10} \approx 63.25$ (ft/s)

34. 460.8 ft

36. About 13.6 ft

37. 25 (mi)

38. 1:10 pm

39. 6 mph

40. 2.4 mi

41. $\frac{544}{3} \approx 181.33$ ft/s

42. 25 mi

43. Time: 6.12245×10^9 s ≈ 194 years; Distance: 1.8367×10^{17} m ≈ 19.4 light-years

44. About 54 mi/h

Section 1.3

1.

2.

3.

4.

5.

6.

7.

8.

9.

10.

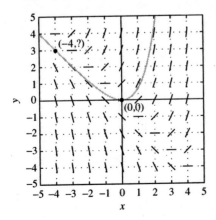

11. A unique solution exists in some neighborhood of $x = 1$.

12. A unique solution exists in some neighborhood of $x = 1$.

13. A unique solution exists in some neighborhood of $x = 0$.

14. Existence but not uniqueness is guaranteed in some neighborhood of $x = 0$.

15. Neither existence nor uniqueness is guaranteed in any neighborhood of $x = 2$.

16. A unique solution exists in some neighborhood of $x = 2$.

17. A unique solution exists in some neighborhood of $x = 0$.

18. Neither existence nor uniqueness is guaranteed.

19. A unique solution exists in some neighborhood of $x = 0$.

20. A unique solution exists in some neighborhood of $x = 0$.

21. Your figure should suggest that $y(-4) \approx 3$; an exact solution of the differential equation gives $y(-4) = 3 + e^{-4} \approx 3.0183$.

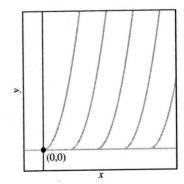

22. $y(-4) \approx -3$

23. Your figure should suggest that $y(2) \approx 1$; the actual value is closer to 1.004.

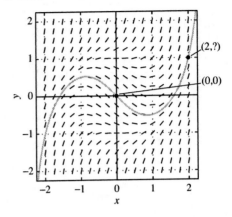

24. $y(2) \approx 1.5$

25. Your figure should suggest that the limiting velocity is about 20 ft/sec (quite survivable) and that the time required to reach 19 ft/sec is a little less than 2 seconds. An exact solution gives $v(t) = 19$ when $t = \frac{5}{8} \ln 20 \approx 1.8723$.

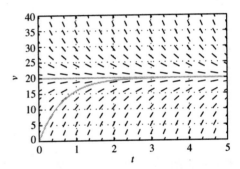

26. A figure suggests that there are 40 deer after about 60 months; a more accurate value is $t \approx 61.61$. The limiting population is 75 deer.

27. The initial value problem $y' = 2\sqrt{y}$, $y(0) = b$ has no solution if $b < 0$; a unique solution if $b > 0$; infinitely many solutions if $b = 0$.

28. The initial value problem $xy' = y$, $y(a) = b$ has a unique solution if $a \neq 0$; infinitely many solutions if $a = b = 0$; no solution if $a = 0$ but $b \neq 0$.

29. The initial value problem $y' = 3y^{2/3}$, $y(a) = b$ always has infinitely many solutions defined for all x. However, if $b \neq 0$

then it has a unique solution near $x = a$.

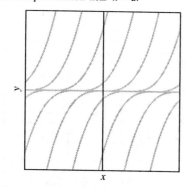

30. The initial value problem $y' = -\sqrt{1 - y^2}$, $y(a) = b$ has a unique solution if $|b| < 1$; no solution if $|b| > 1$, and infinitely many solutions (defined for all x) if $b = \pm 1$.

31. The initial value problem $y' = \sqrt{1 - y^2}$, $y(a) = b$ has a unique solution if $|b| < 1$; no solution if $|b| > 1$, and infinitely many solutions (defined for all x) if $b = \pm 1$.

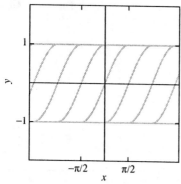

32. The initial value problem $y' = 4x\sqrt{y}$, $y(a) = b$ has infinitely many solutions (defined for all x) if $b \geqq 0$; no solutions if $b < 0$. However, if $b > 0$ then it has a unique solution near $x = a$.

33. The initial value problem $x^2 y' + y^2 = 0$, $y(a) = b$ has a unique solution with initial point (a, b) if $a \neq 0$, no solution if $a = 0$ but $b \neq 0$, infinitely many solutions if $a = b = 0$.

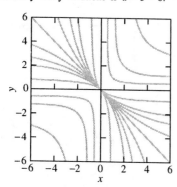

Section 1.4

1. $y(x) = C \exp(-x^2)$ **2.** $y(x) = 1/(x^2 + C)$
3. $y(x) = C \exp(-\cos x)$ **4.** $y(x) = C(1 + x)^4$
5. $y(x) = \sin\left(C + \sqrt{x}\right)$ **6.** $y(x) = (x^{3/2} + C)^2$
7. $y(x) = (2x^{4/3} + C)^{3/2}$ **8.** $y(x) = \sin^{-1}(x^2 + C)$

9. $y(x) = C(1 + x)/(1 - x)$
10. $y(x) = (1 + x)/[1 + C(1 + x)]$
11. $y(x) = (C - x^2)^{-1/2}$ **12.** $y^2 + 1 = Ce^{x^2}$
13. $\ln(y^4 + 1) = C + 4 \sin x$ **14.** $3y + 2y^{3/2} = 3x + 2x^{3/2} + C$
15. $1/(3y^3) - 2/y = 1/x + \ln|x| + C$
16. $y(x) = \sec^{-1}(C\sqrt{1 + x^2})$
17. $\ln|1 + y| = x + \frac{1}{2}x^2 + C$
18. $y(x) = \tan\left(C - \dfrac{1}{x} - x\right)$
19. $y(x) = 2 \exp(e^x)$ **20.** $y(x) = \tan(x^3 + \pi/4)$
21. $y^2 = 1 + \sqrt{x^2 - 16}$ **22.** $y(x) = -3 \exp(x^4 - x)$
23. $y(x) = \frac{1}{2}(1 + e^{2x-2})$ **24.** $y(x) = \frac{\pi}{2} \sin x$
25. $y(x) = x \exp(x^2 - 1)$ **26.** $y(x) = 1/(1 - x^2 - x^3)$
27. $y = \ln(3e^{2x} - 2)$ **28.** $y(x) = \tan^{-1}(\sqrt{x} - 1)$
29. (a) General solution $y(x) = -1/(x - C)$; (b) The singular solution $y(x) \equiv 0$. (c) In the following figure we see that there is a unique solution through every point of the xy-plane.

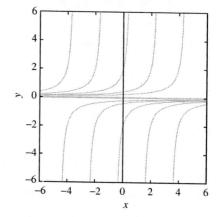

30. General solution $y(x) = (x - C)^2$; singular solution $y(x) \equiv 0$. (a) No solution if $b < 0$; (b) Infinitely many solutions (for all x) if $b \geqq 0$; (c) Two solutions near (a, b) if $b < 0$.

31. Separation of variables gives the same general solution $y = (x - C)^2$ as in Problem 30, but the restriction that $y' = 2\sqrt{y} \geqq 0$ implies that only the *right halves* of the parabolas qualify as solution curves. In the figure below we see that through the point (a, b) there passes (a) No solution curve if $b < 0$, (b) a unique solution curve if $b > 0$, (c) Infinitely many solution curves if $b = 0$.

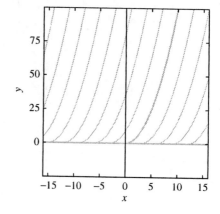

32. General solution $y(x) = \pm \sec(x - C)$; singular solutions $y(x) \equiv \pm 1$.
(a) No solution if $|b| < 1$; (b) A unique solution if $|b| > 1$; (c) Infinitely many solutions if $b = \pm 1$.

33. About 51,840 persons

34. $t \approx 3.87$ hr

35. About 14,735 years

36. Age about 686 years

37. \$21103.48

38. \$44.52

39. 2585 mg

40. About 35 years

41. About 4.86×10^9 years ago

42. About 1.25 billion years

43. After a total of about 63 min have elapsed

44. About 2.41 minutes

45. (a) 0.495 m; (b) $(8.32 \times 10^{-7})I_0$; (c) 3.29 m

46. (a) About 9.60 inches; (b) About 18,200 ft

47. After about 46 days

48. About 6 billion years

49. After about 66 min 40 s

50. (a) $A(t) = 10 \cdot 3^{2t/15}$; (b) About 20.80 pu; (c) About 15.72 years

51. (a) $A(t) = 15 \cdot \left(\frac{2}{3}\right)^{t/5}$; (b) approximately 7.84 su; (c) After about 33.4 months

52. About 120 thousand years ago

53. About 74 thousand years ago

54. 3 hours

55. 972 s

56. At time $t = 2048/1562 \approx 1.31$ (in hours)

58. 1:20 P.M.

59. (a) $y(t) = (8 - 7t)^{2/3}$; (b) at 1:08:34 P.M.; (c) $r = \frac{1}{60}\sqrt{\frac{7}{12}} \approx 0.15$ (in.)

60. About 6 min 3 sec

61. Approximately 14 min 29 s

62. The tank is empty about 14 seconds after 2:00 P.M.

63. (a) 1:53:34 P.M.; (b) $r \approx 0.04442$ ft ≈ 0.53 in.

64. $r = \frac{1}{720}\sqrt{3}$ ft, about $\frac{1}{35}$ in.

65. At approximately 10:29 A.M.

Section 1.5

1. $y(x) = 2(1 - e^{-x})$

2. $y(x) = (3x + C)e^{2x}$

3. $y(x) = e^{-3x}(x^2 + C)$

4. $y(x) = (x + C)e^{x^2}$

5. $y(x) = x + 4x^{-2}$

6. $y(x) = x^2 + 32/x^5$

7. $y(x) = 5x^{1/2} + Cx^{-1/2}$

8. $y(x) = 3x + Cx^{-1/3}$

9. $y(x) = x(7 + \ln x)$

10. $y(x) = 3x^3 + Cx^{3/2}$

11. $y(x) \equiv 0$

12. $y(x) = \frac{1}{4}x^5 - 56x^{-3}$

13. $y(x) = (e^x + e^{-x})/2$

14. $y(x) = x^3 \ln x + 10x^3$

15. $y(x) = [1 - 5\exp(-x^2)]/2$

16. $y(x) = 1 + e^{-\sin x}$

17. $y(x) = (1 + \sin x)/(1 + x)$

18. $y(x) = x^2(\sin x + C)$

19. $y(x) = \frac{1}{2}\sin x + C\csc x$

20. $y(x) = -1 + \exp\left(-x - \frac{1}{2}x^2\right)$

21. $y(x) = x^3 \sin x$

22. $y(x) = (x^3 + 5)e^{+x^2}$

23. $y(x) = x^3(2 + Ce^{-2x})$

24. $y(x) = \frac{1}{3}[1 + 16(x^2 + 4)^{-3/2}]$

25. $y(x) = \left[\exp\left(-\frac{3}{2}x^2\right)\right]\left[3(x^2 + 1)^{3/2} - 2\right]$

26. $x(y) = 1/2y^2 + C/y^4$

27. $x(y) = e^y\left(C + \frac{1}{2}y^2\right)$

28. $x(y) = \frac{1}{2}[y + (1 + y^2)(\tan^{-1} y + C)]$

29. $y(x) = \left[\exp(x^2)\right]\left[C + \frac{1}{2}\sqrt{\pi}\,\text{erf}(x)\right]$

30. $y(x) = x^{1/2}\int_1^x t^{-1/2}\cos t\, dt$

32. (a) $y(x) = \sin x - \cos x$; (b) $y(x) = Ce^{-x} + \sin x - \cos x$; (c) $y(x) = 2e^{-x} + \sin x - \cos x$

33. After about 7 min 41 s

34. About 22.2 days

35. About 5.5452 years

36. (a) $x(t) = (60 - t) - (60 - t)^3/3600$; (b) About 23.09 lb

37. 393.75 lb

38. (a) $x(t) = 50e^{-t/20}$; (b) $y(t) = 150e^{-t/40} - 100e^{-t/20}$; (c) 56.25 lb

39. (b) $y_{\max} = 100e^{-1} \approx 36.79$ (gal)

41. (b) Approximately \$1,308,283

43. $-50.0529, -28.0265, -6.0000, 16.0265, 38.0529$

44. $3.99982, 4.00005, 4.00027, 4.00050, 4.00073$

45. $x(t) = 20(1 - e^{-t/10})$; $x = 10$ after $t = 10\ln 2 \approx 6.93$ months.

46. $x(t) = \frac{20}{101}(101 - 102e^{-t/10} + \cos t + 10\sin t)$; $x = 10$ after $t = 6.47$ months

Section 1.6

1. $x^2 - 2xy - y^2 = C$

2. $y^2 = x^2(\ln x + C)$

3. $y(x) = x(C + \ln|x|)^2$

4. $2\tan^{-1}(y/x) - \ln(y^2/x^2 + 1) = 2\ln x + C$

5. $\ln|xy| = C + xy^{-1}$

6. $2y\ln y = x + Cy$

7. $y^3 = 3x^3(C + \ln|x|)$

8. $y = -x\ln(C - \ln x)$

9. $y(x) = x/(C - \ln|x|)$

10. $x^2 + 2y^2 = Cx^6$

11. $y = C(x^2 + y^2)$

12. $4x^2 + y^2 = x^2(\ln x + C)^2$

13. $y + \sqrt{x^2 + y^2} = Cx^2$

14. $x - \sqrt{x^2 + y^2} = C$

15. $x^2(2xy + y^2) = C$

16. $x = 2\sqrt{x + y + 1} - 2\ln\left(1 + \sqrt{x + y + 1}\right) + C$

17. $y(x) = -4x + 2\tan(2x + C)$

18. $y = \ln(x + y + 1) + C$

19. $y^2 = x/(2 + Cx^5)$

20. $y^3 = 3 + Ce^{-3x^2}$

21. $y^2 = 1/(Ce^{-2x} - 1)$

22. $y^3 = 7x/(7Cx^7 + 15)$

23. $y(x) = (x + Cx^2)^{-3}$

24. $y^2 = e^{2x}/(C + \ln x)$

25. $2x^3y^3 = 3\sqrt{1 + x^4} + C$

26. $y^3 = e^{-x}(x + C)$

27. $y(x) = (x^4 + Cx)^{1/3}$

28. $y = \ln(Cx^2 + x^2e^{2x})$

29. $\sin^2 y = 4x^2 + Cx$

30. $x^2 - 2xe^y - e^{2y} = C$

31. $x^2 + 3xy + y^2 = C$

32. $x^2 - xy + 3y^2 = C$

33. $x^3 + 2xy^2 + 2y^3 = C$

34. $x^3 + x^2y^2 + y^4 = C$

35. $3x^4 + 4y^3 + 12y\ln x = C$

36. $x + e^{xy} + y^2 = C$

37. $\sin x + x\ln y + e^y = C$

38. $x^2 + 2x\tan^{-1} y + \ln(1 + y^2) = C$

39. $5x^3y^3 + 5xy^4 + y^5 = C$

40. $e^x\sin y + x\tan y = C$

41. $x^2y^{-1} + y^2x^{-3} + 2y^{1/2} = C$

42. $xy^{-2/3} + x^{-3/2}y = C$

43. $y(x) = Ax^2 + B$

44. $x(y) = Ay^2 + B$

45. $y(x) = A\cos 2x + B\sin 2x$

46. $y(x) = x^2 + A\ln x + B$

47. $y(x) = A - \ln|x + B|$

48. $y(x) = \ln x + Ax^{-2} + B$

49. $y(x) = \pm(A + Be^x)^{1/2}$

50. $y(x) = \ln|\sec(x + A)| - \frac{1}{2}x^2 + B$

51. $x(y) = -\frac{1}{3}(y^3 + Ay + B)$

52. $Ay^2 - (Ax + B)^2 = 1$

53. $y(x) = A\tan(Ax + B)$

54. $Ay^2(B - x) = 1$

58. $y = \exp(x^2 + C/x^2)$

59. $x^2 - 2xy - y^2 - 2x - 6y = C$

60. $(x + 3y + 3)^5 = C(y - x - 5)$

61. $x = \tan(x - y) + \sec(x - y) + C$

64. $y(x) = x + e^{-x^2} \left[C + \frac{1}{2} \sqrt{\pi} \, \mathrm{erf}(x) \right]^{-1}$

65. $y(x) = x + (C - x)^{-1}$

69. Approximately 3.68 mi

Chapter 1 Review Problems

1. Linear: $y(x) = x^3(C + \ln x)$

2. Separable: $y(x) = x/(3 - Cx - x \ln x)$

3. Homogeneous: $y(x) = x/(C - \ln x)$

4. Exact: $x^2 y^3 + e^x - \cos y = C$

5. Separable: $y(x) = C \exp(x^{-3} - x^{-2})$

6. Separable: $y(x) = x/(1 + Cx + 2x \ln x)$

7. Linear: $y(x) = x^{-2}(C + \ln x)$

8. Homogeneous: $y(x) = 3Cx/(C - x^3) = 3x/(1 + Kx^3)$

9. Bernoulli: $y(x) = (x^2 + Cx^{-1})^2$

10. Separable: $y(x) = \tan \left(C + x + \frac{1}{3} x^3 \right)$

11. Homogeneous: $y(x) = x/(C - 3 \ln x)$

12. Exact: $3x^2 y^3 + 2xy^4 = C$

13. Separable: $y(x) = 1/(C + 2x^2 - x^5)$

14. Homogeneous: $y^2 = x^2/(C + 2 \ln x)$

15. Linear: $y(x) = (x^3 + C)e^{-3x}$

16. Substitution: $v = y - x$; solution: $y - x - 1 = Ce^{2x}(y - x + 1)$

17. Exact: $e^x + e^y + e^{xy} = C$

18. Homogeneous: $y^2 = Cx^2(x^2 - y^2)$

19. Separable: $y(x) = x^2/(x^5 + Cx^2 + 1)$

20. Linear: $y(x) = 2x^{-3/2} + Cx^{-3}$

21. Linear: $y(x) = [C + \ln(x - 1)]/(x + 1)$

22. Bernoulli: $y(x) = (2x^4 + Cx^2)^3$

23. Exact: $xe^y + y \sin x = C$

24. Separable: $y(x) = x^{1/2}/(6x^2 + Cx^{1/2} + 2)$

25. Linear: $y(x) = (x + 1)^{-2}(x^3 + 3x^2 + 3x + C)$
$= x + 1 + K(x + 1)^{-2}$

26. Exact: $3x^{3/2} y^{4/3} - 5x^{6/5} y^{3/2} = C$

27. Bernoulli: $y(x) = x^{-1}(C + \ln x)^{-1/3}$

28. Linear: $y(x) = x^{-1}(C + e^{2x})$

29. Linear: $y(x) = (x^2 + x + C)(2x + 1)^{-1/2}$

30. Substitution: $v = x + y$; solution:
$x = 2(x + y)^{1/2} - 2 \ln[1 + (x + y)^{1/2}] + C$

31. Separable and linear

32. Separable and Bernoulli

33. Exact and homogeneous

34. Exact and homogeneous

35. Separable and linear

36. Separable and Bernoulli

Chapter 2

Section 2.1

1. $x(t) = \dfrac{2}{2 - e^{-t}}$

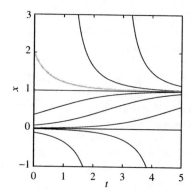

2. $x(t) = \dfrac{10}{1 + 9e^{-10t}}$

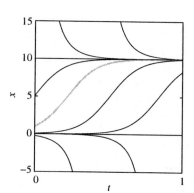

3. $x(t) = \dfrac{2 + e^{-2t}}{2 - e^{-2t}}$

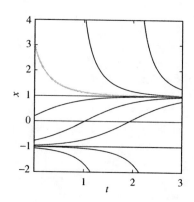

4. $x(t) = \dfrac{3(1 - e^{-12t})}{2(1 + e^{-12t})}$

7. $x(t) = \dfrac{77}{11 - 4e^{-28t}}$

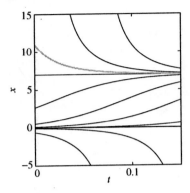

5. $x(t) = \dfrac{40}{8 - 3e^{-15t}}$

8. $x(t) = \dfrac{221}{17 - 4e^{91t}}$

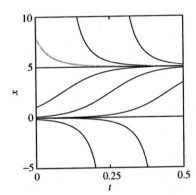

9. 484

10. 20 weeks

11. (b) $P(t) = \left(\frac{1}{2}t + 10\right)^2$

12. $P(t) = \dfrac{240}{20 - t}$

13. $P(t) = \dfrac{180}{30 - t}$

14. $P(t) = \dfrac{P_0}{1 + kP_0 t}$

16. About 27.69 months

17. About 44.22 months

19. About 24.41 months

20. About 42.12 months

21. $\dfrac{200}{1 + e^{-6/5}} \approx 153.7$ million

22. About 34.66 days

23. (a) $\lim\limits_{t \to \infty} x(t) = 200$ grams (b) $\frac{5}{4}\ln 3 \approx 1.37$ seconds

24. About 9.24 days

25. (a) $M = 100$ and $k = 0.0002$; (b) In the year 2035

26. $50 \ln \frac{9}{8} \approx 5.89$ months

27. (a) $100 \ln \frac{9}{5} \approx 58.78$ months; (b) $100 \ln 2 \approx 69.31$ months

28. (a) The alligators eventually die out. (b) Doomsday occurs after about 9 years 2 months.

29. (a) $P(140) \approx 127.008$ million; (b) About 210.544 million; (c) In 2000 we get $P \approx 196.169$, whereas the actual 2000 population was about 281.422 million.

31. $\alpha \approx 0.3915$; 2.15×10^6 cells

37. $k \approx 0.0000668717$, $M \approx 338.027$

38. $k \approx 0.000146679$, $M \approx 208.250$

6. $x(t) = \dfrac{10}{2 + 3e^{15t}}$

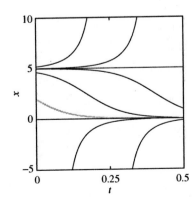

39. $P(t) = P_0 \exp\left(kt + \dfrac{b}{2\pi}\sin 2\pi t\right)$; the colored curve in the figure below shows the graph with $P_0 = 100$, $k = 0.03$, and $b = 0.06$. It oscillates about the black curve which represents

natural growth with $P_0 = 100$ and $k = 0.03$ We see that the two agree at the end of each full year.

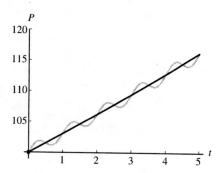

Section 2.2

1. Unstable critical point: $x = 4$;

$$x(t) = 4 + (x_0 - 4)e^t$$

2. Stable critical point: $x = 3$;

$$x(t) = 3 + (x_0 - 3)e^{-t}$$

3. Stable critical point: $x = 0$; unstable critical point: $x = 4$;

$$x(t) = \frac{4x_0}{x_0 + (4 - x_0)e^{4t}}$$

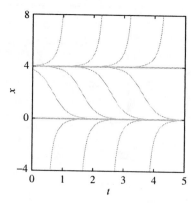

4. Stable critical point: $x = 3$; unstable critical point: $x = 0$;

$$x(t) = \frac{3x_0}{x_0 + (3 - x_0)e^{-3t}}$$

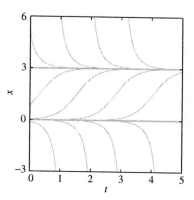

5. Stable critical point: $x = -2$; unstable critical point: $x = 2$;

$$x(t) = \frac{2[x_0 + 2 + (x_0 - 2)e^{4t}]}{x_0 + 2 - (x_0 - 2)e^{4t}}$$

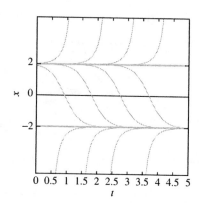

6. Stable critical point: $x = 3$; unstable critical point: $x = -3$;

$$x(t) = \frac{3[x_0 - 3 + (x_0 + 3)e^{6t}]}{3 - x_0 + (x_0 + 3)e^{6t}}$$

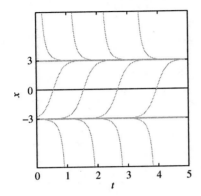

9. Stable critical point: $x = 1$; unstable critical point: $x = 4$;

$$x(t) = \frac{4(1 - x_0) + (x_0 - 4)e^{3t}}{1 - x_0 + (x_0 - 4)e^{3t}}$$

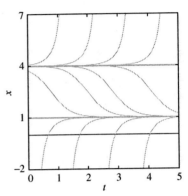

7. Semistable (see Problem 18) critical point: $x = 2$;

$$x(t) = \frac{(2t - 1)x_0 - 4t}{tx_0 - 2t - 1}$$

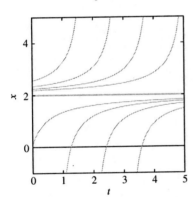

10. Stable critical point: $x = 5$; unstable critical point: $x = 2$;

$$x(t) = \frac{2(5 - x_0) + 5(x_0 - 2)e^{3t}}{5 - x_0 + (x_0 - 2)e^{3t}}$$

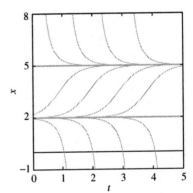

8. Semistable critical point: $x = 3$;

$$x(t) = \frac{(3t + 1)x_0 - 9t}{tx_0 - 3t + 1}$$

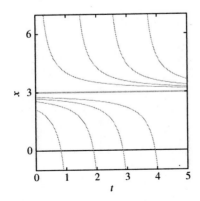

11. Unstable critical point: $x = 1$;

$$\frac{1}{(x(t) - 1)^2} = \frac{1}{(x_0 - 1)^2} - 2t$$

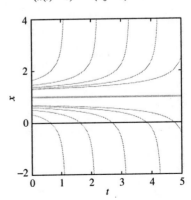

12. Stable critical point: $x = 2$;

$$\frac{1}{(2 - x(t))^2} = \frac{1}{(2 - x_0)^2} + 2t$$

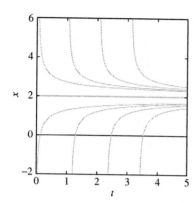

For each of Problems 13 through 18 we show a plot of slope field and typical solution curves. The equilibrium solutions of the given differential equation are labeled, and the stability or instability of each should be clear from the picture.

13.

$x' = (x + 2)(x - 2)^2$

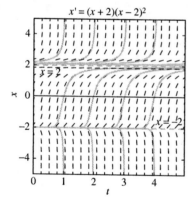

14.

$x' = x(x^2 - 4)$

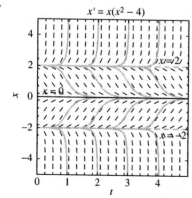

15.

$x' = (x^2 - 4)^2$

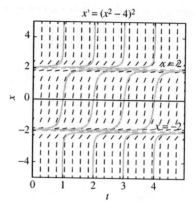

16.

$x' = (x^2 - 4)^3$

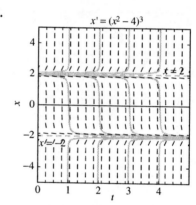

17.

$x' = x^2(x^2 - 4)$

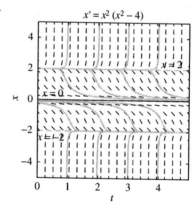

18.

$x' = x^3(x^2 - 4)$

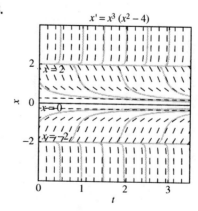

19. There are two critical points if $h < 2\frac{1}{2}$, one critical point if $h = 2\frac{1}{2}$, and no critical points if $h > 2\frac{1}{2}$. The bifurcation diagram is the parabola $(c-5)^2 = 25 - 10h$ in the hc-plane.

20. There are two critical points if $s < \frac{1}{16}$, one critical point if $s = \frac{1}{16}$, and no critical points if $s > \frac{1}{16}$. The bifurcation diagram is the parabola $(2c-5)^2 = 25(1-16s)$ in the sc-plane.

Section 2.3

1. Approximately 31.5 s

3. $400/(\ln 2) \approx 577$ ft

5. $400 \ln 7 \approx 778$ ft

7. (a) 100 ft/s; (b) about 23 s and 1403 ft to reach 90 ft/s

8. (a) 100 ft/s; (b) about 14.7 s and 830 ft to reach 90 ft/s

9. 50 ft/s

10. About 5 min 47 s

11. Time of fall: about 12.5 s

12. Approximately 648 ft

19. Approximately 30.46 ft/s; exactly 40 ft/s

20. Approximately 277.26 ft

22. Approximately 20.67 ft/s; about 484.57 s

23. Approximately 259.304 s

24. (a) About 0.88 cm; (b) about 2.91 km

25. (b) About 1.389 km/s; (c) $r_{max} = 100R/19 \approx 5.26R$

26. Yes

28. (b) After about $8\frac{1}{2}$ minutes it hits the surface at about 4.116 km/s.

29. About 51.427 km

30. Approximately 11.11 km/sec (as compared with the earth's escape velocity of about 11.18 km/s).

Section 2.4

In Problems 1 through 10, we round off the indicated values to 3 decimal places.

1. Approximate values 1.125 and 1.181; true value 1.213

2. Approximate values 1.125 and 1.244; true value 1.359

3. Approximate values 2.125 and 2.221; true value 2.297

4. Approximate values 0.625 and 0.681; true value 0.713

5. Approximate values 0.938 and 0.889; true value 0.851

6. Approximate values 1.750 and 1.627; true value 1.558

7. Approximate values 2.859 and 2.737; true value 2.647

8. Approximate values 0.445 and 0.420; true value 0.405

9. Approximate values 1.267 and 1.278; true value 1.287

10. Approximate values 1.125 and 1.231; true value 1.333

Problems 11 through 24 call for tables of values that would occupy too much space for inclusion here. In Problems 11 through 16, we give first the final x-value, next the corresponding approximate y-values obtained with step sizes $h = 0.01$ and $h = 0.005$, and then the final true y-value. (All y-values rounded off accurate to 4 decimal places.)

11. 1.0, -0.7048, -0.7115, -0.7183

12. 1.0, 2.9864, 2.9931, 3.0000

13. 2.0, 4.8890, 4.8940, 4.8990

14. 2.0, 3.2031, 3.2304, 3.2589

15. 3.0, 3.4422, 3.4433, 3.4444

16. 3.0, 8.8440, 8.8445, 8.8451

In Problems 17 through 24, we give first the final x-value and then the corresponding approximate y-values obtained with step sizes $h = 0.1$, $h = 0.02$, $h = 0.004$, and $h = 0.0008$, respectively. (All y-values rounded off accurate to 4 decimal places.)

17. 1.0, 0.2925, 0.3379, 0.3477, 0.3497

18. 2.0, 1.6680, 1.6771, 1.6790, 1.6794

19. 2.0, 6.1831, 6.3653, 6.4022, 6.4096

20. 2.0, -1.3792, -1.2843, -1.2649, -1.2610

21. 2.0, 2.8508, 2.8681, 2.8716, 2.8723

22. 2.0, 6.9879, 7.2601, 7.3154, 7.3264

23. 1.0, 1.2262, 1.2300, 1.2306, 1.2307

24. 1.0, 0.9585, 0.9918, 0.9984, 0.9997

25. With both step sizes $h = 0.01$ and $h = 0.005$, the approximate velocity after 1 second is 16.0 ft/sec (80% of the limiting velocity of 20 ft/s); after 2 seconds it is 19.2 ft/s (96% of the limiting velocity).

26. With both step sizes $h = 1$ and $h = 0.5$, the approximate population after 5 years is 49 deer (65% of the limiting population of 75 deer); after 10 years it is 66 deer (88% of the limiting population).

27. With successive step sizes $h = 0.1, 0.01, 0.001, \ldots$ the first four approximations to $y(2)$ we obtain are 0.7772, 0.9777, 1.0017, and 1.0042. It therefore seems likely that $y(2) \approx 1.00$.

28. With successive step sizes $h = 0.1, 0.01, 0.001, \ldots$ the first four approximations to $y(2)$ we obtain are 1.2900, 1.4435, 1.4613, and 1.4631. It therefore seems likely that $y(2) \approx 1.46$.

29.

x	$h = 0.15$ y	$h = 0.03$ y	$h = 0.006$ y
-1.0	1.0000	1.0000	1.0000
-0.7	1.0472	1.0512	1.0521
-0.4	1.1213	1.1358	1.1390
-0.1	1.2826	1.3612	1.3835
0.2	0.8900	1.4711	0.8210
0.5	0.7460	1.2808	0.7192

30.

x	$h = 0.1$ y	$h = 0.01$ y
1.8	2.8200	4.3308
1.9	3.9393	7.9425
2.0	5.8521	28.3926

31.

x	$h = 0.1$ y	$h = 0.01$ y
0.7	4.3460	6.4643
0.8	5.8670	11.8425
0.9	8.3349	39.5010

Section 2.5

1.

x	Improved Euler y	Actual y
0.1	1.8100	1.8097
0.2	1.6381	1.6375
0.3	1.4824	1.4816
0.4	1.3416	1.3406
0.5	1.2142	1.2131

Note: In Problems 2 through 10, we give the value of x, the corresponding improved Euler value of y, and the true value of y.

2. 0.5, 1.3514, 1.3191
3. 0.5, 2.2949, 2.2974
4. 0.5, 0.7142, 0.7131
5. 0.5, 0.8526, 0.8513
6. 0.5, 1.5575, 1.5576
7. 0.5, 2.6405, 2.6475
8. 0.5, 0.4053, 0.4055
9. 0.5, 1.2873, 1.2874
10. 0.5, 1.3309, 1.3333

In Problems 11 through 16, we give the final value of x, the corresponding values of y with $h = 0.01$ and with $h = 0.005$, and the true value of y.

11. 1.0, -0.71824, -0.71827, -0.71828
12. 1.0, 2.99995, 2.99999, 3.00000
13. 2.0, 4.89901, 4.89899, 4.89898
14. 2.0, 3.25847, 3.25878, 3.25889
15. 3.0, 3.44445, 3.44445, 3.44444
16. 3.0, 8.84511, 8.84509, 8.84509

In Problems 17 through 24, we give the final value of x and the corresponding values of y for $h = 0.1$, 0.02, 0.004, and 0.0008.

17. 1.0, 0.35183, 0.35030, 0.35023, 0.35023
18. 2.0, 1.68043, 1.67949, 1.67946, 1.67946
19. 2.0, 6.40834, 6.41134, 6.41147, 6.41147
20. 2.0, -1.26092, -1.26003, -1.25999, -1.25999
21. 2.0, 2.87204, 2.87245, 2.87247, 2.87247
22. 2.0, 7.31578, 7.32841, 7.32916, 7.32920
23. 1.0, 1.22967, 1.23069, 1.23073, 1.23073
24. 1.0, 1.00006, 1.00000, 1.00000, 1.00000

25. With both step sizes $h = 0.01$ and $h = 0.005$ the approximate velocity after 1 second is 15.962 ft/s (80% of the limiting velocity of 20 ft/s); after 2 seconds it is 19.185 ft/s (96% of the limiting velocity).

26. With both step sizes $h = 1$ and $h = 0.5$ the approximate population after 5 years is 49.391 deer (65% of the limiting population of 75 deer); after 10 seconds it is 66.113 deer (88% of the limiting population).

27. With successive step sizes $h = 0.1, 0.01, 0.001, \ldots$ the first three approximations to $y(2)$ we obtain are 1.0109, 1.0045, and 1.0045. It therefore seems likely that $y(2) \approx 1.0045$.

28. With successive step sizes $h = 0.1, 0.01, 0.001, \ldots$ the first four approximations to $y(2)$ we obtain are 1.4662, 1.4634, 1.4633, and 1.4633. It therefore seems likely that $y(2) \approx 1.4633$.
29. Impact speed approximately 43.22 m/s
30. Impact speed approximately 43.48 m/s

Section 2.6

1. $y(0.25) \approx 1.55762$; $y(0.25) = 1.55760$.
$y(0.5) \approx 1.21309$; $y(0.5) = 1.21306$.
Solution: $y = 2e^{-x}$

In Problems 2 through 10, we give the approximation to $y(0.5)$, its true value, and the solution.

2. 1.35867, 1.35914; $y = \frac{1}{2}e^{2x}$
3. 2.29740, 2.29744; $y = 2e^x - 1$
4. 0.71309, 0.71306; $y = 2e^{-x} + x - 1$
5. 0.85130, 0.85128; $y = -e^x + x + 2$
6. 1.55759, 1.55760; $u = 2\exp\left(-x^2\right)$
7. 2.64745, 2.64749; $y = 3\exp\left(-x^3\right)$
8. 0.40547, 0.40547; $y = \ln(x + 1)$
9. 1.28743, 1.28743; $y = \tan\frac{1}{4}(x + \pi)$
10. 1.33337, 1.33333; $y = (1 - x^2)^{-1}$
11. *Solution*: $y(x) = 2 - e^x$

x	h = 0.2 y	h = 0.1 y	Exact y
0.0	1.00000	1.00000	1.00000
0.2	0.77860	0.77860	0.77860
0.4	0.50818	0.50818	0.50818
0.6	0.17789	0.17788	0.17788
0.8	-0.22552	-0.22554	-0.22554
1.0	-0.71825	-0.71828	-0.71828

In Problems 12 through 16, we give the final value of x, the corresponding Runge-Kutta approximations with $h = 0.2$ and with $h = 0.1$, the exact value of y, and the solution.

12. 1.0, 2.99996, 3.00000, 3.00000;
$y = 1 + 2/(2 - x)$
13. 2.0, 4.89900, 4.89898, 4.89898;
$y = \sqrt{8 + x^4}$
14. 2.0, 3.25795, 3.25882, 3.25889;
$y = 1/(1 - \ln x)$
15. 3.0, 3.44445, 3.44444, 3.44444;
$y = x + 4x^{-2}$
16. 3.0, 8.84515, 8.84509, 8.84509;
$y = (x^6 - 37)^{1/3}$

In Problems 17 through 24 we give the final value of x and the corresponding values of y with $h = 0.2$, 0.1, 0.05, and 0.025.

17. 1.0, 0.350258, 0.350234, 0.350232, 0.350232
18. 2.0, 1.679513, 1.679461, 1.679459, 1.679459
19. 2.0, 6.411464, 6.411474, 6.411474, 6.411474
20. 2.0, -1.259990, -1.259992, -1.259993, -1.259993
21. 2.0, 2.872467, 2.872468, 2.872468, 2.872468
22. 2.0, 7.326761, 7.328452, 7.328971, 7.329134
23. 1.0, 1.230735, 1.230731, 1.230731, 1.230731

24. 1.0, 1.000000, 1.000000, 1.000000, 1.000000
25. With both step sizes $h = 0.1$ and $h = 0.05$, the approximate velocity after 1 second is 15.962 ft/s (80% of the limiting velocity of 20 ft/s); after 2 seconds it is 19.185 ft/s (96% of the limiting velocity).
26. With both step sizes $h = 6$ and $h = 3$, the approximate population after 5 years is 49.3915 deer (65% of the limiting population of 75 deer); after 10 years it is 66.1136 deer (88% of the limiting population).
27. With successive step sizes $h = 1, 0.1, 0.01, \ldots$ the first four approximations to $y(2)$ we obtain are 1.05722, 1.00447, 1.00445 and 1.00445. Thus it seems likely that $y(2) \approx 1.00445$ accurate to 5 decimal places.
28. With successive step sizes $h = 1, 0.1, 0.01, \ldots$ the first four approximations to $y(2)$ we obtain are 1.48990, 1.46332, 1.46331, and 1.46331. Thus it seems likely that $y(2) \approx 1.4633$ accurate to 5 decimal places.
29. Time aloft: approximately 9.41 seconds
30. Time aloft: approximately 9.41 seconds

Chapter 3

Section 3.1
1. $x = 3$, $y = 2$
2. $x = 5$, $y = -3$
3. $x = -4$, $y = 3$
4. $x = 5$, $y = 4$
5. Inconsistent—no solution
6. Inconsistent—no solution
7. $x = -10 + 4t$, $y = t$ (infinitely many solutions)
8. $x = 4 + 2t$, $y = t$ (infinitely many solutions)
9. $x = 4$, $y = -1$, $z = 3$
10. $x = 3$, $y = 1$, $z = -2$
11. $x = 1$, $y = 3$, $z = -4$
12. $x = 1$, $y = 3$, $z = 5$
13. $x = y = z = 0$
14. $x = 5$, $y = 3$, $z = -4$
15. Inconsistent—no solution
16. Inconsistent—no solution
17. Inconsistent—no solution
18. Inconsistent—no solution
19. $x = 8 + 3t$, $y = 3 + 2t$, $z = t$ (infinitely many solutions)
20. $x = -5t$, $y = 5 + t$, $z = t$ (infinitely many solutions)
21. $x = 3 - 2t$, $y = 2 + 3t$, $z = t$ (infinitely many solutions)
22. $x = -4t$, $y = -5t$, $z = t$ (infinitely many solutions)
23. $y(x) = 3\cos 2x + 4\sin 2x$
24. $y(x) = 5\cosh 3x + 4\sinh 3x$
25. $y(x) = 7e^{5x} + 3e^{-5x}$
26. $y(x) = 23e^{11x} + 21e^{-11x}$
27. $y(x) = 23e^{3x} + 17e^{-5x}$
28. $y(x) = 23e^{3x} - 8e^{7x}$
29. $y(x) = 52e^{x/2} - 45e^{x/3}$
30. $y(x) = 81e^{4x/3} - 40e^{-7x/5}$
31. *Suggestion*: The two lines both pass through the origin.
32. *Suggestion*: Two distinct planes in space either are parallel or intersect in a straight line.
33. (a) No solution (b) A unique solution (c) No solution (d) No solution (e) A unique solution (f) Infinitely many solutions
34. (a) No solution (b) Infinitely many solutions (c) No solution (d) No solution (e) Infinitely many solutions (f) A unique solution

Section 3.2
1. $x_1 = 1$, $x_2 = 0$, $x_3 = 2$
2. $x_1 = 5$, $x_2 = 1$, $x_3 = -3$
3. $x_1 = 13 + 11t$, $x_2 = 2 + 5t$, $x_3 = t$
4. $x_1 = 35 + 33t$, $x_2 = 5 + 7t$, $x_3 = t$
5. $x_1 = 13 + 4t$, $x_2 = 6 + t$, $x_3 = 5 + 3t$, $x_4 = t$
6. $x_1 = 17 + t$, $x_2 = 11 + 3t$, $x_3 = t$, $x_4 = -4$
7. $x_1 = 3 - 8s + 19t$, $x_2 = 7 + 2s - 7t$, $x_3 = s$, $x_4 = t$
8. $x_1 = -25 + 10s + 22t$, $x_2 = s$, $x_3 = 10 - 3t$, $x_4 = t$
9. $x_1 = 1$, $x_2 = 3$, $x_3 = -5$, $x_4 = 6$
10. $x_1 = 63s - 16t$, $x_2 = 13s - 8t$, $x_3 = s$, $x_4 = 5t$, $x_5 = t$
11. $x_1 = 3$, $x_2 = -2$, $x_3 = 4$
12. $x_1 = 5$, $x_2 = -3$, $x_3 = 2$
13. $x_1 = 4 + 3t$, $x_2 = 3 - 2t$, $x_3 = t$
14. $x_1 = 5 + 2t$, $x_2 = t$, $x_3 = 7$
15. Inconsistent—no solution
16. Inconsistent—no solution
17. $x_1 = 3 - 2t$, $x_2 = -4 + t$, $x_3 = 5 - 3t$, $x_4 = t$
18. $x_1 = 4 + 2s - 3t$, $x_2 = s$, $x_3 = 3 - 4t$, $x_4 = t$
19. $x_1 = 3 - s - t$, $x_2 = 5 + 2s - 3t$, $x_3 = s$, $x_4 = t$
20. $x_1 = 2 + 3t$, $x_2 = 1 + s - 2t$, $x_3 = 2 + 2s$, $x_4 = s$, $x_5 = t$
21. $x_1 = 2$, $x_2 = 1$, $x_3 = 3$, $x_4 = 4$
22. $x_1 = 3$, $x_2 = -2$, $x_3 = 4$, $x_4 = -1$
23. (a) None (b) $k \neq 2$ (c) $k = 2$
24. (a) $k \neq 2$ (b) None (c) $k = 4$
25. (a) $k \neq 4$ (b) $k = 4$ (c) None
26. (a) All k (b) None (c) None
27. (a) None (b) $k \neq 11$ (c) $k = 11$
28. No solution unless $c = 2a + 3b$, in which case it has infinitely many solutions.

Section 3.3
1. $\begin{bmatrix} 1 & 0 \\ 0 & 1 \end{bmatrix}$ **2.** $\begin{bmatrix} 1 & 0 \\ 0 & 1 \end{bmatrix}$

3. $\begin{bmatrix} 1 & 0 & 2 \\ 0 & 1 & 3 \end{bmatrix}$ **4.** $\begin{bmatrix} 1 & 0 & 2 \\ 0 & 1 & -1 \end{bmatrix}$

5. $\begin{bmatrix} 1 & 0 & -5 \\ 0 & 1 & -3 \end{bmatrix}$ **6.** $\begin{bmatrix} 1 & 0 & 7 \\ 0 & 1 & -6 \end{bmatrix}$

7. $\begin{bmatrix} 1 & 0 & 5 \\ 0 & 1 & -1 \\ 0 & 0 & 0 \end{bmatrix}$ **8.** $\begin{bmatrix} 1 & 0 & 0 \\ 0 & 1 & 0 \\ 0 & 0 & 1 \end{bmatrix}$

9. $\begin{bmatrix} 1 & 0 & 2 \\ 0 & 1 & 4 \\ 0 & 0 & 0 \end{bmatrix}$ **10.** $\begin{bmatrix} 1 & 0 & -3 \\ 0 & 1 & 5 \\ 0 & 0 & 0 \end{bmatrix}$

11. $\begin{bmatrix} 1 & 3 & 0 \\ 0 & 0 & 1 \\ 0 & 0 & 0 \end{bmatrix}$ **12.** $\begin{bmatrix} 1 & -4 & 0 \\ 0 & 0 & 1 \\ 0 & 0 & 0 \end{bmatrix}$

13. $\begin{bmatrix} 1 & 0 & 0 & 3 \\ 0 & 1 & 0 & -2 \\ 0 & 0 & 1 & 2 \end{bmatrix}$ **14.** $\begin{bmatrix} 1 & 0 & 0 & 4 \\ 0 & 1 & 0 & -3 \\ 0 & 0 & 1 & 5 \end{bmatrix}$

15. $\begin{bmatrix} 1 & 0 & -1 & 2 \\ 0 & 1 & 3 & -1 \\ 0 & 0 & 0 & 0 \end{bmatrix}$ **16.** $\begin{bmatrix} 1 & 0 & 3 & -2 \\ 0 & 1 & 4 & 3 \\ 0 & 0 & 0 & 0 \end{bmatrix}$

17. $\begin{bmatrix} 1 & 0 & 0 & 2 & -3 \\ 0 & 1 & 0 & -1 & 4 \\ 0 & 0 & 1 & -2 & -5 \end{bmatrix}$

18. $\begin{bmatrix} 1 & 0 & 3 & -2 & 3 \\ 0 & 1 & 4 & 5 & 1 \\ 0 & 0 & 0 & 0 & 0 \end{bmatrix}$

19. $\begin{bmatrix} 1 & 0 & 2 & 1 & 3 \\ 0 & 1 & -2 & -3 & 1 \\ 0 & 0 & 0 & 0 & 0 \end{bmatrix}$

20. $\begin{bmatrix} 1 & 2 & 0 & 2 & 3 \\ 0 & 0 & 1 & 1 & 4 \\ 0 & 0 & 0 & 0 & 0 \end{bmatrix}$

21. $x_1 = 3,\ x_2 = -2,\ x_3 = 4$

22. $x_1 = 5,\ x_2 = -3,\ x_3 = 2$

23. $x_1 = 4 + 3t,\ x_2 = 3 - 2t,\ x_3 = t$

24. $x_1 = 5 + 2t,\ x_2 = t,\ x_3 = 7$

25. Inconsistent—no solution

26. Inconsistent—no solution

27. $x_1 = 3 - 2t,\ x_2 = -4 + t,\ x_3 = 5 - 3t,\ x_4 = t$

28. $x_1 = 4 + 2s - 3t,\ x_2 = s,\ x_3 = 3 - 4t,\ x_4 = t$

29. $x_1 = 3 - s - t,\ x_2 = 5 + 2s - 3t,\ x_3 = s,\ x_4 = t$

30. $x_1 = 2 + 3t,\ x_2 = 1 + s - 2t,\ x_3 = 2 + 2s,\ x_4 = s,\ x_5 = t$

31. The sequence $\frac{1}{6}R_3,\ R_2 - 5R_3,\ \frac{1}{4}R_2,\ R_1 - 2R_2,\ R_1 - 3R_3$ of row operations transforms the first matrix to the identity matrix.

33. $\begin{bmatrix} 1 & 0 \\ 0 & 1 \end{bmatrix},\ \begin{bmatrix} 1 & * \\ 0 & 0 \end{bmatrix},\ \begin{bmatrix} 0 & 1 \\ 0 & 0 \end{bmatrix},\ \begin{bmatrix} 0 & 0 \\ 0 & 0 \end{bmatrix}$

Section 3.4

1. $\begin{bmatrix} 5 & -15 \\ 18 & 5 \end{bmatrix}$

2. $\begin{bmatrix} 16 & -9 & -18 \\ -26 & 22 & 15 \end{bmatrix}$

3. $\begin{bmatrix} -26 & 20 \\ 12 & -6 \\ 22 & 18 \end{bmatrix}$

4. $\begin{bmatrix} 44 & -22 & -20 \\ 53 & 10 & -26 \\ 35 & 21 & 94 \end{bmatrix}$

5. $\mathbf{AB} = \begin{bmatrix} -9 & 1 \\ -10 & 12 \end{bmatrix},\ \mathbf{BA} = \begin{bmatrix} -2 & 8 \\ 11 & 5 \end{bmatrix}$

6. $\mathbf{AB} = \begin{bmatrix} 7 & -13 & -24 \\ 23 & 10 & 41 \\ 11 & -8 & 57 \end{bmatrix},\ \mathbf{BA} = \begin{bmatrix} 1 & -17 & -22 \\ 12 & 16 & 7 \\ 27 & -21 & 57 \end{bmatrix}$

7. $\mathbf{AB} = [\ 26\ ],\ \mathbf{BA} = \begin{bmatrix} 3 & 6 & 9 \\ 4 & 8 & 12 \\ 5 & 10 & 15 \end{bmatrix}$

8. $\mathbf{AB} = \begin{bmatrix} 21 & 15 \\ 35 & 0 \end{bmatrix},\ \mathbf{BA} = \begin{bmatrix} 3 & 0 & 9 \\ 7 & -20 & 13 \\ 16 & -25 & 38 \end{bmatrix}$

9. $\mathbf{BA} = \begin{bmatrix} 4 \\ 7 \\ -22 \end{bmatrix}$ but $\mathbf{AB}$ is not defined.

10. $\mathbf{AB} = \begin{bmatrix} 1 & -2 & 13 \\ 5 & -6 & 31 \end{bmatrix}$ but $\mathbf{BA}$ is not defined.

11. $\mathbf{AB} = [\ 11\ \ 1\ \ 5\ \ 3\ ]$ but $\mathbf{BA}$ is not defined.

12. Neither product matrix $\mathbf{AB}$ or $\mathbf{BA}$ is defined.

13. $\mathbf{A(BC)} = \mathbf{(AB)C} = \begin{bmatrix} 32 & 51 \\ -2 & -17 \end{bmatrix}$

14. $\mathbf{A(BC)} = \mathbf{(AB)C} = [\ -3\ ]$

15. $\mathbf{A(BC)} = \mathbf{(AB)C} = \begin{bmatrix} 12 & 15 \\ 8 & 10 \end{bmatrix}$

16. $\mathbf{A(BC)} = \mathbf{(AB)C} = \begin{bmatrix} -4 & -4 & -2 & 2 \\ -9 & -12 & -9 & 12 \\ -14 & -18 & -13 & 17 \end{bmatrix}$

17. $\mathbf{x} = s(5, -2, 1, 0) + t(-4, 7, 0, 1)$

18. $\mathbf{x} = s(3, 1, 0, 0) + t(-6, 0, -9, 1)$

19. $\mathbf{x} = s(-3, 2, -1, 1, 0) + t(1, -6, 8, 0, 1)$

20. $\mathbf{x} = s(3, 1, 0, 0, 0) + t(-7, 0, 2, 10, 0)$

21. $\mathbf{x} = r(1, -2, 1, 0, 0) + s(-2, 3, 0, 1, 0) + t(-7, -4, 0, 0, 1)$

22. $\mathbf{x} = r(1, 1, 0, 0, 0) + s(-7, 0, 1, 1, 0) + t(-3, 0, 2, 0, 1)$

23. $\mathbf{B} = \begin{bmatrix} 2 & -1 \\ -3 & 2 \end{bmatrix}$

24. $\mathbf{B} = \begin{bmatrix} 7 & -4 \\ -5 & 3 \end{bmatrix}$

25. $\mathbf{B} = \begin{bmatrix} 3 & -7 \\ -2 & 5 \end{bmatrix}$

29. $\mathbf{A}^2 = \begin{bmatrix} a^2 + bc & ab + bd \\ ac + dc & bc + d^2 \end{bmatrix},$

$\mathbf{A}^2 + (ad - bc)\mathbf{I} = \begin{bmatrix} a^2 + ad & ab + bd \\ ac + dc & d^2 + ad \end{bmatrix} = \begin{bmatrix} a(a + d) & b(a + d) \\ c(a + d) & d(a + d) \end{bmatrix} = (a + d)\mathbf{A}$

31. (a) $(\mathbf{A} + \mathbf{B})(\mathbf{A} - \mathbf{B}) = \begin{bmatrix} -25 & -34 \\ -71 & -34 \end{bmatrix} \neq \begin{bmatrix} -8 & -45 \\ -44 & -51 \end{bmatrix} = \mathbf{A}^2 - \mathbf{B}^2$

33. $\begin{bmatrix} 1 & 0 \\ 0 & 1 \end{bmatrix},\ \begin{bmatrix} -1 & 0 \\ 0 & -1 \end{bmatrix},\ \begin{bmatrix} +1 & 0 \\ 0 & -1 \end{bmatrix},\ \begin{bmatrix} -1 & 0 \\ 0 & +1 \end{bmatrix}$

35. $\begin{bmatrix} 2 & -1 \\ 2 & -1 \end{bmatrix}$ **37.** $\begin{bmatrix} 0 & 1 \\ -1 & 0 \end{bmatrix}$

39. $\mathbf{A}(c_1\mathbf{x}_1 + c_2\mathbf{x}_2) = c_1\mathbf{Ax}_1 + c_2\mathbf{Ax}_2 = c_1 \cdot \mathbf{0} + c_2 \cdot \mathbf{0} = \mathbf{0}$

43. $\mathbf{A}^2 = \begin{bmatrix} 6 & -3 & -3 \\ -3 & 6 & -3 \\ -3 & -3 & 6 \end{bmatrix} = 3\mathbf{A}$

Section 3.5

1. $\mathbf{A}^{-1} = \begin{bmatrix} 3 & -2 \\ -4 & 3 \end{bmatrix},\ \mathbf{x} = \begin{bmatrix} 3 \\ -2 \end{bmatrix}$

2. $\mathbf{A}^{-1} = \begin{bmatrix} 5 & -7 \\ -2 & 3 \end{bmatrix},\ \mathbf{x} = \begin{bmatrix} -26 \\ 11 \end{bmatrix}$

3. $\mathbf{A}^{-1} = \begin{bmatrix} 6 & -7 \\ -5 & 6 \end{bmatrix},\ \mathbf{x} = \begin{bmatrix} 33 \\ -28 \end{bmatrix}$

4. $\mathbf{A}^{-1} = \begin{bmatrix} 17 & -12 \\ -7 & 5 \end{bmatrix},\ \mathbf{x} = \begin{bmatrix} 25 \\ -10 \end{bmatrix}$

5. $\mathbf{A}^{-1} = \frac{1}{2}\begin{bmatrix} 4 & -2 \\ -5 & 3 \end{bmatrix},\ \mathbf{x} = \frac{1}{2}\begin{bmatrix} 8 \\ -7 \end{bmatrix}$

6. $\mathbf{A}^{-1} = \frac{1}{3}\begin{bmatrix} 6 & -7 \\ -3 & 4 \end{bmatrix},\ \mathbf{x} = \frac{1}{3}\begin{bmatrix} 25 \\ -10 \end{bmatrix}$

7. $\mathbf{A}^{-1} = \frac{1}{4}\begin{bmatrix} 7 & -9 \\ -5 & 7 \end{bmatrix},\ \mathbf{x} = \frac{1}{4}\begin{bmatrix} 3 \\ -1 \end{bmatrix}$

8. $\mathbf{A}^{-1} = \frac{1}{5}\begin{bmatrix} 10 & -15 \\ -5 & 8 \end{bmatrix},\ \mathbf{x} = \frac{1}{5}\begin{bmatrix} 25 \\ -11 \end{bmatrix}$

9. $\mathbf{A}^{-1} = \begin{bmatrix} 5 & -6 \\ -4 & 5 \end{bmatrix}$ **10.** $\mathbf{A}^{-1} = \frac{1}{2}\begin{bmatrix} 6 & -7 \\ -4 & 5 \end{bmatrix}$

11. $\mathbf{A}^{-1} = \begin{bmatrix} -5 & -2 & 5 \\ 2 & 1 & -2 \\ -4 & -3 & 5 \end{bmatrix}$

12. $\mathbf{A}^{-1} = \begin{bmatrix} 18 & 2 & -7 \\ -3 & 0 & 1 \\ -4 & -1 & 2 \end{bmatrix}$

13. $A^{-1} = \begin{bmatrix} -13 & 42 & -5 \\ 3 & -9 & 1 \\ 2 & -7 & 1 \end{bmatrix}$

14. $A^{-1} = \begin{bmatrix} 11 & -7 & -9 \\ -4 & 3 & 3 \\ -2 & 1 & 2 \end{bmatrix}$

15. $A^{-1} = \begin{bmatrix} -22 & 2 & 7 \\ -27 & 3 & 8 \\ 10 & -1 & -3 \end{bmatrix}$

16. $A^{-1} = \frac{1}{3} \begin{bmatrix} -3 & 0 & 3 \\ -1 & -3 & -1 \\ -1 & 3 & 2 \end{bmatrix}$

17. $A^{-1} = \frac{1}{4} \begin{bmatrix} -2 & -6 & -3 \\ -2 & -2 & -1 \\ -2 & -2 & 1 \end{bmatrix}$

18. $A^{-1} = \frac{1}{5} \begin{bmatrix} 1 & 2 & -2 \\ -5 & 0 & 5 \\ -3 & -1 & 6 \end{bmatrix}$

19. $A^{-1} = \frac{1}{6} \begin{bmatrix} -21 & 11 & 8 \\ 9 & -5 & -2 \\ -3 & 3 & 0 \end{bmatrix}$

20. $A^{-1} = \frac{1}{7} \begin{bmatrix} 3 & 1 & 0 \\ -2 & -3 & 7 \\ -1 & 2 & 0 \end{bmatrix}$

21. $A^{-1} = \begin{bmatrix} 0 & 1 & 0 & 0 \\ -2 & 0 & 1 & 0 \\ 1 & 0 & 0 & 0 \\ 0 & -3 & 0 & 1 \end{bmatrix}$

22. $A^{-1} = \begin{bmatrix} 1 & -1 & 1 & 0 \\ 0 & -2 & -1 & 2 \\ 0 & 1 & 1 & -1 \\ -3 & 3 & -5 & 1 \end{bmatrix}$

23. $A^{-1} = \begin{bmatrix} 4 & -3 \\ -5 & 4 \end{bmatrix}$, $X = \begin{bmatrix} 7 & 18 & -35 \\ -9 & -23 & 45 \end{bmatrix}$

24. $A^{-1} = \begin{bmatrix} 7 & -6 \\ -8 & 7 \end{bmatrix}$, $X = \begin{bmatrix} 14 & -30 & 46 \\ -16 & 35 & -53 \end{bmatrix}$

25. $A^{-1} = \begin{bmatrix} 11 & -9 & 4 \\ -2 & 2 & -1 \\ -2 & 1 & 0 \end{bmatrix}$, $X = \begin{bmatrix} 7 & -14 & 15 \\ -1 & 3 & -2 \\ -2 & 2 & -4 \end{bmatrix}$

26. $A^{-1} = \begin{bmatrix} -16 & 3 & 11 \\ 6 & -1 & -4 \\ -13 & 2 & 9 \end{bmatrix}$, $X = \begin{bmatrix} -21 & 9 & 6 \\ 8 & -3 & -2 \\ -17 & 6 & 5 \end{bmatrix}$

27. $A^{-1} = \begin{bmatrix} 7 & -20 & 17 \\ 0 & -1 & 1 \\ -2 & 6 & -5 \end{bmatrix}$,

$X = \begin{bmatrix} 17 & -20 & 24 & -13 \\ 1 & -1 & 1 & -1 \\ -5 & 6 & -7 & 4 \end{bmatrix}$

28. $A^{-1} = \begin{bmatrix} -5 & 5 & 10 \\ -8 & 8 & 15 \\ 24 & -23 & -45 \end{bmatrix}$,

$X = \begin{bmatrix} -5 & 5 & 10 & 1 \\ -8 & 8 & 15 & 7 \\ 24 & -23 & -45 & -13 \end{bmatrix}$

Section 3.6

1. 60
2. 4
3. −210
4. −72

5. 120
6. 60
7. 0
8. 25
9. 30
10. 7
11. 40
12. 10
13. 78
14. −22
15. −74
16. 84
17. 8
18. 135
19. 39
20. 79

21. $\Delta = 1$, $x = 10$, $y = -7$
22. $\Delta = 1$, $x = -1$, $y = 1$
23. $\Delta = 1$, $x = 2$, $y = -4$
24. $\Delta = 1$, $x = 5$, $y = -3$
25. $\Delta = 2$, $x = 6$, $y = -3$
26. $\Delta = -2$, $x = \frac{1}{2}$, $y = 0$
27. $\Delta = 96$, $x_1 = \frac{1}{3}$, $x_2 = -\frac{2}{3}$, $x_3 = -\frac{1}{3}$
28. $\Delta = 35$, $x_1 = \frac{4}{7}$, $x_2 = \frac{3}{7}$, $x_3 = \frac{2}{7}$
29. $\Delta = 23$, $x_1 = 2$, $x_2 = 3$, $x_3 = 0$
30. $\Delta = 56$, $x_1 = -\frac{1}{7}$, $x_2 = \frac{9}{14}$, $x_3 = \frac{2}{7}$
31. $\Delta = 14$, $x_1 = -\frac{8}{7}$, $x_2 = -\frac{10}{7}$, $x_3 = \frac{1}{7}$
32. $\Delta = 6$, $x_1 = -\frac{7}{3}$, $x_2 = 9$, $x_3 = 8$

33. $\det A = -4$, $A^{-1} = \frac{1}{4} \begin{bmatrix} 4 & 4 & 4 \\ 16 & 15 & 13 \\ 28 & 25 & 23 \end{bmatrix}$

34. $\det A = 35$, $A^{-1} = \frac{1}{4} \begin{bmatrix} -2 & -3 & 12 \\ 9 & -4 & -19 \\ 13 & 2 & -8 \end{bmatrix}$

35. $\det A = 35$, $A^{-1} = \frac{1}{35} \begin{bmatrix} -15 & 25 & -26 \\ 10 & -5 & 8 \\ 15 & -25 & 19 \end{bmatrix}$

36. $\det A = 23$, $A^{-1} = \frac{1}{23} \begin{bmatrix} 5 & 20 & -17 \\ 10 & 17 & -11 \\ 1 & 4 & -8 \end{bmatrix}$

37. $\det A = 29$, $A^{-1} = \frac{1}{29} \begin{bmatrix} 11 & -14 & -15 \\ -17 & 19 & 10 \\ 18 & -15 & -14 \end{bmatrix}$

38. $\det A = 6$, $A^{-1} = \frac{1}{6} \begin{bmatrix} -6 & 10 & 2 \\ 15 & -21 & -6 \\ 12 & -18 & -6 \end{bmatrix}$

39. $\det A = 37$, $A^{-1} = \frac{1}{37} \begin{bmatrix} -21 & -1 & -13 \\ 4 & 9 & 6 \\ -6 & 5 & -9 \end{bmatrix}$

40. $\det A = 107$, $A^{-1} = \frac{1}{107} \begin{bmatrix} 9 & 12 & -13 \\ 11 & -21 & -4 \\ -15 & -20 & -14 \end{bmatrix}$

Section 3.7

1. $y(x) = -2 + 3x$
2. $y(x) = 4 - 7x$
3. $y(x) = 3 - 2x^2$
4. $y(x) = 2x + 3x^2$
5. $y(x) = 5 - 3x + x^2$
6. $y(x) = -10 - 7x + 2x^2$
7. $y(x) = \frac{1}{3}(4x + 3x^2 - 4x^3)$
8. $y(x) = 5 + 3x - x^3$
9. $y(x) = 4 + 3x + 2x^2 + x^3$
10. $y(x) = 17 - 5x + 3x^2 - 2x^3$
11. $x^2 + y^2 - 6x - 4y - 12 = 0$, center $(3, 2)$ and radius 5
12. $x^2 + y^2 + 6x - 8y - 75 = 0$, center $(-3, 4)$ and radius 10
13. $x^2 + y^2 + 4x + 4y - 5 = 0$, center $(-3, -2)$ and radius $\sqrt{13}$
14. $x^2 + y^2 - 10x - 24y = 0$, center $(5, 12)$ and radius 13

15. $x^2 - xy + y^2 = 25$

16. $4x^2 - 7xy + 4y^2 = 100$

17. $100x^2 - 199xy + 100y^2 = 100$

18. $400x^2 - 481xy + 225y^2 = 3600$

19. $y = 3 + \dfrac{2}{x}$
20. $y = 10x + \dfrac{8}{x} - \dfrac{16}{x^2}$

21. $x^2 + y^2 + z^2 - 2x - 4y - 6z - 155 = 0$, center $(1,2,3)$ and radius 13

22. $x^2 + y^2 + z^2 - 10x + 14y - 18z - 521 = 0$, center $(5, -7, 9)$ and radius 26

23. $P(t) = 49.061 - 0.0722t + 0.00798t^2$

24. $P(t) = 56.590 + 0.30145t - 0.007375t^2$

25. $P(t) = 62.813 + 1.37915t - 0.012375t^2$

26. $P(t) = 34.838 + 0.7692t + 0.0064t^2$

27. $P(t) = 44.678 + 0.850417t - 0.05105t^2 + 0.000983833t^3$

28. $P(t) = 51.619 + 0.672433t - 0.019565t^2 + 0.000203167t^3$

29. $P(t) = 54.973 + 0.308667t + 0.059515t^2 - 0.00119817t^3$

30. $P(t) = 28.053 + 0.592233t + 0.00907t^2 - 0.0000443333t^3$

31. $P(t) = 39.478 + 0.209692t + 0.0564163t^2 - 0.00292992t^3 + 0.0000391375t^4$

32. $P(t) = 44.461 + 0.7651t - 0.000489167t^2 - 0.000516t^3 + 7.19167 \times 10^{-6}t^4$

33. $P(t) = 47.197 + 1.22537t - 0.077192t^2 + 0.00373475t^3 - 0.0000493292t^4$

34. $P(t) = 20.190 + 1.00003t - 0.031775t^2 + 0.00116067t^3 - 0.000041205t^4$

36. $y = 2x^2 - 6x + 7$

38. $x^2 + y^2 + 6x - 8y - 75 = 0$, center $(-3,4)$ and radius 10

40. $400x^2 - 481xy + 225y^2 - 3600 = 0$

Chapter 4

Section 4.1

1. $\sqrt{51}$, $(5,8,-11)$, $(2,23,0)$

2. 9, $(1,4,-1)$, $(-15,-16,26)$

3. $3\sqrt{21}$, $9\mathbf{i} - 3\mathbf{j} + 3\mathbf{k}$, $-14\mathbf{i} - 21\mathbf{j} + 43\mathbf{k}$

4. $\sqrt{17}$, $4\mathbf{i} - \mathbf{j} - 3\mathbf{k}$, $6\mathbf{i} - 7\mathbf{j} + 12\mathbf{k}$

5. Linearly dependent
6. Linearly independent
7. Linearly independent
8. Linearly dependent
9. $\mathbf{w} = 3\mathbf{u} + 2\mathbf{v}$
10. $\mathbf{w} = 2\mathbf{u} - 3\mathbf{v}$
11. $\mathbf{w} = \mathbf{u} - 2\mathbf{v}$
12. $\mathbf{w} = 3\mathbf{u} + 5\mathbf{v}$
13. $\mathbf{w} = 2\mathbf{u} - 3\mathbf{v}$
14. $\mathbf{w} = 7\mathbf{u} + 5\mathbf{v}$
15. Linearly dependent
16. Linearly dependent
17. Linearly independent
18. Linearly independent
19. Linearly dependent; $a = 3$, $b = 2$, $c = 1$
20. Linearly dependent; $a = -2$, $b = 3$, $c = 1$
21. Linearly dependent; $a = 11$, $b = 4$, $c = -1$
22. Linearly independent
23. Linearly independent
24. Linearly independent
25. $\mathbf{t} = 2\mathbf{u} - \mathbf{v} + 3\mathbf{w}$
26. $\mathbf{t} = \mathbf{u} + 5\mathbf{v} - \mathbf{w}$
27. $\mathbf{t} = 2\mathbf{u} + 6\mathbf{v} + \mathbf{w}$
28. $\mathbf{t} = \mathbf{u} + \mathbf{v} + \mathbf{w}$

Section 4.2

1. W is a subspace of $\mathbf{R}^3$.

2. W is a subspace of $\mathbf{R}^3$.

3. W is not a subspace of $\mathbf{R}^3$.

4. W is not a subspace of $\mathbf{R}^3$.

5. W is a subspace of $\mathbf{R}^4$.

6. W is a subspace of $\mathbf{R}^4$.

7. W is not a subspace of $\mathbf{R}^2$.

8. W is a subspace of $\mathbf{R}^2$.

9. W is not a subspace of $\mathbf{R}^2$.

10. W is not a subspace of $\mathbf{R}^2$.

11. W is a subspace of $\mathbf{R}^4$.

12. W is not a subspace of $\mathbf{R}^4$.

13. W is not a subspace of $\mathbf{R}^4$.

14. W is not a subspace of $\mathbf{R}^4$.

15. $\mathbf{u} = (-1, 0, 1, 0)$ and $\mathbf{v} = (4, -2, 0, 1)$

16. $\mathbf{u} = (-1, -1, 1, 0)$ and $\mathbf{v} = (-5, -3, 0, 1)$

17. $\mathbf{u} = (1, -3, 1, 0)$ and $\mathbf{v} = (-2, 1, 0, 1)$

18. $\mathbf{u} = (2, -1, -2, 1, 0)$ and $\mathbf{v} = (3, -4, 5, 0, 1)$

19. $\mathbf{u} = (1, 2, -1, 0)$

20. $\mathbf{u} = (-5, 3, -2, 1)$

21. $\mathbf{u} = (-3, 2, -4, 1)$

22. $\mathbf{u} = (-6, 4, -3, 1)$

Section 4.3

1. Linearly dependent
2. Linearly dependent
3. Linearly dependent
4. Linearly dependent
5. Linearly independent
6. Linearly independent
7. Linearly independent
8. Linearly dependent
9. $\mathbf{w} = 2\mathbf{v}_1 - 3\mathbf{v}_2$
10. $\mathbf{w} = 7\mathbf{v}_1 + 4\mathbf{v}_2$
11. $\mathbf{w} = \mathbf{v}_1 - 2\mathbf{v}_2$
12. $\mathbf{w} = 2\mathbf{v}_1 + 5\mathbf{v}_2$
13. $\mathbf{w}$ cannot be expressed as a linear combination of $\mathbf{v}_1$ and $\mathbf{v}_2$.
14. $\mathbf{w}$ cannot be expressed as a linear combination of $\mathbf{v}_1$, $\mathbf{v}_2$, and $\mathbf{v}_3$
15. $\mathbf{w} = 3\mathbf{v}_1 - 2\mathbf{v}_2 + 4\mathbf{v}_3$
16. $\mathbf{w} = 6\mathbf{v}_1 - 2\mathbf{v}_2 + 3\mathbf{v}_3$
17. The vectors $\mathbf{v}_1$, $\mathbf{v}_2$, $\mathbf{v}_3$ are linearly independent.
18. $3\mathbf{v}_1 + \mathbf{v}_2 + 5\mathbf{v}_3 = \mathbf{0}$
19. The vectors $\mathbf{v}_1$, $\mathbf{v}_2$, $\mathbf{v}_3$ are linearly independent.
20. The vectors $\mathbf{v}_1$, $\mathbf{v}_2$, $\mathbf{v}_3$ are linearly independent.
21. $\mathbf{v}_1 - 2\mathbf{v}_2 - \mathbf{v}_3 = \mathbf{0}$
22. $7\mathbf{v}_1 + 5\mathbf{v}_2 - 9\mathbf{v}_3 = \mathbf{0}$

Section 4.4

1. The vectors v_1 and v_2 form a basis for $\mathbf{R}^2$.
2. The vectors v_1, v_2, v_3 do not form a basis for $\mathbf{R}^3$.
3. The given vectors do not form a basis for $\mathbf{R}^3$.
4. The given vectors do not form a basis for $\mathbf{R}^4$.
5. The three vectors v_1, v_2, v_3 do not form a basis for $\mathbf{R}^3$.
6. The three given vectors form a basis for $\mathbf{R}^3$.
7. The three given vectors form a basis for $\mathbf{R}^3$.
8. The four given vectors form a basis for $\mathbf{R}^4$.
9. The plane $x - 2y + 5z = 0$ is a 2-dimensional subspace of $\mathbf{R}^3$ with basis consisting of the vectors $v_1 = (2, 1, 0)$ and $v_2 = (-5, 0, 1)$.
10. The plane $y - z = 0$ is a 2-dimensional subspace of $\mathbf{R}^3$ with basis consisting of the vectors $v_1 = (1, 0, 0)$ and $v_2 = (0, 1, 1)$.
11. The line is a 1-dimensional subspace of $\mathbf{R}^3$ with basis consisting of the vector $v = (-3, 1, 1)$.
12. Hence the subspace consisting of all such vectors is 3-dimensional with basis consisting of the vectors $v_1' = (1, 1, 0, 0)$, $v_2 = (1, 0, 1, 0)$, and $v_3 = (1, 0, 0, 1)$.
13. The subspace consisting of all such vectors is 2-dimensional with basis consisting of the vectors $v_1 = (3, 0, 1, 0)$ and $v_2 = (0, 4, 0, 1)$.
14. The subspace consisting of all such vectors is 2-dimensional with basis consisting of the vectors $v_1 = (-2, 1, 0, 0)$ and $v_2 = (0, 0, -3, 1)$.
15. The solution space of the given system is 1-dimensional with basis consisting of the vector $v_1 = (11, 7, 1)$.
16. The solution space of the given system is 1-dimensional with basis consisting of the vector $v_1 = (11, -5, 1)$.
17. The solution space of the given system is 2-dimensional with basis consisting of the vectors $v_1 = (-11, -3, 1, 0)$ and $v_2(-11, -5, 0, 1)$.
18. The solution space of the given system is 2-dimensional with basis consisting of the vectors $v_1 = (-3, 1, 0, 0)$ and $v_2(-25, 0, 5, 1)$.
19. The solution space of the given system is 2-dimensional with basis consisting of the vectors $v_1 = (3, -2, 1, 0)$ and $v_2 = (-4, -3, 0, 1)$.
20. The solution space of the given system is 2-dimensional with basis consisting of the vectors $v_1 = (1, -3, 1, 0)$ and $v_2 = (-2, 1, 0, 1)$.
21. The solution space of the given system is 2-dimensional with basis consisting of the vectors $v_1 = (-1, -1, 1, 0)$ and $v_2 = (-5, -3, 0, 1)$.
22. The solution space of the given system is 2-dimensional with basis consisting of the vectors $v_1 = (2, 1, 0, 0)$ and $v_2 = (-5, 0, -7, 1)$.
23. The solution space of the given system is 1-dimensional with basis consisting of the vector $v_1 = (2, -3, 1, 0)$.
24. The solution space of the given system is 3-dimensional with basis consisting of the vectors $v_1 = (-2, 2, 1, 0, 0)$, $v_2 = (-1, 3, 0, 1, 0)$, and $v_3 = (-3, -1, 0, 0, 1)$.
25. The solution space of the given system is 3-dimensional with basis consisting of the vectors $v_1 = (-2, 1, 0, 0, 0)$, $v_2 = (2, 0, 1, 1, 0)$, and $v_3 = (-3, 0, -4, 0, 1)$.
26. The solution space of the given system is 2-dimensional with basis consisting of the vectors $v_1 = (-2, 1, 2, 1, 0)$ and $v_2 = (3, -4, 5, 0, 1)$.

Section 4.5

1. Row basis: The first and second row vectors of **E**.
   Column basis: The first and second column vectors of **A**.
2. Row basis: The first and second row vectors of **E**.
   Column basis: The first and second column vectors of **A**.
3. Row basis: The first and second row vectors of **E**.
   Column basis: The first and second column vectors of **A**.
4. Row basis: The three row vectors of **E**.
   Column basis: The first three column vectors of **A**.
5. Row basis: The three row vectors of **E**.
   Column basis: The first, second, and fourth column vectors of **A**.
6. Row basis: The three row vectors of **E**.
   Column basis: The first, second, and fourth column vectors of **A**.
7. Row basis: The first two row vectors of **E**.
   Column basis: The first two column vectors of **A**.
8. Row basis: The first three row vectors of **E**.
   Column basis: The first, second, and fourth column vectors of **A**.
9. Row basis: The first three row vectors of **E**.
   Column basis: The first three column vectors of **A**.
10. Row basis: The first three row vectors of **E**.
    Column basis: The first, second, and fourth column vectors of **A**.
11. Row basis: The first three row vectors of **E**.
    Column basis: The first, second, and fifth column vectors of **A**.
12. Row basis: The first three row vectors of **E**.
    Column basis: The first, second, and fifth column vectors of **A**.
13. Linearly independent: v_1 and v_2
14. Linearly independent: v_1 and v_2
15. Linearly independent: v_1, v_2, and v_4
16. Linearly independent: v_1, v_2, v_4, and v_5
17. Basis vectors: v_1, v_2, e_2
18. Basis vectors: v_1, v_2, e_2
19. Basis vectors: v_1, v_2, e_2, e_3
20. Basis vectors: v_1, v_2, e_1, e_3
21. The first and second equations are irredundant.
22. The first and second equations are irredundant.
23. The first, second, and fourth equations are irredundant.
24. The first, second, and fifth equations are irredundant.

Section 4.6

1. Yes, the three vectors are mutually orthogonal.
2. Yes, the three vectors are mutually orthogonal.
3. Yes, the three vectors are mutually orthogonal.
4. Yes, the three vectors are mutually orthogonal.
5. $a^2 = 7$, $b^2 = 7$, $c^2 = 14$
6. $a^2 = 18$, $b^2 = 18$, $c^2 = 36$
7. $a^2 = 19$, $b^2 = 25$, $c^2 = 44$
8. $a^2 = 103$, $b^2 = 112$, $c^2 = 215$
9. $\angle A = \angle B = 45°$
10. $\angle A = \angle B = 45°$
11. $\angle A = 41.08°$, $\angle B = 48.92°$
12. $\angle A = 43.80°$, $\angle B = 46.20°$
13. $u_1 = (2, 1, 0)$, $u_2 = (-3, 0, 1)$
14. $u_1 = (-5, 1, 0)$, $u_2 = (3, 0, 1)$
15. $u_1 = (2, 1, 0, 0)$, $u_2 = (3, 0, 1, 0)$, $u_3 = (-5, 0, 0, 1)$
16. $u_1 = (-7, 1, 0, 0)$, $u_2 = (6, 0, 1, 0)$, $u_3 = (9, 0, 0, 1)$
17. $u_1 = (7, -3, 1, 0)$, $u_2 = (-19, 5, 0, 1)$
18. $u_1 = (-12, -3, 1, 0)$, $u_2 = (16, 7, 0, 1)$

19. $\mathbf{u}_1 = (-13, 4, 1, 0, 0)$, $\mathbf{u}_2 = (4, -3, 0, 1, 0)$,
$\mathbf{u}_3 = (-11, 4, 0, 0, 1)$

20. $\mathbf{u}_1 = (-5, 1, 1, 0, 0)$, $\mathbf{u}_2 = (-12, 4, 0, 1, 0)$,
$\mathbf{u}_3 = (-19, 7, 0, 0, 1)$

21. $\mathbf{u}_1 = (-1, -1, 1, 0, 0)$, $\mathbf{u}_2 = (0, -1, 0, -1, 1)$

22. $\mathbf{u}_1 = (-2, 1, 1, 0, 0)$, $\mathbf{u}_2 = (1, -2, 0, 1, 0)$

Section 4.7

1. It is a subspace.
2. It is a subspace.
3. It is not a subspace.
4. It is not a subspace.
5. It is a subspace.
6. It is not a subspace.
7. It is not a subspace.
8. It is a subspace.
9. It is not a subspace.
10. It is a subspace.
11. It is a subspace.
12. It is not a subspace.
13. The functions $\sin x$ and $\cos x$ are linearly independent.
14. The funtions e^x and xe^x are linearly independent.
15. The functions $(1 + x)$, $(1 - x)$, and $(1 - x^2)$ are linearly independent.
16. The three given polynomials are linearly dependent.
17. The three given trigonometric functions are linearly dependent.
18. The two given linear combinations of $\sin x$ and $\cos x$ are linearly independent.
19. $A = 3$ and $B = -2$.
20. $A = -2$ and $B = C = 1$.
21. $A = 2$ and $B = -2$.
22. $A = -1$, $B = 4$, and $C = -3$.
23. The solution space is 3-dimensional with basis $\{1, x, x^2\}$.
24. The solution space is 4-dimensional with basis $\{1, x, x^2, x^3\}$.
25. The solution space is 2-dimensional with basis $\{1, e^{5x}\}$.
26. The solution space is 2-dimensional with basis $\{1, e^{-10x}\}$.

Chapter 5

Section 5.1

1. $y(x) = \frac{5}{2}e^x - \frac{5}{2}e^{-x}$
2. $y(x) = 2e^{3x} - 3e^{-3x}$
3. $y(x) = 3\cos 2x + 4\sin 2x$
4. $y(x) = 10\cos 5x - 2\sin 5x$
5. $y(x) = 2e^x - e^{2x}$
6. $y(x) = 4e^{2x} + 3e^{-3x}$
7. $y(x) = 6 - 8e^{-x}$
8. $y(x) = \frac{1}{3}(14 - 2e^{3x})$
9. $y(x) = 2e^{-x} + xe^{-x}$
10. $y(x) = 3e^{5x} - 2xe^{5x}$
11. $y(x) = 5e^x \sin x$
12. $y(x) = e^{-3x}(2\cos 2x + 3\sin 2x)$
13. $y(x) = 5x - 2x^2$
14. $y(x) = 3x^2 - 16/x^3$
15. $y(x) = 7x - 5x\ln x$
16. $y(x) = 2\cos(\ln x) + 3\sin(\ln x)$
21. Linearly independent
22. Linearly independent
23. Linearly independent
24. Linearly dependent
25. Linearly independent
26. Linearly independent

28. $y(x) = 1 - 2\cos x - \sin x$

29. There is no contradiction because if the given differential equation is divided by x^2 to get the form in Eq. (8), then the resulting coefficient functions $p(x) = -4/x$ and $q(x) = 6/x^2$ are not continuous at $x = 0$.

33. $y(x) = c_1 e^x + c_2 e^{2x}$
34. $y(x) = c_1 e^{-5x} + c_2 e^{3x}$
35. $y(x) = c_1 + c_2 e^{-5x}$
36. $y(x) = c_1 + c_2 e^{-3x/2}$
37. $y(x) = c_1 e^{-x/2} + c_2 e^x$
38. $y(x) = c_1 e^{-x/2} + c_2 e^{-3x/2}$
39. $y(x) = (c_1 + c_2 x)e^{-x/2}$
40. $y(x) = (c_1 + c_2 x)e^{2x/3}$
41. $y(x) = c_1 e^{-4x/3} + c_2 e^{5x/2}$
42. $y(x) = c_1 e^{-4x/7} + c_2 e^{3x/5}$
43. $y'' + 10y' = 0$
44. $y'' - 100y = 0$
45. $y'' + 20y' + 100y = 0$
46. $y'' - 110y' + 1000y = 0$
47. $y'' = 0$
48. $y'' - 2y' - y = 0$
49. The high point is $\left(\ln\frac{7}{4}, \frac{16}{7}\right)$.
50. $(-\ln 2, -2)$
52. $y(x) = c_1 x + c_2/x$
53. $y(x) = c_1 x^{-4} + c_2 x^3$
54. $y(x) = c_1 x^{-3/2} + c_2 x^{1/2}$
55. $y(x) = c_1 + c_2 \ln x$
56. $y(x) = x^2(c_1 + c_2 \ln x)$

Section 5.2

1. $15 \cdot (2x) - 16 \cdot (3x^2) - 6 \cdot (5x - 8x^2) \equiv 0$
2. $(-4)(5) + (5)(2 - 3x^2) + (1)(10 + 15x^2) \equiv 0$
3. $1 \cdot 0 + 0 \cdot \sin x + 0 \cdot e^x \equiv 0$
4. $(6)(17) + (-51)(2\sin^2 x) + (-34)(3\cos^2 x) \equiv 0$
5. $1 \cdot 17 - 34 \cdot \cos^2 x + 17 \cdot \cos 2x \equiv 0$
6. $(-1)(e^x) + (1)(\cosh x) + (1)(\sinh x) \equiv 0$
13. $y(x) = \frac{4}{3}e^x - \frac{1}{3}e^{-2x}$
14. $y(x) = \frac{1}{2}(3e^x - 6e^{2x} + 3e^{3x})$
15. $y(x) = (2 - 2x + x^2)e^x$
16. $y(x) = -12e^x + 13e^{2x} - 10xe^{2x}$
17. $y(x) = \frac{1}{9}(29 - 2\cos 3x - 3\sin 3x)$
18. $y(x) = e^x(2 - \cos x - \sin x)$
19. $y(x) = x + 2x^2 + 3x^3$
20. $y(x) = 2x - x^{-2} + x^{-2}\ln x$
21. $y(x) = 2\cos x - 5\sin x + 3x$
22. $y(x) = 4e^{2x} - e^{-2x} - 3$
23. $y(x) = e^{-x} + 4e^{3x} - 2$
24. $y(x) = e^x(3\cos x + 4\sin x) + x + 1$
38. $y_2(x) = \frac{1}{x^3}$
39. $y_2(x) = xe^{x/2}$
40. $y_2(x) = xe^x$
41. $y_2(x) = x + 2$
42. $y_2(x) = 1 + x^2$

Section 5.3

1. $y(x) = c_1 e^{2x} + c_2 e^{-2x}$
2. $y(x) = c_1 + c_2 e^{3x/2}$
3. $y(x) = c_1 e^{2x} + c_2 e^{-5x}$
4. $y(x) = c_1 e^{x/2} + c_2 e^{3x}$
5. $y(x) = c_1 e^{-3x} + c_2 x e^{-3x}$
6. $y(x) = e^{-5x/2} \left[c_1 \exp\left(\frac{1}{2}x\sqrt{5}\right) + c_2 \exp\left(-\frac{1}{2}x\sqrt{5}\right) \right]$
7. $y(x) = c_1 e^{3x/2} + c_2 x e^{3x/2}$
8. $y(x) = e^{3x}(c_1 \cos 2x + c_2 \sin 2x)$
9. $y(x) = e^{-4x}(c_1 \cos 3x + c_2 \sin 3x)$
10. $y(x) = c_1 + c_2 x + c_3 x^2 + c_4 e^{-3x/5}$
11. $y(x) = c_1 + c_2 x + c_3 e^{4x} + c_4 x e^{4x}$
12. $y(x) = c_1 + c_2 e^x + c_3 x e^x + c_4 x^2 e^x$
13. $y(x) = c_1 + c_2 e^{-2x/3} + c_3 x e^{-2x/3}$
14. $y(x) = c_1 e^x + c_2 e^{-x} + c_3 \cos 2x + c_4 \sin 2x$
15. $y(x) = c_1 e^{2x} + c_2 x e^{2x} + c_3 e^{-2x} + c_4 x e^{-2x}$
16. $y(x) = (c_1 + c_2 x) \cos 3x + (c_3 + c_4 x) \sin 3x$
17. $y(x) = c_1 \cos\left(x/\sqrt{2}\right) + c_2 \sin\left(x/\sqrt{2}\right) + c_3 \cos\left(2x/\sqrt{3}\right) + c_4 \sin\left(2x/\sqrt{3}\right)$
18. $y(x) = c_1 e^{2x} + c_2 e^{-2x} + c_3 \cos 2x + c_4 \sin 2x$
19. $y(x) = c_1 e^x + c_2 e^{-x} + c_3 x e^{-x}$
20. $y(x) = e^{-x/2}\left[(c_1 + c_2 x)\cos\left(\frac{1}{2}x\sqrt{3}\right) + (c_3 + c_3 x)\sin\left(\frac{1}{2}x\sqrt{3}\right)\right]$
21. $y(x) = 5e^x + 2e^{3x}$
22. $y(x) = e^{-x/3}\left[3\cos\left(x/\sqrt{3}\right) + 5\sqrt{3}\sin\left(x/\sqrt{3}\right)\right]$
23. $y(x) = e^{3x}(3\cos 4x - 2\sin 4x)$
24. $y(x) = \frac{1}{2}(-7 + e^{2x} + 8e^{-x/2})$
25. $y(x) = \frac{1}{4}(-13 + 6x + 9e^{-2x/3})$
26. $y(x) = \frac{1}{5}(24 - 9e^{-5x} - 25xe^{-5x})$
27. $y(x) = c_1 e^x + c_2 e^{-2x} + c_3 x e^{-2x}$
28. $y(x) = c_1 e^{2x} + c_2 e^{-x} + c_3 e^{-x/2}$
29. $y(x) = c_1 e^{-3x} + e^{3x/2}\left[c_2 \cos\left(\frac{3}{2}x\sqrt{3}\right) + c_3 \sin\left(\frac{3}{2}x\sqrt{3}\right)\right]$
30. $y(x) = c_1 e^{-x} + c_2 e^{2x} + c_3 \cos(x\sqrt{3}) + c_4 \sin(x\sqrt{3})$
31. $y(x) = c_1 e^x + e^{-2x}(c_2 \cos 2x + c_3 \sin 2x)$
32. $y(x) = c_1 e^{2x} + (c_2 + c_3 x + c_4 x^2)e^{-x}$
33. $y(x) = c_1 e^{3x} + e^{-3x}(c_2 \cos 3x + c_3 \sin 3x)$
34. $y(x) = c_1 e^{2x/3} + c_2 \cos 2x + c_3 \sin 2x$
35. $y(x) = c_1 e^{-x/2} + c_2 e^{-x/3} + c_3 \cos 2x + c_4 \sin 2x$
36. $y(x) = c_1 e^{7x/9} + e^{-x}(c_2 \cos x + c_3 \sin x)$
37. $y(x) = 11 + 5x + 3x^2 + 7e^x$
38. $y(x) = 2e^{5x} - 2\cos 10x$
39. $y^{(3)} - 6y'' + 12y' - 8y = 0$
40. $y^{(3)} - 2y'' + 4y' - 8y = 0$
41. $y^{(4)} - 16y = 0$
42. $y^{(6)} + 12y^{(4)} + 48y'' + 64y = 0$
44. (a) $x = i, -2i$ (b) $x = -i, 3i$
45. $y(x) = c_1 e^{-ix} + c_2 e^{3ix}$
46. $y(x) = c_1 e^{3ix} + c_2 e^{-2ix}$
47. $y(x) = c_1 \exp\left(\left[1 + i\sqrt{3}\right]x\right) + c_2 \exp\left(-\left[1 + i\sqrt{3}\right]x\right)$
48. $y(x) = \frac{1}{3}\left(e^x + \exp\left[\frac{1}{2}\left(-1 + i\sqrt{3}\right)x\right] + \exp\left[\frac{1}{2}\left(-1 - i\sqrt{3}\right)x\right]\right)$

49. $y(x) = 2e^{2x} - 5e^{-x} + 3\cos x - 9\sin x$
52. $y(x) = c_1 \cos(3\ln x) + c_2 \sin(3\ln x)$
53. $y(x) = x^{-3}[c_1 \cos(4\ln x) + c_2 \sin(4\ln x)]$
54. $y(x) = c_1 + c_2 \ln x + c_3 x^{-3}$
55. $y(x) = c_1 + x^2(c_2 + c_3 \ln x)$
56. $y(x) = c_1 + c_2 \ln x + c_3 (\ln x)^2$
57. $y(x) = c_1 + x^3 \left(c_2 x^{-\sqrt{3}} + c_3 x^{+\sqrt{3}}\right)$
58. $y(x) = x^{-1}[c_1 + c_2 \ln x + c_3 (\ln x)^2]$

Section 5.4

1. Frequency: 2 rad/s   ($1/\pi$ Hz);   period: π s
2. Frequency: 8 rad/sec ($4/\pi$ Hz); period: $\pi/4$ s
3. Amplitude: 2 m;   frequency: 5 rad/s;   period: $2\pi/5$ s
4. (a) $x(t) = \frac{13}{12}\cos(12t - \alpha)$ with $\alpha = 2\pi - \tan^{-1}(5/12) \approx 5.8884$;   (b) Amplitude: $\frac{13}{12}$ m; period: $\pi/6$ s
6. About 7.33 mi
7. About 10450 ft
8. 29.59 in.
10. Amplitude: 100 cm; period: about 2.01 s
11. About 3.8 in.
13. (a) $x(t) = 50(e^{-2t/5} - e^{-t/2})$;   (b) 4.096 exactly
14. (a) $x(t) = 25e^{-t/5}\cos(3t - \alpha)$ with $\alpha = \tan^{-1}(3/4) \approx 0.6435$;   (b) envelope curves $x = \pm 25e^{-t/5}$; pseudoperiod $2\pi/3$
15. $x(t) = 4e^{-2t} - 2e^{-4t}$, overdamped; $u(t) = 2\cos(2\sqrt{2}\,t)$

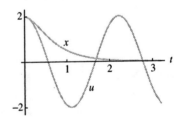

16. $x(t) = 4e^{-3t} - 2e^{-7t}$, overdamped; $u(t) \approx 2\sqrt{\frac{22}{21}}\cos(\sqrt{21}\,t - 0.2149)$

17. $x(t) = 5e^{-4t}(2t + 1)$, critically damped; $u(t) \approx \frac{5}{2}\sqrt{5}\cos(4t - 5.8195)$

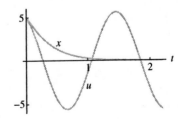

18. $x(t) = 2e^{-3t} \cos\left(4t - \frac{3\pi}{2}\right)$, underdamped; $u(t) = \frac{8}{5} \cos\left(5t - \frac{3\pi}{2}\right)$

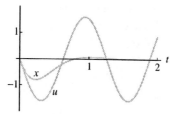

19. $x(t) \approx \frac{1}{3}\sqrt{313}\, e^{-5t/2} \cos(6t - 0.8254)$, underdamped;
$u(t) \approx \frac{4}{13}\sqrt{233} \cos\left(\frac{13}{2}t - 0.5517\right)$

20. $x(t) \approx 13e^{-4t} \cos(2t - 1.1760)$, underdamped;
$u(t) \approx \sqrt{\frac{129}{5}} \cos(2\sqrt{5}\, t - 0.1770)$

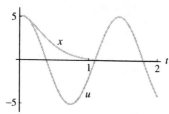

21. $x(t) \approx 10e^{-5t} \cos(10t - 0.9273)$, underdamped;
$u(t) \approx 2\sqrt{14} \cos(5\sqrt{5}\, t - 0.6405)$

22. (b) The time-varying amplitude is $\frac{2}{3}\sqrt{3}$, the frequency is $4\sqrt{3}$ rad/s, and the phase angle is $\pi/6$.

23. (a) $k \approx 7018$ lb/ft; (b) After about 2.47 s

34. Damping constant: $c \approx 11.51$ lb/ft/s; spring constant: $k \approx 189.68$ lb/ft

Section 5.5

1. $y_p(x) = \frac{1}{25}e^{3x}$

2. $y_p(x) = -\frac{1}{4}(5 + 6x)$

3. $y_p(x) = \frac{1}{39}(\cos 3x - 5 \sin 3x)$

4. $y_p(x) = \frac{1}{9}(-4e^x + 3xe^x)$

5. $y_p(x) = \frac{1}{26}(13 + 3\cos 2x - 2\sin 2x)$

6. $y_p(x) = \frac{1}{343}(4 - 56x + 49x^2)$

7. $y_p(x) = -\frac{1}{6}(e^x - e^{-x}) = -\frac{1}{3}\sinh x$

8. $y_p(x) = \frac{1}{4}x \sinh 2x$

9. $y_p(x) = -\frac{1}{3} + \frac{1}{16}(2x^2 - x)e^x$

10. $y_p(x) = \frac{1}{6}(2x \sin 3x - 3x \cos 3x)$

11. $y_p(x) = \frac{1}{8}(3x^2 - 2x)$

12. $y_p(x) = 2x + \frac{1}{2}x \sin x$

13. $y_p(x) = \frac{1}{65}e^x(7 \sin x - 4 \cos x)$

14. $y_p(x) = \frac{1}{24}(-3x^2 e^x + x^3 e^x)$

15. $y_p(x) \equiv -17$

16. $y_p(x) = \frac{1}{81}(45 + e^{3x} - 6xe^{3x} + 9x^2 e^{3x})$

17. $y_p(x) = \frac{1}{4}(x^2 \sin x - x \cos x)$

18. $y_p(x) = -\frac{1}{144}(24xe^x - 19e^{2x} + 6x^2 e^{2x})$

19. $y_p(x) = \frac{1}{8}(10x^2 - 4x^3 + x^4)$

20. $y_p(x) = -7 + \frac{1}{3}xe^x$

21. $y_p(x) = xe^x(A \cos x + B \sin x)$

22. $y_p(x) = Ax^3 + Bx^4 + Cx^5 + Dxe^x$

23. $y_p(x) = Ax \cos 2x + Bx \sin 2x + Cx^2 \cos 2x + Dx^2 \sin 2x$

24. $y_p(x) = Ax + Bx^2 + (Cx + Dx^2)e^{-3x}$

25. $y_p(x) = Axe^{-x} + Bx^2 e^{-x} + Cxe^{-2x} + Dx^2 e^{-2x}$

26. $y_p(x) = (Ax + Bx^2)e^{3x} \cos 2x + (Cx + Dx^2)e^{3x} \sin 2x$

27. $y_p(x) = Ax \cos x + Bx \sin x + Cx \cos 2x + Dx \sin 2x$

28. $y_p(x) = (Ax + Bx^2 + Cx^3)\cos 3x + (Dx + Ex^2 + Fx^3)\sin 3x$

29. $y_p(x) = Ax^3 e^x + Bx^4 e^x + Cxe^{2x} + Dxe^{-2x}$

30. $y_p(x) = (A + Bx + Cx^2)\cos x + (D + Ex + Fx^2)\sin x$

31. $y(x) = \cos 2x + \frac{3}{4}\sin 2x + \frac{1}{2}x$

32. $y(x) = \frac{1}{6}(15e^{-x} - 16e^{-2x} + e^x)$

33. $y(x) = \cos 3x - \frac{2}{15}\sin 3x + \frac{1}{5}\sin 2x$

34. $y(x) = \cos x - \sin x + \frac{1}{2}x \sin x$

35. $y(x) = e^x(2 \cos x - \frac{5}{2}\sin x) + \frac{1}{2}x + 1$

36. $y(x) = \frac{1}{192}(234 + 240x - 9e^{-2x} - 33e^{2x} - 12x^2 - 4x^4)$

37. $y(x) = 4 - 4e^x + 3xe^x + x - \frac{1}{2}x^2 e^x + \frac{1}{6}x^3 e^x$

38. $y(x) = \frac{1}{85}[e^{-x}(176 \cos x + 197 \sin x) - (6 \cos 3x + 7 \sin 3x)]$

39. $y(x) = -3 + 3x - \frac{1}{2}x^2 + \frac{1}{6}x^3 + 4e^{-x} + xe^{-x}$

40. $y(x) = \frac{1}{4}(5e^{-x} + 5e^x + 10 \cos x - 20)$

41. $y_p(x) = 255 - 450x + 30x^2 + 20x^3 + 10x^4 - 4x^5$

42. $y(x) = 10e^{-x} + 35e^{2x} + 210 \cos x + 390 \sin x + y_p(x)$, where $y_p(x)$ is the particular solution of Problem 41.

43. (b) $y(x) = c_1 \cos 2x + c_2 \sin 2x + \frac{1}{4}\cos x - \frac{1}{20}\cos 3x$

44. $y(x) = e^{-x/2}\left[c_1 \cos\left(\frac{1}{2}x\sqrt{3}\right) + c_2 \sin\left(\frac{1}{2}x\sqrt{3}\right)\right] + \frac{1}{26}(-3\cos 2x + 2\sin 2x) + \frac{1}{482}(-15 \cos 4x + 4 \sin 4x)$

45. $y(x) = c_1 \cos 3x + c_2 \sin 3x + \frac{1}{24} - \frac{1}{10}\cos 2x - \frac{1}{56}\cos 4x$

46. $y(x) = c_1 \cos x + c_2 \sin x + \frac{1}{16}(3x \cos x + 3x^2 \sin x) + \frac{1}{128}(3 \sin 3x - 4x \cos 3x)$

47. $y_p(x) = \frac{2}{3}e^x$

48. $y_p(x) = -\frac{1}{12}(6x + 1)e^{-2x}$

49. $y_p(x) = x^2 e^{2x}$

50. $y_p(x) = \frac{1}{16}(4x \cosh 2x - \sinh 2x)$

51. $y_p(x) = -\frac{1}{4}(\cos 2x \cos x - \sin 2x \sin x) + \frac{1}{20}(\cos 5x \cos 2x + \sin 5x \sin 2x) = -\frac{1}{5}\cos 3x$ (!)

52. $y_p(x) = -\frac{1}{6}x \cos 3x$

53. $y_p(x) = \frac{2}{3}x \sin 3x + \frac{2}{9}(\cos 3x) \ln|\cos 3x|$

54. $y_p(x) = -1 - (\cos x) \ln|\csc x - \cot x|$

55. $y_p(x) = \frac{1}{8}(1 - x \sin 2x)$

56. $y_p(x) = -\frac{1}{9}e^x(3x + 2)$

58. $y_p(x) = x^3(\ln x - 1)$

59. $y_p(x) = \frac{1}{4}x^4$

60. $y_p(x) = -\frac{72}{5}x^{4/3}$

61. $y_p(x) = \ln x$

62. $y_p(x) = -x^2 + x \ln\left|\dfrac{1+x}{1-x}\right| + \dfrac{1}{2}(1 + x^2)\ln|1 - x^2|$

Section 5.6

1. $x(t) = 2\cos 2t - 2\cos 3t$

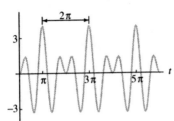

2. $x(t) = \frac{3}{2}\sin 2t - \sin 3t$

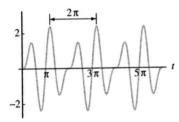

3. $x(t) = \sqrt{138388}\cos(10t - \alpha) + 5\cos(5t - \beta)$ with
$\alpha = 2\pi - \tan^{-1}(1/186) \approx 6.2778$ and
$\beta = \tan^{-1}(4/3) \approx 0.9273$.

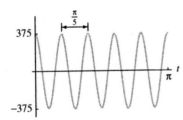

4. $x(t) = 2\sqrt{106}\cos(5t - \alpha) + 10\cos 4t$ with
$\alpha = \pi - \tan^{-1}(9/5) \approx 2.0779$

5. $x(t) = (x_0 - C)\cos\omega_0 t + C\cos\omega t$, where $C = F_0/(k - m\omega^2)$

7. $x_{sp}(t) = \frac{10}{13}\cos(3t - \alpha)$ with $\alpha = \pi - \tan^{-1}(12/5) \approx 1.9656$

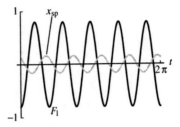

8. $x_{sp}(t) = \frac{4}{25}\cos(5t - \alpha)$ with $\alpha = 2\pi - \tan^{-1}(3/4) \approx 5.6397$

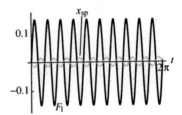

9. $x_{sp}(t) = \frac{3}{\sqrt{40001}}\cos(10t - \alpha)$ with
$\alpha = \pi + \tan^{-1}(199/20) \approx 4.6122$

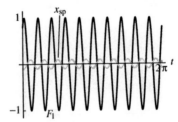

10. $x_{sp}(t) = \frac{10}{793}\sqrt{61}\cos(10t - \alpha)$ with
$\alpha = \pi + \tan^{-1}(171/478) \approx 3.4851$

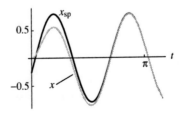

11. $x_{sp}(t) = \frac{\sqrt{10}}{4}\cos(3t - \alpha)$ with $\alpha = \pi - \tan^{-1}(3) \approx 1.8925$
$x_{tr}(t) = \frac{5}{4}\sqrt{2}\,e^{-2t}\cos(t - \beta)$ with $\beta = 2\pi - \tan^{-1}(7) \approx 4.8543$

12. $x_{sp}(t) = \frac{5}{3\sqrt{29}}\cos(3t - \alpha)$ with $\alpha = \pi + \tan^{-1}(2/5) \approx 3.5221$

$x_{tr}(t) = \frac{25}{6\sqrt{29}}e^{-3t}\cos(2t - \beta)$ with $\beta = \tan^{-1}(5/2) \approx 1.1903$

13. $x_{sp}(t) = \frac{300}{\sqrt{1469}}\cos(10t - \alpha)$ with

$\alpha = \pi - \tan^{-1}(10/37) \approx 2.9320$

$x_{tr}(t) = 2\sqrt{\frac{113314}{1469}}\,e^{-t}\cos(5t - \beta)$ with

$\beta = 2\pi - \tan^{-1}(421/12895) \approx 6.2505$

14. $x_{sp}(t) = \sqrt{485}\cos(t - \alpha)$ with $\alpha = \tan^{-1}(22) \approx 1.5254$

$x_{tr}(t) = \sqrt{3665}\,e^{-4t}\cos(3t - \beta)$ with

$\beta = \pi + \tan^{-1}(52/31) \approx 4.1748$

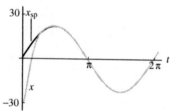

15. $C(\omega) = 2/\sqrt{4 + \omega^4}$; there is no practical resonance frequency.

16. $C(\omega) = 10/\sqrt{25 + 6\omega^2 + \omega^4}$; there is no practical resonance frequency.

17. $C(\omega) = 50/\sqrt{2025 - 54\omega^2 + \omega^4}$; there is practical resonance at frequency $\omega = 3\sqrt{3}$.

18. $C(\omega) = 100/\sqrt{422500 - 1200\omega^2 + \omega^4}$; there is practical resonance at frequency $\omega = 10\sqrt{6}$.

19. $\omega = \sqrt{384}$ rad/sec (approximately 3.12 Hz)

20. $\omega \approx 44.27$ rad/sec (approximately 7.05 Hz)

21. $\omega_0 = \sqrt{(g/L) + (k/m)}$

22. $\omega_0 = \sqrt{k/(m + I/a^2)}$

23. (a) Natural frequency: $\sqrt{10}$ rad/s (approximately 0.50 Hz);
(b) amplitude: approximately 10.625 in.

Chapter 6

Section 6.1

1. $\lambda_1 = 2$: $\mathbf{v}_1 = (1, 1)$; $\lambda_2 = 3$: $\mathbf{v}_2 = (2, 1)$

2. $\lambda_1 = -1$: $\mathbf{v}_1 = (1, 1)$; $\lambda_2 = 2$: $\mathbf{v}_2 = (2, 1)$

3. $\lambda_1 = 2$: $\mathbf{v}_2 = (1, 1)$; $\lambda_2 = 5$: $\mathbf{v}_1 = (2, 1)$

4. $\lambda_1 = 1$: $\mathbf{v}_2 = (1, 1)$; $\lambda_2 = 2$: $\mathbf{v}_1 = (3, 2)$

5. $\lambda_1 = 1$: $\mathbf{v}_2 = (1, 1)$; $\lambda_2 = 4$: $\mathbf{v}_1 = (3, 2)$

6. $\lambda_1 = 2$: $\mathbf{v}_2 = (1, 1)$; $\lambda_2 = 3$: $\mathbf{v}_1 = (4, 3)$

7. $\lambda_1 = 2$: $\mathbf{v}_2 = (1, 1)$; $\lambda_2 = 4$: $\mathbf{v}_1 = (4, 3)$

8. $\lambda_1 = -2$: $\mathbf{v}_2 = (2, 3)$; $\lambda_2 = -1$: $\mathbf{v}_1 = (3, 4)$

9. $\lambda_1 = 3$: $\mathbf{v}_1 = (2, 1)$; $\lambda_2 = 4$: $\mathbf{v}_2 = (5, 2)$

10. $\lambda_1 = 4$: $\mathbf{v}_1 = (2, 1)$; $\lambda_2 = 5$: $\mathbf{v}_2 = (5, 2)$

11. $\lambda_1 = 4$: $\mathbf{v}_2 = (2, 3)$; $\lambda_2 = 5$: $\mathbf{v}_1 = (5, 7)$

12. $\lambda_1 = 3$: $\mathbf{v}_2 = (3, 2)$; $\lambda_2 = 4$: $\mathbf{v}_1 = (5, 3)$

13. $\lambda_1 = 0$: $\mathbf{v}_1 = (0, -1, 2)$; $\lambda_2 = 1$: $\mathbf{v}_2 = (0, -1, 3)$;
$\lambda_3 = 2$: $\mathbf{v}_3 = (1, 0, 2)$

14. $\lambda_1 = 0$: $\mathbf{v}_1 = (0, -1, 2)$; $\lambda_2 = 2$: $\mathbf{v}_2 = (0, -1, 3)$;
$\lambda_3 = 5$: $\mathbf{v}_3 = (1, 0, 2)$

15. $\lambda_1 = 0$: $\mathbf{v}_1 = (1, 1, 0)$; $\lambda_2 = 1$: $\mathbf{v}_2 = (2, 1, 1)$;
$\lambda_3 = 2$: $\mathbf{v}_3 = (1, 0, 2)$

16. $\lambda_1 = 0$: $\mathbf{v}_1 = (1, 1, 1)$; $\lambda_2 = 1$: $\mathbf{v}_2 = (1, 1, 0)$;
$\lambda_3 = 3$: $\mathbf{v}_3 = (-1, 0, 2)$

17. $\lambda_1 = 1$: $\mathbf{v}_1 = (1, 0, 1)$; $\lambda_2 = 2$: $\mathbf{v}_2 = (-1, 1, 2)$;
$\lambda_3 = 3$: $\mathbf{v}_3 = (1, 0, 0)$

18. $\lambda_1 = 1$: $\mathbf{v}_1 = (1, 0, 3)$; $\lambda_2 = 2$: $\mathbf{v}_2 = (0, -1, 3)$;
$\lambda_3 = 3$: $\mathbf{v}_3 = (0, -2, 5)$

19. $\lambda_1 = \lambda_2 = 1$: $\mathbf{v}_1 = (1,0,1)$, $\mathbf{v}_2 = (-3,1,0)$;
$\lambda_3 = 3$, $\mathbf{v}_3 = (1,0,0)$

20. $\lambda_1 = \lambda_2 = 1$: $\mathbf{v}_1 = (1,0,2)$, $\mathbf{v}_2 = (3,2,0)$;
$\lambda_3 = 2$, $\mathbf{v}_3 = (0,-2,5)$

21. $\lambda_1 = 1$: $\mathbf{v}_1 = (1,1,0)$; $\lambda_2 = \lambda_3 = 2$: $\mathbf{v}_2 = (3,2,0)$, $\mathbf{v}_3 = (-1,0,2)$

22. $\lambda_1 = \lambda_2 = -1$: $\mathbf{v}_1 = (1,1,0)$, $\mathbf{v}_2 = (-1,0,2)$;
$\lambda_3 = 2$, $\mathbf{v}_3 = (1,1,1)$

23. $\lambda_1 = 1$: $\mathbf{v}_1 = (1,0,0,0)$; $\lambda_2 = 2$: $\mathbf{v}_2 = (2,1,0,0)$;
$\lambda_3 = 3$: $\mathbf{v}_3 = (3,2,1,0)$; $\lambda_4 = 4$: $\mathbf{v}_4 = (4,3,2,1)$

24. $\lambda_1 = \lambda_2 = 1$: $\mathbf{v}_1 = (1,0,0,0)$, $\mathbf{v}_2 = (0,1,0,0)$;
$\lambda_3 = \lambda_4 = 3$: $\mathbf{v}_3 = (0,0,0,1)$, $\mathbf{v}_4 = (2,2,1,0)$

25. $\lambda_1 = \lambda_2 = 1$: $\mathbf{v}_1 = (1,0,0,0)$, $\mathbf{v}_2 = (0,1,0,0)$;
$\lambda_3 = \lambda_4 = 2$: $\mathbf{v}_3 = (0,0,0,1)$, $\mathbf{v}_4 = (1,1,1,0)$

26. $\lambda_1 = -2$: $\mathbf{v}_1 = (1,0,0,2)$; $\lambda_2 = -1$: $\mathbf{v}_2 = (0,0,1,0)$;
$\lambda_3 = 1$: $\mathbf{v}_3 = (1,0,0,1)$; $\lambda_4 = 2$: $\mathbf{v}_4 = (0,1,0,0)$

27. $\lambda_1 = -i$: $\mathbf{v}_1 = (+i,1)$; $\lambda_2 = +i$: $\mathbf{v}_2 = (-i,1)$

28. $\lambda_1 = -6i$: $\mathbf{v}_1 = (-i,1)$; $\lambda_2 = +6i$: $\mathbf{v}_2 = (+i,1)$

29. $\lambda_1 = -6i$: $\mathbf{v}_1 = (-i,2)$; $\lambda_2 = +6i$: $\mathbf{v}_2 = (+i,2)$

30. $\lambda_1 = -12i$: $\mathbf{v}_1 = (-i,1)$; $\lambda_2 = +12i$: $\mathbf{v}_2 = (+i,1)$

31. $\lambda_1 = -12i$: $\mathbf{v}_1 = (+2i,1)$; $\lambda_2 = +12i$: $\mathbf{v}_2 = (-2i,1)$

32. $\lambda_1 = -12i$: $\mathbf{v}_1 = (-i,3)$; $\lambda_2 = +12i$: $\mathbf{v}_2 = (+i,3)$

40. We find that $\operatorname{Tr}\mathbf{A} = 12$ and $\det\mathbf{A} = 60$, so the characteristic polynomial of the given matrix $\mathbf{A}$ is
$p(\lambda) = -\lambda^3 + 12\lambda^2 + c_1\lambda + 60$. Eigenvalues and eigenvectors:
$\lambda_1 = 3$: $\mathbf{v}_1 = (3,2,1)$; $\lambda_2 = 4$: $\mathbf{v}_2 = (5,7,7)$; $\lambda_3 = 5$:
$\mathbf{v}_3 = (-1,1,2)$

41. We find that $\operatorname{Tr}\mathbf{A} = 8$ and $\det\mathbf{A} = -60$, so the characteristic polynomial of the given matrix $\mathbf{A}$ is
$p(\lambda) = -\lambda^4 - 8\lambda^3 + c_2\lambda^2 + c_1\lambda - 60$. Eigenvalues and eigenvectors: $\lambda_1 = -2$: $\mathbf{v}_1 = (1,0,1,2)$; $\lambda_2 = 2$: $\mathbf{v}_2 = (3,4,0,3)$;
$\lambda_3 = 3$: $\mathbf{v}_3 = (3,1,2,4)$; $\lambda_4 = 5$: $\mathbf{v}_4 = (1,1,0,1)$

Section 6.2

1. $\lambda_1 = 1$, $\lambda_2 = 3$; $\mathbf{P} = \begin{bmatrix} 1 & 2 \\ 1 & 1 \end{bmatrix}$, $\mathbf{D} = \begin{bmatrix} 1 & 0 \\ 0 & 3 \end{bmatrix}$

2. $\lambda_1 = 0$, $\lambda_2 = 2$; $\mathbf{P} = \begin{bmatrix} 1 & 3 \\ 1 & 2 \end{bmatrix}$, $\mathbf{D} = \begin{bmatrix} 0 & 0 \\ 0 & 2 \end{bmatrix}$

3. $\lambda_1 = 2$, $\lambda_2 = 3$; $\mathbf{P} = \begin{bmatrix} 1 & 3 \\ 1 & 2 \end{bmatrix}$, $\mathbf{D} = \begin{bmatrix} 2 & 0 \\ 0 & 3 \end{bmatrix}$

4. $\lambda_1 = 1$, $\lambda_2 = 2$; $\mathbf{P} = \begin{bmatrix} 1 & 4 \\ 1 & 3 \end{bmatrix}$, $\mathbf{D} = \begin{bmatrix} 1 & 0 \\ 0 & 2 \end{bmatrix}$

5. $\lambda_1 = 1$, $\lambda_2 = 3$; $\mathbf{P} = \begin{bmatrix} 1 & 4 \\ 1 & 3 \end{bmatrix}$, $\mathbf{D} = \begin{bmatrix} 1 & 0 \\ 0 & 3 \end{bmatrix}$

6. $\lambda_1 = 1$, $\lambda_2 = 2$; $\mathbf{P} = \begin{bmatrix} 2 & 3 \\ 3 & 4 \end{bmatrix}$, $\mathbf{D} = \begin{bmatrix} 1 & 0 \\ 0 & 2 \end{bmatrix}$

7. $\lambda_1 = 1$, $\lambda_2 = 2$; $\mathbf{P} = \begin{bmatrix} 2 & 5 \\ 1 & 2 \end{bmatrix}$, $\mathbf{D} = \begin{bmatrix} 1 & 0 \\ 0 & 2 \end{bmatrix}$

8. $\lambda_1 = 1$, $\lambda_2 = 2$; $\mathbf{P} = \begin{bmatrix} 3 & 5 \\ 2 & 3 \end{bmatrix}$, $\mathbf{D} = \begin{bmatrix} 1 & 0 \\ 0 & 2 \end{bmatrix}$

9. The double eigenvalue $\lambda_1 = \lambda_2 = 2$ has only the single associated eigenvector $\mathbf{v}_1 = (1,1)$, so the matrix $\mathbf{A}$ is not diagonalizable.

10. The double eigenvalue $\lambda_1 = \lambda_2 = 1$ has only the single associated eigenvector $\mathbf{v}_1 = (2,1)$, so the matrix $\mathbf{A}$ is not diagonalizable.

11. The double eigenvalue $\lambda_1 = \lambda_2 = 2$ has only the single associated eigenvector $\mathbf{v}_1 = (-1,3)$, so the matrix $\mathbf{A}$ is not diagonalizable.

12. The double eigenvalue $\lambda_1 = \lambda_2 = -1$ has only the single associated eigenvector $\mathbf{v}_1 = (-3,4)$, so the matrix $\mathbf{A}$ is not diagonalizable.

13. $\lambda_1 = 1$, $\lambda_2 = \lambda_3 = 2$; $\mathbf{P} = \begin{bmatrix} 1 & 0 & 3 \\ 0 & 0 & 1 \\ 0 & 1 & 0 \end{bmatrix}$, $\mathbf{D} = \begin{bmatrix} 1 & 0 & 0 \\ 0 & 2 & 0 \\ 0 & 0 & 2 \end{bmatrix}$

14. $\lambda_1 = \lambda_2 = 0$, $\lambda_3 = 1$; $\mathbf{P} = \begin{bmatrix} -1 & 1 & 1 \\ 0 & 1 & 1 \\ 2 & 0 & 1 \end{bmatrix}$, $\mathbf{D} = \begin{bmatrix} 0 & 0 & 0 \\ 0 & 0 & 0 \\ 0 & 0 & 1 \end{bmatrix}$

15. $\lambda_1 = 0$, $\lambda_2 = \lambda_3 = 1$; $\mathbf{P} = \begin{bmatrix} 1 & -1 & 3 \\ 1 & 0 & 2 \\ 0 & 2 & 0 \end{bmatrix}$,
$\mathbf{D} = \begin{bmatrix} 0 & 0 & 0 \\ 0 & 1 & 0 \\ 0 & 0 & 1 \end{bmatrix}$

16. $\lambda_1 = \lambda_2 = 1$, $\lambda_3 = 3$; $\mathbf{P} = \begin{bmatrix} 0 & 1 & -1 \\ 0 & 1 & 0 \\ 1 & 0 & 2 \end{bmatrix}$,
$\mathbf{D} = \begin{bmatrix} 1 & 0 & 0 \\ 0 & 1 & 0 \\ 0 & 0 & 3 \end{bmatrix}$

17. $\lambda_1 = -1$, $\lambda_2 = 1$, $\lambda_3 = 2$; $\mathbf{P} = \begin{bmatrix} 1 & -1 & 1 \\ 1 & 0 & 1 \\ 0 & 2 & 1 \end{bmatrix}$,
$\mathbf{D} = \begin{bmatrix} -1 & 0 & 0 \\ 0 & 1 & 0 \\ 0 & 0 & 2 \end{bmatrix}$

18. $\lambda_1 = 1$, $\lambda_2 = 2$, $\lambda_3 = 3$; $\mathbf{P} = \begin{bmatrix} 1 & -1 & 1 \\ 1 & 0 & 1 \\ 0 & 2 & 1 \end{bmatrix}$,
$\mathbf{D} = \begin{bmatrix} 1 & 0 & 0 \\ 0 & 2 & 0 \\ 0 & 0 & 3 \end{bmatrix}$

19. $\lambda_1 = 1$, $\lambda_2 = 2$, $\lambda_3 = 3$; $\mathbf{P} = \begin{bmatrix} 1 & 1 & -1 \\ 1 & 1 & 0 \\ 1 & 0 & 2 \end{bmatrix}$,
$\mathbf{D} = \begin{bmatrix} 1 & 0 & 0 \\ 0 & 2 & 0 \\ 0 & 0 & 3 \end{bmatrix}$

20. $\lambda_1 = 2$, $\lambda_2 = 5$, $\lambda_3 = 6$; $\mathbf{P} = \begin{bmatrix} 1 & 0 & 0 \\ 0 & -1 & -2 \\ 3 & 3 & 5 \end{bmatrix}$,
$\mathbf{D} = \begin{bmatrix} 2 & 0 & 0 \\ 0 & 5 & 0 \\ 0 & 0 & 6 \end{bmatrix}$

21. The triple eigenvalue $\lambda_1 = \lambda_2 = \lambda_3 = 1$ has only the two associated eigenvectors $\mathbf{v}_1 = (0,0,1)$ and $\mathbf{v}_2 = (1,1,0)$, so the matrix $\mathbf{A}$ is not diagonalizable.

22. The triple eigenvalue $\lambda_1 = \lambda_2 = \lambda_3 = 1$ has only the single associated eigenvector $\mathbf{v}_1 = (1,1,1)$, so the matrix $\mathbf{A}$ is not diagonalizable.

23. The eigenvalues $\lambda_1 = \lambda_2 = 1$ and $\lambda_3 = 2$ have only the two associated eigenvectors $\mathbf{v}_1 = (1,1,1)$ and $\mathbf{v}_3 = (1,1,0)$, so the matrix $\mathbf{A}$ is not diagonalizable.

24. The eigenvalues $\lambda_1 = 1$ and $\lambda_2 = \lambda_3 = 2$ have only the two associated eigenvectors $\mathbf{v}_1 = (1,1,0)$ and $\mathbf{v}_2 = (1,1,1)$, so the matrix $\mathbf{A}$ is not diagonalizable.

25. $\lambda_1 = \lambda_2 = -1,\ \lambda_3 = \lambda_4 = 1;\ \mathbf{P} = \begin{bmatrix} 0 & 1 & 0 & 1 \\ 0 & 1 & 1 & 0 \\ 0 & 1 & 0 & 0 \\ 1 & 0 & 0 & 0 \end{bmatrix},$

$\mathbf{D} = \begin{bmatrix} -1 & 0 & 0 & 0 \\ 0 & -1 & 0 & 0 \\ 0 & 0 & 1 & 0 \\ 0 & 0 & 0 & 1 \end{bmatrix}$

26. $\lambda_1 = \lambda_2 = \lambda_3 = 1,\ \lambda_4 = 2;\ \mathbf{P} = \begin{bmatrix} 0 & 0 & 1 & 1 \\ 0 & 1 & 0 & 1 \\ 1 & 0 & 0 & 1 \\ 0 & 0 & 0 & 1 \end{bmatrix},$

$\mathbf{D} = \begin{bmatrix} 1 & 0 & 0 & 0 \\ 0 & 1 & 0 & 0 \\ 0 & 0 & 1 & 0 \\ 0 & 0 & 0 & 2 \end{bmatrix}$

27. The eigenvalues $\lambda_1 = \lambda_2 = \lambda_3 = 1$ and $\lambda_4 = 2$ have only the two associated eigenvectors $\mathbf{v}_1 = (1, 0, 0, 0)$ and $\mathbf{v}_4 = (1, 1, 1, 1)$, so the matrix $\mathbf{A}$ is not diagonalizable.

28. The eigenvalues $\lambda_1 = \lambda_2 = 1$ and $\lambda_3 = \lambda_4 = 2$ have only the two associated eigenvectors $\mathbf{v}_1 = (1, 0, 0, 0)$ and $\mathbf{v}_3 = (1, 1, 1, 0)$, so the matrix $\mathbf{A}$ is not diagonalizable.

Section 6.3

1. $\mathbf{P} = \begin{bmatrix} 1 & 2 \\ 1 & 1 \end{bmatrix},\ \mathbf{D} = \begin{bmatrix} 1 & 0 \\ 0 & 2 \end{bmatrix},\ A^5 = \begin{bmatrix} 63 & -62 \\ 31 & -30 \end{bmatrix}$

2. $\mathbf{P} = \begin{bmatrix} 1 & 2 \\ 1 & 1 \end{bmatrix},\ \mathbf{D} = \begin{bmatrix} -1 & 0 \\ 0 & 2 \end{bmatrix},\ A^5 = \begin{bmatrix} 65 & -66 \\ 33 & -34 \end{bmatrix}$

3. $\mathbf{P} = \begin{bmatrix} 1 & 3 \\ 1 & 2 \end{bmatrix},\ \mathbf{D} = \begin{bmatrix} 0 & 0 \\ 0 & 2 \end{bmatrix},\ A^5 = \begin{bmatrix} 96 & -96 \\ 64 & -64 \end{bmatrix}$

4. $\mathbf{P} = \begin{bmatrix} 1 & 3 \\ 1 & 2 \end{bmatrix},\ \mathbf{D} = \begin{bmatrix} 1 & 0 \\ 0 & 2 \end{bmatrix},\ A^5 = \begin{bmatrix} 94 & -93 \\ 62 & -61 \end{bmatrix}$

5. $\mathbf{P} = \begin{bmatrix} 1 & 4 \\ 1 & 3 \end{bmatrix},\ \mathbf{D} = \begin{bmatrix} 1 & 0 \\ 0 & 2 \end{bmatrix},\ A^5 = \begin{bmatrix} 125 & -124 \\ 93 & -92 \end{bmatrix}$

6. $\mathbf{P} = \begin{bmatrix} 2 & 5 \\ 1 & 2 \end{bmatrix},\ \mathbf{D} = \begin{bmatrix} 1 & 0 \\ 0 & 2 \end{bmatrix},\ A^5 = \begin{bmatrix} 156 & -310 \\ 62 & -123 \end{bmatrix}$

7. $\mathbf{P} = \begin{bmatrix} 1 & 0 & 3 \\ 0 & 0 & 1 \\ 0 & 1 & 0 \end{bmatrix},\ \mathbf{D} = \begin{bmatrix} 1 & 0 & 0 \\ 0 & 2 & 0 \\ 0 & 0 & 2 \end{bmatrix},\ A^5 = \begin{bmatrix} 1 & 93 & 0 \\ 0 & 32 & 0 \\ 0 & 0 & 32 \end{bmatrix}$

8. $\mathbf{P} = \begin{bmatrix} 0 & 1 & 1 \\ 1 & 0 & 0 \\ 2 & 0 & 1 \end{bmatrix},\ \mathbf{D} = \begin{bmatrix} 1 & 0 & 0 \\ 0 & 1 & 0 \\ 0 & 0 & 2 \end{bmatrix},$

$A^5 = \begin{bmatrix} 1 & -62 & 31 \\ 0 & 1 & 0 \\ 0 & -62 & 32 \end{bmatrix}$

9. $\mathbf{P} = \begin{bmatrix} 1 & 1 & -3 \\ 0 & 0 & 1 \\ 0 & 1 & 0 \end{bmatrix},\ \mathbf{D} = \begin{bmatrix} 1 & 0 & 0 \\ 0 & 2 & 0 \\ 0 & 0 & 2 \end{bmatrix},$

$A^5 = \begin{bmatrix} 1 & -93 & 31 \\ 0 & 32 & 0 \\ 0 & 0 & 32 \end{bmatrix}$

10. $\mathbf{P} = \begin{bmatrix} 1 & -1 & 3 \\ 1 & 0 & 2 \\ 0 & 2 & 0 \end{bmatrix},\ \mathbf{D} = \begin{bmatrix} 1 & 0 & 0 \\ 0 & 2 & 0 \\ 0 & 0 & 2 \end{bmatrix},$

$A^5 = \begin{bmatrix} 94 & -93 & 31 \\ 62 & -61 & 31 \\ 0 & 0 & 32 \end{bmatrix}$

11. $\mathbf{P} = \begin{bmatrix} 0 & 0 & -1 \\ -1 & -2 & -42 \\ 3 & 5 & 87 \end{bmatrix},\ \mathbf{D} = \begin{bmatrix} -1 & 0 & 0 \\ 0 & 0 & 0 \\ 0 & 0 & 1 \end{bmatrix},$

$A^{10} = \begin{bmatrix} 1 & 0 & 0 \\ 78 & -5 & -2 \\ -195 & 15 & 6 \end{bmatrix}$

12. $\mathbf{P} = \begin{bmatrix} 1 & 1 & 3 \\ 2 & 0 & 5 \\ 0 & 5 & 0 \end{bmatrix},\ \mathbf{D} = \begin{bmatrix} -1 & 0 & 0 \\ 0 & 1 & 0 \\ 0 & 0 & 1 \end{bmatrix},$

$A^{10} = \begin{bmatrix} 1 & 0 & 0 \\ 0 & 1 & 0 \\ 0 & 0 & 1 \end{bmatrix}$

13. $\mathbf{P} = \begin{bmatrix} -1 & 1 & 1 \\ 0 & 1 & 1 \\ 2 & 0 & 1 \end{bmatrix},\ \mathbf{D} = \begin{bmatrix} -1 & 0 & 0 \\ 0 & 0 & 0 \\ 0 & 0 & 1 \end{bmatrix},$

$A^{10} = \begin{bmatrix} 3 & -3 & 1 \\ 2 & -2 & 1 \\ 0 & 0 & 1 \end{bmatrix}$

14. $\mathbf{P} = \begin{bmatrix} 1 & 1 & 2 \\ 0 & 1 & 1 \\ 2 & 0 & 1 \end{bmatrix},\ \mathbf{D} = \begin{bmatrix} -1 & 0 & 0 \\ 0 & 0 & 0 \\ 0 & 0 & 1 \end{bmatrix},$

$A^{10} = \begin{bmatrix} 3 & -3 & -1 \\ 2 & -2 & -1 \\ 0 & 0 & 1 \end{bmatrix}$

15. $\mathbf{A}^2 - 3\mathbf{A} + 2\mathbf{I} = \mathbf{0},\ \mathbf{A}^3 = \begin{bmatrix} 29 & -28 \\ 21 & -20 \end{bmatrix},\ \mathbf{A}^4 = \begin{bmatrix} 61 & -60 \\ 45 & -44 \end{bmatrix},$

$\mathbf{A}^{-1} = \frac{1}{2}\begin{bmatrix} -2 & 4 \\ -3 & 5 \end{bmatrix}$

16. $\mathbf{A}^2 - 3\mathbf{A} + 2\mathbf{I} = \mathbf{0},\ \mathbf{A}^3 = \begin{bmatrix} 36 & -70 \\ 14 & -27 \end{bmatrix},\ \mathbf{A}^4 = \begin{bmatrix} 76 & -150 \\ 30 & -59 \end{bmatrix},$

$\mathbf{A}^{-1} = \frac{1}{2}\begin{bmatrix} -3 & 10 \\ -2 & 6 \end{bmatrix}$

17. $-\mathbf{A}^3 + 5\mathbf{A}^2 - 8\mathbf{A} + 4\mathbf{I} = \mathbf{0},\ \mathbf{A}^3 = \begin{bmatrix} 1 & 21 & 0 \\ 0 & 8 & 0 \\ 0 & 0 & 8 \end{bmatrix},$

$\mathbf{A}^4 = \begin{bmatrix} 1 & 45 & 0 \\ 0 & 16 & 0 \\ 0 & 0 & 16 \end{bmatrix},\ \mathbf{A}^{-1} = \frac{1}{2}\begin{bmatrix} 2 & -3 & 0 \\ 0 & 1 & 0 \\ 0 & 0 & 1 \end{bmatrix}$

18. $-\mathbf{A}^3 + 4\mathbf{A}^2 - 5\mathbf{A} + 2\mathbf{I} = \mathbf{0},\ \mathbf{A}^3 = \begin{bmatrix} 1 & -14 & 7 \\ 0 & 1 & 0 \\ 0 & -14 & 8 \end{bmatrix},$

$\mathbf{A}^4 = \begin{bmatrix} 1 & -30 & 15 \\ 0 & 1 & 0 \\ 0 & -30 & 16 \end{bmatrix}\ \mathbf{A}^{-1} = \frac{1}{2}\begin{bmatrix} 2 & 2 & -1 \\ 0 & 2 & 0 \\ 0 & 2 & 1 \end{bmatrix}$

19. $-\mathbf{A}^3 + 5\mathbf{A}^2 - 8\mathbf{A} + 4\mathbf{I} = \mathbf{0},\ \mathbf{A}^3 = \begin{bmatrix} 1 & -21 & 7 \\ 0 & 8 & 0 \\ 0 & 0 & 8 \end{bmatrix},$

$\mathbf{A}^4 = \begin{bmatrix} 1 & -45 & 15 \\ 0 & 16 & 0 \\ 0 & 0 & 16 \end{bmatrix},\ \mathbf{A}^{-1} = \frac{1}{2}\begin{bmatrix} 2 & 3 & -1 \\ 0 & 1 & 0 \\ 0 & 0 & 1 \end{bmatrix}$

20. $-\mathbf{A}^3 + 5\mathbf{A}^2 - 8\mathbf{A} + 4\mathbf{I} = \mathbf{0},\ \mathbf{A}^3 = \begin{bmatrix} 22 & -21 & 7 \\ 14 & -13 & 7 \\ 0 & 0 & 8 \end{bmatrix},$

$\mathbf{A}^4 = \begin{bmatrix} 46 & -45 & 15 \\ 30 & -29 & 15 \\ 0 & 0 & 16 \end{bmatrix},\ \mathbf{A}^{-1} = \frac{1}{2}\begin{bmatrix} -1 & 3 & -1 \\ -2 & 4 & -1 \\ 0 & 0 & 1 \end{bmatrix}$

21. $-A^3 + A = 0$, $A^3 = A = \begin{bmatrix} 1 & 0 & 0 \\ 6 & 5 & 2 \\ 21 & -15 & -6 \end{bmatrix}$,

$A^4 = A^2 = \begin{bmatrix} 1 & 0 & 0 \\ 78 & -5 & -2 \\ -195 & 15 & 6 \end{bmatrix}$. Because $\lambda = 0$ is an

eigenvalue, A is singular and A^{-1} does not exist.

22. $-A^3 + A^2 + A - I = 0$, $A^3 = A = \begin{bmatrix} 11 & -6 & -2 \\ 20 & -11 & -4 \\ 0 & 0 & 1 \end{bmatrix} = A$,

$A^4 = \begin{bmatrix} 1 & 0 & 0 \\ 0 & 1 & 0 \\ 0 & 0 & 1 \end{bmatrix} = I$, $A^{-1} = A$

23. $-A^3 + A = 0$, $A^3 = A = \begin{bmatrix} 1 & -1 & 1 \\ 2 & -2 & 1 \\ 4 & -4 & 1 \end{bmatrix}$,

$A^4 = A^2 = \begin{bmatrix} 3 & -3 & 1 \\ 2 & -2 & 1 \\ 0 & 0 & 1 \end{bmatrix}$. Because $\lambda = 0$ is an eigenvalue,

A is singular and A^{-1} does not exist.

24. $-A^3 + A = 0$, $A^3 = A = \begin{bmatrix} 5 & -5 & -3 \\ 2 & -2 & -1 \\ 4 & -4 & -3 \end{bmatrix}$,

$A^4 = A^2 = \begin{bmatrix} 3 & -3 & -1 \\ 2 & -2 & -1 \\ 0 & 0 & 1 \end{bmatrix}$. Because $\lambda = 0$ is an eigenvalue,

A is singular and A^{-1} does not exist.

25. $\mathbf{x}_k = A^k \mathbf{x}_0 = \begin{bmatrix} 1 & -1 \\ 1 & 1 \end{bmatrix} \begin{bmatrix} 1 & 0 \\ 0 & 4/5 \end{bmatrix}^k \frac{1}{2} \begin{bmatrix} 1 & 1 \\ -1 & 1 \end{bmatrix} \mathbf{x}_0 \to =$

$(C_0 + S_0) \begin{bmatrix} 1/2 \\ 1/2 \end{bmatrix}$ as $k \to \infty$. The long-term distribution of population is 50% city, 50% suburban.

26. $\mathbf{x}_k = A^k \mathbf{x}_0 = \begin{bmatrix} 1 & -1 \\ 3 & 1 \end{bmatrix} \begin{bmatrix} 1 & 0 \\ 0 & 4/5 \end{bmatrix}^k \frac{1}{4} \begin{bmatrix} 1 & 1 \\ -3 & 1 \end{bmatrix} \mathbf{x}_0 \to =$

$(C_0 + S_0) \begin{bmatrix} 1/4 \\ 3/4 \end{bmatrix}$ as $k \to \infty$. The long-term distribution of population is 25% city, 75% suburban.

27. $\mathbf{x}_k = A^k \mathbf{x}_0 = \begin{bmatrix} 3 & -1 \\ 5 & 1 \end{bmatrix} \begin{bmatrix} 1 & 0 \\ 0 & 3/5 \end{bmatrix}^k \frac{1}{8} \begin{bmatrix} 1 & 1 \\ -5 & 3 \end{bmatrix} \mathbf{x}_0 \to =$

$(C_0 + S_0) \begin{bmatrix} 3/8 \\ 5/8 \end{bmatrix}$ as $k \to \infty$. The long-term distribution of population is 3/8 city, 5/8 suburban.

28. $\mathbf{x}_k = A^k \mathbf{x}_0 = \begin{bmatrix} 1 & -1 \\ 2 & 1 \end{bmatrix} \begin{bmatrix} 1 & 0 \\ 0 & 7/10 \end{bmatrix}^k \frac{1}{3} \begin{bmatrix} 1 & 1 \\ -2 & 1 \end{bmatrix} \mathbf{x}_0 \to =$

$(C_0 + S_0) \begin{bmatrix} 1/3 \\ 2/3 \end{bmatrix}$ as $k \to \infty$. The long-term distribution of population is 1/3 city, 2/3 suburban.

29. $\mathbf{x}_k = A^k \mathbf{x}_0 = \begin{bmatrix} 1 & -1 \\ 2 & 1 \end{bmatrix} \begin{bmatrix} 1 & 0 \\ 0 & 17/20 \end{bmatrix}^k \frac{1}{3} \begin{bmatrix} 1 & 1 \\ -2 & 1 \end{bmatrix} \mathbf{x}_0 \to =$

$(C_0 + S_0) \begin{bmatrix} 1/3 \\ 2/3 \end{bmatrix}$ as $k \to \infty$. The long-term distribution of population is 1/3 city, 2/3 suburban.

30. $\mathbf{x}_k = A^k \mathbf{x}_0 = \begin{bmatrix} 3 & -1 \\ 4 & 1 \end{bmatrix} \begin{bmatrix} 1 & 0 \\ 0 & 13/20 \end{bmatrix}^k \frac{1}{7} \begin{bmatrix} 1 & 1 \\ -4 & 3 \end{bmatrix} \mathbf{x}_0 \to =$

$(C_0 + S_0) \begin{bmatrix} 3/7 \\ 4/7 \end{bmatrix}$ as $k \to \infty$. The long-term distribution of population is 3/7 city, 4/7 suburban.

31. $\mathbf{x}_k = A^k \mathbf{x}_0 = \begin{bmatrix} 5 & 5 \\ 4 & 2 \end{bmatrix} \begin{bmatrix} 1 & 0 \\ 0 & 4/5 \end{bmatrix}^k \frac{1}{10} \begin{bmatrix} -2 & 5 \\ 4 & -5 \end{bmatrix} \mathbf{x}_0 \to =$

$\begin{bmatrix} 2.5R_0 - F_0 \\ 2R_0 - 0.8F_0 \end{bmatrix}$ as $k \to \infty$. The fox-rabbit population approaches a stable situation with $2.5R_0 - F_0$ foxes and $2R_0 - 0.8F_0$ rabbits.

32. $\mathbf{x}_k = A^k \mathbf{x}_0 = $

$\begin{bmatrix} 10 & 10 \\ 9 & 3 \end{bmatrix} \begin{bmatrix} 21/20 & 0 \\ 0 & 3/4 \end{bmatrix}^k \frac{1}{60} \begin{bmatrix} -3 & 10 \\ 9 & -10 \end{bmatrix} \mathbf{x}_0 \approx$

$\frac{1}{60}(1.05)^k (10R_0 - 3F_0) \begin{bmatrix} 10 \\ 9 \end{bmatrix}$ as when k is sufficiently large. The fox and rabbit populations are both increasing at 5% per year, with 10 foxes for each 9 rabbits.

33. $\mathbf{x}_k = A^k \mathbf{x}_0 = $

$\begin{bmatrix} 10 & 2 \\ 7 & 1 \end{bmatrix} \begin{bmatrix} 19/20 & 0 \\ 0 & 17/20 \end{bmatrix}^k \frac{1}{4} \begin{bmatrix} -1 & 2 \\ 7 & -10 \end{bmatrix} \mathbf{x}_0 \to = \begin{bmatrix} 0 \\ 0 \end{bmatrix}$ as

$k \to \infty$. The fox and rabbit population both die out.

34. $A = PDP^{-1} = \begin{bmatrix} 41 & -30 \\ 56 & -41 \end{bmatrix}$. If n is even then $D^n = I$ so

$A^n = PD^nP^{-1} = PIP^{-1} = I$. If n is odd then
$A^n = A^{n-1}A = IA = A$. Thus $A^{99} = A$ and $A^{100} = I$.

35. $\lambda = \pm 1$ implies that $D^n = I$ if n is even, in which case $A^n = PD^nP^{-1} = I$.

36. $A^2 = I$, so $A^3 = A^2A = IA = A$, $A^4 = A^3A = A^2 = I$, and so forth.

37. $A^2 = -I$, so $A^3 = A^2A = -IA = -A$, $A^4 = A^3A = -A^2 = I$, and so forth.

38. If $B = \begin{bmatrix} 0 & 1 \\ 0 & 0 \end{bmatrix}$ so $B^2 = 0$, and it follows that

$A^n = I + nB = \begin{bmatrix} 1 & n \\ 0 & 1 \end{bmatrix}$.

Chapter 7

Section 7.1

1. $x_1' = x_2$, $x_2' = -7x_1 - 3x_2 + t^2$

2. $x_1' = x_2$, $x_2' = x_3$, $x_3' = x_4$, $x_4' = -x_1 + 3x_2 - 6x_3 + \cos 3t$

3. $x_1' = x_2$, $t^2 x_2' = (1 - t^2)x_1 - tx_2$

4. $x_1' = x_2$, $x_2' = x_3$, $t^3 x_3' = -5x_1 - 3tx_2 + 2t^2 x_3 + \ln t$

5. $x_1' = x_2$, $x_2' = x_3$, $x_3' = x_2^2 + \cos x_1$

6. $x_1' = x_2$, $x_2' = 5x_1 - 4y_1$, $y_1' = y_2$, $y_2' = -4x_1 + 5y_1$

7. $x_1' = x_2$, $y_1' = y_2$, $x_2' = -kx_1 \cdot (x_1^2 + y_1^2)^{-3/2}$,
$y_2' = -ky_1 \cdot (x_1^2 + y_1^2)^{-3/2}$

8. $x_1' = x_2$, $x_2' = -4x_1 + 2y_1 - 3x_2$
$y_1' = y_2$, $y_2' = 3x_1 - y_1 - 2y_2 + \cos t$

9. $x_1' = x_2$, $y_1' = y_2$, $z_1' = z_2$, $x_2' = 3x_1 - y_1 + 2z_1$,
$y_2' = x_1 + y_1 - 4z_1$, $z_2' = 5x_1 - y_1 - z_1$

10. $x_1' = x_2$, $x_2' = x_1(1 - y_1)$
$y_1' = y_2$, $y_2' = y_1(1 - x_1)$

11. $x(t) = A \cos t + B \sin t$, $y(t) = B \cos t - A \sin t$

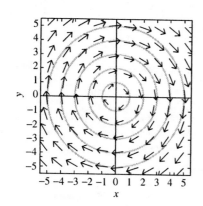

12. $x(t) = Ae^t + Be^{-t}$, $y(t) = Ae^t - Be^{-t}$

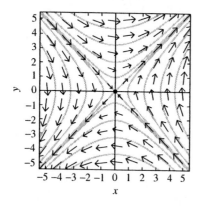

13. $x(t) = A \cos 2t + B \sin 2t$, $y(t) = -B \cos 2t + A \sin 2t$;
$x(t) = \cos 2t$, $y(t) = \sin 2t$

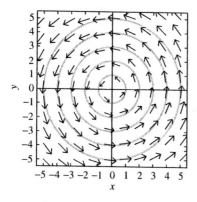

14. $x(t) = A \cos 10t + B \sin 10t$, $y(t) = B \cos 10t - A \sin 10t$;
$x(t) = 3 \cos 10t + 4 \sin 10t$, $y(t) = 4 \cos 10t - 3 \sin 10t$

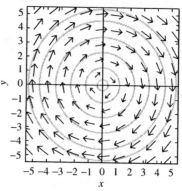

15. $x(t) = A \cos 2t + B \sin 2t$, $y(t) = 4B \cos 2t - 4A \sin 2t$

16. $x(t) = A \cos 4t + B \sin 4t$, $y(t) = \frac{1}{2}B \cos 4t - \frac{1}{2}A \sin 4t$

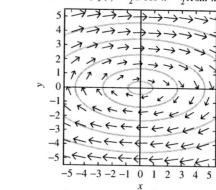

17. $x(t) = Ae^{-3t} + Be^{2t}$, $y(t) = -3Ae^{-3t} + 2Be^{2t}$; $x(t) = e^{2t}$,
$y(t) = 2e^{2t}$

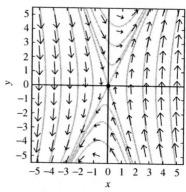

18. $x(t) = Ae^{-2t} + Be^{-5t}$, $y(t) = 2Ae^{-2t} + 5Be^{-5t}$; $A = \frac{17}{3}$ and $B = -\frac{11}{3}$ in the particular solution.

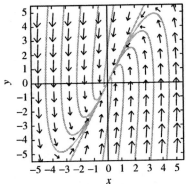

19. $x(t) = -e^{-2t}\sin 3t$, $y(t) = e^{-2t}(3\cos 3t + 2\sin 3t)$

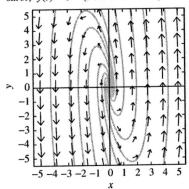

20. $x(t) = (A + Bt)e^{3t}$, $y(t) = (3A + B + 3Bt)e^{3t}$

Section 7.2

1. $(\mathbf{AB})' = \begin{bmatrix} 1 - 8t + 18t^2 & 1 + 2t - 12t^2 + 32t^3 \\ 3 + 3t^2 - 4t^3 & 8t + 3t^2 + 4t^3 \end{bmatrix}$

3. $\mathbf{x} = \begin{bmatrix} x \\ y \end{bmatrix}$, $\mathbf{P}(t) = \begin{bmatrix} 0 & -3 \\ 3 & 0 \end{bmatrix}$, $\mathbf{f}(t) = \begin{bmatrix} 0 \\ 0 \end{bmatrix}$

5. $\mathbf{x} = \begin{bmatrix} x \\ y \end{bmatrix}$, $\mathbf{P}(t) = \begin{bmatrix} 2 & 4 \\ 5 & -1 \end{bmatrix}$, $\mathbf{f}(t) = \begin{bmatrix} 3e^t \\ -t^2 \end{bmatrix}$

7. $\mathbf{x} = \begin{bmatrix} x \\ y \\ z \end{bmatrix}$, $\mathbf{P}(t) = \begin{bmatrix} 0 & 1 & 1 \\ 1 & 0 & 1 \\ 1 & 1 & 0 \end{bmatrix}$, $\mathbf{f}(t) = \begin{bmatrix} 0 \\ 0 \\ 0 \end{bmatrix}$

9. $\mathbf{x} = \begin{bmatrix} x \\ y \\ z \end{bmatrix}$, $\mathbf{P}(t) = \begin{bmatrix} 3 & -4 & 1 \\ 1 & 0 & -3 \\ 0 & 6 & -7 \end{bmatrix}$, $\mathbf{f}(t) = \begin{bmatrix} t \\ t^2 \\ t^3 \end{bmatrix}$

11. $\mathbf{x} = \begin{bmatrix} x_1 \\ x_2 \\ x_3 \\ x_4 \end{bmatrix}$, $\mathbf{P}(t) = \begin{bmatrix} 0 & 1 & 0 & 0 \\ 0 & 0 & 2 & 0 \\ 0 & 0 & 0 & 3 \\ 4 & 0 & 0 & 0 \end{bmatrix}$, $\mathbf{f}(t) = \begin{bmatrix} 0 \\ 0 \\ 0 \\ 0 \end{bmatrix}$

13. $W(t) = e^{3t}$; $\mathbf{x}(t) = \begin{bmatrix} 2c_1 e^t + c_2 e^{2t} \\ -3c_1 e^t - c_2 e^{2t} \end{bmatrix}$

15. $W(t) \equiv 4$; $\mathbf{x}(t) = \begin{bmatrix} c_1 e^{2t} + c_2 e^{-2t} \\ c_1 e^{2t} + 5c_2 e^{-2t} \end{bmatrix}$

17. $W(t) = 7e^{-3t}$; $\mathbf{x}(t) = \begin{bmatrix} 3c_1 e^{2t} + c_2 e^{-5t} \\ 2c_1 e^{2t} + 3c_2 e^{-5t} \end{bmatrix}$

19. $W(t) \equiv 3$; $\mathbf{x}(t) = \begin{bmatrix} c_1 e^{2t} + c_2 e^{-t} \\ c_1 e^{2t} + c_3 e^{-t} \\ c_1 e^{2t} - (c_2 + c_3)e^{-t} \end{bmatrix}$

21. $W(t) = e^{2t}$; $\mathbf{x}(t) = \begin{bmatrix} 3c_1 e^{-2t} + c_2 e^t + c_3 e^{3t} \\ -2c_1 e^{-2t} - c_2 e^t - c_3 e^{3t} \\ 2c_1 e^{-2t} + c_2 e^t \end{bmatrix}$

23. $\mathbf{x} = 2\mathbf{x}_1 - \mathbf{x}_2$ **25.** $\mathbf{x} = 15\mathbf{x}_1 - 4\mathbf{x}_2$

27. $\mathbf{x} = \mathbf{x}_1 + 2\mathbf{x}_2 + \mathbf{x}_3$ **29.** $\mathbf{x} = 3\mathbf{x}_1 - 3\mathbf{x}_2 - 5\mathbf{x}_3$

31. $\mathbf{x} = 3\mathbf{x}_1 + 7\mathbf{x}_2 + \mathbf{x}_3 - 2\mathbf{x}_4$ **32.** $\mathbf{x} = 13\mathbf{x}_1 + 41\mathbf{x}_2 + 3\mathbf{x}_3 - 12\mathbf{x}_4$

33. (a) $\mathbf{x}_2 = t\mathbf{x}_1$, so neither is a constant multiple of the other.
(b) $W(\mathbf{x}_1, \mathbf{x}_2) \equiv 0$, whereas Theorem 2 implies that $W \neq 0$ if $\mathbf{x}_1$ and $\mathbf{x}_2$ were independent solutions of a system of the indicated form.

Section 7.3

1. $x_1(t) = c_1 e^{-t} + c_2 e^{3t}$, $x_2(t) = -c_1 e^{-t} + c_2 e^{3t}$

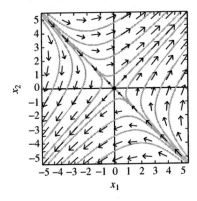

2. $x_1(t) = c_1 e^{-t} + 3c_2 e^{4t}$, $x_2(t) = -c_1 e^{-t} + 2c_2 e^{4t}$

3. General solution $x_1(t) = c_1 e^{-t} + 4c_2 e^{6t}$, $x_2(t) = -c_1 e^{-t} + 3c_2 e^{6t}$
Particular solution $x_1(t) = \frac{1}{7}(-e^{-t} + 8e^{6t})$, $x_2(t) = \frac{1}{7}(e^{-t} + 6e^{6t})$.

4. $x_1(t) = c_1 e^{-2t} + c_2 e^{5t}$, $x_2(t) = -6c_1 e^{-2t} + c_2 e^{5t}$

5. $x_1(t) = c_1 e^{-t} + 7c_2 e^{5t}$, $x_2(t) = c_1 e^{-t} + c_2 e^{5t}$

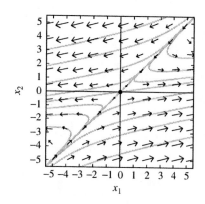

6. General solution $x_1(t) = 5c_1 e^{3t} + c_2 e^{4t}$, $x_2(t) = -6c_1 e^{3t} - c_2 e^{4t}$
Particular solution $x_1(t) = -5e^{3t} + 6e^{4t}$, $x_2(t) = 6e^{3t} - 6e^{4t}$.

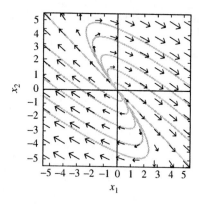

7. $x_1(t) = c_1 e^t + 2c_2 e^{-9t}$, $x_2(t) = c_1 e^t - 3c_2 e^{-9t}$

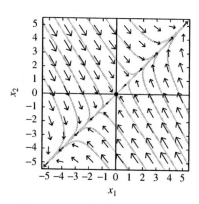

8. $x_1(t) = 5c_1 \cos 2t + 5c_2 \sin 2t$,
$x_2(t) = (c_1 - 2c_2) \cos 2t + (2c_1 + c_2) \sin 2t$

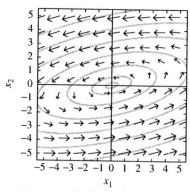

9. General solution $x_1(t) = 5c_1 \cos 4t + 5c_2 \sin 4t$,
$x_2(t) = c_1(2 \cos 4t + 4 \sin 4t) + c_2(2 \sin 4t - 4 \cos 4t)$.
Particular solution $x_1(t) = 2 \cos 4t - \frac{11}{4} \sin 4t$,
$x_2(t) = 3 \cos 4t + \frac{1}{2} \sin 4t$

10. $x_1(t) = -2c_1 \cos 3t - 2c_2 \sin 3t$,
$x_2(t) = (3c_1 + 3c_2) \cos 3t + (3c_2 - 3c_1) \sin 3t$

11. General solution $x_1(t) = e^t(c_1 \cos 2t - c_2 \sin 2t)$,
$x_2(t) = e^t(c_1 \sin 2t + c_2 \cos 2t)$
Particular solution $x_1(t) = -4e^t \sin 2t$, $x_2(t) = 4e^t \cos 2t$

12. $x_1(t) = e^{2t}(-5c_1 \cos 2t - 5c_2 \sin 2t)$,
$x_2(t) = e^{2t}[(c_1 + 2c_2) \cos 2t + (-2c_1 + c_2) \sin 2t]$

13. $x_1(t) = 3e^{2t}(c_1 \cos 3t - c_2 \sin 3t)$,
$x_2(t) = e^{2t}[(c_1 + c_2) \cos 3t + (c_1 - c_2) \sin 3t]$

14. $x_1(t) = e^{3t}(c_1 \cos 4t + c_2 \sin 4t)$,
$x_2(t) = e^{3t}(c_1 \sin 4t - c_2 \cos 4t)$

15. $x_1(t) = 5e^{5t}(c_1 \cos 4t - c_2 \sin 4t)$,
$x_2(t) = e^{5t}[(2c_1 + 4c_2) \cos 4t + (4c_1 - 2c_2) \sin 4t]$

16. $x_1(t) = c_1 e^{-10t} + 2c_2 e^{-100t}$, $x_2(t) = 2c_1 e^{-10t} - 5c_2 e^{-100t}$

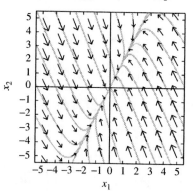

17. $x_1(t) = c_1 e^{9t} + c_2 e^{6t} + c_3,$
$x_2(t) = c_1 e^{9t} - 2c_2 e^{6t},$
$x_3(t) = c_1 e^{9t} + c_2 e^{6t} - c_3$

18. $x_1(t) = c_1 e^{9t} + 4c_3,$
$x_2(t) = 2c_1 e^{9t} + c_2 e^{6t} - c_3,$
$x_3(t) = 2c_1 e^{9t} - c_2 e^{6t} - c_3$

19. $x_1(t) = c_1 e^{6t} + c_2 e^{3t} + c_3 e^{3t},$
$x_2(t) = c_1 e^{6t} - 2c_2 e^{3t},$
$x_3(t) = c_1 e^{6t} + c_2 e^{3t} - c_3 e^{3t}$

20. $x_1(t) = c_1 e^{9t} + c_2 e^{6t} + c_3 e^{2t},$
$x_2(t) = c_1 e^{9t} - 2c_2 e^{6t},$
$x_3(t) = c_1 e^{9t} + c_2 e^{6t} - c_3 e^{2t}$

21. $x_1(t) = 6c_1 + 3c_2 e^{t} + 2c_3 e^{-t},$
$x_2(t) = 2c_1 + c_2 e^{t} + c_3 e^{-t},$
$x_3(t) = 5c_1 + 2c_2 e^{t} + 2c_3 e^{-t}$

22. $x_1(t) = c_2 e^{t} + c_3 e^{3t},$
$x_2(t) = c_1 e^{-2t} - c_2 e^{t} - c_3 e^{3t},$
$x_3(t) = -c_1 e^{-2t} + c_3 e^{3t}$

23. $x_1(t) = c_1 e^{2t} + c_3 e^{3t},$
$x_2(t) = -c_1 e^{2t} + c_2 e^{-2t} - c_3 e^{3t},$
$x_3(t) = -c_2 e^{-2t} + c_3 e^{3t}$

24. $x_1(t) = c_1 e^{t} + c_2(2\cos 2t - \sin 2t) + c_3(\cos 2t + 2\sin 2t)$
$x_2(t) = -c_1 e^{t} - c_2(3\cos 2t + \sin 2t) + c_3(\cos 2t - 3\sin 2t)$
$x_3(t) = c_2(3\cos 2t + \sin 2t) + c_3(3\sin 2t - \cos 2t)$

25. $x_1(t) = c_1 + e^{2t}[(c_2 + c_3)\cos 3t + (-c_2 + c_3)\sin 3t],$
$x_2(t) = -c_1 + 2e^{2t}(-c_2 \cos 3t - c_3 \sin 3t),$
$x_3(t) = 2e^{2t}(c_2 \cos 3t + c_3 \sin 3t)$

26. $x_1(t) = 4e^{3t} - e^{-t}(4\cos t - \sin t),$
$x_2(t) = 9e^{3t} - e^{-t}(9\cos t + 2\sin t),$
$x_3(t) = 17e^{-t}\cos t$

27. $x_1(t) = 15e^{-0.2t},$ $x_2(t) = 15(e^{-0.2t} - e^{-0.4t}).$
The maximum amount ever in tank 2 is $x_2(5\ln 2) = 3.75$ lb.

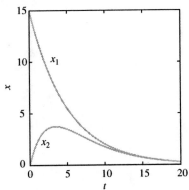

28. $x_1(t) = 15e^{-0.4t},$ $x_2(t) = 40(-e^{-0.4t} + e^{-0.25t}).$
The maximum amount ever in tank 2 is about 6.85 lb.

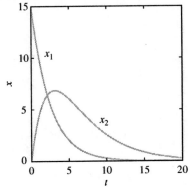

29. $x_1(t) = 10 + 5e^{-0.6t},$ $x_2(t) = 5 - 5e^{-0.6t}$

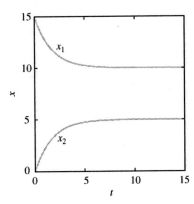

30. $x_1(t) = 5c_1 + c_2 e^{-0.65t},$ $x_2(t) = 8c_1 - c_2 e^{-0.65t}.$

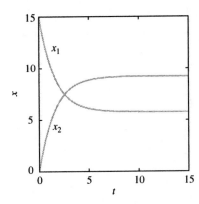

31. $x_1(t) = 27e^{-t},$
$x_2(t) = 27e^{-t} - 27e^{-2t},$
$x_3(t) = 27e^{-t} - 54e^{-2t} + 27e^{-3t}.$
The maximum amount of salt ever in tank 3 is $x_3(\ln 3) = 4$ pounds.

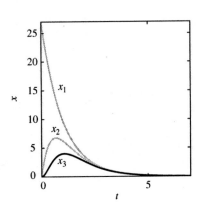

32. $x_1(t) = 45e^{-3t},$
$x_2(t) = -135e^{-3t} + 135e^{-2t},$
$x_3(t) = 135e^{-3t} - 270e^{-2t} + 135e^{-t}.$

The maximum amount of salt ever in tank 3 is $x_3(\ln 3) = 20$ pounds.

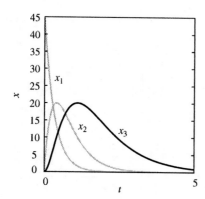

33. $x_1(t) = 45e^{-4t}$,
$x_2(t) = 90e^{-4t} - 90e^{-6t}$,
$x_3(t) = -270e^{-4t} + 135e^{-6t} + 135e^{-2t}$.
The maximum amount of salt ever in tank 3 is
$x_3\left(\frac{1}{2}\ln 3\right) = 20$ pounds.

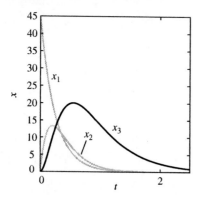

34. $x_1(t) = 40e^{-3t}$,
$x_2(t) = 60e^{-3t} - 60e^{-5t}$,
$x_3(t) = -150e^{-3t} + 75e^{-5t} + 75e^{-t}$.
The maximum amount of salt ever in tank 3 is
$x_3\left(\frac{1}{2}\ln 5\right) \approx 21.4663$ pounds.

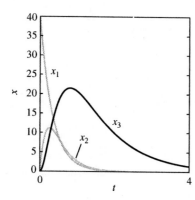

35. $x_1(t) = 10 - \frac{1}{7}\left(55e^{-18t} - 216e^{-11t}\right)$,
$x_2(t) = 3 - \frac{1}{7}\left(165e^{-18t} - 144e^{-11t}\right)$,
$x_3(t) = 20 + \frac{1}{7}\left(220e^{-18t} - 360e^{-11t}\right)$.
The limiting amounts of salt in tanks 1, 2, and 3 are 10 lb, 3 lb,

and 20 lb.

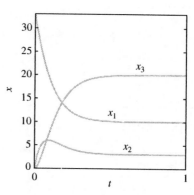

36. $x_1(t) = 4 + e^{-3t/5}[14\cos(3t/10) - 2\sin(3t/10)]$,
$x_2(t) = 10 - e^{-3t/5}[10\cos(3t/10) - 10\sin(3t/10)]$,
$x_3(t) = 4 - e^{-3t/5}[4\cos(3t/10) + 8\sin(3t/10)]$.
The limiting amounts of salt in tanks 1, 2, and 3 are 4 lb, 10 lb, and 4 lb.

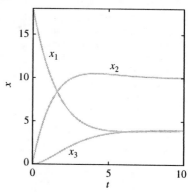

37. $x_1(t) = 30 + e^{-3t}[25\cos(t\sqrt{2}) + 10\sqrt{2}\sin(t\sqrt{2})]$,
$x_2(t) = 10 - e^{-3t}[10\cos(t\sqrt{2}) - \frac{25}{2}\sqrt{2}\sin(t\sqrt{2})]$,
$x_3(t) = 15 - e^{-3t}[15\cos(t\sqrt{2}) + \frac{45}{2}\sqrt{2}\sin(t\sqrt{2})]$.
The limiting amounts of salt in tanks 1, 2, and 3 are 30 lb, 10 lb, and 15 lb.

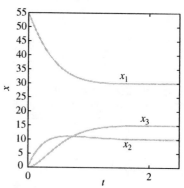

38. $x_1(t) = c_1e^t$,
$x_2(t) = -2c_1e^t + c_2e^{2t}$,
$x_3(t) = 3c_1e^t - 3c_2e^{2t} + c_3e^{3t}$,
$x_4(t) = -4c_1e^t + 6c_2e^{2t} - 4c_3e^{3t} + c_4e^{4t}$

39. $x_1(t) = 3c_1e^t + c_4e^{-2t}$,
$x_2(t) = -2c_1e^t + c_3e^{2t} - c_4e^{-2t}$,
$x_3(t) = 4c_1e^t + c_2e^{-t}$,
$x_4(t) = c_1e^t$

40. $x_1(t) = c_1 e^{2t}$,
$x_2(t) = -3c_1 e^{2t} + 3c_2 e^{-2t} - c_4 e^{-5t}$,
$x_3(t) = c_3 e^{5t}$,
$x_4(t) = -c_2 e^{-2t} - 3c_3 e^{5t}$

41. $x_1(t) = 2e^{10t} + e^{15t} = x_4(t)$, $x_2(t) = -e^{10t} + 2e^{15t} = x_3(t)$

42. $\mathbf{x}(t) = c_1 \begin{bmatrix} 3 \\ -1 \\ 2 \end{bmatrix} + c_2 \begin{bmatrix} 1 \\ 1 \\ 1 \end{bmatrix} e^{2t} + c_3 \begin{bmatrix} 2 \\ -3 \\ 1 \end{bmatrix} e^{5t}$

43. $\mathbf{x}(t) = c_1 \begin{bmatrix} 3 \\ -1 \\ 5 \end{bmatrix} e^{-2t} + c_2 \begin{bmatrix} 1 \\ 1 \\ 1 \end{bmatrix} e^{4t} + c_3 \begin{bmatrix} 1 \\ -1 \\ 3 \end{bmatrix} e^{8t}$

44. $\mathbf{x}(t) = c_1 \begin{bmatrix} 3 \\ -2 \\ 2 \end{bmatrix} e^{-3t} + c_2 \begin{bmatrix} 7 \\ 1 \\ 5 \end{bmatrix} e^{6t} + c_3 \begin{bmatrix} 5 \\ -3 \\ 3 \end{bmatrix} e^{12t}$

45. $\mathbf{x}(t) = c_1 \begin{bmatrix} 1 \\ 1 \\ 1 \\ -1 \end{bmatrix} e^{-3t} + c_2 \begin{bmatrix} 1 \\ 2 \\ -1 \\ 1 \end{bmatrix} + c_3 \begin{bmatrix} 2 \\ 1 \\ 1 \\ 1 \end{bmatrix} e^{3t} + c_4 \begin{bmatrix} 1 \\ -1 \\ 2 \\ -1 \end{bmatrix} e^{6t}$

46. $\mathbf{x}(t) =$
$c_1 \begin{bmatrix} 3 \\ 2 \\ -1 \\ 1 \end{bmatrix} e^{-4t} + c_2 \begin{bmatrix} 1 \\ 2 \\ 2 \\ -1 \end{bmatrix} e^{2t} + c_3 \begin{bmatrix} 1 \\ 1 \\ -1 \\ 1 \end{bmatrix} e^{4t} + c_4 \begin{bmatrix} 3 \\ -2 \\ 3 \\ -3 \end{bmatrix} e^{8t}$

47. $\mathbf{x}(t) = c_1 \begin{bmatrix} 2 \\ 2 \\ 1 \\ -1 \end{bmatrix} e^{-3t} + c_2 \begin{bmatrix} 1 \\ 2 \\ -1 \\ 1 \end{bmatrix} e^{3t} + c_3 \begin{bmatrix} 2 \\ 1 \\ 1 \\ 1 \end{bmatrix} e^{6t} + c_4 \begin{bmatrix} 1 \\ -1 \\ 2 \\ -1 \end{bmatrix} e^{9t}$

48. $\mathbf{x}(t) =$
$c_1 \begin{bmatrix} 1 \\ 2 \\ -1 \\ 2 \end{bmatrix} e^{16t} + c_2 \begin{bmatrix} 2 \\ 5 \\ 1 \\ -1 \end{bmatrix} e^{32t} + c_3 \begin{bmatrix} 3 \\ -1 \\ 1 \\ 2 \end{bmatrix} e^{48t} + c_4 \begin{bmatrix} 1 \\ 1 \\ 2 \\ -3 \end{bmatrix} e^{64t}$

49. $\mathbf{x}(t) =$
$c_1 \begin{bmatrix} 1 \\ 0 \\ 3 \\ 1 \\ 1 \end{bmatrix} e^{-3t} + c_2 \begin{bmatrix} 0 \\ 3 \\ 0 \\ -1 \\ 1 \end{bmatrix} + c_3 \begin{bmatrix} 1 \\ 7 \\ 1 \\ 1 \\ 1 \end{bmatrix} e^{3t} + c_4 \begin{bmatrix} 0 \\ 1 \\ 0 \\ 1 \\ 1 \end{bmatrix} e^{6t} + c_5 \begin{bmatrix} 2 \\ 0 \\ 5 \\ 2 \\ 1 \end{bmatrix} e^{9t}$

50. $\mathbf{x}(t) = c_1 \begin{bmatrix} 0 \\ 1 \\ 1 \\ 1 \\ 0 \\ 1 \end{bmatrix} e^{-7t} + c_2 \begin{bmatrix} 1 \\ 0 \\ 0 \\ 0 \\ 1 \\ 1 \end{bmatrix} e^{-4t} + c_3 \begin{bmatrix} 0 \\ 1 \\ 0 \\ 1 \\ 0 \\ 1 \end{bmatrix} e^{3t} +$

$c_4 \begin{bmatrix} 0 \\ 0 \\ 1 \\ 0 \\ 1 \\ 0 \end{bmatrix} e^{5t} + c_5 \begin{bmatrix} 1 \\ 1 \\ 0 \\ 0 \\ 0 \\ 1 \end{bmatrix} e^{9t} + c_6 \begin{bmatrix} 0 \\ 0 \\ 1 \\ -1 \\ -1 \\ 0 \end{bmatrix} e^{11t}$

Section 7.4

1. The natural frequencies are $\omega_0 = 0$ and $\omega_1 = 2$. In the degenerate natural mode with "frequency" $\omega_0 = 0$ the two masses move linearly with $x_1(t) = x_2(t) = a_0 + b_0 t$. At frequency $\omega_1 = 2$ they oscillate in opposite directions with equal amplitudes.

2. The natural frequencies are $\omega_1 = 1$ and $\omega_2 = 3$. In the natural mode with frequency ω_1, the two masses m_1 and m_2 move in the same direction with equal amplitudes of oscillation. At frequency ω_2 they move in opposite directions with equal amplitudes.

3. The natural frequencies are $\omega_1 = 1$ and $\omega_2 = 2$. In the natural mode with frequency ω_1, the two masses m_1 and m_2 move in the same direction with equal amplitudes of oscillation. In the natural mode with frequency ω_2 they move in opposite directions with the amplitude of oscillation of m_1 twice that of m_2.

4. The natural frequencies are $\omega_1 = 1$ and $\omega_2 = \sqrt{5}$. In the natural mode with frequency ω_1, the two masses m_1 and m_2 move in the same direction with equal amplitudes of oscillation. At frequency ω_2 they move in opposite directions with equal amplitudes.

5. The natural frequencies are $\omega_1 = \sqrt{2}$ and $\omega_2 = 2$. In the natural mode with frequency ω_1, the two masses m_1 and m_2 move in the same direction with equal amplitudes of oscillation. At frequency ω_2 they move in opposite directions with equal amplitudes.

6. The natural frequencies are $\omega_1 = \sqrt{2}$ and $\omega_2 = \sqrt{8}$. In the natural mode with frequency ω_1, the two masses m_1 and m_2 move in the same direction with equal amplitudes of oscillation. In the natural mode with frequency ω_2 they move in opposite directions with the amplitude of oscillation of m_1 twice that of m_2.

7. The natural frequencies are $\omega_1 = 2$ and $\omega_2 = 4$. In the natural mode with frequency ω_1, the two masses m_1 and m_2 move in the same direction with equal amplitudes of oscillation. At frequency ω_2 they move in opposite directions with equal amplitudes.

8. $x_1(t) = 2\cos t + 3\cos 3t - 5\cos 5t$,
$x_2(t) = 2\cos t - 3\cos 3t + \cos 5t$.
We have a superposition of three oscillations, in which the two masses move (1) in the same direction with frequency $\omega_1 = 1$ and equal amplitudes; (2) in opposite directions with frequency $\omega_2 = 3$ and equal amplitudes; (3) in opposite directions with frequency $\omega_3 = 5$ and with the amplitude of motion of m_1 being 5 times that of m_2.

9. $x_1(t) = 5\cos t - 8\cos 2t + 3\cos 3t$,
$x_2(t) = 5\cos t + 4\cos 2t - 9\cos 3t$.
We have a superposition of three oscillations, in which the two masses move (1) in the same direction with frequency $\omega_1 = 1$ and equal amplitudes; (2) in opposite directions with frequency $\omega_2 = 2$ and with the amplitude of motion of m_1 being twice that of m_2; (3) in opposite directions with frequency $\omega_3 = 3$ and with the amplitude of motion of m_2 being 3 times that of m_1.

10. $x_1(t) = \cos 2t - 15\cos 4t + 14\cos t$,
$x_2(t) = \cos 2t + 15\cos 4t + 16\cos t$.
We have a superposition of three oscillations, in which the two masses move (1) in the same direction with frequency $\omega_1 = 1$ and with the amplitude of motion of m_2 being $8/7$ times that of m_1; (2) in the same direction with frequency $\omega_2 = 2$ and equal amplitudes; (3) in opposite directions with frequency $\omega_3 = 4$ and equal amplitudes.

11. (a) The natural frequencies are $\omega_1 = 6$ and $\omega_2 = 8$. In mode 1 the two masses oscillate in the same direction with frequency $\omega_1 = 6$ and with the amplitude of motion of m_1 being twice that of m_2. In mode 2 the two masses oscillate in opposite directions with frequency $\omega_2 = 8$ and with the amplitude of motion of m_2 being 3 times that of m_1.
(b) $x(t) = 2\sin 6t + 19\cos 7t$, $y(t) = \sin 6t + 3\cos 7t$
We have a superposition of (only two) oscillations, in which the two masses move (1) in the same direction with frequency

$\omega_1 = 6$ and with the amplitude of motion of m_1 being twice that of m_2; (2) in the same direction with frequency $\omega_3 = 7$ and with the amplitude of motion of m_1 being 19/3 times that of m_2.

12. The system's three natural modes of oscillation have (1) natural frequency $\omega_1 = \sqrt{2}$ with amplitude ratios $1:0:-1$; (2) natural frequency $\omega_2 = \sqrt{2+\sqrt{2}}$ with amplitude ratios $1:-\sqrt{2}:1$; (3) natural frequency $\omega_3 = \sqrt{2-\sqrt{2}}$ with amplitude ratios $1:\sqrt{2}:1$.

13. The system's three natural modes of oscillation have (1) natural frequency $\omega_1 = 2$ with amplitude ratios $1:0:-1$; (2) natural frequency $\omega_2 = \sqrt{4+2\sqrt{2}}$ with amplitude ratios $1:-\sqrt{2}:1$; (3) natural frequency $\omega_3 = \sqrt{4-2\sqrt{2}}$ with amplitude ratios $1:\sqrt{2}:1$.

15. $x_1(t) = \frac{2}{3}\cos 5t - 2\cos 5\sqrt{3}t + \frac{4}{3}\cos 10t$,
$x_2(t) = \frac{4}{3}\cos 5t + 4\cos 5\sqrt{3}t + \frac{16}{3}\cos 10t$.
We have a superposition of two oscillations with the natural frequencies $\omega_1 = 5$ and $\omega_2 = 5\sqrt{3}$ and a forced oscillation with frequency $\omega = 10$. In each of the two natural oscillations the amplitude of motion of m_2 is twice that of m_1, while in the forced oscillation the amplitude of motion of m_2 is four times that of m_1.

21. (a) $\omega_1 \approx 1.0293$ Hz; $\omega_2 \approx 1.7971$ Hz
(b) $v_1 \approx 28$ mi/h; $v_2 \approx 49$ mi/h

23. $\omega_1 = 2\sqrt{10}$, $v_1 \approx 40.26$ (ft/s (about 27 mi/h),
$\omega_2 = 5\sqrt{5}$, $v_2 \approx 71.18$ ft/s (about 49 mi/h)

24. $\omega_1 \approx 6.1311$, $v_1 \approx 39.03$ ft/s (about 27 mi/h)
$\omega_2 \approx 10.3155$, $v_2 \approx 65.67$ ft/s (about 45 mi/h)

25. $\omega_1 \approx 5.0424$, $v_1 \approx 32.10$ ft/s (about 22 mi/h),
$\omega_2 \approx 9.9158$, $v_2 \approx 63.13$ ft/s (about 43 mi/h)

Section 7.5

1. Repeated eigenvalue $\lambda = -3$, eigenvector $\mathbf{v} = \begin{bmatrix} 1 & -1 \end{bmatrix}^T$;
$x_1(t) = (c_1 + c_2 + c_2 t)e^{-3t}$, $x_2(t) = (-c_1 - c_2 t)e^{-3t}$

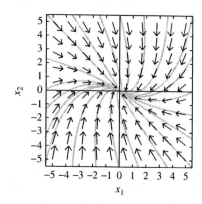

2. Repeated eigenvalue $\lambda = 2$, single eigenvector $\mathbf{v} = \begin{bmatrix} 1 & 1 \end{bmatrix}^T$;
$x_1(t) = (c_1 + c_2 + c_2 t)e^{2t}$, $x_2(t) = (c_1 + c_2 t)e^{2t}$

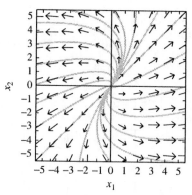

3. Repeated eigenvalue $\lambda = 3$, eigenvector $\mathbf{v} = \begin{bmatrix} -2 & 2 \end{bmatrix}^T$;
$x_1(t) = (-2c_1 + c_2 - 2c_2 t)e^{3t}$, $x_2(t) = (2c_1 + 2c_2 t)e^{3t}$

4. Repeated eigenvalue $\lambda = 4$, single eigenvector $\mathbf{v} = \begin{bmatrix} -1 & 1 \end{bmatrix}^T$;
$x_1(t) = (-c_1 + c_2 - c_2 t)e^{4t}$, $x_2(t) = (c_1 + c_2 t)e^{4t}$

5. Repeated eigenvalue $\lambda = 5$, eigenvector $\mathbf{v} = \begin{bmatrix} 2 & -4 \end{bmatrix}^T$;
$x_1(t) = (2c_1 + c_2 + 2c_2 t)e^{5t}$, $x_2(t) = (-4c_1 - 4c_2 t)e^{5t}$

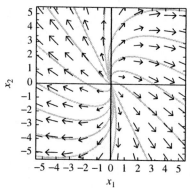

6. Repeated eigenvalue $\lambda = 5$, single eigenvector $\mathbf{v} = \begin{bmatrix} -4 & 4 \end{bmatrix}^T$;
$x_1(t) = (-4c_1 + c_2 - 4c_2 t)e^{5t}$, $x_2(t) = (4c_1 + 4c_2 t)e^{5t}$

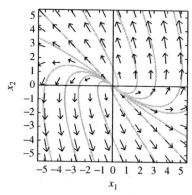

7. Eigenvalues $\lambda = 2, 2, 9$ with three linearly independent eigenvectors; $x_1(t) = c_1 e^{2t} + c_2 e^{2t}$, $x_2(t) = c_1 e^{2t} + c_3 e^{9t}$, $x_3(t) = c_2 e^{2t}$

8. Eigenvalues $\lambda = 7, 13, 13$ with three linearly independent eigenvectors; $x_1(t) = 2c_1 e^{7t} - c_3 e^{13t}$, $x_2(t) = -3c_1 e^{7t} + c_3 e^{13t}$, $x_3(t) = c_1 e^{7t} + c_2 e^{13t}$

9. Eigenvalues $\lambda = 5, 5, 9$ with three linearly independent eigenvectors; $x_1(t) = c_1 e^{5t} + 7c_2 e^{5t} + 3c_3 e^{9t}$, $x_2(t) = 2c_1 e^{5t}$, $x_3(t) = 2c_2 e^{5t} + c_3 e^{9t}$

10. Eigenvalues $\lambda = 3, 3, 7$ with three linearly independent eigenvectors; $x_1(t) = 5c_1e^{3t} - 3c_2e^{3t} + 2c_3e^{7t}$,
$x_2(t) = 2c_1e^{3t} + c_3e^{7t}$, $x_3(t) = c_2e^{3t}$

11. Triple eigenvalue $\lambda = -1$ of defect 2;
$x_1(t) = (-2c_2 + c_3 - 2c_3t)e^{-t}$,
$x_2(t) = (c_1 - c_2 + c_2t - c_3t + \frac{1}{2}c_3t^2)e^{-t}$,
$x_3(t) = (c_2 + c_3t)e^{-t}$

12. Triple eigenvalue $\lambda = -1$ of defect 2;
$x_1(t) = e^{-t}(c_1 + c_3 + c_2t + \frac{1}{2}c_3t^2)$
$x_2(t) = e^{-t}(c_1 + c_2t + \frac{1}{2}c_3t^2)$,
$x_3(t) = e^{-t}(c_2 + c_3t)$

13. Triple eigenvalue $\lambda = -1$ of defect 2;
$x_1(t) = (c_1 + c_2t + \frac{1}{2}c_3t^2)e^{-t}$,
$x_2(t) = (2c_2 + c_3 + 2c_3t)e^{-t}$,
$x_3(t) = (c_2 + c_2t)e^{-t}$

14. Triple eigenvalue $\lambda = -1$ of defect 2;
$x_1(t) = e^{-t}(5c_1 + c_2 + c_3 + 5c_2t + c_3t + \frac{5}{2}c_3t^2)$,
$x_2(t) = e^{-t}(-25c_1 - 5c_2 - 25c_2t - 5c_3t - \frac{25}{2}c_3t^2)$,
$x_3(t) = e^{-t}(-5c_1 + 4c_2 - 5c_2t + 4c_3t - \frac{5}{2}c_3t^2)$

15. Triple eigenvalue $\lambda = 1$ of defect 1;
$x_1(t) = (3c_1 + c_3 - 3c_3t)e^{t}$,
$x_2(t) = (-c_1 + c_3t)e^{t}$, $x_3(t) = (c_2 + c_3t)e^{t}$

16. Triple eigenvalue $\lambda = 1$ of defect 1;
$x_1(t) = e^{t}(3c_1 + 3c_2 + c_3)$
$x_2(t) = e^{t}(-2c_1 - 2c_3t)$,
$x_3(t) = e^{t}(-2c_2 + 2c_3t)$

17. Triple eigenvalue $\lambda = 1$ of defect 1;
$x_1(t) = (2c_1 + c_2)e^{t}$, $x_2(t) = (-3c_2 + c_3 + 6c_3t)e^{t}$,
$x_3(t) = -9(c_1 + c_3t)e^{t}$

18. Triple eigenvalue $\lambda = 1$ of defect 1;
$x_1(t) = e^{t}(-c_1 - 2c_2 + c_3)$,
$x_2(t) = e^{t}(c_2 + c_3t)$,
$x_3(t) = e^{t}(c_1 - 2c_3t)$

19. Double eigenvalues $\lambda = -1$ and $\lambda = 1$, each with defect 1;
$x_1(t) = c_1e^{-t} + c_4e^{t}$,
$x_2(t) = c_3e^{t}$,
$x_3(t) = c_2e^{-t} + 3c_4e^{t}$,
$x_4(t) = c_1e^{-t} - 2c_3e^{t}$

20. Eigenvalue $\lambda = 2$ with multiplicity 4 and defect 3;
$x_1(t) = (c_1 + c_3 + c_2t + c_4t + \frac{1}{2}c_3t^2 + \frac{1}{6}c_4t^3)e^{2t}$,
$x_2(t) = (c_2 + c_3t + \frac{1}{2}c_4t^2)e^{2t}$,
$x_3(t) = (c_3 + c_4t)e^{2t}$, $x_4(t) = c_4e^{2t}$

21. Eigenvalue $\lambda = 1$ with multiplicity 4 and defect 2;
$x_1(t) = (-2c_2 + c_3 - 2c_3t)e^{t}$, $x_2(t) = (c_2 + c_3t)e^{t}$,
$x_3(t) = (c_2 + c_4 + c_3t)e^{t}$, $x_4(t) = (c_1 + c_2t + \frac{1}{2}c_3t^2)e^{t}$

22. Eigenvalue $\lambda = 1$ with multiplicity 4 and defect 2;
$x_1(t) = (c_1 + 3c_2 + c_4 + c_2t + 3c_3t + \frac{1}{2}c_3t^2)e^{t}$,
$x_2(t) = -(2c_2 - c_3 + 2c_3t)e^{t}$, $x_3(t) = (c_2 + c_3t)e^{t}$,
$x_4(t) = -(2c_1 + 6c_2 + 2c_2t + 6c_3t + c_3t^2)e^{t}$

23. $\mathbf{x}(t) = c_1\mathbf{v}_1e^{-t} + (c_2\mathbf{v}_2 + c_3\mathbf{v}_3)e^{3t}$ with $\mathbf{v}_1 = \begin{bmatrix} 1 & -1 & 2 \end{bmatrix}^T$,
$\mathbf{v}_2 = \begin{bmatrix} 4 & 0 & 9 \end{bmatrix}^T$, $\mathbf{v}_3 = \begin{bmatrix} 0 & 2 & 1 \end{bmatrix}^T$

24. $\mathbf{x}(t) = c_1\mathbf{v}_1e^{-t} + (c_2\mathbf{v}_2 + c_3\mathbf{v}_3)e^{3t}$ with $\mathbf{v}_1 = \begin{bmatrix} 5 & 3 & -3 \end{bmatrix}^T$,
$\mathbf{v}_2 = \begin{bmatrix} 4 & 0 & -1 \end{bmatrix}^T$, $\mathbf{v}_3 = \begin{bmatrix} 2 & -1 & 0 \end{bmatrix}^T$

25. $\mathbf{x}(t) = \left[c_1\mathbf{v}_1 + c_2(\mathbf{v}_1t + \mathbf{v}_2) + c_3\left(\frac{1}{2}\mathbf{v}_1t^2 + \mathbf{v}_2t + \mathbf{v}_3\right) \right] e^{2t}$ with
$\mathbf{v}_1 = \begin{bmatrix} -1 & 0 & -1 \end{bmatrix}^T$, $\mathbf{v}_2 = \begin{bmatrix} -4 & -1 & 0 \end{bmatrix}^T$, and
$\mathbf{v}_3 = \begin{bmatrix} 1 & 0 & 0 \end{bmatrix}^T$

26. $\mathbf{x}(t) = \left[c_1\mathbf{v}_1 + c_2(\mathbf{v}_1t + \mathbf{v}_2) + c_3\left(\frac{1}{2}\mathbf{v}_1t^2 + \mathbf{v}_2t + \mathbf{v}_3\right) \right] e^{3t}$ with
$\mathbf{v}_1 = \begin{bmatrix} 0 & 2 & 2 \end{bmatrix}^T$, $\mathbf{v}_3 = \begin{bmatrix} 2 & 1 & -3 \end{bmatrix}^T$, and
$\mathbf{v}_3 = \begin{bmatrix} 1 & 0 & 0 \end{bmatrix}^T$

27. $\mathbf{x}(t) = [c_1\mathbf{v}_1 + c_2(\mathbf{v}_1t + \mathbf{v}_2) + c_3\mathbf{v}_3]e^{2t}$ with $\mathbf{v}_1 = \begin{bmatrix} -5 & 3 & 8 \end{bmatrix}^T$,
$\mathbf{v}_2 = \begin{bmatrix} 1 & 0 & 0 \end{bmatrix}^T$, $\mathbf{v}_3 = \begin{bmatrix} 1 & 1 & 0 \end{bmatrix}^T$

28. $\mathbf{x}(t) = \left[c_1\mathbf{v}_1 + c_2(\mathbf{v}_1t + \mathbf{v}_2) + c_3\left(\frac{1}{2}\mathbf{v}_1t^2 + \mathbf{v}_2t + \mathbf{v}_3\right) \right] e^{2t}$ with
$\mathbf{v}_1 = \begin{bmatrix} 119 & -289 & 0 \end{bmatrix}^T$, $\mathbf{v}_2 = \begin{bmatrix} -17 & 34 & 17 \end{bmatrix}^T$, and
$\mathbf{v}_3 = \begin{bmatrix} 1 & 0 & 0 \end{bmatrix}^T$

29. $\mathbf{x}(t) = [c_1\mathbf{v}_1 + c_2(\mathbf{v}_1t + \mathbf{v}_2)]e^{-t} + [c_3\mathbf{v}_3 + c_4(\mathbf{v}_3t + \mathbf{v}_4)]e^{2t}$ with
$\mathbf{v}_1 = \begin{bmatrix} 1 & -3 & -1 & -2 \end{bmatrix}^T$, $\mathbf{v}_2 = \begin{bmatrix} 0 & 1 & 0 & 0 \end{bmatrix}^T$,
$\mathbf{v}_3 = \begin{bmatrix} 0 & -1 & 1 & 0 \end{bmatrix}^T$, $\mathbf{v}_4 = \begin{bmatrix} 0 & 0 & 2 & 1 \end{bmatrix}^T$

30. $\mathbf{x}(t) = [c_1\mathbf{v}_1 + c_2(\mathbf{v}_1t + \mathbf{v}_2)]e^{-t} + [c_3\mathbf{v}_3 + c_4(\mathbf{v}_3t + \mathbf{v}_4)]e^{2t}$, with
$\mathbf{v}_1 = \begin{bmatrix} 0 & 1 & -1 & -3 \end{bmatrix}^T$, $\mathbf{v}_2 = \begin{bmatrix} 0 & 0 & 1 & 2 \end{bmatrix}^T$,
$\mathbf{v}_3 = \begin{bmatrix} -1 & 0 & 0 & 0 \end{bmatrix}^T$, $\mathbf{v}_4 = \begin{bmatrix} 0 & 0 & 3 & 5 \end{bmatrix}^T$

31. $\mathbf{x}(t) = [c_1\mathbf{v}_1 + c_2(\mathbf{v}_1t + \mathbf{v}_2)$
$+ c_3\left(\frac{1}{2}\mathbf{v}_1t^2 + \mathbf{v}_2t + \mathbf{v}_3\right) + c_4\mathbf{v}_4] e^{t}$ with
$\mathbf{v}_1 = \begin{bmatrix} 42 & 7 & -21 & -42 \end{bmatrix}^T$, $\mathbf{v}_2 = \begin{bmatrix} 34 & 22 & -10 & -27 \end{bmatrix}^T$,
$\mathbf{v}_3 = \begin{bmatrix} -1 & 0 & 0 & 0 \end{bmatrix}^T$, $\mathbf{v}_4 = \begin{bmatrix} 0 & 1 & 3 & 0 \end{bmatrix}^T$

32. $\mathbf{x}(t) = (c_1\mathbf{v}_1 + c_2\mathbf{v}_2)e^{2t} + (c_3\mathbf{v}_3 + c_4\mathbf{v}_4 + c_5\mathbf{v}_5)e^{3t}$ with
$\mathbf{v}_1 = \begin{bmatrix} 8 & 0 & -3 & 1 & 0 \end{bmatrix}^T$, $\mathbf{v}_2 = \begin{bmatrix} 1 & 0 & 0 & 0 & 3 \end{bmatrix}^T$,
$\mathbf{v}_3 = \begin{bmatrix} 3 & -2 & -1 & 0 & 0 \end{bmatrix}^T$, $\mathbf{v}_4 = \begin{bmatrix} 2 & -2 & 0 & -3 & 0 \end{bmatrix}^T$,
$\mathbf{v}_5 = \begin{bmatrix} 1 & -1 & 0 & 0 & 3 \end{bmatrix}^T$

33. $\mathbf{x}_1(t) = \begin{bmatrix} \cos 4t & \sin 4t & 0 & 0 \end{bmatrix}^T e^{3t}$,
$\mathbf{x}_2(t) = \begin{bmatrix} -\sin 4t & \cos 4t & 0 & 0 \end{bmatrix}^T e^{3t}$,
$\mathbf{x}_3(t) = \begin{bmatrix} t\cos 4t & t\sin 4t & \cos 4t & \sin 4t \end{bmatrix}^T e^{3t}$,
$\mathbf{x}_4(t) = \begin{bmatrix} -t\sin 4t & t\cos 4t & -\sin 4t & \cos 4t \end{bmatrix}^T e^{3t}$

34. $\mathbf{x}_1(t) = \begin{bmatrix} \sin 3t \\ 3\cos 3t - 3\sin 3t \\ 0 \\ \sin 3t \end{bmatrix} e^{2t}$,

$\mathbf{x}_2(t) = \begin{bmatrix} -\cos 3t \\ 3\sin 3t + 3\cos 3t \\ 0 \\ -\cos 3t \end{bmatrix} e^{2t}$,

$\mathbf{x}_3(t) = \begin{bmatrix} 3\cos 3t + t\sin 3t \\ (3t-10)\cos 3t - (3t+9)\sin 3t \\ \sin 3t \\ t\sin 3t \end{bmatrix} e^{2t}$,

$\mathbf{x}_4(t) = \begin{bmatrix} -t\cos 3t + 3\sin 3t \\ (3t+9)\cos 3t + (3t-10)\sin 3t \\ -\cos 3t \\ -t\cos 3t \end{bmatrix} e^{2t}$

35. $x_1(t) = x_2(t) = v_0(1 - e^{-t})$; $\lim_{t\to\infty} x_1(t) = \lim_{t\to\infty} x_2(t) = v_0$

36. $x_1(t) = v_0(2 - 2e^{-t} - te^{-t})$,
$x_2(t) = v_0(2 - 2e^{-t} - te^{-t} - \frac{1}{2}t^2e^{-t})$; $\lim_{t\to\infty} x_1(t) = \lim_{t\to\infty} x_2(t) = 2v_0$

In Problems 37, 39, 41, 43, and 45 we give a nonsingular matrix $\mathbf{Q}$ and a Jordan-form matrix $\mathbf{J}$ such that $\mathbf{A} = \mathbf{QJQ}^{-1}$. Any scalar multiple of $\mathbf{Q}$ will do the same job.

37. $\mathbf{Q} = \begin{bmatrix} 1 & 4 & -2 \\ -1 & 0 & 9 \\ 2 & 9 & 0 \end{bmatrix}$, $\mathbf{J} = \begin{bmatrix} -1 & 0 & 0 \\ 0 & 3 & 0 \\ 0 & 0 & 3 \end{bmatrix}$

39. $\mathbf{Q} = \begin{bmatrix} 1 & 4 & -1 \\ 0 & 1 & 0 \\ 1 & 0 & 0 \end{bmatrix}$, $\mathbf{J} = \begin{bmatrix} 2 & 1 & 0 \\ 0 & 2 & 1 \\ 0 & 0 & 2 \end{bmatrix}$

41. $\mathbf{Q} = \begin{bmatrix} 0 & -5 & 0 \\ 1 & 3 & 0 \\ 1 & 8 & 1 \end{bmatrix}$, $\mathbf{J} = \begin{bmatrix} 2 & 0 & 0 \\ 0 & 2 & 1 \\ 0 & 0 & 2 \end{bmatrix}$

43. $Q = \begin{bmatrix} -1 & 0 & 0 & 0 \\ 3 & -1 & -1 & 2 \\ 1 & 0 & 1 & 0 \\ 2 & 0 & 0 & 1 \end{bmatrix}$, $J = \begin{bmatrix} -1 & 1 & 0 & 0 \\ 0 & -1 & 0 & 0 \\ 0 & 0 & 2 & 1 \\ 0 & 0 & 0 & 2 \end{bmatrix}$

45. $Q = \begin{bmatrix} -30 & 432 & 360 & 0 \\ -7 & 72 & 228 & 0 \\ 9 & -216 & -108 & 0 \\ 30 & -432 & -288 & 12 \end{bmatrix}$, $J = \begin{bmatrix} 1 & 0 & 0 & 0 \\ 0 & 1 & 1 & 0 \\ 0 & 0 & 1 & 1 \\ 0 & 0 & 0 & 1 \end{bmatrix}$

Section 7.6

The format for the first eight answers is this: $(x(t), y(t))$ at $t = 0.2$ by the Euler method, by the improved Euler method, by the Runge-Kutta method, and finally the actual values.

1. $(0.8800, 2.5000)$, $(0.9600, 2.6000)$, $(1.0027, 2.6401)$, $(1.0034, 2.6408)$

2. $(0.8100, -0.8100)$, $(0.8200, -0.8200)$, $(0.8187, -0.8187)$, $(0.8187, -0.8187)$

3. $(2.8100, 2.3100)$, $(3.2200, 2.6200)$, $(3.6481, 2.9407)$, $(3.6775, 2.9628)$

4. $(3.3100, -1.6200)$, $(3.8200, -2.0400)$, $(4.2274, -2.4060)$, $(4.2427, -2.4205)$

5. $(-0.5200, 2.9200)$, $(-0.8400, 2.4400)$, $(-0.5712, 2.4485)$, $(-0.5793, 2.4488)$

6. $(-1.7600, 4.6800)$, $(-1.9200, 4.5600)$, $(-1.9029, 4.4995)$, $(-1.9025, 4.4999)$

7. $(3.1200, 1.6800)$, $(3.2400, 1.7600)$, $(3.2816, 1.7899)$, $(3.2820, 1.7902)$

8. $(2.1600, -0.6300)$, $(2.5200, -0.4600)$, $(2.5320, -0.3867)$, $(2.5270, -0.3889)$

9. At $t = 1$ we obtain $(x, y) = (3.99261, 6.21770)$ $(h = 0.1)$ and $(3.99234, 6.21768)$ $(h = 0.05)$; the actual value is $(3.99232, 6.21768)$.

10. At $t = 1$ we obtain $(x, y) = (1.31498, 1.02537)$ $(h = 0.1)$ and $(1.31501, 1.02538)$ $(h = 0.05)$; the actual value is $(1.31501, 1.02538)$.

11. At $t = 1$ we obtain $(x, y) = (-0.05832, 0.56664)$ $(h = 0.1)$ and $(-0.05832, 0.56665)$ $(h = 0.05)$; the actual value is $(-0.05832, 0.56665)$.

12. We solved $x' = y$, $y' = -x + \sin t$, $x(0) = y(0) = 0$. With $h = 0.1$ and also with $h = 0.05$ we obtain the actual value $x(1.0) \approx 0.15058$.

13. Runge-Kutta, $h = 0.1$: about 1050 ft in about 7.7 s

14. Runge-Kutta, $h = 0.1$: about 1044 ft in about 7.8 s

15. Runge-Kutta, $h = 1.0$: about 83.83 mi in about 168 s

16. At 40°: 5.0 s, 352.9 ft; at 45°: 5.4 s, 347.2 ft; at 50°: 5.8 s, 334.2 ft (all values approximate)

17. At 39.0° the range is about 352.7 ft. At 39.5° it is 352.8; at 40°, 352.9; at 40.5°, 352.6; at 41.0°, 352.1.

18. Just under 57.5°

19. Approximately 253 ft/s

20. Maximum height: about 1005 ft, attained in about 5.6 s; range: about 1880 ft; time aloft: about 11.6 s

21. Runge-Kutta with $h = 0.1$ yields these results: (a) 21400 ft, 46 s, 518 ft/s; (b) 8970 ft, 17.5 s; (c) 368 ft/s (at $t \approx 23$).

Appendix A

1. $y_0 = 3$, $y_1 = 3 + 3x$, $y_2 = 3 + 3x + \frac{3}{2}x^2$, $y_3 = 3 + 3x + \frac{3}{2}x^2 + \frac{1}{2}x^3$, $y_4 = 3 + 3x + \frac{3}{2}x^2 + \frac{1}{2}x^3 + \frac{1}{8}x^4$; $y(x) = 3e^x$

3. $y_0 = 1$, $y_1 = 1 - x^2$, $y_2 = 1 - x^2 + \frac{1}{2}x^4$, $y_3 = 1 - x^2 + \frac{1}{2}x^4 - \frac{1}{6}x^6$, $y_4 = 1 - x^2 + \frac{1}{2}x^4 - \frac{1}{6}x^6 + \frac{1}{24}x^8$; $y(x) = \exp\left(-x^2\right)$

5. $y_0 = 0$, $y_1 = 2x$, $y_2 = 2x + 2x^2$, $y_3 = 2x + 2x^2 + \frac{4}{3}x^3$, $y_4 = 2x + 2x^2 + \frac{4}{3}x^3 + \frac{2}{3}x^4$; $y(x) = e^{2x} - 1$

7. $y_0 = 0$, $y_1 = x^2$, $y_2 = x^2 + \frac{1}{2}x^4$, $y_3 = x^2 + \frac{1}{2}x^4 + \frac{1}{6}x^6$, $y_4 = x^2 + \frac{1}{2}x^4 + \frac{1}{6}x^6 + \frac{1}{24}x^8$; $y(x) = \exp(x^2) - 1$

9. $y_0 = 1$, $y_1 = (1 + x) + \frac{1}{2}x^2$, $y_2 = (1 + x + x^2) + \frac{1}{6}x^3$, $y_3 = \left(1 + x + x^2 + \frac{1}{3}x^3\right) + \frac{1}{24}x^4$; $y(x) = 2e^x - 1 - x = 1 + x + x^2 + \frac{1}{3}x^3 + \cdots$

11. $y_0 = 1$, $y_1 = 1 + x$, $y_2 = (1 + x + x^2) + \frac{1}{3}x^3$, $y_3 = (1 + x + x^2 + x^3) + \frac{2}{3}x^4 + \frac{1}{3}x^5 + \frac{1}{9}x^6 + \frac{1}{63}x^7$; $y(x) = \frac{1}{1 - x} = 1 + x + x^2 + x^3 + x^4 + x^5 + \cdots$

12. $y_0 = 1$, $y_1 = 1 + \frac{1}{2}x$, $y_2 = 1 + \frac{1}{2}x + \frac{3}{8}x^3 + \frac{1}{8}x^3 + \frac{1}{64}x^4$, $y_3 = 1 + \frac{1}{2}x + \frac{3}{8}x^2 + \frac{5}{16}x^3 + \frac{13}{64}x^4 + \cdots$; $y(x) = (1 - x)^{-1/2}$

13. $\begin{bmatrix} x_0 \\ y_0 \end{bmatrix} = \begin{bmatrix} 1 \\ -1 \end{bmatrix}$, $\begin{bmatrix} x_1 \\ y_1 \end{bmatrix} = \begin{bmatrix} 1 + 3t \\ -1 + 3t \end{bmatrix}$, $\begin{bmatrix} x_2 \\ y_2 \end{bmatrix} = \begin{bmatrix} 1 + 3t + \frac{1}{2}t^2 \\ -1 + 5t - \frac{1}{2}t^2 \end{bmatrix}$, $\begin{bmatrix} x_3 \\ y_3 \end{bmatrix} = \begin{bmatrix} 1 + 3t + \frac{1}{2}t^2 + \frac{1}{3}t^3 \\ -1 + 5t - \frac{1}{2}t^2 + \frac{5}{6}t^3 \end{bmatrix}$

14. $\mathbf{x}(t) = \begin{bmatrix} e^t + te^t \\ e^t \end{bmatrix}$

16. $y_3(1) \approx 0.350185$

INDEX

Boldface page numbers indicate where terms are defined.

UNIT B

DIFFERENTIAL EQUATIONS AND BOUNDARY VALUE PROBLEMS

Computing and Modeling

Third Edition

C. Henry Edwards

David E. Penney

CHAPTER 7

Laplace Transform Methods

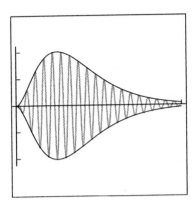

7.1 Laplace Transforms and Inverse Transforms

$$D\{f(t)\} = f'(t)$$

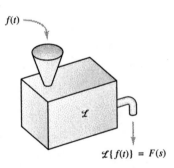

$$\mathcal{L}\{f(t)\} = F(s)$$

FIGURE 7.1.1. Transformation of a function: $\mathcal{L}$ in analogy with D.

In Chapter 3 we saw that linear differential equations with constant coefficients have numerous applications and can be solved systematically. There are common situations, however, in which the alternative methods of this chapter are preferable. For example, recall the differential equations

$$mx'' + cx' + kx = F(t) \quad \text{and} \quad LI'' + RI' + \frac{1}{C}I = E'(t)$$

corresponding to a mass-spring-dashpot system and a series RLC circuit, respectively. It often happens in practice that the forcing term, $F(t)$ or $E'(t)$, has discontinuities— for example, when the voltage supplied to an electrical circuit is turned off and on periodically. In this case the methods of Chapter 3 can be quite awkward, and the Laplace transform method is more convenient.

The differentiation operator D can be viewed as a transformation which, when applied to the function $f(t)$, yields the new function $D\{f(t)\} = f'(t)$. The Laplace transformation $\mathcal{L}$ involves the operation of integration and yields the new function $\mathcal{L}\{f(t)\} = F(s)$ of a new independent variable s. The situation is diagrammed in Fig. 7.1.1. After learning in this section how to compute the Laplace transform $F(s)$ of a function $f(t)$, we will see in Section 7.2 that the Laplace transform converts a *differential* equation in the unknown function $f(t)$ into an *algebraic* equation in $F(s)$. Because algebraic equations are generally easier to solve than differential equations, this is one method that simplifies the problem of finding the solution $f(t)$.

547

Definition: The Laplace Transform

Given a function $f(t)$ defined for all $t \geq 0$, the *Laplace transform* of f is the function F defined as follows:

➤
$$F(s) = \mathcal{L}\{f(t)\} = \int_0^\infty e^{-st} f(t)\, dt \tag{1}$$

for all values of s for which the improper integral converges.

Recall that an **improper integral** over an infinite interval is defined as a limit of integrals over bounded intervals; that is,

$$\int_a^\infty g(t)\, dt = \lim_{b \to \infty} \int_a^b g(t)\, dt. \tag{2}$$

If the limit in (2) exists, then we say that the improper integral **converges;** otherwise, it **diverges** or fails to exist. Note that the integrand of the improper integral in (1) contains the parameter s in addition to the variable of integration t. Therefore, when the integral in (1) converges, it converges not merely to a number, but to a *function* F of s. As in the following examples, it is typical for the improper integral in the definition of $\mathcal{L}\{f(t)\}$ to converge for some values of s and diverge for others.

Example 1

With $f(t) \equiv 1$ for $t \geq 0$, the definition of the Laplace transform in (1) gives

$$\mathcal{L}\{1\} = \int_0^\infty e^{-st}\, dt = \left[-\frac{1}{s} e^{-st} \right]_0^\infty = \lim_{b \to \infty} \left[-\frac{1}{s} e^{-bs} + \frac{1}{s} \right],$$

and therefore

$$\mathcal{L}\{1\} = \frac{1}{s} \quad \text{for} \quad s > 0. \tag{3}$$

As in (3), it's good practice to specify the domain of the Laplace transform—in problems as well as in examples. Also, in this computation we have used the common abbreviation

$$\left[g(t) \right]_a^\infty = \lim_{b \to \infty} \left[g(t) \right]_a^b. \tag{4}$$

∎

Remark: The limit we computed in Example 1 would not exist if $s < 0$, for then $(1/s)e^{-bs}$ would become unbounded as $b \to +\infty$. Hence $\mathcal{L}\{1\}$ is defined only for $s > 0$. This is typical of Laplace transforms; the domain of a transform is normally of the form $s > a$ for some number a. ∎

Example 2

With $f(t) = e^{at}$ for $t \geq 0$, we obtain

$$\mathcal{L}\{e^{at}\} = \int_0^\infty e^{-st} e^{at}\, dt = \int_0^\infty e^{-(s-a)t}\, dt = \left[-\frac{e^{-(s-a)t}}{s-a} \right]_{t=0}^\infty.$$

If $s - a > 0$, then $e^{-(s-a)t} \to 0$ as $t \to +\infty$, so it follows that

$$\blacktriangleright \qquad \mathcal{L}\{e^{at}\} = \frac{1}{s-a} \quad \text{for} \quad s > a. \qquad (5)$$

Note here that the improper integral giving $\mathcal{L}\{e^{at}\}$ diverges if $s \leqq a$. It is worth noting also that the formula in (5) holds if a is a complex number. For then, with $a = \alpha + i\beta$,

$$e^{-(s-a)t} = e^{i\beta t}e^{-(s-\alpha)t} \to 0$$

as $t \to +\infty$, provided that $s > \alpha = \text{Re}(a)$; recall that $e^{i\beta t} = \cos \beta t + i \sin \beta t$. $\blacksquare$

The Laplace transform $\mathcal{L}\{t^a\}$ of a power function is most conveniently expressed in terms of the **gamma function** $\Gamma(x)$, which is defined for $x > 0$ by the formula

$$\blacktriangleright \qquad \Gamma(x) = \int_0^\infty e^{-t}t^{x-1} \, dt. \qquad (6)$$

For an elementary discussion of $\Gamma(x)$, see the subsection on the gamma function in Section 8.5, where it is shown that

$$\Gamma(1) = 1 \qquad (7)$$

and that

$$\Gamma(x + 1) = x\Gamma(x) \qquad (8)$$

for $x > 0$. It then follows that if n is a positive integer, then

$$\begin{aligned}
\Gamma(n + 1) &= n\Gamma(n) \\
&= n \cdot (n-1)\Gamma(n-1) \\
&= n \cdot (n-1) \cdot (n-2)\Gamma(n-2) \\
&\;\;\vdots \\
&= n(n-1)(n-2)\cdots 2 \cdot \Gamma(2) \\
&= n(n-1)(n-2)\cdots 2 \cdot 1 \cdot \Gamma(1);
\end{aligned}$$

thus

$$\blacktriangleright \qquad \Gamma(n + 1) = n! \qquad (9)$$

if n is a positive integer. Therefore, the function $\Gamma(x + 1)$, which is defined and continuous for all $x > -1$, agrees with the factorial function for $x = n$, a positive integer.

Example 3 Suppose that $f(t) = t^a$ where a is real and $a > -1$. Then

$$\mathcal{L}\{t^a\} = \int_0^\infty e^{-st}t^a \, dt.$$

If we substitute $u = st$, $t = u/s$, and $dt = du/s$ in this integral, we get

$$\mathcal{L}\{t^a\} = \frac{1}{s^{a+1}} \int_0^\infty e^{-u}u^a \, du = \frac{\Gamma(a+1)}{s^{a+1}} \qquad (10)$$

for all $s > 0$ (so that $u = st > 0$). Because $\Gamma(n + 1) = n!$ if n is a nonnegative integer, we see that

$$\mathcal{L}\{t^n\} = \frac{n!}{s^{n+1}} \quad \text{for} \quad s > 0. \tag{11}$$

For instance,

$$\mathcal{L}\{t\} = \frac{1}{s^2}, \quad \mathcal{L}\{t^2\} = \frac{2}{s^3}, \quad \text{and} \quad \mathcal{L}\{t^3\} = \frac{6}{s^4}.$$

As in Problems 1 and 2, these formulas can be derived immediately from the definition, without the use of the gamma function. ∎

Linearity of Transforms

It is not necessary for us to proceed much further in the computation of Laplace transforms directly from the definition. Once we know the Laplace transforms of several functions, we can combine them to obtain transforms of other functions. The reason is that the Laplace transformation is a *linear* operation.

THEOREM 1: Linearity of the Laplace Transform

If a and b are constants, then

$$\mathcal{L}\{af(t) + bg(t)\} = a\mathcal{L}\{f(t)\} + b\mathcal{L}\{g(t)\} \tag{12}$$

for all s such that the Laplace transforms of the functions f and g both exist. ▲

The proof of Theorem 1 follows immediately from the linearity of the operations of taking limits and of integration:

$$\mathcal{L}\{af(t) + bg(t)\} = \int_0^\infty e^{-st}[af(t) + bg(t)]\, dt$$

$$= \lim_{c \to \infty} \int_0^c e^{-st}[af(t) + bg(t)]\, dt$$

$$= a\left(\lim_{c \to \infty} \int_0^c e^{-st}f(t)\, dt\right) + b\left(\lim_{c \to \infty} \int_0^c e^{-st}g(t)\, dt\right)$$

$$= a\mathcal{L}\{f(t)\} + b\mathcal{L}\{g(t)\}.$$

Example 4 The computation of $\mathcal{L}\{t^{n/2}\}$ is based on the known special value

$$\Gamma\left(\frac{1}{2}\right) = \sqrt{\pi} \tag{13}$$

of the gamma function. For instance, it follows that

$$\Gamma\left(\frac{5}{2}\right) = \frac{3}{2}\Gamma\left(\frac{3}{2}\right) = \frac{3}{2} \cdot \frac{1}{2}\Gamma\left(\frac{1}{2}\right) = \frac{3}{4}\sqrt{\pi},$$

using the formula $\Gamma(x+1) = x\Gamma(x)$ in (9), first with $x = \frac{3}{2}$ and then with $x = \frac{1}{2}$. Now the formulas in (10) through (12) yield

$$\mathcal{L}\{3t^2 + 4t^{3/2}\} = 3 \cdot \frac{2!}{s^3} + \frac{4\Gamma\left(\frac{5}{2}\right)}{s^{5/2}} = \frac{6}{s^3} + 3\sqrt{\frac{\pi}{s^5}}. \qquad \blacksquare$$

Example 5   Recall that $\cosh kt = (e^{kt} + e^{-kt})/2$. If $k > 0$, then Theorem 1 and Example 2 together give

$$\mathcal{L}\{\cosh kt\} = \frac{1}{2}\mathcal{L}\{e^{kt}\} + \frac{1}{2}\mathcal{L}\{e^{-kt}\} = \frac{1}{2}\left(\frac{1}{s-k} + \frac{1}{s+k}\right);$$

that is,

$$\mathcal{L}\{\cosh kt\} = \frac{s}{s^2 - k^2} \qquad \text{for } s > k > 0. \qquad (14)$$

Similarly,

$$\mathcal{L}\{\sinh kt\} = \frac{k}{s^2 - k^2} \qquad \text{for } s > k > 0. \qquad (15)$$

Because $\cos kt = (e^{ikt} + e^{-ikt})/2$, the formula in (5) (with $a = ik$) yields

$$\mathcal{L}\{\cos kt\} = \frac{1}{2}\left(\frac{1}{s-ik} + \frac{1}{s+ik}\right) = \frac{1}{2} \cdot \frac{2s}{s^2 - (ik)^2},$$

and thus

$$\mathcal{L}\{\cos kt\} = \frac{s}{s^2 + k^2} \qquad \text{for } s > 0. \qquad (16)$$

(The domain follows from $s > \text{Re}(ik) = 0$.) Similarly,

$$\mathcal{L}\{\sin kt\} = \frac{k}{s^2 + k^2} \qquad \text{for } s > 0. \qquad (17)$$
$\blacksquare$

Example 6   Applying linearity, the formula in (16), and a familiar trigonometric identity, we get

$$\mathcal{L}\{3e^{2t} + 2\sin^2 3t\} = \mathcal{L}\{3e^{2t} + 1 - \cos 6t\}$$

$$= \frac{3}{s-2} + \frac{1}{s} - \frac{s}{s^2 + 36}$$

$$= \frac{3s^3 + 144s - 72}{s(s-2)(s^2 + 36)} \qquad \text{for } s > 0. \qquad \blacksquare$$

Inverse Transforms

According to Theorem 3 of this section, no two different functions that are both continuous for all $t \geq 0$ can have the same Laplace transform. Thus if $F(s)$ is the transform of some continuous function $f(t)$, then $f(t)$ is uniquely determined. This observation allows us to make the following definition: If $F(s) = \mathcal{L}\{f(t)\}$, then we call $f(t)$ the **inverse Laplace transform** of $F(s)$ and write

$$f(t) = \mathcal{L}^{-1}\{F(s)\}. \tag{18}$$

Example 7

$$\mathcal{L}^{-1}\left\{\frac{1}{s^3}\right\} = \frac{1}{2}t^2, \quad \mathcal{L}^{-1}\left\{\frac{1}{s+2}\right\} = e^{-2t}, \quad \mathcal{L}^{-1}\left\{\frac{2}{s^2+9}\right\} = \frac{2}{3}\sin 3t,$$

and so on. ∎

NOTATION: FUNCTIONS AND THEIR TRANSFORMS. Throughout this chapter we denote functions of t by lowercase letters. The transform of a function will always be denoted by that same letter capitalized. Thus $F(s)$ is the Laplace transform of $f(t)$ and $x(t)$ is the inverse Laplace transform of $X(s)$.

A table of Laplace transforms serves a purpose similar to that of a table of integrals. The table in Fig. 7.1.2 lists the transforms derived in this section; many additional transforms can be derived from these few, using various general properties of the Laplace transformation (which we will discuss in subsequent sections).

Piecewise Continuous Functions

As we remarked at the beginning of this section, we need to be able to handle certain types of discontinuous functions. The function $f(t)$ is said to be **piecewise continuous** on the bounded interval $a \leq t \leq b$ provided that $[a, b]$ can be subdivided into finitely many abutting subintervals in such a way that

1. f is continuous in the interior of each of these subintervals; and
2. $f(t)$ has a finite limit as t approaches each endpoint of each subinterval from its interior.

$f(t)$	$F(s)$	
1	$\dfrac{1}{s}$	$(s > 0)$
t	$\dfrac{1}{s^2}$	$(s > 0)$
t^n $(n \geq 0)$	$\dfrac{n!}{s^{n+1}}$	$(s > 0)$
t^a $(a > -1)$	$\dfrac{\Gamma(a+1)}{s^{a+1}}$	$(s > 0)$
e^{at}	$\dfrac{1}{s-a}$	$(s > 0)$
$\cos kt$	$\dfrac{s}{s^2+k^2}$	$(s > 0)$
$\sin kt$	$\dfrac{k}{s^2+k^2}$	$(s > 0)$
$\cosh kt$	$\dfrac{s}{s^2-k^2}$	$(s > |k|)$
$\sinh kt$	$\dfrac{k}{s^2-k^2}$	$(s > |k|)$
$u(t-a)$	$\dfrac{e^{-as}}{s}$	$(s > 0)$

FIGURE 7.1.2. A short table of Laplace transforms.

We say that f is piecewise continuous for $t \geq 0$ if it is piecewise continuous on every bounded subinterval of $[0, +\infty)$. Thus a piecewise continuous function has only simple discontinuities (if any) and only at isolated points. At such points the value of the function experiences a finite jump, as indicated in Fig. 7.1.3. The **jump in $f(t)$ at the point** c is defined to be $f(c+) - f(c-)$, where

$$f(c+) = \lim_{\epsilon \to 0^+} f(c+\epsilon) \quad \text{and} \quad f(c-) = \lim_{\epsilon \to 0^+} f(c-\epsilon).$$

Perhaps the simplest piecewise continuous (but discontinuous) function is the **unit step function**, whose graph appears in Fig. 7.1.4. It is defined as follows:

$$u(t) = \begin{cases} 0 & \text{for } t < 0, \\ 1 & \text{for } t \geq 0. \end{cases} \tag{19}$$

Because $u(t) = 1$ for $t \geq 0$ and because the Laplace transform involves only the values of a function for $t \geq 0$, we see immediately that

$$\mathcal{L}\{u(t)\} = \frac{1}{s} \quad (s > 0). \tag{20}$$

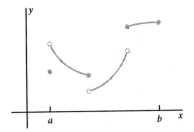

FIGURE 7.1.3. The graph of a piecewise continuous function; the solid dots indicate values of the function at discontinuities.

FIGURE 7.1.4. The graph of the unit step function.

FIGURE 7.1.5. The unit step function $u_a(t)$ has a jump at $t = a$.

The graph of the unit step function $u_a(t) = u(t - a)$ appears in Fig. 7.1.5. Its jump occurs at $t = a$ rather than at $t = 0$; equivalently,

$$u_a(t) = u(t - a) = \begin{cases} 0 & \text{for } t < a, \\ 1 & \text{for } t \geqq a. \end{cases} \tag{21}$$

Example 8   Find $\mathcal{L}\{u_a(t)\}$ if $a > 0$.

Solution   We begin with the definition of the Laplace transform. We obtain

$$\mathcal{L}\{u_a(t)\} = \int_0^\infty e^{-st} u_a(t)\, dt = \int_a^\infty e^{-st}\, dt = \lim_{b \to \infty} \left[-\frac{e^{-st}}{s} \right]_{t=a}^b ;$$

consequently,

$$\mathcal{L}\{u_a(t)\} = \frac{e^{-as}}{s} \quad (s > 0, \ a > 0). \tag{22}$$

∎

General Properties of Transforms

It is a familiar fact from calculus that the integral

$$\int_a^b g(t)\, dt$$

exists if g is piecewise continuous on the bounded interval $[a, b]$. Hence if f is piecewise continuous for $t \geqq 0$, it follows that the integral

$$\int_0^b e^{-st} f(t)\, dt$$

exists for all $b < +\infty$. But in order for $F(s)$—the limit of this last integral as $b \to +\infty$—to exist, we need some condition to limit the rate of growth of $f(t)$ as $t \to +\infty$. The function f is said to be **of exponential order** as $t \to +\infty$ if there exist nonnegative constants M, c, and T such that

$$|f(t)| \leqq Me^{ct} \quad \text{for } t \geqq T. \tag{23}$$

Thus a function is of exponential order provided that it grows no more rapidly (as $t \to +\infty$) than a constant multiple of some exponential function with a linear exponent. The particular values of M, c, and T are not so important. What is important is that some such values exist so that the condition in (23) is satisfied.

Every polynomial $p(t)$ is of exponential order, with $M = c = 1$ in (23); this follows from the fact that $p(t)/e^t \to 0$ as $t \to +\infty$. The function $g(t) = e^{t^2}$ is an example of one that is *not* of exponential order—because

$$\lim_{t \to \infty} \frac{e^{t^2}}{e^{ct}} = \lim_{t \to \infty} e^{t^2 - ct} = +\infty,$$

the condition in (23) cannot hold for any [finite] value of M. The condition in (23) merely says that $f(t)/e^{ct}$ is *bounded* for t sufficiently large. In particular, any bounded function—such as $\cos kt$ or $\sin kt$—is of exponential order.

THEOREM 2: Existence of Laplace Transforms

If the function f is piecewise continuous for $t \geq 0$ and is of exponential order as $t \to +\infty$, then its Laplace transform $F(s) = \mathcal{L}\{f(t)\}$ exists. More precisely, if f is piecewise continuous and satisfies the condition in (23), then $F(s)$ exists for all $s > c$.

Proof: First we note that we can take $T = 0$ in (23). For by piecewise continuity, $|f(t)|$ is bounded on $[0, T]$. Increasing M in (23) if necessary, we can therefore assume that $|f(t)| \leq M$ if $0 \leq t \leq T$. Because $e^{ct} \geq 1$ for $t \geq 0$, it then follows that $|f(t)| \leq Me^{ct}$ for all $t \geq 0$.

By a standard theorem on convergence of improper integrals—the fact that absolute convergence implies convergence—it suffices for us to prove that the integral

$$\int_0^\infty |e^{-st} f(t)| \, dt$$

exists for $s > c$. To do this, it suffices in turn to show that the value of the integral

$$\int_0^b |e^{-st} f(t)| \, dt$$

remains bounded as $b \to +\infty$. But the fact that $|f(t)| \leq Me^{ct}$ for all $t \geq 0$ implies that

$$\int_0^b |e^{-st} f(t)| \, dt \leq \int_0^b |e^{-st} Me^{ct}| \, dt = M \int_0^b e^{-(s-c)t} \, dt$$

$$\leq M \int_0^\infty e^{-(s-c)t} \, dt = \frac{M}{s - c}$$

if $s > c$. This proves Theorem 2. ▲

We have shown, moreover, that

$$|F(s)| \leq \int_0^\infty |e^{-st} f(t)| \, dt \leq \frac{M}{s - c} \tag{24}$$

if $s > c$. When we take limits as $s \to +\infty$, we get the following result.

COROLLARY: $F(s)$ for s Large

If $f(t)$ satisfies the hypotheses of Theorem 2, then

$$\lim_{s \to \infty} F(s) = 0. \qquad (25)$$

▲

The condition in (25) severely limits the functions that can be Laplace transforms. For instance, the function $G(s) = s/(s+1)$ cannot be the Laplace transform of any "reasonable" function because its limit as $s \to +\infty$ is 1, not 0. More generally, a rational function—a quotient of two polynomials—can be (and is, as we shall see) a Laplace transform only if the degree of its numerator is less than that of its denominator.

On the other hand, the hypotheses of Theorem 2 are sufficient, but not necessary, conditions for existence of the Laplace transform of $f(t)$. For example, the function $f(t) = 1/\sqrt{t}$ fails to be piecewise continuous (at $t = 0$), but nevertheless (Example 3 with $a = -\frac{1}{2} > -1$) its Laplace transform

$$\mathcal{L}\{t^{-1/2}\} = \frac{\Gamma\left(\frac{1}{2}\right)}{s^{1/2}} = \sqrt{\frac{\pi}{s}}$$

both exists and violates the condition in (24), which would imply that $sF(s)$ remains bounded as $s \to +\infty$.

The remainder of this chapter is devoted largely to techniques for solving a differential equation by first finding the Laplace transform of its solution. It is then vital for us to know that this uniquely determines the solution of the differential equation; that is, that the function of s we have found has only one inverse Laplace transform that could be the desired solution. The following theorem is proved in Chapter 6 of Churchill's *Operational Mathematics*, 3rd ed. (New York: McGraw-Hill, 1972).

THEOREM 3: Uniqueness of Inverse Laplace Transforms

Suppose that the functions $f(t)$ and $g(t)$ satisfy the hypotheses of Theorem 2, so that their Laplace transforms $F(s)$ and $G(s)$ both exist. If $F(s) = G(s)$ for all $s > c$ (for some c), then $f(t) = g(t)$ wherever on $[0, +\infty)$ both f and g are continuous.

▲

Thus two piecewise continuous functions of exponential order with the same Laplace transform can differ only at their isolated points of discontinuity. This is of no importance in most practical applications, so we may regard inverse Laplace transforms as being essentially unique. In particular, two solutions of a differential equation must both be continuous, and hence must be the same solution if they have the same Laplace transform.

Historical Remark: Laplace transforms have an interesting history. The integral in the definition of the Laplace transform probably appeared first in the work of Euler. It is customary in mathematics to name a technique or theorem for the next person after Euler to discover it (else there will be several hundred different examples of "Euler's theorem"). In this case, the next person was the French mathematician

Pierre Simon de Laplace (1749–1827), who employed such integrals in his work on probability theory. The so-called operational techniques for solving differential equations, which are based on Laplace transforms, were not exploited by Laplace. Indeed, they were discovered and popularized by practicing engineers—notably the English electrical engineer Oliver Heaviside (1850–1925). These techniques were successfully and widely applied before they had been rigorously justified, and around the beginning of the twentieth century their validity was the subject of considerable controversy.

7.1 Problems

Apply the definition in (1) to find directly the Laplace transforms of the functions described (by formula or graph) in Problems 1 through 10.

1. $f(t) = t$

2. $f(t) = t^2$

3. $f(t) = e^{3t+1}$

4. $f(t) = \cos t$

5. $f(t) = \sinh t$

6. $f(t) = \sin^2 t$

7.

FIGURE 7.1.6.

8.

FIGURE 7.1.7.

9.

FIGURE 7.1.8.

10.

FIGURE 7.1.9.

Use the transforms in Fig. 7.1.2 to find the Laplace transforms of the functions in Problems 11 through 22. A preliminary integration by parts may be necessary.

11. $f(t) = \sqrt{t} + 3t$

12. $f(t) = 3t^{5/2} - 4t^3$

13. $f(t) = t - 2e^{3t}$

14. $f(t) = t^{3/2} - e^{-10t}$

15. $f(t) = 1 + \cosh 5t$

16. $f(t) = \sin 2t + \cos 2t$

17. $f(t) = \cos^2 2t$

18. $f(t) = \sin 3t \cos 3t$

19. $f(t) = (1 + t)^3$

20. $f(t) = te^t$

21. $f(t) = t \cos 2t$

22. $f(t) = \sinh^2 3t$

Use the transforms in Fig. 7.1.2 to find the inverse Laplace transforms of the functions in Problems 23 through 32.

23. $F(s) = \dfrac{3}{s^4}$

24. $F(s) = s^{-3/2}$

25. $F(s) = \dfrac{1}{s} - \dfrac{2}{s^{5/2}}$

26. $F(s) = \dfrac{1}{s+5}$

27. $F(s) = \dfrac{3}{s-4}$

28. $F(s) = \dfrac{3s+1}{s^2+4}$

29. $F(s) = \dfrac{5-3s}{s^2+9}$

30. $F(s) = \dfrac{9+s}{4-s^2}$

31. $F(s) = \dfrac{10s-3}{25-s^2}$

32. $F(s) = 2s^{-1}e^{-3s}$

33. Derive the transform of $f(t) = \sin kt$ by the method used in the text to derive the formula in (16).

34. Derive the transform of $f(t) = \sinh kt$ by the method used in the text to derive the formula in (14).

35. Use the tabulated integral

$$\int e^{ax} \cos bx\, dx = \frac{e^{ax}}{a^2+b^2}(a \cos bx + b \sin bx) + C$$

to obtain $\mathcal{L}\{\cos kt\}$ directly from the definition of the Laplace transform.

36. Show that the function $f(t) = \sin(e^{t^2})$ is of exponential order as $t \to +\infty$ but that its derivative is not.

37. Given $a > 0$, let $f(t) = 1$ if $0 \leqq t < a$, $f(t) = 0$ if $t \geqq a$. First, sketch the graph of the function f, making clear its value at $t = a$. Then express f in terms of unit step functions to show that $\mathcal{L}\{f(t)\} = s^{-1}(1 - e^{-as})$.

38. Given that $0 < a < b$, let $f(t) = 1$ if $a \leqq t < b$, $f(t) = 0$ if either $t < a$ or $t \geqq b$. First, sketch the graph of the function f, making clear its values at $t = a$ and $t = b$. Then express f in terms of unit step functions to show that $\mathcal{L}\{f(t)\} = s^{-1}(e^{-as} - e^{-bs})$.

39. The *unit staircase function* is defined as follows:

$$f(t) = n \quad \text{if} \quad n - 1 \leqq t < n, \quad n = 1, 2, 3, \ldots.$$

(a) Sketch the graph of f to see why its name is appropriate. **(b)** Show that

$$f(t) = \sum_{n=0}^{\infty} u(t - n)$$

for all $t \geqq 0$. **(c)** Assume that the Laplace transform of the infinite series in part (b) can be taken termwise (it can). Apply the geometric series to obtain the result

$$\mathcal{L}\{f(t)\} = \frac{1}{s(1 - e^{-s})}.$$

40. **(a)** The graph of the function f is shown in Fig. 7.1.10. Show that f can be written in the form

$$f(t) = \sum_{n=0}^{\infty} (-1)^n u(t - n).$$

(b) Use the method of Problem 39 to show that

$$\mathcal{L}\{f(t)\} = \frac{1}{s(1 + e^{-s})}.$$

FIGURE 7.1.10. The graph of the function of Problem 40.

41. The graph of the *square wave function* $g(t)$ is shown in Fig. 7.1.11. Express g in terms of the function f of Problem 40 and hence deduce that

$$\mathcal{L}\{g(t)\} = \frac{1 - e^{-s}}{s(1 + e^{-s})} = \frac{1}{s} \tanh \frac{s}{2}.$$

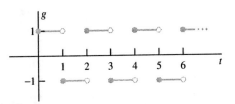

FIGURE 7.1.11. The graph of the function of Problem 41.

42. Given constants a and b, define $h(t)$ for $t \geqq 0$ by

$$h(t) = \begin{cases} a & \text{if } n - 1 \leqq t < n \text{ and } n \text{ is odd;} \\ b & \text{if } n - 1 \leqq t < n \text{ and } n \text{ is even.} \end{cases}$$

Sketch the graph of h and apply one of the preceding problems to show that

$$\mathcal{L}\{h(t)\} = \frac{a + be^{-s}}{s(1 + e^{-s})}.$$

7.1 Application: Computer Algebra Transforms and Inverse Transforms

If $f(t) = t \cos 3t$, then the definition of the Laplace transform gives the improper integral

$$F(s) = \mathcal{L}\{f(t)\} = \int_0^{\infty} te^{-st} \cos 3t \, dt,$$

whose evaluation would appear to require a tedious integration by parts. Consequently a computer algebra Laplace transforms package is useful for the quick calculation of transforms. *Maple* contains the integral transforms package **inttrans** and *Mathematica* contains the package **Calculus:LaplaceTransform**. The *Maple* commands

```
with(inttrans):
f := t*cos(3*t):
F := laplace(f, t, s);
F := simplify(expand( F ));
```

or the *Mathematica* commands

```
Needs["Calculus`LaplaceTransform`"]
f = t*Cos[3*t];
F = LaplaceTransform[f, t, s]
Simplify[Expand[ F ]]
```

yield immediately the Laplace transform $F(s) = (s^2 - 9)/(s^2 + 9)^2$.

If you execute these commands you'll see why it's a good idea to routinely "expand and simplify" the result when calculating a Laplace transform. We can recover the original function $f(t)$ with the *Maple* command

```
invlaplace(F, s, t);
```

or the *Mathematica* command

```
InverseLaplaceTransform[F, s, t]
```

(although again we may want to expand and simplify before taking a close look at the result).

Remark: Note carefully the order of s and t in the preceding commands—first t, then s when transforming; first s, then t when inverse transforming. ∎

You can use these computer algebra commands to check the answers to Problems 11 through 32 in this section, as well as a few interesting problems of your own selection.

7.2 Transformation of Initial Value Problems

We now discuss the application of Laplace transforms to solve a linear differential equation with constant coefficients, such as

$$ax''(t) + bx'(t) + cx(t) = f(t), \tag{1}$$

with given initial conditions $x(0) = x_0$ and $x'(0) = x'_0$. By the linearity of the Laplace transformation, we can transform Eq. (1) by separately taking the Laplace transform of each term in the equation. The transformed equation is

$$a\mathcal{L}\{x''(t)\} + b\mathcal{L}\{x'(t)\} + c\mathcal{L}\{x(t)\} = \mathcal{L}\{f(t)\}; \tag{2}$$

it involves the transforms of the derivatives x' and x'' of the unknown function $x(t)$. The key to the method is Theorem 1, which tells us how to express the transform of the *derivative* of a function in terms of the transform of the function itself.

THEOREM 1: Transforms of Derivatives

Suppose that the function $f(t)$ is continuous and piecewise smooth for $t \geqq 0$ and is of exponential order as $t \to +\infty$, so that there exist nonnegative constants M, c, and T such that

$$|f(t)| \leqq Me^{ct} \quad \text{for } t \geqq T. \tag{3}$$

Then $\mathcal{L}\{f'(t)\}$ exists for $s > c$, and

$$\mathcal{L}\{f'(t)\} = s\mathcal{L}\{f(t)\} - f(0) = sF(s) - f(0). \tag{4}$$

▲

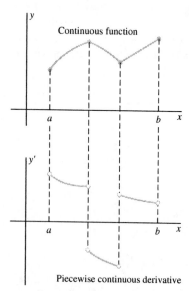

Continuous function

Piecewise continuous derivative

FIGURE 7.2.1. The discontinuities of f' correspond to "corners" on the graph of f.

The function f is called **piecewise smooth** on the bounded interval $[a, b]$ if it is piecewise continuous on $[a, b]$ and differentiable except at finitely many points, with $f'(t)$ being piecewise continuous on $[a, b]$. We may assign arbitrary values to $f(t)$ at the isolated points at which f is not differentiable. We say that f is piecewise smooth for $t \geqq 0$ if it is piecewise smooth on every bounded subinterval of $[0, +\infty)$. Figure 7.2.1 indicates how "corners" on the graph of f correspond to discontinuities in its derivative f'.

The main idea of the proof of Theorem 1 is exhibited best by the case in which $f'(t)$ is continuous (not merely piecewise continuous) for $t \geq 0$. Then, beginning with the definition of $\mathcal{L}\{f'(t)\}$ and integrating by parts, we get

$$\mathcal{L}\{f'(t)\} = \int_0^\infty e^{-st} f'(t)\, dt = \left[e^{-st} f(t) \right]_{t=0}^\infty + s \int_0^\infty e^{-st} f(t)\, dt.$$

Because of (3), the integrated term $e^{-st} f(t)$ approaches zero (when $s > c$) as $t \to +\infty$, and its value at the lower limit $t = 0$ contributes $-f(0)$ to the evaluation of the preceding expression. The integral that remains is simply $\mathcal{L}\{f(t)\}$; by Theorem 2 of Section 7.1, the integral converges when $s > c$. Then $\mathcal{L}\{f'(t)\}$ exists when $s > c$, and its value is that given in Eq. (4). We will defer the case in which $f'(t)$ has isolated discontinuities to the end of this section.

Solution of Initial Value Problems

In order to transform Eq. (1), we need the transform of the second derivative as well. If we assume that $g(t) = f'(t)$ satisfies the hypotheses of Theorem 1, then that theorem implies that

$$\begin{aligned}
\mathcal{L}\{f''(t)\} = \mathcal{L}\{g'(t)\} &= s\mathcal{L}\{g(t)\} - g(0) \\
&= s\mathcal{L}\{f'(t)\} - f'(0) \\
&= s[s\mathcal{L}\{f(t)\} - f(0)] - f'(0),
\end{aligned}$$

and thus

➤
$$\mathcal{L}\{f''(t)\} = s^2 F(s) - s f(0) - f'(0). \tag{5}$$

A repetition of this calculation gives

$$\mathcal{L}\{f'''(t)\} = s\mathcal{L}\{f''(t)\} - f''(0) = s^3 F(s) - s^2 f(0) - s f'(0) - f''(0). \tag{6}$$

After finitely many such steps we obtain the following extension of Theorem 1.

COROLLARY: Transforms of Higher Derivatives

Suppose that the functions f, f', f'', ..., $f^{(n-1)}$ are continuous and piecewise smooth for $t \geq 0$, and that each of these functions satisfies the conditions in (3) with the same values of M and c. Then $\mathcal{L}\{f^{(n)}(t)\}$ exists when $s > c$, and

➤
$$\begin{aligned}
\mathcal{L}\{f^{(n)}(t)\} &= s^n \mathcal{L}\{f(t)\} - s^{n-1} f(0) - s^{n-2} f'(0) - \cdots - f^{(n-1)}(0) \\
&= s^n F(s) - s^{n-1} f(0) - \cdots - s f^{(n-2)}(0) - f^{(n-1)}(0). \tag{7}
\end{aligned}$$

▲

Example 1   Solve the initial value problem

$$x'' - x' - 6x = 0; \quad x(0) = 2, \quad x'(0) = -1.$$

Solution   With the given initial values, Eqs. (4) and (5) yield

$$\mathcal{L}\{x'(t)\} = s\mathcal{L}\{x(t)\} - x(0) = sX(s) - 2$$

and

$$\mathcal{L}\{x''(t)\} = s^2\mathcal{L}\{x(t)\} - sx(0) - x'(0) = s^2X(s) - 2s + 1,$$

where (according to our convention about notation) $X(s)$ denotes the Laplace transform of the (unknown) function $x(t)$. Hence the transformed equation is

$$\left[s^2X(s) - 2s + 1\right] - [sX(s) - 2] - 6[X(s)] = 0,$$

which we quickly simplify to

$$(s^2 - s - 6)X(s) - 2s + 3 = 0.$$

Thus

$$X(s) = \frac{2s - 3}{s^2 - s - 6} = \frac{2s - 3}{(s - 3)(s + 2)}.$$

By the method of partial fractions (of integral calculus), there exist constants A and B such that

$$\frac{2s - 3}{(s - 3)(s + 2)} = \frac{A}{s - 3} + \frac{B}{s + 2},$$

and multiplication of both sides of this equation by $(s - 3)(s + 2)$ yields the identity

$$2s - 3 = A(s + 2) + B(s - 3).$$

If we substitute $s = 3$, we find that $A = \frac{3}{5}$; substitution of $s = -2$ shows that $B = \frac{7}{5}$. Hence

$$X(s) = \mathcal{L}\{x(t)\} = \frac{\frac{3}{5}}{s - 3} + \frac{\frac{7}{5}}{s + 2}.$$

Because $\mathcal{L}^{-1}\{1/(s - a)\} = e^{at}$, it follows that

$$x(t) = \tfrac{3}{5}e^{3t} + \tfrac{7}{5}e^{-2t}$$

is the solution of the original initial value problem. Note that we did not first find the general solution of the differential equation. The Laplace transform method directly yields the desired particular solution, automatically taking into account—via Theorem 1 and its corollary—the given initial conditions. ∎

Example 2   Solve the initial value problem

$$x'' + 4x = \sin 3t; \quad x(0) = x'(0) = 0.$$

Such a problem arises in the motion of a mass-and-spring system with external force, as shown in Fig. 7.2.2.

Solution

FIGURE 7.2.2. A mass-and-spring system satisfying the initial value problem in Example 2. The mass is initially at rest in its equilibrium position.

Because both initial values are zero, Eq. (5) yields $\mathcal{L}\{x''(t)\} = s^2 X(s)$. We read the transform of $\sin 3t$ from the table in Fig. 7.1.2 (Section 7.1) and thereby get the transformed equation

$$s^2 X(s) + 4X(s) = \frac{3}{s^2 + 9}.$$

Therefore,

$$X(s) = \frac{3}{(s^2 + 4)(s^2 + 9)}.$$

The method of partial fractions calls for

$$\frac{3}{(s^2 + 4)(s^2 + 9)} = \frac{As + B}{s^2 + 4} + \frac{Cs + D}{s^2 + 9}.$$

The fact that there are no terms of odd degree on the left-hand side suggests that we set $A = C = 0$, because nonzero values for A or C would lead to terms of odd degree—but no such terms are present in the numerator on the left. So we replace A and C with zero, then multiply both sides by $(s^2 + 4)(s^2 + 9)$. The result is the identity

$$3 = B(s^2 + 9) + D(s^2 + 4) = (B + D)s^2 + (9B + 4D).$$

When we equate coefficients of like powers of s we get the linear equations

$$B + D = 0,$$
$$9B + 4D = 3,$$

which are readily solved for $B = \frac{3}{5}$ and $D = -\frac{3}{5}$. Hence

$$X(s) = \mathcal{L}\{x(t)\} = \frac{3}{10} \cdot \frac{2}{s^2 + 4} - \frac{1}{5} \cdot \frac{3}{s^2 + 9}.$$

Because $\mathcal{L}\{\sin 2t\} = 2/(s^2 + 4)$ and $\mathcal{L}\{\sin 3t\} = 3/(s^2 + 9)$, it follows that

$$x(t) = \tfrac{3}{10} \sin 2t - \tfrac{1}{5} \sin 3t.$$

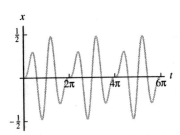

FIGURE 7.2.3. The position function $x(t)$ in Example 2.

Figure 7.2.3 shows the graph of this period 2π position function of the mass. Note that the Laplace transform method again gives the solution directly, without the necessity of first finding the complementary function and a particular solution of the original nonhomogeneous differential equation. Thus nonhomogeneous equations are solved in exactly the same manner as are homogeneous equations. ∎

Examples 1 and 2 illustrate the solution procedure that is outlined in Fig. 7.2.4.

Linear Systems

Laplace transforms are used frequently in engineering problems to solve linear systems in which the coefficients are all constants. When initial conditions are specified, the Laplace transform reduces such a linear system of differential equations to a linear system of algebraic equations in which the unknowns are the transforms of the solution functions. As Example 3 illustrates, the technique for a system is essentially the same as for a single linear differential equation with constant coefficients.

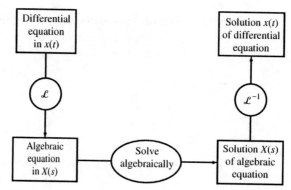

FIGURE 7.2.4. Using the Laplace transform to solve an initial value problem.

Example 3   Solve the system

$$2x'' = -6x + 2y,$$
$$y'' = 2x - 2y + 40\sin 3t, \tag{8}$$

subject to the initial conditions

$$x(0) = x'(0) = y(0) = y'(0) = 0. \tag{9}$$

Thus the force $f(t) = 40\sin 3t$ is suddenly applied to the second mass of Fig. 7.2.5 at the time $t = 0$ when the system is at rest in its equilibrium position.

FIGURE 7.2.5. A mass-and-spring system satisfying the initial value problem in Example 3. Both masses are initially at rest in their equilibrium positions.

Solution   We write $X(s) = \mathcal{L}\{x(t)\}$ and $Y(s) = \mathcal{L}\{y(t)\}$. Then the initial conditions in (9) imply that

$$\mathcal{L}\{x''(t)\} = s^2 X(s) \quad \text{and} \quad \mathcal{L}\{y''(t)\} = s^2 Y(s).$$

Because $\mathcal{L}\{\sin 3t\} = 3/(s^2 + 9)$, the transforms of the equations in (8) are the equations

$$2s^2 X(s) = -6X(s) + 2Y(s),$$
$$s^2 Y(s) = 2X(s) - 2Y(s) + \frac{120}{s^2 + 9}.$$

Thus the transformed system is

$$(s^2 + 3)X(s) \qquad - Y(s) = 0,$$
$$-2X(s) + (s^2 + 2)Y(s) = \frac{120}{s^2 + 9}. \tag{10}$$

The determinant of this pair of linear equations in $X(s)$ and $Y(s)$ is

$$\begin{vmatrix} s^2 + 3 & -1 \\ -2 & s^2 + 2 \end{vmatrix} = (s^2 + 3)(s^2 + 2) - 2 = (s^2 + 1)(s^2 + 4),$$

and we readily solve—using Cramer's rule, for instance—the system in (10) for

$$X(s) = \frac{120}{(s^2 + 1)(s^2 + 4)(s^2 + 9)} = \frac{5}{s^2 + 1} - \frac{8}{s^2 + 4} + \frac{3}{s^2 + 9} \qquad (11a)$$

and

$$Y(s) = \frac{120(s^2 + 3)}{(s^2 + 1)(s^2 + 4)(s^2 + 9)} = \frac{10}{s^2 + 1} + \frac{8}{s^2 + 4} - \frac{18}{s^2 + 9}. \qquad (11b)$$

The partial fraction decompositions in Eqs. (11a) and (11b) are readily found using the method of Example 2. For instance, noting that the denominator factors are linear in s^2, we can write

$$\frac{120}{(s^2 + 1)(s^2 + 4)(s^2 + 9)} = \frac{A}{s^2 + 1} + \frac{B}{s^2 + 4} + \frac{C}{s^2 + 9},$$

and it follows that

$$120 = A(s^2 + 4)(s^2 + 9) + B(s^2 + 1)(s^2 + 9) + C(s^2 + 1)(s^2 + 4). \qquad (12)$$

Substitution of $s^2 = -1$ (that is, $s = i$, a zero of the factor $s^2 + 1$) in Eq. (12) gives $120 = A \cdot 3 \cdot 8$, so $A = 5$. Similarly, substitution of $s^2 = -4$ in Eq. (12) yields $B = -8$, and substitution of $s^2 = -9$ yields $C = 3$. Thus we obtain the partial fraction decomposition shown in Eq. (11a).

At any rate, the inverse Laplace transforms of the expressions in Eqs. (11a) and (11b) give the solution

$$x(t) = 5 \sin t - 4 \sin 2t + \sin 3t,$$
$$y(t) = 10 \sin t + 4 \sin 2t - 6 \sin 3t.$$

Figure 7.2.6 shows the graphs of these two period 2π position functions of the two masses. ∎

FIGURE 7.2.6. The position functions $x(t)$ and $y(t)$ in Example 3.

The Transform Perspective

Let us regard the general constant-coefficient second-order equation as the equation of motion

$$mx'' + cx' + kx = f(t)$$

FIGURE 7.2.7. A mass-spring-dashpot system with external force $f(t)$.

of the familiar mass-spring-dashpot system (Fig. 7.2.7). Then the transformed equation is

$$m\left[s^2 X(s) - sx(0) - x'(0)\right] + c\left[sX(s) - x(0)\right] + kX(s) = F(s). \qquad (13)$$

Note that Eq. (13) is an *algebraic* equation—indeed, a linear equation—in the "unknown" $X(s)$. This is the source of the power of the Laplace transform method:

> Linear *differential* equations are transformed into readily solved *algebraic* equations.

If we solve Eq. (13) for $X(s)$, we get

$$X(s) = \frac{F(s)}{Z(s)} + \frac{I(s)}{Z(s)}, \tag{14}$$

where

$$Z(s) = ms^2 + cs + k \quad \text{and} \quad I(s) = mx(0)s + mx'(0) + cx(0).$$

Note that $Z(s)$ depends only on the physical system itself. Thus Eq. (14) presents $X(s) = \mathcal{L}\{x(t)\}$ as the sum of a term depending only on the external force and one depending only on the initial conditions. In the case of an underdamped system, these two terms are the transforms

$$\mathcal{L}\{x_{sp}(t)\} = \frac{F(s)}{Z(s)} \quad \text{and} \quad \mathcal{L}\{x_{tr}(t)\} = \frac{I(s)}{Z(s)}$$

of the steady periodic solution and the transient solution, respectively. The only potential difficulty in finding these solutions is in finding the inverse Laplace transform of the right-hand side in Eq. (14). Much of the remainder of this chapter is devoted to finding Laplace transforms and inverse transforms. In particular, we seek those methods that are sufficiently powerful to enable us to solve problems that—unlike those in Examples 1 and 2—cannot be solved readily by the methods of Chapter 3.

Additional Transform Techniques

Example 4   Show that

$$\mathcal{L}\{te^{at}\} = \frac{1}{(s-a)^2}.$$

Solution   If $f(t) = te^{at}$, then $f(0) = 0$ and $f'(t) = e^{at} + ate^{at}$. Hence Theorem 1 gives

$$\mathcal{L}\{e^{at} + ate^{at}\} = \mathcal{L}\{f'(t)\} = s\mathcal{L}\{f(t)\} = s\mathcal{L}\{te^{at}\}.$$

It follows from the linearity of the transform that

$$\mathcal{L}\{e^{at}\} + a\mathcal{L}\{te^{at}\} = s\mathcal{L}\{te^{at}\}.$$

Hence

$$\mathcal{L}\{te^{at}\} = \frac{\mathcal{L}\{e^{at}\}}{s-a} = \frac{1}{(s-a)^2} \tag{15}$$

because $\mathcal{L}\{e^{at}\} = 1/(s-a)$.   ■

Example 5 Find $\mathcal{L}\{t \sin kt\}$.

Solution Let $f(t) = t \sin kt$. Then $f(0) = 0$ and

$$f'(t) = \sin kt + kt \cos kt.$$

The derivative involves the new function $t \cos kt$, so we note that $f'(0) = 0$ and differentiate again. The result is

$$f''(t) = 2k \cos kt - k^2 t \sin kt.$$

But $\mathcal{L}\{f''(t)\} = s^2 \mathcal{L}\{f(t)\}$ by the formula in (5) for the transform of the second derivative, and $\mathcal{L}\{\cos kt\} = s/(s^2 + k^2)$, so we have

$$\frac{2ks}{s^2 + k^2} - k^2 \mathcal{L}\{t \sin kt\} = s^2 \mathcal{L}\{t \sin kt\}.$$

Finally, we solve this equation for

$$\mathcal{L}\{t \sin kt\} = \frac{2ks}{(s^2 + k^2)^2}. \tag{16}$$

This procedure is considerably more pleasant than the alternative of evaluating the integral

$$\mathcal{L}\{t \sin kt\} = \int_0^\infty t e^{-st} \sin kt \, dt. \qquad\blacksquare$$

Examples 4 and 5 exploit the fact that if $f(0) = 0$, then differentiation of f corresponds to multiplication of its transform by s. It is reasonable to expect the inverse operation of integration (antidifferentiation) to correspond to division of the transform by s.

THEOREM 2: Transforms of Integrals

If $f(t)$ is a piecewise continuous function for $t \geq 0$ and satisfies the condition of exponential order $|f(t)| \leq Me^{ct}$ for $t \geq T$, then

$$\mathcal{L}\left\{ \int_0^t f(\tau) \, d\tau \right\} = \frac{1}{s} \mathcal{L}\{f(t)\} = \frac{F(s)}{s} \tag{17}$$

for $s > c$. Equivalently,

$$\mathcal{L}^{-1}\left\{ \frac{F(s)}{s} \right\} = \int_0^t f(\tau) \, d\tau. \tag{18}$$

Proof: Because f is piecewise continuous, the fundamental theorem of calculus implies that

$$g(t) = \int_0^t f(\tau) \, d\tau$$

is continuous and that $g'(t) = f(t)$ where f is continuous; thus g is continuous and piecewise smooth for $t \geq 0$. Furthermore,

$$|g(t)| \leq \int_0^t |f(\tau)| \, d\tau \leq M \int_0^t e^{c\tau} \, d\tau = \frac{M}{c}(e^{ct} - 1) < \frac{M}{c} e^{ct},$$

so $g(t)$ is of exponential order as $t \to +\infty$. Hence we can apply Theorem 1 to g; this gives

$$\mathcal{L}\{f(t)\} = \mathcal{L}\{g'(t)\} = s\mathcal{L}\{g(t)\} - g(0).$$

Now $g(0) = 0$, so division by s yields

$$\mathcal{L}\left\{ \int_0^t f(\tau)\, d\tau \right\} = \mathcal{L}\{g(t)\} = \frac{\mathcal{L}\{f(t)\}}{s},$$

which completes the proof.   ▲

Example 6   Find the inverse Laplace transform of

$$G(s) = \frac{1}{s^2(s-a)}.$$

Solution   In effect, Eq. (18) means that we can delete a factor of s from the denominator, find the inverse transform of the resulting simpler expression, and finally integrate from 0 to t (to "correct" for the missing factor s). Thus

$$\mathcal{L}^{-1}\left\{ \frac{1}{s(s-a)} \right\} = \int_0^t \mathcal{L}^{-1}\left\{ \frac{1}{s-a} \right\} d\tau = \int_0^t e^{a\tau}\, d\tau = \frac{1}{a}(e^{at} - 1).$$

We now repeat the technique to obtain

$$\mathcal{L}^{-1}\left\{ \frac{1}{s^2(s-a)} \right\} = \int_0^t \mathcal{L}^{-1}\left\{ \frac{1}{s(s-a)} \right\} d\tau = \int_0^t \frac{1}{a}(e^{a\tau} - 1)\, d\tau$$

$$= \left[\frac{1}{a}\left(\frac{1}{a}e^{a\tau} - \tau \right) \right]_0^t = \frac{1}{a^2}(e^{at} - at - 1).$$

This technique is often a more convenient way than the method of partial fractions for finding an inverse transform of a fraction of the form $P(s)/[s^n Q(s)]$.   ∎

Proof of Theorem 1:   We conclude this section with the proof of Theorem 1 in the general case in which f' is merely piecewise continuous. We need to prove that the limit

$$\lim_{b \to \infty} \int_0^b e^{-st} f'(t)\, dt$$

exists and also need to find its value. With b fixed, let $t_1, t_2, \ldots, t_{k-1}$ be the points interior to the interval $[0, b]$ at which f' is discontinuous. Let $t_0 = 0$ and $t_k = b$. Then we can integrate by parts on each interval (t_{n-1}, t_n) where f' is continuous. This yields

$$\int_0^b e^{-st} f'(t)\, dt = \sum_{n=1}^{k} \int_{t_{n-1}}^{t_n} e^{-st} f'(t)\, dt$$

$$= \sum_{n=1}^{k} \left(\left[e^{-st} f(t) \right]_{t_{n-1}}^{t_n} + s \int_{t_{n-1}}^{t_n} e^{-st} f(t)\, dt \right)$$

$$= -f(0) - \sum_{n=1}^{k-1} e^{-st_n} j_f(t_n) + e^{-sb} f(b) + s \int_0^b e^{-st} f(t)\, dt, \qquad (19)$$

where

$$j_f(t_n) = f(t_n+) - f(t_n-) \tag{20}$$

is the jump in $f(t)$ at $t = t_n$. But because f is continuous, each jump is zero: $j_f(t_n) = 0$ for all n. Moreover, if $b > c$, then $e^{-sb}f(b) \to 0$ as $b \to +\infty$. Therefore when we take the limit in (19) as $b \to +\infty$, we get the desired result:

$$\mathcal{L}\{f'(t)\} = s\mathcal{L}\{f(t)\} - f(0). \qquad \blacktriangle$$

Extension of Theorem 1

Suppose that the original function $f(t)$ is itself only piecewise continuous (instead of continuous), with its (finite jump) discontinuities located at the points t_1, t_2, t_3, ... Assuming that $\mathcal{L}\{f'(t)\}$ exists, when we take the limit in (19) as $b \to +\infty$, we get

$$\mathcal{L}\{f'(t)\} = sF(s) - f(0) - \sum_{n=1}^{\infty} e^{-st_n} j_f(t_n). \tag{21}$$

$\blacktriangle$

Example 7

Let $f(t) = 1 + [\![t]\!]$ be the unit staircase function; its graph is shown in Fig. 7.2.8. Then $f(0) = 1$, $f'(t) \equiv 0$, and $j_f(n) = 1$ for each integer $n = 1, 2, 3, \ldots$. Hence Eq. (21) yields

$$0 = sF(s) - 1 - \sum_{n=1}^{\infty} e^{-ns},$$

so the Laplace transform of $f(t)$ is

$$F(s) = \frac{1}{s}\sum_{n=0}^{\infty} e^{-ns} = \frac{1}{s(1 - e^{-s})}.$$

In the last step we used the formula for the sum of a geometric series,

$$\sum_{n=0}^{\infty} x^n = \frac{1}{1 - x},$$

with $x = e^{-s} < 1$. $\blacksquare$

FIGURE 7.2.8. The graph of the unit staircase function of Example 7.

7.2 Problems

Use Laplace transforms to solve the initial value problems in Problems 1 through 16.

1. $x'' + 4x = 0$; $x(0) = 5$, $x'(0) = 0$
2. $x'' + 9x = 0$; $x(0) = 3$, $x'(0) = 4$
3. $x'' - x' - 2x = 0$; $x(0) = 0$, $x'(0) = 2$
4. $x'' + 8x' + 15x = 0$; $x(0) = 2$, $x'(0) = -3$

5. $x'' + x = \sin 2t$; $x(0) = 0 = x'(0)$
6. $x'' + 4x = \cos t$; $x(0) = 0 = x'(0)$
7. $x'' + x = \cos 3t$; $x(0) = 1$, $x'(0) = 0$
8. $x'' + 9x = 1$; $x(0) = 0 = x'(0)$
9. $x'' + 4x' + 3x = 1$; $x(0) = 0 = x'(0)$
10. $x'' + 3x' + 2x = t$; $x(0) = 0$, $x'(0) = 2$
11. $x' = 2x + y$, $y' = 6x + 3y$; $x(0) = 1$, $y(0) = -2$

12. $x' = x + 2y$, $y' = x + e^{-t}$; $x(0) = y(0) = 0$

13. $x' + 2y' + x = 0$, $x' - y' + y = 0$; $x(0) = 0$, $y(0) = 1$

14. $x'' + 2x + 4y = 0$, $y'' + x + 2y = 0$; $x(0) = y(0) = 0$, $x'(0) = y'(0) = -1$

15. $x'' + x' + y' + 2x - y = 0$, $y'' + x' + y' + 4x - 2y = 0$; $x(0) = y(0) = 1$, $x'(0) = y'(0) = 0$

16. $x' = x + z$, $y' = x + y$, $z' = -2x - z$; $x(0) = 1$, $y(0) = 0$, $z(0) = 0$

Apply Theorem 2 to find the inverse Laplace transforms of the functions in Problems 17 through 24.

17. $F(s) = \dfrac{1}{s(s - 3)}$

18. $F(s) = \dfrac{3}{s(s + 5)}$

19. $F(s) = \dfrac{1}{s(s^2 + 4)}$

20. $F(s) = \dfrac{2s + 1}{s(s^2 + 9)}$

21. $F(s) = \dfrac{1}{s^2(s^2 + 1)}$

22. $F(s) = \dfrac{1}{s(s^2 - 9)}$

23. $F(s) = \dfrac{1}{s^2(s^2 - 1)}$

24. $F(s) = \dfrac{1}{s(s + 1)(s + 2)}$

25. Apply Theorem 1 to derive $\mathcal{L}\{\sin kt\}$ from the formula for $\mathcal{L}\{\cos kt\}$.

26. Apply Theorem 1 to derive $\mathcal{L}\{\cosh kt\}$ from the formula for $\mathcal{L}\{\sinh kt\}$.

27. (a) Apply Theorem 1 to show that

$$\mathcal{L}\{t^n e^{at}\} = \frac{n}{s - a}\mathcal{L}\{t^{n-1}e^{at}\}.$$

(b) Deduce that $\mathcal{L}\{t^n e^{at}\} = n!/(s - a)^{n+1}$ for $n = 1, 2, 3, \ldots$.

Apply Theorem 1 as in Example 5 to derive the Laplace transforms in Problems 28 through 30.

28. $\mathcal{L}\{t \cos kt\} = \dfrac{s^2 - k^2}{(s^2 + k^2)^2}$

29. $\mathcal{L}\{t \sinh kt\} = \dfrac{2ks}{(s^2 - k^2)^2}$

30. $\mathcal{L}\{t \cosh kt\} = \dfrac{s^2 + k^2}{(s^2 - k^2)^2}$

31. Apply the results in Example 5 and Problem 28 to show that

$$\mathcal{L}^{-1}\left\{\frac{1}{(s^2 + k^2)^2}\right\} = \frac{1}{2k^3}(\sin kt - kt \cos kt).$$

Apply the extension of Theorem 1 in Eq. (21) to derive the Laplace transforms given in Problems 32 through 37.

32. $\mathcal{L}\{u(t - a)\} = s^{-1}e^{-as}$ for $a > 0$.

33. If $f(t) = 1$ on the interval $[a, b]$ (where $0 < a < b$) and $f(t) = 0$ otherwise, then

$$\mathcal{L}\{f(t)\} = \frac{e^{-as} - e^{-bs}}{s}.$$

34. If $f(t) = (-1)^{[\![t]\!]}$ is the square wave function whose graph is shown in Fig. 7.2.9, then

$$\mathcal{L}\{f(t)\} = \frac{1}{s}\tanh\frac{s}{2}.$$

(Suggestion: Use the geometric series.)

FIGURE 7.2.9. The graph of the square wave function of Problem 34.

35. If $f(t)$ is the *unit on-off function* whose graph is shown in Fig. 7.2.10, then

$$\mathcal{L}\{f(t)\} = \frac{1}{s(1 + e^{-s})}.$$

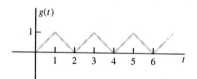

FIGURE 7.2.10. The graph of the off-on function of Problem 35.

36. If $g(t)$ is the *triangular wave function* whose graph is shown in Fig. 7.2.11, then

$$\mathcal{L}\{g(t)\} = \frac{1}{s^2}\tanh\frac{s}{2}.$$

FIGURE 7.2.11. The graph of the triangular wave function of Problem 36.

37. If $f(t)$ is the *sawtooth function* whose graph is shown in Fig. 7.2.12, then

$$\mathcal{L}\{f(t)\} = \frac{1}{s^2} - \frac{e^{-s}}{s(1 - e^{-s})}.$$

(Suggestion: Note that $f'(t) \equiv 1$ where it is defined.)

FIGURE 7.2.12. The graph of the sawtooth function of Problem 37.

7.2 Application: Transforms of Initial Value Problems

The typical computer algebra system knows Theorem 1 and its corollary, and hence can transform not only functions (as in the Section 7.1 project), but also entire initial value problems. We illustrate the technique here with *Mathematica*, and in the Section 7.3 project with *Maple*. Consider the initial value problem

$$x'' + 4x = \sin 3t, \quad x(0) = x'(0) = 0$$

of Example 2. First we define the differential equation with its initial conditions, then load the Laplace transform package.

```
de = x''[t] + 4*x[t] == Sin[3*t]
inits = {x[0] -> 0,x'[0] -> 0}
Needs["Calculus`LaplaceTransform`"]
```

The Laplace transform of the differential equation is given by

```
DE = LaplaceTransform[ de, t, s ]
```

The result of this command—which we do not show explicitly here—is a linear (algebraic) equation in the as yet unknown `LaplaceTransform[x[t],t,s]`. We proceed to solve for this transform $X(s)$ of the unknown function $x(t)$ and substitute the initial conditions.

```
X = Solve[DE, LaplaceTransform[x[t],t,s]]
X = X // Last // Last // Last
X = X /. inits
```

$$\frac{3}{(s^2 + 4)(s^2 + 9)}$$

Finally we need only compute an inverse transform to find $x(t)$.

```
x = InverseLaplaceTransform[X,s,t] // Expand
```

$$\frac{3}{10} \sin(2t) - \frac{1}{5} \sin(3t)$$

Of course we could probably get this result immediately with `DSolve`, but the intermediate output generated by the steps shown here can be quite instructive. You can try it for yourself with the initial value problems in Problems 1 through 16.

7.3 Translation and Partial Fractions

As illustrated by Examples 1 and 2 of Section 7.2, the solution of a linear differential equation with constant coefficients can often be reduced to the matter of finding the inverse Laplace transform of a rational function of the form

$$R(s) = \frac{P(s)}{Q(s)} \tag{1}$$

where the degree of $P(s)$ is less than that of $Q(s)$. The technique for finding $\mathcal{L}^{-1}\{R(s)\}$ is based on the same method of partial fractions that we use in elementary calculus to integrate rational functions. The following two rules describe the **partial fraction decomposition** of $R(s)$, in terms of the factorization of the denominator $Q(s)$ into linear factors and irreducible quadratic factors corresponding to the real and complex zeros, respectively, of $Q(s)$.

RULE 1: Linear Factor Partial Fractions

The part of the partial fraction decomposition of $R(s)$ corresponding to the linear factor $s - a$ of multiplicity n is a sum of n partial fractions, having the form

$$\frac{A_1}{s - a} + \frac{A_2}{(s - a)^2} + \cdots + \frac{A_n}{(s - a)^n}, \tag{2}$$

where A_1, A_2, ..., and A_n are constants. ▲

RULE 2: Quadratic Factor Partial Fractions

The part of the partial fraction decomposition corresponding to the irreducible quadratic factor $(s - a)^2 + b^2$ of multiplicity n is a sum of n partial fractions, having the form

$$\frac{A_1 s + B_1}{(s - a)^2 + b^2} + \frac{A_2 s + B_2}{[(s - a)^2 + b^2]^2} + \cdots + \frac{A_n s + B_n}{[(s - a)^2 + b^2]^n}, \tag{3}$$

where A_1, A_2, ..., A_n, B_1, B_2, ..., and B_n are constants. ▲

Finding $\mathcal{L}^{-1}\{R(s)\}$ involves two steps. First we must find the partial fraction decomposition of $R(s)$, and then we must find the inverse Laplace transform of each of the individual partial fractions of the types that appear in (2) and (3). The latter step is based on the following elementary property of Laplace transforms.

THEOREM 1: Translation on the s-Axis

If $F(s) = \mathcal{L}\{f(t)\}$ exists for $s > c$, then $\mathcal{L}\{e^{at} f(t)\}$ exists for $s > a + c$, and

➤ $$\mathcal{L}\{e^{at} f(t)\} = F(s - a). \tag{4}$$

Equivalently,

➤ $$\mathcal{L}^{-1}\{F(s - a)\} = e^{at} f(t). \tag{5}$$

Thus the translation $s \to s - a$ in the transform corresponds to multiplication of the original function of t by e^{at}.

Proof: If we simply replace s with $s - a$ in the definition of $F(s) = \mathcal{L}\{f(t)\}$, we obtain

$$F(s - a) = \int_0^\infty e^{-(s-a)t} f(t)\, dt = \int_0^\infty e^{-st} \left[e^{at} f(t) \right] dt = \mathcal{L}\{e^{at} f(t)\}.$$

This is Eq. (4), and it is clear that Eq. (5) is the same. ▲

If we apply the translation theorem to the formulas for the Laplace transforms of t^n, $\cos kt$, and $\sin kt$ that we already know—multiplying each of these functions by e^{at} and replacing s with $s - a$ in the transforms—we get the following additions to the table in Fig. 7.1.2.

$f(t)$	$F(s)$		
$e^{at} t^n$	$\dfrac{n!}{(s-a)^{n+1}}$ $(s > a)$		(6)
$e^{at} \cos kt$	$\dfrac{s-a}{(s-a)^2 + k^2}$ $(s > a)$		(7)
$e^{at} \sin kt$	$\dfrac{k}{(s-a)^2 + k^2}$ $(s > a)$		(8)

For ready reference, all the Laplace transforms derived in this chapter are listed in the table of transforms that appears in the endpapers.

Example 1

Consider a mass-and-spring system with $m = \frac{1}{2}$, $k = 17$, and $c = 3$ in mks units (Fig. 7.3.1). As usual, let $x(t)$ denote the displacement of the mass m from its equilibrium position. If the mass is set in motion with $x(0) = 3$ and $x'(0) = 1$, find $x(t)$ for the resulting damped free oscillations.

Solution

The differential equation is $\frac{1}{2}x'' + 3x' + 17x = 0$, so we need to solve the initial value problem

$$x'' + 6x' + 34x = 0; \quad x(0) = 3, \quad x'(0) = 1.$$

We take the Laplace transform of each term of the differential equation. Because [obviously] $\mathcal{L}\{0\} \equiv 0$, we get the equation

$$\left[s^2 X(s) - 3s - 1\right] + 6\left[sX(s) - 3\right] + 34X(s) = 0,$$

which we solve for

$$X(s) = \frac{3s + 19}{s^2 + 6s + 34} = 3 \cdot \frac{s+3}{(s+3)^2 + 25} + 2 \cdot \frac{5}{(s+3)^2 + 25}.$$

Applying the formulas in (7) and (8) with $a = -3$ and $k = 5$, we now see that

$$x(t) = e^{-3t}\left(3\cos 5t + 2\sin 5t\right).$$

Figure 7.3.2 shows the graph of this rapidly decaying damped oscillation. ∎

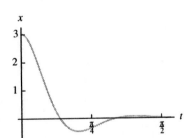

FIGURE 7.3.1. The mass-spring-dashpot system of Example 1.

FIGURE 7.3.2. The position function $x(t)$ in Example 1.

Example 2 illustrates a useful technique for finding the partial fraction coefficients in the case of nonrepeated linear factors.

Example 2

Find the inverse Laplace transform of

$$R(s) = \frac{s^2 + 1}{s^3 - 2s^2 - 8s}.$$

Solution Note that the denominator of $R(s)$ factors as $Q(s) = s(s + 2)(s - 4)$. Hence

$$\frac{s^2 + 1}{s^3 - 2s^2 - 8s} = \frac{A}{s} + \frac{B}{s + 2} + \frac{C}{s - 4}.$$

Multiplication of each term of this equation by $Q(s)$ yields

$$s^2 + 1 = A(s + 2)(s - 4) + Bs(s - 4) + Cs(s + 2).$$

When we successively substitute the three zeros $s = 0$, $s = -2$, and $s = 4$ of the denominator $Q(s)$ in this equation, we get the results

$$-8A = 1, \quad 12B = 5, \quad \text{and} \quad 24C = 17.$$

Thus $A = -\frac{1}{8}$, $B = \frac{5}{12}$, and $C = \frac{17}{24}$, so

$$\frac{s^2 + 1}{s^3 - 2s^2 - 8s} = -\frac{\frac{1}{8}}{s} + \frac{\frac{5}{12}}{s + 2} + \frac{\frac{17}{24}}{s - 4},$$

and therefore

$$\mathcal{L}^{-1}\left\{\frac{s^2 + 1}{s^3 - 2s^2 - 8s}\right\} = -\frac{1}{8} + \frac{5}{12}e^{-2t} + \frac{17}{24}e^{4t}. \qquad \blacksquare$$

Example 3 illustrates a differentiation technique for finding the partial fraction coefficients in the case of repeated linear factors.

Example 3 Solve the initial value problem

$$y'' + 4y' + 4y = t^2; \quad y(0) = y'(0) = 0.$$

Solution The transformed equation is

$$s^2 Y(s) + 4s Y(s) + 4Y(s) = \frac{2}{s^3}.$$

Thus

$$Y(s) = \frac{2}{s^3(s + 2)^2} = \frac{A}{s^3} + \frac{B}{s^2} + \frac{C}{s} + \frac{D}{(s + 2)^2} + \frac{E}{s + 2}. \qquad (9)$$

To find A, B, and C, we multiply both sides by s^3 to obtain

$$\frac{2}{(s + 2)^2} = A + Bs + Cs^2 + s^3 F(s), \qquad (10)$$

where $F(s) = D(s + 2)^{-2} + E(s + 2)^{-1}$ is the sum of the two partial fractions corresponding to $(s + 2)^2$. Substitution of $s = 0$ in Eq. (10) yields $A = \frac{1}{2}$. To find B and C, we differentiate Eq. (10) twice to obtain

$$\frac{-4}{(s + 2)^3} = B + 2Cs + 3s^2 F(s) + s^3 F'(s) \qquad (11)$$

and

$$\frac{12}{(s+2)^4} = 2C + 6sF(s) + 6s^2 F'(s) + s^3 F''(s). \tag{12}$$

Now substitution of $s = 0$ in Eq. (11) yields $B = -\frac{1}{2}$, and substitution of $s = 0$ in Eq. (12) yields $C = \frac{3}{8}$.

To find D and E, we multiply each side in Eq. (9) by $(s+2)^2$ to get

$$\frac{2}{s^3} = D + E(s+2) + (s+2)^2 G(s), \tag{13}$$

where $G(s) = As^{-3} + Bs^{-2} + Cs^{-1}$, and then differentiate to obtain

$$-\frac{6}{s^4} = E + 2(s+2)G(s) + (s+2)^2 G'(s). \tag{14}$$

Substitution of $s = -2$ in Eqs. (13) and (14) now yields $D = -\frac{1}{4}$ and $E = -\frac{3}{8}$. Thus

$$Y(s) = \frac{\frac{1}{2}}{s^3} - \frac{\frac{1}{2}}{s^2} + \frac{\frac{3}{8}}{s} - \frac{\frac{1}{4}}{(s+2)^2} - \frac{\frac{3}{8}}{s+2},$$

so the solution of the given initial value problem is

$$y(t) = \tfrac{1}{4}t^2 - \tfrac{1}{2}t + \tfrac{3}{8} - \tfrac{1}{4}te^{-2t} - \tfrac{3}{8}e^{-2t}. \qquad \blacksquare$$

Examples 4, 5, and 6 illustrate techniques for dealing with quadratic factors in partial fraction decompositions.

Example 4

Consider the mass-spring-dashpot system as in Example 1, but with initial conditions $x(0) = x'(0) = 0$ and with the imposed external force $F(t) = 15 \sin 2t$. Find the resulting transient motion and steady periodic motion of the mass.

Solution

The initial value problem we need to solve is

$$x'' + 6x' + 34x = 30 \sin 2t; \quad x(0) = x'(0) = 0.$$

The transformed equation is

$$s^2 X(s) + 6s X(s) + 34 X(s) = \frac{60}{s^2+4}.$$

Hence

$$X(s) = \frac{60}{(s^2+4)[(s+3)^2+25]} = \frac{As+B}{s^2+4} + \frac{Cs+D}{(s+3)^2+25}.$$

When we multiply both sides by the common denominator, we get

$$60 = (As+B)[(s+3)^2+25] + (Cs+D)(s^2+4). \tag{15}$$

To find A and B, we substitute the zero $s = 2i$ of the quadratic factor $s^2 + 4$ in Eq. (15); the result is

$$60 = (2iA + B)[(2i+3)^2 + 25],$$

which we simplify to

$$60 = (-24A + 30B) + (60A + 12B)i.$$

We now equate real parts and imaginary parts on each side of this equation to obtain the two linear equations

$$-24A + 30B = 60 \quad \text{and} \quad 60A + 12B = 0,$$

which are readily solved for $A = -\frac{10}{29}$ and $B = \frac{50}{29}$.

To find C and D, we substitute the zero $s = -3 + 5i$ of the quadratic factor $(s+3)^2 + 25$ in Eq. (15) and get

$$60 = [C(-3+5i) + D][(-3+5i)^2 + 4],$$

which we simplify to

$$60 = (186C - 12D) + (30C - 30D)i.$$

Again we equate real parts and imaginary parts; this yields the two linear equations

$$186C - 12D = 60 \quad \text{and} \quad 30C - 30D = 0,$$

and we readily find their solution to be $C = D = \frac{10}{29}$.

With these values of the coefficients A, B, C, and D, our partial fractions decomposition of $X(s)$ is

$$X(s) = \frac{1}{29}\left(\frac{-10s + 50}{s^2 + 4} + \frac{10s + 10}{(s+3)^2 + 25}\right)$$

$$= \frac{1}{29}\left(\frac{-10s + 25 \cdot 2}{s^2 + 4} + \frac{10(s+3) - 4 \cdot 5}{(s+3)^2 + 25}\right).$$

After we compute the inverse Laplace transforms, we get the position function

$$x(t) = \frac{5}{29}(-2\cos 2t + 5\sin 2t) + \frac{2}{29}e^{-3t}(5\cos 5t - 2\sin 5t).$$

The terms of circular frequency 2 constitute the steady periodic forced oscillation of the mass, whereas the exponentially damped terms of circular frequency 5 constitute its transient motion, which disappears very rapidly (see Fig. 7.3.3). Note that the transient motion is nonzero even though both initial conditions are zero. ∎

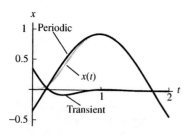

FIGURE 7.3.3. The periodic forced oscillation $x_{\text{sp}}(t)$, damped transient motion $x_{\text{tr}}(t)$, and solution $x(t) = x_{\text{sp}}(t) + x_{\text{tr}}(t)$ in Example 4.

Resonance and Repeated Quadratic Factors

The following two inverse Laplace transforms are useful in inverting partial fractions that correspond to the case of repeated quadratic factors:

$$\mathcal{L}^{-1}\left\{\frac{s}{(s^2 + k^2)^2}\right\} = \frac{1}{2k}t\sin kt, \tag{16}$$

$$\mathcal{L}^{-1}\left\{\frac{1}{(s^2 + k^2)^2}\right\} = \frac{1}{2k^3}(\sin kt - kt\cos kt). \tag{17}$$

These follow from Example 5 and Problem 31 of Section 7.2, respectively. Because of the presence in Eqs. (16) and (17) of the terms $t\sin kt$ and $t\cos kt$, a repeated quadratic factor ordinarily signals the phenomenon of resonance in an undamped mechanical or electrical system.

Example 5 Use Laplace transforms to solve the initial value problem

$$x'' + \omega_0^2 x = F_0 \sin \omega t; \quad x(0) = 0 = x'(0)$$

that determines the undamped forced oscillations of a mass on a spring.

Solution When we transform the differential equation, we get the equation

$$s^2 X(s) + \omega_0^2 X(s) = \frac{F_0 \omega}{s^2 + \omega^2}, \quad \text{so} \quad X(s) = \frac{F_0 \omega}{(s^2 + \omega^2)(s^2 + \omega_0^2)}.$$

If $\omega \neq \omega_0$, we find without difficulty that

$$X(s) = \frac{F_0 \omega}{\omega^2 - \omega_0^2} \left(\frac{1}{s^2 + \omega_0^2} - \frac{1}{s^2 + \omega^2} \right),$$

so it follows that

$$x(t) = \frac{F_0 \omega}{\omega^2 - \omega_0^2} \left(\frac{1}{\omega_0} \sin \omega_0 t - \frac{1}{\omega} \sin \omega t \right).$$

But if $\omega = \omega_0$, we have

$$X(s) = \frac{F_0 \omega_0}{(s^2 + \omega_0^2)^2},$$

so Eq. (17) yields the resonance solution

$$x(t) = \frac{F_0}{2\omega_0^2} (\sin \omega_0 t - \omega_0 t \cos \omega_0 t). \tag{18}$$

∎

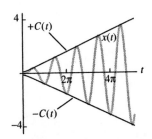

FIGURE 7.3.4. The resonance solution in (18) with $\omega_0 = \frac{1}{2}$ and $F_0 = 1$, together with its envelope curves $x = \pm C(t)$.

Remark: The solution curve defined in Eq. (18) bounces back and forth (see Fig. 7.3.4) between the "envelope curves" $x = \pm C(t)$ that are obtained by writing (18) in the form

$$x(t) = A(t) \cos \omega_0 t + B(t) \sin \omega_0 t$$

and then defining the usual "amplitude" $C = \sqrt{A^2 + B^2}$. In this case we find that

$$C(t) = \frac{F_0}{2\omega_0^2} \sqrt{\omega_0^2 t^2 + 1}.$$

This technique for constructing envelope curves of resonance solutions is illustrated further in the application material for this section. ∎

Example 6   Solve the initial value problem

$$y^{(4)} + 2y'' + y = 4te^t; \quad y(0) = y'(0) = y''(0) = y^{(3)}(0) = 0.$$

Solution   First we observe that

$$\mathcal{L}\{y''(t)\} = s^2 Y(s), \quad \mathcal{L}\{y^{(4)}(t)\} = s^4 Y(s), \quad \text{and} \quad \mathcal{L}\{te^t\} = \frac{1}{(s-1)^2}.$$

Hence the transformed equation is

$$(s^4 + 2s^2 + 1)Y(s) = \frac{4}{(s-1)^2}.$$

Thus our problem is to find the inverse transform of

$$
\begin{aligned}
Y(s) &= \frac{4}{(s-1)^2(s^2+1)^2} \\
&= \frac{A}{(s-1)^2} + \frac{B}{s-1} + \frac{Cs+D}{(s^2+1)^2} + \frac{Es+F}{s^2+1}.
\end{aligned}
\tag{19}
$$

If we multiply by the common denominator $(s-1)^2(s^2+1)^2$, we get the equation

$$
\begin{aligned}
A(s^2+1)^2 &+ B(s-1)(s^2+1)^2 + Cs(s-1)^2 \\
&+ D(s-1)^2 + Es(s-1)^2(s^2+1) + F(s-1)^2(s^2+1) = 4.
\end{aligned}
\tag{20}
$$

Upon substituting $s = 1$ we find that $A = 1$.

Equation (20) is an identity that holds for all values of s. To find the values of the remaining coefficients, we substitute in succession the values $s = 0$, $s = -1$, $s = 2$, $s = -2$, and $s = 3$ in Eq. (20). This yields the system

$$
\begin{aligned}
-B + D + F &= 3, \\
-8B - 4C + 4D - 8E + 8F &= 0, \\
25B + 2C + D + 10E + 5F &= -21, \\
-75B - 18C + 9D - 90E + 45F &= -21, \\
200B + 12C + 4D + 120E + 40F &= -96
\end{aligned}
\tag{21}
$$

of five linear equations in B, C, D, E, and F. With the aid of a calculator programmed to solve linear systems, we find that $B = -2$, $C = 2$, $D = 0$, $E = 2$, and $F = 1$.

We now substitute in Eq. (18) the coefficients we have found, and thus obtain

$$Y(s) = \frac{1}{(s-1)^2} - \frac{2}{s-1} + \frac{2s}{(s^2+1)^2} + \frac{2s+1}{s^2+1}.$$

Recalling Eq. (16), the translation property, and the familiar transforms of $\cos t$ and $\sin t$, we see finally that the solution of the given initial value problem is

$$y(t) = (t-2)e^t + (t+1)\sin t + 2\cos t. \quad \blacksquare$$

7.3 Problems

Apply the translation theorem to find the Laplace transforms of the functions in Problems 1 through 4.

1. $f(t) = t^4 e^{\pi t}$

2. $f(t) = t^{3/2} e^{-4t}$

3. $f(t) = e^{-2t} \sin 3\pi t$

4. $f(t) = e^{-1/2} \cos 2 \left(t - \frac{1}{8}\pi\right)$

Apply the translation theorem to find the inverse Laplace transforms of the functions in Problems 5 through 10.

5. $F(s) = \dfrac{3}{2s - 4}$

6. $F(s) = \dfrac{s - 1}{(s + 1)^3}$

7. $F(s) = \dfrac{1}{s^2 + 4s + 4}$

8. $F(s) = \dfrac{s + 2}{s^2 + 4s + 5}$

9. $F(s) = \dfrac{3s + 5}{s^2 - 6s + 25}$

10. $F(s) = \dfrac{2s - 3}{9s^2 - 12s + 20}$

Use partial fractions to find the inverse Laplace transforms of the functions in Problems 11 through 22.

11. $F(s) = \dfrac{1}{s^2 - 4}$

12. $F(s) = \dfrac{5s - 6}{s^2 - 3s}$

13. $F(s) = \dfrac{5 - 2s}{s^2 + 7s + 10}$

14. $F(s) = \dfrac{5s - 4}{s^3 - s^2 - 2s}$

15. $F(s) = \dfrac{1}{s^3 - 5s^2}$

16. $F(s) = \dfrac{1}{(s^2 + s - 6)^2}$

17. $F(s) = \dfrac{1}{s^4 - 16}$

18. $F(s) = \dfrac{s^3}{(s - 4)^4}$

19. $F(s) = \dfrac{s^2 - 2s}{s^4 + 5s^2 + 4}$

20. $F(s) = \dfrac{1}{s^4 - 8s^2 + 16}$

21. $F(s) = \dfrac{s^2 + 3}{(s^2 + 2s + 2)^2}$

22. $F(s) = \dfrac{2s^3 - s^2}{(4s^2 - 4s + 5)^2}$

Use the factorization

$$s^4 + 4a^4 = (s^2 - 2as + 2a^2)(s^2 + 2as + 2a^2)$$

to derive the inverse Laplace transforms listed in Problems 23 through 26.

23. $\mathcal{L}^{-1}\left\{\dfrac{s^3}{s^4 + 4a^4}\right\} = \cosh at \cos at$

24. $\mathcal{L}^{-1}\left\{\dfrac{s}{s^4 + 4a^4}\right\} = \dfrac{1}{2a^2}\sinh at \sin at$

25. $\mathcal{L}^{-1}\left\{\dfrac{s^2}{s^4 + 4a^4}\right\} = \dfrac{1}{2a}(\cosh at \sin at + \sinh at \cos at)$

26. $\mathcal{L}^{-1}\left\{\dfrac{1}{s^4 + 4a^4}\right\} = \dfrac{1}{4a^3}(\cosh at \sin at - \sinh at \cos at)$

Use Laplace transforms to solve the initial value problems in Problems 27 through 38.

27. $x'' + 6x' + 25x = 0$; $x(0) = 2, x'(0) = 3$

28. $x'' - 6x' + 8x = 2$; $x(0) = x'(0) = 0$

29. $x'' - 4x = 3t$; $x(0) = x'(0) = 0$

30. $x'' + 4x' + 8x = e^{-t}$; $x(0) = x'(0) = 0$

31. $x^{(3)} + x'' - 6x' = 0$; $x(0) = 0, \ x'(0) = x''(0) = 1$

32. $x^{(4)} - x = 0$; $x(0) = 1, \ x'(0) = x''(0) = x^{(3)}(0) = 0$

33. $x^{(4)} + x = 0$; $x(0) = x'(0) = x''(0) = 0, \ x^{(3)}(0) = 1$

34. $x^{(4)} + 13x'' + 36x = 0$; $x(0) = x''(0) = 0, \ x'(0) = 2, \ x^{(3)}(0) = -13$

35. $x^{(4)} + 8x'' + 16x = 0$; $x(0) = x'(0) = x''(0) = 0, \ x^{(3)}(0) = 1$

36. $x^{(4)} + 2x'' + x = e^{2t}$; $x(0) = x'(0) = x''(0) = x^{(3)}(0) = 0$

37. $x'' + 4x' + 13x = te^{-t}$; $x(0) = 0, \ x'(0) = 2$

38. $x'' + 6x' + 18x = \cos 2t$; $x(0) = 1, \ x'(0) = -1$

Problems 39 and 40 illustrate two types of resonance in a mass-spring-dashpot system with given external force $f(t)$ and with the initial conditions $x(0) = x'(0) = 0$.

39. Suppose that $m = 1$, $k = 9$, $c = 0$, and $f(t) = 6\cos 3t$. Use the inverse transform given in Eq. (16) to derive the solution $x(t) = t\sin 3t$. Construct a figure that illustrates the resonance that occurs.

40. Suppose that $m = 1$, $k = 9.04$, $c = 0.4$, and $f(t) = 6e^{-t/5}\cos 3t$. Derive the solution

$$x(t) = te^{-t/5}\sin 3t.$$

Show that the maximum value of the amplitude function $A(t) = te^{-t/5}$ is $A(5) = 5/e$. Thus (as indicated in Fig. 7.3.5) the oscillations of the mass increase in amplitude during the first 5 s before being damped out as $t \to +\infty$.

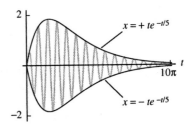

FIGURE 7.3.5. The graph of the damped oscillation in Problem 40.

7.3 Application: Damping and Resonance Investigations

Here we outline a *Maple* investigation of the behavior of the mass-spring-dashpot system

$$mx'' + cx' + kx = F(t), \quad x(0) = x'(0) = 0 \tag{1}$$

with parameter values

$$m := 25; \qquad c := 10; \qquad k := 226;$$

in response to a variety of possible external forces:

1. $F(t) \equiv 0$:

This is the case of free damped oscillations, similar to those illustrated in Fig. 3.4.12.

2. $F(t) = 901 \cos 3t$:

With this periodic external force you should see a steady periodic oscillation with an exponentially damped transient motion (as illustrated in Fig. 3.6.13).

3. $F(t) = 900e^{-t/5} \cos 3t$:

Now the periodic external force is exponentially damped, and the transform $X(s)$ includes a repeated quadratic factor that signals the presence of a resonance phenomenon. The response $x(t)$ is a constant multiple of that shown in Fig. 7.3.5.

4. $F(t) = 900te^{-t/5} \cos 3t$:

We have inserted the factor t to make it a bit more interesting. The solution in this case is illustrated below.

5. $F(t) = 162t^3 e^{-t/5} \cos 3t$:

In this case you'll find that the transform $X(s)$ involves the *fifth* power of a quadratic factor, and its inverse transform by manual methods would be impossibly tedious.

To illustrate the *Maple* approach, we first set up the differential equation corresponding to Case 4.

```
F := 900*t*exp(-t/5)*cos(3*t);
de := m*diff(x(t),t$2) + c*diff(x(t),t) + k*x(t) = F;
```

Then we apply the Laplace transform and substitute the initial conditions.

```
with(inttrans):
DE := laplace(de, t, s):
X(s) := solve(DE, laplace(x(t), t, s)):
X(s) := simplify(subs(x(0)=0, D(x)(0)=0, X(s)));
```

At this point the command `factor(denom(X(s)))` shows that

$$X(s) = \frac{22500(25s^2 + 10s - 224)}{(25s^2 + 10s + 226)^3}.$$

The cubed quadratic factor would be difficult to handle manually, but the command

```
x(t) := invlaplace(X(s), s, t);
```

soon yields

$$x(t) = e^{-t/5} \left(t \cos 3t + \left(3t^2 - \tfrac{1}{3} \right) \sin 3t \right).$$

The amplitude function for these damped oscillations is defined by

```
C(t) := exp(-t/5)*sqrt(t^2 + (3*t^2 - 1/3)^2);
```

and finally the command

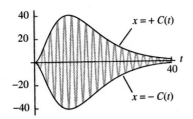

FIGURE 7.3.6. The resonance solution and its envelope curves in Case 4.

```
plot({x(t), C(t), -C(t)}, t=0..40);
```

produces the plot shown in Fig. 7.3.6. The resonance resulting from the repeated quadratic factor consists of a temporary buildup before the oscillations are damped out.

For each of Cases 1 through 5 you can enter the appropriate external force and re-execute the commands listed previously. To see the advantage of using Laplace transforms, set up the differential equation **de** for Case 5 and examine the result of the command

```
dsolve({de, x(0)=0, D(x)(0)=0}, x(t));
```

Of course you can substitute your own favorite mass-spring-dashpot parameters for those used here. But it will simplify the calculations if you choose m, c, and k so that

$$mr^2 + cr + k = (pr + a)^2 + b^2 \tag{2}$$

where p, a, and b are integers. One way is to select the latter integers first, then use Eq. (2) to determine m, c, and k.

7.4 Derivatives, Integrals, and Products of Transforms

The Laplace transform of the (initially unknown) solution of a differential equation is sometimes recognizable as the product of the transforms of two *known* functions. For example, when we transform the initial value problem

$$x'' + x = \cos t; \quad x(0) = x'(0) = 0,$$

we get

$$X(s) = \frac{s}{(s^2 + 1)^2} = \frac{s}{s^2 + 1} \cdot \frac{1}{s^2 + 1} = \mathcal{L}\{\cos t\} \cdot \mathcal{L}\{\sin t\}.$$

This strongly suggests that there ought to be a way of combining the two functions $\sin t$ and $\cos t$ to obtain a function $x(t)$ whose transform is the *product* of *their* transforms. But obviously $x(t)$ is *not* simply the product of $\cos t$ and $\sin t$, because

$$\mathcal{L}\{\cos t \sin t\} = \mathcal{L}\left\{\tfrac{1}{2} \sin 2t\right\} = \frac{1}{s^2 + 4} \neq \frac{s}{(s^2 + 1)^2}.$$

Thus $\mathcal{L}\{\cos t \sin t\} \neq \mathcal{L}\{\cos t\} \cdot \mathcal{L}\{\sin t\}$.

Theorem 1 of this section will tell us that the function

$$h(t) = \int_0^t f(\tau)g(t - \tau)\, d\tau \tag{1}$$

has the desired property that

$$\mathcal{L}\{h(t)\} = H(s) = F(s) \cdot G(s). \tag{2}$$

The new function of t defined as the integral in (1) depends only on f and g and is called the *convolution* of f and g. It is denoted by $f * g$, the idea being that it is a new type of product of f and g, so tailored that its transform is the product of the transforms of f and g.

Definition: The Convolution of Two Functions

The **convolution** $f * g$ of the piecewise continuous functions f and g is defined for $t \geqq 0$ as follows:

➤
$$(f * g)(t) = \int_0^t f(\tau)g(t - \tau)\, d\tau. \qquad (3)$$

We will also write $f(t) * g(t)$ when convenient. In terms of the convolution product, Theorem 1 of this section says that

➤
$$\mathcal{L}\{f * g\} = \mathcal{L}\{f\} \cdot \mathcal{L}\{g\}.$$

If we make the substitution $u = t - \tau$ in the integral in (3), we see that

$$f(t) * g(t) = \int_0^t f(\tau)g(t - \tau)\, d\tau = \int_t^0 f(t - u)g(u)(-du)$$

$$= \int_0^t g(u)f(t - u)\, du = g(t) * f(t).$$

Thus the convolution is *commutative*: $f * g = g * f$.

Example 1

The convolution of $\cos t$ and $\sin t$ is

$$(\cos t) * (\sin t) = \int_0^t \cos \tau \sin(t - \tau)\, d\tau.$$

We apply the trigonometric identity

$$\cos A \sin B = \tfrac{1}{2}\left[\sin(A + B) - \sin(A - B)\right]$$

to obtain

$$(\cos t) * (\sin t) = \int_0^t \tfrac{1}{2}\left[\sin t - \sin(2\tau - t)\right]\, d\tau$$

$$= \tfrac{1}{2}\left[\tau \sin t + \tfrac{1}{2}\cos(2\tau - t)\right]_{\tau=0}^{t};$$

that is,

$$(\cos t) * (\sin t) = \tfrac{1}{2}t \sin t.$$

And we recall from Example 5 of Section 7.2 that the Laplace transform of $\tfrac{1}{2}t \sin t$ is indeed $s/(s^2 + 1)^2$. ∎

Theorem 1 is proved at the end of this section.

THEOREM 1: The Convolution Property

Suppose that $f(t)$ and $g(t)$ are piecewise continuous for $t \geqq 0$ and that $|f(t)|$ and $|g(t)|$ are bounded by Me^{ct} as $t \to +\infty$. Then the Laplace transform of the convolution $f(t) * g(t)$ exists for $s > c$; moreover,

➤
$$\mathcal{L}\{f(t) * g(t)\} = \mathcal{L}\{f(t)\} \cdot \mathcal{L}\{g(t)\} \qquad (4)$$

and

$$\mathcal{L}^{-1}\{F(s) \cdot G(s)\} = f(t) * g(t).$$ (5)

Thus we can find the inverse transform of the product $F(s) \cdot G(s)$, provided that we can evaluate the integral

$$\mathcal{L}^{-1}\{F(s) \cdot G(s)\} = \int_0^t f(\tau)g(t - \tau)\, d\tau.$$ (5')

Example 2 illustrates the fact that convolution often provides a convenient alternative to the use of partial fractions for finding inverse transforms.

Example 2   With $f(t) = \sin 2t$ and $g(t) = e^t$, convolution yields

$$\mathcal{L}^{-1}\left\{\frac{2}{(s-1)(s^2+4)}\right\} = (\sin 2t) * e^t = \int_0^t e^{t-\tau} \sin 2\tau\, d\tau$$

$$= e^t \int_0^t e^{-\tau} \sin 2\tau\, d\tau = e^t \left[\frac{e^{-\tau}}{5}(-\sin 2\tau - 2\cos 2\tau)\right]_0^t,$$

so

$$\mathcal{L}^{-1}\left\{\frac{2}{(s-1)(s^2+4)}\right\} = \frac{2}{5}e^t - \frac{1}{5}\sin 2t - \frac{2}{5}\cos 2t. \qquad \blacksquare$$

Differentiation of Transforms

According to Theorem 1 of Section 7.2, if $f(0) = 0$ then differentiation of $f(t)$ corresponds to multiplication of its transform by s. Theorem 2, proved at the end of this section, tells us that differentiation of the transform $F(s)$ corresponds to multiplication of the original function $f(t)$ by $-t$.

THEOREM 2: Differentiation of Transforms

If $f(t)$ is piecewise continuous for $t \geq 0$ and $|f(t)| \leq Me^{ct}$ as $t \to +\infty$, then

$$\mathcal{L}\{-tf(t)\} = F'(s)$$ (6)

for $s > c$. Equivalently,

$$f(t) = \mathcal{L}^{-1}\{F(s)\} = -\frac{1}{t}\mathcal{L}^{-1}\{F'(s)\}.$$ (7)

Repeated application of Eq. (6) gives

$$\mathcal{L}\{t^n f(t)\} = (-1)^n F^{(n)}(s)$$ (8)

for $n = 1, 2, 3, \ldots$.

Example 3   Find $\mathcal{L}\{t^2 \sin kt\}$.

Solution   Equation (8) gives

$$\mathcal{L}\{t^2 \sin kt\} = (-1)^2 \frac{d^2}{ds^2}\left(\frac{k}{s^2 + k^2}\right)$$

$$= \frac{d}{ds}\left[\frac{-2ks}{(s^2 + k^2)^2}\right] = \frac{6ks^2 - 2k^3}{(s^2 + k^2)^3}. \tag{9}$$

The form of the differentiation property in Eq. (7) is often helpful in finding an inverse transform when the *derivative* of the transform is easier to work with than the transform itself.

Example 4   Find $\mathcal{L}^{-1}\{\tan^{-1}(1/s)\}$.

Solution   The derivative of $\tan^{-1}(1/s)$ is a simple rational function, so we apply Eq. (7):

$$\mathcal{L}^{-1}\left\{\tan^{-1}\frac{1}{s}\right\} = -\frac{1}{t}\mathcal{L}^{-1}\left\{\frac{d}{ds}\tan^{-1}\frac{1}{s}\right\} = -\frac{1}{t}\mathcal{L}^{-1}\left\{\frac{-1/s^2}{1 + (1/s)^2}\right\}$$

$$= -\frac{1}{t}\mathcal{L}^{-1}\left\{\frac{-1}{s^2 + 1}\right\} = -\frac{1}{t}(-\sin t).$$

Therefore,

$$\mathcal{L}^{-1}\left\{\tan^{-1}\frac{1}{s}\right\} = \frac{\sin t}{t}.$$

Equation (8) can be applied to transform a linear differential equation having polynomial, rather than constant, coefficients. The result will be a differential equation involving the transform; whether this procedure leads to success depends, of course, on whether we can solve the new equation more readily than the old one.

Example 5   Let $x(t)$ be the solution of Bessel's equation of order zero,

$$tx'' + x' + tx = 0,$$

such that $x(0) = 1$ and $x'(0) = 0$. This solution of Bessel's equation is customarily denoted by $J_0(t)$. Because

$$\mathcal{L}\{x'(t)\} = sX(s) - 1 \quad \text{and} \quad \mathcal{L}\{x''(t)\} = s^2X(s) - s,$$

and because x and x'' are each multiplied by t, application of Eq. (7) yields the transformed equation

$$-\frac{d}{ds}\left[s^2X(s) - s\right] + [sX(s) - 1] - \frac{d}{ds}[X(s)] = 0.$$

The result of differentiation and simplification is the differential equation

$$(s^2 + 1)X'(s) + sX(s) = 0.$$

This equation is separable—

$$\frac{X'(s)}{X(s)} = -\frac{s}{s^2 + 1};$$

its general solution is

$$X(s) = \frac{C}{\sqrt{s^2 + 1}}.$$

In Problem 39 we outline the argument that $C = 1$. Because $X(s) = \mathcal{L}\{J_0(t)\}$, it follows that

$$\mathcal{L}\{J_0(t)\} = \frac{1}{\sqrt{s^2 + 1}}. \tag{10}$$

■

Integration of Transforms

Differentiation of $F(s)$ corresponds to multiplication of $f(t)$ by t (together with a change of sign). It is therefore natural to expect that integration of $F(s)$ will correspond to division of $f(t)$ by t. Theorem 3, proved at the end of this section, confirms this, provided that the resulting quotient $f(t)/t$ remains well behaved as $t \to 0$ from the right; that is, provided that

$$\lim_{t \to 0^+} \frac{f(t)}{t} \quad \text{exists and is finite.} \tag{11}$$

THEOREM 3: Integration of Transforms

Suppose that $f(t)$ is piecewise continuous for $t \geqq 0$, that $f(t)$ satisfies the condition in (11), and that $|f(t)| \leqq Me^{ct}$ as $t \to +\infty$. Then

$$\mathcal{L}\left\{\frac{f(t)}{t}\right\} = \int_s^\infty F(\sigma)\,d\sigma \tag{12}$$

for $s > c$. Equivalently,

$$f(t) = \mathcal{L}^{-1}\{F(s)\} = t\mathcal{L}^{-1}\left\{\int_s^\infty F(\sigma)\,d\sigma\right\}. \tag{13}$$

▲

Example 6 Find $\mathcal{L}\{(\sinh t)/t\}$.

Solution We first verify that the condition in (11) holds:

$$\lim_{t \to 0} \frac{\sinh t}{t} = \lim_{t \to 0} \frac{e^t - e^{-t}}{2t} = \lim_{t \to 0} \frac{e^t + e^{-t}}{2} = 1,$$

with the aid of l'Hôpital's rule. Then Eq. (12), with $f(t) = \sinh t$, yields

$$\mathcal{L}\left\{\frac{\sinh t}{t}\right\} = \int_s^\infty \mathcal{L}\{\sinh t\}\,d\sigma = \int_s^\infty \frac{d\sigma}{\sigma^2 - 1}$$

$$= \frac{1}{2}\int_s^\infty \left(\frac{1}{\sigma - 1} - \frac{1}{\sigma + 1}\right) d\sigma = \frac{1}{2}\left[\ln\frac{\sigma - 1}{\sigma + 1}\right]_s^\infty.$$

Therefore,

$$\mathcal{L}\left\{\frac{\sinh t}{t}\right\} = \frac{1}{2}\ln\frac{s + 1}{s - 1},$$

because $\ln 1 = 0$. ∎

The form of the integration property in Eq. (13) is often helpful in finding an inverse transform when the indefinite *integral* of the transform is easier to handle than the transform itself.

Example 7 Find $\mathcal{L}^{-1}\{2s/(s^2 - 1)^2\}$.

Solution We could use partial fractions, but it is much simpler to apply Eq. (13). This gives

$$\mathcal{L}^{-1}\left\{\frac{2s}{(s^2 - 1)^2}\right\} = t\mathcal{L}^{-1}\left\{\int_s^\infty \frac{2\sigma}{(\sigma^2 - 1)^2}\,d\sigma\right\}$$

$$= t\mathcal{L}^{-1}\left\{\left[\frac{-1}{\sigma^2 - 1}\right]_s^\infty\right\} = t\mathcal{L}^{-1}\left\{\frac{1}{s^2 - 1}\right\},$$

and therefore

$$\mathcal{L}^{-1}\left\{\frac{2s}{(s^2 - 1)^2}\right\} = t\sinh t.$$ ∎

*Proofs of Theorems

Proof of Theorem 1: The transforms $F(s)$ and $G(s)$ exist when $s > c$ by Theorem 2 of Section 7.1. The definition of the Laplace transform gives

$$G(s) = \int_0^\infty e^{-su} g(u)\,du = \int_{-\tau}^\infty e^{-s(t - \tau)} g(t - \tau)\,dt \quad (u = t - \tau),$$

and therefore

$$G(s) = e^{s\tau}\int_0^\infty e^{-st} g(t - \tau)\,dt,$$

because we may *define* $f(t)$ and $g(t)$ to be zero for $t < 0$. Then

$$F(s)G(s) = G(s)\int_0^\infty e^{-s\tau} f(\tau)\,d\tau = \int_0^\infty e^{-s\tau} f(\tau)G(s)\,d\tau$$

$$= \int_0^\infty e^{-s\tau} f(\tau)\left(e^{s\tau}\int_0^\infty e^{-st} g(t - \tau)\,dt\right) d\tau$$

$$= \int_0^\infty \left(\int_0^\infty e^{-st} f(\tau)g(t - \tau)\,dt\right) d\tau.$$

Now our hypotheses on f and g imply that the order of integration may be reversed. (The proof of this requires a discussion of uniform convergence of improper integrals, and can be found in Chapter 2 of Churchill's *Operational Mathematics*, 3rd ed. (New York: McGraw-Hill, 1972).) Hence

$$F(s)G(s) = \int_0^\infty \left(\int_0^\infty e^{-st} f(\tau) g(t - \tau) \, d\tau \right) dt$$

$$= \int_0^\infty e^{-st} \left(\int_0^t f(\tau) g(t - \tau) \, d\tau \right) dt$$

$$= \int_0^\infty e^{-st} [f(t) * g(t)] \, dt,$$

and therefore,

$$F(s)G(s) = \mathcal{L}\{f(t) * g(t)\}.$$

We replace the upper limit of the inner integral with t because $g(t-\tau) = 0$ whenever $\tau > t$. This completes the proof of Theorem 1. ▲

Proof of Theorem 2: Because

$$F(s) = \int_0^\infty e^{-st} f(t) \, dt,$$

differentiation under the integral sign yields

$$F(s) = \frac{d}{ds} \int_0^\infty e^{-st} f(t) \, dt$$

$$= \int_0^\infty \frac{d}{ds} \left[e^{-st} f(t) \right] dt = \int_0^\infty e^{-st} [-t f(t)] \, dt;$$

thus

$$F'(s) = \mathcal{L}\{-t f(t)\},$$

which is Eq. (6). We obtain Eq. (7) by applying $\mathcal{L}^{-1}$ and then dividing by $-t$. The validity of differentiation under the integral sign depends on uniform convergence of the resulting integral; this is discussed in Chapter 2 of the book by Churchill just mentioned. ▲

Proof of Theorem 3: By definition,

$$F(\sigma) = \int_0^\infty e^{-\sigma t} f(t) \, dt.$$

So integration of $F(\sigma)$ from s to $+\infty$ gives

$$\int_s^\infty F(\sigma) \, d\sigma = \int_s^\infty \left(\int_0^\infty e^{-\sigma t} f(t) \, dt \right) d\sigma.$$

Under the hypotheses of the theorem, the order of integration may be reversed (see Churchill's book again); it follows that

$$\int_s^\infty F(\sigma)\,d\sigma = \int_0^\infty \left(\int_s^\infty e^{-\sigma t} f(t)\,d\sigma \right) dt$$

$$= \int_0^\infty \left[\frac{e^{-\sigma t}}{-t} \right]_{\sigma=s}^\infty f(t)\,dt$$

$$= \int_0^\infty e^{-st} \frac{f(t)}{t}\,dt = \mathcal{L}\left\{ \frac{f(t)}{t} \right\}.$$

This verifies Eq. (12), and Eq. (13) follows upon first applying $\mathcal{L}^{-1}$ and then multiplying by t.

▲

7.4 Problems

Find the convolution $f(t) * g(t)$ in Problems 1 through 6.

1. $f(t) = t$, $g(t) \equiv 1$
2. $f(t) = t$, $g(t) = e^{at}$
3. $f(t) = g(t) = \sin t$
4. $f(t) = t^2$, $g(t) = \cos t$
5. $f(t) = g(t) = e^{at}$
6. $f(t) = e^{at}$, $g(t) = e^{bt}$ $(a \neq b)$

Apply the convolution theorem to find the inverse Laplace transforms of the functions in Problems 7 through 14.

7. $F(s) = \dfrac{1}{s(s-3)}$
8. $F(s) = \dfrac{1}{s(s^2+4)}$

9. $F(s) = \dfrac{1}{(s^2+9)^2}$
10. $F(s) = \dfrac{1}{s^2(s^2+k^2)}$

11. $F(s) = \dfrac{s^2}{(s^2+4)^2}$
12. $F(s) = \dfrac{1}{s(s^2+4s+5)}$

13. $F(s) = \dfrac{s}{(s-3)(s^2+1)}$
14. $F(s) = \dfrac{s}{s^4+5s^2+4}$

In Problems 15 through 22, apply either Theorem 2 or Theorem 3 to find the Laplace transform of $f(t)$.

15. $f(t) = t \sin 3t$
16. $f(t) = t^2 \cos 2t$
17. $f(t) = te^{2t} \cos 3t$
18. $f(t) = te^{-t} \sin^2 t$
19. $f(t) = \dfrac{\sin t}{t}$
20. $f(t) = \dfrac{1 - \cos 2t}{t}$
21. $f(t) = \dfrac{e^{3t} - 1}{t}$
22. $f(t) = \dfrac{e^t - e^{-t}}{t}$

Find the inverse transforms of the functions in Problems 23 through 28.

23. $F(s) = \ln \dfrac{s-2}{s+2}$
24. $F(s) = \ln \dfrac{s^2+1}{s^2+4}$

25. $F(s) = \ln \dfrac{s^2+1}{(s+2)(s-3)}$
26. $F(s) = \tan^{-1} \dfrac{3}{s+2}$

27. $F(s) = \ln \left(1 + \dfrac{1}{s^2} \right)$
28. $F(s) = \dfrac{s}{(s^2+1)^3}$

In Problems 29 through 34, transform the given differential equation to find a nontrivial solution such that $x(0) = 0$.

29. $tx'' + (t-2)x' + x = 0$
30. $tx'' + (3t-1)x' + 3x = 0$
31. $tx'' - (4t+1)x' + 2(2t+1)x = 0$
32. $tx'' + 2(t-1)x' - 2x = 0$
33. $tx'' - 2x' + tx = 0$
34. $tx'' + (4t-2)x' + (13t-4)x = 0$
35. Apply the convolution theorem to show that

$$\mathcal{L}^{-1}\left\{ \frac{1}{(s-1)\sqrt{s}} \right\} = \frac{2e^t}{\sqrt{\pi}} \int_0^{\sqrt{t}} e^{-u^2}\,du = e^t \operatorname{erf}\sqrt{t}.$$

(*Suggestion:* Substitute $u = \sqrt{t}$.)

In Problems 36 through 38, apply the convolution theorem to derive the indicated solution $x(t)$ of the given differential equation with initial conditions $x(0) = x'(0) = 0$.

36. $x'' + 4x = f(t)$; $x(t) = \dfrac{1}{2} \displaystyle\int_0^t f(t-\tau) \sin 2\tau\,d\tau$

37. $x'' + 2x' + x = f(t)$; $x(t) = \displaystyle\int_0^t \tau e^{-\tau} f(t-\tau)\,d\tau$

38. $x'' + 4x' + 13x = f(t)$;

$$x(t) = \frac{1}{3} \int_0^t f(t-\tau)e^{-2\tau} \sin 3\tau\,d\tau$$

Termwise Inverse Transformation of Series

In Chapter 2 of Churchill's Operational Mathematics, the following theorem is proved. Suppose that $f(t)$ is continuous for $t \geqq 0$, that $f(t)$ is of exponential order as $t \to +\infty$, and that

$$F(s) = \sum_{n=0}^\infty \frac{a_n}{s^{n+k+1}}$$

where $0 \leqq k < 1$ *and the series converges absolutely for* $s > c$.
Then

$$f(t) = \sum_{n=0}^{\infty} \frac{a_n t^{n+k}}{\Gamma(n+k+1)}.$$

Apply this result in Problems 39 through 41.

39. In Example 5 it was shown that

$$\mathcal{L}\{J_0(t)\} = \frac{C}{\sqrt{s^2+1}} = \frac{C}{s}\left(1 + \frac{1}{s^2}\right)^{-1/2}.$$

Expand with the aid of the binomial series and then compute the inverse transformation term by term to obtain

$$J_0(t) = C\sum_{n=0}^{\infty} \frac{(-1)^n t^{2n}}{2^{2n}(n!)^2}.$$

Finally, note that $J_0(0) = 1$ implies that $C = 1$.

40. Expand the function $F(s) = s^{-1/2}e^{-1/s}$ in powers of s^{-1} to show that

$$\mathcal{L}^{-1}\left\{\frac{1}{\sqrt{s}}e^{-1/s}\right\} = \frac{1}{\sqrt{\pi t}}\cos 2\sqrt{t}.$$

41. Show that

$$\mathcal{L}^{-1}\left\{\frac{1}{s}e^{-1/s}\right\} = J_0\left(2\sqrt{t}\right).$$

7.5 Periodic and Piecewise Continuous Input Functions

FIGURE 7.5.1. The graph of the unit step function at $t = a$.

Mathematical models of mechanical or electrical systems often involve functions with discontinuities corresponding to external forces that are turned abruptly on or off. One such simple off-on function is the **unit step function** at $t = a$; its formula is

$$u_a(t) = u(t-a) = \begin{cases} 0 & \text{if } t < a, \\ 1 & \text{if } t \geqq a, \end{cases} \tag{1}$$

and its graph appears in Fig. 7.5.1.

In Example 8 of Section 7.1 we saw that if $a \geqq 0$, then

$$\blacktriangleright \qquad\qquad \mathcal{L}\{u(t-a)\} = \frac{e^{-as}}{s}. \tag{2}$$

Because $\mathcal{L}\{u(t)\} = 1/s$, Eq. (2) implies that multiplication of the transform of $u(t)$ by e^{-as} corresponds to the translation $t \to t - a$ in the original independent variable. Theorem 1 tells us that this fact, when properly interpreted, is a general property of the Laplace transformation.

THEOREM 1: Translation on the *t*-Axis

If $\mathcal{L}\{f(t)\}$ exists for $s > c$, then

$$\mathcal{L}\{u(t-a)f(t-a)\} = e^{-as}F(s) \tag{3a}$$

and

$$\mathcal{L}^{-1}\{e^{-as}F(s)\} = u(t-a)f(t-a) \tag{3b}$$

for $s > c + a$.   ▲

Note that

$$u(t-a)f(t-a) = \begin{cases} 0 & \text{if } t < a, \\ f(t-a) & \text{if } t \geqq a. \end{cases} \tag{4}$$

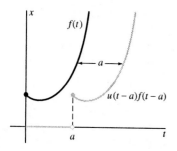

FIGURE 7.5.2. Translation of $f(t)$ a units to the right.

Thus Theorem 1 implies that $\mathcal{L}^{-1}\{e^{-as}F(s)\}$ is the function whose graph for $t \geq a$ is the translation a units to the right of the graph of $f(t)$. Note that the part of the graph of $f(t)$ to the left of $t = 0$ is cut off and not translated (Fig. 7.5.2).

Proof of Theorem 1: From the definition of $\mathcal{L}\{f(t)\}$, we get

$$e^{-as}F(s) = e^{-as}\int_0^\infty e^{-s\tau}f(\tau)\,d\tau = \int_0^\infty e^{-s(\tau+a)}f(\tau)\,d\tau.$$

The substitution $t = \tau + a$ then yields

$$e^{-as}F(s) = \int_a^\infty e^{-st}f(t-a)\,dt.$$

From Eq. (4) we see that this is the same as

$$e^{-as}F(s) = \int_0^\infty e^{-st}u(t-a)f(t-a)\,dt = \mathcal{L}\{u(t-a)f(t-a)\},$$

because $u(t-a)f(t-a) = 0$ for $t < a$. This completes the proof of Theorem 1. ▲

Example 1

With $f(t) = \frac{1}{2}t^2$, Theorem 1 gives

$$\mathcal{L}^{-1}\left\{\frac{e^{-as}}{s^3}\right\} = u(t-a)\frac{1}{2}(t-a)^2 = \begin{cases} 0 & \text{if } t < a, \\ \frac{1}{2}(t-a)^2 & \text{if } t \geq a \end{cases} \qquad \text{(Fig. 7.5.3).} \quad \blacksquare$$

Example 2

Find $\mathcal{L}\{g(t)\}$ if

$$g(t) = \begin{cases} 0 & \text{if } t < 3, \\ t^2 & \text{if } t \geq 3 \end{cases} \qquad \text{(Fig. 7.5.4).}$$

Solution

Before applying Theorem 1, we must first write $g(t)$ in the form $u(t-3)f(t-3)$. The function $f(t)$ whose translation 3 units to the right agrees (for $t \geq 3$) with $g(t) = t^2$ is $f(t) = (t+3)^2$ because $f(t-3) = t^2$. But then

$$F(s) = \mathcal{L}\{t^2 + 6t + 9\} = \frac{2}{s^3} + \frac{6}{s^2} + \frac{9}{s},$$

so now Theorem 1 yields

$$\mathcal{L}\{g(t)\} = \mathcal{L}\{u(t-3)f(t-3)\} = e^{-3s}F(s) = e^{-3s}\left(\frac{2}{s^3} + \frac{6}{s^2} + \frac{9}{s}\right). \quad \blacksquare$$

Example 3

Find $\mathcal{L}\{f(t)\}$ if

$$f(t) = \begin{cases} \cos 2t & \text{if } 0 \leq t < 2\pi, \\ 0 & \text{if } t \geq 2\pi \end{cases} \qquad \text{(Fig. 7.5.5).}$$

FIGURE 7.5.3. The graph of the inverse transform of Example 1.

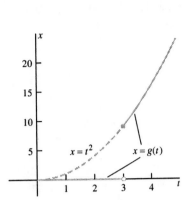

FIGURE 7.5.4. The graph of the function $g(t)$ of Example 2.

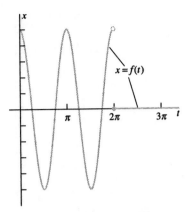

FIGURE 7.5.5. The function $f(t)$ of Examples 3 and 4

Solution We note first that

$$f(t) = [1 - u(t - 2\pi)]\cos 2t = \cos 2t - u(t - 2\pi)\cos 2(t - 2\pi)$$

because of the periodicity of the cosine function. Hence Theorem 1 gives

$$\mathcal{L}\{f(t)\} = \mathcal{L}\{\cos 2t\} - e^{-2\pi s}\mathcal{L}\{\cos 2t\} = \frac{s(1 - e^{-2\pi s})}{s^2 + 4}.$$ ∎

Example 4 A mass that weighs 32 lb (mass $m = 1$ slug) is attached to the free end of a long light spring that is stretched 1 ft by a force of 4 lb ($k = 4$ lb/ft). The mass is initially at rest in its equilibrium position. Beginning at time $t = 0$ (seconds), an external force $f(t) = \cos 2t$ is applied to the mass, but at time $t = 2\pi$ this force is turned off (abruptly discontinued) and the mass is allowed to continue its motion unimpeded. Find the resulting position function $x(t)$ of the mass.

Solution We need to solve the initial value problem

$$x'' + 4x = f(t); \quad x(0) = x'(0) = 0,$$

where $f(t)$ is the function of Example 3. The transformed equation is

$$(s^2 + 4)X(s) = F(s) = \frac{s(1 - e^{-2\pi s})}{s^2 + 4},$$

so

$$X(s) = \frac{s}{(s^2 + 4)^2} - e^{-2\pi s}\frac{s}{(s^2 + 4)^2}.$$

Because

$$\mathcal{L}^{-1}\left\{\frac{s}{(s^2 + 4)^2}\right\} = \tfrac{1}{4}t\sin 2t$$

by Eq. (16) of Section 7.3, it follows from Theorem 1 that

$$x(t) = \tfrac{1}{4}t\sin 2t - u(t - 2\pi)\cdot\tfrac{1}{4}(t - 2\pi)\sin 2(t - 2\pi)$$

$$= \tfrac{1}{4}[t - u(t - 2\pi)\cdot(t - 2\pi)]\sin 2t.$$

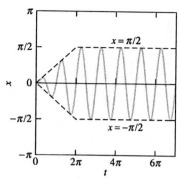

FIGURE 7.5.6. The graph of the function $x(t)$ of Example 4.

If we separate the cases $t < 2\pi$ and $t \geq 2\pi$, we find that the position function may be written in the form

$$x(t) = \begin{cases} \frac{1}{4}t \sin 2t & \text{if } t < 2\pi, \\ \frac{1}{2}\pi \sin 2t & \text{if } t \geq 2\pi. \end{cases}$$

As indicated by the graph of $x(t)$ shown in Fig. 7.5.6, the mass oscillates with circular frequency $\omega = 2$ and with linearly increasing amplitude until the force is removed at time $t = 2\pi$. Thereafter, the mass continues to oscillate with the same frequency but with constant amplitude $\pi/2$. The force $F(t) = \cos 2t$ would produce pure resonance if continued indefinitely, but we see that its effect ceases immediately at the moment it is turned off. ∎

If we were to attack Example 4 with the methods of Chapter 3, we would need to solve one problem for the interval $0 \leq t < 2\pi$ and then solve a new problem with different initial conditions for the interval $t \geq 2\pi$. In such a situation the Laplace transform method enjoys the distinct advantage of not requiring the solution of different problems on different intervals.

Example 5

Consider the RLC circuit shown in Fig. 7.5.7, with $R = 110\ \Omega$, $L = 1$ H, $C = 0.001$ F, and a battery supplying $E_0 = 90$ V. Initially there is no current in the circuit and no charge on the capacitor. At time $t = 0$ the switch is closed and left closed for 1 second. At time $t = 1$ it is opened and left open thereafter. Find the resulting current in the circuit.

Solution

We recall from Section 3.7 the basic series circuit equation

$$L\frac{di}{dt} + Ri + \frac{1}{C}q = e(t); \tag{5}$$

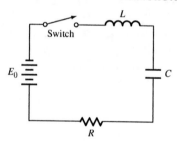

FIGURE 7.5.7. The series RLC circuit of Example 5.

we use lowercase letters for current, charge, and voltage and reserve uppercase letters for their transforms. With the given circuit elements, Eq. (5) is

$$\frac{di}{dt} + 110i + 1000q = e(t), \tag{6}$$

where $e(t) = 90[1 - u(t-1)]$, corresponding to the opening and closing of the switch.

In Section 3.7 our strategy was to differentiate both sides of Eq. (5), then apply the relation

$$i = \frac{dq}{dt} \tag{7}$$

to obtain the second-order equation

$$L\frac{d^2i}{dt^2} + R\frac{di}{dt} + \frac{1}{C}i = e'(t).$$

Here we do not use that method, because $e'(t) = 0$ except at $t = 1$, whereas the jump from $e(t) = 90$ when $t < 1$ to $e(t) = 0$ when $t > 1$ would seem to require that $e'(1) = -\infty$. Thus $e'(t)$ appears to have an infinite discontinuity at $t = 1$. This phenomenon will be discussed in Section 7.6. For now, we will simply note that it is an odd situation and circumvent it rather than attempt to deal with it here.

To avoid the possible problem at $t = 1$, we observe that the initial value $q(0) = 0$ and Eq. (7) yield, upon integration,

$$q(t) = \int_0^t i(\tau)\, d\tau. \tag{8}$$

We substitute Eq. (8) in Eq. (5) to obtain

$$L\frac{di}{dt} + Ri + \frac{1}{C}\int_0^t i(\tau)\, d\tau = e(t). \tag{9}$$

This is the **integrodifferential equation** of a series RLC circuit; it involves both the integral and the derivative of the unknown function $i(t)$. The Laplace transform method works well with such an equation.

In the present example, Eq. (9) is

$$\frac{di}{dt} + 110i + 1000\int_0^t i(\tau)\, d\tau = 90[1 - u(t-1)]. \tag{10}$$

Because

$$\mathcal{L}\left\{\int_0^t i(\tau)\, d\tau\right\} = \frac{I(s)}{s}$$

by Theorem 2 of Section 7.2 on transforms of integrals, the transformed equation is

$$sI(s) + 110I(s) + 1000\frac{I(s)}{s} = \frac{90}{s}(1 - e^{-s}).$$

We solve this equation for $I(s)$ to obtain

$$I(s) = \frac{90(1 - e^{-s})}{s^2 + 110s + 1000}.$$

But

$$\frac{90}{s^2 + 110s + 1000} = \frac{1}{s + 10} - \frac{1}{s + 100},$$

so we have

$$I(s) = \frac{1}{s + 10} - \frac{1}{s + 100} - e^{-s}\left(\frac{1}{s + 10} - \frac{1}{s + 100}\right).$$

We now apply Theorem 1 with $f(t) = e^{-10t} - e^{-100t}$; thus the inverse transform is

$$i(t) = e^{-10t} - e^{-100t} - u(t-1)\left[e^{-10(t-1)} - e^{-100(t-1)}\right].$$

After we separate the cases $t < 1$ and $t \geq 1$, we find that the current in the circuit is given by

$$i(t) = \begin{cases} e^{-10t} - e^{-100t} & \text{if } t < 1, \\ e^{-10t} - e^{-10(t-1)} - e^{-100t} + e^{-100(t-1)} & \text{if } t \geq 1. \end{cases}$$

The portion $e^{-10t} - e^{-100t}$ of the solution would describe the current if the switch were left closed for all t rather than being open for $t \geq 1$. ∎

Transforms of Periodic Functions

FIGURE 7.5.8. The graph of a function with period p.

Periodic forcing functions in practical mechanical or electrical systems often are more complicated than pure sines or cosines. The nonconstant function $f(t)$ defined for $t \geq 0$ is said to be **periodic** if there is a number $p > 0$ such that

$$f(t + p) = f(t) \tag{11}$$

for all $t \geq 0$. The least positive value of p (if any) for which Eq. (11) holds is called the **period** of f. Such a function is shown in Fig. 7.5.8. Theorem 2 simplifies the computation of the Laplace transform of a periodic function.

THEOREM 2: Transforms of Periodic Functions

Let $f(t)$ be periodic with period p and piecewise continuous for $t \geq 0$. Then the transform $F(s) = \mathcal{L}\{f(t)\}$ exists for $s > 0$ and is given by

$$F(s) = \frac{1}{1 - e^{-ps}} \int_0^p e^{-st} f(t)\, dt. \tag{12}$$

Proof: The definition of the Laplace transform gives

$$F(s) = \int_0^\infty e^{-st} f(t)\, dt = \sum_{n=0}^\infty \int_{np}^{(n+1)p} e^{-st} f(t)\, dt.$$

The substitution $t = \tau + np$ in the nth integral following the summation sign yields

$$\int_{np}^{(n+1)p} e^{-st} f(t)\, dt = \int_0^p e^{-s(\tau + np)} f(\tau + np)\, d\tau = e^{-nps} \int_0^p e^{-s\tau} f(\tau)\, d\tau$$

because $f(\tau + np) = f(\tau)$ by periodicity. Thus

$$F(s) = \sum_{n=0}^\infty \left(e^{-nps} \int_0^p e^{-s\tau} f(\tau)\, d\tau \right)$$

$$= \left(1 + e^{-ps} + e^{-2ps} + \cdots \right) \int_0^p e^{-s\tau} f(\tau)\, d\tau.$$

Consequently,

$$F(s) = \frac{1}{1 - e^{-ps}} \int_0^p e^{-s\tau} f(\tau)\, d\tau.$$

We use the geometric series

$$\frac{1}{1 - x} = 1 + x + x^2 + x^3 + \cdots,$$

with $x = e^{-ps} < 1$ (for $s > 0$) to sum the series in the final step. Thus we have derived Eq. (12). ▲

The principal advantage of Theorem 2 is that it enables us to find the Laplace transform of a periodic function without the necessity of an explicit evaluation of an improper integral.

Example 6

FIGURE 7.5.9. The graph of the square wave function of Example 6.

Figure 7.5.9 shows the graph of the square wave function $f(t) = (-1)^{\llbracket t/a \rrbracket}$ of period $p = 2a$; $\llbracket x \rrbracket$ denotes the greatest integer not exceeding x. By Theorem 2 the Laplace transform of $f(t)$ is

$$F(s) = \frac{1}{1 - e^{-2as}} \int_0^{2a} e^{-st} f(t)\, dt$$

$$= \frac{1}{1 - e^{-2as}} \left(\int_0^a e^{-st}\, dt + \int_a^{2a} (-1)e^{-st}\, dt \right)$$

$$= \frac{1}{1 - e^{-2as}} \left(\left[-\frac{1}{s} e^{-st} \right]_0^a - \left[-\frac{1}{s} e^{-st} \right]_a^{2a} \right)$$

$$= \frac{(1 - e^{-as})^2}{s(1 - e^{-2as})} = \frac{1 - e^{-as}}{s(1 + e^{-as})}.$$

Therefore,

$$F(s) = \frac{1 - e^{-as}}{s(1 + e^{-as})} \tag{13a}$$

$$= \frac{e^{as/2} - e^{-as/2}}{s(e^{as/2} + e^{-as/2})} = \frac{1}{s} \tanh \frac{as}{2}. \tag{13b}$$

∎

Example 7

FIGURE 7.5.10. The graph of the triangular wave function of Example 7.

Figure 7.5.10 shows the graph of a triangular wave function $g(t)$ of period $p = 2a$. Because the derivative $g'(t)$ is the square wave function of Example 6, it follows from the formula in (13b) and Theorem 2 of Section 7.2 that the transform of this triangular wave function is

$$G(s) = \frac{F(s)}{s} = \frac{1}{s^2} \tanh \frac{as}{2}. \tag{14}$$

∎

Example 8

Consider a mass-spring-dashpot system with $m = 1$, $c = 4$, and $k = 20$ in appropriate units. Suppose that the system is initially at rest at equilibrium ($x(0) = x'(0) = 0$) and that the mass is acted on beginning at time $t = 0$ by the external force $f(t)$ whose graph is shown in Fig. 7.5.11: the square wave with amplitude 20 and period 2π. Find the position function $f(t)$.

Solution   The initial value problem is

$$x'' + 4x' + 20x = f(t); \quad x(0) = x'(0) = 0.$$

The transformed equation is

$$s^2 X(s) + 4s X(s) + 20 X(s) = F(s). \tag{15}$$

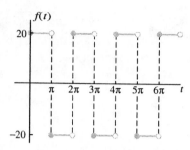

FIGURE 7.5.11. The graph of the external force function of Example 8.

From Example 6 with $a = \pi$ we see that the transform of $f(t)$ is

$$F(s) = \frac{20}{s} \cdot \frac{1 - e^{-\pi s}}{1 + e^{-\pi s}}$$

$$= \frac{20}{s} \left(1 - e^{-\pi s}\right) \left(1 - e^{-\pi s} + e^{-2\pi s} - e^{-3\pi s} + \cdots \right)$$

$$= \frac{20}{s} \left(1 - 2e^{-\pi s} + 2e^{-2\pi s} - 2e^{-3\pi s} + \cdots \right),$$

so that

$$F(s) = \frac{20}{s} + \frac{40}{s} \sum_{n=1}^{\infty} (-1)^n e^{-n\pi s}. \tag{16}$$

Substitution of Eq. (16) in Eq. (15) yields

$$X(s) = \frac{F(s)}{s^2 + 4s + 20}$$

$$= \frac{20}{s[(s+2)^2 + 16]} + 2 \sum_{n=1}^{\infty} (-1)^n \frac{20 e^{-n\pi s}}{s[(s+2)^2 + 16]}. \tag{17}$$

From the transform in Eq. (8) of Section 7.3, we get

$$\mathcal{L}^{-1} \left\{ \frac{20}{(s+2)^2 + 16} \right\} = 5e^{-2t} \sin 4t,$$

so by Theorem 2 of Section 7.2 we have

$$g(t) = \mathcal{L}^{-1} \left\{ \frac{20}{s[(s+2)^2 + 16]} \right\} = \int_0^t 5e^{-2\tau} \sin 4\tau \, d\tau.$$

Using a tabulated formula for $\int e^{at} \sin bt \, dt$, we get

$$g(t) = 1 - e^{-2t} \left(\cos 4t + \tfrac{1}{2} \sin 4t \right) = 1 - h(t), \tag{18}$$

where

$$h(t) = e^{-2t} \left(\cos 4t + \tfrac{1}{2} \sin 4t \right). \tag{19}$$

Now we apply Theorem 1 to find the inverse transform of the right-hand term in Eq. (17). The result is

$$x(t) = g(t) + 2 \sum_{n=1}^{\infty} (-1)^n u(t - n\pi) g(t - n\pi), \tag{20}$$

and we note that for any fixed value of t the sum in Eq. (20) is finite. Moreover,

$$g(t - n\pi) = 1 - e^{-2(t-n\pi)} \left[\cos 4(t - n\pi) + \tfrac{1}{2} \sin 4(t - n\pi) \right]$$

$$= 1 - e^{2n\pi} e^{-2t} \left(\cos 4t + \tfrac{1}{2} \sin 4t \right).$$

Therefore,

$$g(t - n\pi) = 1 - e^{2n\pi} h(t). \tag{21}$$

Hence if $0 < t < \pi$, then

$$x(t) = 1 - h(t).$$

If $\pi < t < 2\pi$, then

$$x(t) = [1 - h(t)] - 2\left[1 - e^{2\pi} h(t)\right] = -1 + h(t) - 2h(t)\left[1 - e^{2\pi}\right].$$

If $2\pi < t < 3\pi$, then

$$x(t) = [1 - h(t)] - 2\left[1 - e^{2\pi} h(t)\right] + 2\left[1 - e^{4\pi} h(t)\right]$$

$$= 1 + h(t) - 2h(t)\left[1 - e^{2\pi} + e^{4\pi}\right].$$

The general expression for $n\pi < t < (n+1)\pi$ is

$$x(t) = h(t) + (-1)^n - 2h(t)\left[1 - e^{2\pi} + \cdots + (-1)^n e^{2n\pi}\right]$$

$$= h(t) + (-1)^n - 2h(t)\frac{1 + (-1)^n e^{2(n+1)\pi}}{1 + e^{2\pi}}, \tag{22}$$

which we obtained with the aid of the familiar formula for the sum of a finite geometric progression. A rearrangement of Eq. (22) finally gives, with the aid of Eq. (19),

$$x(t) = \frac{e^{2\pi} - 1}{e^{2\pi} + 1} e^{-2t} \left(\cos 4t + \tfrac{1}{2} \sin 4t \right) + (-1)^n$$

$$- \frac{2 \cdot (-1)^n e^{2\pi}}{e^{2\pi} + 1} e^{-2(t-n\pi)} \left(\cos 4t + \tfrac{1}{2} \sin 4t \right) \tag{23}$$

for $n\pi < t < (n+1)\pi$. The first term in Eq. (23) is the transient solution

$$x_{\text{tr}}(t) \approx (0.9963) e^{-2t} \left(\cos 4t + \tfrac{1}{2} \sin 4t \right) \approx (1.1139) e^{-2t} \cos(4t - 0.4636). \tag{24}$$

The last two terms in Eq. (23) give the steady periodic solution x_{sp}. To investigate it, we write $\tau = t - n\pi$ for t in the interval $n\pi < t < (n+1)\pi$. Then

$$x_{\text{sp}}(t) = (-1)^n \left[1 - \frac{2e^{2\pi}}{e^{2\pi} + 1} e^{-2\tau} \left(\cos 4\tau + \tfrac{1}{2} \sin 4\tau \right) \right] \tag{25}$$

$$\approx (-1)^n \left[1 - (2.2319) e^{-2\tau} \cos(4\tau - 0.4636) \right].$$

Figure 7.5.12 shows the graph of $x_{\text{sp}}(t)$. Its most interesting feature is the appearance of periodically damped oscillations with a frequency *four times* that of the imposed force $f(t)$. In Chapter 9 (Fourier Series) we will see why a periodic external force sometimes excites oscillations at a higher frequency than the imposed frequency. ∎

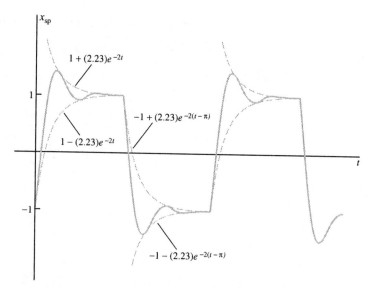

FIGURE 7.5.12. The graph of the steady periodic solution for Example 8; note the "periodically damped" oscillations with frequency four times that of the imposed force.

7.5 Problems

Find the inverse Laplace transform $f(t)$ of each function given in Problems 1 through 10. Then sketch the graph of f.

1. $F(s) = \dfrac{e^{-3s}}{s^2}$

2. $F(s) = \dfrac{e^{-s} - e^{-3s}}{s^2}$

3. $F(s) = \dfrac{e^{-s}}{s + 2}$

4. $F(s) = \dfrac{e^{-s} - e^{2-2s}}{s - 1}$

5. $F(s) = \dfrac{e^{-\pi s}}{s^2 + 1}$

6. $F(s) = \dfrac{se^{-s}}{s^2 + \pi^2}$

7. $F(s) = \dfrac{1 - e^{-2\pi s}}{s^2 + 1}$

8. $F(s) = \dfrac{s(1 - e^{-2s})}{s^2 + \pi^2}$

9. $F(s) = \dfrac{s(1 + e^{-3s})}{s^2 + \pi^2}$

10. $F(s) = \dfrac{2s(e^{-\pi s} - e^{-2\pi s})}{s^2 + 4}$

Find the Laplace transforms of the functions given in Problems 11 through 22.

11. $f(t) = 2$ if $0 \le t < 3$; $f(t) = 0$ if $t \ge 3$
12. $f(t) = 1$ if $1 \le t \le 4$; $f(t) = 0$ if $t < 1$ or if $t > 4$
13. $f(t) = \sin t$ if $0 \le t \le 2\pi$; $f(t) = 0$ if $t > 2\pi$
14. $f(t) = \cos \pi t$ if $0 \le t \le 2$; $f(t) = 0$ if $t > 2$
15. $f(t) = \sin t$ if $0 \le t \le 3\pi$; $f(t) = 0$ if $t > 3\pi$
16. $f(t) = \sin 2t$ if $\pi \le t \le 2\pi$; $f(t) = 0$ if $t < \pi$ or if $t > 2\pi$
17. $f(t) = \sin \pi t$ if $2 \le t \le 3$; $f(t) = 0$ if $t < 2$ or if $t > 3$
18. $f(t) = \cos \frac{1}{2}\pi t$ if $3 \le t \le 5$; $f(t) = 0$ if $t < 3$ or if $t > 5$
19. $f(t) = 0$ if $t < 1$; $f(t) = t$ if $t \ge 1$
20. $f(t) = t$ if $t \le 1$; $f(t) = 1$ if $t > 1$
21. $f(t) = t$ if $t \le 1$; $f(t) = 2 - t$ if $1 \le t \le 2$; $f(t) = 0$ if $t > 2$
22. $f(t) = t^3$ if $1 \le t \le 2$; $f(t) = 0$ if $t < 1$ or if $t > 2$

23. Apply Theorem 2 with $p = 1$ to verify that $\mathcal{L}\{1\} = 1/s$.
24. Apply Theorem 2 to verify that $\mathcal{L}\{\cos kt\} = s/(s^2 + k^2)$.
25. Apply Theorem 2 to show that the Laplace transform of the square wave function of Fig. 7.5.13 is

$$\mathcal{L}\{f(t)\} = \frac{1}{s(1 + e^{-as})}.$$

FIGURE 7.5.13. The graph of the square wave function of Problem 25.

26. Apply Theorem 2 to show that the Laplace transform of the sawtooth function $f(t)$ of Fig. 7.5.14 is

$$F(s) = \frac{1}{as^2} - \frac{e^{-as}}{s(1 - e^{-as})}.$$

FIGURE 7.5.14. The graph of the sawtooth function of Problem 26.

27. Let $g(t)$ be the staircase function of Fig. 7.5.15. Show that $g(t) = (t/a) - f(t)$, where f is the sawtooth function of Fig. 7.5.14, and hence deduce that

$$\mathcal{L}\{g(t)\} = \frac{e^{-as}}{s(1 - e^{-as})}.$$

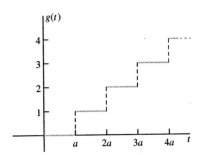

FIGURE 7.5.15. The graph of the staircase function of Problem 27.

28. Suppose that $f(t)$ is a periodic function of period $2a$ with $f(t) = t$ if $0 \le t < a$ and $f(t) = 0$ if $a \le t < 2a$. Find $\mathcal{L}\{f(t)\}$.

29. Suppose that $f(t)$ is the half-wave rectification of $\sin kt$, shown in Fig. 7.5.16. Show that

$$\mathcal{L}\{f(t)\} = \frac{k}{(s^2 + k^2)(1 - e^{-\pi s/k})}.$$

FIGURE 7.5.16. The half-wave rectification of $\sin kt$.

30. Let $g(t) = u(t - \pi/k) f(t - \pi/k)$, where $f(t)$ is the function of Problem 29 and $k > 0$. Note that $h(t) = f(t) + g(t)$ is the full-wave rectification of $\sin kt$ shown in Fig. 7.5.17. Hence deduce from Problem 29 that

$$\mathcal{L}\{h(t)\} = \frac{k}{s^2 + k^2} \coth \frac{\pi s}{2k}.$$

FIGURE 7.5.17. The full-wave rectification of $\sin kt$.

In Problems 31 through 35, the values of mass m, spring constant k, dashpot resistance c, and force f(t) are given for a mass-spring-dashpot system with external forcing function. Solve the initial value problem

$$mx'' + cx' + kx = f(t), \quad x(0) = x'(0) = 0$$

and construct the graph of the position function x(t).

31. $m = 1$, $k = 4$, $c = 0$; $f(t) = 1$ if $0 \le t < \pi$, $f(t) = 0$ if $t \ge \pi$

32. $m = 1$, $k = 4$, $c = 5$; $f(t) = 1$ if $0 \le t < 2$, $f(t) = 0$ if $t \ge 2$

33. $m = 1$, $k = 9$, $c = 0$; $f(t) = \sin t$ if $0 \le t \le 2\pi$, $f(t) = 0$ if $t > 2\pi$

34. $m = 1$, $k = 1$, $c = 0$; $f(t) = t$ if $0 \le t < 1$, $f(t) = 0$ if $t \ge 1$

35. $m = 1$, $k = 4$, $c = 4$; $f(t) = t$ if $0 \le t \le 2$, $f(t) = 0$ if $t > 2$

In Problems 36 through 40, the values of the elements of an RLC circuit are given. Solve the initial value problem

$$L\frac{di}{dt} + Ri + \frac{1}{C}\int_0^t i(\tau)\,d\tau = e(t); \quad i(0) = 0$$

with the given impressed voltage e(t).

36. $L = 0$, $R = 100$, $C = 10^{-3}$; $e(t) = 100$ if $0 \le t < 1$; $e(t) = 0$ if $t \ge 1$

37. $L = 1$, $R = 0$, $C = 10^{-4}$; $e(t) = 100$ if $0 \le t < 2\pi$; $e(t) = 0$ if $t \ge 2\pi$

38. $L = 1$, $R = 0$, $C = 10^{-4}$; $e(t) = 100\sin 10t$ if $0 \le t < \pi$; $e(t) = 0$ if $t \ge \pi$

39. $L = 1$, $R = 150$, $C = 2 \times 10^{-4}$; $e(t) = 100t$ if $0 \le t < 1$; $e(t) = 0$ if $t \ge 1$

40. $L = 1$, $R = 100$, $C = 4 \times 10^{-4}$; $e(t) = 50t$ if $0 \le t < 1$; $e(t) = 0$ if $t \ge 1$

In Problems 41 and 42, a mass-spring-dashpot system with external force f(t) is described. Under the assumption that $x(0) = x'(0) = 0$, use the method of Example 8 to find the transient and steady periodic motions of the mass. Then construct the graph of the position function x(t). If you would like to check your graph using a numerical DE solver, it may be useful to note that the function

$$f(t) = A[2u((t - \pi)(t - 2\pi)(t - 3\pi) \cdot$$
$$(t - 4\pi)(t - 5\pi)(t - 6\pi)) - 1]$$

has the value $+A$ if $0 < t < \pi$, the value $-A$ if $\pi < t < 2\pi$, and so forth, and hence agrees on the interval $[0, 6\pi]$ with the square wave function that has amplitude A and period 2π. (See also the definition of a square wave function in terms of sawtooth and triangular wave functions in the application material for this section.)

41. $m = 1$, $k = 4$, $c = 0$; $f(t)$ is a square wave function with amplitude 4 and period 2π.

42. $m = 1$, $k = 10$, $c = 2$; $f(t)$ is a square wave function with amplitude 10 and period 2π.

7.5 Application: Engineering Functions

Periodic piecewise linear functions occur so frequently as input functions in engineering applications that they are sometimes called **engineering functions.** Computations with such functions are readily handled by computer algebra systems. In *Mathematica*, for instance, we can define

```
SawTooth[t_] := 2 t - 2 Floor[t] - 1
TriangularWave[t_] := Abs[2 SawTooth[(2 t - 1)/4]] - 1
SquareWave[t_] := Sign[ TriangularWave[t] ]
```

Plot each of the functions to verify that it has period 2 and that its name is aptly chosen. For instance, the result of

```
Plot[ SquareWave[t], {t, 0, 6}];
```

should look like Fig. 7.5.9. If $f(t)$ is one of these engineering functions and $p > 0$, then the function $f(2t/p)$ will have period p. To illustrate this, try

```
Plot[ TriangularWave[ 2 t/p ], {t, 0, 3 p}];
```

with various values of p.

Now let's consider the mass-spring-dashpot equation

```
diffEq = m x''[t] + c x'[t] + k x[t] == input
```

with selected parameter values and an input forcing function with period p and amplitude F_0.

```
m = 4; c = 8; k = 5; p = 1; F0 = 4;
input = F0 SquareWave[2 t/p];
```

You can plot this **input** function to verify that it has period 1:

```
Plot[ input, {t, 0, 10}];
```

Finally, let's suppose that the mass is initially at rest in its equilibrium position and solve numerically the resulting initial value problem.

```
response = NDSolve[ {diffEq, x[0] == 0, x'[0] == 0},
                x, {t, 0, 10}, MaxSteps -> 1000 ]
Plot[ x[t] /. response, {t, 0, 10}];
```

FIGURE 7.5.18. Response $x(t)$ to period 1 square wave input.

In the resulting Fig. 7.5.18 we see that after an initial transient dies out, the response function $x(t)$ settles down (as expected?) to a periodic oscillation with the same period as the input.

Investigate this initial value problem with several mass-spring-dashpot parameters—for instance, selected digits of your student ID number—and with input engineering functions having various amplitudes and periods.

7.6 Impulses and Delta Functions

Consider a force $f(t)$ that acts only during a very short time interval $a \le t \le b$, with $f(t) = 0$ outside this interval. A typical example would be the *impulsive force* of a bat striking a ball—the impact is almost instantaneous. A quick surge of voltage (resulting from a lightning bolt, for instance) is an analogous electrical phenomenon. In such a situation it often happens that the principal effect of the force depends

only on the value of the integral

$$p = \int_a^b f(t) \, dt \qquad (1)$$

and does not depend otherwise on precisely how $f(t)$ varies with time t. The number p in Eq. (1) is called the **impulse** of the force $f(t)$ over the interval $[a, b]$.

In the case of a force $f(t)$ that acts on a particle of mass m in linear motion, integration of Newton's law

$$f(t) = mv'(t) = \frac{d}{dt}[mv(t)]$$

yields

$$p = \int_a^b \frac{d}{dt}[mv(t)] \, dt = mv(b) - mv(a). \qquad (2)$$

Thus the impulse of the force is equal to the change in momentum of the particle. So if change in momentum is the only effect with which we are concerned, we need know only the impulse of the force; we need know neither the precise function $f(t)$ nor even the precise time interval during which it acts. This is fortunate, because in a situation such as that of a batted ball, we are unlikely to have such detailed information about the impulsive force that acts on the ball.

Our strategy for handling such a situation is to set up a reasonable mathematical model in which the unknown force $f(t)$ is replaced with a simple and explicit force that has the same impulse. Suppose for simplicity that $f(t)$ has impulse 1 and acts during some brief time interval beginning at time $t = a \geq 0$. Then we can select a fixed number $\epsilon > 0$ that approximates the length of this time interval and replace $f(t)$ with the specific function

$$d_{a,\epsilon}(t) = \begin{cases} \dfrac{1}{\epsilon} & \text{if } a \leq t < a + \epsilon, \\[2mm] 0 & \text{otherwise.} \end{cases} \qquad (3)$$

FIGURE 7.6.1. The graph of the impulse function $d_{a,\epsilon}(t)$.

This is a function of t, with a and ϵ being parameters that specify the time interval $[a, a + \epsilon]$. If $b \geq a + \epsilon$, then we see (Fig. 7.6.1) that the impulse of $d_{a,\epsilon}$ over $[a, b]$ is

$$p = \int_a^b d_{a,\epsilon}(t) \, dt = \int_a^{a+\epsilon} \frac{1}{\epsilon} \, dt = 1.$$

Thus $d_{a,\epsilon}$ has a *unit* impulse, whatever the number ϵ may be. Essentially the same computation gives

$$\int_0^\infty d_{a,\epsilon}(t) \, dt = 1. \qquad (4)$$

Because the precise time interval during which the force acts seems unimportant, it is tempting to think of an *instantaneous impulse* that occurs precisely at the instant $t = a$. We might try to model such an instantaneous unit impulse by taking the limit as $\epsilon \to 0$, thereby defining

$$\delta_a(t) = \lim_{\epsilon \to 0} d_{a,\epsilon}(t), \qquad (5)$$

where $a \geqq 0$. If we could also take the limit under the integral sign in Eq. (4), then it would follow that

$$\int_0^\infty \delta_a(t)\,dt = 1. \tag{6}$$

But the limit in Eq. (5) gives

$$\delta_a(t) = \begin{cases} +\infty & \text{if } t = a, \\ 0 & \text{if } t \neq a. \end{cases} \tag{7}$$

Obviously, no function can satisfy both (6) and (7)—if a function is zero except at a single point, then its integral is not 1 but zero. Nevertheless, the symbol $\delta_a(t)$ is very useful. However interpreted, it is called the **Dirac delta function** at a after the British theoretical physicist P. A. M. Dirac (1902–1984), who in the early 1930s introduced a "function" allegedly enjoying the properties in Eqs. (6) and (7).

Delta Functions as Operators

The following computation motivates the meaning that we will attach here to the symbol $\delta_a(t)$. If $g(t)$ is continuous function, then the mean value theorem for integrals implies that

$$\int_a^{a+\epsilon} g(t)\,dt = \epsilon g\left(\bar{t}\right)$$

for some point $\bar{t}$ in $[a, a + \epsilon]$. It follows that

$$\lim_{\epsilon \to 0} \int_0^\infty g(t)d_{a,\epsilon}(t)\,dt = \lim_{\epsilon \to 0} \int_a^{a+\epsilon} g(t) \cdot \frac{1}{\epsilon}\,dt = \lim_{\epsilon \to 0} g\left(\bar{t}\right) = g(a) \tag{8}$$

by continuity of g at $t = a$. If $\delta_a(t)$ *were* a function in the strict sense of the definition, and if we could interchange the limit and the integral in Eq. (8), we therefore could conclude that

$$\int_0^\infty g(t)\delta_a(t)\,dt = g(a). \tag{9}$$

We take Eq. (9) as the *definition* (!) of the symbol $\delta_a(t)$. Although we call it the delta function, it is not a genuine function; instead, it specifies the *operation*

$$\int_0^\infty \cdots \delta_a(t)\,dt$$

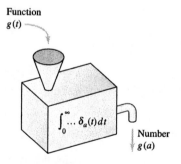

Function $g(t)$

$\int_0^\infty \cdots \delta_a(t)\,dt$

Number $g(a)$

FIGURE 7.6.2. A diagram illustrating how the delta function "sifts out" the value $g(a)$.

which—when applied to a continuous function $g(t)$—sifts out or selects the value $g(a)$ of this function at the point $a \geqq 0$. This idea is shown schematically in Fig. 7.6.2. Note that we will use the symbol $\delta_a(t)$ only in the context of integrals such as that in Eq. (9), or when it will appear subsequently in such an integral.

For instance, if we take $g(t) = e^{-st}$ in Eq. (9), the result is

$$\int_0^\infty e^{-st}\delta_a(t)\,dt = e^{-as}. \tag{10}$$

We therefore *define* the Laplace transform of the delta function to be

$$\mathcal{L}\{\delta_a(t)\} = e^{-as} \quad (a \geqq 0). \tag{11}$$

If we write

$$\delta(t) = \delta_0(t) \quad \text{and} \quad \delta(t-a) = \delta_a(t), \tag{12}$$

then (11) with $a = 0$ gives

$$\mathcal{L}\{\delta(t)\} = 1. \tag{13}$$

Note that if $\delta(t)$ were an actual function, then Eq. (13) would contradict the corollary to Theorem 2 of Section 7.1. There is no problem here; $\delta(t)$ is not a function, and Eq. (13) is our *definition* of $\mathcal{L}\{\delta(t)\}$.

Delta Function Inputs

Now, finally, suppose that we are given a mechanical system whose response $x(t)$ to the external force $f(t)$ is determined by the differential equation

$$Ax'' + Bx' + Cx = f(t). \tag{14}$$

To investigate the response of this system to a unit impulse at the instant $t = a$, it seems reasonable to replace $f(t)$ with $\delta_a(t)$ and begin with the equation

$$Ax'' + Bx' + Cx = \delta_a(t). \tag{15}$$

But what is meant by the solution of such an equation? We will call $x(t)$ a solution of Eq. (15) provided that

$$x(t) = \lim_{\epsilon \to 0} x_\epsilon(t), \tag{16}$$

where $x_\epsilon(t)$ is a solution of

$$Ax'' + Bx' + Cx = d_{a,\epsilon}(t). \tag{17}$$

Because

$$d_{a,\epsilon}(t) = \frac{1}{\epsilon}[u_a(t) - u_{a+\epsilon}(t)] \tag{18}$$

is an ordinary function, Eq. (17) makes sense. For simplicity suppose the initial conditions to be $x(0) = x'(0) = 0$. When we transform Eq. (17), writing $X_\epsilon = \mathcal{L}\{x_\epsilon\}$, we get the equation

$$(As^2 + Bs + C)X_\epsilon(s) = \frac{1}{\epsilon}\left(\frac{e^{-as}}{s} - \frac{e^{-(a+\epsilon)s}}{s}\right) = \left(e^{-as}\right)\frac{1 - e^{-s\epsilon}}{s\epsilon}.$$

If we take the limit in the last equation as $\epsilon \to 0$, and note that

$$\lim_{\epsilon \to 0}\frac{1 - e^{-s\epsilon}}{s\epsilon} = 1$$

by l'Hôpital's rule, we get the equation

$$(As^2 + Bs + C)X(s) = e^{-as}, \tag{19}$$

if

$$X(s) = \lim_{\epsilon \to 0} X_\epsilon(x).$$

Note that this is precisely the same result that we would obtain if we transformed Eq. (15) directly, using the fact that $\mathcal{L}\{\delta_a(t)\} = e^{-as}$.

On this basis it is reasonable to solve a differential equation involving a delta function by employing the Laplace transform method exactly as if $\delta_a(t)$ were an ordinary function. It is important to verify that the solution so obtained agrees with the one defined in Eq. (16), but this depends on a highly technical analysis of the limiting procedures involved; we consider it beyond the scope of the present discussion. The formal method is valid in all the examples of this section and will produce correct results in the subsequent problem set.

Example 1   A mass $m = 1$ is attached to a spring with constant $k = 4$; there is no dashpot. The mass is released from rest with $x(0) = 3$. At the instant $t = 2\pi$ the mass is struck with a hammer, providing an impulse $p = 8$. Determine the motion of the mass.

Solution   We need to solve the initial value problem

$$x'' + 4x = 8\delta_{2\pi}(t); \quad x(0) = 3, \quad x'(0) = 0.$$

We apply the Laplace transform to get

$$s^2 X(s) - 3s + 4X(s) = 8e^{-2\pi s},$$

so

$$X(s) = \frac{3s}{s^2 + 4} + \frac{8e^{-2\pi s}}{s^2 + 4}.$$

Recalling the transforms of sine and cosine, as well as the theorem on translations on the t-axis (Theorem 1 of Section 7.5), we see that the inverse transform is

$$x(t) = 3\cos 2t + 4u(t - 2\pi)\sin 2(t - 2\pi)$$
$$= 3\cos 2t + 4u_{2\pi}(t)\sin 2t.$$

Because $3\cos 2t + 4\sin 2t = 5\cos(2t - \alpha)$ with $\alpha = \tan^{-1}(4/3) \approx 0.9273$, separation of the cases $t < 2\pi$ and $t \geqq 2\pi$ gives

$$x(t) \approx \begin{cases} 3\cos 2t & \text{if } t \leqq 2\pi, \\ 5\cos(2t - 0.9273) & \text{if } t \geqq 2\pi. \end{cases}$$

The resulting motion is shown in Fig. 7.6.3. Note that the impulse at $t = 2\pi$ results in a visible discontinuity in the velocity at $t = 2\pi$, as it instantaneously increases the amplitude of the oscillations of the mass from 3 to 5.   ∎

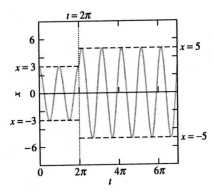

FIGURE 7.6.3. The motion of the mass of Example 1.

Delta Functions and Step Functions

It is useful to regard the delta function $\delta_a(t)$ as the derivative of the unit step function $u_a(t)$. To see why this is reasonable, consider the continuous approximation $u_{a,\epsilon}(t)$ to $u_a(t)$ shown in Fig. 7.6.4. We readily verify that

$$\frac{d}{dt}u_{a,\epsilon}(t) = d_{a,\epsilon}(t).$$

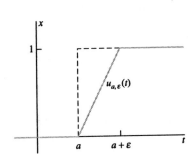

FIGURE 7.6.4. Approximation of $u_a(t)$ by $u_{a,\epsilon}(t)$.

Because

$$u_a(t) = \lim_{\epsilon \to 0} u_{a,\epsilon}(t) \quad \text{and} \quad \delta_a(t) = \lim_{\epsilon \to 0} d_{a,\epsilon}(t),$$

an interchange of limits and derivatives yields

$$\frac{d}{dt}u_a(t) = \lim_{\epsilon \to 0}\frac{d}{dt}u_{a,\epsilon}(t) = \lim_{\epsilon \to 0} d_{a,\epsilon}(t),$$

and therefore

$$\frac{d}{dt}u_a(t) = \delta_a(t) = \delta(t - a). \tag{20}$$

We may regard this as the *formal definition* of the derivative of the unit step function, although $u_a(t)$ is not differentiable in the ordinary sense at $t = a$.

Example 2

We return to the RLC circuit of Example 5 of Section 7.5, with $R = 110\ \Omega$, $L = 1$ H, $C = 0.001$ F, and a battery supplying $e_0 = 90$ V. Suppose that the circuit is initially passive—no current and no charge. At time $t = 0$ the switch is closed and at time $t = 1$ it is opened and left open. Find the resulting current $i(t)$ in the circuit.

Solution

In Section 7.5 we circumvented the discontinuity in the voltage by employing the integrodifferential form of the circuit equation. Now that delta functions are available, we may begin with the ordinary circuit equation

$$Li'' + Ri' + \frac{1}{C}i = e'(t).$$

In this example we have

$$e(t) = 90 - 90u(t - 1) = 90 - 90u_1(t),$$

so $e'(t) = -90\delta(t-1)$ by Eq. (20). Hence we want to solve the initial value problem

$$i'' + 110i' + 1000i = -90\delta(t-1); \quad i(0) = 0, \quad i'(0) = 90. \tag{21}$$

The fact that $i'(0) = 90$ comes from substitution of $t = 0$ in the equation

$$Li'(t) + Ri(t) + \frac{1}{C}q(t) = e(t)$$

with the numerical values $i(0) = q(0) = 0$ and $e(0) = 90$.

When we transform the problem in (21), we get the equation

$$s^2 I(s) - 90 + 110sI(s) + 1000I(s) = -90e^{-s}.$$

Hence

$$I(s) = \frac{90(1 - e^{-s})}{s^2 + 110s + 1000}.$$

This is precisely the same transform $I(s)$ we found in Example 5 of Section 7.5, so inversion of $I(s)$ yields the same solution $i(t)$ recorded there. ∎

Example 3   Consider a mass on a spring with $m = k = 1$ and $x(0) = x'(0) = 0$. At each of the instants $t = 0, \pi, 2\pi, 3\pi, \ldots, n\pi, \ldots$, the mass is struck a hammer blow with a unit impulse. Determine the resulting motion.

Solution   We need to solve the initial value problem

$$x'' + x = \sum_{n=0}^{\infty} \delta_{n\pi}(t); \quad x(0) = 0 = x'(0).$$

Because $\mathcal{L}\{\delta_{n\pi}(t)\} = e^{-n\pi s}$, the transformed equation is

$$s^2 X(s) + X(s) = \sum_{n=0}^{\infty} e^{-n\pi s},$$

so

$$X(s) = \sum_{n=0}^{\infty} \frac{e^{-n\pi s}}{s^2 + 1}.$$

We compute the inverse Laplace transform term by term; the result is

$$x(t) = \sum_{n=0}^{\infty} u(t - n\pi) \sin(t - n\pi).$$

Because $\sin(t - n\pi) = (-1)^n \sin t$ and $u(t - n\pi) = 0$ for $t < n\pi$, we see that if $n\pi < t < (n+1)\pi$, then

$$x(t) = \sin t - \sin t + \sin t - \cdots + (-1)^n \sin t;$$

that is,

$$x(t) = \begin{cases} \sin t & \text{if } n \text{ is even,} \\ 0 & \text{if } n \text{ is odd.} \end{cases}$$

Hence $x(t)$ is the half-wave rectification of $\sin t$ shown in Fig. 7.6.5. The physical explanation is that the first hammer blow (at time $t = 0$) starts the mass moving to the right; just as it returns to the origin, the second hammer blow stops it dead; it remains motionless until the third hammer blow starts it moving again, and so on. Of course, if the hammer blows are not perfectly synchronized then the motion of the mass will be quite different. ∎

FIGURE 7.6.5. The half-wave rectification of $\sin t$.

Systems Analysis and Duhamel's Principle

Consider a physical system in which the *output* or *response* $x(t)$ to the *input* function $f(t)$ is described by the differential equation

$$ax'' + bx' + cx = f(t), \tag{22}$$

where the constant coefficients a, b, and c are determined by the physical parameters of the system and are independent of $f(t)$. The mass-spring-dashpot system and the series RLC circuit are familiar examples of this general situation.

For simplicity we assume that the system is initially passive: $x(0) = x'(0) = 0$. Then the transform of Eq. (22) is

$$as^2 X(s) + bs X(s) + c X(s) = F(s),$$

so

$$X(s) = \frac{F(s)}{as^2 + bs + c} = W(s)F(s). \tag{23}$$

The function

$$W(s) = \frac{1}{as^2 + bs + c} \tag{24}$$

is called the **transfer function** of the system. Thus the transform of the response to the input $f(t)$ is the product of $W(s)$ and the transform $F(s)$.

The function

$$w(t) = \mathcal{L}^{-1}\{W(s)\} \tag{25}$$

is called the **weight function** of the system. From Eq. (24) we see by convolution that

$$x(t) = \int_0^t w(\tau)f(t - \tau)\,d\tau. \tag{26}$$

This formula is **Duhamel's principle** for the system. What is important is that the weight function $w(t)$ is determined completely by the parameters of the system. Once $w(t)$ has been determined, the integral in (26) gives the response of the system to an arbitrary input function $f(t)$.

Example 4

Consider a mass-spring-dashpot system (initially passive) that responds to the external force $f(t)$ in accord with the equation $x'' + 6x' + 10x = f(t)$. Then

$$W(s) = \frac{1}{s^2 + 6s + 10} = \frac{1}{(s + 3)^2 + 1},$$

so the weight function is $w(t) = e^{-3t}\sin t$. Then Duhamel's principle implies that the response $x(t)$ to the force $f(t)$ is

$$x(t) = \int_0^t e^{-3\tau}(\sin \tau)f(t - \tau)\,d\tau. \qquad\blacksquare$$

Note that

$$W(s) = \frac{1}{as^2 + bs + c} = \frac{\mathcal{L}\{\delta(t)\}}{as^2 + bs + c}.$$

Consequently, it follows from Eq. (23) that the weight function is simply the response of the system to the delta function input $\delta(t)$. For this reason $w(t)$ is sometimes called the **unit impulse response**. A response that is usually easier to measure in practice is the response $h(t)$ to the unit step function $u(t)$; $h(t)$ is the **unit step response**. Because $\mathcal{L}\{u(t)\} = 1/s$, we see from Eq. (23) that the transform of $h(t)$ is

$$H(s) = \frac{W(s)}{s}.$$

It follows from the formula for transforms of integrals that

$$h(t) = \int_0^t w(\tau)\,d\tau, \quad \text{so that} \quad w(t) = h'(t). \tag{27}$$

Thus the weight function, or unit impulse response, is the derivative of the unit step response. Substitution of (27) in Duhamel's principle gives

$$x(t) = \int_0^t h'(t)f(t - \tau)\,d\tau \tag{28}$$

for the response of the system to the input $f(t)$.

APPLICATIONS: To describe a typical application of Eq. (28), suppose that we are given a complex series circuit containing many inductors, resistors, and capacitors. Assume that its circuit equation is a linear equation of the form in (22), but with i in place of x. What if the coefficients a, b, and c are unknown, perhaps only because they are too difficult to compute? We would still want to know the current $i(t)$ corresponding to any input $f(t) = e'(t)$. We connect the circuit to a linearly increasing voltage $e(t) = t$, so that $f(t) = e'(t) = 1 = u(t)$, and measure the response $h(t)$ with an ammeter. We then compute the derivative $h'(t)$, either numerically or graphically. Then according to Eq. (28), the output current $i(t)$ corresponding to the input voltage $e(t)$ will be given by

$$i(t) = \int_0^t h'(\tau)e'(t - \tau)\,d\tau$$

(using the fact that $f(t) = e'(t)$).

HISTORICAL REMARK: In conclusion, we remark that around 1950, after engineers and physicists had been using delta functions widely and fruitfully for about 20 years without rigorous justification, the French mathematician Laurent Schwartz developed a rigorous mathematical theory of *generalized functions* that supplied the missing logical foundation for delta function techniques. Every piecewise continuous ordinary function is a generalized function, but the delta function is an example of a generalized function that is not an ordinary function.

7.6 Problems

Solve the initial value problems in Problems 1 through 8, and graph each solution function $x(t)$.

1. $x'' + 4x = \delta(t);\ x(0) = x'(0) = 0$
2. $x'' + 4x = \delta(t) + \delta(t - \pi);\ x(0) = x'(0) = 0$
3. $x'' + 4x' + 4x = 1 + \delta(t - 2);\ x(0) = x'(0) = 0$
4. $x'' + 2x' + x = t + \delta(t);\ x(0) = 0,\ x'(0) = 1$
5. $x'' + 2x' + 2x = 2\delta(t - \pi);\ x(0) = x'(0) = 0$
6. $x'' + 9x = \delta(t - 3\pi) + \cos 3t;\ x(0) = x'(0) = 0$
7. $x'' + 4x' + 5x = \delta(t - \pi) + \delta(t - 2\pi);\ x(0) = 0,\ x'(0) = 2$
8. $x'' + 2x' + x = \delta(t) - \delta(t - 2);\ x(0) = x'(0) = 2$

Apply Duhamel's principle to write an integral formula for the solution of each initial value problem in Problems 9 through 12.

9. $x'' + 4x = f(t);\ x(0) = x'(0) = 0$
10. $x'' + 6x' + 9x = f(t);\ x(0) = x'(0) = 0$
11. $x'' + 6x' + 8x = f(t);\ x(0) = x'(0) = 0$
12. $x'' + 4x' + 8x = f(t);\ x(0) = x'(0) = 0$

13. This problem deals with a mass m, initially at rest at the origin, that receives an impulse p at time $t = 0$. **(a)** Find the solution $x_\epsilon(t)$ of the problem

$$mx'' = p\,d_{0,\epsilon}(t);\quad x(0) = x'(0) = 0.$$

(b) Show that $\lim_{\epsilon \to 0} x_\epsilon(t)$ agrees with the solution of the problem

$$mx'' = p\delta(t);\quad x(0) = x'(0) = 0.$$

(c) Show that $mv = p$ for $t > 0$ ($v = dx/dt$).

14. Verify that $u'(t - a) = \delta(t - a)$ by solving the problem

$$x' = \delta(t - a);\quad x(0) = 0$$

to obtain $x(t) = u(t - a)$.

15. This problem deals with a mass m on a spring (with constant k) that receives an impulse $p_0 = mv_0$ at time $t = 0$. Show that the initial value problems

$$mx'' + kx = 0;\quad x(0) = 0,\quad x'(0) = v_0$$

and

$$mx'' + kx = p_0\delta(t);\quad x(0) = 0,\quad x'(0) = 0$$

have the same solution. Thus the effect of $p_0\delta(t)$ is, indeed, to impart to the particle an initial momentum p_0.

16. This is a generalization of Problem 15. Show that the problems

$$ax'' + bx' + cx = f(t);\quad x(0) = 0,\quad x'(0) = v_0$$

and

$$ax'' + bx' + cx = f(t) + av_0\delta(t);\quad x(0) = x'(0) = 0$$

have the same solution for $t > 0$. Thus the effect of the term $av_0\delta(t)$ is to supply the initial condition $x'(0) = v_0$.

17. Consider an initially passive RC circuit (no inductance) with a battery supplying e_0 volts. **(a)** If the switch to the battery is closed at time $t = a$ and opened at time $t = b > a$ (and left open thereafter), show that the current in the circuit satisfies the initial value problem

$$Ri' + \frac{1}{C}i = e_0\delta(t - a) - e_0\delta(t - b);\quad i(0) = 0.$$

(b) Solve this problem if $R = 100\ \Omega$, $C = 10^{-4}$ F, $e_0 = 100$ V, $a = 1$ (s), and $b = 2$ (s). Show that $i(t) > 0$ if $1 < t < 2$ and that $i(t) < 0$ if $t > 2$.

18. Consider an initially passive LC circuit (no resistance) with a battery supplying e_0 volts. **(a)** If the switch is closed at time $t = 0$ and opened at time $t = a > 0$, show that the current in the circuit satisfies the initial value problem

$$Li'' + \frac{1}{C}i = e_0\delta(t) - e_0\delta(t - a);$$

$$i(0) = i'(0) = 0.$$

(b) If $L = 1$ H, $C = 10^{-2}$ F, $e_0 = 10$ V, and $a = \pi$ (s), show that

$$i(t) = \begin{cases} \sin 10t & \text{if } t < \pi, \\ 0 & \text{if } t > \pi. \end{cases}$$

Thus the current oscillates through five cycles and then stops abruptly when the switch is opened (Fig. 7.6.6).

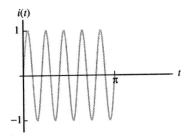

FIGURE 7.6.6. The current function of Problem 18.

19. Consider the LC circuit of Problem 18(b), except suppose that the switch is alternately closed and opened at times $t = 0, \pi/10, 2\pi/10, \dots$ **(a)** Show that $i(t)$ satisfies the initial value problem

$$i'' + 100i = 10\sum_{n=0}^{\infty}(-1)^n\delta\left(t - \frac{n\pi}{10}\right);\quad i(0) = i'(0) = 0.$$

(b) Solve this initial value problem to show that

$$i(t) = (n + 1)\sin 10t \quad \text{if} \quad \frac{n\pi}{10} < t < \frac{(n + 1)\pi}{10}.$$

Thus a resonance phenomenon occurs (see Fig. 7.6.7).

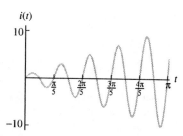

FIGURE 7.6.7. The current function of Problem 19.

20. Repeat Problem 19, except suppose that the switch is alternately closed and opened at times $t = 0$, $\pi/5$, $2\pi/5$, $\ldots$, $n\pi/5$, $\ldots$. Now show that if

$$\frac{n\pi}{5} < t < \frac{(n+1)\pi}{5},$$

then

$$i(t) = \begin{cases} \sin 10t & \text{if } n \text{ is even;} \\ 0 & \text{if } n \text{ is odd.} \end{cases}$$

Thus the current in alternate cycles of length $\pi/5$ first executes a sine oscillation during one cycle, then is dormant during the next cycle, and so on (see Fig. 7.6.8).

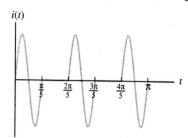

FIGURE 7.6.8. The current function of Problem 20.

21. Consider an RLC circuit in series with a battery, with $L = 1$ H, $R = 60$ Ω, $C = 10^{-3}$ F, and $e_0 = 10$ V. **(a)** Suppose that the switch is alternately closed and opened at times $t = 0$, $\pi/10$, $2\pi/10$, $\ldots$. Show that $i(t)$ satisfies the initial value problem

$$i'' + 60i' + 1000i = 10 \sum_{n=0}^{\infty}(-1)^n \delta\left(t - \frac{n\pi}{10}\right);$$

$$i(0) = i'(0) = 0.$$

(b) Solve this problem to show that if

$$\frac{n\pi}{10} < t < \frac{(n+1)\pi}{10},$$

then

$$i(t) = \frac{e^{3n\pi+3\pi} - 1}{e^{3\pi} - 1} e^{-30t} \sin 10t.$$

Construct a figure showing the graph of this current function.

22. Consider a mass $m = 1$ on a spring with constant $k = 1$, initially at rest, but struck with a hammer at each of the instants $t = 0$, 2π, 4π, $\ldots$. Suppose that each hammer blow imparts an impulse of $+1$. Show that the position function $x(t)$ of the mass satisfies the initial value problem

$$x'' + x = \sum_{n=0}^{\infty} \delta(t - 2n\pi); \quad x(0) = x'(0) = 0.$$

Solve this problem to show that if $2n\pi < t < 2(n+1)\pi$, then $x(t) = (n+1)\sin t$. Thus resonance occurs because the mass is struck each time it passes through the origin moving to the right—in contrast with Example 3, in which the mass was struck each time it returned to the origin. Finally, construct a figure showing the graph of this position function.

C H A P T E R

Power Series Methods

8.1 Introduction and Review of Power Series

In Section 3.3 we saw that solving a homogeneous linear differential equation with constant coefficients can be reduced to the algebraic problem of finding the roots of its characteristic equation. There is no similar procedure for solving linear differential equations with *variable* coefficients, at least not routinely and in finitely many steps. With the exception of special types, such as the occasional equation that can be solved by inspection, linear equations with variable coefficients generally require the power series techniques of this chapter.

These techniques suffice for many of the nonelementary differential equations that appear most frequently in applications. Perhaps the most important (because of its applications in such areas as acoustics, heat flow, and electromagnetic radiation) is **Bessel's equation** of order n:

$$x^2 y'' + xy' + (x^2 - n^2)y = 0.$$

Legendre's equation of order n is important in many applications. It has the form

$$(1 - x^2)y'' - 2xy' + n(n + 1)y = 0.$$

In this section we introduce the **power series method** in its simplest form and, along the way, state (without proof) several theorems that constitute a review of the basic facts about power series. Recall first that a **power series** in [powers of] $x - a$ is an infinite series of the form

$$\sum_{n=0}^{\infty} c_n(x - a)^n = c_0 + c_1(x - a) + c_2(x - a)^2 + \cdots + c_n(x - a)^n + \cdots. \quad (1)$$

If $a = 0$, this is a power series in x:

$$\sum_{n=0}^{\infty} c_n x^n = c_0 + c_1 x + c_2 x^2 + \cdots + c_n x^n + \cdots. \quad (2)$$

609

We will confine our review mainly to power series in x, but every general property of power series in x can be converted to a general property of power series in $x - a$ by replacement of x with $x - a$.

The power series in (2) **converges** on the interval I provided that the limit

$$\sum_{n=0}^{\infty} c_n x^n = \lim_{N \to \infty} \sum_{n=0}^{N} c_n x^n \tag{3}$$

exists for all x in I. In this case the sum

$$f(x) = \sum_{n=0}^{\infty} c_n x^n \tag{4}$$

is defined on I, and we call the series $\sum c_n x^n$ a **power series representation** of the function f on I. The following power series representations of elementary functions should be familiar to you from introductory calculus:

$$e^x = \sum_{n=0}^{\infty} \frac{x^n}{n!} = 1 + x + \frac{x^2}{2!} + \frac{x^3}{3!} + \cdots ; \tag{5}$$

$$\cos x = \sum_{n=0}^{\infty} \frac{(-1)^n x^{2n}}{(2n)!} = 1 - \frac{x^2}{2!} + \frac{x^4}{4!} - \cdots ; \tag{6}$$

$$\sin x = \sum_{n=0}^{\infty} \frac{(-1)^n x^{2n+1}}{(2n+1)!} = x - \frac{x^3}{3!} + \frac{x^5}{5!} - \cdots ; \tag{7}$$

$$\cosh x = \sum_{n=0}^{\infty} \frac{x^{2n}}{(2n)!} = 1 + \frac{x^2}{2!} + \frac{x^4}{4!} + \cdots ; \tag{8}$$

$$\sinh x = \sum_{n=0}^{\infty} \frac{x^{2n+1}}{(2n+1)!} = x + \frac{x^3}{3!} + \frac{x^5}{5!} + \cdots ; \tag{9}$$

$$\ln(1 + x) = \sum_{n=1}^{\infty} \frac{(-1)^{n+1} x^n}{n} = x - \frac{x^2}{2} + \frac{x^3}{3} - \cdots ; \tag{10}$$

$$\frac{1}{1 - x} = \sum_{n=0}^{\infty} x^n = 1 + x + x^2 + x^3 + \cdots ; \tag{11}$$

and

$$(1 + x)^\alpha = 1 + \alpha x + \frac{\alpha(\alpha - 1)x^2}{2!} + \frac{\alpha(\alpha - 1)(\alpha - 2)x^3}{3!} + \cdots . \tag{12}$$

In compact summation notation, we observe the usual conventions that $0! = 1$ and that $x^0 = 1$ for all x, including $x = 0$. The series in (5) through (9) converge to the indicated functions for all x. In contrast, the series in (10) and (11) converge if $|x| < 1$ but diverge if $|x| > 1$. (What if $|x| = 1$?) The series in (11) is the **geometric series**. The series in (12), with α an arbitrary real number, is the **binomial series**. If α is a nonnegative integer, then the binomial series converges for all x. Otherwise it converges if $|x| < 1$ and diverges if $|x| > 1$; its behavior for $|x| = 1$ depends on the value of α.

Remark: Power series such as those listed in (5) through (12) are often derived as Taylor series. The **Taylor series** with **center** $x = a$ of the function f is the power series

$$\sum_{n=0}^{\infty} \frac{f^{(n)}(a)}{n!}(x-a)^n = f(a) + f'(a)(x-a) + \frac{f''(a)}{2!}(x-a)^2 + \cdots \qquad (13)$$

in powers of $x - a$, under the hypothesis that f is infinitely differentiable at $x = a$ (so that the coefficients in Eq. (13) are all defined). If $a = 0$, then the series in (13) is the **Maclaurin series**

$$\sum_{n=0}^{\infty} \frac{f^{(n)}(0)}{n!}x^n = f(0) + f'(0)x + \frac{f''(0)}{2!}x^2 + \frac{f^{(3)}(0)}{3!}x^3 + \cdots. \qquad (13')$$

For example, suppose that $f(x) = e^x$. Then $f^{(n)}(x) = e^x$, and hence $f^{(n)}(0) = 1$ for all $n \geq 0$. In this case Eq. (13′) reduces to the **exponential series** in (5). ∎

Power Series Operations

If the Taylor series of the function f converges to $f(x)$ for all x in some open interval containing a, then we say that the function f is **analytic** at $x = a$. For example, every polynomial is analytic everywhere and every rational function is analytic wherever its denominator is nonzero. More generally, if the two functions f and g are both analytic at $x = a$, then so are their sum $f + g$ and their product $f \cdot g$, as is their quotient f/g if $g(a) \neq 0$.

For instance, the function $h(x) = \tan x = (\sin x)/(\cos x)$ is analytic at $x = 0$ because $\cos 0 = 1 \neq 0$ and the sine and cosine functions are analytic (by virtue of their convergent power series representations in Eqs. (6) and (7)). It is rather awkward to compute the Taylor series of the tangent function using Eq. (13) because of the way in which its successive derivatives grow in complexity (try it!). Fortunately, power series may be manipulated algebraically in much the same way as polynomials. For example, if

$$f(x) = \sum_{n=0}^{\infty} a_n x^n \quad \text{and} \quad g(x) = \sum_{n=0}^{\infty} b_n x^n, \qquad (14)$$

then

$$f(x) + g(x) = \sum_{n=0}^{\infty} (a_n + b_n)x^n \qquad (15)$$

and

$$f(x)g(x) = \sum_{n=0}^{\infty} c_n x^n$$

$$= a_0 b_0 + (a_0 b_1 + a_1 b_0)x + (a_0 b_2 + a_1 b_1 + a_2 b_0)x^2 + \cdots, \qquad (16)$$

where $c_n = a_0 b_n + a_1 b_{n-1} + \cdots + a_n b_0$. The series in (15) is the result of **termwise addition** and the series in (16) is the result of **formal multiplication**—multiplying each term of the first series by each term of the second and then collecting coefficients of like powers of x. (Thus the processes strongly resemble addition and multiplication of ordinary polynomials.) The series in (15) and (16) converge to $f(x) + g(x)$ and $f(x)g(x)$, respectively, on any open interval on which both the series in (14) converge. For example,

$$\sin x \cos x = \left(x - \frac{1}{6}x^3 + \frac{1}{120}x^5 - \cdots \right) \left(1 - \frac{1}{2}x^2 + \frac{1}{24}x^4 - \cdots \right)$$

$$= x + \left(-\frac{1}{6} - \frac{1}{2} \right) x^3 + \left(\frac{1}{24} + \frac{1}{12} + \frac{1}{120} \right) x^5 + \cdots$$

$$= x - \frac{4}{6}x^3 + \frac{16}{120}x^5 - \cdots$$

$$= \frac{1}{2} \left[(2x) - \frac{(2x)^3}{3!} + \frac{(2x)^5}{5!} - \cdots \right] = \frac{1}{2}\sin 2x$$

for all x.

Similarly, the quotient of two power series can be computed by long division, as illustrated by the computation shown in Fig. 8.1.1. This division of the Taylor series for $\cos x$ into that for $\sin x$ yields the first few terms of the series

$$\tan x = x + \frac{1}{3}x^3 + \frac{2}{15}x^5 + \frac{17}{315}x^7 + \cdots. \tag{17}$$

Division of power series is more treacherous than multiplication; the series thus obtained for f/g may fail to converge at some points where the series for f and g both converge. For example, the sine and cosine series converge for all x, but the tangent series in (17) converges only if $|x| < \pi/2$.

The Power Series Method

The **power series method** for solving a differential equation consists of substituting the power series

$$\blacktriangleright \qquad \qquad y = \sum_{n=0}^{\infty} c_n x^n \tag{18}$$

in the differential equation and then attempting to determine what the coefficients $c_0, c_1, c_2, \ldots$ must be in order that the power series will satisfy the differential equation. This is reminiscent of the method of undetermined coefficients, but now we have infinitely many coefficients somehow to determine. This method is not always successful, but when it is we obtain an infinite series representation of a solution, in contrast to the "closed form" solutions that our previous methods have yielded.

Before we can substitute the power series in (18) in a differential equation, we must first know what to substitute for the derivatives y', y'', ... The following theorem (stated without proof) tells us that the derivative y' of $y = \sum c_n x^n$ is obtained

$$
\begin{array}{r}
x \;+\; \dfrac{x^3}{3} \;+\; \dfrac{2x^5}{15} \;+\; \dfrac{17x^7}{315} \;+\; \cdots
\end{array}
$$

$$
1 - \dfrac{x^2}{2} + \dfrac{x^4}{24} - \dfrac{x^6}{720} + \cdots \;\Big)\; x \;-\; \dfrac{x^3}{6} \;+\; \dfrac{x^5}{120} \;-\; \dfrac{x^7}{5040} \;+\; \cdots
$$

$$
\underline{x \;-\; \dfrac{x^3}{2} \;+\; \dfrac{x^5}{24} \;-\; \dfrac{x^7}{720} \;+\; \cdots}
$$

$$
\dfrac{x^3}{3} \;-\; \dfrac{x^5}{30} \;+\; \dfrac{x^7}{840} \;+\; \cdots
$$

$$
\underline{\dfrac{x^3}{3} \;-\; \dfrac{x^5}{6} \;+\; \dfrac{x^7}{72} \;-\; \cdots}
$$

$$
\dfrac{2x^5}{15} \;-\; \dfrac{4x^7}{315} \;+\; \cdots
$$

$$
\underline{\dfrac{2x^5}{15} \;-\; \dfrac{x^7}{15} \;+\; \cdots}
$$

$$
\dfrac{17x^7}{315} \;+\; \cdots
$$

$$
\vdots
$$

FIGURE 8.1.1. Obtaining the series for $\tan x$ by division of series.

by the simple procedure of writing the sum of the derivatives of the individual terms in the series for y.

THEOREM 1: Termwise Differentiation of Power Series

If the power series representation

$$
f(x) = \sum_{n=0}^{\infty} c_n x^n = c_0 + c_1 x + c_2 x^2 + c_3 x^3 + \cdots \tag{19}
$$

of the function f converges on the open interval I, then f is differentiable on I, and

$$
f'(x) = \sum_{n=1}^{\infty} n c_n x^{n-1} = c_1 + 2c_2 x + 3c_3 x^2 + \cdots \tag{20}
$$

at each point of I. ▲

For example, differentiation of the geometric series

$$
\frac{1}{1-x} = \sum_{n=0}^{\infty} x^n = 1 + x + x^2 + x^3 + \cdots \tag{11}
$$

gives

$$\frac{1}{(1-x)^2} = \sum_{n=1}^{\infty} nx^{n-1} = 1 + 2x + 3x^2 + 4x^3 + \cdots.$$

The process of determining the coefficients in the series $y = \sum c_n x^n$ so that it will satisfy a given differential equation depends also on Theorem 2. This theorem—stated without proof—tells us that if two power series represent the same function, then they are the same series. In particular, the Taylor series in (13) is the only power series (in powers of $x - a$) that represents the function f.

THEOREM 2: Identity Principle

If

$$\sum_{n=0}^{\infty} a_n x^n = \sum_{n=0}^{\infty} b_n x^n$$

for every point x in some open interval I, then $a_n = b_n$ for all $n \geq 0$. ▲

In particular, if $\sum a_n x^n = 0$ for all x in some open interval, it follows from Theorem 2 that $a_n = 0$ for all $n \geq 0$.

Example 1   Solve the equation $y' + 2y = 0$.

Solution   We substitute the series

➤
$$y = \sum_{n=0}^{\infty} c_n x^n \quad \text{and} \quad y' = \sum_{n=1}^{\infty} nc_n x^{n-1},$$

and obtain

$$\sum_{n=1}^{\infty} nc_n x^{n-1} + 2 \sum_{n=0}^{\infty} c_n x^n = 0. \tag{21}$$

To compare coefficients here, we need the general term in each sum to be the term containing x^n. To accomplish this, we shift the index of summation in the first sum. To see how to do this, note that

$$\sum_{n=1}^{\infty} nc_n x^{n-1} = c_1 + 2c_2 x + 3c_3 x^2 + \cdots = \sum_{n=0}^{\infty} (n+1)c_{n+1} x^n.$$

Thus we can replace n with $n+1$ if, at the same time, we start counting one step lower; that is, at $n = 0$ rather than at $n = 1$. This is a shift of $+1$ in the index of summation. The result of making this shift in Eq. (21) is the identity

$$\sum_{n=0}^{\infty} (n+1)c_{n+1} x^n + 2 \sum_{n=0}^{\infty} c_n x^n = 0;$$

that is,

$$\sum_{n=0}^{\infty} [(n+1)c_{n+1} + 2c_n] x^n = 0.$$

If this equation holds on some interval, then it follows from the identity principle that $(n+1)c_{n+1} + 2c_n = 0$ for all $n \geq 0$; consequently,

$$c_{n+1} = -\frac{2c_n}{n+1} \tag{22}$$

for all $n \geq 0$. Equation (22) is a **recurrence relation** from which we can successively compute $c_1, c_2, c_3, \ldots$ in terms of c_0; the latter will turn out to be the arbitrary constant that we expect to find in a general solution of a first-order differential equation.

With $n = 0$, Eq. (22) gives

$$c_1 = -\frac{2c_0}{1}.$$

With $n = 1$, Eq. (22) gives

$$c_2 = -\frac{2c_1}{2} = +\frac{2^2 c_0}{1 \cdot 2} = \frac{2^2 c_0}{2!}.$$

With $n = 2$, Eq. (22) gives

$$c_3 = -\frac{2c_2}{3} = -\frac{2^3 c_0}{1 \cdot 2 \cdot 3} = -\frac{2^3 c_0}{3!}.$$

By now it should be clear that after n such steps, we will have

$$c_n = (-1)^n \frac{2^n c_0}{n!}, \qquad n \geq 1.$$

(This is easy to prove by induction on n.) Consequently, our solution takes the form

$$y(x) = \sum_{n=0}^{\infty} c_n x^n = \sum_{n=0}^{\infty} (-1)^n \frac{2^n c_0}{n!} x^n = c_0 \sum_{n=0}^{\infty} \frac{(-2x)^n}{n!} = c_0 e^{-2x}.$$

In the final step we have used the familiar exponential series in Eq. (5) to identify our power series solution as the same solution $y(x) = c_0 e^{-2x}$ we could have obtained by the method of separation of variables. ∎

Shift of Index of Summation

In the solution of Example 1 we wrote

$$\sum_{n=1}^{\infty} nc_n x^{n-1} = \sum_{n=0}^{\infty} (n+1)c_{n+1} x^n \tag{23}$$

by shifting the index of summation by $+1$ in the series on the left. That is, we simultaneously *increased* the index of summation by 1 (replacing n with $n+1$, $n \to n+1$) and *decreased* the starting point by 1, from $n = 1$ to $n = 0$, thereby obtaining the series on the right. This procedure is valid because each infinite series in (23) is simply a compact notation for the single series

$$c_1 + 2c_2 x + 3c_3 x^2 + 4c_4 x^3 + \cdots. \tag{24}$$

More generally, we can shift the index of summation by k in an infinite series by simultaneously *increasing* the summation index by k ($n \to n+k$) and *decreasing* the starting point by k. For instance, a shift by $+2$ ($n \to n+2$) yields

$$\sum_{n=3}^{\infty} a_n x^{n-1} = \sum_{n=1}^{\infty} a_{n+2} x^{n+1}.$$

If k is negative, we interpret a "decrease by k" as an increase by $-k = |k|$. Thus a shift by -2 ($n \to n-2$) in the index of summation yields

$$\sum_{n=1}^{\infty} n c_n x^{n-1} = \sum_{n=3}^{\infty} (n-2) c_{n-2} x^{n-3};$$

we have *decreased* the index of summation by 2 but *increased* the starting point by 2, from $n = 1$ to $n = 3$. You should check that the summation on the right is merely another representation of the series in (24).

We know that the power series obtained in Example 1 converges for all x because it is an exponential series. More commonly, a power series solution is not recognizable in terms of the familiar elementary functions. When we get an unfamiliar power series solution, we need a way of finding where it converges. After all, $y = \sum c_n x^n$ is merely an *assumed* form of the solution. The procedure illustrated in Example 1 for finding the coefficients $\{c_n\}$ is merely a formal process and may or may not be valid. Its validity—in applying Theorem 1 to compute y' and applying Theorem 2 to obtain a recurrence relation for the coefficients—depends on the convergence of the initially *unknown* series $y = \sum c_n x^n$. Hence this formal process is justified only if in the end we can show that the power series we obtain converges on some open interval. If so, it then represents a solution of the differential equation on that interval. The following theorem (which we state without proof) may be used for this purpose.

THEOREM 3: Radius of Convergence

Given the power series $\sum c_n x^n$, suppose that the limit

$$\rho = \lim_{n \to \infty} \left| \frac{c_n}{c_{n+1}} \right| \tag{25}$$

exists (ρ is finite) or is infinite (in this case we will write $\rho = \infty$). Then

(a) If $\rho = 0$, then the series diverges for all $x \neq 0$.

(b) If $0 < \rho < \infty$, then $\sum c_n x^n$ converges if $|x| < \rho$ and diverges if $|x| > \rho$.

(c) If $\rho = \infty$, then the series converges for all x. ▲

The number ρ in (25) is called the **radius of convergence** of the power series $\sum c_n x^n$. For instance, for the power series obtained in Example 1, we have

$$\rho = \lim_{n \to \infty} \left| \frac{(-1)^n 2^n c_0 / n!}{(-1)^{n+1} 2^{n+1} c_0 / (n+1)!} \right| = \lim_{n \to \infty} \frac{n+1}{2} = \infty,$$

and consequently the series we obtained in Example 1 converges for all x. Even if the limit in (25) fails to exist, there always will be a number ρ such that exactly one of the three alternatives in Theorem 3 holds. This number may be difficult to find, but for the power series we will consider in this chapter, Eq. (25) will be quite sufficient for computing the radius of convergence.

Example 2 Solve the equation $(x - 3)y' + 2y = 0$.

Solution As before, we substitute

$$\blacktriangleright \qquad y = \sum_{n=0}^{\infty} c_n x^n \quad \text{and} \quad y' = \sum_{n=1}^{\infty} n c_n x^{n-1}$$

to obtain

$$(x - 3) \sum_{n=1}^{\infty} n c_n x^{n-1} + 2 \sum_{n=0}^{\infty} c_n x^n = 0,$$

so that

$$\sum_{n=1}^{\infty} n c_n x^n - 3 \sum_{n=1}^{\infty} n c_n x^{n-1} + 2 \sum_{n=0}^{\infty} c_n x^n = 0.$$

In the first sum we can replace $n = 1$ with $n = 0$ with no effect on the sum. In the second sum we shift the index of summation by $+1$. This yields

$$\sum_{n=0}^{\infty} n c_n x^n - 3 \sum_{n=0}^{\infty} (n + 1) c_{n+1} x^n + 2 \sum_{n=0}^{\infty} c_n x^n = 0;$$

that is,

$$\sum_{n=0}^{\infty} [n c_n - 3(n + 1) c_{n+1} + 2 c_n] x^n = 0.$$

The identity principle then gives

$$n c_n - 3(n + 1) c_{n+1} + 2 c_n = 0,$$

from which we obtain the recurrence relation

$$\blacktriangleright \qquad c_{n+1} = \frac{n + 2}{3(n + 1)} c_n \qquad \text{for} \quad n \geq 0.$$

We apply this formula with $n = 0$, $n = 1$, and $n = 2$, in turn, and find that

$$c_1 = \frac{2}{3} c_0, \quad c_2 = \frac{3}{3 \cdot 2} c_1 = \frac{3}{3^2} c_0, \quad \text{and} \quad c_3 = \frac{4}{3 \cdot 3} c_2 = \frac{4}{3^3} c_0.$$

This is almost enough to make the pattern evident; it is not difficult to show by induction on n that

$$\blacktriangleright \qquad c_n = \frac{n + 1}{3^n} c_0 \quad \text{if} \quad n \geq 1.$$

Hence our proposed power series solution is

$$y(x) = c_0 \sum_{n=0}^{\infty} \frac{n + 1}{3^n} x^n. \tag{26}$$

Its radius of convergence is

$$\rho = \lim_{n\to\infty} \left| \frac{c_n}{c_{n+1}} \right| = \lim_{n\to\infty} \frac{3n+3}{n+2} = 3.$$

Thus the series in (26) converges if $-3 < x < 3$ and diverges if $|x| > 3$. In this particular example we can explain why. An elementary solution (obtained by separation of variables) of our differential equation is $y = 1/(3-x)^2$. If we differentiate termwise the geometric series

$$\frac{1}{3-x} = \frac{\frac{1}{3}}{1 - \frac{x}{3}} = \frac{1}{3} \sum_{n=0}^{\infty} \frac{x^n}{3^n},$$

we get a constant multiple of the series in (26). Thus this series (with the arbitrary constant c_0 appropriately chosen) represents the solution

$$y(x) = \frac{1}{(3-x)^2}$$

on the interval $-3 < x < 3$, and the singularity at $x = 3$ is the reason why the radius of convergence of the power series solution turned out to be $\rho = 3$. ∎

Example 3 Solve the equation $x^2 y' = y - x - 1$.

Solution We make the usual substitutions $y = \sum c_n x^n$ and $y' = \sum n c_n x^{n-1}$, which yield

$$x^2 \sum_{n=1}^{\infty} n c_n x^{n-1} = -1 - x + \sum_{n=0}^{\infty} c_n x^n$$

so that

$$\sum_{n=1}^{\infty} n c_n x^{n+1} = -1 - x + \sum_{n=0}^{\infty} c_n x^n.$$

Because of the presence of the two terms -1 and $-x$ on the right-hand side, we need to split off the first two terms, $c_0 + c_1 x$, of the series on the right for comparison. If we also shift the index of summation on the left by -1 (replace $n = 1$ with $n = 2$ and n with $n - 1$), we get

$$\sum_{n=2}^{\infty} (n-1) c_{n-1} x^n = -1 - x + c_0 + c_1 x + \sum_{n=2}^{\infty} c_n x^n.$$

Because the left-hand side contains neither a constant term nor a term containing x to the first power, the identity principle now yields $c_0 = 1$, $c_1 = 1$, and $c_n = (n-1)c_{n-1}$ for $n \geq 2$. It follows that

$$c_2 = 1 \cdot c_1 = 1!, \quad c_3 = 2 \cdot c_2 = 2!, \quad c_4 = 3 \cdot c_3 = 3!,$$

and, in general, that

➤

$$c_n = (n-1)! \quad \text{for} \quad n \geq 2.$$

Thus we obtain the power series

$$y(x) = 1 + x + \sum_{n=2}^{\infty} (n-1)! \, x^n.$$

But the radius of convergence of this series is

$$\rho = \lim_{n \to \infty} \frac{(n-1)!}{n!} = \lim_{n \to \infty} \frac{1}{n} = 0,$$

so the series converges only for $x = 0$. What does this mean? Simply that the given differential equation does not have a [convergent] power series solution of the assumed form $y = \sum c_n x^n$. This example serves as a warning that the simple act of writing $y = \sum c_n x^n$ involves an assumption that may be false. ∎

Example 4   Solve the equation $y'' + y = 0$.

Solution   If we assume a solution of the form

➤
$$y = \sum_{n=0}^{\infty} c_n x^n,$$

we find that

➤
$$y' = \sum_{n=1}^{\infty} n c_n x^{n-1} \quad \text{and} \quad y'' = \sum_{n=2}^{\infty} n(n-1) c_n x^{n-2}.$$

Substitution for y and y'' in the differential equation then yields

$$\sum_{n=2}^{\infty} n(n-1) c_n x^{n-2} + \sum_{n=0}^{\infty} c_n x^n = 0.$$

We shift the index of summation in the first sum by $+2$ (replace $n = 2$ with $n = 0$ and n with $n + 2$). This gives

$$\sum_{n=0}^{\infty} (n+2)(n+1) c_{n+2} x^n + \sum_{n=0}^{\infty} c_n x^n = 0.$$

The identity $(n+2)(n+1)c_{n+2} + c_n = 0$ now follows from the identity principle, and thus we obtain the recurrence relation

➤
$$c_{n+2} = -\frac{c_n}{(n+1)(n+2)} \tag{27}$$

for $n \geq 0$. It is evident that this formula will determine the coefficients c_n with even subscript in terms of c_0 and those of odd subscript in terms of c_1; c_0 and c_1 are not predetermined and thus will be the two arbitrary constants we expect to find in a general solution of a second-order equation.

    When we apply the recurrence relation in (27) with $n = 0$, 2, and 4 in turn, we get

$$c_2 = -\frac{c_0}{2!}, \quad c_4 = \frac{c_0}{4!}, \quad \text{and} \quad c_6 = -\frac{c_0}{6!}.$$

Taking $n = 1$, 3, and 5 in turn, we find that

$$c_3 = -\frac{c_1}{3!}, \quad c_5 = \frac{c_1}{5!}, \quad \text{and} \quad c_7 = -\frac{c_1}{7!}.$$

Again, the pattern is clear; we leave it for you to show (by induction) that for $k \geq 1$,

$$c_{2k} = \frac{(-1)^k c_0}{(2k)!} \quad \text{and} \quad c_{2k+1} = \frac{(-1)^k c_1}{(2k+1)!}.$$

Thus we get the power series solution

$$y(x) = c_0 \left(1 - \frac{x^2}{2!} + \frac{x^4}{4!} - \frac{x^6}{6!} + \cdots \right) + c_1 \left(x - \frac{x^3}{3!} + \frac{x^5}{5!} - \frac{x^7}{7!} + \cdots \right);$$

that is, $y(x) = c_0 \cos x + c_1 \sin x$. Note that we have no problem with the radius of convergence here; the Taylor series for the sine and cosine functions converge for all x. ∎

The solution of Example 4 can bear further comment. Suppose that we had never heard of the sine and cosine functions, let alone their Taylor series. We would then have discovered the two power series solutions

$$C(x) = \sum_{n=0}^{\infty} \frac{(-1)^n x^{2n}}{(2n)!} = 1 - \frac{x^2}{2!} + \frac{x^4}{4!} - \cdots \qquad (28)$$

and

$$S(x) = \sum_{n=0}^{\infty} \frac{(-1)^n x^{2n+1}}{(2n+1)!} = x - \frac{x^3}{3!} + \frac{x^5}{5!} - \cdots \qquad (29)$$

of the differential equation $y'' + y = 0$. It is clear that $C(0) = 1$ and that $S(0) = 0$. After verifying that the two series in (28) and (29) converge for all x, we can differentiate them term by term to find that

$$C'(x) = -S(x) \quad \text{and} \quad S'(x) = C(x). \qquad (30)$$

Consequently, $C'(0) = 0$ and $S'(0) = 1$. Thus with the aid of the power series method (all the while knowing nothing about the sine and cosine functions), we have discovered that $y = C(x)$ is the unique solution of

$$y'' + y = 0$$

that satisfies the initial conditions $y(0) = 1$ and $y'(0) = 0$, and that $y = S(x)$ is the unique solution that satisfies the initial conditions $y(0) = 0$ and $y'(0) = 1$. It follows that $C(x)$ and $S(x)$ are linearly independent, and—recognizing the importance of the differential equation $y'' + y = 0$—we can agree to call C the *cosine* function and S the *sine* function. Indeed, all the usual properties of these two functions can be established, using only their initial values (at $x = 0$) and the derivatives in (30); there is no need to refer to triangles or even to angles. (Can you use the series in (28) and (29) to show that $[C(x)]^2 + [S(x)]^2 = 1$ for all x?) This demonstrates that the cosine and sine functions are fully determined by the differential equation $y'' + y = 0$ of which they are the natural linearly independent solutions. Figures 8.1.2 and 8.1.3 show how the geometric character of the graphs of $\cos x$ and $\sin x$ is revealed by the graphs of the Taylor polynomial approximations that we get by truncating the infinite series in (28) and (29).

This is by no means an uncommon situation. Many important special functions of mathematics occur in the first instance as power series solutions of differential equations and thus are in practice *defined* by means of these power series. In the remaining sections of this chapter we will see numerous examples of such functions.

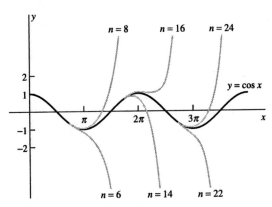

FIGURE 8.1.2. Taylor polynomial approximations to $\cos x$.

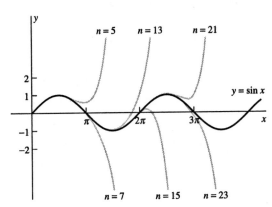

FIGURE 8.1.3. Taylor polynomial approximations to $\sin x$.

8.1 Problems

In Problems 1 through 10, find a power series solution of the given differential equation. Determine the radius of convergence of the resulting series, and use the series in Eqs. (5) through (12) to identify the series solution in terms of familiar elementary functions. (Of course, no one can prevent you from checking your work by also solving the equations by the methods of earlier chapters!)

1. $y' = y$
2. $y' = 4y$
3. $2y' + 3y = 0$
4. $y' + 2xy = 0$
5. $y' = x^2 y$
6. $(x - 2)y' + y = 0$
7. $(2x - 1)y' + 2y = 0$
8. $2(x + 1)y' = y$
9. $(x - 1)y' + 2y = 0$
10. $2(x - 1)y' = 3y$

In Problems 11 through 14, use the method of Example 4 to find two linearly independent power series solutions of the given differential equation. Determine the radius of convergence of each series, and identify the general solution in terms of familiar elementary functions.

11. $y'' = y$
12. $y'' = 4y$
13. $y'' + 9y = 0$
14. $y'' + y = x$

Show (as in Example 3) that the power series method fails to yield a power series solution of the form $y = \sum c_n x^n$ for the differential equations in Problems 15 through 18.

15. $xy' + y = 0$
16. $2xy' = y$
17. $x^2 y' + y = 0$
18. $x^3 y' = 2y$

In Problems 19 through 22, first derive a recurrence relation giving c_n for $n \geq 2$ in terms of c_0 or c_1 (or both). Then apply the given initial conditions to find the values of c_0 and c_1. Next determine c_n (in terms of n, as in the text) and, finally, identify the particular solution in terms of familiar elementary functions.

19. $y'' + 4y = 0$; $y(0) = 0$, $y'(0) = 3$
20. $y'' - 4y = 0$; $y(0) = 2$, $y'(0) = 0$
21. $y'' - 2y' + y = 0$; $y(0) = 0$, $y'(0) = 1$
22. $y'' + y' - 2y = 0$; $y(0) = 1$, $y'(0) = -2$
23. Show that the equation

$$x^2 y'' + x^2 y' + y = 0$$

has no power series solution of the form $y = \sum c_n x^n$.
24. Establish the binomial series in (12) by means of the following steps. **(a)** Show that $y = (1 + x)^\alpha$ satisfies the initial value problem $(1 + x)y' = \alpha y$, $y(0) = 1$. **(b)** Show that the power series method gives the binomial series in (12) as the solution of the initial value problem in part (a), and that this series converges if $|x| < 1$. **(c)** Explain why the validity of the binomial series given in (12) follows from parts (a) and (b).
25. For the initial value problem

$$y'' = y' + y, \quad y(0) = 0, \quad y(1) = 1$$

derive the power series solution

$$y(x) = \sum_{n=1}^{\infty} \frac{F_n}{n!} x^n$$

where $\{F_n\}_{n=0}^{\infty}$ is the sequence 0, 1, 1, 2, 3, 5, 8, 13, ... of *Fibonacci numbers* defined by $F_0 = 0$, $F_1 = 1$, $F_n = F_{n-2} + F_{n-1}$ for $n > 1$.

26. (a) Show that the solution of the initial value problem

$$y' = 1 + y^2, \quad y(0) = 0$$

is $y(x) = \tan x$. **(b)** Because $y(x) = \tan x$ is an odd function with $y'(0) = 1$, its Taylor series is of the form

$$y = x + c_3 x^3 + c_5 x^5 + c_7 x^7 + \cdots.$$

Substitute this series in $y' = 1 + y^2$ and equate like powers of x to derive the following relations:

$$3c_3 = 1, \qquad\qquad 5c_5 = 2c_3,$$
$$7c_7 = 2c_5 + (c_3)^2, \qquad 9c_9 = 2c_7 + 2c_3 c_5,$$
$$11c_{11} = 2c_9 + 2c_3 c_7 + (c_5)^2.$$

(c) Conclude that

$$\tan x = x + \frac{1}{3}x^3 + \frac{2}{15}x^5 + \frac{17}{315}x^7$$
$$+ \frac{62}{2835}x^9 + \frac{1382}{155925}x^{11} + \cdots.$$

27. This section introduces the use of infinite series to solve differential equations. Conversely, differential equations

can sometimes be used to sum infinite series. For example, consider the infinite series

$$1 + \frac{1}{1!} - \frac{1}{2!} + \frac{1}{3!} + \frac{1}{4!} - \frac{1}{5!} + \cdots;$$

note the $+ + - + + - \cdots$ pattern of signs superimposed on the terms of the series for the number e. We could evaluate this series if we could obtain a formula for the function

$$f(x) = 1 + x - \frac{1}{2!}x^2 + \frac{1}{3!}x^3 + \frac{1}{4!}x^4 - \frac{1}{5!}x^5 + \cdots,$$

because the sum of the numerical series in question is simply $f(1)$. **(a)** It's possible to show that the power series given here converges for all x and that termwise differentiation is valid. Given these facts, show that $f(x)$ satisfies the initial value problem

$$y^{(3)} = y; \quad y(0) = y'(0) = 1, \quad y''(0) = -1.$$

(b) Solve this initial value problem to show that

$$f(x) = \frac{1}{3}e^x + \frac{2}{3}e^{-x/2}\left(\cos\frac{\sqrt{3}}{2}x + \sqrt{3}\sin\frac{\sqrt{3}}{2}x\right).$$

For a suggestion, see Problem 48 of Section 3.3. **(c)** Evaluate $f(1)$ to find the sum of the numerical series given here.

8.2 Series Solutions Near Ordinary Points

The power series method introduced in Section 8.1 can be applied to linear equations of any order, but its most important applications are to homogeneous second-order linear differential equations of the form

$$A(x)y'' + B(x)y' + C(x)y = 0, \tag{1}$$

where the coefficients A, B, and C are analytic functions of x. Indeed, in most applications these coefficient functions are simple polynomials.

We saw in Example 3 of Section 8.1 that the series method does not always yield a series solution. To discover when it does succeed, we rewrite Eq. (1) in the form

$$\blacktriangleright \qquad y'' + P(x)y' + Q(x)y = 0 \tag{2}$$

with leading coefficient 1, and with $P = B/A$ and $Q = C/A$. Note that $P(x)$ and $Q(x)$ will generally fail to be analytic at points where $A(x)$ vanishes. For instance, consider the equation

$$xy'' + y' + xy = 0. \tag{3}$$

The coefficient functions in (3) are continuous everywhere. But in the form of (2) it is the equation

$$y'' + \frac{1}{x}y' + y = 0 \tag{4}$$

with $P(x) = 1/x$ not analytic at $x = 0$.

The point $x = a$ is called an **ordinary point** of Eq. (2)—and of the equivalent Eq. (1)—provided that the functions $P(x)$ and $Q(x)$ are both analytic at $x = a$. Otherwise, $x = a$ is a **singular point**. Thus the only singular point of Eqs. (3) and (4) is $x = 0$. Recall that a quotient of analytic functions is analytic wherever the denominator is nonzero. It follows that, if $A(a) \neq 0$ in Eq. (1) with analytic coefficients, then $x = a$ is an ordinary point. If $A(x)$, $B(x)$, and $C(x)$ are *polynomials* with no common factors, then $x = a$ is an ordinary point if and only if $A(a) \neq 0$.

Example 1   The point $x = 0$ is an ordinary point of the equation

$$xy'' + (\sin x)y' + x^2 y = 0,$$

despite the fact that $A(x) = x$ vanishes at $x = 0$. The reason is that

$$P(x) = \frac{\sin x}{x} = \frac{1}{x}\left(x - \frac{x^3}{3!} + \frac{x^5}{5!} - \cdots\right) = 1 - \frac{x^2}{3!} + \frac{x^4}{5!} - \cdots$$

is nevertheless analytic at $x = 0$ because the division by x yields a convergent power series. ∎

Example 2   The point $x = 0$ is *not* an ordinary point of the equation

$$y'' + x^2 y' + x^{1/2} y = 0.$$

For while $P(x) = x^2$ is analytic at the origin, $Q(x) = x^{1/2}$ is not. The reason is that $Q(x)$ is not differentiable at $x = 0$ and hence is not analytic there. (Theorem 1 of Section 8.1 implies that an analytic function must be differentiable.) ∎

Example 3   The point $x = 0$ is an ordinary point of the equation

$$(1 - x^3)y'' + (7x^2 + 3x^5)y' + (5x - 13x^4)y = 0$$

because the coefficient functions $A(x)$, $B(x)$, and $C(x)$ are polynomials with $A(0) \neq 0$. ∎

Theorem 2 of Section 3.1 implies that Eq. (2) has two linearly independent solutions on any open interval where the coefficient functions $P(x)$ and $Q(x)$ are continuous. The basic fact for our present purpose is that near an *ordinary* point a, these solutions will be power series in powers of $x - a$. A proof of the following theorem can be found in Chapter 3 of Coddington, *An Introduction to Ordinary Differential Equations* (Englewood Cliffs, N.J.: Prentice Hall, 1961).

THEOREM 1: Solutions Near an Ordinary Point

Suppose that a is an ordinary point of the equation

$$A(x)y'' + B(x)y' + C(x)y = 0; \tag{1}$$

that is, the functions $P = B/A$ and $Q = C/A$ are analytic at $x = a$. Then Eq. (1) has two linearly independent solutions, each of the form

➤
$$y(x) = \sum_{n=0}^{\infty} c_n(x - a)^n. \tag{5}$$

The radius of convergence of any such series solution is at least as large as the distance from a to the nearest (real or complex) singular point of Eq. (1). The coefficients in the series in (5) can be determined by its substitution in Eq. (1). ▲

Example 4   Determine the radius of convergence guaranteed by Theorem 1 of a series solution of

$$(x^2 + 9)y'' + xy' + x^2y = 0 \tag{6}$$

in powers of x. Repeat for a series in powers of $x - 4$.

Solution   This example illustrates the fact that we must take into account complex singular points as well as real ones. Because

$$P(x) = \frac{x}{x^2 + 9} \quad \text{and} \quad Q(x) = \frac{x^2}{x^2 + 9},$$

the only singular points of Eq. (6) are $\pm 3i$. The distance (in the complex plane) of each of these from 0 is 3, so a series solution of the form $\sum c_n x^n$ has radius of convergence at least 3. The distance of each singular point from 4 is 5, so a series solution of the form $\sum c_n(x - 4)^n$ has radius of convergence at least 5 (see Fig. 8.2.1). ∎

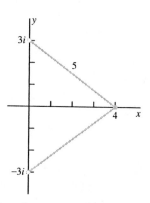

FIGURE 8.2.1.   Radius of convergence as distance to nearest singularity.

Example 5   Find the general solution in powers of x of

$$(x^2 - 4)y'' + 3xy' + y = 0. \tag{7}$$

Then find the particular solution with $y(0) = 4$, $y'(0) = 1$.

Solution   The only singular points of Eq. (7) are ± 2, so the series we get will have radius of convergence at least 2. Substitution of

$$\blacktriangleright \qquad y = \sum_{n=0}^{\infty} c_n x^n, \quad y' = \sum_{n=1}^{\infty} nc_n x^{n-1}, \quad \text{and} \quad y'' = \sum_{n=2}^{\infty} n(n-1)c_n x^{n-2}$$

in Eq. (7) yields

$$\sum_{n=2}^{\infty} n(n-1)c_n x^n - 4 \sum_{n=2}^{\infty} n(n-1)c_n x^{n-2} + 3 \sum_{n=1}^{\infty} nc_n x^n + \sum_{n=0}^{\infty} c_n x^n = 0.$$

We can begin the first and third summations at $n = 0$ as well, because no nonzero terms are thereby introduced. We shift the index of summation in the second sum by $+2$, replacing n with $n + 2$ and using the initial value $n = 0$. This gives

$$\sum_{n=0}^{\infty} n(n-1)c_n x^n - 4 \sum_{n=0}^{\infty} (n+2)(n+1)c_{n+2} x^n + 3 \sum_{n=0}^{\infty} nc_n x^n + \sum_{n=0}^{\infty} c_n x^n = 0.$$

After collecting coefficients of c_n and c_{n+2}, we obtain

$$\sum_{n=0}^{\infty} \left[(n^2 + 2n + 1)c_n - 4(n+2)(n+1)c_{n+2} \right] x^n = 0.$$

The identity principle yields

$$(n+1)^2 c_n - 4(n+2)(n+1)c_{n+2} = 0,$$

which leads to the recurrence relation

$$\blacktriangleright \qquad c_{n+2} = \frac{(n+1)c_n}{4(n+2)} \qquad\qquad (8)$$

for $n \geq 0$. With $n = 0$, 2, and 4 in turn, we get

$$c_2 = \frac{c_0}{4 \cdot 2}, \quad c_4 = \frac{3c_2}{4 \cdot 4} = \frac{3c_0}{4^2 \cdot 2 \cdot 4}, \quad \text{and} \quad c_6 = \frac{5c_4}{4 \cdot 6} = \frac{3 \cdot 5 c_0}{4^3 \cdot 2 \cdot 4 \cdot 6}.$$

Continuing in this fashion, we evidently would find that

$$c_{2n} = \frac{1 \cdot 3 \cdot 5 \cdots (2n-1)}{4^n \cdot 2 \cdot 4 \cdots (2n)} c_0.$$

With the common notation

$$(2n+1)!! = 1 \cdot 3 \cdot 5 \cdots (2n+1) = \frac{(2n+1)!}{2^n \cdot n!}$$

and the observation that $2 \cdot 4 \cdot 6 \cdots (2n) = 2^n \cdot n!$, we finally obtain

$$\blacktriangleright \qquad c_{2n} = \frac{(2n-1)!!}{2^{3n} \cdot n!} c_0. \qquad\qquad (9)$$

(We also used the fact that $4^n \cdot 2^n = 2^{3n}$.)

With $n = 1$, 3, and 5 in Eq. (8), we get

$$c_3 = \frac{2c_1}{4 \cdot 3}, \quad c_5 = \frac{4c_3}{4 \cdot 5} = \frac{2 \cdot 4c_1}{4^2 \cdot 3 \cdot 5}, \quad \text{and} \quad c_7 = \frac{6c_5}{4 \cdot 7} = \frac{2 \cdot 4 \cdot 6c_1}{4^3 \cdot 3 \cdot 5 \cdot 7}.$$

It is apparent that the pattern is

$$\blacktriangleright \qquad c_{2n+1} = \frac{2 \cdot 4 \cdot 6 \cdots (2n)}{4^n \cdot 1 \cdot 3 \cdot 5 \cdots (2n+1)} c_1 = \frac{n!}{2^n \cdot (2n+1)!!} c_1. \tag{10}$$

The formula in (9) gives the coefficients of even subscript in terms of c_0; the formula in (10) gives the coefficients of odd subscript in terms of c_1. After we separately collect the terms of the series of even and odd degree, we get the general solution

$$y(x) = c_0 \left(1 + \sum_{n=1}^{\infty} \frac{(2n-1)!!}{2^{3n} \cdot n!} x^{2n} \right) + c_1 \left(x + \sum_{n=1}^{\infty} \frac{n!}{2^n \cdot (2n+1)!!} x^{2n+1} \right). \tag{11}$$

Alternatively,

$$y(x) = c_0 \left(1 + \frac{1}{8}x^2 + \frac{3}{128}x^4 + \frac{5}{1024}x^6 + \cdots \right)$$

$$+ c_1 \left(x + \frac{1}{6}x^3 + \frac{1}{30}x^5 + \frac{1}{140}x^7 + \cdots \right). \tag{11'}$$

Because $y(0) = c_0$ and $y'(0) = c_1$, the given initial conditions imply that $c_0 = 4$ and $c_1 = 1$. Using these values in Eq. (11'), the first few terms of the particular solution satisfying $y(0) = 4$ and $y'(0) = 1$ are

$$y(x) = 4 + x + \frac{1}{2}x^2 + \frac{1}{6}x^3 + \frac{3}{32}x^4 + \frac{1}{30}x^5 + \cdots. \tag{12}$$

$\blacksquare$

Remark: As in Example 5, substitution of $y = \sum c_n x^n$ in a linear second-order equation with $x = 0$ an ordinary point typically leads to a recurrence relation that can be used to express each of the successive coefficients c_2, c_3, c_4, ... in terms of the first two, c_0 and c_1. In this event two linearly independent solutions are obtained as follows. Let $y_0(x)$ be the solution obtained with $c_0 = 1$ and $c_1 = 0$, and let $y_1(x)$ be the solution obtained with $c_0 = 0$ and $c_1 = 1$. Then

$$y_0(0) = 1, \quad y_0'(0) = 0 \quad \text{and} \quad y_1(0) = 0, \quad y_1'(0) = 1,$$

so it is clear that y_0 and y_1 are linearly independent. In Example 5, $y_0(x)$ and $y_1(x)$ are defined by the two series that appear on the right-hand side in Eq. (11), which expresses the general solution in the form $y = c_0 y_0 + c_1 y_1$. $\blacksquare$

Translated Series Solutions

If in Example 5 we had sought a particular solution with given initial values $y(a)$ and $y'(a)$, we would have needed the general solution in the form

$$y(x) = \sum_{n=0}^{\infty} c_n(x - a)^n; \tag{13}$$

that is, in powers of $x - a$ rather than in powers of x. For only with a solution of the form in (13) is it true that the initial conditions

$$y(a) = c_0 \quad \text{and} \quad y'(a) = c_1$$

determine the arbitrary constants c_0 and c_1 in terms of the initial values of y and y'. Consequently, to solve an initial value problem, we need a series expansion of the general solution centered at the point where the initial conditions are specified.

Example 6 Solve the initial value problem

$$(t^2 - 2t - 3)\frac{d^2y}{dt^2} + 3(t - 1)\frac{dy}{dt} + y = 0; \quad y(1) = 4, \quad y'(1) = -1. \tag{14}$$

Solution We need a general solution of the form $\sum c_n(t - 1)^n$. But instead of substituting this series in (14) to determine the coefficients, it simplifies the computations if we first make the substitution $x = t - 1$, so that we wind up looking for a series of the form $\sum c_n x^n$ after all. To transform Eq. (14) into one with the new independent variable x, we note that

$$t^2 - 2t - 3 = (x + 1)^2 - 2(x + 1) - 3 = x^2 - 4,$$

$$\frac{dy}{dt} = \frac{dy}{dx}\frac{dx}{dt} = \frac{dy}{dx} = y',$$

and

$$\frac{d^2y}{dt^2} = \left[\frac{d}{dx}\left(\frac{dy}{dx}\right)\right]\frac{dx}{dt} = \frac{d}{dx}(y') = y'',$$

where primes denote differentiation with respect to x. Hence we transform Eq. (14) into

$$(x^2 - 4)y'' + 3xy' + y = 0$$

with initial conditions $y = 4$ and $y' = 1$ at $x = 0$ (corresponding to $t = 1$). This is the initial value problem we solved in Example 5, so the particular solution in (12) is available. We substitute $t - 1$ for x in Eq. (12) and thereby obtain the desired particular solution

$$y(t) = 4 + (t - 1) + \frac{1}{2}(t - 1)^2 + \frac{1}{6}(t - 1)^3$$

$$+ \frac{3}{32}(t - 1)^4 + \frac{1}{30}(t - 1)^5 + \cdots.$$

This series converges if $-1 < t < 3$. (Why?) A series such as this can be used to estimate numerical values of the solution. For instance,

$$y(0.8) = 4 + (-0.2) + \frac{1}{2}(-0.2)^2 + \frac{1}{6}(-0.2)^3$$

$$+ \frac{3}{32}(-0.2)^4 + \frac{1}{30}(-0.2)^5 + \cdots,$$

so that $y(0.8) \approx 3.8188$.   ∎

The last computation in Example 6 illustrates the fact that series solutions of differential equations are useful not only for establishing general properties of a solution, but also for numerical computations when an expression of the solution in terms of elementary functions is unavailable.

Types of Recurrence Relations

The formula in Eq. (8) is an example of a **two-term** recurrence relation; it expresses each coefficient in the series in terms of *one* of the preceding coefficients. A **many-term** recurrence relation expresses each coefficient in the series in terms of two or more preceding coefficients. In the case of a many-term recurrence relation, it is generally inconvenient or even impossible to find a formula that gives the typical coefficient c_n in terms of n. The next example shows what we sometimes can do with a three-term recurrence relation.

Example 7   Find two linearly independent solutions of

$$y'' - xy' - x^2 y = 0. \tag{15}$$

Solution   We make the usual substitution of the power series $y = \sum c_n x^n$. This results in the equation

$$\sum_{n=2}^{\infty} n(n-1)c_n x^{n-2} - \sum_{n=1}^{\infty} nc_n x^n - \sum_{n=0}^{\infty} c_n x^{n+2} = 0.$$

We can start the second sum at $n = 0$ without changing anything else. To make each term include x^n in its general term, we shift the index of summation in the first sum by $+2$ (replace n with $n+2$), and we shift it by -2 in the third sum (replace n with $n-2$). These shifts yield

$$\sum_{n=0}^{\infty} (n+2)(n+1)c_{n+2} x^n - \sum_{n=0}^{\infty} nc_n x^n - \sum_{n=2}^{\infty} c_{n-2} x^n = 0.$$

The common range of these three summations is $n \geq 2$, so we must separate the terms corresponding to $n = 0$ and $n = 1$ in the first two sums before collecting coefficients of x^n. This gives

$$2c_2 + 6c_3 x - c_1 x + \sum_{n=2}^{\infty} [(n+2)(n+1)c_{n+2} - nc_n - c_{n-2}] x^n = 0.$$

The identity principle now implies that $2c_2 = 0$, that $c_3 = \frac{1}{6}c_1$, and the three-term recurrence relation

$$c_{n+2} = \frac{nc_n + c_{n-2}}{(n+2)(n+1)} \tag{16}$$

for $n \geqq 2$. In particular,

$$c_4 = \frac{2c_2 + c_0}{12}, \quad c_5 = \frac{3c_3 + c_1}{20}, \quad c_6 = \frac{4c_4 + c_2}{30},$$

$$c_7 = \frac{5c_5 + c_3}{42}, \quad c_8 = \frac{6c_6 + c_4}{56}. \tag{17}$$

Thus all values of c_n for $n \geq 4$ are given in terms of the arbitrary constants c_0 and c_1 because $c_2 = 0$ and $c_3 = \frac{1}{6}c_1$.

To get our first solution y_1 of Eq. (15), we choose $c_0 = 1$ and $c_1 = 0$, so that $c_2 = c_3 = 0$. Then the formulas in (17) yield

$$c_4 = \frac{1}{12}, \quad c_5 = 0, \quad c_6 = \frac{1}{90}, \quad c_7 = 0, \quad c_8 = \frac{3}{1120};$$

thus

$$y_1(x) = 1 + \frac{1}{12}x^4 + \frac{1}{90}x^6 + \frac{3}{1120}x^8 + \cdots . \tag{18}$$

Because $c_1 = c_3 = 0$, it is clear from Eq. (16) that this series contains only terms of even degree.

To obtain a second linearly independent solution y_2 of Eq. (15), we take $c_0 = 0$ and $c_1 = 1$, so that $c_2 = 0$ and $c_3 = \frac{1}{6}$. Then the formulas in (17) yield

$$c_4 = 0, \quad c_5 = \frac{3}{40}, \quad c_6 = 0, \quad c_7 = \frac{13}{1008},$$

so that

$$y_2(x) = x + \frac{1}{6}x^3 + \frac{3}{40}x^5 + \frac{13}{1008}x^7 + \cdots . \tag{19}$$

Because $c_0 = c_2 = 0$, it is clear from Eq. (16) that this series contains only terms of odd degree. The solutions $y_1(x)$ and $y_2(x)$ are linearly independent because $y_1(0) = 1$ and $y_1'(0) = 0$, whereas $y_2(0) = 0$ and $y_2'(0) = 1$. A general solution of Eq. (15) is a linear combination of the power series in (18) and (19). Equation (15) has no singular points, so the power series representing $y_1(x)$ and $y_2(x)$ converge for all x. ∎

The Legendre Equation

The **Legendre equation** of order α is the second-order linear differential equation

$$\blacktriangleright \qquad (1 - x^2)y'' - 2xy' + \alpha(\alpha + 1)y = 0, \tag{20}$$

where the real number α satisfies the inequality $\alpha > -1$. This differential equation has extensive applications, ranging from numerical integration formulas (such as Gaussian quadrature) to the problem of determining the steady-state temperature within a solid spherical ball when the temperatures at points of its boundary are known. The only singular points of the Legendre equation are at $+1$ and -1, so it has two linearly independent solutions that can be expressed as power series in powers of x with radius of convergence at least 1. The substitution $y = \sum c_m x^m$ in Eq. (20) leads (see Problem 31) to the recurrence relation

$$c_{m+2} = -\frac{(\alpha - m)(\alpha + m + 1)}{(m+1)(m+2)}c_m \qquad (21)$$

for $m \geqq 0$. We are using m as the index of summation because we have another role for n to play.

In terms of the arbitrary constants c_0 and c_1, Eq. (21) yields

$$c_2 = -\frac{\alpha(\alpha+1)}{2!}c_0,$$

$$c_3 = -\frac{(\alpha-1)(\alpha+2)}{3!}c_1,$$

$$c_4 = \frac{\alpha(\alpha-2)(\alpha+1)(\alpha+3)}{4!}c_0,$$

$$c_5 = \frac{(\alpha-1)(\alpha-3)(\alpha+2)(\alpha+4)}{5!}c_1.$$

We can show without much trouble that for $m > 0$,

$$c_{2m} = (-1)^m \frac{\alpha(\alpha-2)(\alpha-4)\cdots(\alpha-2m+2)(\alpha+1)(\alpha+3)\cdots(\alpha+2m-1)}{(2m)!}c_0 \quad (22)$$

and

$$c_{2m+1} = (-1)^m \frac{(\alpha-1)(\alpha-3)\cdots(\alpha-2m+1)(\alpha+2)(\alpha+4)\cdots(\alpha+2m)}{(2m+1)!}c_1. \quad (23)$$

Alternatively,

$$c_{2m} = (-1)^m a_{2m} c_0 \quad \text{and} \quad c_{2m+1} = (-1)^m a_{2m+1} c_1,$$

where a_{2m} and a_{2m+1} denote the fractions in Eqs. (22) and (23), respectively. With this notation, we get two linearly independent power series solutions

$$y_1(x) = c_0 \sum_{m=0}^{\infty} (-1)^m a_{2m} x^{2m} \quad \text{and} \quad y_2(x) = c_1 \sum_{m=0}^{\infty} (-1)^m a_{2m+1} x^{2m+1} \qquad (24)$$

of Legendre's equation of order α.

Now suppose that $\alpha = n$, a nonnegative *integer.* If $\alpha = n$ is even, we see from Eq. (22) that $a_{2m} = 0$ when $2m > n$. In this case, $y_1(x)$ is a *polynomial* of degree n and y_2 is a (nonterminating) infinite series. If $\alpha = n$ is an odd positive integer, we see from Eq. (23) that $a_{2m+1} = 0$ when $2m+1 > n$. In this case, $y_2(x)$ is a *polynomial* of degree n and y_1 is a (nonterminating) infinite series. Thus in either case, one of the two solutions in (24) is a polynomial and the other is a nonterminating series.

With an appropriate choice (made separately for each n) of the arbitrary constants c_0 (n even) or c_1 (n odd), the nth-degree polynomial solution of Legendre's equation of order n,

$$(1 - x)^2 y'' - 2xy' + n(n + 1)y = 0, \tag{25}$$

is denoted by $P_n(x)$ and is called the **Legendre polynomial** of degree n. It is customary (for a reason indicated in Problem 32) to choose the arbitrary constant so that the coefficient of x^n in $P_n(x)$ is $(2n)! / \left[2^n (n!)^2\right]$. It then turns out that

$$P_n(x) = \sum_{k=0}^{N} \frac{(-1)^k (2n - 2k)!}{2^n k! (n - k)! (n - 2k)!} x^{n-2k}, \tag{26}$$

where $N = [\![n/2]\!]$, the integral part of $n/2$. The first six Legendre polynomials are

$$P_0(x) \equiv 1, \qquad\qquad P_1(x) = x,$$

$$P_2(x) = \frac{1}{2}(3x^2 - 1), \qquad\qquad P_3(x) = \frac{1}{2}(5x^3 - 3x),$$

$$P_4(x) = \frac{1}{8}(35x^4 - 30x^2 + 3), \qquad P_5(x) = \frac{1}{8}(63x^5 - 70x^3 + 15x),$$

and their graphs are shown in Fig. 8.2.2.

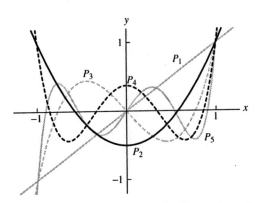

FIGURE 8.2.2. Graphs $y = P_n(x)$ of the Legendre polynomials for $n = 1, 2, 3, 4,$ and 5. The graphs are distinguished by the fact that all n zeros of $P_n(x)$ lie in the interval $-1 < x < 1$.

8.2 Problems

Find general solutions in powers of x of the differential equations in Problems 1 through 15. State the recurrence relation and the guaranteed radius of convergence in each case.

1. $(x^2 - 1)y'' + 4xy' + 2y = 0$
2. $(x^2 + 2)y'' + 4xy' + 2y = 0$
3. $y'' + xy' + y = 0$
4. $(x^2 + 1)y'' + 6xy' + 4y = 0$
5. $(x^2 - 3)y'' + 2xy' = 0$
6. $(x^2 - 1)y'' - 6xy' + 12y = 0$
7. $(x^2 + 3)y'' - 7xy' + 16y = 0$
8. $(2 - x^2)y'' - xy' + 16y = 0$
9. $(x^2 - 1)y'' + 8xy' + 12y = 0$
10. $3y'' + xy' - 4y = 0$
11. $5y'' - 2xy' + 10y = 0$
12. $y'' - x^2y' - 3xy = 0$
13. $y'' + x^2y' + 2xy = 0$
14. $y'' + xy = 0$ (an *Airy equation*)
15. $y'' + x^2y = 0$

Use power series to solve the initial value problems in Problems 16 and 17.

16. $(1 + x^2)y'' + 2xy' - 2y = 0$; $y(0) = 0$, $y'(0) = 1$
17. $y'' + xy' - 2y = 0$; $y(0) = 1$, $y'(0) = 0$

Solve the initial value problems in Problems 18 through 22. First make a substitution of the form $t = x - a$, then find a solution $\sum c_n t^n$ of the transformed differential equation. State the interval of values of x for which Theorem 1 of this section guarantees convergence.

18. $y'' + (x - 1)y' + y = 0$; $y(1) = 2$, $y'(1) = 0$
19. $(2x - x^2)y'' - 6(x - 1)y' - 4y = 0$; $y(1) = 0$, $y'(1) = 1$
20. $(x^2 - 6x + 10)y'' - 4(x - 3)y' + 6y = 0$; $y(3) = 2$, $y'(3) = 0$
21. $(4x^2 + 16x + 17)y'' = 8y$; $y(-2) = 1$, $y'(-2) = 0$
22. $(x^2 + 6x)y'' + (3x + 9)y' - 3y = 0$; $y(-3) = 0$, $y'(-3) = 2$

In Problems 23 through 26, find a three-term recurrence relation for solutions of the form $y = \sum c_n x^n$. Then find the first three nonzero terms in each of two linearly independent solutions.

23. $y'' + (1 + x)y = 0$
24. $(x^2 - 1)y'' + 2xy' + 2xy = 0$
25. $y'' + x^2 y' + x^2 y = 0$
26. $(1 + x^3)y'' + x^4 y = 0$
27. Solve the initial value problem

$$y'' + xy' + (2x^2 + 1)y = 0; \quad y(0) = 1, y'(0) = -1.$$

Determine sufficiently many terms to compute $y(1/2)$ accurate to four decimal places.

In Problems 28 through 30, find the first three nonzero terms in each of two linearly independent solutions of the form $y = \sum c_n x^n$. Substitute known Taylor series for the analytic functions and retain enough terms to compute the necessary coefficients.

28. $y'' + e^{-x}y = 0$
29. $(\cos x)y'' + y = 0$
30. $xy'' + (\sin x)y' + xy = 0$
31. Derive the recurrence relation in (21) for the Legendre equation.
32. Follow the steps outlined in this problem to establish **Rodrigues's formula**

$$P_n(x) = \frac{1}{n! \, 2^n} \frac{d^n}{dx^n}(x^2 - 1)^n$$

for the nth-degree Legendre polynomial. **(a)** Show that $v = (x^2 - 1)^n$ satisfies the differential equation

$$(1 - x^2)v' + 2nxv = 0.$$

Differentiate each side of this equation to obtain

$$(1 - x^2)v'' + 2(n - 1)xv' + 2nv = 0.$$

(b) Differentiate each side of the last equation n times in succession to obtain

$$(1 - x^2)v^{(n+2)} - 2xv^{(n+1)} + n(n + 1)v^{(n)} = 0.$$

Thus $u = v^{(n)} = D^n(x^2 - 1)^n$ satisfies Legendre's equation of order n. **(c)** Show that the coefficient of x^n in u is $(2n)!/n!$; then state why this proves Rodrigues' formula. (Note that the coefficient of x^n in $P_n(x)$ is $(2n)! / [2^n(n!)^2]$.)

33. The **Hermite equation** of order α is

$$y'' - 2xy' + 2\alpha y = 0.$$

(a) Derive the two power series solutions

$$y_1 = 1 + \sum_{m=1}^{\infty} (-1)^m \frac{2^m \alpha(\alpha - 2) \cdots (\alpha - 2m + 2)}{(2m)!} x^{2m}$$

and

$$y_2 = x$$

$$+ \sum_{m=1}^{\infty} (-1)^m \frac{2^m(\alpha - 1)(\alpha - 3) \cdots (\alpha - 2m + 1)}{(2m + 1)!} x^{2m+1}.$$

Show that y_1 is a polynomial if α is an even integer, whereas y_2 is a polynomial if α is an odd integer. **(b)** The **Hermite polynomial** of degree n is denoted by $H_n(x)$. It is the nth-degree polynomial solution of Hermite's equation, multiplied by a suitable constant so that the coefficient of x^n is 2^n. Show that the first six Hermite polynomials are

$$H_0(x) \equiv 1, \qquad\qquad H_1(x) = 2x,$$
$$H_2(x) = 4x^2 - 2, \qquad H_3(x) = 8x^3 - 12x,$$
$$H_4(x) = 16x^4 - 48x^2 + 12,$$
$$H_5(x) = 32x^5 - 160x^3 + 120x.$$

A general formula for the Hermite polynomials is

$$H_n(x) = (-1)^n e^{x^2} \frac{d^n}{dx^n}\left(e^{-x^2}\right).$$

Verify that this formula does in fact give an nth-degree polynomial. It is interesting to use a computer algebra system to investigate the conjecture that (for each n) the zeros of the Hermite polynomials $H_n(x)$ and H_{n+1} are "interlaced"—that is, the n zeros of H_n line in the n bounded open intervals whose endpoints are successive pairs of zeros of H_{n+1}.

34. The discussion following Example 4 in Section 8.1 suggests that the differential equation $y'' + y = 0$ could be used to introduce and define the familiar sine and cosine functions. In a similar fashion, the *Airy equation*

$$y'' = xy$$

serves to introduce two new special functions that appear in applications ranging from radio waves to molecular vibrations. Derive the first three or four terms of two different power series solutions of the Airy equation. Then verify that your results agree with the formulas

$$y_1(x) = 1 + \sum_{k=1}^{\infty} \frac{1 \cdot 4 \cdots (3k-2)}{(3k)!} x^{3k}$$

and

$$y_2(x) = x + \sum_{k=1}^{\infty} \frac{2 \cdot 5 \cdots (3k-1)}{(3k+1)!} x^{3k+1}$$

for the solutions that satisfy the initial conditions $y_1(0) = 1$, $y_1'(0) = 0$ and $y_2(0) = 0$, $y_2'(0) = 1$, respectively. The special combinations

$$\text{Ai}(x) = \frac{y_1(x)}{3^{2/3}\Gamma(\frac{2}{3})} - \frac{y_2(x)}{3^{1/3}\Gamma(\frac{1}{3})}$$

and

$$\text{Bi}(x) = \frac{y_1(x)}{3^{1/6}\Gamma(\frac{2}{3})} + \frac{y_2(x)}{3^{-1/6}\Gamma(\frac{1}{3})}$$

define the standard *Airy functions* that appear in mathematical tables and computer algebra systems. Their graphs shown in Fig. 8.2.3 exhibit trigonometric-like oscillatory behavior for $x < 0$, whereas $\text{Ai}(x)$ decreases exponentially and $\text{Bi}(x)$ increases exponentially as $x \to +\infty$. It is interesting to use a computer algebra system to investigate how many terms must be retained in the y_1- and y_2-series above to produce a figure that is visually indistinguishable from Fig. 8.2.3 (which is based on high-precision approximations to the Airy functions).

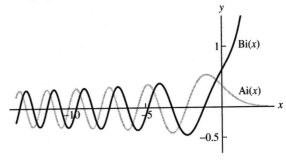

FIGURE 8.2.3. The Airy function graphs $y = \text{Ai}(x)$ and $y = \text{Bi}(x)$.

8.2 Application: Automatic Computation of Series Coefficients

Repeated application of a recurrence relation to grind out successive coefficients is—especially in the case of a recurrence relation with three or more terms—a tedious aspect of the infinite series method. Here we illustrate the use of a computer algebra system for this task. In Example 7 we saw that the coefficients in the series solution $y = \sum c_n x^n$ of the differential equation $y'' - xy' - x^2 y = 0$ are given in terms of the two arbitrary coefficients c_0 and c_1 by

$$c_2 = 0, \quad c_3 = \frac{c_1}{6}, \quad \text{and} \quad c_{n+2} = \frac{nc_n + c_{n-2}}{(n+2)(n+1)} \quad \text{for} \quad n \geq 2. \tag{1}$$

It would appear to be a routine matter to implement such a recurrence relation, but a twist results from the fact that a typical computer system array is indexed by the subscripts 1, 2, 3, ..., rather than by the subscripts 0, 1, 2, ... that match the exponents in the successive terms of a power series that begins with a constant term. For this reason we first rewrite our proposed power series solution in the form

$$y = \sum_{n=0}^{\infty} c_n x^n = \sum_{n=1}^{\infty} b_n x^{n-1} \tag{2}$$

where $b_n = c_{n-1}$ for each $n \geq 1$. Then the first two conditions in (1) imply that $b_3 = 0$ and $b_4 = \frac{1}{6}b_2$; also, the recurrence relation (with n replaced with $n-1$) yields the new recurrence relation

$$b_{n+2} = c_{n+1} = \frac{(n-1)c_{n-1} + c_{n-3}}{(n+1)n} = \frac{(n-1)b_n + b_{n-2}}{n(n+1)}. \tag{3}$$

Now we are ready to begin. Suppose that we want to calculate the terms through the 10th degree in (2) with the initial conditions $b_1 = b_2 = 1$. Then either the *Maple* commands

```
k := 11:                 # k terms
b := array(1..k):
b[1] := 1:               # arbitrary
b[2] := 1:               # arbitrary
b[3] := 0:
b[4] := b[2]/6:
for n from 3 by 1 to k - 2 do
   b[n+2] := ((n-1)*b[n] + b[n-2])/(n*(n+1));
   od;
```

or the *Mathematica* commands

```
k = 11;                  (* k terms *)
b = Table[0, {n,1,k}];
b[[1]] = 1;              (* arbitrary *)
b[[2]] = 1;              (* arbitrary *)
b[[3]] = 0;
b[[4]] = b[[2]]/6;
For[n=3, n<=k-2,
    b[[n+2]]=((n-1)*b[[n]] + b[[n-2]])/(n*(n+1)); n=n+1];
```

quickly yield the coefficients $\{b_n\}$ corresponding to the solution

$y(x) =$

$$1 + x + \frac{x^3}{6} + \frac{x^4}{12} + \frac{3x^5}{40} + \frac{x^6}{90} + \frac{13x^7}{1008} + \frac{3x^8}{1120} + \frac{119x^9}{51840} + \frac{41x^{10}}{113400} + \cdots . \quad (4)$$

You might note that the even- and odd-degree terms here agree with those shown in Eqs. (18) and (19), respectively, of Example 7.

The MATLAB commands

```
k = 11;                  % k terms
b = 0*(1:k);
b(1) = 1;                % arbitrary
b(2) = 1;                % arbitrary
b(3) = 0;
b(4) = b(2)/6;
for n = 3:k-2
    b(n+2) = ((n-1)*b(n) + b(n-2))/(n*(n+1));
    end
format rat, b
```

give the same results, *except that* the coefficient b_{10} of x^9 is shown as 73/31801 rather than the correct value 119/51840 shown in Eq. (4). It happens that

$$\frac{73}{31801} \approx 0.0022955253 \quad \text{while} \quad \frac{119}{51840} \approx 0.0022955247,$$

so the two rational fractions agree when rounded to 9 decimal places. The explanation is that (unlike *Mathematica* and *Maple*) MATLAB works internally with decimal rather than exact arithmetic. But at the end its **format rat** algorithm converts a correct 14-place approximation for b_{10} into an incorrect rational fraction that's "close but no cigar."

You can substitute $b_1 = 1$, $b_2 = 0$ and $b_1 = 0$, $b_2 = 1$ separately (instead of $b_1 = b_2 = 1$) in the commands shown here to derive partial sums of the two linearly independent solutions displayed in Eqs. (18) and (19) of Example 7. This technique can be applied to any of the examples and problems in this section.

8.3 Regular Singular Points

We now investigate the solution of the homogeneous second-order linear equation

$$A(x)y'' + B(x)y' + C(x)y = 0 \qquad (1)$$

near a singular point. Recall that if the functions A, B, and C are polynomials having no common factors, then the singular points of Eq. (1) are simply those points where $A(x) = 0$. For instance, $x = 0$ is the only singular point of the Bessel equation of order n,

$$x^2 y'' + xy' + (x^2 - n^2)y = 0,$$

whereas the Legendre equation of order n,

$$(1 - x^2)y'' - 2xy' + n(n+1)y = 0,$$

has the two singular points $x = -1$ and $x = 1$. It turns out that some of the features of the solutions of such equations of the most importance for applications are largely determined by their behavior near their singular points.

We will restrict our attention to the case in which $x = 0$ is a singular point of Eq. (1). A differential equation having $x = a$ as a singular point is easily transformed by the substitution $t = x - a$ into one having a corresponding singular point at 0. For example, let us substitute $t = x - 1$ into the Legendre equation of order n. Because

$$y' = \frac{dy}{dx} = \frac{dy}{dt}\frac{dt}{dx} = \frac{dy}{dt},$$

$$y'' = \frac{d^2 y}{dx^2} = \left[\frac{d}{dt}\left(\frac{dy}{dx}\right)\right]\frac{dt}{dx} = \frac{d^2 y}{dt^2},$$

and $1 - x^2 = 1 - (t+1)^2 = -2t - t^2$, we get the equation

$$-t(t+2)\frac{d^2 y}{dt^2} - 2(t+1)\frac{dy}{dt} + n(n+1)y = 0.$$

This new equation has the singular point $t = 0$ corresponding to $x = 1$ in the original equation; it has also the singular point $t = -2$ corresponding to $x = -1$.

Types of Singular Points

A differential equation having a singular point at 0 ordinarily will *not* have power series solutions of the form $y(x) = \sum c_n x^n$, so the straightforward method of Section 8.2 fails in this case. To investigate the form that a solution of such an equation might take, we assume that Eq. (1) has analytic coefficient functions and rewrite it in the standard form

$$y'' + P(x)y' + Q(x)y = 0, \qquad (2)$$

where $P = B/A$ and $Q = C/A$. Recall that $x = 0$ is an ordinary point (as opposed to a singular point) of Eq. (2) if the functions $P(x)$ and $Q(x)$ are analytic at $x = 0$; that is, if $P(x)$ and $Q(x)$ have convergent power series expansions in powers of x on some open interval containing $x = 0$. Now it can be proved that each of the functions $P(x)$ and $Q(x)$ *either* is analytic *or* approaches $\pm\infty$ as $x \to 0$.

Consequently, $x = 0$ is a singular point of Eq. (2) provided that either $P(x)$ or $Q(x)$ (or both) approaches $\pm\infty$ as $x \to 0$. For instance, if we rewrite the Bessel equation of order n in the form

$$y'' + \frac{1}{x}y' + \left(1 - \frac{n^2}{x^2}\right)y = 0,$$

we see that $P(x) = 1/x$ and $Q(x) = 1 - (n/x)^2$ both approach infinity as $x \to 0$.

We will see presently that the power series method can be generalized to apply near the singular point $x = 0$ of Eq. (2), provided that $P(x)$ approaches infinity no more rapidly than $1/x$, and $Q(x)$ no more rapidly than $1/x^2$, as $x \to 0$. This is a way of saying that $P(x)$ and $Q(x)$ have only "weak" singularities at $x = 0$. To state this more precisely, we rewrite Eq. (2) in the form

➤
$$y'' + \frac{p(x)}{x}y' + \frac{q(x)}{x^2}y = 0, \tag{3}$$

where

➤
$$p(x) = xP(x) \quad \text{and} \quad q(x) = x^2Q(x). \tag{4}$$

Definition: Regular Singular Point

The singular point $x = 0$ of Eq. (3) is a **regular singular point** if the functions $p(x)$ and $q(x)$ are both analytic at $x = 0$. Otherwise it is an **irregular singular point**.

In particular, the singular point $x = 0$ is a *regular* singular point if $p(x)$ and $q(x)$ are both polynomials. For instance, we see that $x = 0$ is a regular singular point of Bessel's equation of order n by writing that equation in the form

$$y'' + \frac{1}{x}y' + \frac{x^2 - n^2}{x^2}y = 0,$$

noting that $p(x) \equiv 1$ and $q(x) = x^2 - n^2$ are both polynomials in x.

By contrast, consider the equation

$$2x^3y'' + (1 + x)y' + 3xy = 0,$$

which has the singular point $x = 0$. If we write this equation in the form of (3), we get

$$y'' + \frac{(1 + x)/(2x^2)}{x}y' + \frac{\frac{3}{2}}{x^2}y = 0.$$

Because

$$p(x) = \frac{1 + x}{2x^2} = \frac{1}{2x^2} + \frac{1}{2x} \to \infty$$

as $x \to 0$ (although $q(x) \equiv \frac{3}{2}$ is a polynomial), we see that $x = 0$ is an irregular singular point. We will not discuss the solution of differential equations near irregular singular points; this is a considerably more advanced topic than the solution of differential equations near regular singular points.

Example 1   Consider the differential equation

$$x^2(1+x)y'' + x(4-x^2)y' + (2+3x)y = 0.$$

In the standard form $y'' + Py' + Qy = 0$ it is

$$y'' + \frac{4-x^2}{x(1+x)}y' + \frac{2+3x}{x^2(1+x)}y = 0.$$

Because

$$P(x) = \frac{4-x^2}{x(1+x)} \quad \text{and} \quad Q(x) = \frac{2+3x}{x^2(1+x)}$$

both approach ∞ as $x \to 0$, we see that $x = 0$ is a singular point. To determine the nature of this singular point we write the differential equation in the form of Eq. (3):

$$y'' + \frac{(4-x^2)/(1+x)}{x}y' + \frac{(2+3x)/(1+x)}{x^2}y = 0.$$

Thus

$$p(x) = \frac{4-x^2}{1+x} \quad \text{and} \quad q(x) = \frac{2+3x}{1+x}.$$

Because a quotient of polynomials is analytic wherever the denominator is nonzero, we see that $p(x)$ and $q(x)$ are both analytic at $x = 0$. Hence $x = 0$ is a *regular singular point* of the given differential equation. ∎

    It may happen that when we begin with a differential equation in the general form in Eq. (1) and rewrite it in the form in (3), the functions $p(x)$ and $q(x)$ as given in (4) are indeterminate forms at $x = 0$. In this case the situation is determined by the limits

$$p_0 = p(0) = \lim_{x \to 0} p(x) = \lim_{x \to 0} xP(x) \tag{5}$$

and

$$q_0 = q(0) = \lim_{x \to 0} q(x) = \lim_{x \to 0} x^2 Q(x). \tag{6}$$

If $p_0 = 0 = q_0$, then $x = 0$ may be an ordinary point. Otherwise, if the limits in both (5) and (6) exist and are *finite*, then $x = 0$ is a regular singular point. If either limit fails to exist or is infinite, then $x = 0$ is an irregular singular point.

    Remark: The most common case in applications, for the differential equation written in the form

$$y'' + \frac{p(x)}{x}y' + \frac{q(x)}{x^2}y = 0, \tag{3}$$

is that the functions $p(x)$ and $q(x)$ are *polynomials*. In this case $p_0 = p(0)$ and $q_0 = q(0)$ are simply the constant terms of these polynomials, so there is no need to evaluate the limits in Eqs. (5) and (6). ∎

| Example 2 | To investigate the nature of the point $x = 0$ for the differential equation |

$$x^4 y'' + (x^2 \sin x)y' + (1 - \cos x)y = 0,$$

we first write it in the form in (3):

$$y'' + \frac{(\sin x)/x}{x}y' + \frac{(1 - \cos x)/x^2}{x^2}y = 0.$$

Then l'Hôpital's rule gives the values

$$p_0 = \lim_{x \to 0} \frac{\sin x}{x} = \lim_{x \to 0} \frac{\cos x}{1} = 1$$

and

$$q_0 = \lim_{x \to 0} \frac{1 - \cos x}{x^2} = \lim_{x \to 0} \frac{\sin x}{2x} = \frac{1}{2}$$

for the limits in Eqs. (5) and (6). While not both are zero, we see that $x = 0$ is a regular singular point because each limit is finite. Alternatively, we could write

$$p(x) = \frac{\sin x}{x} = \frac{1}{x}\left(x - \frac{x^3}{3!} + \frac{x^5}{5!} - \cdots\right) = 1 - \frac{x^2}{3!} + \frac{x^4}{5!} - \cdots$$

and

$$q(x) = \frac{1 - \cos x}{x^2} = \frac{1}{x^2}\left[1 - \left(1 - \frac{x^2}{2!} + \frac{x^4}{4!} - \frac{x^6}{6!} + \cdots\right)\right]$$

$$= \frac{1}{2!} - \frac{x^2}{4!} + \frac{x^4}{6!} - \cdots.$$

These (convergent) power series show explicitly that $p(x)$ and $q(x)$ are analytic and moreover that $p_0 = p(0) = 1$ and $q_0 = q(0) = \frac{1}{2}$. ∎

The Method of Frobenius

We now approach the task of actually finding solutions of a second-order linear differential equation near the regular singular point $x = 0$. The simplest such equation is the constant-coefficient *equidimensional equation*

$$x^2 y'' + p_0 x y' + q_0 y = 0 \tag{7}$$

to which Eq. (3) reduces when $p(x) \equiv p_0$ and $q(x) \equiv q_0$ are constants. In this case we can verify by direct substitution that the simple power function $y(x) = x^r$ is a solution of Eq. (7) if and only if r is a root of the quadratic equation

$$r(r - 1) + p_0 r + q_0 = 0. \tag{8}$$

In the general case, in which $p(x)$ and $q(x)$ are power series rather than constants, it is a reasonable conjecture that our differential equation might have a solution of the form

➤ $$y(x) = x^r \sum_{n=0}^{\infty} c_n x^n = \sum_{n=0}^{\infty} c_n x^{n+r} = c_0 x^r + c_1 x^{r+1} + c_2 x^{r+2} + \cdots \tag{9}$$

—the product of x^r and a power series. This turns out to be a very fruitful conjecture; according to Theorem 1 (soon to be stated formally), every equation of the form in (1) having $x = 0$ as a regular singular point does, indeed, have at least one such solution. This fact is the basis for the **method of Frobenius**, named for the German mathematician Georg Frobenius (1848–1917), who discovered the method in the 1870s.

An infinite series of the form in (9) is called a **Frobenius series**. Note that a Frobenius series is generally *not* a power series. For instance, with $r = -\frac{1}{2}$ the series in (9) takes the form

$$y = c_0 x^{-1/2} + c_1 x^{1/2} + c_2 x^{3/2} + c_3 x^{5/2} + \cdots \, ;$$

it is not a series in *integral* powers of x.

To investigate the possible existence of Frobenius series solutions, we begin with the equation

$$x^2 y'' + x p(x) y' + q(x) y = 0 \tag{10}$$

obtained by multiplying the equation in (3) by x^2. If $x = 0$ is a regular singular point, then $p(x)$ and $q(x)$ are analytic at $x = 0$, so

$$\begin{aligned} p(x) &= p_0 + p_1 x + p_2 x^2 + p_3 x^3 + \cdots, \\ q(x) &= q_0 + q_1 x + q_2 x^2 + q_3 x^3 + \cdots. \end{aligned} \tag{11}$$

Suppose that Eq. (10) has the Frobenius series solution

$$y = \sum_{n=0}^{\infty} c_n x^{n+r}. \tag{12}$$

We may (and always do) assume that $c_0 \neq 0$ because the series must have a first nonzero term. Termwise differentiation in Eq. (12) leads to

$$y' = \sum_{n=0}^{\infty} c_n (n + r) x^{n+r-1} \tag{13}$$

and

$$y'' = \sum_{n=0}^{\infty} c_n (n + r)(n + r - 1) x^{n+r-2}. \tag{14}$$

Substitution of the series in Eqs. (11) through (14) in Eq. (10) now yields

$$\begin{aligned} \big[r(r-1) c_0 x^r + (r+1) r c_1 x^{r+1} + \cdots \big] \\ + \big[p_0 x + p_1 x^2 + \cdots \big] \cdot \big[r c_0 x^{r-1} + (r+1) c_1 x^r + \cdots \big] \\ + \big[q_0 + q_1 x + \cdots \big] \cdot \big[c_0 x^r + c_1 x^{r+1} + \cdots \big] = 0. \end{aligned} \tag{15}$$

The lowest power of x that appears in Eq. (15) is x^r. If Eq. (15) is to be satisfied identically, then the coefficient $r(r-1)c_0 + p_0 r c_0 + q_0 c_0$ of x^r must vanish. Because $c_0 \neq 0$, it follows that r must satisfy the quadratic equation

$$r(r-1) + p_0 r + q_0 = 0 \tag{16}$$

of precisely the same form as that obtained with the equidimensional equation in (7). Equation (16) is called the **indicial equation** of the differential equation in (10), and its two roots (possibly equal) are the **exponents** of the differential equation (at the regular singular point $x = 0$).

Our derivation of Eq. (16) shows that *if* the Frobenius series $y = x^r \sum c_n x^n$ is to be a solution of the differential equation in (10), *then* the exponent r must be one of the roots r_1 and r_2 of the indicial equation in (16). If $r_1 \neq r_2$, it follows that there are two possible Frobenius series solutions, whereas if $r_1 = r_2$ there is only one possible Frobenius series solution; the second solution cannot be a Frobenius series. The exponents r_1 and r_2 in the possible Frobenius series solutions are determined (using the indicial equation) by the values $p_0 = p(0)$ and $q_0 = q(0)$ that we have discussed. In practice, particularly when the coefficients in the differential equation in the original form in (1) are polynomials, the simplest way of finding p_0 and q_0 is often to write the equation in the form

$$y'' + \frac{p_0 + p_1 x + p_2 x^2 + \cdots}{x} y' + \frac{q_0 + q_1 x + q_2 x^2 + \cdots}{x^2} y = 0. \qquad (17)$$

Then inspection of the series that appear in the two numerators reveals the constants p_0 and q_0.

Example 3 Find the exponents in the possible Frobenius series solutions of the equation

$$2x^2(1 + x)y'' + 3x(1 + x)^3 y' - (1 - x^2)y = 0.$$

Solution We divide each term by $2x^2(1 + x)$ to recast the differential equation in the form

$$y'' + \frac{\frac{3}{2}(1 + 2x + x^2)}{x} y' + \frac{-\frac{1}{2}(1 - x)}{x^2} y = 0,$$

and thus see that $p_0 = \frac{3}{2}$ and $q_0 = -\frac{1}{2}$. Hence the indicial equation is

$$r(r - 1) + \frac{3}{2}r - \frac{1}{2} = r^2 + \frac{1}{2}r - \frac{1}{2} = (r + 1)(r - \frac{1}{2}) = 0,$$

with roots $r_1 = \frac{1}{2}$ and $r_2 = -1$. The two possible Frobenius series solutions are then of the forms

$$y_1(x) = x^{1/2} \sum_{n=0}^{\infty} a_n x^n \quad \text{and} \quad y_2(x) = x^{-1} \sum_{n=0}^{\infty} b_n x^n. \qquad \blacksquare$$

Frobenius Series Solutions

Once the exponents r_1 and r_2 are known, the coefficients in a Frobenius series solution are determined by substitution of the series in Eqs. (12) through (14) in the differential equation, essentially the same method as was used to determine coefficients in power series solutions in Section 8.2. If the exponents r_1 and r_2 are complex conjugates, then there always exist two linearly independent Frobenius series solutions. We will restrict our attention here to the case in which r_1 and r_2 are both real. We also will seek solutions only for $x > 0$. Once such a solution has been found, we need only replace x^{r_1} with $|x|^{r_1}$ to obtain a solution for $x < 0$. The following theorem is proved in Chapter 4 of Coddington's *An Introduction to Ordinary Differential Equations*.

THEOREM 1: Frobenius Series Solutions

Suppose that $x = 0$ is a regular singular point of the equation

➤ $$x^2 y'' + xp(x)y' + q(x)y = 0. \tag{10}$$

Let $\rho > 0$ denote the minimum of the radii of convergence of the power series

$$p(x) = \sum_{n=0}^{\infty} p_n x^n \quad \text{and} \quad q(x) = \sum_{n=0}^{\infty} q_n x^n.$$

Let r_1 and r_2 be the roots, with $r_1 \geq r_2$, of the indicial equation $r(r-1) + p_0 r + q_0 = 0$. Then

(a) For $x > 0$, there exists a solution of Eq. (10) of the form

➤ $$y_1(x) = x^{r_1} \sum_{n=0}^{\infty} a_n x^n \quad (a_0 \neq 0) \tag{18}$$

corresponding to the larger root r_1.

(b) If $r_1 - r_2$ is neither zero nor a positive integer, then there exists a second linearly independent solution for $x > 0$ of the form

➤ $$y_2(x) = x^{r_2} \sum_{n=0}^{\infty} b_n x^n \quad (b_0 \neq 0) \tag{19}$$

corresponding to the smaller root r_2.

The radii of convergence of the power series in Eqs. (18) and (19) are each at least ρ. The coefficients in these series can be determined by substituting the series in the differential equation

$$x^2 y'' + xp(x)y' + q(x)y = 0. \qquad \blacktriangle$$

We have already seen that if $r_1 = r_2$, then there can exist only one Frobenius series solution. It turns out that, if $r_1 - r_2$ is a positive integer, there may or may not exist a second Frobenius series solution of the form in Eq. (19) corresponding to the smaller root r_2. These exceptional cases are discussed in Section 8.4. Examples 4 through 6 illustrate the process of determining the coefficients in those Frobenius series solutions that are guaranteed by Theorem 1.

Example 4 Find the Frobenius series solutions of

$$2x^2 y'' + 3xy' - (x^2 + 1)y = 0. \tag{20}$$

Solution First we divide each term by $2x^2$ to put the equation in the form in (17):

$$y'' + \frac{\frac{3}{2}}{x} y' + \frac{-\frac{1}{2} - \frac{1}{2}x^2}{x^2} y = 0. \tag{21}$$

We now see that $x = 0$ is a regular singular point, and that $p_0 = \frac{3}{2}$ and $q_0 = -\frac{1}{2}$. Because $p(x) \equiv \frac{3}{2}$ and $q(x) = -\frac{1}{2} - \frac{1}{2}x^2$ are polynomials, the Frobenius series we obtain will converge for all $x > 0$. The indicial equation is

$$r(r-1) + \tfrac{3}{2}r - \tfrac{1}{2} = \left(r - \tfrac{1}{2}\right)(r + 1) = 0,$$

so the exponents are $r_1 = \frac{1}{2}$ and $r_2 = -1$. They do not differ by an integer, so Theorem 1 guarantees the existence of two linearly independent Frobenius series solutions. Rather than separately substituting

$$y_1 = x^{1/2} \sum_{n=0}^{\infty} a_n x^n \quad \text{and} \quad y_2 = x^{-1} \sum_{n=0}^{\infty} b_n x^n$$

in Eq. (20), it is more efficient to begin by substituting $y = x^r \sum c_n x^n$. We will then get a recurrence relation that depends on r. With the value $r_1 = \frac{1}{2}$ it becomes a recurrence relation for the series for y_1, whereas with $r_2 = -1$ it becomes a recurrence relation for the series for y_2.

When we substitute

> $$y = \sum_{n=0}^{\infty} c_n x^{n+r}, \quad y' = \sum_{n=0}^{\infty} (n+r)c_n x^{n+r-1},$$

and

> $$y'' = \sum_{n=0}^{\infty} (n+r)(n+r-1)c_n x^{n+r-2}$$

in Eq. (20)—the original differential equation, rather than Eq. (21)—we get

$$2\sum_{n=0}^{\infty} (n+r)(n+r-1)c_n x^{n+r} + 3\sum_{n=0}^{\infty} (n+r)c_n x^{n+r}$$

$$- \sum_{n=0}^{\infty} c_n x^{n+r+2} - \sum_{n=0}^{\infty} c_n x^{n+r} = 0. \qquad (22)$$

At this stage there are several ways to proceed. A good standard practice is to shift indices so that each exponent will be the same as the smallest one present. In this example, we shift the index of summation in the third sum by -2 to reduce its exponent from $n+r+2$ to $n+r$. This gives

$$2\sum_{n=0}^{\infty} (n+r)(n+r-1)c_n x^{n+r} + 3\sum_{n=0}^{\infty} (n+r)c_n x^{n+r}$$

$$- \sum_{n=2}^{\infty} c_{n-2} x^{n+r} - \sum_{n=0}^{\infty} c_n x^{n+r} = 0. \qquad (23)$$

The common range of summation is $n \geq 2$, so we must treat $n = 0$ and $n = 1$ separately. Following our standard practice, the terms corresponding to $n = 0$ will always give the indicial equation

$$[2r(r-1) + 3r - 1]c_0 = 2\left(r^2 + \tfrac{1}{2}r - \tfrac{1}{2}\right)c_0 = 0.$$

The terms corresponding to $n = 1$ yield

$$[2(r + 1)r + 3(r + 1) - 1]c_1 = (2r^2 + 5r + 2)c_1 = 0.$$

Because the coefficient $2r^2 + 5r + 2$ of c_1 is nonzero whether $r = \frac{1}{2}$ or $r = -1$, it follows that

$$c_1 = 0 \tag{24}$$

in either case.

The coefficient of x^{n+r} in Eq. (23) is

$$2(n + r)(n + r - 1)c_n + 3(n + r)c_n - c_{n-2} - c_n = 0.$$

We solve for c_n and simplify to obtain the recurrence relation

$$\blacktriangleright \qquad c_n = \frac{c_{n-2}}{2(n + r)^2 + (n + r) - 1} \qquad \text{for } n \geq 2. \tag{25}$$

CASE 1: $r_1 = \frac{1}{2}$.   We now write a_n in place of c_n and substitute $r = \frac{1}{2}$ in Eq. (25). This gives the recurrence relation

$$\blacktriangleright \qquad a_n = \frac{a_{n-2}}{2n^2 + 3n} \qquad \text{for } n \geq 2. \tag{26}$$

With this formula we can determine the coefficients in the first Frobenius solution y_1. In view of Eq. (24) we see that $a_n = 0$ whenever n is odd. With $n = 2$, 4, and 6 in Eq. (26), we get

$$a_2 = \frac{a_0}{14}, \quad a_4 = \frac{a_2}{44} = \frac{a_0}{616}, \quad \text{and} \quad a_6 = \frac{a_4}{90} = \frac{a_0}{55440}.$$

Hence the first Frobenius solution is

$$y_1(x) = a_0 x^{1/2} \left(1 + \frac{x^2}{14} + \frac{x^4}{616} + \frac{x^6}{55440} + \cdots \right).$$

CASE 2: $r_2 = -1$.   We now write b_n in place of c_n and substitute $r = -1$ in Eq. (25). This gives the recurrence relation

$$\blacktriangleright \qquad b_n = \frac{b_{n-2}}{2b^2 - 3n} \qquad \text{for } n \geq 2. \tag{27}$$

Again, Eq. (24) implies that $b_n = 0$ for n odd. With $n = 2$, 4, and 6 in (27), we get

$$b_2 = \frac{b_0}{2}, \quad b_4 = \frac{b_2}{20} = \frac{b_0}{40}, \quad \text{and} \quad b_6 = \frac{b_4}{54} = \frac{b_0}{2160}.$$

Hence the second Frobenius solution is

$$y_2(x) = b_0 x^{-1} \left(1 + \frac{x^2}{2} + \frac{x^4}{40} + \frac{x^6}{2160} + \cdots \right). \qquad \blacksquare$$

Example 5 Find a Frobenius solution of Bessel's equation of order zero,

$$x^2 y'' + x y' + x^2 y = 0. \tag{28}$$

Solution   In the form of (17), Eq. (28) becomes

$$y'' + \frac{1}{x} y' + \frac{x^2}{x^2} y = 0.$$

Hence $x = 0$ is a regular singular point with $p(x) \equiv 1$ and $q(x) = x^2$, so our series will converge for all $x > 0$. Because $p_0 = 1$ and $q_0 = 0$, the indicial equation is

$$r(r - 1) + r = r^2 = 0.$$

Thus we obtain only the single exponent $r = 0$, and so there is only one Frobenius series solution

$$y(x) = x^0 \sum_{n=0}^{\infty} c_n x^n$$

of Eq. (28); it is in fact a power series.
Thus we substitute $y = \sum c_n x^n$ in (28); the result is

$$\sum_{n=0}^{\infty} n(n-1) c_n x^n + \sum_{n=0}^{\infty} n c_n x^n + \sum_{n=0}^{\infty} c_n x^{n+2} = 0.$$

We combine the first two sums and shift the index of summation in the third by -2 to obtain

$$\sum_{n=0}^{\infty} n^2 c_n x^n + \sum_{n=2}^{\infty} c_{n-2} x^n = 0.$$

The term corresponding to x^0 gives $0 = 0$: no information. The term corresponding to x^1 gives $c_1 = 0$, and the term for x^n yields the recurrence relation

$$c_n = -\frac{c_{n-2}}{n^2} \quad \text{for } n \geq 2. \tag{29}$$

Because $c_1 = 0$, we see that $c_n = 0$ whenever n is odd. Substituting $n = 2, 4,$ and 6 in Eq. (29), we get

$$c_2 = -\frac{c_0}{2^2}, \quad c_4 = -\frac{c_2}{4^2} = \frac{c_0}{2^2 \cdot 4^2}, \quad \text{and} \quad c_6 = -\frac{c_4}{6^2} = -\frac{c_0}{2^2 \cdot 4^2 \cdot 6^2}.$$

Evidently, the pattern is

$$c_{2n} = \frac{(-1)^n c_0}{2^2 \cdot 4^2 \cdots (2n)^2} = \frac{(-1)^n c_0}{2^{2n} (n!)^2}.$$

The choice $c_0 = 1$ gives us one of the most important special functions in mathematics, the **Bessel function of order zero of the first kind**, denoted by $J_0(x)$. Thus

$$J_0(x) = \sum_{n=0}^{\infty} \frac{(-1)^n x^{2n}}{2^{2n} (n!)^2} = 1 - \frac{x^2}{4} + \frac{x^4}{64} - \frac{x^6}{2304} + \cdots. \tag{30}$$

In this example we have not been able to find a second linearly independent solution of Bessel's equation of order zero. We will derive that solution in Section 8.4; it will not be a Frobenius series. ∎

When $r_1 - r_2$ Is an Integer

Recall that, if $r_1 - r_2$ is a positive integer, then Theorem 1 guarantees only the existence of the Frobenius series solution corresponding to the larger exponent r_1. Example 6 illustrates the fortunate case in which the series method nevertheless yields a second Frobenius series solution. The case in which the second solution is not a Frobenius series will be discussed in Section 8.4.

Example 6   Find the Frobenius series solutions of

$$xy'' + 2y' + xy = 0. \tag{31}$$

Solution   In standard form the equation becomes

$$y'' + \frac{2}{x}y' + \frac{x^2}{x^2}y = 0,$$

so we see that $x = 0$ is a regular singular point with $p_0 = 2$ and $q_0 = 0$. The indicial equation

$$r(r-1) + 2r = r(r+1) = 0$$

has roots $r_1 = 0$ and $r_2 = -1$, which differ by an integer. In this case when $r_1 - r_2$ is an integer, it is better to depart from the standard procedure of Example 4 and begin our work with the *smaller* exponent. As you will see, the recurrence relation will then tell us whether or not a second Frobenius series solution exists. If it does exist, our computations will simultaneously yield *both* Frobenius series solutions. If the second solution does not exist, we begin anew with the larger exponent $r = r_1$ to obtain the one Frobenius series solution guaranteed by Theorem 1.

Hence we begin by substituting

$$y = x^{-1} \sum_{n=0}^{\infty} c_n x^n = \sum_{n=0}^{\infty} c_n x^{n-1}$$

in Eq. (31). This gives

$$\sum_{n=0}^{\infty} (n-1)(n-2)c_n x^{n-2} + 2\sum_{n=0}^{\infty} (n-1)c_n x^{n-2} + \sum_{n=0}^{\infty} c_n x^n = 0.$$

We combine the first two sums and shift the index by -2 in the third to obtain

$$\sum_{n=0}^{\infty} n(n-1)c_n x^{n-2} + \sum_{n=2}^{\infty} c_{n-2} x^{n-2} = 0. \tag{32}$$

The cases $n = 0$ and $n = 1$ reduce to

$$0 \cdot c_0 = 0 \quad \text{and} \quad 0 \cdot c_1 = 0.$$

Hence we have *two* arbitrary constants c_0 and c_1 and therefore can expect to find a general solution incorporating two linearly independent Frobenius series solutions. If, for $n = 1$, we had obtained an equation such as $0 \cdot c_1 = 3$, which can be satisfied for *no* choice of c_1, this would have told us that no second Frobenius series solution could exist.

Now knowing that all is well, from (32) we read the recurrence relation

$$c_n = -\frac{c_{n-2}}{n(n-1)} \qquad \text{for } n \geq 2. \tag{33}$$

The first few values of n give

$$c_2 = -\frac{1}{2 \cdot 1}c_0, \qquad\qquad c_3 = -\frac{1}{3 \cdot 2}c_1,$$

$$c_4 = -\frac{1}{4 \cdot 3}c_2 = \frac{c_0}{4!}, \qquad c_5 = -\frac{1}{5 \cdot 4}c_3 = \frac{c_1}{5!},$$

$$c_6 = -\frac{1}{6 \cdot 5}c_4 = -\frac{c_0}{6!}, \qquad c_7 = -\frac{1}{7 \cdot 6}c_6 = -\frac{c_1}{7!};$$

evidently the pattern is

$$c_{2n} = \frac{(-1)^n c_0}{(2n)!}, \qquad c_{2n+1} = \frac{(-1)^n c_1}{(2n+1)!}$$

for $n \geq 1$. Therefore, a general solution of Eq. (31) is

$$y(x) = x^{-1} \sum_{n=0}^{\infty} c_n x^n$$

$$= \frac{c_0}{x}\left(1 - \frac{x^2}{2!} + \frac{x^4}{4!} - \cdots\right) + \frac{c_1}{x}\left(x - \frac{x^3}{3!} + \frac{x^5}{5!} - \cdots\right)$$

$$= \frac{c_0}{x}\sum_{n=0}^{\infty}\frac{(-1)^n x^{2n}}{(2n)!} + \frac{c_1}{x}\sum_{n=0}^{\infty}\frac{(-1)^n x^{2n+1}}{(2n+1)!}.$$

Thus

$$y(x) = \frac{1}{x}(c_0 \cos x + c_1 \sin x).$$

We have thus found a general solution expressed as a linear combination of the two Frobenius series solutions

$$y_1(x) = \frac{\cos x}{x} \quad \text{and} \quad y_2(x) = \frac{\sin x}{x}. \tag{34}$$

As indicated in Fig. 8.3.1, one of these Frobenius series solutions is bounded but the other is unbounded near the regular singular point $x = 0$—a common occurrence in the case of exponents differing by an integer. ∎

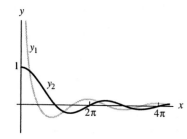

FIGURE 8.3.1. The solutions $y_1(x) = \dfrac{\cos x}{x}$ and $y_2(x) = \dfrac{\sin x}{x}$ in Example 6.

Summary

When confronted with a linear second-order differential equation

$$A(x)y'' + B(x)y' + C(x)y = 0$$

with analytic coefficient functions, in order to investigate the possible existence of series solutions we first write the equation in the standard form

➤
$$y'' + P(x)y' + Q(x)y = 0.$$

If $P(x)$ and $Q(x)$ are both analytic at $x = 0$, then $x = 0$ is an ordinary point, and the equation has two linearly independent power series solutions.

Otherwise, $x = 0$ is a singular point, and we next write the differential equation in the form

➤
$$y'' + \frac{p(x)}{x}y' + \frac{q(x)}{x^2}y = 0.$$

If $p(x)$ and $q(x)$ are both analytic at $x = 0$, then $x = 0$ is a regular singular point. In this case we find the two exponents r_1 and r_2 (assumed real, and with $r_1 \geqq r_2$) by solving the indicial equation

➤
$$r(r - 1) + p_0 r + q_0 = 0,$$

where $p_0 = p(0)$ and $q_0 = q(0)$. There always exists a Frobenius series solution $y = x^{r_1} \sum a_n x^n$ associated with the larger exponent r_1, and if $r_1 - r_2$ is not an integer, the existence of a second Frobenius series solution $y_2 = x^{r_2} \sum b_n x^n$ is also guaranteed.

8.3 Problems

In Problems 1 through 8, determine whether $x = 0$ is an ordinary point, a regular singular point, or an irregular singular point. If it is a regular singular point, find the exponents of the differential equation at $x = 0$.

1. $xy'' + (x - x^3)y' + (\sin x)y = 0$
2. $xy'' + x^2 y' + (e^x - 1)y = 0$
3. $x^2 y'' + (\cos x)y' + xy = 0$
4. $3x^3 y'' + 2x^2 y' + (1 - x^2)y = 0$
5. $x(1 + x)y'' + 2y' + 3xy = 0$
6. $x^2(1 - x^2)y'' + 2xy' - 2y = 0$
7. $x^2 y'' + (6\sin x)y' + 6y = 0$
8. $(6x + 2x^3)y'' + 21xy' + 9(x^2 - 1)y = 0$

If $x = a \neq 0$ is a singular point of a second-order linear differential equation, then the substitution $t = x - a$ transforms it into a differential equation having $t = 0$ as a singular point. We then attribute to the original equation at $x = a$ the behavior of the new equation at $t = 0$. Classify (as regular or irregular) the singular points of the differential equations in Problems 9 through 16.

9. $(1 - x)y'' + xy' + x^2 y = 0$
10. $(1 - x)^2 y'' + (2x - 2)y' + y = 0$
11. $(1 - x^2)y'' - 2xy' + 12y = 0$
12. $(x - 2)^3 y'' + 3(x - 2)^2 y' + x^3 y = 0$
13. $(x^2 - 4)y'' + (x - 2)y' + (x + 2)y = 0$
14. $(x^2 - 9)^2 y'' + (x^2 + 9)y' + (x^2 + 4)y = 0$
15. $(x - 2)^2 y'' - (x^2 - 4)y' + (x + 2)y = 0$

16. $x^3(1 - x)y'' + (3x + 2)y' + xy = 0$

Find two linearly independent Frobenius series solutions (for $x > 0$) of each of the differential equations in Problems 17 through 26.

17. $4xy'' + 2y' + y = 0$
18. $2xy'' + 3y' - y = 0$
19. $2xy'' - y' - y = 0$
20. $3xy'' + 2y' + 2y = 0$
21. $2x^2 y'' + xy' - (1 + 2x^2)y = 0$
22. $2x^2 y'' + xy' - (3 - 2x^2)y = 0$
23. $6x^2 y'' + 7xy' - (x^2 + 2)y = 0$
24. $3x^2 y'' + 2xy' + x^2 y = 0$
25. $2xy'' + (1 + x)y' + y = 0$
26. $2xy'' + (1 - 2x^2)y' - 4xy = 0$

Use the method of Example 6 to find two linearly independent Frobenius series solutions of the differential equations in Problems 27 through 31. Then construct a graph showing their graphs for $x > 0$.

27. $xy'' + 2y' + 9xy = 0$
28. $xy'' + 2y' - 4xy = 0$
29. $4xy'' + 8y' + xy = 0$
30. $xy'' - y' + 4x^3 y = 0$
31. $4x^2 y'' - 4xy' + (3 - 4x^2)y = 0$

In Problems 32 through 34, find the first three nonzero terms of each of two linearly independent Frobenius series solutions.

32. $2x^2y'' + x(x+1)y' - (2x+1)y = 0$

33. $(2x^2 + 5x^3)y'' + (3x - x^2)y' - (1+x)y = 0$

34. $2x^2y'' + (\sin x)y' - (\cos x)y = 0$

35. Note that $x = 0$ is an irregular point of the equation

$$x^2y'' + (3x - 1)y' + y = 0.$$

(a) Show that $y = x^r \sum c_n x^n$ can satisfy this equation only if $r = 0$. **(b)** Substitute $y = \sum c_n x^n$ to derive the "formal" solution $y = \sum n! x^n$. What is the radius of convergence of this series?

36. (a) Suppose that A and B are nonzero constants. Show that the equation $x^2y'' + Ay' + By = 0$ has at most one solution of the form $y = x^r \sum c_n x^n$. **(b)** Repeat part (a) with the equation $x^3y'' + Axy' + By = 0$. **(c)** Show that the equation $x^3y'' + Ax^2y' + By = 0$ has no Frobenius series solution. (*Suggestion:* In each case substitute $y = x^r \sum c_n x^n$ in the given equation to determine the possible values of r.)

37. (a) Use the method of Frobenius to derive the solution $y_1 = x$ of the equation $x^3y'' - xy' + y = 0$. **(b)** Verify by substitution the second solution $y_2 = xe^{-1/x}$. Does y_2 have a Frobenius series representation?

38. Apply the method of Frobenius to Bessel's equation of order $\frac{1}{2}$,

$$x^2y'' + xy' + \left(x^2 - \tfrac{1}{4}\right)y = 0,$$

to derive its general solution for $x > 0$,

$$y(x) = c_0\frac{\cos x}{\sqrt{x}} + c_1\frac{\sin x}{\sqrt{x}}.$$

Figure 8.3.2 shows the graphs of the two indicated solutions.

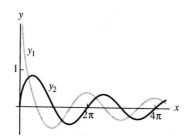

FIGURE 8.3.2. The solutions $y_1(x) = \dfrac{\cos x}{\sqrt{x}}$ and $y_2(x) = \dfrac{\sin x}{\sqrt{x}}$ in Problem 38.

39. (a) Show that Bessel's equation of order 1,

$$x^2y'' + xy' + (x^2 - 1)y = 0,$$

has exponents $r_1 = 1$ and $r_2 = -1$ at $x = 0$, and that the Frobenius series corresponding to $r_1 = 1$ is

$$J_1(x) = \frac{x}{2}\sum_{n=0}^{\infty}\frac{(-1)^n x^{2n}}{n!\,(n+1)!\,2^{2n}}.$$

(b) Show that there is no Frobenius solution corresponding to the smaller exponent $r_2 = -1$; that

is, show that it is impossible to determine the coefficients in

$$y_2(x) = x^{-1}\sum_{n=0}^{\infty}c_n x^n.$$

40. Consider the equation $x^2y'' + xy' + (1-x)y = 0$. **(a)** Show that its exponents are $\pm i$, so it has complex-valued Frobenius series solutions

$$y_+ = x^i\sum_{n=0}^{\infty}p_n x^n \quad \text{and} \quad y_- = x^{-i}\sum_{n=0}^{\infty}q_n x^n$$

with $p_0 = q_0 = 1$. **(b)** Show that the recursion formula is

$$c_n = \frac{c_{n-1}}{n^2 + 2rn}.$$

Apply this formula with $r = i$ to obtain $p_n = c_n$, then with $r = -i$ to obtain $q_n = c_n$. Conclude that p_n and q_n are complex conjugates: $p_n = a_n + ib_n$ and $q_n = a_n - ib_n$, where the numbers $\{a_n\}$ and $\{b_n\}$ are real. **(c)** Deduce from part (b) that the differential equation given in this problem has real-valued solutions of the form

$$y_1(x) = A(x)\cos(\ln x) - B(x)\sin(\ln x),$$
$$y_2(x) = A(x)\sin(\ln x) + B(x)\cos(\ln x),$$

where $A(x) = \sum a_n x^n$ and $B(x) = \sum b_n x^n$.

41. Consider the differential equation

$$x(x-1)(x+1)^2y'' + 2x(x-3)(x+1)y' - 2(x-1)y = 0$$

that appeared in an advertisement for a symbolic algebra program in the March 1984 issue of the *American Mathematical Monthly*. **(a)** Show that $x = 0$ is a regular singular point with exponents $r_1 = 1$ and $r_2 = 0$. **(b)** It follows from Theorem 1 that this differential equation has a power series solution of the form

$$y_1(x) = x + c_2 x^2 + c_3 x^3 + \cdots.$$

Substitute this series (with $c_1 = 1$) in the differential equation to show that $c_2 = -2$, $c_3 = 3$, and

$$c_{n+2} = \frac{(n^2 - n)c_{n-1} + (n^2 - 5n - 2)c_n - (n^2 + 7n + 4)c_{n+1}}{(n+1)(n+2)}$$

for $n \geq 2$. **(c)** Use the recurrence relation in part (b) to prove by induction that $c_n = (-1)^{n+1}n$ for $n \geq 1$ (!). Hence deduce (using the geometric series) that

$$y_1(x) = \frac{x}{(1+x)^2}$$

for $0 < x < 1$.

42. This problem is a brief introduction to Gauss's **hypergeometric equation**

$$x(1-x)y'' + [\gamma - (\alpha + \beta + 1)x]y' - \alpha\beta y = 0, \qquad (35)$$

where α, β, and γ are constants. This famous equation has wide-ranging applications in mathematics and physics. **(a)** Show that $x = 0$ is a regular singular point of Eq. (35), with exponents 0 and $1 - \gamma$. **(b)** If γ is not zero or a negative integer, it follows (why?) that Eq. (35) has a power series solution

$$y(x) = x^0 \sum_{n=0}^{\infty} c_n x^n = \sum_{n=0}^{\infty} c_n x^n$$

with $c_0 \neq 0$. Show that the recurrence relation for this series is

$$c_{n+1} = \frac{(\alpha + n)(\beta + n)}{(\gamma + n)(1 + n)} c_n$$

for $n \geq 0$. **(c)** Conclude that with $c_0 = 1$ the series in part (b) is

$$y(x) = 1 + \sum_{n=0}^{\infty} \frac{\alpha_n \beta_n}{n! \, \gamma_n} x^n \qquad (36)$$

where $\alpha_n = \alpha(\alpha + 1)(\alpha + 2)\cdots(\alpha + n - 1)$ for $n \geq 1$, and β_n and γ_n are defined similarly. **(d)** The series in (36) is known as the **hypergeometric series** and is commonly denoted by $F(\alpha, \beta, \gamma, x)$. Show that

(i) $F(1, 1, 1, x) = \dfrac{1}{1 - x}$ (the geometric series);

(ii) $xF(1, 1, 2, -x) = \ln(1 + x)$;

(iii) $xF\left(\frac{1}{2}, 1, \frac{3}{2}, -x^2\right) = \tan^{-1} x$;

(iv) $F(-k, 1, 1, -x) = (1 + x)^k$ (the binomial series).

8.3 Application: Automating the Frobenius Series Method

Here we illustrate the use of a computer algebra system such as *Maple* to apply the method of Frobenius. More complete versions of this application—illustrating the use of *Maple*, *Mathematica*, and MATLAB—can be found in the computing applications manual that accompanies this text. We consider the differential equation

$$2x^2 y'' + 3xy' - (x^2 + 1)y = 0 \qquad (1)$$

of Example 4 in this section, where we found the two indicial roots $r_1 = \frac{1}{2}$ and $r_2 = -1$.

Beginning with the indicial root $r_1 = \frac{1}{2}$, we first write the initial seven terms of a proposed Frobenius series solution:

```
a := array(0..6):
y := x^(1/2)*sum( a[n]*x^(n), n = 0..6);
```

$$y := \sqrt{x}\left(a_0 + a_1 x + a_2 x^2 + a_3 x^3 + a_4 x^4 + a_5 x^5 + a_6 x^6\right)$$

Then we substitute this series (actually, partial sum) into the left-hand side of Eq. (1).

```
deq1 := 2*x^2*diff(y,x$2) + 3*x*diff(y,x) - (x^2 + 1)*y:
```

Evidently $x^{3/2}$ will factor out upon simplification, so we multiply by $x^{-3/2}$ and then collect coefficients of like powers of x.

```
deq2 := collect( x^(-3/2)*simplify(deq1), x);
```

$$deq2 := -x^7 a_6 - x^6 a_5 + (90a_6 - a_4)x^5 + (-a_3 + 65a_5)x^4$$
$$+ (-a_2 + 44a_4)x^3 + (-a_1 + 27a_3)x^2 + (14a_2 - a_0)x + 5a_1$$

We see here the equations that the successive coefficients must satisfy. We can select them automatically by defining an array, then filling the elements of this array by equating to zero (in turn) each of the coefficients in the series.

```
eqs := array(0..5):
for n from 0 to 5 do
    eqs[n] := coeff(deq1,x,n) = 0: od:
coeffEqs := convert(eqs, set);
```

$$coeffEqs := \{5a_1 = 0, \; -a_2 + 44a_4 = 0, \; -a_3 + 65a_5 = 0,$$
$$90a_6 - a_4 = 0, \; 14a_2 - a_0 = 0, \; -a_1 + 27a_3 = 0\}$$

We now have a collection of six linear equations relating the seven coefficients (a_0 through a_6). Hence we can proceed to solve for the successive coefficients in terms of a_0.

```
succCoeffs := convert([seq(a[n], n=1..6)], set);
ourCoeffs := solve(coeffEqs, succCoeffs);
```

$$ourCoeffs := \left\{ a_1 = 0, \; a_6 = \frac{1}{55440}a_0, \; a_4 = \frac{1}{616}a_0, \right.$$

$$\left. a_2 = \frac{1}{14}a_0, \; a_5 = 0, \; a_3 = 0 \right\}$$

Thus we get the first particular solution

$$y_1(x) = a_0 x^{1/2} \left(1 + \frac{x^2}{14} + \frac{x^4}{616} + \frac{x^6}{55440} + \cdots \right)$$

found in Example 4. You can now repeat this process, beginning with the indicial root $r_2 = -1$, to derive similarly the second particular solution.

In the following problems, use this method to derive Frobenius series solutions that can be checked against the given known general solutions.

1. $xy'' - y' + 4x^3 y = 0$, $\quad y(x) = A\cos x^2 + B\sin x^2$
2. $xy'' - 2y' + 9x^5 y = 0$, $\quad y(x) = A\cos x^3 + B\sin x^3$
3. $4xy'' - 2y' + y = 0$, $\quad y(x) = A\cos\sqrt{x} + B\sin\sqrt{x}$
4. $xy'' + 2y' + xy = 0$, $\quad y(x) = \frac{1}{x}(A\cos x + B\sin x)$
5. $4xy'' + 6y' + y = 0$, $\quad y(x) = \frac{1}{\sqrt{x}}\left(A\cos\sqrt{x} + B\sin\sqrt{x}\right)$
6. $x^2 y'' + xy' + (4x^4 - 1)y = 0$, $\quad y(x) = \frac{1}{x}(A\cos x^2 + B\sin x^2)$
7. $xy'' + 3y' + 4x^3 y = 0$, $\quad y(x) = \frac{1}{x^2}(A\cos x^2 + B\sin x^2)$
8. $x^2 y'' + x^2 y' - 2y = 0$, $\quad y(x) = \frac{1}{x}[A(2 - x) + B(2 + x)e^{-x}]$

Problems 9 through 11 involve the arctangent series

$$\tan^{-1} x = x - \frac{x^3}{3} + \frac{x^5}{5} - \frac{x^7}{7} + \cdots .$$

9. $(x + x^3)y'' + (2 + 4x^2)y' + 2xy = 0$, $\quad y(x) = \frac{1}{x}(A + B\tan^{-1} x)$

10. $(2x + 2x^2)y'' + (3 + 5x)y' + y = 0$, $\quad y(x) = \frac{1}{\sqrt{x}}\left(A + B\tan^{-1}\sqrt{x}\right)$

11. $(x + x^5)y'' + (3 + 7x^4)y' + 8x^3 y = 0$, $\quad y(x) = \frac{1}{x^2}(A + B\tan^{-1} x^2)$

8.4 Method of Frobenius: The Exceptional Cases

We continue our discussion of the equation

$$y'' + \frac{p(x)}{x}y' + \frac{q(x)}{x^2}y = 0 \qquad (1)$$

where $p(x)$ and $q(x)$ are analytic at $x = 0$, and $x = 0$ is a regular singular point. If the roots r_1 and r_2 of the indicial equation

$$\phi(r) = r(r-1) + p_0 r + q_0 = 0 \qquad (2)$$

do not differ by an integer, then Theorem 1 of Section 8.3 guarantees that Eq. (1) has two linearly independent Frobenius series solutions. We consider now the more complex situation in which $r_1 - r_2$ is an integer. If $r_1 = r_2$, then there is only one exponent available, and thus there can be only one Frobenius series solution. But we saw in Example 6 of Section 8.3 that if $r_1 = r_2 + N$, with N a positive integer, then it is possible that a second Frobenius series solution exists. We will also see that it is possible that such a solution does not exist. In fact, the second solution involves $\ln x$ when it is not a Frobenius series. As you will see in Examples 3 and 4, these exceptional cases occur in the solution of Bessel's equation. For applications, this is the most important second-order linear differential equation with variable coefficients.

The Nonlogarithmic Case with $r_1 = r_2 + N$

In Section 8.3 we derived the indicial equation by substituting the power series $p(x) = \sum p_n x^n$ and $q(x) = \sum q_n x^n$ and the Frobenius series

$$y(x) = x^r \sum_{n=0}^{\infty} c_n x^n = \sum_{n=0}^{\infty} c_n x^{n+r} \qquad (c_0 \neq 0) \qquad (3)$$

in the differential equation in the form

$$x^2 y'' + xp(x)y' + q(x)y = 0. \qquad (4)$$

The result of this substitution, after collection of the coefficients of like powers of x, is an equation of the form

$$\sum_{n=0}^{\infty} F_n(r)x^{n+r} = 0 \qquad (5)$$

in which the coefficients depend on r. It turns out that the coefficient of x^r is

$$F_0(r) = [r(r-1) + p_0 r + q_0]c_0 = \phi(r)c_0, \qquad (6)$$

which gives the indicial equation because $c_0 \neq 0$ by assumption; also, for $n \geq 1$, the coefficient of x^{n+r} has the form

$$F_n(r) = \phi(r+n)c_n + L_n(r; c_0, c_1, \ldots, c_{n-1}). \qquad (7)$$

Here L_n is a certain linear combination of $c_0, c_1, \ldots, c_{n-1}$. Although the exact formula is not necessary for our purposes, it happens that

$$L_n = \sum_{k=0}^{n-1} [(r+k)p_{n-k} + q_{n-k}]c_k. \tag{8}$$

Because all the coefficients in (5) must vanish for the Frobenius series to be a solution of Eq. (4), it follows that the exponent r and the coefficients $c_0, c_1, \ldots, c_n$ must satisfy the equation

$$\phi(r+n)c_n + L_n(r; c_0, c_1, \ldots, c_{n-1}) = 0. \tag{9}$$

This is a *recurrence relation* for c_n in terms of $c_0, c_1, \ldots, c_{n-1}$.

Now suppose that $r_1 = r_2 + N$ with N a positive integer. If we use the larger exponent r_1 in Eq. (9), then the coefficient $\phi(r_1 + n)$ of c_n will be nonzero for every $n \geq 1$ because $\phi(r) = 0$ only when $r = r_1$ and when $r = r_2 < r_1$. Once $c_0, c_1, \ldots, c_{n-1}$ have been determined, we therefore can solve Eq. (9) for c_n and continue to compute successive coefficients in the Frobenius series solution corresponding to the exponent r_1.

But when we use the smaller exponent r_2, there is a potential difficulty in computing c_N. For in this case $\phi(r_2 + N) = 0$, so Eq. (9) becomes

$$0 \cdot c_N + L_N(r_2; c_0, c_1, \ldots, c_{N-1}) = 0. \tag{10}$$

At this stage $c_0, c_1, \ldots, c_{N-1}$ have already been determined. If it happens that

$$L_N(r_2; c_0, c_1, \ldots, c_{N-1}) = 0,$$

then we can choose c_N arbitrarily and continue to determine the remaining coefficients in a second Frobenius series solution. But if it happens that

$$L_N(r_2; c_0, c_1, \ldots, c_{N-1}) \neq 0,$$

then Eq. (10) is not satisfied with any choice of c_N; in this case there cannot exist a second Frobenius series solution corresponding to the smaller exponent r_2. Examples 1 and 2 illustrate these two possibilities.

Example 1

Consider the equation

$$x^2 y'' + (6x + x^2)y' + xy = 0. \tag{11}$$

Here $p_0 = 6$ and $q_0 = 0$, so the indicial equation is

$$\phi(r) = r(r-1) + 6r = r^2 + 5r = 0 \tag{12}$$

with roots $r_1 = 0$ and $r_2 = -5$; the roots differ by the integer $N = 5$. We substitute the Frobenius series $y = \sum c_n x^{n+r}$ and get

$$\sum_{n=0}^{\infty} (n+r)(n+r-1)c_n x^{n+r} + 6 \sum_{n=0}^{\infty} (n+r)c_n x^{n+r}$$

$$+ \sum_{n=0}^{\infty} (n+r)c_n x^{n+r+1} + \sum_{n=0}^{\infty} c_n x^{n+r+1} = 0.$$

When we combine the first two and also the last two sums, and in the latter shift the index by -1, the result is

$$\sum_{n=0}^{\infty}[(n+r)^2+5(n+r)]c_nx^{n+r}+\sum_{n=1}^{\infty}(n+r)c_{n-1}x^{n+r}=0.$$

The terms corresponding to $n=0$ give the indicial equation in (12), whereas for $n \geq 1$ we get the equation

$$[(n+r)^2+5(n+r)]c_n+(n+r)c_{n-1}=0, \tag{13}$$

which in this example corresponds to the general solution in (9). Note that the coefficient of c_n is $\phi(n+r)$.

We now follow the recommendation in Section 8.3 for the case $r_1=r_2+N$: We begin with the smaller root $r_2=-5$. With $r_2=-5$, Eq. (13) reduces to

$$\blacktriangleright \qquad\qquad n(n-5)c_n+(n-5)c_{n-1}=0. \tag{14}$$

If $n \neq 5$, we can solve this equation for c_n to obtain the recurrence relation

$$\blacktriangleright \qquad\qquad c_n=-\frac{c_{n-1}}{n}\qquad\text{for }n\neq 5. \tag{15}$$

This yields

$$c_1=-c_0, \qquad\qquad\qquad c_2=-\frac{c_1}{2}=\frac{c_0}{2},$$

$$c_3=-\frac{c_2}{3}=-\frac{c_0}{6}, \qquad\text{and}\qquad c_4=-\frac{c_3}{4}=\frac{c_0}{24}. \tag{16}$$

In the case $r_1=r_2+N$, it is always the coefficient c_N that requires special consideration. Here $N=5$, and for $n=5$ Eq. (14) takes the form $0 \cdot c_5+0=0$. Hence c_5 is a second arbitrary constant, and we can compute additional coefficients, still using the recursion formula in (15):

$$c_6=-\frac{c_5}{6}, \quad c_7=-\frac{c_6}{7}=\frac{c_5}{6\cdot 7}, \quad c_8=-\frac{c_7}{8}=-\frac{c_5}{6\cdot 7\cdot 8}, \tag{17}$$

and so on.

When we combine the results in (16) and (17), we get

$$y=x^{-5}\sum_{n=0}^{\infty}c_nx^n$$

$$=c_0x^{-5}\left(1-x+\frac{x^2}{2}-\frac{x^3}{6}+\frac{x^4}{24}\right)$$

$$+c_5x^{-5}\left(x^5-\frac{x^6}{6}+\frac{x^7}{6\cdot 7}-\frac{x^8}{6\cdot 7\cdot 8}+\cdots\right)$$

in terms of the two arbitrary constants c_0 and c_5. Thus we have found the two Frobenius series solutions

$$y_1(x)=x^{-5}\left(1-x+\frac{x^2}{2}-\frac{x^3}{6}+\frac{x^4}{24}\right)$$

and

$$y_2(x) = 1 + \sum_{n=1}^{\infty} \frac{(-1)^n x^n}{6 \cdot 7 \cdots (n+5)} = 1 + 120 \sum_{n=1}^{\infty} \frac{(-1)^n x^n}{(n+5)!}$$

of Eq. (11). ∎

Example 2   Determine whether or not the equation

$$x^2 y'' - xy' + (x^2 - 8)y = 0 \tag{18}$$

has two linearly independent Frobenius series solutions.

Solution   Here $p_0 = -1$ and $q_0 = -8$, so the indicial equation is

$$\phi(r) = r(r-1) - r - 8 = r^2 - 2r - 8 = 0$$

with roots $r_1 = 4$ and $r_2 = -2$ differing by $N = 6$. On substitution of $y = \sum c_n x^{n+r}$ in Eq. (18), we get

$$\sum_{n=0}^{\infty} (n+r)(n+r-1)c_n x^{n+r} - \sum_{n=0}^{\infty} (n+r)c_n x^{n+r}$$

$$+ \sum_{n=0}^{\infty} c_n x^{n+r+2} - 8 \sum_{n=0}^{\infty} c_n x^{n+r} = 0.$$

If we shift the index by -2 in the third sum and combine the other three sums, we get

$$\sum_{n=0}^{\infty} [(n+r)^2 - 2(n+r) - 8]c_n x^{n+r} + \sum_{n=2}^{\infty} c_{n-2} x^{n+r} = 0.$$

The coefficient of x^r gives the indicial equation, and the coefficient of x^{r+1} gives

$$\left[(r+1)^2 - 2(r+1) - 8\right] c_1 = 0.$$

Because the coefficient of c_1 is nonzero both for $r = 4$ and for $r = -2$, it follows that $c_1 = 0$ in each case. For $n \geq 2$ we get the equation

➤ $$\left[(n+r)^2 - 2(n+r) - 8\right] c_n + c_{n-2} = 0, \tag{19}$$

which corresponds in this example to the general equation in (9); note that the coefficient of c_n is $\phi(n+r)$.

We work first with the smaller root $r = r_2 = -2$. Then Eq. (19) becomes

➤ $$n(n-6)c_n + c_{n-2} = 0 \tag{20}$$

for $n \geq 2$. For $n \neq 6$ we can solve for the recurrence relation

➤ $$c_n = -\frac{c_{n-2}}{n(n-6)} \qquad (n \geq 2,\ n \neq 6). \tag{21}$$

Because $c_1 = 0$, this formula gives

$$c_2 = \frac{c_0}{8}, \qquad\qquad c_3 = 0,$$

$$c_4 = \frac{c_2}{8} = \frac{c_0}{64}, \qquad \text{and} \qquad c_5 = 0.$$

Now Eq. (20) with $n = 6$ reduces to

$$0 \cdot c_6 + \frac{c_0}{64} = 0.$$

But $c_0 \neq 0$ by assumption, and hence there is no way to choose c_6 so that this equation holds. Thus there is *no* Frobenius series solution corresponding to the smaller root $r_2 = -2$.

To find the single Frobenius series solution corresponding to the larger root $r_1 = 4$, we substitute $r = 4$ in Eq. (19) to obtain the recurrence relation

$$\blacktriangleright \qquad\qquad c_n = -\frac{c_{n-2}}{n(n+6)} \qquad (n \geq 2). \qquad\qquad (22)$$

This gives

$$c_2 = -\frac{c_0}{2 \cdot 8}, \quad c_4 = -\frac{c_2}{4 \cdot 10} = \frac{c_0}{2 \cdot 4 \cdot 8 \cdot 10}.$$

The general pattern is

$$c_{2n} = \frac{(-1)^n c_0}{2 \cdot 4 \cdots (2n) \cdot 8 \cdot 10 \cdots (2n+6)} = \frac{(-1)^n 6 c_0}{2^{2n} n! \, (n+3)!}.$$

This yields the Frobenius series solution

$$y_1(x) = x^4 \left(1 + 6 \sum_{n=1}^{\infty} \frac{(-1)^n x^{2n}}{2^{2n} n! \, (n+3)!} \right)$$

of Eq. (18). ∎

Reduction of Order

When only a single Frobenius series solution exists, we need an additional technique. We discuss here the method of **reduction of order**, which enables us to use one known solution y_1 of a second-order homogeneous linear differential equation to find a second linearly independent solution y_2. Consider the second-order equation

$$\blacktriangleright \qquad\qquad y'' + P(x)y' + Q(x)y = 0 \qquad\qquad (23)$$

on an open interval I on which P and Q are continuous. Suppose that we know one solution y_1 of Eq. (23). By Theorem 2 of Section 3.1, there exists a second linearly independent solution y_2; our problem is to find y_2. Equivalently, we would like to find the quotient

$$v(x) = \frac{y_2(x)}{y_1(x)}. \qquad\qquad (24)$$

Once we know $v(x)$, y_2 will then be given by

$$y_2(x) = v(x)y_1(x). \tag{25}$$

We begin by substituting the expression in (25) in Eq. (23), using the derivatives

$$y_2' = vy_1' + v'y_1 \quad \text{and} \quad y_2'' = vy_1'' + 2v'y_1' + v''y_1.$$

We get

$$\left[vy_1'' + 2v'y_1' + v''y_1 \right] + P \left[vy_1' + v'y_1 \right] + Qvy_1 = 0,$$

and rearrangement gives

$$v \left[y_1'' + Py_1' + Qy_1 \right] + v''y_1 + 2v'y_1' + Pv'y_1 = 0.$$

But the bracketed expression in this last equation vanishes because y_1 is a solution of Eq. (23). This leaves the equation

$$v''y_1 + (2y_1' + Py_1)v' = 0. \tag{26}$$

The key to the success of this method is that Eq. (26) is *linear* in v'. Thus the substitution in (25) has reduced the second-order linear equation in (23) to the first-order (in v') linear equation in (26). If we write $u = v'$ and assume that $y_1(x)$ never vanishes on I, then Eq. (26) yields

$$u' + \left(2\frac{y_1'}{y_1} + P(x) \right) u = 0. \tag{27}$$

An integrating factor for Eq. (27) is

$$\rho = \exp \left(\int \left(2\frac{y_1'}{y_1} + P(x) \right) dx \right) = \exp \left(2 \ln |y_1| + \int P(x)\, dx \right);$$

thus

$$\rho(x) = y_1^2 \exp \left(\int P(x)\, dx \right).$$

We now integrate the equation in (27) to obtain

$$uy_1^2 \exp \left(\int P(x)\, dx \right) = C, \quad \text{so} \quad v' = u = \frac{C}{y_1^2} \exp \left(-\int P(x)\, dx \right).$$

Another integration now gives

$$\frac{y_2}{y_1} = v = C \int \frac{\exp \left(-\int P(x)\, dx \right)}{y_1^2}\, dx + K.$$

With the particular choices $C = 1$ and $K = 0$, we get

➤
$$y_2 = y_1 \int \frac{\exp \left(-\int P(x)\, dx \right)}{y_1^2}\, dx. \tag{28}$$

This formula provides a second solution $y_2(x)$ of Eq. (23) on any interval where $y_1(x)$ is never zero. Note that because an exponential function never vanishes, $y_2(x)$ is a nonconstant multiple of $y_1(x)$, so y_1 and y_2 are linearly independent solutions.

The Logarithmic Cases

We now investigate the general form of the second solution of the equation

$$\blacktriangleright \qquad y'' + \frac{p(x)}{x} y' + \frac{q(x)}{x^2} y = 0, \qquad (1)$$

under the assumption that its exponents r_1 and $r_2 = r_1 - N$ differ by the integer $N \geq 0$. We assume that we have already found the Frobenius series solution

$$\blacktriangleright \qquad y_1(x) = x^{r_1} \sum_{n=0}^{\infty} a_n x^n \qquad (a_0 \neq 0) \qquad (29)$$

for $x > 0$ corresponding to the larger exponent r_1. Let us write $P(x)$ for $p(x)/x$ and $Q(x)$ for $q(x)/x^2$. Thus we can rewrite Eq. (1) in the form $y'' + Py' + Qy = 0$ of Eq. (23).

Because the indicial equation has roots r_1 and $r_2 = r_1 - N$, it can be factored easily:

$$r^2 + (p_0 - 1)r + q_0 = (r - r_1)(r - r_1 + N)$$
$$= r^2 + (N - 2r_1)r + (r_1^2 - r_1 N) = 0,$$

so we see that

$$p_0 - 1 = N - 2r_1;$$

that is,

$$-p_0 - 2r_1 = -1 - N. \qquad (30)$$

In preparation for use of the reduction of order formula in (28), we write

$$P(x) = \frac{p_0 + p_1 x + p_2 x^2 + \cdots}{x} = \frac{p_0}{x} + p_1 + p_2 x + \cdots.$$

Then

$$\exp\left(-\int P(x)\,dx\right) = \exp\left(-\int \left[\frac{p_0}{x} + p_1 + p_2 x + \cdots\right] dx\right)$$
$$= \exp\left(-p_0 \ln x - p_1 x - \tfrac{1}{2} p_2 x^2 - \cdots\right)$$
$$= x^{-p_0} \exp\left(-p_1 x - \tfrac{1}{2} p_2 x^2 - \cdots\right),$$

so that

$$\exp\left(-\int P(x)\,dx\right) = x^{-p_0}\left(1 + A_1 x + A_2 x^2 + \cdots\right). \qquad (31)$$

In the last step we have used the fact that a composition of analytic functions is analytic and therefore has a power series representation; the initial coefficient of that series in (31) is 1 because $e^0 = 1$.

We now substitute (29) and (31) in (28); with the choice $a_0 = 1$ in (29), this yields

$$y_2 = y_1 \int \frac{x^{-p_0}\left(1 + A_1 x + A_2 x^2 + \cdots\right)}{x^{2r_1}\left(1 + a_1 x + a_2 x^2 + \cdots\right)^2} \, dx.$$

We expand the denominator and simplify:

$$y_2 = y_1 \int \frac{x^{-p_0 - 2r_1} \left(1 + A_1 x + A_2 x^2 + \cdots \right)}{1 + B_1 x + B_2 x^2 + \cdots} \, dx$$

$$= y_1 \int x^{-1-N} \left(1 + C_1 x + C_2 x^2 + \cdots \right) dx \tag{32}$$

(we used long division and (30) in the last step). We now consider separately the cases $N = 0$ and $N > 0$. We want to ascertain the general form of y_2 without keeping track of specific coefficients.

CASE 1: EQUAL EXPONENTS ($r_1 = r_2$). With $N = 0$, Eq. (32) gives

$$y_2 = y_1 \int \left(\frac{1}{x} + C_1 + C_2 x^2 + \cdots \right) dx$$

$$= y_1 \ln x + y_1 \left(C_1 x + \tfrac{1}{2} C_2 x^2 + \cdots \right)$$

$$= y_1 \ln x + x^{r_1} (1 + a_1 x + \cdots) \left(C_1 x + \tfrac{1}{2} C_2 x^2 + \cdots \right)$$

$$= y_1 \ln x + x^{r_1} \left(b_0 x + b_1 x^2 + b_2 x^3 + \cdots \right).$$

Consequently, in the case of equal exponents, the general form of y_2 is

➤
$$y_2(x) = y_1(x) \ln x + x^{1+r_1} \sum_{n=0}^{\infty} b_n x^n. \tag{33}$$

Note the logarithmic term; it is always present when $r_1 = r_2$.

CASE 2: POSITIVE INTEGRAL DIFFERENCE ($r_1 = r_2 + N$). With $N > 0$, Eq. (32) gives

$$y_2 = y_1 \int x^{-1-N} \left(1 + C_1 x + C_2 x^2 + \cdots + C_N x^N + \cdots \right) dx$$

$$= y_1 \int \left(\frac{C_N}{x} + \frac{1}{x^{N+1}} + \frac{C_1}{x^N} + \cdots \right) dx$$

$$= C_N y_1 \ln x + y_1 \left(\frac{x^{-N}}{-N} + \frac{C_1 x^{-N+1}}{-N+1} + \cdots \right)$$

$$= C_N y_1 \ln x + x^{r_2 + N} \left(\sum_{n=0}^{\infty} a_n x^n \right) x^{-N} \left(-\frac{1}{N} + \frac{C_1 x}{-N+1} + \cdots \right),$$

so that

➤
$$y_2(x) = C_N y_1(x) \ln x + x^{r_2} \sum_{n=0}^{\infty} b_n x^n, \tag{34}$$

where $b_0 = -a_0/N \neq 0$. This gives the general form of y_2 in the case of exponents differing by a positive integer. Note the coefficient C_N that appears in (34) but not in (33). If it happens that $C_N = 0$, then there is no logarithmic term; if so, Eq. (1) has a second Frobenius series solution (as in Example 1).

In our derivation of Eqs. (33) and (34)—which exhibit the general form of the second solution in the cases $r_1 = r_2$ and $r_1 - r_2 = N > 0$, respectively—we have said nothing about the radii of convergence of the various power series that appear. Theorem 1 (next) is a summation of the preceding discussion and also tells where the series in (33) and (34) converge. As in Theorem 1 of Section 8.3, we restrict our attention to solutions for $x > 0$.

THEOREM 1: The Exceptional Cases

Suppose that $x = 0$ is a regular singular point of the equation

$$x^2 y'' + x p(x) y' + q(x) y = 0. \tag{4}$$

Let $\rho > 0$ denote the minimum of the radii of convergence of the power series

$$p(x) = \sum_{n=0}^{\infty} p_n x^n \quad \text{and} \quad q(x) = \sum_{n=0}^{\infty} q_n x^n.$$

Let r_1 and r_2 be the roots, with $r_1 \geqq r_2$, of the indicial equation

$$r(r-1) + p_0 r + q_0 = 0.$$

(a) If $r_1 = r_2$, then Eq. (4) has two solutions y_1 and y_2 of the forms

➤ $$y_1(x) = x^{r_1} \sum_{n=0}^{\infty} a_n x^n \qquad (a_0 \neq 0) \tag{35a}$$

and

➤ $$y_2(x) = y_1(x) \ln x + x^{r_1+1} \sum_{n=0}^{\infty} b_n x^n. \tag{35b}$$

(b) If $r_1 - r_2 = N$, a positive integer, then Eq. (4) has two solutions y_1 and y_2 of the forms

➤ $$y_1(x) = x^{r_1} \sum_{n=0}^{\infty} a_n x^n \qquad (a_0 \neq 0) \tag{36a}$$

and

➤ $$y_2(x) = C y_1(x) \ln x + x^{r_2} \sum_{n=0}^{\infty} b_n x^n. \tag{36b}$$

In Eq. (36b), $b_0 \neq 0$ but C may be either zero or nonzero, so the logarithmic term may or may not actually be present in this case. The radii of convergence of the power series of this theorem are all at least ρ. The coefficients in these series (and the constant C in Eq. (36b)) may be determined by direct substitution of the series in the differential equation in (4). ▲

Example 3 We will illustrate the case $r_1 = r_2$ by deriving the second solution of Bessel's equation of order zero,

$$x^2 y'' + xy' + x^2 y = 0, \tag{37}$$

for which $r_1 = r_2 = 0$. In Example 5 of Section 8.3 we found the first solution

$$y_1(x) = J_0(x) = \sum_{n=0}^{\infty} \frac{(-1)^n x^{2n}}{2^{2n}(n!)^2} \tag{38}$$

According to Eq. (35b) the second solution will have the form

$$y_2 = y_1 \ln x + \sum_{n=1}^{\infty} b_n x^n. \tag{39}$$

The first two derivatives of y_2 are

$$y_2' = y_1' \ln x + \frac{y_1}{x} + \sum_{n=1}^{\infty} nb_n x^{n-1}$$

and

$$y_2'' = y_1'' \ln x + \frac{2y_1'}{x} - \frac{y_1}{x^2} + \sum_{n=2}^{\infty} n(n-1)b_n x^{n-2}.$$

We substitute these in Eq. (37) and use the fact that $J_0(x)$ also satisfies this equation to obtain

$$
\begin{aligned}
0 &= x^2 y_2'' + xy_2' + x^2 y_2 \\
&= \left[x^2 y_1'' + xy_1' + x^2 y_1 \right] \ln x + 2xy_1' \\
&\quad + \sum_{n=2}^{\infty} n(n-1)b_n x^n + \sum_{n=1}^{\infty} nb_n x^n + \sum_{n=1}^{\infty} b_n x^{n+2},
\end{aligned}
$$

and it follows that

$$0 = 2\sum_{n=1}^{\infty} \frac{(-1)^n 2n x^{2n}}{2^{2n}(n!)^2} + b_1 x + 2^2 b_2 x^2 + \sum_{n=3}^{\infty} (n^2 b_n + b_{n-2}) x^n. \tag{40}$$

The only term involving x in Eq. (40) is $b_1 x$, so $b_1 = 0$. But $n^2 b_n + b_{n-2} = 0$ if n is odd, and it follows that all the coefficients of odd subscript in y_2 vanish.

Now we examine the coefficients with even subscripts in Eq. (40). First we see that

$$b_2 = -2 \cdot \frac{(-1)(2)}{2^2 \cdot 2^2 \cdot (1!)^2} = \frac{1}{4}. \tag{41}$$

For $n \geq 2$, we read the recurrence relation

$$(2n)^2 b_{2n} + b_{2n-2} = -\frac{(2)(-1)^n (2n)}{2^{2n}(n!)^2} \tag{42}$$

from (40). Nonhomogeneous recurrence relations such as (42) are typical of the exceptional cases of the method of Frobenius, and their solution often requires a bit of ingenuity. The usual strategy depends on detecting the most conspicuous dependence of b_{2n} on n. We note the presence of $2^{2n}(n!)^2$ on the right-hand side in (42); in conjunction with the coefficient $(2n)^2$ on the left-hand side, we are induced to think of b_{2n} as *something* divided by $2^{2n}(n!)^2$. Noting also the alternation of sign, we make the substitution

$$b_{2n} = \frac{(-1)^{n+1} c_{2n}}{2^{2n}(n!)^2},\tag{43}$$

in the expectation that the recurrence relation for c_{2n} will be simpler than the one for b_{2n}. We chose $(-1)^{n+1}$ rather than $(-1)^n$ because $b_2 = \frac{1}{4} > 0$; with $n = 1$ in (43), we get $c_2 = 1$. Substitution of (43) in (42) gives

$$(2n)^2 \frac{(-1)^{n+1} c_{2n}}{2^{2n}(n!)^2} + \frac{(-1)^n c_{2n-2}}{2^{2n-2}[(n-1)!]^2} = \frac{(-2)(-2)^n(2n)}{2^{2n}(n!)^2},$$

which boils down to the extremely simple recurrence relation

$$c_{2n} = c_{2n-2} + \frac{1}{n}.$$

Thus

$$c_4 = c_2 + \frac{1}{2} = 1 + \frac{1}{2},$$

$$c_6 = c_4 + \frac{1}{3} = 1 + \frac{1}{2} + \frac{1}{3},$$

$$c_8 = c_6 + \frac{1}{4} = 1 + \frac{1}{2} + \frac{1}{3} + \frac{1}{4},$$

and so on. Evidently,

$$c_{2n} = 1 + \frac{1}{2} + \frac{1}{3} + \cdots + \frac{1}{n} = H_n,\tag{44}$$

where we denote by H_n the nth partial sum of the harmonic series $\sum(1/n)$.

Finally, keeping in mind that the coefficients of odd subscript are all zero, we substitute (43) and (44) in (39) to obtain the second solution

$$y_2(x) = J_0(x) \ln x + \sum_{n=1}^{\infty} \frac{(-1)^{n+1} H_n x^{2n}}{2^{2n}(n!)^2}$$

$$= J_0(x) \ln x + \frac{x^2}{4} - \frac{3x^4}{128} + \frac{11x^6}{13824} - \cdots\tag{45}$$

of Bessel's equation of order zero. The power series in (45) converges for all x. The most commonly used linearly independent [of $J_0(x)$] second solution is

$$Y_0(x) = \frac{2}{\pi}(\gamma - \ln 2)y_1 + \frac{2}{\pi}y_2;$$

that is,

$$Y_0(x) = \frac{2}{\pi} \left[\left(\gamma + \ln \frac{x}{2} \right) J_0(x) + \sum_{n=1}^{\infty} \frac{(-1)^{n+1} H_n x^{2n}}{2^{2n}(n!)^2} \right], \tag{46}$$

where γ denotes *Euler's constant*:

$$\gamma = \lim_{n \to \infty} (H_n - \ln n) \approx 0.57722. \tag{47}$$

This particular combination $Y_0(x)$ is chosen because of its nice behavior as $x \to +\infty$; it is called the **Bessel function of order zero of the second kind.** ∎

Example 4

As an alternative to the method of substitution, we illustrate the case $r_1 - r_2 = N$ by employing the technique of reduction of order to derive a second solution of Bessel's equation of order 1,

$$x^2 y'' + xy' + (x^2 - 1)y = 0; \tag{48}$$

the associated indicial equation has roots $r_1 = 1$ and $r_2 = -1$. According to Problem 39 of Section 8.3, one solution of Eq. (48) is

$$y_1(x) = J_1(x) = \frac{x}{2} \sum_{n=0}^{\infty} \frac{(-1)^n x^{2n}}{2^{2n} n! \, (n+1)!} = \frac{x}{2} - \frac{x^3}{16} + \frac{x^5}{384} - \frac{x^7}{18432} + \cdots. \tag{49}$$

With $P(x) = 1/x$ from (48), the reduction of order formula in (28) yields

$$y_2 = y_1 \int \frac{1}{xy_1^2} \, dx$$

$$= y_1 \int \frac{1}{x(x/2 - x^3/16 + x^5/384 - x^7/18432 + \cdots)^2} \, dx$$

$$= y_1 \int \frac{4}{x^3(1 - x^2/8 + x^4/192 - x^6/9216 + \cdots)^2} \, dx$$

$$= 4y_1 \int \frac{1}{x^3(1 - x^2/4 + 5x^4/192 - 7x^6/4608 + \cdots)} \, dx$$

$$= 4y_1 \int \frac{1}{x^3} \left(1 + \frac{x^2}{4} + \frac{7x^4}{192} + \frac{19x^6}{4608} + \cdots \right) dx$$

$$= 4y_1 \int \left(\frac{1}{4x} + \frac{1}{x^3} + \frac{7x}{192} + \frac{19x^3}{4608} + \cdots \right) dx$$

$$= y_1 \ln x + 4y_1 \left(-\frac{1}{2x^2} + \frac{7x^2}{384} + \frac{19x^4}{18432} + \cdots \right).$$

Thus

$$y_2(x) = y_1(x) \ln x - \frac{1}{x} + \frac{x}{8} + \frac{x^3}{32} - \frac{11x^5}{4608} + \cdots. \tag{50}$$

Note that the technique of reduction of order readily yields the first several terms of the series, but does not provide a recurrence relation that can be used to determine the general term of the series.

With a computation similar to that shown in Example 3 (but more complicated —see Problem 21), the method of substitution can be used to derive the solution

$$y_3(x) = y_1(x) \ln x - \frac{1}{x} + \sum_{n=1}^{\infty} \frac{(-1)^n (H_n + H_{n-1}) x^{2n-1}}{2^{2n} n! (n-1)!}, \tag{51}$$

where H_n is defined in (44) for $n \geq 1$; $H_0 = 0$. The reader can verify that the terms shown in Eq. (50) agree with

$$y_2(x) = \frac{3}{4} J_1(x) + y_3(x). \tag{52}$$

The most commonly used linearly independent [of J_1] solution of Bessel's equation of order 1 is the combination

$$Y_1(x) = \frac{2}{\pi}(\gamma - \ln 2) y_1(x) + \frac{2}{\pi} y_3(x)$$

$$= \frac{2}{\pi} \left[\left(\gamma + \ln \frac{x}{2} \right) J_1(x) - \frac{1}{x} + \sum_{n=1}^{\infty} \frac{(-1)^n (H_n + H_{n-1}) x^{2n-1}}{2^{2n} n! (n-1)!} \right]. \tag{53}$$

Examples 3 and 4 illustrate two methods of finding the solution in the logarithmic cases—direct substitution and reduction of order. A third alternative is outlined in Problem 19.

8.4 Problems

In Problems 1 through 8, either apply the method of Example 1 to find two linearly independent Frobenius series solutions, or find one such solution and show (as in Example 2) that a second such solution does not exist.

1. $xy'' + (3 - x)y' - y = 0$
2. $xy'' + (5 - x)y' - y = 0$
3. $xy'' + (5 + 3x)y' + 3y = 0$
4. $5xy'' + (30 + 3x)y' + 3y = 0$
5. $xy'' - (4 + x)y' + 3y = 0$
6. $2xy'' - (6 + 2x)y' + y = 0$
7. $x^2y'' + (2x + 3x^2)y' - 2y = 0$
8. $x(1 - x)y'' - 3y' + 2y = 0$

In Problems 9 through 14, first find the first four nonzero terms in a Frobenius series solution of the given differential equation. Then use the reduction of order technique (as in Example 4) to find the logarithmic term and the first three nonzero terms in a second linearly independent solution.

9. $xy'' + y' - xy = 0$
10. $x^2y'' - xy' + (x^2 + 1)y = 0$
11. $x^2y'' + (x^2 - 3x)y' + 4y = 0$

12. $x^2y'' + x^2y' - 2y = 0$
13. $x^2y'' + (2x^2 - 3x)y' + 3y = 0$
14. $x^2y'' + x(1 + x)y' - 4y = 0$
15. Begin with

$$J_0(x) = 1 - \frac{x^2}{4} + \frac{x^4}{64} - \frac{x^6}{2304} + \cdots.$$

Using the method of reduction of order, derive the second linearly independent solution

$$y_2(x) = J_0(x) \ln x + \frac{x^2}{4} - \frac{3x^4}{128} + \frac{11x^6}{13284} - \cdots$$

of Bessel's equation of order zero.
16. Find two linearly independent Frobenius series solutions of Bessel's equation of order $\frac{3}{2}$,

$$x^2y'' + xy' + \left(x^2 - \frac{9}{4} \right) y = 0.$$

17. **(a)** Verify that $y_1(x) = xe^x$ is one solution of

$$x^2y'' - x(1 + x)y' + y = 0.$$

(b) Note that $r_1 = r_2 = 1$. Substitute

$$y_2 = y_1 \ln x + \sum_{n=1}^{\infty} b_n x^{n+1}$$

in the differential equation to deduce that $b_1 = -1$ and that

$$nb_n - b_{n-1} = -\frac{1}{n!} \quad \text{for } n \geq 2.$$

(c) Substitute $b_n = c_n/n!$ in this recurrence relation and conclude from the result that $c_n = -H_n$. Thus the second solution is

$$y_2(x) = xe^x \ln x - \sum_{n=1}^{\infty} \frac{H_n x^{n+1}}{n!}.$$

18. Consider the equation $xy'' - y = 0$, which has exponents $r_1 = 1$ and $r_2 = 0$ at $x = 0$. **(a)** Derive the Frobenius series solution

$$y_1(x) = \sum_{n=1}^{\infty} \frac{x^n}{n!\,(n-1)!}.$$

(b) Substitute

$$y_2 = Cy_1 \ln x + \sum_{n=0}^{\infty} b_n x^n$$

in the equation $xy'' - y = 0$ to derive the recurrence relation

$$n(n+1)b_{n+1} - b_n = -\frac{2n+1}{(n+1)!\,n!}C.$$

Conclude from this result that a second solution is

$$y_2(x) = y_1(x) \ln x + 1 - \sum_{n=1}^{\infty} \frac{H_n + H_{n-1}}{n!\,(n-1)!} x^n.$$

19. Suppose that the differential equation

$$L[y] = x^2 y'' + xp(x)y' + q(x)y = 0 \tag{54}$$

has equal exponents $r_1 = r_2$ at the regular singular point $x = 0$, so that its indicial equation is

$$\phi(r) = (r - r_1)^2 = 0.$$

Let $c_0 = 1$ and define $c_n(r)$ for $n \geq 1$ by using Eq. (9); that is,

$$c_n(r) = -\frac{L_n(r; c_0, c_1, \ldots, c_{n-1})}{\phi(r+n)}. \tag{55}$$

Then define the function $y(x,r)$ of x and r to be

$$y(x,r) = \sum_{n=0}^{\infty} c_n(r)x^{n+r}. \tag{56}$$

(a) Deduce from the discussion preceding Eq. (9) that

$$L[y(x,r)] = x^r(r - r_1)^2. \tag{57}$$

Hence deduce that

$$y_1 = y(x, r_1) = \sum_{n=0}^{\infty} c_n(r_1)x^{n+r_1} \tag{58}$$

is one solution of Eq. (54). **(b)** Differentiate Eq. (57) with respect to r to show that

$$L[y_r(x, r_1)] = \frac{\partial}{\partial r}\left[x^r(r - r_1)^2 \right]\Bigg|_{r=r_1} = 0.$$

Deduce that $y_2 = y_r(x, r_1)$ is a second solution of Eq. (54). **(c)** Differentiate Eq. (58) with respect to r to show that

$$y_2 = y_1 \ln x + x^{r_1} \sum_{n=1}^{\infty} c_n'(r_1)x^n. \tag{59}$$

20. Use the method of Problem 19 to derive both the solutions in (38) and (45) of Bessel's equation of order zero. The following steps outline this computation. **(a)** Take $c_0 = 1$; show that Eq. (55) reduces in this case to

$$(r+1)^2 c_1(r) = 0 \quad \text{and}$$
$$c_n(r) = -\frac{c_{n-2}(r)}{(n+r)^2} \quad \text{for } n \geq 2. \tag{60}$$

(b) Next show that $c_1(0) = c_1'(0) = 0$, and then deduce from (60) that $c_n(0) = c_n'(0) = 0$ for n odd. Hence you need to compute $c_n(0)$ and $c_n'(0)$ only for n even. **(c)** Deduce from (60) that

$$c_{2n}(r) = \frac{(-1)^n}{(r+2)^2(r+4)^2 \cdots (r+2n)^2}. \tag{61}$$

With $r = r_1 = 0$ in (58), this gives $J_0(x)$. **(d)** Differentiate (61) to show that

$$c_{2n}'(0) = \frac{(-1)^{n+1}H_n}{2^{2n}(n!)^2}.$$

Substitution of this result in (59) gives the second solution in (45).

21. Derive the logarithmic solution in (51) of Bessel's equation of order 1 by the method of substitution. The following steps outline this computation. **(a)** Substitute

$$y_2 = CJ_1(x) \ln x + x^{-1}\left(1 + \sum_{n=1}^{\infty} b_n x^n\right)$$

in Bessel's equation to obtain

$$-b_1 + x + \sum_{n=2}^{\infty}[(n^2 - 1)b_{n+1} + b_{n-1}]x^n$$
$$+ C\left[x + \sum_{n=1}^{\infty} \frac{(-1)^n(2n+1)x^{2n+1}}{2^{2n}(n+1)!\,n!}\right] = 0. \tag{62}$$

(b) Deduce from Eq. (62) that $C = -1$ and that $b_n = 0$ for n odd. **(c)** Next deduce the recurrence relation

$$\left[(2n+1)^2 - 1\right] b_{2n+2} + b_{2n} = \frac{(-1)^n(2n+1)}{2^{2n}(n+1)!\,n!} \qquad (63)$$

for $n \geq 1$. Note that if b_2 is chosen arbitrarily, then b_{2n} is determined for all $n > 1$. **(d)** Take $b_2 = \frac{1}{4}$ and substitute

$$b_{2n} = \frac{(-1)^n c_{2n}}{2^{2n}(n-1)!\,n!}$$

in Eq. (63) to obtain

$$c_{2n+2} - c_{2n} = \frac{1}{n+1} + \frac{1}{n}.$$

(e) Note that $c_2 = 1 = H_1 + H_0$ and deduce that

$$c_{2n} = H_n + H_{n-1}.$$

8.4 Application: The Exceptional Case by Reduction of Order

Here we illustrate the use of a computer algebra system such as *Mathematica* to implement the reduction of order formula in Eq. (28) of this section. More complete versions of this application—using *Maple*, *Mathematica*, and MATLAB—can be found in the computing applications manual that accompanies this text. To illustrate the method, we will derive a second solution of Bessel's equation of order zero, beginning with the known power series solution

$$J_0(x) = \sum_{n=0}^{\infty}(-1)^n \frac{x^{2n}}{2^{2n}(n!)^2},$$

which we enter in the form

```
y1 = Sum[ ((-x^2/4)^n) / (n!)^2, {n, 0, 5}] + O[x]^12
```

Then with

```
P = 1/x;
```

we need only substitute in the integral in Eq. (28):

```
integral = Integrate[ Exp[ -Integrate[P,x]]/y1^2, x ]
```

$$\log(x) + \frac{x^2}{4} + \frac{5x^4}{128} + \frac{23x^6}{3456} + \frac{677x^8}{589824} + \frac{7313x^{10}}{36864000} + O(x^{12})$$

Then—multiplying `J0 = y1` times the logarithm and the series terms separately—the computation

```
y2 = J0*Log[x] + y1*(integral - Log[x])
```

yields the second solution

$$J_0(x)\log(x) + \frac{x^2}{4} - \frac{3x^4}{128} + \frac{11x^6}{13824} - \frac{25x^8}{1769472} + \frac{137x^{10}}{884736000} + O(x^{12})$$

of Bessel's equation of order zero (as we see it in Eq. (45) of the text).

After verifying (with your computer algebra system) the computations we present here, you can begin with the power series for $J_1(x)$ in Eq. (49) of this section and derive similarly the second solution in (50) of Bessel's equation of order 1. Problems 9 through 14 can also be partially automated in this way.

8.5 Bessel's Equation

We have already seen several cases of Bessel's equation of order $p \geqq 0$,

$$x^2 y'' + xy' + (x^2 - p^2)y = 0. \tag{1}$$

Its solutions are now called Bessel functions of order p. Such functions first appeared in the 1730s in the work of Daniel Bernoulli and Euler on the oscillations of a vertically suspended chain. The equation itself appears in a 1764 article by Euler on the vibrations of a circular drumhead, and Fourier used Bessel functions in his classical treatise on heat (1822). But their general properties were first studied systematically in an 1824 memoir by the German astronomer and mathematician Friedrich W. Bessel (1784–1846), who was investigating the motion of planets. The standard source of information on Bessel functions is G. N. Watson's *A Treatise on the Theory of Bessel Functions*, 2nd ed. (Cambridge: Cambridge University Press, 1944). Its 36 pages of references, which cover only the period up to 1922, give some idea of the vast literature of this subject.

Bessel's equation in (1) has indicial equation $r^2 - p^2 = 0$, with roots $r = \pm p$. If we substitute $y = \sum c_m x^{m+r}$ in Eq. (1), we find in the usual manner that $c_1 = 0$ and that

$$\left[(m+r)^2 - p^2 \right] c_m + c_{m-2} = 0 \tag{2}$$

for $m \geqq 2$. The verification of Eq. (2) is left to the reader (Problem 6).

The Case $r = p > 0$

If we use $r = p$ and write a_m in place of c_m, then Eq. (2) yields the recursion formula

$$a_m = -\frac{a_{m-2}}{m(2p+m)}. \tag{3}$$

Because $a_1 = 0$, it follows that $a_m = 0$ for all odd values of m. The first few even coefficients are

$$a_2 = -\frac{a_0}{2(2p+2)} = -\frac{a_0}{2^2(p+1)},$$

$$a_4 = -\frac{a_2}{4(2p+4)} = \frac{a_0}{2^4 \cdot 2(p+1)(p+2)},$$

$$a_6 = -\frac{a_4}{6(2p+6)} = -\frac{a_0}{2^6 \cdot 2 \cdot 3(p+1)(p+2)(p+3)}.$$

The general pattern is

$$a_{2m} = \frac{(-1)^m a_0}{2^{2m} m! \, (p+1)(p+2) \cdots (p+m)},$$

so with the larger root $r = p$ we get the solution

$$y_1(x) = a_0 \sum_{m=0}^{\infty} \frac{(-1)^m x^{2m+p}}{2^{2m} m! \, (p+1)(p+2) \cdots (p+m)}. \tag{4}$$

If $p = 0$ this is the only Frobenius series solution; with $a_0 = 1$ as well, it is the function $J_0(x)$ we have seen before.

The Case $r = -p < 0$

If we use $r = -p$ and write b_m in place of c_m, Eq. (2) takes the form

$$m(m - 2p)b_m + b_{m-2} = 0 \tag{5}$$

for $m \geq 2$, whereas $b_1 = 0$. We see that there is a potential difficulty if it happens that $2p$ is a positive integer—that is, if p is either a positive integer or an odd positive integral multiple of $\frac{1}{2}$. For then when $m = 2p$, Eq. (5) is simply $0 \cdot b_m + b_{m-2} = 0$. Thus if $b_{m-2} \neq 0$, then no value of b_m can satisfy this equation.

But if p is an odd positive integral multiple of $\frac{1}{2}$, we can circumvent this difficulty. For suppose that $p = k/2$ where k is an odd positive integer. Then we need only choose $b_m = 0$ for all odd values of m. The crucial step is the kth step,

$$k(k - k)b_k + b_{k-2} = 0;$$

and this equation will hold because $b_k = b_{k-2} = 0$.

Hence if p is *not* a positive integer, we take $b_m = 0$ for m odd and define the coefficients of even subscript in terms of b_0 by means of the recursion formula

$$b_m = -\frac{b_{m-2}}{m(m - 2p)}, \qquad m \geq 2. \tag{6}$$

In comparing (6) with (3), we see that (6) will lead to the same result as that in (4), except with p replaced with $-p$. Thus in this case we obtain the second solution

$$y_2(x) = b_0 \sum_{m=0}^{\infty} \frac{(-1)^m x^{2m-p}}{2^{2m} m! \, (-p + 1)(-p + 2) \cdots (-p + m)}. \tag{7}$$

The series in (4) and (7) converge for all $x > 0$ because $x = 0$ is the only singular point of Bessel's equation. If $p > 0$, then the leading term in y_1 is $a_0 x^p$, whereas the leading term in y_2 is $b_0 x^{-p}$. Hence $y_1(0) = 0$, but $y_2(x) \to \pm\infty$ as $x \to 0$, so it is clear that y_1 and y_2 are linearly independent solutions of Bessel's equation of order $p > 0$.

The Gamma Function

The formulas in (4) and (7) can be simplified by use of the **gamma function** $\Gamma(x)$, which is defined for $x > 0$ by

$$\Gamma(x) = \int_0^{\infty} e^{-t} t^{x-1} \, dt. \tag{8}$$

It is not difficult to show that this improper integral converges for each $x > 0$. The gamma function is a generalization for $x > 0$ of the factorial function $n!$, which is defined only if n is a nonnegative integer. To see the way in which $\Gamma(x)$ is a generalization of $n!$, we note first that

$$\Gamma(1) = \int_0^{\infty} e^{-t} \, dt = \lim_{b \to \infty} \left[-e^{-t} \right]_0^b = 1. \tag{9}$$

Then we integrate by parts with $u = t^x$ and $dv = e^{-t}\,dt$:

$$\Gamma(x+1) = \lim_{b \to \infty} \int_0^b e^{-t} t^x\,dt = \lim_{b \to \infty} \left(\left[-e^{-t} t^x \right]_0^b + \int_0^b x e^{-t} t^{x-1}\,dt \right)$$

$$= x \left(\lim_{b \to \infty} \int_0^b e^{-t} t^{x-1}\,dt \right);$$

that is,

$$\Gamma(x+1) = x\Gamma(x). \tag{10}$$

This is the most important property of the gamma function.

If we combine Eqs. (9) and (10), we see that

$$\Gamma(2) = 1 \cdot \Gamma(1) = 1!, \quad \Gamma(3) = 2 \cdot \Gamma(2) = 2!, \quad \Gamma(4) = 3 \cdot \Gamma(3) = 3!,$$

and in general that

$$\Gamma(n+1) = n! \qquad \text{for } n \geq 0 \text{ an integer.} \tag{11}$$

An important special value of the gamma function is

$$\Gamma\left(\tfrac{1}{2}\right) = \int_0^\infty e^{-t} t^{-1/2}\,dt = 2 \int_0^\infty e^{-u^2}\,du = \sqrt{\pi}, \tag{12}$$

where we have substituted u^2 for t in the first integral; the fact that

$$\int_0^\infty e^{-u^2}\,du = \frac{\sqrt{\pi}}{2}$$

is known, but is far from obvious.

Although $\Gamma(x)$ is defined in (8) only for $x > 0$, we can use the recursion formula in (10) to define $\Gamma(x)$ whenever x is neither zero nor a negative integer. If $-1 < x < 0$, then

$$\Gamma(x) = \frac{\Gamma(x+1)}{x};$$

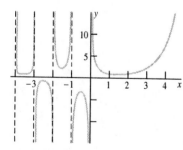

FIGURE 8.5.1. The graph of the extended gamma function.

the right-hand side is defined because $0 < x + 1 < 1$. The same formula may then be used to extend the definition of $\Gamma(x)$ to the open interval $(-2, -1)$, then to the open interval $(-3, -2)$, and so on. The graph of the gamma function thus extended is shown in Fig. 8.5.1. The student who would like to pursue this fascinating topic further should consult Artin's *The Gamma Function* (New York: Holt, Rinehart and Winston, 1964). In only 39 pages, this is one of the finest expositions in the entire literature of mathematics.

Bessel Functions of the First Kind

If we choose $a_0 = 1/[2^p\Gamma(p + 1)]$ in (4), where $p > 0$, and note that

$$\Gamma(p + m + 1) = (p + m)(p + m - 1)\cdots(p + 2)(p + 1)\Gamma(p + 1)$$

by repeated application of Eq. (10), we can write the **Bessel function of the first kind of order** p very concisely with the aid of the gamma function:

$$\blacktriangleright \qquad J_p(x) = \sum_{m=0}^{\infty} \frac{(-1)^m}{m!\,\Gamma(p + m + 1)}\left(\frac{x}{2}\right)^{2m+p}. \qquad (13)$$

Similarly, if $p > 0$ is not an integer, we choose $b_0 = 1/[2^{-p}\Gamma(-p + 1)]$ in (7) to obtain the linearly independent second solution

$$\blacktriangleright \qquad J_{-p}(x) = \sum_{m=0}^{\infty} \frac{(-1)^m}{m!\,\Gamma(-p + m + 1)}\left(\frac{x}{2}\right)^{2m-p} \qquad (14)$$

of Bessel's equation of order p. If p is not an integer, we have the general solution

$$y(x) = c_1 J_p(x) + c_2 J_{-p}(x) \qquad (15)$$

for $x > 0$; x^p must be replaced with $|x|^p$ in Eqs. (13) through (15) to get the correct solutions for $x < 0$.

If $p = n$, a nonnegative integer, then Eq. (13) gives

$$\blacktriangleright \qquad J_n(x) = \sum_{m=0}^{\infty} \frac{(-1)^m}{m!\,(m + n)!}\left(\frac{x}{2}\right)^{2m+n} \qquad (16)$$

for the Bessel functions of the first kind of integral order. Thus

$$J_0(x) = \sum_{m=0}^{\infty} \frac{(-1)^m x^{2m}}{2^{2m}(m!)^2} = 1 - \frac{x^2}{2^2} + \frac{x^4}{2^2 \cdot 4^2} - \frac{x^6}{2^2 \cdot 4^2 \cdot 6^2} + \cdots \qquad (17)$$

and

$$J_1(x) = \sum_{m=0}^{\infty} \frac{(-1)^m 2^{2m+1}}{2^{2m+1} m!\,(m + 1)!} = \frac{x}{2} - \frac{1}{2!}\left(\frac{x}{2}\right)^3 + \frac{1}{2!\cdot 3!}\left(\frac{x}{2}\right)^5 - \cdots. \qquad (18)$$

The graphs of $J_0(x)$ and $J_1(x)$ are shown in Fig. 8.5.2. In a general way they resemble damped cosine and sine oscillations, respectively (see Problem 27). Indeed, if you examine the series in (17), you can see part of the reason why $J_0(x)$ and $\cos x$ *might* be similar—only minor changes in the denominators in (17) are needed to produce the Taylor series for $\cos x$. As suggested by Fig. 8.5.2, the zeros of the functions $J_0(x)$ and $J_1(x)$ are *interlaced*—between any two consecutive zeros of $J_0(x)$ there is precisely one zero of $J_1(x)$ (Problem 26) and vice versa. The first four zeros of $J_0(x)$ are approximately 2.4048, 5.5201, 8.6537, and 11.7915. For n large, the nth zero of $J_0(x)$ is approximately $\left(n - \frac{1}{4}\right)\pi$; the nth zero of $J_1(x)$ is approximately $\left(n + \frac{1}{4}\right)\pi$. Thus the interval between consecutive zeros of either $J_0(x)$ or $J_1(x)$ is approximately π—another similarity with $\cos x$ and $\sin x$. You can see the way the accuracy of these approximations increases with increasing n by rounding the entries in the table in Fig. 8.5.3 to two decimal places.

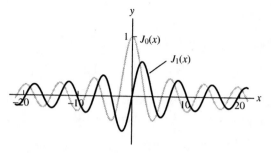

FIGURE 8.5.2. The graphs of the Bessel functions $J_0(x)$ and $J_1(x)$.

FIGURE 8.5.3. Zeros of $J_0(x)$ and $J_1(x)$.

n	nth zero of $J_0(x)$	$\left(n - \frac{1}{4}\right)\pi$	nth zero of $J_1(x)$	$\left(n + \frac{1}{4}\right)\pi$
1	2.4048	2.3562	3.8317	3.9270
2	5.5201	5.4978	7.0156	7.0686
3	8.6537	8.6394	10.1735	10.2102
4	11.7915	11.7810	13.3237	13.3518
5	14.9309	14.9226	16.4706	16.4934

It turns out that $J_p(x)$ is an elementary function if the order p is half an odd integer. For instance, on substitution of $p = \frac{1}{2}$ and $p = -\frac{1}{2}$ in Eqs. (13) and (14), respectively, the results can be recognized (Problem 2) as

$$J_{1/2}(x) = \sqrt{\frac{2}{\pi x}} \sin x \quad \text{and} \quad J_{-1/2}(x) = \sqrt{\frac{2}{\pi x}} \cos x. \qquad (19)$$

Bessel Functions of the Second Kind

The methods of Section 8.4 must be used to find linearly independent second solutions of integral order. A very complicated generalization of Example 3 in that section gives the formula

$$Y_n(x) = \frac{2}{\pi}\left(\gamma + \ln\frac{x}{2}\right) J_n(x) - \frac{1}{\pi}\sum_{m=0}^{n-1}\frac{2^{n-2m}(n-m-1)!}{m!\, x^{n-2m}}$$

$$- \frac{1}{\pi}\sum_{m=0}^{\infty}\frac{(-1)^m(H_m + H_{m+n})}{m!\,(m+n)!}\left(\frac{x}{2}\right)^{n+2m}, \qquad (20)$$

with the notation used there. If $n = 0$ then the first sum in (20) is taken to be zero. Here, $Y_n(x)$ is called the **Bessel function of the second kind of integral order** $n \geq 0$.

The general solution of Bessel's equation of integral order n is

$$y(x) = c_1 J_n(x) + c_2 Y_n(x). \qquad (21)$$

It is important to note that $Y_n(x) \to -\infty$ as $x \to 0$ (Fig. 8.5.4). Hence $c_2 = 0$ in Eq. (21) if $y(x)$ is continuous at $x = 0$. Thus if $y(x)$ is a *continuous* solution of Bessel's equation of order n, it follows that

$$y(x) = cJ_n(x)$$

for some constant c. Because $J_0(0) = 1$, we see in addition that if $n = 0$, then $c = y(0)$. In Section 10.4 we will see that this single fact regarding Bessel functions has numerous physical applications.

Figure 8.5.5 illustrates the fact that for $n > 1$ the graphs of $J_n(x)$ and $Y_n(x)$ look generally like those of $J_1(x)$ and $Y_1(x)$. In particular, $J_n(0) = 0$ while $Y_n(x) \to -\infty$ as $x \to 0^+$, and both functions undergo damped oscillation as $x \to +\infty$.

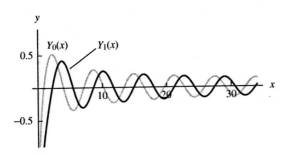

FIGURE 8.5.4. The graphs of the Bessel functions $Y_0(x)$ and $Y_1(x)$.

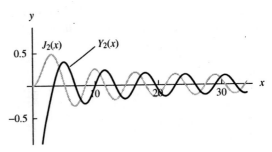

FIGURE 8.5.5. The graphs of the Bessel functions $J_2(x)$ and $Y_2(x)$.

Bessel Function Identities

Bessel functions are analogous to trigonometric functions in that they satisfy a large number of standard identities of frequent utility, especially in the evaluation of integrals involving Bessel functions. Differentiation of

$$J_p(x) = \sum_{m=0}^{\infty} \frac{(-1)^m}{m!\,\Gamma(p+m+1)} \left(\frac{x}{2}\right)^{2m+p} \tag{13}$$

in the case that p is a nonnegative integer gives

$$\frac{d}{dx}\left[x^p J_p(x)\right] = \frac{d}{dx} \sum_{m=0}^{\infty} \frac{(-1)^m x^{2m+2p}}{2^{2m+p} m!\,(p+m)!}$$

$$= \sum_{m=0}^{\infty} \frac{(-1)^m x^{2m+2p-1}}{2^{2m+p-1} m!\,(p+m-1)!}$$

$$= x^p \sum_{m=0}^{\infty} \frac{(-1)^m x^{2m+p-1}}{2^{2m+p-1} m!\,(p+m-1)!},$$

and thus we have shown that

$$\frac{d}{dx}\left[x^p J_p(x)\right] = x^p J_{p-1}(x). \tag{22}$$

Similarly,

$$\frac{d}{dx}\left[x^{-p} J_p(x)\right] = -x^{-p} J_{p+1}(x). \tag{23}$$

If we carry out the differentiations in Eqs. (22) and (23) and then divide the resulting identities by x^p and x^{-p}, respectively, we obtain (Problem 8) the identities

$$J_p'(x) = J_{p-1}(x) - \frac{p}{x} J_p(x) \tag{24}$$

and

$$J_p'(x) = \frac{p}{x} J_p(x) - J_{p+1}(x). \tag{25}$$

Thus we may express the derivatives of Bessel functions in terms of Bessel functions themselves. Subtraction of Eq. (25) from Eq. (24) gives the recursion formula

$$J_{p+1}(x) = \frac{2p}{x} J_p(x) - J_{p-1}(x),$$

(26)

which can be used to express Bessel functions of high order in terms of Bessel functions of lower orders. In the form

$$J_{p-1}(x) = \frac{2p}{x} J_p(x) - J_{p+1}(x),$$

(27)

it can be used to express Bessel functions of large negative order in terms of Bessel functions of numerically smaller negative orders.

The identities in Eqs. (22) through (27) hold wherever they are meaningful— that is, whenever no Bessel functions of negative integral order appear. In particular, they hold for all nonintegral values of p.

Example 1 With $p = 0$, Eq. (22) gives

$$\int x J_0(x)\, dx = x J_1(x) + C.$$

Similarly, with $p = 0$, Eq. (23) gives

$$\int J_1(x)\, dx = -J_0(x) + C.$$ ∎

Example 2 Using first $p = 2$ and then $p = 1$ in Eq. (26), we get

$$J_3(x) = \frac{4}{x} J_2(x) - J_1(x) = \frac{4}{x} \left[\frac{2}{x} J_1(x) - J_0(x) \right] - J_1(x),$$

so that

$$J_3(x) = -\frac{4}{x} J_0(x) + \left(\frac{8}{x^2} - 1 \right) J_1(x).$$

With similar manipulations every Bessel function of positive integral order can be expressed in terms of $J_0(x)$ and $J_1(x)$. ∎

Example 3 To antidifferentiate $x J_2(x)$, we first note that

$$\int x^{-1} J_2(x)\, dx = -x^{-1} J_1(x) + C$$

by Eq. (23) with $p = 1$. We therefore write

$$\int x J_2(x)\, dx = \int x^2 \left[x^{-1} J_2(x) \right] dx$$

and integrate by parts with

$$u = x^2, \qquad\qquad dv = x^{-1} J_2(x)\, dx,$$
$$du = 2x\, dx, \qquad \text{and} \qquad v = -x^{-1} J_1(x).$$

This gives

$$\int x J_2(x)\, dx = -x J_1(x) + 2 \int J_1(x)\, dx = -x J_1(x) - 2 J_0(x) + C,$$

with the aid of the second result of Example 1. ∎

The Parametric Bessel Equation

The **parametric Bessel equation of order** n is

$$x^2 y'' + xy' + (\alpha^2 x^2 - n^2)y = 0, \tag{28}$$

where α is a positive parameter. As we will see in Chapter 10, this equation appears in the solution of Laplace's equation in polar coordinates. It is easy to see (Problem 9) that the substitution $t = \alpha x$ transforms Eq. (28) into the (standard) Bessel equation

$$t^2 \frac{d^2 y}{dt^2} + t \frac{dy}{dt} + (t^2 - n^2)y = 0 \tag{29}$$

with general solution $y(t) = c_1 J_n(t) + c_2 Y_n(t)$. Hence the general solution of Eq. (28) is

$$y(x) = c_1 J_n(\alpha x) + c_2 Y_n(\alpha x). \tag{30}$$

Now consider the eigenvalue problem

$$
\begin{aligned}
x^2 y'' + xy' + (\lambda x^2 - n^2) &= 0, \\
y(L) &= 0
\end{aligned}
\tag{31}
$$

on the interval $[0, L]$. We seek the *positive* values of λ for which there exists a nontrivial solution of (31) that is *continuous* on $[0, L]$. If we write $\lambda = \alpha^2$, then the differential equation in (31) is that in Eq. (28), so its general solution is given in Eq. (30). Because $Y_n(x) \to -\infty$ as $x \to 0$ but $J_n(0)$ is finite, the continuity of $y(x)$ requires that $c_2 = 0$. Thus $y(x) = c_1 J_n(\alpha x)$. The endpoint condition $y(L) = 0$ now implies that $z = \alpha L$ must be a (positive) root of the equation

$$J_n(z) = 0. \tag{32}$$

For $n > 1$, $J_n(x)$ oscillates rather like $J_1(x)$ in Fig. 8.5.2 and hence has an infinite sequence of positive zeros $\gamma_{n1}, \gamma_{n2}, \gamma_{n3}, \ldots$ (see Fig 8.5.6). It follows that the kth positive eigenvalue of the problem in (31) is

$$\lambda_k = (\alpha_k)^2 = \frac{(\gamma_{nk})^2}{L^2}, \tag{33}$$

and that its associated eigenfunction is

$$y_k(x) = J_n\left(\frac{\gamma_{nk}}{L}x\right). \tag{34}$$

The roots γ_{nk} of Eq. (32) for $n \leq 8$ and $k \leq 20$ are tabulated in Table 9.5 of M. Abramowitz and I. A. Stegun, *Handbook of Mathematical Functions* (New York: Dover, 1965).

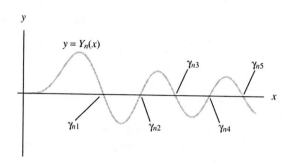

FIGURE 8.5.6. The positive zeros γ_{n1}, γ_{n2}, γ_{n3}, ... of the Bessel function $J_n(x)$.

8.5 Problems

1. Differentiate termwise the series for $J_0(x)$ to show directly that $J_0'(x) = -J_1(x)$ (another analogy with the cosine and sine functions).

2. (a) Deduce from Eqs. (10) and (12) that

$$\Gamma\left(n + \tfrac{1}{2}\right) = \frac{1 \cdot 3 \cdot 5 \cdots (2n - 1)}{2^n} \sqrt{\pi}.$$

(b) Use the result of part (a) to verify the formulas in Eq. (19) for $J_{1/2}(x)$ and $J_{-1/2}(x)$, and construct a figure showing the graphs of these functions.

3. (a) Suppose that m is a positive integer. Show that

$$\Gamma\left(m + \tfrac{2}{3}\right) = \frac{2 \cdot 5 \cdot 8 \cdots (3m - 1)}{3^m} \Gamma\left(\tfrac{2}{3}\right).$$

(b) Conclude from part (a) and Eq. (13) that

$$J_{-1/3}(x) =$$
$$\frac{(x/2)^{-1/3}}{\Gamma\left(\tfrac{2}{3}\right)} \left(1 + \sum_{m=1}^{\infty} \frac{(-1)^m 3^m x^{2m}}{2^{2m} m! \cdot 2 \cdot 5 \cdots (3m - 1)}\right).$$

4. Apply Eqs. (19), (26), and (27) to show that

$$J_{3/2}(x) = \sqrt{\frac{2}{\pi x^3}} (\sin x - x \cos x)$$

and

$$J_{-3/2}(x) = -\sqrt{\frac{2}{\pi x^3}} (\cos x + x \sin x).$$

Construct a figure showing the graphs of these two functions.

5. Express $J_4(x)$ in terms of $J_0(x)$ and $J_1(x)$.

6. Derive the recursion formula in Eq. (2) for Bessel's equation.

7. Verify the identity in (23) by termwise differentiation.

8. Deduce the identities in Eqs. (24) and (25) from those in Eqs. (22) and (23).

9. Verify that the substitution $t = \alpha x$ transforms the parametric Bessel equation in (28) into the equation in (29).

10. Show that

$$4J_p''(x) = J_{p-2}(x) - 2J_p(x) + J_{p+2}(x).$$

11. Use the relation $\Gamma(x + 1) = x\Gamma(x)$ to deduce from Eqs. (13) and (14) that if p is not a negative integer, then

$$J_p(x) =$$
$$\frac{(x/2)^p}{\Gamma(p + 1)} \left[1 + \sum_{m=1}^{\infty} \frac{(-1)^m (x/2)^{2m}}{m! \, (p + 1)(p + 2) \cdots (p + m)}\right].$$

This form is more convenient for the computation of $J_p(x)$ because only the single value $\Gamma(p+1)$ of the gamma function is required.

12. Use the series of Problem 11 to find $y(0) = \lim_{x \to 0} y(x)$ if

$$y(x) = x^2 \left[\frac{J_{5/2}(x) + J_{-5/2}(x)}{J_{1/2}(x) + J_{-1/2}(x)}\right].$$

Use a computer algebra system to graph $y(x)$ for x near 0. Does the graph corroborate your value of $y(0)$?

Any integral of the form $\int x^m J_n(x)\, dx$ can be evaluated in terms of Bessel functions and the indefinite integral $\int J_0(x)\, dx$. The latter integral cannot be simplified further, but the function $\int_0^x J_0(t)\, dt$ is tabulated in Table 11.1 of Abramowitz and Stegun. Use the identities in Eqs. (22) and (23) to evaluate the integrals in Problems 13 through 21.

13. $\int x^2 J_0(x)\, dx$

14. $\int x^3 J_0(x)\, dx$

15. $\int x^4 J_0(x)\, dx$

16. $\int x J_1(x)\, dx$

17. $\int x^2 J_1(x)\, dx$

18. $\int x^3 J_1(x)\, dx$

19. $\int x^4 J_1(x)\, dx$

20. $\int J_2(x)\, dx$

21. $\int J_3(x)\, dx$

22. Prove that

$$J_0(x) = \frac{1}{\pi} \int_0^\pi \cos(x \sin \theta) \, d\theta$$

by showing that the right-hand side satisfies Bessel's equation of order zero and has the value $J_0(0)$ when $x = 0$. Explain why this constitutes a proof.

23. Prove that

$$J_1(x) = \frac{1}{\pi} \int_0^\pi \cos(\theta - x \sin \theta) \, d\theta$$

by showing that the right-hand side satisfies Bessel's equation of order 1 and that its derivative has the value $J_1'(0)$ when $x = 0$. Explain why this constitutes a proof.

24. It can be shown that

$$J_n(x) = \frac{1}{\pi} \int_0^\pi \cos(n\theta - x \sin \theta) \, d\theta.$$

With $n \geqq 2$, show that the right-hand side satisfies Bessel's equation of order n and also agrees with the values $J_n(0)$ and $J_n'(0)$. Explain why this does *not* suffice to prove the preceding assertion.

25. Deduce from Problem 22 that

$$J_0(x) = \frac{1}{2\pi} \int_0^{2\pi} e^{ix \sin \theta} \, d\theta.$$

(*Suggestion*: Show first that

$$\int_0^{2\pi} e^{ix \sin \theta} \, d\theta = \int_0^\pi \left(e^{ix \sin \theta} + e^{-ix \sin \theta} \right) d\theta;$$

then use Euler's formula.)

26. Use Eqs. (22) and (23) and Rolle's theorem to prove that between any two consecutive zeros of $J_n(x)$ there is precisely one zero of $J_{n+1}(x)$. Use a computer algebra system to construct a figure illustrating this fact with $n = 10$ (for instance).

27. **(a)** Show that the substitution $y = x^{-1/2}z$ in Bessel's equation of order p,

$$x^2 y'' + xy' + (x^2 - p^2)y = 0,$$

yields

$$z'' + \left(1 - \frac{p^2 - \frac{1}{4}}{x^2} \right) z = 0.$$

(b) If x is so large that $\left(p^2 - \frac{1}{4} \right) / x^2$ is negligible, then the latter equation reduces to $z'' + z \approx 0$. Explain why this suggests (without proving it) that if $y(x)$ is a solution of Bessel's equation, then

$$y(x) \approx x^{-1/2}(A \cos x + B \sin x)$$
$$= Cx^{-1/2} \cos(x - \alpha) \tag{35}$$

with C and α constants, and x large.

Asymptotic Approximations

It is known that the choices $C = \sqrt{2/\pi}$ and $\alpha = (2n+1)\pi/4$ in (35) yield the best approximation to $J_n(x)$ for x large:

$$J_n(x) \approx \sqrt{\frac{2}{\pi x}} \cos\left(x - \tfrac{1}{4}(2n+1)\pi\right). \tag{36}$$

Similarly,

$$Y_n(x) \approx \sqrt{\frac{2}{\pi x}} \sin\left(x - \tfrac{1}{4}(2n+1)\pi\right). \tag{37}$$

In particular,

$$J_0(x) \approx \sqrt{\frac{2}{\pi x}} \cos\left(x - \tfrac{1}{4}\pi\right)$$

and

$$Y_0(x) \approx \sqrt{\frac{2}{\pi x}} \sin\left(x - \tfrac{1}{4}\pi\right)$$

if x is large. These are *asymptotic approximations* in that the ratio of the two sides in each approximation approaches unity as $x \to +\infty$.

8.6 Applications of Bessel Functions

The importance of Bessel functions stems not only from the frequent appearance of Bessel's equation in applications, but also from the fact that the solutions of many other second-order linear differential equations can be expressed in terms of Bessel functions. To see how this comes about, we begin with Bessel's equation of order p in the form

$$z^2 \frac{d^2 w}{dz^2} + z \frac{dw}{dz} + (z^2 - p^2)w = 0, \tag{1}$$

and substitute

$$w = x^{-\alpha} y, \qquad z = kx^\beta. \tag{2}$$

Then a routine (but lengthy) transformation of Eq. (1) yields

$$x^2 y'' + (1 - 2\alpha)xy' + (\alpha^2 - \beta^2 p^2 + \beta^2 k^2 x^{2\beta})y = 0;$$

that is,

➤
$$x^2 y'' + Axy' + (B + Cx^q)y = 0, \tag{3}$$

where the constants A, B, C, and q are given by

$$A = 1 - 2\alpha, \quad B = \alpha^2 - \beta^2 p^2, \quad C = \beta^2 k^2, \quad \text{and} \quad q = 2\beta. \tag{4}$$

It is a simple matter to solve the equations in (4) for

➤
$$\alpha = \frac{1 - A}{2}, \qquad \beta = \frac{q}{2}, $$
$$k = \frac{2\sqrt{C}}{q}, \qquad \text{and} \qquad p = \frac{\sqrt{(1 - A)^2 - 4B}}{q}. \tag{5}$$

Under the assumption that the square roots in (5) are real, it follows that the general solution of Eq. (3) is

$$y(x) = x^\alpha w(z) = x^\alpha w(kx^\beta),$$

where

$$w(z) = c_1 J_p(z) + c_2 Y_{-p}(z)$$

(assuming that p is not an integer) is the general solution of the Bessel equation in (1). This establishes the following result.

THEOREM 1: Solutions in Bessel Functions

If $C > 0$, $q \neq 0$, and $(1 - A)^2 \geqq 4B$, then the general solution (for $x > 0$) of Eq. (3) is

➤
$$y(x) = x^\alpha \left[c_1 J_p(kx^\beta) + c_2 J_{-p}(kx^\beta) \right], \tag{6}$$

where α, β, k, and p are given by the equations in (5). If p is an integer, then J_{-p} is to be replaced with Y_p. ▲

Example 1   Solve the equation

$$4x^2 y'' + 8xy' + (x^4 - 3)y = 0. \tag{7}$$

Solution   To compare Eq. (7) with Eq. (3), we rewrite the former as

$$x^2 y'' + 2xy' + \left(-\tfrac{3}{4} + \tfrac{1}{4}x^4\right) y = 0$$

and see that $A = 2$, $B = -\tfrac{3}{4}$, $C = \tfrac{1}{4}$, and $q = 4$. Then the equations in (5) give $\alpha = -\tfrac{1}{2}$, $\beta = 2$, $k = \tfrac{1}{4}$, and $p = \tfrac{1}{2}$. Thus the general solution in (6) of Eq. (7) is

$$y(x) = x^{-1/2} \left[c_1 J_{1/2}\left(\tfrac{1}{4}x^2\right) + c_2 J_{-1/2}\left(\tfrac{1}{4}x^2\right) \right].$$

If we recall from Eq. (19) of Section 8.5 that

$$J_{1/2}(z) = \sqrt{\frac{2}{\pi z}} \sin z \quad \text{and} \quad J_{-1/2}(z) = \sqrt{\frac{2}{\pi z}} \cos z,$$

we see that a general solution of Eq. (7) can be written in the elementary form

$$y(x) = x^{-3/2} \left(A \cos \frac{x^2}{4} + B \sin \frac{x^2}{4} \right). \qquad \blacksquare$$

Example 2   Solve the Airy equation

$$y'' + 9xy = 0. \qquad (8)$$

Solution   First we rewrite the given equation in the form

$$x^2 y'' + 9x^3 y = 0.$$

This is the special case of Eq. (3) with $A = B = 0$, $C = 9$, and $q = 3$. It follows from the equations in (5) that $\alpha = \frac{1}{2}$, $\beta = \frac{3}{2}$, $k = 2$, and $p = \frac{1}{3}$. Thus the general solution of Eq. (8) is

$$y(x) = x^{1/2} \left[c_1 J_{1/3}(2x^{3/2}) + c_2 J_{-1/3}(2x^{3/2}) \right]. \qquad \blacksquare$$

Buckling of a Vertical Column

For a practical application, we now consider the problem of determining when a uniform vertical column will buckle under its own weight. We take $x = 0$ at the free top end of the column and $x = L > 0$ at its bottom; we assume that the bottom is rigidly imbedded in the ground, perhaps in concrete; see Fig. 8.6.1. Denote the angular deflection of the column at the point x by $\theta(x)$. From the theory of elasticity it follows that

$$EI \frac{d^2\theta}{dx^2} + g\rho x\theta = 0, \qquad (9)$$

FIGURE 8.6.1. The buckling column.

where E is the Young's modulus of the material of the column, I is its cross-sectional moment of inertia, ρ is the linear density of the column, and g is gravitational acceleration. The boundary conditions are

$$\theta'(0) = 0, \quad \theta(L) = 0. \qquad (10)$$

We will accept (9) and (10) as an appropriate statement of the problem and attempt to solve it in this form. With

$$\lambda = \gamma^2 = \frac{g\rho}{EI}, \qquad (11)$$

we have the eigenvalue problem

$$\theta'' + \gamma^2 x\theta = 0; \quad \theta'(0) = 0, \quad \theta(L) = 0. \qquad (12)$$

The column can buckle only if there is a nontrivial solution of (12); otherwise the column will remain in its undeflected vertical position.

The differential equation in (12) is an Airy equation similar to the one in Example 2. It has the form of Eq. (3) with $A = B = 0$, $C = \gamma^2$, and $q = 3$. The equations in (5) give $\alpha = \frac{1}{2}$, $\beta = \frac{3}{2}$, $k = \frac{2}{3}\gamma$, and $p = \frac{1}{3}$. So the general solution is

$$\theta(x) = x^{1/2}\left[c_1 J_{1/3}\left(\tfrac{2}{3}\gamma x^{3/2}\right) + c_2 J_{-1/3}\left(\tfrac{2}{3}\gamma x^{3/2}\right)\right]. \tag{13}$$

In order to apply the initial conditions, we substitute $p = \pm\frac{1}{3}$ in

$$J_p(x) = \sum_{m=0}^{\infty} \frac{(-1)^m}{m!\,\Gamma(p+m+1)}\left(\frac{x}{2}\right)^{2m+p},$$

and find after some simplifications that

$$\theta(x) = \frac{c_1\gamma^{1/3}}{3^{1/3}\Gamma\left(\tfrac{4}{3}\right)}\left(x - \frac{\gamma^2 x^4}{12} + \frac{\gamma^4 x^7}{504} - \cdots\right)$$

$$+ \frac{c_2 3^{1/3}}{\gamma^{1/3}\Gamma\left(\tfrac{2}{3}\right)}\left(1 - \frac{\gamma^2 x^3}{6} + \frac{\gamma^4 x^6}{180} - \cdots\right).$$

From this it is clear that the endpoint condition $\theta'(0) = 0$ implies that $c_1 = 0$, so

$$\theta(x) = c_2 x^{1/2} J_{-1/3}\left(\tfrac{2}{3}\gamma x^{3/2}\right). \tag{14}$$

The endpoint condition $\theta(L) = 0$ now gives

$$J_{-1/3}\left(\tfrac{2}{3}\gamma L^{3/2}\right) = 0. \tag{15}$$

Thus the column will buckle only if $z = \frac{2}{3}\gamma L^{3/2}$ is a root of the equation $J_{-1/3}(z) = 0$. The graph of

$$J_{-1/3}(z) = \frac{(z/2)^{-1/3}}{\Gamma\left(\tfrac{2}{3}\right)}\left(1 + \sum_{m=1}^{\infty} \frac{(-1)^m 3^m z^{2m}}{2^{2m}\, m!\cdot 2\cdot 5\cdots(3m-1)}\right) \tag{16}$$

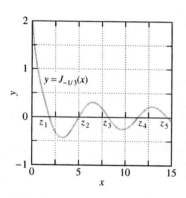

FIGURE 8.6.2. The graph of $J_{-1/3}(x)$.

(see Problem 3 of Section 8.5) is shown in Fig. 8.6.2, where we see that the smallest positive zero z_1 is a bit less than 2. Most technical computing systems can find roots like this one. For instance, each of the computer system commands

```
fsolve(BesselJ(-1/3,x)=0, x, 1..2)          (Maple)
FindRoot[BesselJ[-1/3,x]==0, {x,2}]          (Mathematica)
fzero('besselj(-1/3,x)', 2)                  (MATLAB)
```

yield the value $z_1 = 1.86635$ (rounded accurate to five decimal places).

The shortest length L_1 for which the column will buckle under its own weight is

$$L_1 = \left(\frac{3z_1}{2\gamma}\right)^{2/3} = \left[\frac{3z_1}{2}\left(\frac{EI}{\rho g}\right)^{1/2}\right]^{2/3}.$$

If we substitute $z_1 \approx 1.86635$ and $\rho = \delta A$, where δ is the volumetric density of the material of the column and A is its cross-sectional area, we finally get

$$L_1 \approx (1.986)\left(\frac{EI}{g\delta A}\right)^{1/3} \tag{17}$$

for the critical buckling length. For example, with a steel column or rod for which $E = 2.8 \times 10^7$ lb/in.^{2} and $g\delta = 0.28$ lb/in.^{3}, the formula in (17) gives the results shown in the table in Fig. 8.6.3.

Cross Section of Rod	Shortest Buckling Length L_1
Circular with $r = 0.5$ in.	30 ft 6 in.
Circular with $r = 1.5$ in.	63 ft 5 in.
Annular with $r_{inner} = 1.25$ in. and $r_{outer} = 1.5$ in.	75 ft 7 in.

FIGURE 8.6.3.

We have used the familiar formulas $A = \pi r^2$ and $I = \frac{1}{4}\pi r^4$ for a circular disk. The data in the table show why flagpoles are hollow.

8.6 Problems

In Problems 1 through 12, express the general solution of the given differential equation in terms of Bessel functions.

1. $x^2 y'' - xy' + (1 + x^2)y = 0$
2. $xy'' + 3y' + xy = 0$
3. $xy'' - y' + 36x^3 y = 0$
4. $x^2 y'' - 5xy' + (8 + x)y = 0$
5. $36x^2 y'' + 60xy' + (9x^3 - 5)y = 0$
6. $16x^2 y'' + 24xy' + (1 + 144x^3)y = 0$
7. $x^2 y'' + 3xy' + (1 + x^2)y = 0$
8. $4x^2 y'' - 12xy' + (15 + 16x)y = 0$
9. $16x^2 y'' - (5 - 144x^3)y = 0$
10. $2x^2 y'' - 3xy' - 2(14 - x^5)y = 0$
11. $y'' + x^4 y = 0$
12. $y'' + 4x^3 y = 0$
13. Apply Theorem 1 to show that the general solution of

$$xy'' + 2y' + xy = 0$$

is $y(x) = x^{-1}(A \cos x + B \sin x)$.
14. Verify that the substitutions in (2) in Bessel's equation (Eq. (1)) yield Eq. (3).
15. **(a)** Show that the substitution

$$y = -\frac{1}{u}\frac{du}{dx}$$

transforms the Riccati equation $dy/dx = x^2 + y^2$ into $u'' + x^2 u = 0$. **(b)** Show that the general solution of $dy/dx = x^2 + y^2$ is

$$y(x) = x\frac{J_{3/4}\left(\frac{1}{2}x^2\right) - cJ_{-3/4}\left(\frac{1}{2}x^2\right)}{cJ_{1/4}\left(\frac{1}{2}x^2\right) + J_{-1/4}\left(\frac{1}{2}x^2\right)}.$$

(*Suggestion:* Apply the identities in Eqs. (22) and (23) of Section 8.5.)

16. **(a)** Substitute the series of Problem 11 of Section 8.5 in the result of Problem 15 here to show that the solution of the initial value problem

$$\frac{dy}{dx} = x^2 + y^2, \quad y(0) = 0$$

is

$$y(x) = x\frac{J_{3/4}\left(\frac{1}{2}x^2\right)}{J_{-1/4}\left(\frac{1}{2}x^2\right)}.$$

(b) Deduce similarly that the solution of the initial value problem

$$\frac{dy}{dx} = x^2 + y^2, \quad y(0) = 1$$

is

$$y(x) = x\frac{2\Gamma\left(\frac{3}{4}\right)J_{3/4}\left(\frac{1}{2}x^2\right) + \Gamma\left(\frac{1}{4}\right)J_{-3/4}\left(\frac{1}{2}x^2\right)}{2\Gamma\left(\frac{3}{4}\right)J_{-1/4}\left(\frac{1}{2}x^2\right) - \Gamma\left(\frac{1}{4}\right)J_{1/4}\left(\frac{1}{2}x^2\right)}.$$

Some solution curves of the equation $dy/dx = x^2 + y^2$ are shown in Fig. 8.6.4. The location of the asymptotes where $y(x) \to +\infty$ can be found by using Newton's method to find the zeros of the denominators in the formulas for the solutions as listed here.

FIGURE 8.6.4. Solution curves of $\frac{dy}{dx} = x^2 + y^2$.

17. Figure 8.6.5 shows a linearly tapered rod with circular cross section, subject to an axial force P of compression. As in Section 3.8, its deflection curve $y = y(x)$ satisfies the endpoint value problem

$$EIy'' + Py = 0; \quad y(a) = y(b) = 0. \quad (18)$$

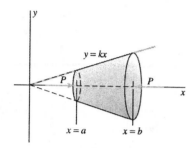

FIGURE 8.6.5. The tapered rod of Problem 17.

Here, however, the moment of inertia $I = I(x)$ of the cross section at x is given by

$$I(x) = \frac{1}{4}\pi(kx)^4 = I_0 \cdot \left(\frac{x}{b}\right)^4,$$

where $I_0 = I(b)$, the value of I at $x = b$. Substitution of $I(x)$ in the differential equation in (18) yields the eigenvalue problem

$$x^4 y'' + \lambda y = 0, \quad y(a) = y(b) = 0,$$

where $\lambda = \mu^2 = Pb^4/EI_0$. **(a)** Apply the theorem of this section to show that the general solution of $x^4 y'' + \mu^2 y = 0$ is

$$y(x) = x\left(A\cos\frac{\mu}{x} + B\sin\frac{\mu}{x}\right).$$

(b) Conclude that the nth eigenvalue is given by $\mu_n = n\pi ab/L$, where $L = b - a$ is the length of the rod, and hence that the nth buckling force is

$$P_n = \frac{n^2\pi^2}{L^2}\left(\frac{a}{b}\right)^2 EI_0.$$

Note that if $a = b$, this result reduces to Eq. (28) of Section 3.8.

18. Consider a variable-length pendulum as indicated in Fig. 8.6.6. Assume that its length is increasing linearly with time, $L(t) = a + bt$. It can be shown that the oscillations of this pendulum satisfy the differential equation

$$L\theta'' + 2L'\theta' + g\theta = 0$$

under the usual condition that θ is so small that $\sin\theta$ is very well approximated by θ: $\theta \approx \sin\theta$. Substitute $L = a + bt$ to derive the general solution

$$\theta(t) = \frac{1}{\sqrt{L}}\left[AJ_1\left(\frac{2}{b}\sqrt{gL}\right) + BY_1\left(\frac{2}{b}\sqrt{gL}\right)\right].$$

For the application of this solution to a discussion of the steadily descending pendulum ("its nether extremity was formed of a crescent of glittering steel, about a foot in length from horn to horn; the horns upward, and the under edge as keen as that of a razor ... and the whole hissed as it swung through the air ... down and still down it came") of Edgar Allan Poe's macabre classic "The Pit and the Pendulum," see the article by Borrelli, Coleman, and Hobson in the March 1985 issue of *Mathematics Magazine* (Vol. 58, pp. 78–83).

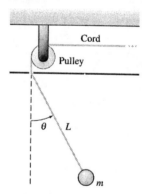

FIGURE 8.6.6. A variable length pendulum.

8.6 Application: Riccati Equations and Modified Bessel Functions

A Riccati equation is one of the form

$$\frac{dy}{dx} = A(x)y^2 + B(x)y + C(x).$$

Many Riccati equations like the ones listed next can be solved explicitly in terms of Bessel functions.

$$\frac{dy}{dx} = x^2 + y^2; \quad (1)$$

$$\frac{dy}{dx} = x^2 - y^2; \quad (2)$$

$$\frac{dy}{dx} = y^2 - x^2; \tag{3}$$

$$\frac{dy}{dx} = x + y^2; \tag{4}$$

$$\frac{dy}{dx} = x - y^2; \tag{5}$$

$$\frac{dy}{dx} = y^2 - x. \tag{6}$$

For example, Problem 15 in this section says that the general solution of Eq. (1) is given by

$$y(x) = x \frac{J_{3/4}\left(\frac{1}{2}x^2\right) - cJ_{-3/4}\left(\frac{1}{2}x^2\right)}{cJ_{1/4}\left(\frac{1}{2}x^2\right) + J_{-1/4}\left(\frac{1}{2}x^2\right)}. \tag{7}$$

See whether the symbolic DE solver command in your computer algebra system, such as the *Maple* command

```
dsolve(diff(y(x),x) = x^2 + y(x)^2, y(x))
```

or the *Mathematica* command

```
DSolve[ y'[x] == x^2 + y[x]^2, y[x], x ]
```

agrees with Eq. (7). If Bessel functions other than those appearing in Eq. (7) are involved, you may need to apply the identities in (26) and (27) of Section 8.5 to transform the computer's "answer" to (7). Then see whether your system can take the limit as $x \to 0$ in (7) to show that the arbitrary constant c is given in terms of the initial value $y(0)$ by

$$c = -\frac{y(0)\Gamma\left(\frac{1}{4}\right)}{2\Gamma\left(\frac{3}{4}\right)}. \tag{8}$$

Now you should be able to use built-in Bessel functions to plot typical solution curves like those shown in Fig. 8.6.4.

Next, investigate similarly one of the other equations in (2) through (6). Each has a general solution of the same general form in (7)—a quotient of linear combinations of Bessel functions. In addition to $J_p(x)$ and $Y_p(x)$, these solutions may involve the *modified Bessel functions*

$$I_p(x) = i^{-p}J_p(ix)$$

and

$$K_p(x) = \frac{\pi}{2}i^{-p}\left[J_p(ix) + Y_p(ix)\right]$$

that satisfy the *modified Bessel equation*

$$x^2 y'' + xy' - (x^2 + p^2)y = 0$$

of order p. For instance, the general solution of Eq. (5) is given for $x > 0$ by

$$y(x) = x^{1/2} \frac{I_{2/3}\left(\frac{2}{3}x^{3/2}\right) - cI_{-2/3}\left(\frac{2}{3}x^{3/2}\right)}{I_{-1/3}\left(\frac{2}{3}x^{3/2}\right) - cI_{1/3}\left(\frac{2}{3}x^{3/2}\right)}, \tag{9}$$

where

$$c = -\frac{y(0)\Gamma\left(\frac{1}{3}\right)}{3^{1/3}\Gamma\left(\frac{2}{3}\right)}. \tag{10}$$

Figure 8.6.7 shows some typical solution curves, together with the parabola $y^2 = x$ that appears to bear an interesting relation to Eq. (6)—we see a funnel near $y = +\sqrt{x}$ and a spout near $y = -\sqrt{x}$.

The Bessel functions with imaginary argument that appear in the definitions of $I_p(x)$ and $K_p(x)$ may look exotic, but the power series of the modified function $I_n(x)$ is simply that of the unmodified function $J_n(x)$ except without the alternating minus signs. For instance,

$$I_0(x) = 1 + \frac{x^2}{4} + \frac{x^4}{64} + \frac{x^6}{2304} + \cdots$$

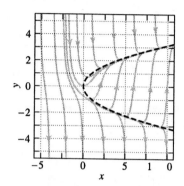

FIGURE 8.6.7. Solution curves of $\dfrac{dy}{dx} = x - y^2$.

and

$$I_1(x) = \frac{x}{2} + \frac{x^3}{16} + \frac{x^5}{384} + \frac{x^7}{18432} + \cdots.$$

Check these power series expansions using your computer algebra system—look at **BesselI** in either *Maple* or *Mathematica*—and compare them with Eqs. (17) and (18) in Section 8.5.

The second-order differential equations with the same right-hand sides as in Eqs. (1) through (6) have interesting solutions which, however, cannot be expressed in terms of elementary functions and/or "known" special functions such as Bessel functions. Nevertheless, they can be investigated using an ODE plotter. For instance, the interesting pattern in Fig. 8.6.8 shows solution curves of the second-order equation

$$y'' = y^2 - x \tag{11}$$

with the same initial value $y(0) = 0$ but different slopes $y'(0) = -3.3, -3.1, \ldots, 0.7$. Equation (11) is a form of the *first Painlevé transcendant,* an equation that arose historically in the classification of nonlinear second-order differential equations in terms of their critical points (see Chapter 14 of E. L. Ince, *Ordinary Differential Equations*, New York: Dover Publications, 1956). Figure 8.6.8 was suggested by an article by Anne Noonburg containing a similar figure in the Spring 1993 issue of the *C•ODE•E Newsletter*.

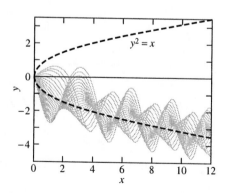

FIGURE 8.6.8. The first Painleve transcendant $y'' = y^2 - x$, $y(0) = 0$, $y'(0) = -3.3, -3.1, \ldots, 0.7$.

Finally, here's a related example that was inspired by a *Maple* demonstration package. The *Maple* `dsolve` command yields the general solution

$$y(x) = x^{-1}(c_1 J_{10}(x) + c_2 Y_{10}(x))$$
$$+ x^{-11}(1857945600 + 51609600x^2 + 806400x^4 + 9600x^6 + 100x^8 + x^{10}) \quad (12)$$

of the nonhomogeneous second-order equation

$$x^2 y'' + 3xy' + (x^2 - 99)y = x. \quad (13)$$

Show that Theorem 1 in this section explains the "Bessel part" of the alleged solution in Eq. (12). Can you explain where the rational function part comes from, or at least verify it? For further examples of this sort, you can replace the coefficient 99 in Eq. (13) with $r^2 - 1$, where r is an *even* integer, and/or replace the x on the right-hand side with x^s, where s is an *odd* integer. (With parities other than these, more exotic special functions are involved.)

C H A P T E R

9

Fourier Series Methods

9.1 Periodic Functions and Trigonometric Series

As motivation for the subject of Fourier series, we consider the differential equation

$$\frac{d^2x}{dt^2} + \omega_0^2 x = f(t) \tag{1}$$

that models the behavior of a mass-and-spring system with natural [circular] frequency ω_0, moving under the influence of an external force of magnitude $f(t)$ per unit mass. As we saw in Section 3.6, a particular solution of Eq. (1) can easily be found by the method of undetermined coefficients if $f(t)$ is a simple harmonic function—a sine or cosine function. For instance, the equation

$$\frac{d^2x}{dt^2} + \omega_0^2 x = A \cos \omega t \tag{2}$$

with $\omega^2 \neq \omega_0^2$ has the particular solution

$$x_p(t) = \frac{A}{\omega_0^2 - \omega^2} \cos \omega t, \tag{3}$$

which is readily found by beginning with the trial solution $x_p(t) = a \cos \omega t$.

Now suppose, more generally, that the force function $f(t)$ in Eq. (1) is a linear combination of simple harmonic functions. Then, on the basis of Eq. (3) and the analogous formula with sine in place of cosine, we can apply the principle of superposition to construct a particular solution of Eq. (1). For example, consider

684

the equation

$$\frac{d^2 x}{dt^2} + \omega_0^2 x = \sum_{n=1}^{N} A_n \cos \omega_n t, \qquad (4)$$

in which ω_0^2 is equal to none of the ω_n^2. Equation (4) has the particular solution

$$x_p(t) = \sum_{n=1}^{N} \frac{A_n}{\omega_0^2 - \omega_n^2} \cos \omega_n t, \qquad (5)$$

obtained by adding the solutions given in Eq. (3) corresponding to the N terms on the right-hand side in Eq. (4).

Mechanical (and electrical) systems often involve periodic forcing functions that are not [simply] finite linear combinations of sines and cosines. Nevertheless, as we will soon see, any reasonably nice periodic function $f(t)$ has a representation as an *infinite series* of trigonometric terms. This fact opens the way toward solving Eq. (1) by superposition of trigonometric "building blocks," with the finite sum in Eq. (5) replaced with an infinite series.

Definition: Periodic Function

The function $f(t)$ defined for all t is said to be **periodic** provided that there exists a positive number p such that

➤
$$f(t + p) = f(t) \qquad (6)$$

for all t. The number p is then called a **period** of the function f.

Note that the period of a periodic function is not unique; for example, if p is a period of $f(t)$, then so are the numbers $2p$, $3p$, and so on. Indeed, every positive number is a period of any constant function.

If there exists a smallest positive number P such that $f(t)$ is periodic with period P, then we call P *the* period of f. For instance, the period of the functions $g(t) = \cos nt$ and $h(t) = \sin nt$ (where n is a positive integer) is $2\pi/n$ because

$$\cos n\left(t + \frac{2\pi}{n}\right) = \cos(nt + 2\pi) = \cos nt$$

and

$$\sin n\left(t + \frac{2\pi}{n}\right) = \sin(nt + 2\pi) = \sin nt. \qquad (7)$$

FIGURE 9.1.1. A square wave function.

Moreover, 2π itself is a period of the functions $g(t)$ and $h(t)$. Ordinarily we will have no need to refer to the smallest period of a function $f(t)$ and will simply say that $f(t)$ has period p if p is any period of $f(t)$.

In Section 7.5 we saw several examples of piecewise continuous periodic functions. For instance, the square wave function having the graph shown in Fig. 9.1.1 has period 2π.

Because $g(t) = \cos nt$ and $h(t) = \sin nt$ each have period 2π, any linear combination of sines and cosines of integral multiples of t, such as

$$f(t) = 3 + \cos t - \sin t + 5 \cos 2t + 17 \sin 3t,$$

has period 2π. But every such linear combination is continuous, so the square wave function cannot be expressed in such manner. In his celebrated treatise *The Analytic Theory of Heat* (1822), the French scientist Joseph Fourier (1768–1830) made the remarkable assertion that every function $f(t)$ with period 2π can be represented by an *infinite* trigonometric series of the form

$$\frac{a_0}{2} + \sum_{n=1}^{\infty} (a_n \cos nt + b_n \sin nt). \tag{8}$$

We will see in Section 9.2 that under rather mild restrictions on the function $f(t)$, this is so! An infinite series of the form in (8) is called a *Fourier series*, and the representation of functions by Fourier series is one of the most widely used techniques in applied mathematics, especially for the solution of partial differential equations (see Sections 9.5 through 9.7).

Fourier Series of Period 2π Functions

In this section we will confine our attention to functions of period 2π. We want to determine what the coefficients in the Fourier series in (8) must be if it is to converge to a given function $f(t)$ of period 2π. For this purpose we need the following integrals, in which m and n denote positive integers (Problems 27 through 29):

$$\int_{-\pi}^{\pi} \cos mt \cos nt \, dt = \begin{cases} 0 & \text{if } m \neq n, \\ \pi & \text{if } m = n. \end{cases} \tag{9}$$

$$\int_{-\pi}^{\pi} \sin mt \sin nt \, dt = \begin{cases} 0 & \text{if } m \neq n, \\ \pi & \text{if } m = n. \end{cases} \tag{10}$$

$$\int_{-\pi}^{\pi} \cos mt \sin nt \, dt = 0 \quad \text{for all } m \text{ and } n. \tag{11}$$

These formulas imply that the functions $\cos nt$ and $\sin nt$ for $n = 1, 2, 3, \ldots$ constitute a *mutually orthogonal* set of functions on the interval $[-\pi, \pi]$. Two real-valued functions $u(t)$ and $v(t)$ are said to be **orthogonal** on the interval $[a, b]$ provided that

$$\int_{a}^{b} u(t)v(t) \, dt = 0. \tag{12}$$

Suppose now that the piecewise continuous function $f(t)$ of period 2π has a Fourier series representation

$$f(t) = \frac{a_0}{2} + \sum_{m=1}^{\infty} (a_m \cos mt + b_m \sin mt), \tag{13}$$

in the sense that the infinite series on the right converges to the value $f(t)$ for every t. We assume in addition that, when the infinite series in Eq. (13) is multiplied by any continuous function, the resulting series can be integrated term by term. Then the result of termwise integration of Eq. (13) itself from $t = -\pi$ to $t = \pi$ is

$$\int_{-\pi}^{\pi} f(t)\,dt = \frac{a_0}{2}\int_{-\pi}^{\pi} 1\,dt$$

$$+ \sum_{m=1}^{\infty}\left(a_m\int_{-\pi}^{\pi}\cos mt\,dt\right) + \sum_{m=1}^{\infty}\left(b_m\int_{-\pi}^{\pi}\sin mt\,dt\right) = \pi a_0$$

because all the trigonometric integrals vanish. Hence

$$a_0 = \frac{1}{\pi}\int_{-\pi}^{\pi} f(t)\,dt. \tag{14}$$

If we first multiply each side in Eq. (13) by $\cos nt$ and then integrate termwise, the result is

$$\int_{-\pi}^{\pi} f(t)\cos nt\,dt = \frac{a_0}{2}\int_{-\pi}^{\pi}\cos nt\,dt$$

$$+ \sum_{m=1}^{\infty}\left(a_m\int_{-\pi}^{\pi}\cos mt\cos nt\,dt\right) + \sum_{m=1}^{\infty}\left(b_m\int_{-\pi}^{\pi}\sin mt\cos nt\,dt\right);$$

it then follows from Eq. (11) that

$$\int_{-\pi}^{\pi} f(t)\cos nt\,dt = \sum_{m=1}^{\infty} a_m\left(\int_{-\pi}^{\pi}\cos mt\cos nt\,dt\right). \tag{15}$$

But of all the integrals (for $m = 1, 2, 3, \ldots$) on the right-hand side in (15), only the one for which $m = n$ is nonzero. Thus Eq. (9) yields

$$\int_{-\pi}^{\pi} f(t)\cos nt\,dt = a_n\int_{-\pi}^{\pi}\cos^2 nt\,dt = \pi a_n,$$

so the value of the coefficient a_n is

$$a_n = \frac{1}{\pi}\int_{-\pi}^{\pi} f(t)\cos nt\,dt. \tag{16}$$

Note that with $n = 0$, the formula in (16) reduces to Eq. (14); this explains why we denote the constant term in the original Fourier series by $\frac{1}{2}a_0$ (rather than simply a_0). If we multiply each side in Eq. (13) by $\sin nt$ and then integrate termwise, we find in a similar way that

$$b_n = \frac{1}{\pi}\int_{-\pi}^{\pi} f(t)\sin nt\,dt. \tag{17}$$

In short, we have found that if the series in (13) converges to $f(t)$ and if the termwise integrations carried out here are valid, then the coefficients in the series must have the values given in Eqs. (16) and (17). This motivates us to *define* the Fourier series of a periodic function by means of these formulas, whether or not the resulting series converges to the function (or even converges at all).

> **Definition: Fourier Series and Fourier Coefficients**
>
> Let $f(t)$ be a piecewise continuous function of period 2π that is defined for all t. Then the **Fourier series** of $f(t)$ is the series
>
> $$\frac{a_0}{2} + \sum_{n=1}^{\infty} (a_n \cos nt + b_n \sin nt), \qquad (18)$$
>
> where the **Fourier coefficients** a_n and b_n are defined by means of the formulas
>
> $$a_n = \frac{1}{\pi} \int_{-\pi}^{\pi} f(t) \cos nt \, dt \qquad (16)$$
>
> for $n = 0, 1, 2, 3, \ldots$ and
>
> $$b_n = \frac{1}{\pi} \int_{-\pi}^{\pi} f(t) \sin nt \, dt \qquad (17)$$
>
> for $n = 1, 2, 3, \ldots$.

It can (and often does) happen that the Fourier series of a function fails to converge to the function at certain points in the domain of the function. We will therefore write

$$f(t) \sim \frac{a_0}{2} + \sum_{n=1}^{\infty} (a_n \cos nt + b_n \sin nt), \qquad (19)$$

not using an equals sign between the function and its Fourier series until we have discussed convergence of Fourier series in Section 9.2.

Suppose that the piecewise continuous function $f(t)$ as given initially is defined only on the interval $[-\pi, \pi]$, and assume that $f(-\pi) = f(\pi)$. Then we can extend f so that its domain includes all real numbers by means of the periodicity condition $f(t + 2\pi) = f(t)$ for all t. We continue to denote this extension of the original function by f, and note that it automatically has period 2π. Its graph looks the same on every interval of the form

$$(2n - 1)\pi \leqq t \leqq (2n + 1)\pi$$

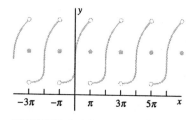

FIGURE 9.1.2. Extending a function to produce a periodic function.

where n is an integer (Fig. 9.1.2). For instance, the square wave function of Fig. 9.1.1 can be described as the period 2π function such that

$$f(t) = \begin{cases} -1 & \text{if } -\pi < t < 0; \\ +1 & \text{if } 0 < t < \pi; \\ 0 & \text{if } t = -\pi, 0, \text{ or } \pi. \end{cases} \qquad (20)$$

Thus the square wave function is the period 2π function defined on one full period by means of Eq. (20).

We need to consider Fourier series of piecewise continuous functions because many functions that appear in applications are only piecewise continuous, not continuous. Note that the integrals in Eqs. (16) and (17) exist if $f(t)$ is piecewise continuous, so every piecewise continuous function has a Fourier series.

Example 1 Find the Fourier series of the square wave function defined in Eq. (20).

Solution It is always a good idea to calculate a_0 separately, using Eq. (14). Thus

$$a_0 = \frac{1}{\pi} \int_{-\pi}^{\pi} f(t)\,dt = \frac{1}{\pi} \int_{-\pi}^{0} (-1)\,dt + \frac{1}{\pi} \int_{0}^{\pi} (+1)\,dt$$

$$= \frac{1}{\pi}(-\pi) + \frac{1}{\pi}(\pi) = 0.$$

We split the first integral into two integrals because $f(t)$ is defined by different formulas on the intervals $(-\pi, 0)$ and $(0, \pi)$; the values of $f(t)$ at the endpoints of these intervals do not affect the values of the integrals.

Equation (16) yields (for $n > 0$)

$$a_n = \frac{1}{\pi} \int_{-\pi}^{\pi} f(t) \cos nt\,dt = \frac{1}{\pi} \int_{-\pi}^{0} (-\cos nt)\,dt + \frac{1}{\pi} \int_{0}^{\pi} \cos nt\,dt$$

$$= \frac{1}{\pi}\left[-\frac{1}{n} \sin nt\right]_{-\pi}^{0} + \frac{1}{\pi}\left[\frac{1}{n} \sin nt\right]_{0}^{\pi} = 0.$$

And Eq. (17) yields

$$b_n = \frac{1}{\pi} \int_{-\pi}^{\pi} f(t) \sin nt\,dt = \frac{1}{\pi} \int_{-\pi}^{0} (-\sin nt)\,dt + \frac{1}{\pi} \int_{0}^{\pi} \sin nt\,dt$$

$$= \frac{1}{\pi}\left[\frac{1}{n} \cos nt\right]_{-\pi}^{0} + \frac{1}{\pi}\left[-\frac{1}{n} \cos nt\right]_{0}^{\pi}$$

$$= \frac{2}{n\pi}(1 - \cos n\pi) = \frac{2}{n\pi}[1 - (-1)^n].$$

Thus $a_n = 0$ for all $n \geqq 0$, and

$$b_n = \begin{cases} \dfrac{4}{n\pi} & \text{for } n \text{ odd}; \\[2mm] 0 & \text{for } n \text{ even}. \end{cases}$$

The last result follows because $\cos(-n\pi) = \cos(n\pi) = (-1)^n$. With these values of the Fourier coefficients, we obtain the Fourier series

$$f(t) \sim \frac{4}{\pi} \sum_{n \text{ odd}} \frac{\sin nt}{n} = \frac{4}{\pi}\left(\sin t + \frac{1}{3} \sin 3t + \frac{1}{5} \sin 5t + \cdots\right). \tag{21}$$

Here we have introduced the useful abbreviation

$$\sum_{n \text{ odd}} \quad \text{for} \quad \sum_{\substack{n=1 \\ n \text{ odd}}}^{\infty}$$

—for example,

$$\sum_{n \text{ odd}} \frac{1}{n} = 1 + \frac{1}{3} + \frac{1}{5} + \cdots.$$

Figure 9.1.3 shows the graphs of several of the partial sums

$$S_N(t) = \frac{4}{\pi} \sum_{n=1}^{N} \frac{\sin(2n-1)t}{2n-1}$$

of the Fourier series in (21). Note that as t approaches a discontinuity of $f(t)$ from either side, the value of $S_n(t)$ tends to overshoot the limiting value of $f(t)$—either $+1$ or -1 in this case. This behavior of a Fourier series near a point of discontinuity of its function is typical and is known as **Gibbs's phenomenon.** ∎

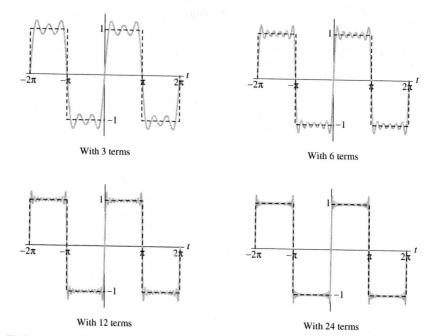

With 3 terms

With 6 terms

With 12 terms

With 24 terms

FIGURE 9.1.3. Graphs of partial sums of the Fourier series of the square wave function (Example 1) with $N = 3, 6, 12,$ and 24 terms.

The following integral formulas, easily derived by integration by parts, are useful in computing Fourier series of polynomial functions:

$$\int u \cos u \, du = \cos u + u \sin u + C; \tag{22}$$

$$\int u \sin u \, du = \sin u - u \cos u + C; \tag{23}$$

$$\int u^n \cos u \, du = u^n \sin u - n \int u^{n-1} \sin u \, du; \tag{24}$$

$$\int u^n \sin u \, du = -u^n \cos u + n \int u^{n-1} \cos u \, du. \tag{25}$$

Example 2   Find the Fourier series of the period 2π function that is defined in one period to be

$$
f(t) = \begin{cases} 0 & \text{if } -\pi < t \leqq 0; \\ t & \text{if } 0 \leqq t < \pi; \\ \dfrac{\pi}{2} & \text{if } t = \pm\pi. \end{cases} \tag{26}
$$

The graph of f is shown in Fig. 9.1.4.

Solution   The values of $f(\pm\pi)$ are irrelevant because they have no effect on the values of the integrals that yield the Fourier coefficients. Because $f(t) \equiv 0$ on the interval $(-\pi, 0)$, each integral from $t = -\pi$ to $t = \pi$ may be replaced with an integral from $t = 0$ to $t = \pi$. Equations (14), (16), and (17) therefore give

FIGURE 9.1.4. The periodic function of Example 2.

$$
a_0 = \frac{1}{\pi} \int_0^\pi t\, dt = \frac{1}{\pi} \left[\frac{1}{2} t^2 \right]_0^\pi = \frac{\pi}{2};
$$

$$
a_n = \frac{1}{\pi} \int_0^\pi t \cos nt\, dt = \frac{1}{n^2\pi} \int_0^{n\pi} u \cos u\, du \qquad \left(u = nt,\ t = \frac{u}{n} \right)
$$

$$
= \frac{1}{n^2\pi} \Big[\cos u + u \sin u \Big]_0^{n\pi} \qquad \text{(by Eq. (22))}
$$

$$
= \frac{1}{n^2\pi} [(-1)^n - 1].
$$

Consequently, $a_n = 0$ if n is even and $n \geqq 2$;

$$
a_n = -\frac{2}{n^2\pi} \qquad \text{if } n \text{ is odd.}
$$

Next,

$$
b_n = \frac{1}{\pi} \int_0^\pi t \sin nt\, dt = \frac{1}{n^2\pi} \int_0^{n\pi} u \sin u\, du
$$

$$
= \frac{1}{n^2\pi} \Big[\sin u - u \cos u \Big]_0^{n\pi} \qquad \text{(by Eq. (20))}
$$

$$
= -\frac{1}{n} \cos n\pi.
$$

Thus

$$
b_n = \frac{(-1)^{n+1}}{n} \qquad \text{for all } n \geqq 1.
$$

Therefore, the Fourier series of $f(t)$ is

$$
f(t) \sim \frac{\pi}{4} - \frac{2}{\pi} \sum_{n \text{ odd}} \frac{\cos nt}{n^2} + \sum_{n=1}^\infty \frac{(-1)^{n+1} \sin nt}{n}. \tag{27}
$$

∎

If $f(t)$ is a function of period 2π, it is readily verified (Problem 30) that

$$\int_{-\pi}^{\pi} f(t)\, dt = \int_{a}^{a+2\pi} f(t)\, dt \qquad (28)$$

for all a. That is, the integral of $f(t)$ over one interval of length 2π is equal to its integral over any other such interval. In case $f(t)$ is given explicitly on the interval $[0, 2\pi]$ rather than on $[-\pi, \pi]$, it may be more convenient to compute its Fourier coefficients as

$$a_n = \frac{1}{\pi} \int_{0}^{2\pi} f(t) \cos nt\, dt \qquad (29a)$$

and

$$b_n = \frac{1}{\pi} \int_{0}^{2\pi} f(t) \sin nt\, dt. \qquad (29b)$$

9.1 Problems

In Problems 1 through 10, sketch the graph of the function f defined for all t by the given formula, and determine whether it is periodic. If so, find its smallest period.

1. $f(t) = \sin 3t$

2. $f(t) = \cos 2\pi t$

3. $f(t) = \cos \dfrac{3t}{2}$

4. $f(t) = \sin \dfrac{\pi t}{3}$

5. $f(t) = \tan t$

6. $f(t) = \cot 2\pi t$

7. $f(t) = \cosh 3t$

8. $f(t) = \sinh \pi t$

9. $f(t) = |\sin t|$

10. $f(t) = \cos^2 3t$

In Problems 11 through 26, the values of a period 2π function $f(t)$ in one full period are given. Sketch several periods of its graph and find its Fourier series.

11. $f(t) \equiv 1$, $-\pi \leqq t \leqq \pi$

12. $f(t) = \begin{cases} +3, & -\pi < t \leqq 0; \\ -3, & 0 < t \leqq \pi \end{cases}$

13. $f(t) = \begin{cases} 0, & -\pi < t \leqq 0; \\ 1, & 0 < t \leqq \pi \end{cases}$

14. $f(t) = \begin{cases} 3, & -\pi < t \leqq 0; \\ -2, & 0 < t \leqq \pi \end{cases}$

15. $f(t) = t, -\pi < t \leqq \pi$

16. $f(t) = t, 0 < t < 2\pi$

17. $f(t) = |t|, -\pi \leqq t \leqq \pi$

18. $f(t) = \begin{cases} \pi + t, & -\pi < t \leqq 0; \\ \pi - t, & 0 < t \leqq \pi \end{cases}$

19. $f(t) = \begin{cases} \pi + t, & -\pi \leqq t < 0; \\ 0, & 0 \leqq t \leqq \pi \end{cases}$

20. $f(t) = \begin{cases} 0, & -\pi \leqq t < -\pi/2; \\ 1, & -\pi/2 \leqq t \leqq \pi/2; \\ 0, & \pi/2 < t \leqq \pi \end{cases}$

21. $f(t) = t^2$, $-\pi \leqq t \leqq \pi$

22. $f(t) = t^2$, $0 \leqq t < 2\pi$

23. $f(t) = \begin{cases} 0, & -\pi \leqq t \leqq 0; \\ t^2, & 0 \leqq t < \pi \end{cases}$

24. $f(t) = |\sin t|$, $-\pi \leqq t \leqq \pi$

25. $f(t) = \cos^2 2t$, $-\pi \leqq t \leqq \pi$

26. $f(t) = \begin{cases} 0, & -\pi \leqq t \leqq 0; \\ \sin t, & 0 \leqq t \leqq \pi \end{cases}$

27. Verify Eq. (9). (*Suggestion:* Use the trigonometric identity

$$\cos A \cos B = \tfrac{1}{2}\left[\cos(A + B) + \cos(A - B)\right].)$$

28. Verify Eq. (10).

29. Verify Eq. (11).

30. Let $f(t)$ be a piecewise continuous function with period P. **(a)** Suppose that $0 \leqq a < P$. Substitute $u = t - P$ to show that

$$\int_{P}^{a+P} f(t)\, dt = \int_{0}^{a} f(t)\, dt.$$

Conclude that

$$\int_{a}^{a+P} f(t)\, dt = \int_{0}^{P} f(t)\, dt.$$

(b) Given A, choose n so that $A = nP + a$ with $0 \leqq a < P$. Then substitute $v = t - nP$ to show that

$$\int_{A}^{A+P} f(t)\, dt = \int_{a}^{a+P} f(t)\, dt = \int_{0}^{P} f(t)\, dt.$$

31. Multiply each side in Eq. (13) by $\sin nt$ and then integrate term by term to derive Eq. (17).

9.2 General Fourier Series and Convergence

In Section 9.1 we defined the Fourier series of a periodic function of period 2π. Now let $f(t)$ be a function that is piecewise continuous for all t and has arbitrary period $P > 0$. We write

$$P = 2L,\tag{1}$$

so L is the **half-period** of the function f. Let us define the function g as follows:

$$g(u) = f\left(\frac{Lu}{\pi}\right)\tag{2}$$

for all u. Then

$$g(u + 2\pi) = f\left(\frac{Lu}{\pi} + 2L\right) = f\left(\frac{Lu}{\pi}\right) = g(u),$$

and hence $g(u)$ is also periodic and has period 2π. Consequently, g has the Fourier series

$$g(u) \sim \frac{a_0}{2} + \sum_{n=1}^{\infty}(a_n \cos nu + b_n \sin nu)\tag{3}$$

with Fourier coefficients

$$a_n = \frac{1}{\pi}\int_{-\pi}^{\pi} g(u) \cos nu\, du\tag{4a}$$

and

$$b_n = \frac{1}{\pi}\int_{-\pi}^{\pi} g(u) \sin nu\, du.\tag{4b}$$

If we now write

$$t = \frac{Lu}{\pi}, \quad u = \frac{\pi t}{L}, \quad f(t) = g(u),\tag{5}$$

then

$$f(t) = g\left(\frac{\pi t}{L}\right) \sim \frac{a_0}{2} + \sum_{n=1}^{\infty}\left(a_n \cos\frac{n\pi t}{L} + b_n \frac{n\pi t}{L}\right),\tag{6}$$

and then substitution of (5) in (4) yields

$$a_n = \frac{1}{\pi}\int_{-\pi}^{\pi} g(u) \cos nu\, du \qquad \left(u = \frac{\pi t}{L}, \ du = \frac{\pi}{L}\, dt\right)$$

$$= \frac{1}{L}\int_{-L}^{L} g\left(\frac{\pi t}{L}\right) \cos\frac{n\pi t}{L}\, dt.$$

Therefore,

$$a_n = \frac{1}{L} \int_{-L}^{L} f(t) \cos \frac{n\pi t}{L} \, dt; \tag{7}$$

similarly,

$$b_n = \frac{1}{L} \int_{-L}^{L} f(t) \sin \frac{n\pi t}{L} \, dt. \tag{8}$$

This computation motivates the following definition of the Fourier series of a periodic function of period $2L$.

Definition: Fourier Series and Fourier Coefficients

Let $f(t)$ be a piecewise continuous function of period $2L$ that is defined for all t. Then the **Fourier series** of $f(t)$ is the series

➤
$$f(t) \sim \frac{a_0}{2} + \sum_{n=1}^{\infty} \left(a_n \cos \frac{n\pi t}{L} + b_n \sin \frac{n\pi t}{L} \right), \tag{6}$$

where the **Fourier coefficients** $\{a_n\}_0^{\infty}$ and $\{b_n\}_1^{\infty}$ are defined to be

➤
$$a_n = \frac{1}{L} \int_{-L}^{L} f(t) \cos \frac{n\pi t}{L} \, dt \tag{7}$$

and

➤
$$b_n = \frac{1}{L} \int_{-L}^{L} f(t) \sin \frac{n\pi t}{L} \, dt. \tag{8}$$

With $n = 0$, Eq. (7) takes the simple form

$$a_0 = \frac{1}{L} \int_{-L}^{L} f(t) \, dt, \tag{9}$$

which demonstrates that the constant term $\frac{1}{2} a_0$ in the Fourier series of f is simply the average value of $f(t)$ on the interval $[-L, L]$.

As a consequence of Problem 30 of Section 9.1, we may evaluate the integrals in (7) and (8) over any other interval of length $2L$. For instance, if $f(t)$ is given by a single formula for $0 < t < 2L$, it may be more convenient to compute the integrals

$$a_n = \frac{1}{L} \int_0^{2L} f(t) \cos \frac{n\pi t}{L} \, dt \tag{10a}$$

and

$$b_n = \frac{1}{L} \int_0^{2L} f(t) \sin \frac{n\pi t}{L} \, dt. \tag{10b}$$

Example 1   Figure 9.2.1 shows the graph of a square wave function with period 4. Find its Fourier series.

Solution   Here, $L = 2$; also, $f(t) = -1$ if $-2 < t < 0$, while $f(t) = 1$ if $0 < t < 2$. Hence Eqs. (7), (8), and (9) yield

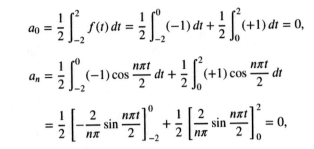

$$a_0 = \frac{1}{2}\int_{-2}^{2} f(t)\,dt = \frac{1}{2}\int_{-2}^{0}(-1)\,dt + \frac{1}{2}\int_{0}^{2}(+1)\,dt = 0,$$

$$a_n = \frac{1}{2}\int_{-2}^{0}(-1)\cos\frac{n\pi t}{2}\,dt + \frac{1}{2}\int_{0}^{2}(+1)\cos\frac{n\pi t}{2}\,dt$$

$$= \frac{1}{2}\left[-\frac{2}{n\pi}\sin\frac{n\pi t}{2}\right]_{-2}^{0} + \frac{1}{2}\left[\frac{2}{n\pi}\sin\frac{n\pi t}{2}\right]_{0}^{2} = 0,$$

FIGURE 9.2.1. The square wave of Example 1.

and

$$b_n = \frac{1}{2}\int_{-2}^{0}(-1)\sin\frac{n\pi t}{2}\,dt + \frac{1}{2}\int_{0}^{2}(+1)\sin\frac{n\pi t}{2}\,dt$$

$$+ \frac{1}{2}\left[\frac{2}{n\pi}\cos\frac{n\pi t}{2}\right]_{-2}^{0} + \frac{1}{2}\left[-\frac{2}{n\pi}\cos\frac{n\pi t}{2}\right]_{0}^{2}$$

$$= \frac{2}{n\pi}\left[1-(-1)^n\right] = \begin{cases} \dfrac{4}{n\pi} & \text{if } n \text{ is odd,} \\[2mm] 0 & \text{if } n \text{ is even.} \end{cases}$$

Thus the Fourier series is

$$f(t) \sim \frac{4}{\pi}\sum_{n\text{ odd}}\frac{1}{n}\sin\frac{n\pi t}{2} \qquad\qquad (11a)$$

$$= \frac{4}{\pi}\left(\sin\frac{\pi t}{2} + \frac{1}{3}\sin\frac{3\pi t}{2} + \frac{1}{5}\sin\frac{5\pi t}{2} + \cdots\right). \qquad (11b)$$

∎

The Convergence Theorem

We want to impose conditions on the periodic function f that are enough to guarantee that its Fourier series actually converges to $f(t)$ at least at those values of t at which f is continuous. Recall that the function f is said to be *piecewise continuous* on the interval $[a, b]$ provided that there is a finite partition of $[a, b]$ with endpoints

$$a = t_0 < t_1 < t_2 < \cdots < t_{n-1} < t_n = b$$

such that

1. f is continuous on each open interval $t_{i-1} < t < t_i$; and
2. At each endpoint t_i of such a subinterval the limit of $f(t)$, as t approaches t_i from within the subinterval, exists and is finite.

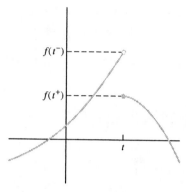

FIGURE 9.2.2. A finite jump discontinuity.

The function f is called *piecewise continuous* for all t if it is piecewise continuous on every bounded interval. It follows that a piecewise continuous function is continuous except possibly at isolated points, and that at each such point of discontinuity, the one-sided limits

$$f(t+) = \lim_{u \to t^+} f(u) \quad \text{and} \quad f(t-) = \lim_{u \to t^-} f(u) \tag{12}$$

both exist and are finite. Thus a piecewise continuous function has only isolated "finite jump" discontinuities like the one shown in Fig. 9.2.2.

The square wave and sawtooth functions that we saw in Chapter 7 are typical examples of periodic piecewise continuous functions. The function $f(t) = \tan t$ is a periodic function (of period π) that is not piecewise continuous because it has infinite discontinuities. The function $g(t) = \sin(1/t)$ is not piecewise continuous on $[-1, 1]$ because its one-sided limits at $t = 0$ do not exist. The function

$$h(t) = \begin{cases} t & \text{if } t = \dfrac{1}{n} \quad (n \text{ an integer}), \\ 0 & \text{otherwise} \end{cases}$$

on $[-1, 1]$ has one-sided limits everywhere, but is not piecewise continuous because its discontinuities are not isolated—it has the infinite sequence $\{1/n\}_1^\infty$ of discontinuities; a piecewise continuous function can have only finitely many discontinuities in any bounded interval.

Note that a piecewise continuous function need not be defined at its isolated points of discontinuity. Alternatively, it can be defined arbitrarily at such points. For instance, the square wave function f of Fig. 9.2.1 is piecewise continuous no matter what its values might be at the points $\dots, -4, -2, 0, 2, 4, 6, \dots$ at which it is discontinuous. Its derivative f' is also piecewise continuous; $f'(t) = 0$ unless t is an even integer, in which case $f'(t)$ is undefined.

The piecewise continuous function f is said to be **piecewise smooth** provided that its derivative f' is piecewise continuous. Theorem 1 (next) tells us that the Fourier series of a piecewise smooth function converges everywhere. More general Fourier convergence theorems—with weaker hypotheses on the periodic function f—are known. But the hypothesis that f is piecewise smooth is easy to check and is satisfied by most functions encountered in practical applications. A proof of the following theorem may be found in G. P. Tolstov, *Fourier Series* (New York: Dover, 1976).

THEOREM 1: Convergence of Fourier Series

Suppose that the periodic function f is piecewise smooth. Then its Fourier series in (6) converges

(a) to the value $f(t)$ at each point where f is continuous, and

(b) to the value $\frac{1}{2}[f(t+) + f(t-)]$ at each point where f is discontinuous. ▲

Note that $\frac{1}{2}[f(t+) + f(t-)]$ is the *average* of the right-hand and left-hand limits of f at the point t. If f is continuous at t, then $f(t) = f(t+) = f(t-)$, so

$$f(t) = \frac{f(t+) + f(t-)}{2}. \tag{13}$$

Hence Theorem 1 could be rephrased as follows: The Fourier series of a piecewise smooth function f converges for *every* t to the average value in (13). For this reason it is customary to write

$$f(t) = \frac{a_0}{2} + \sum_{n=1}^{\infty} \left(a_n \cos \frac{n\pi t}{L} + b_n \sin \frac{n\pi t}{L} \right), \tag{14}$$

with the understanding that the piecewise smooth function f has been redefined (if necessary) at each of its points of discontinuity in order to satisfy the average value condition in (13).

Example 1

Continued

Figure 9.2.1 shows us at a glance that if t_0 is an even integer, then

$$\lim_{t \to t_0^+} f(t) = +1 \quad \text{and} \quad \lim_{t \to t_0^-} f(t) = -1.$$

Hence

$$\frac{f(t_0+) + f(t_0-)}{2} = 0.$$

Note that, in accord with Theorem 1, the Fourier series of $f(t)$ in (11) clearly converges to zero if n is an even integer (because $\sin n\pi = 0$). ∎

Example 2

Let $f(t)$ be a function of period 2 with $f(t) = t^2$ if $0 < t < 2$. We define $f(t)$ for t an even integer by the average value condition in (13); consequently, $f(t) = 2$ if t is an even integer. The graph of the function f appears in Fig. 9.2.3. Find its Fourier series.

Solution

Here $L = 1$, and it is most convenient to integrate from $t = 0$ to $t = 2$. Then

$$a_0 = \frac{1}{1} \int_0^2 t^2 \, dt = \left[\frac{1}{3} t^3 \right]_0^2 = \frac{8}{3}.$$

With the aid of the integral formulas in Eqs. (22) through (25) of Section 9.1, we obtain

$$a_n = \int_0^2 t^2 \cos n\pi t \, dt$$

$$= \frac{1}{n^3 \pi^3} \int_0^{2n\pi} u^2 \cos u \, du \qquad \left(u = n\pi t, \ t = \frac{u}{n\pi} \right)$$

$$= \frac{1}{n^3 \pi^3} \left[u^2 \sin u - 2 \sin u + 2u \cos u \right]_0^{2n\pi} = \frac{4}{n^2 \pi^2};$$

$$b_n = \int_0^2 t^2 \sin n\pi t \, dt = \frac{1}{n^3 \pi^3} \int_0^{2n\pi} u^2 \sin u \, du$$

$$= \frac{1}{n^3 \pi^3} \left[-u^2 \cos u + 2 \cos u + 2u \sin u \right]_0^{2n\pi} = -\frac{4}{n\pi}.$$

FIGURE 9.2.3. The period 2 function of Example 2.

Hence the Fourier series of f is

$$f(t) = \frac{4}{3} + \frac{4}{\pi^2} \sum_{n=1}^{\infty} \frac{\cos n\pi t}{n^2} - \frac{4}{\pi} \sum_{n=1}^{\infty} \frac{\sin n\pi t}{n}, \tag{15}$$

and Theorem 1 assures us that this series converges to $f(t)$ for all t. ∎

We can draw some interesting consequences from the Fourier series in (15). If we substitute $t = 0$ on each side, we find that

$$f(0) = 2 = \frac{4}{3} + \frac{4}{\pi^2} \sum_{n=1}^{\infty} \frac{1}{n^2}.$$

On solving for the series, we obtain the lovely summation

➤ $$\sum_{n=1}^{\infty} \frac{1}{n^2} = 1 + \frac{1}{2^2} + \frac{1}{3^2} + \frac{1}{4^2} + \cdots = \frac{\pi^2}{6} \tag{16}$$

that was discovered by Euler. If we substitute $t = 1$ in Eq. (15), we get

$$f(1) = 1 = \frac{4}{3} + \frac{4}{\pi^2} \sum_{n=1}^{\infty} \frac{(-1)^n}{n^2},$$

which yields

$$\sum_{n=1}^{\infty} \frac{(-1)^{n+1}}{n^2} = 1 - \frac{1}{2^2} + \frac{1}{3^2} - \frac{1}{4^2} + \cdots = \frac{\pi^2}{12}. \tag{17}$$

If we add the series in Eqs. (16) and (17) and then divide by 2, the "even" terms cancel and the result is

$$\sum_{n \text{ odd}} \frac{1}{n^2} = 1 + \frac{1}{3^2} + \frac{1}{5^2} + \frac{1}{7^2} + \cdots = \frac{\pi^2}{8}. \tag{18}$$

9.2 Problems

In Problems 1 through 14, the values of a periodic function $f(t)$ in one full period are given; at each discontinuity the value of $f(t)$ is that given by the average value condition in (13). Sketch the graph of f and find its Fourier series.

1. $f(t) = \begin{cases} -2, & -3 < t < 0; \\ 2, & 0 < t < 3 \end{cases}$

2. $f(t) = \begin{cases} 0, & -5 < t < 0; \\ 1, & 0 < t < 5 \end{cases}$

3. $f(t) = \begin{cases} 2, & -2\pi < t < 0; \\ -1, & 0 < t < 2\pi \end{cases}$

4. $f(t) = t, \quad -2 < t < 2$

5. $f(t) = t, \quad -2\pi < t < 2\pi$

6. $f(t) = t, \quad 0 < t < 3$

7. $f(t) = |t|, \quad -1 < t < 1$

8. $f(t) = \begin{cases} 0, & 0 < t < 1; \\ 1, & 1 < t < 2; \\ 0, & 2 < t < 3 \end{cases}$

9. $f(t) = t^2, \quad -1 < t < 1$

10. $f(t) = \begin{cases} 0, & -2 < t < 0; \\ t^2, & 0 < t < 2 \end{cases}$

11. $f(t) = \cos \frac{\pi t}{2}, \quad -1 < t < 1$

12. $f(t) = \sin \pi t, \quad 0 < t < 1$

13. $f(t) = \begin{cases} 0, & -1 < t < 0; \\ \sin \pi t, & 0 < t < 1 \end{cases}$

14. $f(t) = \begin{cases} 0, & -2\pi < t < 0; \\ \sin t, & 0 < t < 2\pi \end{cases}$

15. (a) Suppose that f is a function of period 2π with $f(t) = t^2$ for $0 < t < 2\pi$. Show that

$$f(t) = \frac{4\pi^2}{3} + 4 \sum_{n=1}^{\infty} \frac{\cos nt}{n^2} - 4\pi \sum_{n=1}^{\infty} \frac{\sin nt}{n}$$

and sketch the graph of f, indicating the value at each discontinuity. **(b)** Deduce the series summations in Eqs. (16) and (17) from the Fourier series in part (a).

16. (a) Suppose that f is a function of period 2 such that $f(t) = 0$ if $-1 < t < 0$ and $f(t) = t$ if $0 < t < 1$. Show that

$$f(t) = \frac{1}{4} - \frac{2}{\pi^2} \sum_{n \text{ odd}} \frac{\cos n\pi t}{n^2} + \frac{1}{\pi} \sum_{n=1}^{\infty} \frac{(-1)^{n+1} \sin n\pi t}{n},$$

and sketch the graph of f, indicating the value at each discontinuity. **(b)** Deduce the series summation in Eq. (18) from the Fourier series in part (a).

17. (a) Suppose that f is a function of period 2 with $f(t) = t$ for $0 < t < 2$. Show that

$$f(t) = 1 - \frac{2}{\pi} \sum_{n=1}^{\infty} \frac{\sin n\pi t}{n}$$

and sketch the graph of f, indicating the value at each discontinuity. **(b)** Substitute an appropriate value of t to deduce **Leibniz's series**

$$1 - \frac{1}{3} + \frac{1}{5} - \frac{1}{7} + \cdots = \frac{\pi}{4}.$$

Derive the Fourier series listed in Problems 18 through 21, and graph the period 2π function to which each series converges.

18. $\displaystyle\sum_{n=1}^{\infty} \frac{\sin nt}{n} = \frac{\pi - t}{2} \quad (0 < t < 2\pi)$

19. $\displaystyle\sum_{n=1}^{\infty} \frac{(-1)^{n+1} \sin nt}{n} = \frac{t}{2} \quad (-\pi < t < \pi)$

20. $\displaystyle\sum_{n=1}^{\infty} \frac{\cos nt}{n^2} = \frac{3t^2 - 6\pi t + 2\pi^2}{12} \quad (0 < t < 2\pi)$

21. $\displaystyle\sum_{n=1}^{\infty} \frac{(-1)^{n+1} \cos nt}{n^2} = \frac{\pi^2 - 3t^2}{12} \quad (-\pi < t < \pi)$

22. Suppose that $p(t)$ is a polynomial of degree n. Show by repeated integration by parts that

$$\int p(t)g(t) \, dt = p(t)G_1(t) - p'(t)G_2(t)$$
$$+ p''(t)G_3(t) - \cdots + (-1)^n p^{(n)}(t)G_{n+1}(t)$$

where $G_k(t)$ denotes the kth iterated antiderivative $G_k(t) = (D^{-1})^k g(t)$. This formula is useful in computing Fourier coefficients of polynomials.

23. Apply the integral formula of Problem 22 to show that

$$\int t^4 \cos t \, dt = t^4 \sin t + 4t^3 \cos t$$
$$- 12t^2 \sin t - 24t \cos t + 24 \sin t + C$$

and that

$$\int t^4 \sin t \, dt = -t^4 \cos t + 4t^3 \sin t$$
$$+ 12t^2 \cos t - 24t \sin t - 24 \cos t + C.$$

24. (a) Show that for $0 < t < 2\pi$,

$$t^4 = \frac{16\pi^4}{5} + 16 \sum_{n=1}^{\infty} \left(\frac{2\pi^2}{n^2} - \frac{3}{n^4} \right) \cos nt$$
$$+ 16\pi \sum_{n=1}^{\infty} \left(\frac{3}{n^3} - \frac{\pi^2}{n} \right) \sin nt$$

and sketch the graph of f, indicating the value at each discontinuity. **(b)** From the Fourier series in part (a), deduce the summations

$$\sum_{n=1}^{\infty} \frac{1}{n^4} = \frac{\pi^4}{90}, \qquad \sum_{n=1}^{\infty} \frac{(-1)^{n+1}}{n^4} = \frac{7\pi^4}{720},$$

and

$$\sum_{n \text{ odd}} \frac{1}{n^4} = \frac{\pi^4}{96}.$$

25. (a) Find the Fourier series of the period 2π function f with $f(t) = t^3$ if $-\pi < t < \pi$. **(b)** Use the series of part (a) to derive the summation

$$1 - \frac{1}{3^3} + \frac{1}{5^3} - \frac{1}{7^3} + \cdots = \frac{\pi^3}{32}$$

and sketch the graph of f, indicating the value at each discontinuity. **(c)** *Attempt* to evaluate the series

$$\sum_{n=1}^{\infty} \frac{1}{n^3} = 1 + \frac{1}{2^3} + \frac{1}{3^3} + \frac{1}{4^3} + \cdots$$

by substituting an appropriate value of t in the Fourier series of part (a). Is your attempt successful? Explain.

9.2 Application: Computer Algebra Calculation of Fourier Coefficients

A computer algebra system can greatly ease the burden of calculation of the Fourier coefficients of a given function $f(t)$. In the case of a function that is defined "piece-wise," we must take care to "split" the integral according to the different intervals of definition of the function. We illustrate the method by deriving the Fourier series of the period 2π square wave function defined on $(-\pi, \pi)$ by

$$f(t) = \begin{cases} -1 & \text{if} \quad -\pi < t < 0, \\ +1 & \text{if} \quad 0 < t < \pi. \end{cases} \tag{1}$$

In this case the function is defined by different formulas on two different intervals, so each Fourier coefficient integral from $-\pi$ to π must be calculated as the sum of two integrals:

$$a_n = \frac{1}{\pi} \int_{-\pi}^{0} (-1) \cos nt \, dt + \frac{1}{\pi} \int_{0}^{\pi} (+1) \cos nt \, dt,$$

$$b_n = \frac{1}{\pi} \int_{-\pi}^{0} (-1) \sin nt \, dt + \frac{1}{\pi} \int_{0}^{\pi} (+1) \sin nt \, dt. \tag{2}$$

We can define the coefficients in (2) as functions of n by the *Maple* commands

```
a := n -> (1/Pi)*(int(-cos(n*t), t=-Pi..0) +
                  int(+cos(n*t), t=0..Pi)):
b := n -> (1/Pi)*(int(-sin(n*t), t=-Pi..0) +
                  int(+sin(n*t), t=0..Pi)):
```

or by the *Mathematica* commands

```
a[n_] := (1/Pi)*(Integrate[-Cos[n*t], {t, -Pi, 0}] +
                 Integrate[+Cos[n*t], {t, 0, Pi}])
b[n_] := (1/Pi)*(Integrate[-Sin[n*t], {t, -Pi, 0}] +
                 Integrate[+Sin[n*t], {t, 0, Pi}])
```

Because the function $f(t)$ in Eq. (1) is odd, we naturally find that $a_n \equiv 0$. Hence the *Maple* commands

```
fourierSum := sum(b(n)*sin(n*t), n=1..9);
plot(fourierSum, t=-2*Pi..4*Pi);
```

or the *Mathematica* commands

```
fourierSum = Sum[b[n]*Sin[n*t], {n,1,9}]
Plot[fourierSum, {t, -2*Pi, 4*Pi}];
```

yield the partial sum

$$\sum_{n=1}^{9} b_n \sin nt = \frac{4}{\pi} \left(\sin t + \frac{\sin 3t}{3} + \frac{\sin 5t}{5} + \frac{\sin 7t}{7} + \frac{\sin 9t}{9} \right)$$

and generate a graph like one of those in Fig. 9.1.3. The corresponding MATLAB commands are entirely analogous and can be found in the applications manual that accompanies this text.

To practice the symbolic derivation of Fourier series in this manner, you can begin by verifying the Fourier series calculated manually in Examples 1 and 2 of this section. Then Problems 1 through 21 are fair game. Finally, the period 2π triangular wave and trapezoidal wave functions illustrated in Figs. 9.2.4 and 9.2.5 have especially interesting Fourier series that we invite you to discover for yourself.

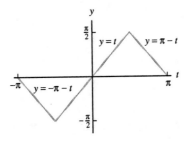

FIGURE 9.2.4. The triangular wave.

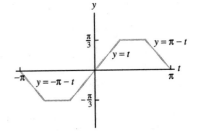

FIGURE 9.2.5. The trapezoidal wave.

9.3 Fourier Sine and Cosine Series

Certain properties of functions are reflected prominently in their Fourier series. The function f defined for all t is said to be **even** if

$$f(-t) = f(t) \tag{1}$$

for all t; f is **odd** if

$$f(-t) = -f(t) \tag{2}$$

for all t. The first condition implies that the graph of $y = f(t)$ is symmetric with respect to the y-axis, whereas the condition in (2) implies that the graph of an odd function is symmetric with respect to the origin (see Fig. 9.3.1). The functions $f(t) = t^{2n}$ and $g(t) = \cos t$ are even functions, whereas the functions $f(t) = t^{2n+1}$ and $g(t) = \sin t$ are odd. We will see that the Fourier series of an even periodic function has only cosine terms and that the Fourier series of an odd periodic function has only sine terms.

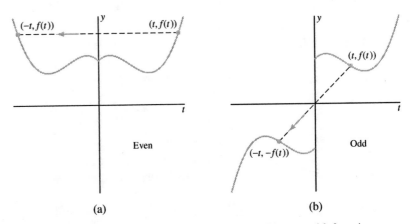

FIGURE 9.3.1. (a) An even function; (b) an odd function.

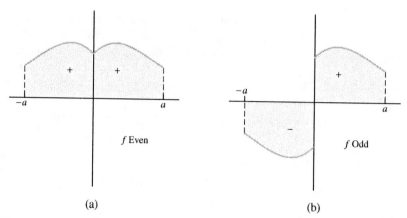

FIGURE 9.3.2. Area under the graph of (a) an even function and (b) an odd.

Addition and cancellation of areas as indicated in Fig. 9.3.2 reminds us of the following basic facts about integrals of even and odd functions over an interval $[-a, a]$ that is symmetric around the origin.

$$\text{If } f \text{ is even:} \quad \int_{-a}^{a} f(t)\,dt = 2 \int_{0}^{a} f(t)\,dt. \tag{3}$$

$$\text{If } f \text{ is odd:} \quad \int_{-a}^{a} f(t)\,dt = 0. \tag{4}$$

These facts are easy to verify analytically (Problem 17).

It follows immediately from Eqs. (1) and (2) that the product of two even functions is even, as is the product of two odd functions; the product of an even function and an odd function is odd. In particular, if $f(t)$ is an *even* periodic function of period $2L$, then $f(t)\cos(n\pi t/L)$ is even, whereas $f(t)\sin(n\pi t/L)$ is odd, because the cosine function is even and the sine function is odd. When we compute the Fourier coefficients of f, we therefore get

$$a_n = \frac{1}{L} \int_{-L}^{L} f(t)\cos \frac{n\pi t}{L}\,dt = \frac{2}{L} \int_{0}^{L} f(t)\cos \frac{n\pi t}{L}\,dt \tag{5a}$$

and

$$b_n = \frac{1}{L} \int_{-L}^{L} f(t)\sin \frac{n\pi t}{L}\,dt = 0 \tag{5b}$$

because of (3) and (4). Hence the Fourier series of the *even* function f of period $2L$ has only *cosine* terms:

$$f(t) = \frac{a_0}{2} + \sum_{n=1}^{\infty} a_n \cos \frac{n\pi t}{L} \qquad (f \text{ even}) \tag{6}$$

with the values of a_n given by Eq. (5a). If $f(t)$ is *odd*, then $f(t)\cos(n\pi t/L)$ is odd, whereas $f(t)\sin(n\pi t/L)$ is even, so

$$a_n = \frac{1}{L} \int_{-L}^{L} f(t)\cos \frac{n\pi t}{L}\,dt = 0 \tag{7a}$$

and

$$b_n = \frac{1}{L} \int_{-L}^{L} f(t) \sin \frac{n\pi t}{L} \, dt = \frac{2}{L} \int_{0}^{L} f(t) \sin \frac{n\pi t}{L} \, dt. \tag{7b}$$

Hence the Fourier series of the *odd* function f of period $2L$ has only *sine* terms:

$$f(t) = \sum_{n=1}^{\infty} b_n \sin \frac{n\pi t}{L} \qquad (f \text{ odd}) \tag{8}$$

with the coefficients b_n given in Eq. (7b).

Even and Odd Extensions

In all our earlier discussion and examples, we began with a periodic function defined *for all* t; the Fourier series of such a function is uniquely determined by the Fourier coefficient formulas. In many practical situations, however, we begin with a function f defined only on an interval of the form $0 < t < L$, and we want to represent its values on this interval by a Fourier series of period $2L$. The first step is the necessary extension of f to the interval $-L < t < 0$. Granted this, we may extend f to the entire real line by the periodicity condition $f(t+2L) = f(t)$ (and use the average value property should any discontinuities arise). But *how* we define f for $-L < t < 0$ is our choice, and the Fourier series representation for $f(t)$ on $(0, L)$ that we obtain will depend on that choice. Specifically, different choices of the extension of f to the interval $(-L, 0)$ will yield different Fourier series that converge to the same function $f(t)$ in the original interval $0 < t < L$, but converge to the different extensions of f on the interval $-L < t < 0$.

In practice, given $f(t)$ defined for $0 < t < L$, we generally make one of two natural choices—we extend f to obtain either an even function or an odd function. The **even period $2L$ extension** of f is the function f_E defined as

$$f_E(t) = \begin{cases} f(t) & \text{if} \quad 0 < t < L; \\ f(-t) & \text{if} \ -L < t < 0 \end{cases} \tag{9}$$

and by $f_E(t+2L) = f_E(t)$ for all t. The values of $f_E(t)$ for t an integral multiple of L are not important because they cannot affect the Fourier series of f_E. The Fourier series of the even extension f_E, given by Eqs. (5) and (6), will contain only cosine terms and is called the *Fourier cosine series* of the original function f.

The **odd period $2L$ extension** of f is the function f_O defined as

$$f_O(t) = \begin{cases} f(t) & \text{if} \quad 0 < t < L; \\ -f(-t) & \text{if} \ -L < t < 0 \end{cases} \tag{10}$$

and by $f_O(t + 2L) = f_O(t)$ for all t. The Fourier series of the odd extension f_O, given by Eqs. (7) and (8), will contain only sine terms and is called the *Fourier sine series* of the original function f.

Definition: Fourier Cosine and Sine Series

Suppose that the function $f(t)$ is piecewise continuous on the interval $[0, L]$. Then the **Fourier cosine series** of f is the series

➤
$$f(t) = \frac{a_0}{2} + \sum_{n=1}^{\infty} a_n \cos \frac{n\pi t}{L} \qquad (11)$$

with

➤
$$a_n = \frac{2}{L} \int_0^L f(t) \cos \frac{n\pi t}{L} \, dt. \qquad (12)$$

The **Fourier sine series** of f is the series

➤
$$f(t) = \sum_{n=1}^{\infty} b_n \sin \frac{n\pi t}{L} \qquad (13)$$

with

➤
$$b_n = \frac{2}{L} \int_0^L f(t) \sin \frac{n\pi t}{L} \, dt. \qquad (14)$$

Assuming that f is piecewise smooth and satisfies the average value condition $f(t) = \frac{1}{2}[f(t+) + f(t-)]$ at each of its isolated discontinuities, Theorem 1 of Section 9.2 implies that each of the two series in (11) and (13) converges to $f(t)$ for all t in the interval $0 < t < L$. Outside this interval, the cosine series in (11) converges to the even period $2L$ extension of f, whereas the sine series in (13) converges to the odd period $2L$ extension of f. In many cases of interest we have no concern with the values of f outside the original interval $(0, L)$, and therefore the choice between (11) and (12) or (13) and (14) is determined by whether we prefer to represent $f(t)$ in the interval $(0, L)$ by a cosine series or a sine series. (See Example 2 for a situation that dictates our choice between a Fourier cosine series and a Fourier sine series to represent a given function.)

Example 1

Suppose that $f(t) = t$ for $0 < t < L$. Find both the Fourier cosine series and the Fourier sine series for f.

Solution Equation (12) gives

$$a_0 = \frac{2}{L} \int_0^L t \, dt = \frac{2}{L} \left[\frac{1}{2} t^2 \right]_0^L = L$$

and

$$a_n = \frac{2}{L} \int_0^L t \cos \frac{n\pi t}{L} \, dt = \frac{2L}{n^2 \pi^2} \int_0^{n\pi} u \cos u \, du$$

$$= \frac{2L}{n^2 \pi^2} \Big[u \sin u + \cos u \Big]_0^{n\pi} = \begin{cases} -\dfrac{4L}{n^2 \pi^2} & \text{for } n \text{ odd;} \\ \quad 0 & \text{for } n \text{ even.} \end{cases}$$

Thus the Fourier cosine series of f is

$$t = \frac{L}{2} - \frac{4L}{\pi^2}\left(\cos\frac{\pi t}{L} + \frac{1}{3^2}\cos\frac{3\pi t}{L} + \frac{1}{5^2}\cos\frac{5\pi t}{L} + \cdots\right) \tag{15}$$

for $0 < t < L$. Next, Eq. (14) gives

$$b_n = \frac{2}{L}\int_0^L t\sin\frac{n\pi t}{L}\,dt = \frac{2L}{n^2\pi^2}\int_0^{n\pi} u\sin u\,du$$

$$= \frac{2L}{n^2\pi^2}\Big[-u\cos u + \sin u\Big]_0^{n\pi} = \frac{2L}{n\pi}(-1)^{n+1}.$$

Thus the Fourier sine series of f is

$$t = \frac{2L}{\pi}\left(\sin\frac{\pi t}{L} - \frac{1}{2}\sin\frac{2\pi t}{L} + \frac{1}{3}\sin\frac{3\pi t}{L} - \cdots\right) \tag{16}$$

FIGURE 9.3.3. The even period $2L$ extension of f.

for $0 < t < L$. The series in Eq. (15) converges to the even period $2L$ extension of f shown in Fig. 9.3.3; the series in Eq. (16) converges to the odd period $2L$ extension shown in Fig. 9.3.4. ∎

FIGURE 9.3.4. The odd period $2L$ extension of f.

Termwise Differentiation of Fourier Series

In this and in subsequent sections, we want to consider Fourier series as possible solutions of differential equations. In order to substitute a Fourier series for the unknown dependent variable in a differential equation to check whether it is a solution, we first need to differentiate the series in order to compute the derivatives that appear in the equation. Care is required here; term-by-term differentiation of an infinite series of variable terms is not always valid. Theorem 1 gives sufficient conditions for the validity of termwise differentiation of a Fourier series.

THEOREM 1: Termwise Differentiation of Fourier Series

Suppose that the function f is continuous for all t, periodic with period $2L$, and that its derivative f' is piecewise smooth for all t. Then the Fourier series of f' is the series

$$f'(t) = \sum_{n=1}^{\infty}\left(-\frac{n\pi}{L}a_n\sin\frac{n\pi t}{L} + \frac{n\pi}{L}b_n\cos\frac{n\pi t}{L}\right) \tag{17}$$

obtained by termwise differentiation of the Fourier series

$$f(t) = \frac{a_0}{2} + \sum_{n=1}^{\infty}\left(a_n\cos\frac{n\pi t}{L} + b_n\sin\frac{n\pi t}{L}\right). \tag{18}$$

Proof: The point of the theorem is that the differentiated series in Eq. (17) actually converges to $f'(t)$ (with the usual proviso about average values). But because f' is periodic and piecewise smooth, we know from Theorem 1 of Section 9.2 that the Fourier series of f' converges to $f'(t)$:

$$f'(t) = \frac{\alpha_0}{2} + \sum_{n=1}^{\infty}\left(\alpha_n\cos\frac{n\pi t}{L} + \beta_n\sin\frac{n\pi t}{L}\right). \tag{19}$$

In order to prove Theorem 1, it therefore suffices to show that the series in Eqs. (17) and (19) are identical. We will do so under the additional hypothesis that f' is continuous everywhere. Then

$$\alpha_0 = \frac{1}{L} \int_{-L}^{L} f'(t)\, dt = \frac{1}{L} \Big[f(t) \Big]_{-L}^{L} = 0$$

because $f(L) = f(-L)$ by periodicity, and

$$\alpha_n = \frac{1}{L} \int_{-L}^{L} f'(t) \cos \frac{n\pi t}{L}\, dt$$

$$= \frac{1}{L} \left[f(t) \cos \frac{n\pi t}{L} \right]_{-L}^{L} + \frac{n\pi}{L} \cdot \frac{1}{L} \int_{-L}^{L} f(t) \sin \frac{n\pi t}{L}\, dt$$

—integration by parts. It follows that

$$\alpha_n = \frac{n\pi}{L} b_n.$$

Similarly, we find that

$$\beta_n = -\frac{n\pi}{L} a_n,$$

and therefore the series in Eqs. (17) and (19) are, indeed, identical.   ▲

     Whereas the assumption that the derivative f' is continuous is merely a convenience—the proof of Theorem 1 can be strengthened to allow isolated discontinuities in f'—it is important to note that the conclusion of Theorem 1 generally fails when f itself is discontinuous. For example, consider the Fourier series

$$t = \frac{2L}{\pi} \left(\sin \frac{\pi t}{L} - \frac{1}{2} \sin \frac{2\pi t}{L} + \frac{1}{3} \sin \frac{3\pi t}{L} - \cdots \right), \tag{16}$$

$-L < t < L$, of the discontinuous sawtooth function having the graph shown in Fig. 9.3.4. All the hypotheses of Theorem 1 are satisfied apart from the continuity of f, and f has only isolated jump discontinuities. But the series

$$2 \left(\cos \frac{\pi t}{L} - \cos \frac{2\pi t}{L} + \cos \frac{3\pi t}{L} - \cdots \right) \tag{20}$$

obtained by differentiating the series in Eq. (16) term by term diverges (for instance, when $t = 0$ and when $t = L$), and therefore termwise differentiation of the series in Eq. (16) is not valid.

     By contrast, consider the [continuous] triangular wave function $f(t)$ having the graph shown in Fig. 9.3.3, with $f(t) = |t|$ for $-L < t < L$. This function satisfies all the hypotheses of Theorem 1, so its Fourier series

$$f(t) = \frac{L}{2} - \frac{4L}{\pi^2} \left(\cos \frac{\pi t}{L} + \frac{1}{3^2} \cos \frac{3\pi t}{L} + \frac{1}{5^2} \cos \frac{5\pi t}{L} + \cdots \right) \tag{15}$$

can be differentiated termwise. The result is

$$f'(t) = \frac{4}{\pi} \left(\sin \frac{\pi t}{L} + \frac{1}{3} \sin \frac{3\pi t}{L} + \frac{1}{5} \sin \frac{5\pi t}{L} + \cdots \right), \tag{21}$$

which is the Fourier series of the period $2L$ square wave function that takes the value -1 for $-L < t < 0$ and $+1$ for $0 < t < L$.

Fourier Series Solutions of Differential Equations

In the remainder of this chapter and in Chapter 10, we will frequently need to solve endpoint value problems of the general form

$$ax'' + bx' + cx = f(t) \quad (0 < t < L); \tag{22}$$
$$x(0) = x(L) = 0, \tag{23}$$

where the function $f(t)$ is given. We might consider applying the techniques of Chapter 3, solving the problem by

1. First finding the general solution $x_c = c_1 x_1 + c_2 x_2$ of the associated homogeneous differential equation;
2. Then finding a single particular solution x_p of the nonhomogeneous equation in (22); and
3. Finally, determining the constants c_1 and c_2 so that $x = x_c + x_p$ satisfies the endpoint conditions in (23).

In many problems, the following Fourier series method is more convenient and more useful. We first extend the definition of the function $f(t)$ to the interval $-L < t < 0$ in an appropriate way, and then to the entire real line by the periodicity conditions $f(t+2L) = f(t)$. Then the function f, if piecewise smooth, has a Fourier series

$$f(t) = \frac{A_0}{2} + \sum_{n=1}^{\infty} \left(A_n \cos \frac{n\pi t}{L} + B_n \sin \frac{n\pi t}{L} \right), \tag{24}$$

which has coefficients $\{A_n\}$ and $\{B_n\}$ that we can and do compute. We then assume that the differential equation in (22) has a solution $x(t)$ with a Fourier series

$$x(t) = \frac{a_0}{2} + \sum_{n=1}^{\infty} \left(a_n \cos \frac{n\pi t}{L} + b_n \sin \frac{n\pi t}{L} \right) \tag{25}$$

that may validly be differentiated twice termwise. We attempt to determine the coefficients in Eq. (25) by first substituting the series in Eqs. (24) and (25) into the differential equation in (22) and then equating coefficients of like terms. If this procedure is carried out in such a way that the resulting series in Eq. (25) also satisfies the endpoint conditions in (23), then we have a "formal Fourier series solution" of the original endpoint value problem; that is, a solution subject to verification of the assumed termwise differentiability. Example 2 illustrates this process.

Example 2 Find a formal Fourier series solution of the endpoint value problem

$$x'' + 4x = 4t, \tag{26}$$
$$x(0) = x(1) = 0. \tag{27}$$

Solution Here $f(t) = 4t$ for $0 < t < 1$. A crucial first step—which we did not make explicit in the preceding outline—is to choose a periodic extension $f(t)$ so that each term in its Fourier series satisfies the endpoint conditions in (27). For this purpose we choose the odd period 2 extension, because each term of the form $\sin n\pi t$ satisfies (27). Then from the series in Eq. (16) with $L = 1$, we get the Fourier series

$$4t = \frac{8}{\pi} \sum_{n=1}^{\infty} \frac{(-1)^{n+1}}{n} \sin n\pi t \tag{28}$$

for $0 < t < 1$. We therefore anticipate a sine series solution

$$x(t) = \sum_{n=1}^{\infty} b_n \sin n\pi t, \tag{29}$$

noting that any such series will satisfy the endpoint conditions in (27). When we substitute the series in (28) and (29) in Eq. (26), the result is

$$\sum_{n=1}^{\infty} (-n^2\pi^2 + 4)b_n \sin n\pi t = \frac{8}{\pi} \sum_{n=1}^{\infty} \frac{(-1)^{n+1}}{n} \sin n\pi t. \tag{30}$$

We next equate coefficients of like terms in Eq. (30). This yields

$$b_n = \frac{8 \cdot (-1)^{n+1}}{n\pi(4 - n^2\pi^2)},$$

so our formal Fourier series solution is

$$x(t) = \frac{8}{\pi} \sum_{n=1}^{\infty} \frac{(-1)^{n+1} \sin n\pi t}{n(4 - n^2\pi^2)}. \tag{31}$$

In Problem 16 we ask you to derive the exact solution

$$x(t) = t - \frac{\sin 2t}{\sin 2} \qquad (0 \leqq t \leqq 1), \tag{32}$$

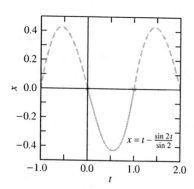

FIGURE 9.3.5. Graph of the solution in Example 2.

and to verify that (31) is the Fourier series of the odd period 2 extension of this solution.

   The dashed curve in Fig. 9.3.5 was plotted by summing 10 terms of the Fourier series in (31). The solid curve for $0 \leqq t \leqq 2$ is the graph of the exact solution in (32).   ■

Termwise Integration of Fourier Series

Theorem 2 guarantees that the Fourier series of a piecewise continuous periodic function can always be integrated term by term, whether or not it converges! A proof is outlined in Problem 25.

THEOREM 2: Termwise Integration of Fourier Series

Suppose that f is a piecewise continuous periodic function with period $2L$ and Fourier series

$$f(t) \sim \frac{a_0}{2} + \sum_{n=1}^{\infty} \left(a_n \cos \frac{n\pi t}{L} + b_n \sin \frac{n\pi t}{L} \right), \tag{33}$$

which may not converge. Then

$$\int_0^t f(s)\, ds = \frac{a_0 t}{2} + \sum_{n=1}^{\infty} \frac{L}{n\pi} \left[a_n \sin \frac{n\pi t}{L} - b_n \left(\cos \frac{n\pi t}{L} - 1 \right) \right], \tag{34}$$

with the series on the right-hand side convergent for all t. Note that the series in Eq. (34) is the result of term-by-term integration of the series in (33). ▲

Example 3 Let us attempt to verify the conclusion of Theorem 2 in the case that $f(t)$ is the period 2π function such that

$$f(t) = \begin{cases} -1, & -\pi < t < 0; \\ +1, & 0 < t < \pi. \end{cases} \tag{35}$$

By Example 1 of Section 9.1, the Fourier series of f is

$$f(t) = \frac{4}{\pi} \left(\sin t + \frac{1}{3} \sin 3t + \frac{1}{5} \sin 5t + \cdots \right). \tag{36}$$

Theorem 2 then implies that

$$F(t) = \int_0^t f(s)\, ds$$

$$= \int_0^t \frac{4}{\pi} \left(\sin s + \frac{1}{3} \sin 3s + \frac{1}{5} \sin 5s + \cdots \right) ds$$

$$= \frac{4}{\pi} \left[(1 - \cos t) + \frac{1}{3^2}(1 - \cos 3t) + \frac{1}{5^2}(1 - \cos 5t) + \cdots \right].$$

Thus

$$F(t) = \frac{4}{\pi} \left(1 + \frac{1}{3^2} + \frac{1}{5^2} + \cdots \right)$$

$$\quad - \frac{4}{\pi} \left(\cos t + \frac{1}{3^2} \cos 3t + \frac{1}{5^2} \cos 5t + \cdots \right). \tag{37}$$

On the other hand, direct integration of (35) yields

$$F(t) = \int_0^t f(s)\, ds = |t| = \begin{cases} -t, & -\pi < t < 0, \\ t, & 0 < t < \pi. \end{cases}$$

We know from Example 1 in this section (with $L = \pi$) that

$$|t| = \frac{\pi}{2} - \frac{4}{\pi}\left(\cos t + \frac{1}{3^2}\cos 3t + \frac{1}{5^2}\cos 5t + \cdots\right). \tag{38}$$

We also know from Eq. (18) of Section 9.2 that

$$1 + \frac{1}{3^2} + \frac{1}{5^2} + \frac{1}{7^2} + \cdots = \frac{\pi^2}{8},$$

so it follows that the two series in Eqs. (37) and (38) are indeed identical. ■

9.3 Problems

In Problems 1 through 10, a function $f(t)$ defined on an interval $0 < t < L$ is given. Find the Fourier cosine and sine series of f and sketch the graphs of the two extensions of f to which these two series converge.

1. $f(t) = 1,\ 0 < t < \pi$

2. $f(t) = 1 - t,\ 0 < t < 1$

3. $f(t) = 1 - t,\ 0 < t < 2$

4. $f(t) = \begin{cases} t, & 0 < t \leq 1; \\ 2 - t, & 1 \leq t < 2 \end{cases}$

5. $f(t) = \begin{cases} 0, & 0 < t < 1; \\ 1, & 1 < t < 2; \\ 0, & 2 < t < 3 \end{cases}$

6. $f(t) = t^2,\ 0 < t < \pi$

7. $f(t) = t(\pi - t),\ 0 < t < \pi$

8. $f(t) = t - t^2,\ 0 < t < 1$

9. $f(t) = \sin t,\ 0 < t < \pi$

10. $f(t) = \begin{cases} \sin t, & 0 < t \leq \pi \\ 0, & \pi \leq t < 2\pi \end{cases}$

Find formal Fourier series solutions of the endpoint value problems in Problems 11 through 14.

11. $x'' + 2x = 1,\ x(0) = x(\pi) = 0$

12. $x'' - 4x = 1,\ x(0) = x(\pi) = 0$

13. $x'' + x = t,\ x(0) = x(1) = 0$

14. $x'' + 2x = t,\ x(0) = x(2) = 0$

15. Find a formal Fourier series solution of the endpoint value problem

$$x'' + 2x = t, \quad x'(0) = x'(\pi) = 0.$$

(*Suggestion:* Use a Fourier cosine series in which each term satisfies the endpoint conditions.)

16. (a) Derive the solution $x(t) = t - (\sin 2t)/(\sin 2)$ of the endpoint value problem

$$x'' + 4x = 4t, \quad x(0) = x(1) = 0.$$

(b) Show that the series in Eq. (31) is the Fourier sine series of the solution in part (a).

17. (a) Suppose that f is an even function. Show that

$$\int_{-a}^0 f(t)\, dt = \int_0^a f(t)\, dt.$$

(b) Suppose that f is an odd function. Show that

$$\int_{-a}^0 f(t)\, dt = -\int_0^a f(t)\, dt.$$

18. By Example 2 of Section 9.2, the Fourier series of the period 2 function f with $f(t) = t^2$ for $0 < t < 2$ is

$$f(t) = \frac{4}{3} + \frac{4}{\pi^2}\sum_{n=1}^{\infty}\frac{\cos n\pi t}{n^2} - \frac{4}{\pi}\sum_{n=1}^{\infty}\frac{\sin n\pi t}{n}.$$

Show that the termwise derivative of this series does not converge to $f'(t)$.

19. Begin with the Fourier series

$$t = 2\sum_{n=1}^{\infty}\frac{(-1)^{n+1}}{n}\sin nt, \quad -\pi < t < \pi,$$

and integrate termwise three times in succession to obtain the series

$$\frac{1}{24}t^4 = \frac{\pi^2 t^2}{12} - 2\sum_{n=1}^{\infty}\frac{(-1)^n}{n^4}\cos nt + 2\sum_{n=1}^{\infty}\frac{(-1)^n}{n^4}.$$

20. Substitute $t = \pi/2$ and $t = \pi$ in the series of Problem 19 to obtain the summations

$$\sum_{n=1}^{\infty} \frac{1}{n^4} = \frac{\pi^4}{90}, \quad \sum_{n=1}^{\infty} \frac{(-1)^{n+1}}{n^4} = \frac{7\pi^4}{720},$$

and

$$1 + \frac{1}{3^4} + \frac{1}{5^4} + \frac{1}{7^4} + \cdots = \frac{\pi^4}{96}.$$

21. (*Odd half-multiple sine series*) Let $f(t)$ be given for $0 < t < L$, and define $F(t)$ for $0 < t < 2L$ as follows:

$$F(t) = \begin{cases} f(t), & 0 < t < L; \\ f(2L - t), & L < t < 2L. \end{cases}$$

Thus the graph of $F(t)$ is symmetric around the line $t = L$ (Fig. 9.3.6). Then the period $4L$ Fourier sine series of F is

$$F(t) = \sum_{n=1}^{\infty} b_n \sin \frac{n\pi t}{2L},$$

where

$$b_n = \frac{1}{L} \int_0^L f(t) \sin \frac{n\pi t}{2L} \, dt$$
$$+ \frac{1}{L} \int_L^{2L} f(2L - t) \sin \frac{n\pi t}{2L} \, dt.$$

Substitute $s = 2L - t$ in the second integral to derive the series (for $0 < t < L$)

$$f(t) = \sum_{n \text{ odd}} b_n \sin \frac{n\pi t}{2L},$$

where

$$b_n = \frac{2}{L} \int_0^L f(t) \sin \frac{n\pi t}{2L} \, dt \quad (n \text{ odd}).$$

FIGURE 9.3.6. Construction of F from f in Problem 21.

22. (*Odd half-multiple cosine series*) Let $f(t)$ be given for $0 < t < L$, and define $G(t)$ for $0 < t < 2L$ as follows:

$$G(t) = \begin{cases} f(t), & 0 < t < L; \\ -f(2L - t), & L < t < 2L. \end{cases}$$

Use the period $4L$ Fourier cosine series of $G(t)$ to derive the series (for $0 < t < L$)

$$f(t) = \sum_{n \text{ odd}} a_n \cos \frac{n\pi t}{2L},$$

where

$$a_n = \frac{2}{L} \int_0^L f(t) \cos \frac{n\pi t}{2L} \, dt \quad (n \text{ odd}).$$

23. Given: $f(t) = t$, $0 < t < \pi$. Derive the odd half-multiple sine series (Problem 21)

$$f(t) = \frac{8}{\pi} \sum_{n \text{ odd}} \frac{(-1)^{(n-1)/2}}{n^2} \sin \frac{nt}{2}.$$

24. Given the endpoint value problem

$$x'' - x = t, \quad x(0) = 0, \quad x'(\pi) = 0,$$

note that any constant multiple of $\sin(nt/2)$ with n odd satisfies the endpoint conditions. Hence use the odd half-multiple sine series of Problem 23 to derive the formal Fourier series solution

$$x(t) = \frac{32}{\pi} \sum_{n \text{ odd}} \frac{(-1)^{(n+1)/2}}{n^2(n^2 + 4)} \sin \frac{nt}{2}.$$

25. In this problem we outline the proof of Theorem 2. Suppose that $f(t)$ is a piecewise continuous period $2L$ function. Define

$$F(t) = \int_0^t \left[f(s) - \tfrac{1}{2}a_0 \right] ds,$$

where $\{a_n\}$ and $\{b_n\}$ denote the Fourier coefficients of $f(t)$. **(a)** Show directly that $F(t + 2L) = F(t)$, so that F is a continuous period $2L$ function and therefore has a convergent Fourier series

$$F(t) = \frac{A_0}{2} + \sum_{n=1}^{\infty} \left(A_n \cos \frac{n\pi t}{L} + B_n \sin \frac{n\pi t}{L} \right).$$

(b) Suppose that $n \geqq 1$. Show by direct computation that

$$A_n = -\frac{L}{n\pi} b_n \quad \text{and} \quad B_n = \frac{L}{n\pi} a_n.$$

(c) Thus

$$\int_0^t f(s) \, ds = \frac{t}{2} a_0 + \frac{1}{2} A_0$$
$$+ \sum_{n=1}^{\infty} \frac{L}{n\pi} \left(a_n \sin \frac{n\pi t}{L} - b_n \cos \frac{n\pi t}{L} \right).$$

Finally, substitute $t = 0$ to see that

$$\frac{1}{2} A_0 = \sum_{n=1}^{\infty} \frac{L}{n\pi} b_n.$$

9.3 Application: **Fourier Series of Piecewise Smooth Functions**

Most computer algebra systems permit the use of unit step functions for the efficient derivation of Fourier series of "piecewise-defined" functions. Here we illustrate the use of *Maple* for this purpose. *Mathematica* and MATLAB versions can be found in the applications manual that accompanies this text.

Let the "unit function" unit(t, a, b) have the value 1 on the interval $a \leq t < b$ and the value 0 otherwise. Then we can define a given piecewise smooth function $f(t)$ as a "linear combination" of different unit functions corresponding to the separate intervals on which the function is smooth, with the unit function for each interval multiplied by the formula defining $f(t)$ on that interval. For example, consider the even period 2π function whose graph is shown in Fig. 9.3.7. This "trapezoidal wave function" is defined for $0 < t < \pi$ by

$$f(t) = \frac{\pi}{3}\text{unit}\left(t, 0, \frac{\pi}{6}\right)$$

$$+ \left(\frac{\pi}{2} - t\right)\text{unit}\left(t, \frac{\pi}{6}, \frac{5\pi}{6}\right) + \left(-\frac{\pi}{3}\right)\text{unit}\left(t, \frac{5\pi}{6}, \pi\right). \tag{1}$$

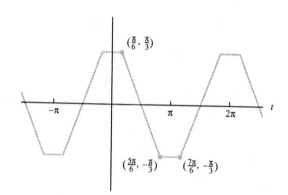

FIGURE 9.3.7. Even period 2π trapezoidal wave function.

The unit step function (with values 0 for $t < 0$ and 1 for $t > 0$) is available in *Maple* as the "Heaviside function." For instance, Heaviside$(-2) = 0$ and Heaviside$(3) = 1$. The unit function on the interval $[a, b]$ can be defined by

```
unit := (t,a,b) -> Heaviside(t-a) - Heaviside(t-b):
```

Then the trapezoidal wave function in Eq. (1) is defined for $0 \leq t \leq \pi$ by

```
f := t -> (Pi/3)*unit(t, 0, Pi/6) +
          (Pi/2 - t)*unit(t, Pi/6, 5*Pi/6) +
          (-Pi/3)*unit(t, 5*Pi/6, Pi):
```

We can now calculate the Fourier coefficients in the cosine series $f(t) = \frac{1}{2}a_0 + \sum a_n \cos nt$.

```
a := n -> (2/Pi)*int(f(t)*cos(n*t), t=0..Pi);
```

We then find that a typical partial sum of the series is given by

```
fourierSum := a(0)/2 + sum(a(n)*cos(n*t), n=1..25);
```

$$fourierSum := 2\frac{\sqrt{3}}{\pi}\frac{\cos(t)}{} - \frac{2}{25}\frac{\sqrt{3}}{\pi}\frac{\cos(5t)}{} - \frac{2}{49}\frac{\sqrt{3}}{\pi}\frac{\cos(7t)}{}$$

$$+ \frac{2}{121}\frac{\sqrt{3}}{\pi}\frac{\cos(11t)}{} + \frac{2}{169}\frac{\sqrt{3}}{\pi}\frac{\cos(13t)}{} - \frac{2}{289}\frac{\sqrt{3}}{\pi}\frac{\cos(17t)}{}$$

$$- \frac{2}{361}\frac{\sqrt{3}}{\pi}\frac{\cos(19t)}{} + \frac{2}{529}\frac{\sqrt{3}}{\pi}\frac{\cos(23t)}{} + \frac{2}{625}\frac{\sqrt{3}}{\pi}\frac{\cos(25t)}{}$$

Thus we discover the lovely Fourier series

$$f(t) = \frac{2\sqrt{3}}{\pi} \sum \frac{(\pm)\cos nt}{n^2} \tag{2}$$

with a +--++--++ pattern of signs, and where the summation is taken over all odd positive integers n that are *not* multiples of 3. You can enter the command

```
plot(fourierSum, t=-2*Pi..3*Pi);
```

to verify that this Fourier series is consistent with Fig. 9.3.7.

You can then apply this method to find the Fourier series of the following period 2π functions.

1. The even square wave function whose graph is shown in Fig. 9.3.8.
2. The even and odd triangular wave functions whose graphs are shown in Figs. 9.2.4 and 9.3.9.
3. The odd trapezoidal wave function whose graph is shown in Fig. 9.2.5.

Then find similarly the Fourier series of some piecewise smooth functions of your own choice, perhaps ones that have periods other than 2π and are neither even nor odd.

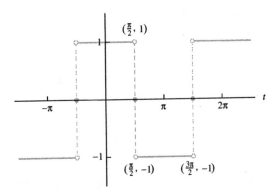

FIGURE 9.3.8. Even period 2π square wave function.

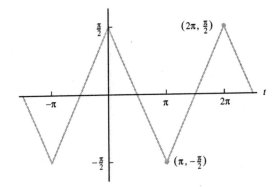

FIGURE 9.3.9. Even period 2π triangular wave function.

9.4 Applications of Fourier Series

We consider first the motion of a mass m on a spring with Hooke's constant k under the influence of a *periodic* external force $F(t)$, as indicated in Fig. 9.4.1. Its displacement $x(t)$ from equilibrium satisfies the familiar equation

$$mx'' + kx = F(t). \tag{1}$$

FIGURE 9.4.1. A mass-and-spring system with external force.

The general solution of Eq. (1) is of the form

$$x(t) = c_1 \cos \omega_0 t + c_2 \sin \omega_0 t + x_p(t), \tag{2}$$

where $\omega_0 = \sqrt{k/m}$ is the natural frequency of the system and $x_p(t)$ is a particular solution of Eq. (1). The values c_1 and c_2 would be determined by the initial conditions. Here we want to use Fourier series to find a *periodic* particular solution of Eq. (1). We will denote it by $x_{sp}(t)$ and call it a **steady periodic solution.**

We assume for simplicity that $F(t)$ is an odd function with period $2L$, so its Fourier series has the form

$$F(t) = \sum_{n=1}^{\infty} B_n \sin \frac{n\pi t}{L}. \tag{3}$$

If $n\pi/L$ is not equal to ω_0 for any positive integer n, we can determine a steady periodic solution of the form

$$x_{sp}(t) = \sum_{n=1}^{\infty} b_n \sin \frac{n\pi t}{L} \tag{4}$$

by substituting the series in Eqs. (3) and (4) in Eq. (1) to find the coefficients in Eq. (4). Example 1 illustrates this procedure.

Example 1

Suppose that $m = 2$ kg, $k = 32$ N/m, and that $F(t)$ is an odd periodic force with a period of 2 s given in one period by

$$F(t) = \begin{cases} +10\,\text{N} & \text{if } 0 < t < 1; \\ -10\,\text{N} & \text{if } 1 < t < 2. \end{cases} \tag{5}$$

Find the steady periodic motion $x_{sp}(t)$.

Solution

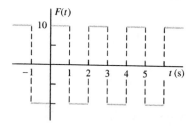

FIGURE 9.4.2. The graph of the forcing function of Example 1.

The graph of the periodic forcing function $F(t)$ is shown in Fig. 9.4.2. By essentially the same computation as in Example 1 of Section 9.1, the Fourier series of $F(t)$ is

$$F(t) = \frac{40}{\pi} \sum_{n \text{ odd}} \frac{\sin n\pi t}{n}; \tag{6}$$

note that it contains only terms corresponding to n odd. When we substitute this series and

$$x_{sp}(t) = \sum_{n \text{ odd}} b_n \sin n\pi t, \tag{7}$$

a trial solution likewise containing only odd terms, into Eq. (1) with $m = 2$ and $k = 32$, we get

$$\sum_{n \text{ odd}} b_n(-2n^2\pi^2 + 32) \sin n\pi t = \frac{40}{\pi} \sum_{n \text{ odd}} \frac{\sin n\pi t}{n}.$$

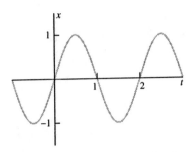

FIGURE 9.4.3. The graph of $x_{sp}(t)$.

We equate coefficients of like terms; the result is that

$$b_n = \frac{20}{n\pi(16 - n^2\pi^2)} \qquad \text{for } n \text{ odd.}$$

Hence

$$x_{sp}(t) = \frac{20}{\pi} \sum_{n \text{ odd}} \frac{\sin n\pi t}{n(16 - n^2\pi^2)}. \tag{8}$$

The fact that each term in Eq. (8) is symmetric around $t = \frac{1}{2}$ suggests that $x_{sp}(t)$ is maximal when $t = \frac{1}{2}$, as does the graph in Fig. 9.4.3. Assuming this, we find the amplitude of the steady periodic motion to be

$$x_{sp}\left(\tfrac{1}{2}\right) = \frac{20}{\pi} \sum_{n \text{ odd}} \frac{1}{n(16 - n^2\pi^2)} \sin \frac{n\pi}{2}.$$

The first 10 terms yield $x\left(\tfrac{1}{2}\right) \approx 1.063$ m. ∎

If there is a nonzero term $B_N \sin(N\pi t/L)$ in the Fourier series of $F(t)$ for which $N\pi/L = \omega_0$, then this term causes **pure resonance**. The reason is that the equation

$$mx'' + kx = B_N \sin \omega_0 t$$

has the resonance solution

$$x(t) = -\frac{B_N}{2m\omega_0} t \cos \omega_0 t$$

if $\omega_0 = \sqrt{k/m}$. The solution corresponding to Eq. (4) in this case is then

$$x(t) = -\frac{B_N}{2m\omega_0} t \cos \omega_0 t + \sum_{n \neq N} \frac{B_N}{m(\omega_0^2 - n^2\pi^2/L^2)} \sin \frac{n\pi t}{L}. \tag{9}$$

Example 2   Suppose that $m = 2$ kg and $k = 32$ N/m as in Example 1. Determine whether pure resonance will occur if $F(t)$ is the odd periodic function defined in one period to be

(a) $F(t) = \begin{cases} +10, & 0 < t < \pi; \\ -10, & \pi < t < 2\pi. \end{cases}$

(b) $F(t) = 10t, \quad -\pi < t < \pi$.

Solution   (a) The natural frequency is $\omega_0 = 4$, and the Fourier series of $F(t)$ is

$$F(t) = \frac{40}{\pi}\left(\sin t + \frac{1}{3}\sin 3t + \frac{1}{5}\sin 5t + \cdots \right).$$

Because this series contains no $\sin 4t$ term, no resonance occurs.

(b) In this case the Fourier series is

$$F(t) = 20 \sum_{n=1}^{\infty} \frac{(-1)^{n+1}}{n} \sin nt.$$

Pure resonance occurs because of the presence of the term containing the factor $\sin 4t$. ∎

Example 3 illustrates the *near resonance* that can occur when a single term in the solution is magnified because its frequency is close to the natural frequency ω_0.

Example 3   Find a steady periodic solution of

$$x'' + 10x = F(t), \tag{10}$$

where $F(t)$ is the period 4 function with $F(t) = 5t$ for $-2 < t < 2$ and Fourier series

$$F(t) = \frac{20}{\pi} \sum_{n=1}^{\infty} \frac{(-1)^{n+1}}{n} \sin \frac{n\pi t}{2}. \tag{11}$$

Solution   When we substitute Eq. (11) and

$$x_{\text{sp}}(t) = \sum_{n=1}^{\infty} b_n \sin \frac{n\pi t}{2}$$

in (10), we obtain

$$\sum_{n=1}^{\infty} b_n \left(-\frac{n^2\pi^2}{4} + 10 \right) \sin \frac{n\pi t}{2} = \frac{20}{\pi} \sum_{n=1}^{\infty} \frac{(-1)^{n+1}}{n} \sin \frac{n\pi t}{2}.$$

We equate coefficients of like terms and then solve for b_n to get the steady periodic solution

$$x_{\text{sp}}(t) = \frac{80}{\pi} \sum_{n=1}^{\infty} \frac{(-1)^{n+1}}{n(40 - n^2\pi^2)} \sin \frac{n\pi t}{2}$$

$$\approx (0.8452) \sin \frac{\pi t}{2} - (24.4111) \sin \frac{2\pi t}{2} - (0.1738) \sin \frac{3\pi t}{2} + \cdots.$$

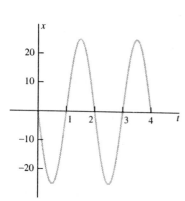

FIGURE 9.4.4. The graph of $x_{\text{sp}}(t)$.

The very large magnitude of the second term results from the fact that $\omega_0 = \sqrt{10} \approx \pi = 2\pi/2$. Thus the dominant motion of a spring with the differential equation in (10) would be an oscillation with frequency π radians per second, period 2 s, and amplitude about 24, consistent with the graph of $x_{\text{sp}}(t)$ shown in Fig. 9.4.4. ∎

Damped Forced Oscillations

FIGURE 9.4.5. A damped mass-and-spring system with external force.

Now we consider the motion of a mass m attached both to a spring with Hooke's constant k and to a dashpot with damping constant c, under the influence of a *periodic* external force $F(t)$ (Fig. 9.4.5). The displacement $x(t)$ of the mass from equilibrium satisfies the equation

$$mx'' + cx' + kx = F(t). \tag{12}$$

We recall from Problem 25 of Section 3.6 that the steady periodic solution of Eq. (12) with $F(t) = F_0 \sin \omega t$ is

$$x(t) = \frac{F_0}{\sqrt{(k - m\omega^2)^2 + (c\omega)^2}} \sin(\omega t - \alpha), \tag{13}$$

where

$$\alpha = \tan^{-1} \frac{c\omega}{k - m\omega^2}, \quad 0 \le \alpha \le \pi. \tag{14}$$

If $F(t)$ is an odd period $2L$ function with Fourier series

$$F(t) = \sum_{n=1}^{\infty} B_n \sin \frac{n\pi t}{L}, \tag{15}$$

then the preceding formulas yield, by superposition, the steady periodic solution

$$x_{\text{sp}}(t) = \sum_{n=1}^{\infty} \frac{B_n \sin(\omega_n t - \alpha_n)}{\sqrt{(k - m\omega_n^2)^2 + (c\omega_n)^2}}, \tag{16}$$

where $\omega_n = n\pi/L$ and α_n is the angle determined by Eq. (14) with this value of ω. Example 4 illustrates the interesting fact that the dominant frequency of the steady periodic solution can be an *integral multiple* of the frequency of the force $F(t)$.

| Example 4 | Suppose that $m = 3$ kg, $c = 0.02$ N/m/s, $k = 27$ N/m, and $F(t)$ is the odd period 2π function with $F(t) = \pi t - t^2$ if $0 < t < \pi$. Find the steady periodic motion $x_{\text{sp}}(t)$. |

Solution We find that the Fourier series of $F(t)$ is

$$F(t) = \frac{8}{\pi} \left(\sin t + \frac{1}{3^3} \sin 3t + \frac{1}{5^3} \sin 5t + \cdots \right). \tag{17}$$

Thus $B_n = 0$ for n even, $B_n = 8/(\pi n^3)$ for n odd, and $\omega_n = n$. Equation (16) gives

$$x_{\text{sp}}(t) = \frac{8}{\pi} \sum_{n \text{ odd}} \frac{\sin(nt - \alpha_n)}{n^3 \sqrt{(27 - 3n^2)^2 + (0.02n)^2}} \tag{18}$$

with

$$\alpha_n = \tan^{-1} \frac{(0.02)n}{27 - 3n^2}, \quad 0 \le \alpha_n \le \pi. \tag{19}$$

With the aid of a programmable calculator, we find that

$$x_{\text{sp}}(t) \approx (0.1061) \sin(t - 0.0008) + (1.5719) \sin\left(3t - \tfrac{1}{2}\pi\right)$$
$$+ (0.0004) \sin(5t - 3.1437) + (0.0001) \sin(7t - 3.1428) + \cdots. \tag{20}$$

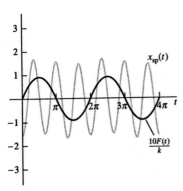

FIGURE 9.4.6. The imposed force and the resulting steady periodic motion in Example 4.

Because the coefficient corresponding to $n = 3$ is much larger than the others, the response of this system is approximately a sinusoidal motion with frequency *three times* that of the input force. Figure 9.4.6 shows $x_{\text{sp}}(t)$ in comparison with the scaled force $10F(t)/k$ that has the appropriate dimension of distance.

What is happening here is this: The mass $m = 3$ on a spring with $k = 27$ has (if we ignore the small effect of the dashpot) a natural frequency $\omega_0 = \sqrt{k/m} = 3$ rad/s. The imposed external force $F(t)$ has a [smallest] period of 2π s and hence a fundamental frequency of 1 rad/s. Consequently, the term corresponding to $n = 3$ in the Fourier series of $F(t)$ (in Eq. (17)) has the same frequency as the natural frequency of the system. Thus near resonance vibrations occur, with the mass completing essentially *three* oscillations for every single oscillation of the external force. This is the physical effect of the dominant $n = 3$ term on the right-hand side in Eq. (20). For instance, you can push a friend in a swing quite high even if you push the swing only every *third* time it returns to you. This also explains why some transformers "hum" at a frequency much higher than 60 Hz.

This is a general phenomenon that must be taken into account in the design of mechanical systems. To avoid the occurrence of abnormally large and potentially destructive near resonance vibrations, the system must be so designed that it is not subject to any external periodic force, some *integral multiple* of whose fundamental frequency is close to a natural frequency of vibration. ∎

9.4 Problems

Find the steady periodic solution $x_{sp}(t)$ of each of the differential equations in 1 through 6. Use a computer algebra system to plot enough terms of the series to determine the visual appearance of the graph of $x_{sp}(t)$.

1. $x'' + 5x = F(t)$, where $F(t)$ is the function of period 2π such that $F(t) = 3$ if $0 < t < \pi$, $F(t) = -3$ if $\pi < t < 2\pi$.

2. $x'' + 10x = F(t)$, where $F(t)$ is the even function of period 4 such that $F(t) = 3$ if $0 < t < 1$, $F(t) = -3$ if $1 < t < 2$.

3. $x'' + 3x = F(t)$, where $F(t)$ is the odd function of period 2π such that $F(t) = 2t$ if $0 < t < \pi$.

4. $x'' + 4x = F(t)$, where $F(t)$ is the even function of period 4 such that $F(t) = 2t$ if $0 < t < 2$.

5. $x'' + 10x = F(t)$, where $F(t)$ is the odd function of period 2 such that $F(t) = t - t^2$ if $0 < t < 1$.

6. $x'' + 2x = F(t)$, where $F(t)$ is the even function of period 2π such that $F(t) = \sin t$ if $0 < t < \pi$.

In each of Problems 7 through 12, the mass m and Hooke's constant k for a mass-and-spring system are given. Determine whether or not pure resonance will occur under the influence of the given external periodic force $F(t)$.

7. $m = 1$, $k = 9$; $F(t)$ is the odd function of period 2π with $F(t) = 1$ for $0 < t < \pi$.

8. $m = 2$, $k = 10$; $F(t)$ is the odd function of period 2 with $F(t) = 1$ for $0 < t < 1$.

9. $m = 3$, $k = 12$; $F(t)$ is the odd function of period 2π with $F(t) = 3$ for $0 < t < \pi$.

10. $m = 1$, $k = 4\pi^2$; $F(t)$ is the odd function of period 2 with $F(t) = 2t$ for $0 < t < 1$.

11. $m = 3$, $k = 48$; $F(t)$ is the even function of period 2π with $F(t) = t$ for $0 < t < \pi$.

12. $m = 2$, $k = 50$; $F(t)$ is the odd function of period 2π with $F(t) = \pi t - t^2$ for $0 < t < \pi$.

In each of Problems 13 through 16, the values of m, c, and k for a damped mass-and-spring system are given. Find the steady periodic motion—in the form of Eq. (16)—of the mass under the influence of the given external force $F(t)$. Compute the coefficients and phase angles for the first three nonzero terms in the series for $x_{sp}(t)$.

13. $m = 1$, $c = 0.1$, $k = 4$; $F(t)$ is the force of Problem 1.

14. $m = 2$, $c = 0.1$, $k = 18$; $F(t)$ is the force of Problem 3.

15. $m = 3$, $c = 1$, $k = 30$; $F(t)$ is the force of Problem 5.

16. $m = 1$, $c = 0.01$, $k = 4$; $F(t)$ is the force of Problem 4.

17. Consider a forced damped mass-and-spring system with $m = \frac{1}{4}$ slug, $c = 0.6$ lb/ft/s, $k = 36$ lb/ft. The force $F(t)$ is the period 2 (s) function with $F(t) = 15$ if $0 < t < 1$, $F(t) = -15$ if $1 < t < 2$. **(a)** Find the steady periodic solution in the form

$$x_{sp}(t) = \sum_{n=1}^{\infty} b_n \sin(n\pi t - \alpha_n).$$

(b) Find the location—to the nearest tenth of an inch—of the mass when $t = 5$ s.

18. Consider a forced damped mass-and-spring system with $m = 1$, $c = 0.01$, and $k = 25$. The force $F(t)$ is the odd function of period 2π with $F(t) = t$ if $0 < t < \pi/2$, $F(t) = \pi - t$ if $\pi/2 < t < \pi$. Find the steady periodic motion; compute enough terms of its series to see that the dominant frequency of the motion is *five* times that of the external force.

9.5 Heat Conduction and Separation of Variables

The most important applications of Fourier series are to the solution of partial differential equations by means of the method of separation of variables that we introduce in this section. Recall that a *partial differential equation* is one containing one or more *partial* derivatives of a dependent variable that is a function of at least two independent variables. An example is the **one-dimensional heat equation**

$$\frac{\partial u}{\partial t} = k\frac{\partial^2 u}{\partial x^2}, \tag{1}$$

in which the dependent variable u is an unknown function of x and t, and k is a given constant.

The Heated Rod

Equation (1) models the variation of temperature u with position x and time t in a heated rod that extends along the x-axis. We assume that the rod has uniform cross section with area A perpendicular to the axis and that it is made of a homogeneous material. We assume further that the cross section of the rod is so small that u is constant on each cross section, and that the lateral surface of the rod is insulated so that no heat can pass through it. Then u will, indeed, be a function of x and t, and heat will flow along the rod in only the x-direction. In general, we envision heat as flowing like a fluid from the warmer to the cooler parts of a body.

The **heat flux** $\phi(x, t)$ in the rod is the rate of flow of heat at time t across a unit area of the cross section at x. Typical units for ϕ are calories per second per square centimeter. The derivation of Eq. (1) is based on the empirical principle that

$$\phi = -K\frac{\partial u}{\partial x}, \tag{2}$$

where the proportionality constant K is called the **thermal conductivity** of the material of the rod. The minus sign in Eq. (2) corresponds to the fact that heat flows in the negative x-direction when $u_x > 0$, whereas ϕ is positive for heat flow in the positive x-direction; in short, heat flows from a hot place to a cold place, not vice versa.

Now consider a small segment of the rod corresponding to the interval $[x, x + \Delta x]$, as shown in Fig. 9.5.1. The rate of flow R (in calories per second) of heat *into* this segment through its two ends is

$$R = A\phi(x, t) - A\phi(x + \Delta x, t) = KA[u_x(x + \Delta x, t) - u_x(x, t)]. \tag{3}$$

FIGURE 9.5.1. Net flow of heat into a short segment of the rod.

The resulting time rate of change u_t of the temperature in the segment depends on its density δ (grams per cubic centimeter) and specific heat c (both assumed constant). The **specific heat** c is the amount of heat (in calories) required to raise by $1°$ the temperature of 1 g of material. Consequently $c\delta u$ calories of heat are required to raise 1 cm^3 of the material from temperature zero to temperature u. A short slice of the rod of length dx has volume $A\,dx$, so $c\delta u A\,dx$ calories of heat are required to raise the temperature of this slice from 0 to u. The **heat content**

$$Q(t) = \int_x^{x+\Delta x} c\delta A u(x, t)\,dx \tag{4}$$

of the segment $[x, x + \Delta x]$ of the rod is the amount of heat needed to raise it from zero to the given temperature $u(x, t)$. Because heat enters and leaves the segment only through its ends, we see from Eq. (3) that

$$Q'(t) = KA[u_x(x + \Delta x, t) - u_x(x, t)], \tag{5}$$

because $R = dQ/dt$. Thus by differentiating Eq. (4) within the integral and applying the mean value theorem for integrals, we see that

$$Q'(t) = \int_x^{x+\Delta x} c\delta A u_t(x,t)\, dx = c\delta A u_t(\overline{x},t)\, \Delta x \tag{6}$$

for some $\overline{x}$ in $(x, x + \Delta x)$. Upon equating the values in Eqs. (5) and (6), we get

$$c\delta A u_t(\overline{x},t)\, \Delta x = KA[u_x(x + \Delta x, t) - u_x(x,t)], \tag{7}$$

so

$$u_t(\overline{x},t) = k\, \frac{u_x(x + \Delta x, t) - u_x(x,t)}{\Delta x}, \tag{8}$$

where

$$k = \frac{K}{c\delta} \tag{9}$$

is the **thermal diffusivity** of the material. Finally, by taking the limit in Eq. (8) as $\Delta x \to 0$ and $\overline{x} \to x$, we obtain the one-dimensional heat equation

$$\frac{\partial u}{\partial t} = k\, \frac{\partial^2 u}{\partial x^2}. \tag{1}$$

Thus the temperature $u(x,t)$ in the thin rod with insulated sides must satisfy this partial differential equation.

Boundary Conditions

Now suppose that the rod has finite length L, extending from $x = 0$ to $x = L$. Its temperature function $u(x,t)$ will be determined among all possible solutions of Eq. (1) by appropriate subsidiary conditions. In fact, whereas a solution of an ordinary differential equation involves arbitrary constants, a solution of a partial differential equation generally involves arbitrary *functions*. In the case of the heated rod, we can specify its temperature function $f(x)$ at time $t = 0$. This gives the *initial condition*

$$u(x,0) = f(x). \tag{10}$$

We may also specify fixed temperatures at the two ends of the rod. For instance, if each end were clamped against a large block of ice at temperature zero, we would have the *endpoint conditions*

$$u(0,t) = u(L,t) = 0 \qquad \text{(for all } t). \tag{11}$$

Combining all this, we get the **boundary value problem**

$$\frac{\partial u}{\partial t} = k\, \frac{\partial^2 u}{\partial x^2} \qquad (0 < x < L, \quad t > 0); \tag{12a}$$

$$u(0,t) = u(L,t) = 0, \tag{12b}$$

$$u(x,0) = f(x). \tag{12c}$$

FIGURE 9.5.2. A geometric interpretation of the boundary value problem in Eqs. (12a)–(12c).

Figure 9.5.2 gives a geometric interpretation of the boundary value problem in (12): We are to find a function $u(x, t)$ that is continuous on the unbounded strip (including its boundary) shaded in the xt-plane. This function must satisfy the differential equation in (12a) at each interior point of the strip, and on the boundary of the strip must have the values prescribed by the *boundary conditions* in (12b) and (12c). Physical intuition suggests that if $f(x)$ is a reasonable function, then there will exist one and only one such function $u(x, t)$.

Instead of having fixed temperatures, the two ends of the rod might be insulated. In this case no heat would flow through either end, so we see from Eq. (2) that the conditions in (12b) would be replaced in the boundary value problem by the endpoint conditions

$$u_x(0, t) = u_x(L, t) = 0 \tag{13}$$

(for all t). Alternatively, the rod could be insulated at one end and have a fixed temperature at the other. This and other endpoint possibilities are discussed in the Problems.

Superposition of Solutions

Note that the heat equation in (12a) is *linear*. That is, any linear combination $u = c_1 u_1 + c_2 u_2$ of two solutions of (12a) is also a solution of (12a); this follows immediately from the linearity of partial differentiation. It is also true that if u_1 and u_2 each satisfy the conditions in (12b), then so does any linear combination $u = c_1 u_1 + c_2 u_2$. The conditions in (12b) are therefore called **homogeneous** boundary conditions (though a more descriptive term might be *linear* boundary conditions). By contrast, the final boundary condition in (12c) is not homogeneous; it is a **nonhomogeneous** boundary condition.

Our overall strategy for solving the boundary value problem in (12) will be to find functions u_1, u_2, u_3, ... that satisfy both the partial differential equation in (12a) and the homogeneous boundary conditions in (12b), and then attempt to combine these functions by superposition, as if they were building blocks, in the hope of obtaining a solution $u = c_1 u_1 + c_2 u_2 + \cdots$ that satisfies the nonhomogeneous condition in (12c) as well. Example 1 illustrates this approach.

Example 1   It is easy to verify by direct substitution that each of the functions

$$u_1(x, t) = e^{-t} \sin x, \quad u_2(x, t) = e^{-4t} \sin 2x, \quad \text{and} \quad u_3(x, t) = e^{-9t} \sin 3x$$

satisfies the equation $u_t = u_{xx}$. Use these functions to construct a solution of the boundary value problem

$$\frac{\partial u}{\partial t} = \frac{\partial^2 u}{\partial x^2} \quad (0 < x < \pi, \ t > 0); \tag{14a}$$

$$u(0, t) = u(\pi, t) = 0, \tag{14b}$$

$$u(x, 0) = 80 \sin^3 x = 60 \sin x - 20 \sin 3x. \tag{14c}$$

Solution   Any linear combination of the form

$$u(x, t) = c_1 u_1(x, t) + c_2 u_2(x, t) + c_3 u_3(x, t)$$
$$= c_1 e^{-t} \sin x + c_2 e^{-4t} \sin 2x + c_3 e^{-9t} \sin 3x$$

satisfies both the differential equation in (14a) and the homogeneous conditions in (14b). Because

$$u(x, 0) = c_1 \sin x + c_2 \sin 2x + c_3 \sin 3x,$$

we see that we can also satisfy the nonhomogeneous condition in (14c) simply by choosing $c_1 = 60$, $c_2 = 0$, and $c_3 = -20$. Thus a solution of the given boundary value problem is

$$u(x, t) = 60e^{-t} \sin x - 20e^{-9t} \sin 3x. \qquad ■$$

The boundary value problem in Example 1 is exceptionally simple in that only a finite number of homogeneous solutions are needed to satisfy by superposition the nonhomogeneous boundary condition. It is more usual that an infinite sequence u_1, u_2, u_3, ... of functions satisfying (12a) and (12b) is required. If so, we write the infinite series

➤
$$u(x, t) = \sum_{n=1}^{\infty} c_n u_n(x, t) \qquad (15)$$

and then attempt to determine the coefficients c_1, c_2, c_3, ... in order to satisfy (12c) as well. The following principle summarizes the properties of this infinite series that must be verified to ensure that we have a solution of the boundary value problem in (12).

PRINCIPLE: Superposition of Solutions

Suppose that each of the functions u_1, u_2, u_3, ... satisfies both the differential equation in (12a) (for $0 < x < L$ and $t > 0$) and the homogeneous conditions in (12b). Suppose also that the coefficients in Eq. (15) are chosen to meet the following three criteria:

1. For $0 < x < L$ and $t > 0$, the function determined by the series in (15) is continuous and termwise differentiable (once with respect to t and twice with respect to x).

2. $\displaystyle\sum_{n=1}^{\infty} c_n u_n(x, 0) = f(x).$

3. The function $u(x, t)$ determined by Eq. (15) interior to the strip $0 \leqq x \leqq L$ and $t \geqq 0$, and by the boundary conditions in (12b) and (12c) on its boundary, is continuous.

Then $u(x, t)$ is a solution of the boundary value problem in (12). ▲

In the method of separation of variables described next, we concentrate on finding the solutions u_1, u_2, u_3, ... satisfying the homogeneous conditions and on determining the coefficients so that the series in Eq. (15) satisfies the nonhomogeneous conditions upon substitution of $t = 0$. At this point we have only a *formal* series solution of the boundary value problem—one that is subject to verification of the continuity and differentiability conditions given in part (1) of the superposition principle stated here. If the function $f(x)$ in (12c) is piecewise smooth, it can be proved that a formal series solution always satisfies the restrictions and, moreover, is the unique solution of the boundary value problem. For a proof, see Chapter 6 of R. V. Churchill and J. W. Brown, *Fourier Series and Boundary Value Problems*, 3rd ed. (New York: McGraw-Hill, 1978).

Separation of Variables

This method of solving the boundary value problem in (12) for the heated rod was introduced by Fourier in his study of heat cited in Section 9.1. We first search for the *building block* functions $u_1, u_2, u_3, \ldots$ that satisfy the differential equation $u_t = ku_{xx}$ and the homogeneous conditions $u(0, t) = u(L, t) = 0$, with each of these functions being of the special form

$$u(x, t) = X(x)T(t) \tag{16}$$

in which the variables x and t are "separated." Substitution of Eq. (16) in $u_t = ku_{xx}$ yields $XT' = kX''T$, where for brevity we write T' for $T'(t)$ and X'' for $X''(x)$. Division of both sides by kXT then gives

$$\frac{X''}{X} = \frac{T'}{kT}. \tag{17}$$

The left-hand side of Eq. (17) is a function of x alone, but the right-hand side is a function of t alone. If t is held constant on the right-hand side, then the left-hand side X''/X must remain constant as x varies. Similarly, if x is held constant on the left-hand side, then the right-hand side T'/kT must remain constant as t varies. Consequently, equality can hold only if each of these two expressions is the same *constant*, which for convenience we denote by $-\lambda$. Thus Eq. (17) becomes

$$\frac{X''}{X} = \frac{T'}{kT} = -\lambda, \tag{18}$$

which consists of the two equations

$$X''(x) + \lambda X(x) = 0, \tag{19}$$
$$T'(t) + \lambda kT(t) = 0. \tag{20}$$

It follows that the product function $u(x, t) = X(x)T(t)$ satisfies the partial differential equation $u_t = ku_{xx}$ if $X(x)$ and $T(t)$ separately satisfy the ordinary differential equations in (19) and (20) for some value of the constant λ.

We focus first on $X(x)$. The homogeneous endpoint conditions are

$$u(x, 0) = X(0)T(t) = 0, \qquad u(L, t) = X(L)T(t) = 0. \tag{21}$$

If $T(t)$ is to be a nontrivial function of t, then (21) can hold only if $X(0) = X(L) = 0$. Thus $X(x)$ must satisfy the endpoint value problem

$$X'' + \lambda X = 0,$$
$$X(0) = 0, \quad X(L) = 0. \tag{22}$$

This is actually an eigenvalue problem of the type we discussed in Section 3.8. Indeed, we saw in Example 3 of that section that (22) has a nontrivial solution if and only if λ is one of the eigenvalues

$$\lambda_n = \frac{n^2\pi^2}{L^2}, \qquad n = 1, 2, 3, \ldots, \tag{23}$$

and that an eigenfunction associated with λ_n is

$$X_n(x) = \sin \frac{n\pi x}{L}, \qquad n = 1, 2, 3, \ldots. \tag{24}$$

Recall that the reasoning behind (23) and (24) is as follows. If $\lambda = 0$, then (22) obviously implies that $X(x) \equiv 0$. If $\lambda = -\alpha^2 < 0$, then

$$X(x) = A \cosh \alpha x + B \sinh \alpha x,$$

and then the conditions $X(0) = 0 = X(L)$ imply that $A = B = 0$. Hence the only possibility for a nontrivial eigenfunction is that $\lambda = \alpha^2 > 0$. Then

$$X(x) = A \cos \alpha x + B \sin \alpha x,$$

and the conditions $X(0) = 0 = X(L)$ then imply that $A = 0$ and that $\alpha = n\pi/L$ for some positive integer n. Whenever separation of variables leads to an unfamiliar eigenvalue problem, we generally must consider separately the cases $\lambda = 0$, $\lambda = -\alpha^2 < 0$, and $\lambda = \alpha^2 > 0$.

Now we turn our attention to Eq. (20), knowing that the constant λ must be one of the eigenvalues listed in (23). For the nth of these possibilities we write Eq. (20) as

$$T_n' + \frac{n^2 \pi^2 k}{L^2} T_n = 0, \tag{25}$$

in anticipation of a different solution $T_n(t)$ for each different positive integer n. A nontrivial solution of this equation is

$$T_n(t) = \exp\left(-n^2 \pi^2 k t / L^2\right). \tag{26}$$

We omit the arbitrary constant of integration because it will (in effect) be inserted later.

To summarize our progress, we have discovered the two associated sequences $\{X_n\}_1^\infty$ and $\{T_n\}_1^\infty$ of functions given in (24) and (26). Together they yield the sequence of product functions

$$u_n(x, t) = X_n(x) T_n(t) = \exp\left(-n^2 \pi^2 k t / L^2\right) \sin \frac{n\pi x}{L}, \tag{27}$$

$n = 1, 2, 3, \ldots.$ Each of these functions satisfies both the heat equation $u_t = k u_{xx}$ and the homogeneous conditions $u(0, t) = u(L, t) = 0$. Now we combine these functions (*superposition*) to attempt to satisfy the nonhomogeneous condition $u(x, 0) = f(x)$ as well. We therefore form the infinite series

$$u(x, t) = \sum_{n=1}^\infty c_n u_n(x, t) = \sum_{n=1}^\infty c_n \exp\left(-n^2 \pi^2 k t / L^2\right) \sin \frac{n\pi x}{L}. \tag{28}$$

It remains only to determine the constant coefficients $\{c_n\}_1^\infty$ so that

$$u(x, 0) = \sum_{n=1}^\infty c_n \sin \frac{n\pi x}{L} = f(x). \tag{29}$$

But this will be the Fourier sine series of $f(x)$ on $[0, L]$ provided that we choose

$$c_n = b_n = \frac{2}{L} \int_0^L f(x) \sin \frac{n\pi x}{L} \, dx \tag{30}$$

for each $n = 1, 2, 3, \ldots$. Thus we have the following result.

THEOREM 1: The Heated Rod with Zero Endpoint Temperatures

The boundary value problem in (12) for a heated rod with zero endpoint temperatures has the formal series solution

$$u(x,t) = \sum_{n=1}^{\infty} b_n \exp\left(-n^2\pi^2 kt/L^2\right) \sin \frac{n\pi x}{L}, \tag{31}$$

where the $\{b_n\}$ are the Fourier sine coefficients in Eq. (30) of the rod's initial temperature function $f(x) = u(x, 0)$. ▲

Remark: By taking the limit in (31) termwise as $t \to \infty$, we get $u(x, \infty) \equiv 0$, as we expect because the two ends of the rod are held at temperature zero. ■

The series solution in Eq. (31) usually converges quite rapidly, unless t is quite small, because of the presence of the negative exponential factors. Therefore it is practical for numerical computations. For use in problems and examples, values of the thermal diffusivity constant k for some common materials are listed in the table in Fig. 9.5.3.

Material	k (cm^2/s)
Silver	1.70
Copper	1.15
Aluminum	0.85
Iron	0.15
Concrete	0.005

FIGURE 9.5.3. Some thermal diffusivity constants.

Example 2

Suppose that a rod of length $L = 50$ cm is immersed in steam until its temperature is $u_0 = 100°$C throughout. At time $t = 0$, its lateral surface is insulated and its two ends are imbedded in ice at $0°$C. Calculate the rod's temperature at its midpoint after half an hour if it is made of (a) iron; (b) concrete.

Solution

The boundary value problem for this rod's temperature function $u(x, t)$ is

$$u_t = ku_{xx},$$
$$u(0, t) = u(L, t) = 0;$$
$$u(x, 0) = u_0.$$

Recall the square-wave series

$$f(t) = \frac{4}{\pi} \sum_{n \text{ odd}} \frac{1}{n} \sin \frac{n\pi t}{L} = \begin{cases} +1 & \text{if } 0 < t < L, \\ -1 & \text{if } -L < t < 0 \end{cases}$$

that we derived in Example 1 of Section 9.2. It follows that the Fourier sine series of $f(x) \equiv u_0$ is

$$f(x) = \frac{4u_0}{\pi} \sum_{n \text{ odd}} \frac{1}{n} \sin \frac{n\pi x}{L}$$

for $0 < x < L$. Hence the Fourier coefficients in Eq. (31) are given by

$$b_n = \begin{cases} \dfrac{4u_0}{n\pi} & \text{for } n \text{ odd,} \\[2mm] 0 & \text{for } n \text{ even,} \end{cases}$$

and therefore the rod's temperature function is given by

$$u(x,t) = \frac{4u_0}{\pi} \sum_{n \text{ odd}} \frac{1}{n} \exp\left(-\frac{n^2\pi^2 kt}{L^2}\right) \sin\frac{n\pi x}{L}.$$

Figure 9.5.4 shows the graph $y = u(x,t)$ with $u_0 = 100$ and $L = 50$. As t increases we see the maximum temperature of the rod (evidently at its midpoint) steadily decreasing. The temperature at the midpoint $x = 25$ after $t = 1800$ seconds is

$$u(25, 1800) = \frac{400}{\pi} \sum_{n \text{ odd}} \frac{(-1)^{n+1}}{n} \exp\left(-\frac{18n^2\pi^2 k}{25}\right).$$

(a) With $k = 0.15$ for iron, this series gives

$$u(25, 1800) \approx 43.8519 - 0.0029 + 0.0000 - \cdots \approx 43.85°\text{C}.$$

(b) With $k = 0.005$ for concrete, it gives

$$\begin{aligned} u(25, 1800) \approx\ & 122.8795 - 30.8257 + 10.4754 - 3.1894 \\ & + 0.7958 - 0.1572 + 0.0242 - 0.0029 \\ & + 0.0003 - 0.0000 + \cdots \approx 100.00°\text{C}. \end{aligned}$$

Thus concrete is a very effective insulator. ∎

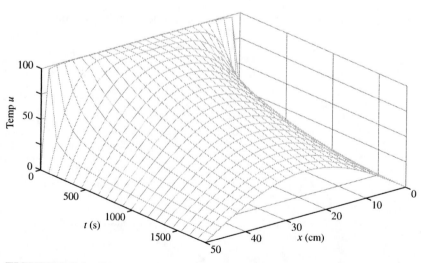

FIGURE 9.5.4. The graph of the temperature function $u(x,t)$ in Example 2.

Insulated Endpoint Conditions

We now consider the boundary value problem

$$\frac{\partial u}{\partial t} = k\frac{\partial^2 u}{\partial x^2} \qquad (0 < x < L, \ \ t > 0); \tag{32a}$$

$$u_x(0,t) = u_x(L,t) = 0, \tag{32b}$$

$$u(x,0) = f(x), \tag{32c}$$

which corresponds to a rod of length L with initial temperature $f(x)$, but with its two ends insulated. The separation of variables $u(x,t) = X(x)T(t)$ proceeds as in Eqs. (16) through (20) without change. But the homogeneous endpoint conditions in (32b) yield $X'(0) = X'(L) = 0$. Thus $X(x)$ must satisfy the endpoint value problem

$$\begin{aligned} X'' + \lambda X &= 0; \\ X'(0) &= 0, \quad X'(L) = 0. \end{aligned} \tag{33}$$

We must consider separately the possibilities $\lambda = 0$, $\lambda = -\alpha^2 < 0$, and $\lambda = \alpha^2 > 0$ for the eigenvalues.

With $\lambda = 0$, the general solution of $X'' = 0$ is $X(x) = Ax + B$, so $X'(x) = A$. Hence the endpoint conditions in (33) require $A = 0$, but B may be nonzero. Because a constant multiple of an eigenfunction is an eigenfunction, we can choose any constant value we wish for B. Thus, with $B = 1$, we have the zero eigenvalue and associated eigenfunction

$$\lambda_0 = 0, \quad X_0(x) \equiv 1. \tag{34}$$

With $\lambda = 0$ in Eq. (20), we get $T'(t) = 0$, so we may take $T_0(t) \equiv 1$ as well.

With $\lambda = -\alpha^2 < 0$, the general solution of the equation $X'' - \alpha^2 X = 0$ is

$$X(x) = A\cosh\alpha x + B\sinh\alpha x,$$

and we readily verify that $X'(0) = X'(L) = 0$ only if $A = B = 0$. Thus there are no negative eigenvalues.

With $\lambda = \alpha^2 > 0$, the general solution of $X'' + \alpha^2 X = 0$ is

$$\begin{aligned} X(x) &= A\cos\alpha x + B\sin\alpha x, \\ X'(x) &= -A\alpha\sin\alpha x + B\alpha\cos\alpha x. \end{aligned}$$

Hence $X'(0) = 0$ implies that $B = 0$, and then

$$X'(L) = -A\alpha\sin\alpha L = 0$$

requires that αL be an integral multiple of π, because $\alpha \neq 0$ and $A \neq 0$ if we are to have a nontrivial solution. Thus we have the infinite sequence of eigenvalues and associated eigenfunctions

$$\lambda_n = \alpha_n^2 = \frac{n^2\pi^2}{L^2}, \quad X_n(x) = \cos\frac{n\pi x}{L} \tag{35}$$

for $n = 1, 2, 3, \ldots$. Just as before, the solution of Eq. (20) with $\lambda = n^2\pi^2/L^2$ is $T_n(t) = \exp\left(-n^2\pi^2 kt/L^2\right)$.

Therefore, the product functions satisfying the homogeneous conditions are

$$u_0(x,t) \equiv 1; \quad u_n(x,t) = \exp\left(n^2\pi^2 kt/L^2\right)\cos\frac{n\pi x}{L} \qquad (36)$$

for $n = 1, 2, 3, \ldots$. Hence the trial solution is

$$u(x,t) = c_0 + \sum_{n=1}^{\infty} c_n \exp\left(-n^2\pi^2 kt/L^2\right)\cos\frac{n\pi x}{L}. \qquad (37)$$

To satisfy the nonhomogeneous condition $u(x,0) = f(x)$, we obviously want Eq. (37) to reduce when $t = 0$ to the Fourier cosine series

$$f(x) = \frac{a_0}{2} + \sum_{n=1}^{\infty} a_n \cos\frac{n\pi x}{L}, \qquad (38)$$

where

$$a_n = \frac{2}{L}\int_0^L f(x)\cos\frac{n\pi x}{L}\,dx \qquad (39)$$

for $n = 0, 1, 2, \ldots$. Thus we have the following result.

THEOREM 2: Heated Rod with Insulated Ends

The boundary value problem in (32) for a heated rod with insulated ends has the formal series solution

$$u(x,t) = \frac{a_0}{2} + \sum_{n=1}^{\infty} a_n \exp\left(-n^2\pi^2 kt/L^2\right)\cos\frac{n\pi x}{L} \qquad (40)$$

where the $\{a_n\}$ are the Fourier cosine coefficients in (39) of the rod's initial temperature function $f(x) = u(x,0)$.   ▲

Remark: Note that

$$\lim_{t\to\infty} u(x,t) = \frac{a_0}{2} = \frac{1}{L}\int_0^L f(x)\,dx, \qquad (41)$$

the average value of the initial temperature. With both the lateral surface and the ends of the rod insulated, its original heat content ultimately distributes itself uniformly throughout the rod.   ■

Example 3

We consider the same 50-cm rod as in Example 2, but now suppose that its initial temperature is given by the "triangular function" graphed in Fig. 9.5.5. At time $t = 0$, the rod's lateral surface *and* its two ends are insulated. Then its temperature function $u(x,t)$ satisfies the boundary value problem

$$u_t = ku_{xx},$$
$$u_x(0,t) = u_x(50,t) = 0,$$
$$u(x,0) = f(x).$$

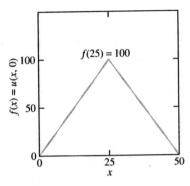

FIGURE 9.5.5. The graph of the initial temperature function $u(x, 0) = f(x)$ in Example 3.

Now substitution of $L = 25$ in the even triangular-wave series of Eq. (15) in Section 9.3 (where the length of the interval is denoted by $2L$), followed by multiplication by 4, yields the Fourier cosine series

$$f(x) = 50 - \frac{400}{\pi^2} \sum_{n \text{ odd}} \frac{1}{n^2} \cos \frac{n\pi x}{25}$$

(for $0 < x < 50$) of our initial temperature function. But in order to match terms with the series in (40) with $L = 50$, we need to exhibit terms of the form $\cos(n\pi x/50)$ rather than terms of the form $\cos(n\pi x/25)$. Hence we replace n with $n/2$ throughout and thereby rewrite the series in the form

$$f(x) = 50 - \frac{1600}{\pi^2} \sum_{n=2, 6, 10, \dots} \frac{1}{n^2} \cos \frac{n\pi x}{50};$$

note that the summation runs through all positive integers of the form $4m - 2$. Then Theorem 2 implies that the rod's temperature function is given by

$$u(x, t) = 50 - \frac{1600}{n^2} \sum_{n=2, 6, 10, \dots} \frac{1}{n^2} \exp\left(-\frac{n^2 \pi^2 k t}{2500}\right) \cos \frac{n\pi x}{50}.$$

Figure 9.5.6 shows the graph $u = u(x, t)$ for the first 1200 seconds, and we see the temperature in the rod beginning with a sharp maximum at the midpoint $x = 25$, but rapidly "averaging out" as the heat in the rod is redistributed with increasing t. ∎

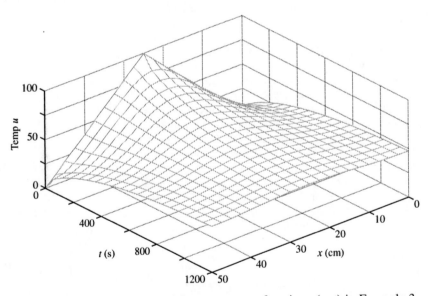

FIGURE 9.5.6. The graph of the temperature function $u(x, t)$ in Example 3.

Finally, we point out that, although we set up the boundary value problems in (12) and (32) for a rod of length L, they also model the temperature $u(x, t)$ within the infinite slab $0 \leq x \leq L$ in three-dimensional space if its initial temperature $f(x)$ depends only on x and its two faces $x = 0$ and $x = L$ are either both insulated or both held at temperature zero.

9.5 Problems

Solve the boundary value problems in Problems 1 through 12.

1. $u_t = 3u_{xx}$, $0 < x < \pi$, $t > 0$; $u(0,t) = u(\pi,t) = 0$,
   $u(x,0) = 4\sin 2x$

2. $u_t = 10u_{xx}$, $0 < x < 5$, $t > 0$; $u_x(0,t) = u_x(5,t) = 0$,
   $u(x,0) = 7$

3. $u_t = 2u_{xx}$, $0 < x < 1$, $t > 0$; $u(0,t) = u(1,t) = 0$,
   $u(x,0) = 5\sin \pi x - \frac{1}{5}\sin 3\pi x$

4. $u_t = u_{xx}$, $0 < x < \pi$, $t > 0$; $u(0,t) = u(\pi,t) = 0$,
   $u(x,0) = 4\sin 4x \cos 2x$

5. $u_t = 2u_{xx}$, $0 < x < 3$, $t > 0$; $u_x(0,t) = u_x(3,t) = 0$,
   $u(x,0) = 4\cos \frac{2}{3}\pi x - 2\cos \frac{4}{3}\pi x$

6. $2u_t = u_{xx}$, $0 < x < 1$, $t > 0$; $u(0,t) = u(1,t) = 0$,
   $u(x,0) = 4\sin \pi x \cos^3 \pi x$

7. $3u_t = u_{xx}$, $0 < x < 2$, $t > 0$; $u_x(0,t) = u_x(2,t) = 0$,
   $u(x,0) = \cos^2 2\pi x$

8. $u_t = u_{xx}$, $0 < x < 2$, $t > 0$; $u_x(0,t) = u_x(2,t) = 0$,
   $u(x,0) = 10\cos \pi x \cos 3\pi x$

9. $10u_t = u_{xx}$, $0 < x < 5$, $t > 0$; $u(0,t) = u(5,t) = 0$,
   $u(x,0) = 25$

10. $5u_t = u_{xx}$, $0 < x < 10$, $t > 0$; $u(0,t) = u(10,t) = 0$,
    $u(x,0) = 4x$

11. $5u_t = u_{xx}$, $0 < x < 10$, $t > 0$; $u_x(0,t) = u_x(10,t) = 0$,
    $u(x,0) = 4x$

12. $u_t = u_{xx}$, $0 < x < 100$, $t > 0$; $u(0,t) = u(100,t) = 0$,
    $u(x,0) = x(100 - x)$

13. Suppose that a rod 40 cm long with insulated lateral surface is heated to a uniform temperature of $100°C$, and that at time $t = 0$ its two ends are embedded in ice at $0°C$. **(a)** Find the formal series solution for the temperature $u(x,t)$ of the rod. **(b)** In the case the rod is made of copper, show that after 5 min the temperature at its midpoint is about $15°C$. **(c)** In the case the rod is made of concrete, use the first term of the series to find the time required for its midpoint to cool to $15°C$.

14. A copper rod 50 cm long with insulated lateral surface has initial temperature $u(x,0) = 2x$, and at time $t = 0$ its two ends are insulated. **(a)** Find $u(x,t)$. **(b)** What will its temperature be at $x = 10$ after 1 min? **(c)** After approximately how long will its temperature at $x = 10$ be $45°C$?

15. The two faces of the slab $0 \leq x \leq L$ are kept at temperature zero, and the initial temperature of the slab is given by $u(x,0) = A$ (a constant) for $0 < x < L/2$, $u(x,0) = 0$ for $L/2 < x < L$. Derive the formal series solution

    $u(x,t) =$

    $$\frac{4A}{\pi} \sum_{n=1}^{\infty} \frac{\sin^2(n\pi/4)}{n} \exp\left(-n^2\pi^2 kt/L^2\right) \sin \frac{n\pi x}{L}.$$

16. Two iron slabs are each 25 cm thick. Initially one is at temperature $100°C$ throughout and the other is at temperature $0°C$. At time $t = 0$ they are placed face to face, and their outer faces are kept at $0°C$. **(a)** Use the result of Problem 15 to verify that after a half hour the temperature of their common face is approximately $22°C$. **(b)** Suppose that the two slabs are instead made of concrete. How long will it be until their common face reaches a temperature of $22°C$?

17. (Steady-state and transient temperatures) Let a laterally insulated rod with initial temperature $u(x,0) = f(x)$ have fixed endpoint temperatures $u(0,t) = A$ and $u(L,t) = B$. **(a)** It is observed empirically that as $t \to +\infty$, $u(x,t)$ approaches a **steady-state temperature** $u_{ss}(x)$ that corresponds to setting $u_t = 0$ in the boundary value problem. Thus $u_{ss}(x)$ is the solution of the endpoint value problem

    $$\frac{\partial^2 u_{ss}}{\partial x^2} = 0; \quad u_{ss}(0) = A, \quad u_{ss}(L) = B.$$

    Find $u_{ss}(x)$. **(b)** The **transient temperature** $u_{tr}(x,t)$ is defined to be

    $$u_{tr}(x,t) = u(x,t) - u_{ss}(x).$$

    Show that u_{tr} satisfies the boundary value problem

    $$\frac{\partial u_{tr}}{\partial t} = k\frac{\partial^2 u_{tr}}{\partial x^2};$$

    $$u_{tr}(0,t) = u_{tr}(L,t) = 0,$$

    $$u_{tr}(x,0) = g(x) = f(x) - u_{ss}(x).$$

    (c) Conclude from the formulas in (30) and (31) that

    $u(x,t) = u_{ss}(x) + u_{tr}(x,t)$

    $$= u_{ss}(x) + \sum_{n=1}^{\infty} c_n \exp\left(-n^2\pi^2 kt/L^2\right) \sin \frac{n\pi x}{L},$$

    where

    $$c_n = \frac{2}{L} \int_0^L [f(x) - u_{ss}(x)] \sin \frac{n\pi x}{L} \, dx.$$

18. Suppose that a laterally insulated rod with length $L = 50$ and thermal diffusivity $k = 1$ has initial temperature $u(x,0) = 0$ and endpoint temperatures $u(0,t) = 0$, $u(50,t) = 100$. Apply the result of Problem 17 to show that

    $u(x,t) =$

    $$2x - \frac{200}{\pi} \sum_{n=1}^{\infty} \frac{(-1)^{n+1}}{n} \exp\left(-n^2\pi^2 kt/2500\right) \sin \frac{n\pi x}{50}.$$

19. Suppose that heat is generated within a laterally insulated rod at the rate of $q(x,t)$ calories per second per cubic centimeter. Extend the derivation of the heat equation in this section to derive the equation

    $$\frac{\partial u}{\partial t} = k\frac{\partial^2 u}{\partial x^2} + \frac{q(x,t)}{c\delta}.$$

20. Suppose that current flowing through a laterally insulated rod generates heat at a constant rate; then Problem 19 yields the equation

$$\frac{\partial u}{\partial t} = k\frac{\partial^2 u}{\partial x^2} + C.$$

Assume the boundary conditions $u(0,t) = u(L,t) = 0$ and $u(x,0) = f(x)$. **(a)** Find the steady-state temperature $u_{ss}(x)$ determined by

$$0 = k\frac{d^2 u_{ss}}{dx^2} + C, \quad u_{ss}(0) = u_{ss}(L) = 0.$$

(b) Show that the transient temperature

$$u_{tr}(x,t) = u(x,t) - u_{ss}(x)$$

satisfies the boundary value problem

$$\frac{\partial u_{tr}}{\partial t} = k\frac{\partial^2 u_{tr}}{\partial x^2};$$

$$u_{tr}(0,t) = u_{tr}(L,t) = 0,$$

$$u_{tr}(x,0) = g(x) = f(x) - u_{ss}(x).$$

Hence conclude from the formulas in (34) and (35) that

$$u(x,t) = u_{ss}(x) + \sum_{n=1}^{\infty} c_n \exp\left(-n^2\pi^2 kt/L^2\right) \sin\frac{n\pi x}{L},$$

where

$$c_n = \frac{2}{L}\int_0^L [f(x) - u_{ss}(x)]\sin\frac{n\pi x}{L}\,dx.$$

21. The answer to part (a) of Problem 20 is $u_{ss}(x) = Cx(L-x)/2k$. If $f(x) \equiv 0$ in Problem 20, so the rod being heated is initially at temperature zero, deduce from the result of part (b) that

$$u(x,t) = \frac{Cx}{2k}(L-x)$$

$$- \frac{4CL^2}{k\pi^3}\sum_{n\ \text{odd}}\frac{1}{n^3}\exp\left(-n^2\pi^2 kt/L^2\right)\sin\frac{n\pi x}{L}.$$

22. Consider the temperature $u(x,t)$ in a bare slender wire with $u(0,t) = u(L,t) = 0$ and $u(x,0) = f(x)$. Instead of being laterally insulated, the wire loses heat to a surrounding medium (at fixed temperature zero) at a rate

proportional to $u(x,t)$. **(a)** Conclude from Problem 19 that

$$\frac{\partial u}{\partial t} = k\frac{\partial^2 u}{\partial x^2} - hu,$$

where h is a positive constant. **(b)** Then substitute

$$u(x,t) = e^{-ht}v(x,t)$$

to show that $v(x,t)$ satisfies the boundary value problem having the solution given in (30) and (31). Hence conclude that

$$u(x,t) = e^{-ht}\sum_{n=1}^{\infty} c_n \exp\left(-n^2\pi^2 kt/L^2\right)\sin\frac{n\pi x}{L},$$

where

$$c_n = \frac{2}{L}\int_0^L f(x)\sin\frac{n\pi x}{L}\,dx.$$

23. Consider a slab with thermal conductivity K occupying the region $0 \leq x \leq L$. Suppose that, in accord with Newton's law of cooling, each face of the slab loses heat to the surrounding medium (at temperature zero) at the rate of Hu calories per second per square centimeter. Deduce from Eq. (2) that the temperature $u(x,t)$ in the slab satisfies the boundary conditions

$$hu(0,t) - u_x(0,t) = 0 = hu(L,t) + u_x(L,t),$$

where $h = H/K$.

24. Suppose that a laterally insulated rod with length L, thermal diffusivity k, and initial temperature $u(x,0) = f(x)$ is insulated at the end $x = L$ and held at temperature zero at $x = 0$. **(a)** Separate the variables to show that the eigenfunctions are

$$X_n(x) = \sin\frac{n\pi x}{2L}$$

for n odd. **(b)** Use the odd half-multiple sine series of Problem 21 in Section 9.3 to derive the solution

$$u(x,t) = \sum_{n\ \text{odd}} c_n \exp\left(-n^2\pi^2 kt/4L^2\right)\sin\frac{n\pi x}{2L},$$

where

$$c_n = \frac{2}{L}\int_0^L f(x)\sin\frac{n\pi x}{2L}\,dx.$$

9.5 Application: Heated Rod Investigations

First let's investigate numerically the temperature function

$$u(x,t) = \frac{4u_0}{\pi}\sum_{n\ \text{odd}}\frac{1}{n}\exp\left(-\frac{n^2\pi^2 kt}{L^2}\right)\sin\frac{n\pi x}{L}$$

of the heated rod of Example 2, having length $L = 50$ cm, uniform initial temperature $u_0 = 100°C$, and thermal diffusivity $k = 0.15$ (for iron). The following

MATLAB function sums the first N nonzero terms of this series.

```
function u = u(x,t)
k = 0.15;                % diffusivity of iron
L = 50;                  % length of rod
u0 = 100;                % initial temperature
S = 0;                   % initial sum
N = 50;                  % number of terms
for n = 1:2:2*N+1;
     S = S +(1/n)*exp(-n^2*pi^2*k*t/L^2).*sin(n*pi*x/L);
end
u = 4*u0*S/pi;
```

This function was used to plot Figs. 9.5.7 through 9.5.10. The corresponding *Maple* and *Mathematica* functions are provided in the applications manual that accompanies this text. As a practical matter, $N = 50$ terms suffice to give the value $u(x, t)$ after 10 seconds (or longer) with two decimal places of accuracy throughout the interval $0 \leqq x \leqq 50$. (How might you check this assertion?)

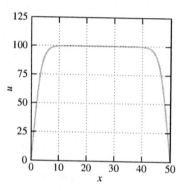

FIGURE 9.5.7. The graph of $u(x, 30)$ giving rod temperatures after 30 seconds.

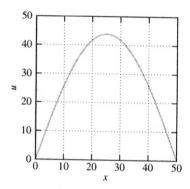

FIGURE 9.5.8. The graph of $u(x, 1800)$ giving rod temperature after 30 minutes.

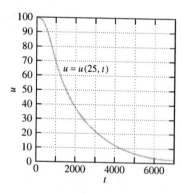

FIGURE 9.5.9. The graph of $u(25, t)$ giving the midpoint temperatures of the rod.

FIGURE 9.5.10. Magnification of the graph of $u(25, t)$ giving the midpoint temperatures of the rod.

The graph of $u(x, 30)$ in Fig. 9.5.7 shows that after 30 seconds the rod has cooled appreciably only near its two ends and still has temperature near 100°C for $10 \leqq x \leqq 40$. Figure 9.5.8 shows the graph of $u(x, 1800)$ after 30 minutes and illustrates the fact (?) that the rod's maximum temperature is always at its midpoint, where $x = 25$.

The graph of $u(25, t)$ for a two-hour period shown in Fig. 9.5.9 indicates that the midpoint temperature takes something more than 1500 seconds (25 minutes) to fall to 50°. Figure 9.5.10 shows a magnification of the graph near its intersection point with the horizontal line $u = 50$ and indicates that this actually takes about 1578 seconds (26 min 18 s).

For your very own rod with constant initial temperature $f(x) = T_0 = 100$ to investigate in this manner, let

$$L = 100 + 10p \quad \text{and} \quad k = 1 + (0.1)q,$$

where p is the largest and q is the smallest nonzero digit of your student ID number.

1. If the two ends of the rod are both held at temperature zero, then determine how long (to the nearest second) it will take for the rod's midpoint temperature to fall to 50°.

2. If the end $x = L$ of the rod is insulated, but the end $x = 0$ is held at temperature zero, then the temperature function $u(x, t)$ is given by the Fourier series in Problem 24 of this section. Determine how long it will be until the maximum temperature anywhere in the rod is 50°.

9.6 Vibrating Strings and the One-Dimensional Wave Equation

Although Fourier systematized the method of separation of variables, trigonometric series solutions of partial differential equations had appeared earlier in eighteenth-century investigations of vibrating strings by Euler, d'Alembert, and Daniel Bernoulli. To derive the partial differential equation that models the vibrations of a string, we begin with a flexible uniform string with linear density ρ (in grams per centimeter or slugs per foot) stretched under a tension of T (dynes or pounds) between the fixed points $x = 0$ and $x = L$. Suppose that, as the string vibrates in the xy-plane around its equilibrium position, each point moves parallel to the y-axis, so we can denote by $y(x, t)$ the displacement at time t of the point x of the string. Then, for any fixed value of t, the shape of the string at time t is the curve $y = y(x, t)$. We assume also that the deflection of the string remains so slight that the approximation $\sin\theta \approx \tan\theta = y_x(x, t)$ is quite accurate (Fig. 9.6.1). Finally, we assume that in addition to the internal forces of tension acting tangentially to the string, it is acted on by an external vertical force with linear density $F(x)$ in such units as dynes per centimeter or pounds per foot.

We want to apply Newton's second law $F = ma$ to the short segment of string of mass $\rho\Delta x$ corresponding to the interval $[x, x + \Delta x]$, with a being the vertical acceleration $y_{tt}(\bar{x}, t)$ of its midpoint. Reading the vertical components of the force shown in Fig. 9.6.1, we get

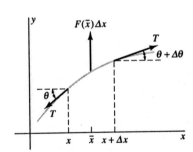

FIGURE 9.6.1. Forces on a short segment of the vibrating string.

$$(\rho\,\Delta x) \cdot y_{tt}(\bar{x}, t) \approx T\sin(\theta + \Delta\theta) - T\sin\theta + F(\bar{x})\,\Delta x$$
$$\approx Ty_x(x + \Delta x, t) - Ty_x(x, t) + F(\bar{x})\,\Delta x,$$

so division by Δx yields

$$\rho y_{tt}(\bar{x}, t) \approx T\frac{y_x(x + \Delta x, t) - y_x(x, t)}{\Delta x} + F(\bar{x}).$$

When we take the limit as $\Delta x \to 0$ and $\bar{x} \to x$, we obtain the partial differential equation

➤
$$\rho \frac{\partial^2 y}{\partial t^2} = T \frac{\partial^2 y}{\partial x^2} + F(x) \tag{1}$$

that describes the vertical vibrations of a flexible string with constant linear density ρ and tension T under the influence of an external vertical force with linear density $F(x)$.

If we set

$$a^2 = \frac{T}{\rho} \tag{2}$$

and set $F(x) \equiv 0$ in Eq. (1), we get the **one-dimensional wave equation**

➤
$$\frac{\partial^2 y}{\partial t^2} = a^2 \frac{\partial^2 y}{\partial x^2} \tag{3}$$

that models the *free* vibrations of a uniform flexible string.

The fixed ends of the string at the points $x = 0$ and $x = L$ on the x-axis correspond to the *endpoint conditions*

$$y(0, t) = y(L, t) = 0. \tag{4}$$

Our intuition about the physics of the situation suggests that the motion of the string will be determined if we specify both its **initial position function**

$$y(x, 0) = f(x) \qquad (0 < x < L) \tag{5}$$

and its **initial velocity function**

$$y_t(x, 0) = g(x) \qquad (0 < x < L). \tag{6}$$

On combining Eqs. (3) through (6), we get the boundary value problem

➤
$$\frac{\partial^2 y}{\partial t^2} = a^2 \frac{\partial^2 y}{\partial x^2} \qquad (0 < x < L, \ t > 0); \tag{7a}$$

$$y(0, t) = y(L, t) = 0, \tag{7b}$$

$$y(x, 0) = f(x) \qquad (0 < x < L), \tag{7c}$$

$$y_t(x, 0) = g(x) \qquad (0 < x < L) \tag{7d}$$

for the displacement function $y(x, t)$ of a freely vibrating string with fixed ends, initial position $f(x)$, and initial velocity $g(x)$.

Solution by Separation of Variables

Like the heat equation, the wave equation in (7a) is linear: Any linear combination of two solutions is again a solution. Another similarity is that the endpoint conditions in (7b) are homogeneous. Unfortunately, the conditions in both (7c) and (7d) are nonhomogeneous; we must deal with *two* nonhomogeneous boundary conditions.

As we described in Section 9.5, the method of separation of variables involves superposition of solutions satisfying the homogeneous conditions to obtain a solution that also satisfies a single nonhomogeneous boundary condition. To adapt the technique to the situation at hand, we adopt the "divide and conquer" strategy of splitting the problem in (7) into the following two separate boundary value problems, each involving only a single nonhomogeneous boundary condition:

Problem A	Problem B
$y_{tt} = a^2 y_{xx};$	$y_{tt} = a^2 y_{xx};$
$y(0,t) = y(L,t) = 0,$	$y(0,t) = y(L,t) = 0,$
$y(x,0) = f(x),$	$y(x,0) = 0,$
$y_t(x,0) = 0.$	$y_t(x,0) = g(x).$

If we can separately find a solution $y_A(x,t)$ of Problem A and a solution $y_B(x,t)$ of Problem B, then their sum $y(x,t) = y_A(x,t) + y_B(x,t)$ will be a solution of the original problem in (7) because

$$y(x,0) = y_A(x,0) + y_B(x,0) = f(x) + 0 = f(x)$$

and

$$y_t(x,0) = \{y_A\}_t(x,0) + \{y_B\}_t(x,0) = 0 + g(x) = g(x).$$

So let us attack Problem A with the method of separation of variables. Substitution of

$$y(x,t) = X(x)T(t) \tag{8}$$

in $y_{tt} = a^2 y_{xx}$ yields $XT'' = a^2 X''T$ where (as before) we write X'' for $X''(x)$ and T'' for $T''(t)$. Therefore,

$$\frac{X''}{X} = \frac{T''}{a^2 T}. \tag{9}$$

The functions X''/X of x and $T''/a^2 T$ of t can agree for all x and t only if each is equal to the same constant. Consequently, we may conclude that

$$\frac{X''}{X} = \frac{T''}{a^2 T} = -\lambda \tag{10}$$

for some constant λ; the minus sign is inserted here merely to facilitate recognition of the eigenvalue problem in (13). Thus our partial differential equation separates into the two ordinary differential equations

$$X'' + \lambda X = 0, \tag{11}$$

$$T'' + \lambda a^2 T = 0. \tag{12}$$

The endpoint conditions

$$y(0,t) = X(0)T(t) = 0, \quad y(L,t) = X(L)T(t) = 0$$

require that $X(0) = X(L) = 0$ if $T(t)$ is nontrivial. Hence $X(x)$ must satisfy the now familiar eigenvalue problem

$$X'' + \lambda X = 0, \quad X(0) = X(L) = 0. \tag{13}$$

As in Eqs. (23) and (24) of Section 9.5, the eigenvalues of this problem are the numbers

$$\lambda_n = \frac{n^2\pi^2}{L^2}, \quad n = 1, 2, 3, \ldots, \tag{14}$$

and the eigenfunction associated with λ_n is

$$X_n(x) = \sin\frac{n\pi x}{L}, \quad n = 1, 2, 3, \ldots. \tag{15}$$

Now we turn to Eq. (12). The homogeneous initial condition

$$y_t(x, 0) = X(x)T'(0) = 0$$

implies that $T'(0) = 0$. Therefore, the solution $T_n(t)$ associated with the eigenvalue $\lambda_n = n^2\pi^2/L^2$ must satisfy the conditions

$$T_n'' + \frac{n^2\pi^2 a^2}{L^2}T_n = 0, \quad T_n'(0) = 0. \tag{16}$$

The general solution of the differential equation in (16) is

$$T_n(t) = A_n\cos\frac{n\pi at}{L} + B_n\sin\frac{n\pi at}{L}. \tag{17}$$

Its derivative

$$T_n'(t) = \frac{n\pi a}{L}\left(-A_n\sin\frac{n\pi at}{L} + B_n\cos\frac{n\pi at}{L}\right)$$

satisfies the condition $T_n'(0) = 0$ if $B_n = 0$. Thus a nontrivial solution of (16) is

$$T_n(t) = \cos\frac{n\pi at}{L}. \tag{18}$$

We combine the results in Eqs. (15) and (18) to obtain the infinite sequence of product functions

$$y_n(x, t) = X_n(x)T_n(t) = \cos\frac{n\pi at}{L}\sin\frac{n\pi x}{L}, \tag{19}$$

$n = 1, 2, 3, \ldots$. Each of these *building block* functions satisfies both the wave equation $y_{tt} = a^2 y_{xx}$ and the homogeneous boundary conditions in Problem A. By superposition we get the infinite series

$$y_n(x, t) = \sum_{n=1}^{\infty} A_n X_n(x)T_n(t) = \sum_{n=1}^{\infty} A_n\cos\frac{n\pi at}{L}\sin\frac{n\pi x}{L}. \tag{20}$$

It remains only to choose the coefficients $\{A_n\}$ to satisfy the nonhomogeneous boundary condition

$$y(x, 0) = \sum_{n=1}^{\infty} A_n\sin\frac{n\pi x}{L} = f(x) \tag{21}$$

for $0 < x < L$. But this will be the Fourier sine series of $f(x)$ on $[0, L]$ provided that we choose

➤
$$A_n = \frac{2}{L} \int_0^L f(x) \sin \frac{n\pi x}{L} \, dx. \tag{22}$$

Thus we see finally that a formal series solution of Problem A is

➤
$$y(x, t) = \sum_{n=1}^{\infty} A_n \cos \frac{n\pi a t}{L} \sin \frac{n\pi x}{L}, \tag{23}$$

with the coefficients $\{A_n\}_1^{\infty}$ computed using Eq. (22). Note that the series in (23) is obtained from the Fourier sine series of $f(x)$ simply by inserting the factor $\cos(n\pi a t / L)$ in the nth term. Note also that this term has [circular] frequency $\omega_n = n\pi a / L$.

Example 1 It follows immediately that the solution of the boundary value problem

$$\frac{\partial^2 y}{\partial t^2} = 4\frac{\partial^2 y}{\partial x^2} \qquad (0 < x < \pi, \quad t > 0);$$

$$y(0, t) = y(\pi, t) = 0,$$

$$y(x, 0) = \tfrac{1}{10} \sin^3 x = \tfrac{3}{40} \sin x - \tfrac{1}{40} \sin 3x,$$

$$y_t(x, 0) = 0,$$

for which $L = \pi$ and $a = 2$, is

$$y(x, t) = \tfrac{3}{40} \cos 2t \sin x - \tfrac{1}{40} \cos 6t \sin 3x.$$

The reason is that we are given explicitly the Fourier sine series of $f(x)$ with $A_1 = \tfrac{3}{40}$, $A_3 = -\tfrac{1}{40}$, and $A_n = 0$ otherwise.   ∎

Example 2 **A plucked string** Figure 9.6.2 shows the initial position function $f(x)$ for a stretched string (of length L) that is set in motion by moving its midpoint $x = L/2$ aside the distance $\tfrac{1}{2}bL$ and then releasing it from rest at time $t = 0$. The corresponding boundary value problem is

$$y_{tt} = a^2 y_{xx} \qquad (0 < x < L, \quad t > 0);$$
$$y(0, t) = y(L, t) = 0,$$
$$y(x, 0) = f(x),$$
$$y_t(x, 0) = 0,$$

where $f(x) = bx$ for $0 \leqq x \leqq L/2$ and $f(x) = b(L - x)$ for $L/2 \leqq x \leqq L$. Find $y(x, t)$.

FIGURE 9.6.2. The initial position of the plucked string of Example 2.

Solution The nth Fourier sine coefficient of $f(x)$ is

$$A_n = \frac{2}{L} \int_0^L f(x) \sin \frac{n\pi x}{L} \, dx$$

$$= \frac{2}{L} \int_0^{L/2} bx \sin \frac{n\pi x}{L} \, dx + \frac{2}{L} \int_{L/2}^L b(L - x) \sin \frac{n\pi x}{L} \, dx;$$

it follows that

$$A_n = \frac{4bL}{n^2\pi^2} \sin \frac{n\pi}{2}.$$

Hence Eq. (23) yields the formal series solution

$$y(x,t) = \frac{4bL}{\pi^2} \sum_{n=1}^{\infty} \frac{1}{n^2} \sin \frac{n\pi}{2} \cos \frac{n\pi at}{L} \sin \frac{n\pi x}{L}$$

$$= \frac{4bL}{\pi^2} \left(\cos \frac{\pi at}{L} \sin \frac{\pi x}{L} - \frac{1}{3^2} \cos \frac{3\pi at}{L} \sin \frac{3\pi x}{L} + \cdots \right). \quad (24)$$

Music

Numerous familiar musical instruments employ vibrating strings to generate the sounds they produce. When a string vibrates with a given frequency, vibrations at this frequency are transmitted through the air—in the form of periodic variations in air density called **sound waves**—to the ear of the listener. For example, middle C is a *tone* with a frequency of approximately 256 Hz. When several tones are heard simultaneously, the combination is perceived as harmonious if the ratios of their frequencies are nearly ratios of small whole numbers; otherwise many perceive the combinations as dissonant.

The series in Eq. (23) represents the motion of a string as a superposition of infinitely many vibrations with different frequencies. The *n*th term

$$A_n \cos \frac{n\pi at}{L} \sin \frac{n\pi x}{L}$$

represents a vibration with frequency

$$\nu_n = \frac{\omega_n}{2\pi} = \frac{n\pi a/L}{2\pi} = \frac{n}{2L} \sqrt{\frac{T}{\rho}} \quad \text{(Hz)}. \quad (25)$$

The lowest of these frequencies,

$$\nu_1 = \frac{1}{2L} \sqrt{\frac{T}{\rho}} \quad \text{(Hz)}, \quad (26)$$

is called the **fundamental frequency,** and it is ordinarily predominant in the sound we hear. The frequency $\nu_n = n\nu_1$ of the *n*th **overtone** or **harmonic** is an integral multiple of ν_1, and this is why the sound of a single vibrating string is harmonious rather than dissonant.

Note in Eq. (26) that the fundamental frequency ν_1 is proportional to $\sqrt{T}$ and inversely proportional to L and to $\sqrt{\rho}$. Thus we can double this frequency—and hence get a fundamental tone one **octave** higher—either by halving the length L or by quadrupling the tension T. The initial conditions do *not* affect ν_1; instead, they determine the coefficients in (23) and hence the extent to which the higher harmonics contribute to the sound produced. Therefore the initial conditions affect the **timbre,** or overall frequency mixture, rather than the fundamental frequency. (Technically this is true only for relatively small displacements of the string; if you strike a piano key rather forcefully you can detect a slight and brief initial deviation from the usual frequency of the note.)

According to one (rather simplistic) theory of hearing, the loudness of the sound produced by a vibrating string is proportional to its total [kinetic plus potential] energy, which is given by

$$E = \frac{1}{2} \int_0^L \left[\rho \left(\frac{\partial y}{\partial t} \right)^2 + T \left(\frac{\partial y}{\partial x} \right)^2 \right] dx. \qquad (27)$$

In Problem 17 we ask you to show that substitution of the series in (23) in the formula in (27) yields

$$E = \frac{\pi^2 T}{4L} \sum_{n=1}^{\infty} n^2 A_n^2. \qquad (28)$$

The ratio of the nth term $n^2 A_n^2$ to the sum $\sum n^2 A_n^2$ is then the portion of the whole sound attributable to the nth harmonic.

We illustrate this theory with the series in (24), which describes the motion of the plucked string of Example 2. Note that the even harmonics are missing, and that $A_n = 4bL/(\pi^2 n^2)$ for n odd. Hence Eq. (28) gives

$$E = \frac{\pi^2 T}{4L} \sum_{n \text{ odd}} n^2 \frac{16 b^2 L^2}{\pi^4 n^4} = \frac{4b^2 LT}{\pi^2} \sum_{n \text{ odd}} \frac{1}{n^2},$$

so the proportion of the sound associated with the nth harmonic (for n odd) is

$$\frac{1/n^2}{\displaystyle\sum_{n \text{ odd}} 1/n^2} = \frac{1/n^2}{\pi^2/8} = \frac{8}{\pi^2 n^2}.$$

Substituting $n = 1$ and $n = 3$, we find that 81.06% of the sound of the string of Example 2 is associated with the fundamental tone and 9.01% with the harmonic corresponding to $n = 3$.

The d'Alembert Solution

In contrast with series solutions of the heat equation, formal series solutions of the wave equation ordinarily do *not* possess sufficient termwise differentiability to permit verification of the solution by application of a superposition theorem analogous to the one stated in Section 9.5. For instance, termwise differentiation of the series in (24) would yield the series

$$\frac{\partial^2 y}{\partial x^2} = -\frac{4b}{L} \sum_{n=1}^{\infty} \sin \frac{n\pi}{2} \cos \frac{n\pi at}{L} \sin \frac{n\pi x}{L},$$

which generally fails to converge, because the "convergence factor" $1/n^2$ has disappeared after the second differentiation.

There is, however, an alternative approach that both verifies the solution in (23) and yields valuable additional information about it. If we apply the trigonometric identity

$$2 \sin A \cos B = \sin(A + B) + \sin(A - B)$$

with $A = n\pi x/L$ and $B = n\pi at/L$, then (23) gives

$$y(x,t) = \sum_{n=1}^{\infty} A_n \sin \frac{n\pi x}{L} \cos \frac{n\pi at}{L}$$

$$= \frac{1}{2} \sum_{n=1}^{\infty} A_n \sin \frac{n\pi}{L}(x+at) + \frac{1}{2} \sum_{n=1}^{\infty} A_n \sin \frac{n\pi}{L}(x-at). \qquad (29)$$

But by definition of the coefficients,

$$\sum_{n=1}^{\infty} A_n \sin \frac{n\pi x}{L} = F(x)$$

for all x, where $F(x)$ is the *odd* extension of period $2L$ of the initial position function $f(x)$. Hence Eq. (29) means that

➤ $$y(x,t) = \tfrac{1}{2}\left[F(x+at) + F(x-at)\right]. \qquad (30)$$

Therefore, the series in (23) converges to the expression on the right-hand side in (30), which is known as the **d'Alembert form** of the solution of Problem A for the vibrating string. Moreover, using the chain rule it is easy to verify (Problems 13 and 14) that the function $y(x,t)$ defined in (30) does, indeed, satisfy the equation $y_{tt} = a^2 y_{xx}$ (under the assumption that F is twice differentiable), as well as the boundary conditions $y(0,t) = y(L,t) = 0$ and $y(x,0) = f(x)$.

For any function $F(x)$, the functions $F(x+at)$ and $F(x-at)$ represent "waves" moving to the left and right, respectively, along the x-axis with speed a. This fact is illustrated in Fig. 9.6.3, which shows the graphs of these two functions for successive values of t, in a typical case where the initial position function $F(x)$ is a pulse function centered at the midpoint $x = \pi/2$ of a string of length $L = \pi$

FIGURE 9.6.3. The pulse $F(x)$ produces two waves—one moving to the left, one to the right.

with $a = 1$ (so the fundamental period of vibration is 2π). Thus the d'Alembert solution in (30) expresses $y(x, t)$ as a superposition of two waves moving in opposite directions with speed a. This is why the equation $y_{tt} = a^2 y_{xx}$ is called the *wave equation*.

Strings with Initial Velocity

The separation of variables solution of Problem B, with initial conditions $y(x, 0) = 0$ and $y_t(x, 0) = g(x)$, proceeds precisely as did that of Problem A until Eq. (16) is reached. But then $y(x, 0) = X(x)T(0) = 0$ implies that $T(0) = 0$, so instead of (16) we have

$$\frac{d^2 T_n}{dt^2} + \frac{n^2 \pi^2 a^2}{L^2} T_n = 0, \quad T_n(0) = 0. \tag{31}$$

From Eq. (17) we see that a nontrivial solution of (31) is

$$T_n(t) = \sin \frac{n\pi a t}{L}. \tag{32}$$

The resulting formal power series solution is therefore of the form

$$\blacktriangleright \qquad y(x, t) = \sum_{n=1}^{\infty} B_n \sin \frac{n\pi a t}{L} \sin \frac{n\pi x}{L}, \tag{33}$$

so we want to choose the coefficients $\{B_n\}$ so that

$$y_t(x, 0) = \sum_{n=1}^{\infty} B_n \frac{n\pi a}{L} \sin \frac{n\pi x}{L} = g(x). \tag{34}$$

Thus we want $B_n \cdot n\pi a / L$ to be the Fourier sine coefficient b_n of $g(x)$ on $[0, L]$:

$$B_n \frac{n\pi a}{L} = b_n = \frac{2}{L} \int_0^L g(x) \sin \frac{n\pi x}{L} \, dx.$$

Hence we choose

$$\blacktriangleright \qquad B_n = \frac{2}{n\pi a} \int_0^L g(x) \sin \frac{n\pi x}{L} \, dx \tag{35}$$

in order for $y(x, t)$ in (33) to be a formal series solution of Problem B.

Example 3

Consider a string on a guitar lying crosswise in the back of a pickup trick that at time $t = 0$ slams into a brick wall with speed v_0. Then $g(x) \equiv v_0$, so

$$B_n = \frac{2}{n\pi a} \int_0^L v_0 \sin \frac{n\pi x}{L} \, dx = \frac{2v_0 L}{n^2 \pi^2 a} \left[1 - (-1)^n \right].$$

Hence the series in (33) gives

$$y(x, t) = \frac{4v_0 L}{\pi^2 a} \sum_{n \text{ odd}} \frac{1}{n^2} \sin \frac{n\pi a t}{L} \sin \frac{n\pi x}{L}. \qquad \blacksquare$$

If we differentiate the series in (33) termwise with respect to t, we get

$$y_t(x,t) = \sum_{n=1}^{\infty} b_n \sin \frac{n\pi x}{L} \cos \frac{n\pi at}{L} = \tfrac{1}{2}[G(x+at) + G(x-at)], \qquad (36)$$

where G is the odd period $2L$ extension of the initial velocity function $g(x)$, using the same device as in the derivation of Eq. (30). In Problem 15 we ask you to deduce that

$$y(x,t) = \frac{1}{2a}[H(x+at) + H(x-at)], \qquad (37)$$

where the function $H(x)$ is defined to be

$$H(x) = \int_0^x G(s)\,ds. \qquad (38)$$

If, finally, a string has both a nonzero initial position function $y(x,0) = f(x)$ and a nonzero initial velocity function $y_t(x,0) = g(x)$, then we can obtain its displacement function by adding the d'Alembert solutions of Problems A and B given in Eqs. (30) and (37), respectively. Hence the vibrations of this string with general initial conditions are described by

$$y(x,t) = \frac{1}{2}[F(x+at) + F(x-at)] + \frac{1}{2a}[H(x+at) + H(x-at)], \qquad (39)$$

a superposition of four waves moving along the x-axis with speed a, two moving to the left and two moving to the right.

9.6 Problems

Solve the boundary value problems in Problems 1 through 10.

1. $y_{tt} = 4y_{xx}$, $0 < x < \pi$, $t > 0$; $y(0,t) = y(\pi,t) = 0$,
$y(x,0) = \frac{1}{10}\sin 2x$, $y_t(x,0) = 0$

2. $y_{tt} = y_{xx}$, $0 < x < 1$, $t > 0$; $y(0,t) = y(1,t) = 0$,
$y(x,0) = \frac{1}{10}\sin \pi x - \frac{1}{20}\sin 3\pi x$, $y_t(x,0) = 0$

3. $4y_{tt} = y_{xx}$, $0 < x < \pi$, $t > 0$; $y(0,t) = y(\pi,t) = 0$,
$y(x,0) = y_t(x,0) = \frac{1}{10}\sin x$

4. $4y_{tt} = y_{xx}$, $0 < x < 2$, $t > 0$; $y(0,t) = y(2,t) = 0$,
$y(x,0) = \frac{1}{5}\sin \pi x \cos \pi x$, $y_t(x,0) = 0$

5. $y_{tt} = 25y_{xx}$, $0 < x < 3$, $t > 0$; $y(0,t) = y(3,t) = 0$,
$y(x,0) = \frac{1}{4}\sin \pi x$, $y_t(x,0) = 10\sin 2\pi x$

6. $y_{tt} = 100y_{xx}$, $0 < x < \pi$, $t > 0$; $y(0,t) = y(\pi,t) = 0$,
$y(x,0) = x(\pi - x)$, $y_t(x,0) = 0$

7. $y_{tt} = 100y_{xx}$, $0 < x < 1$, $t > 0$; $y(0,t) = y(1,t) = 0$,
$y(x,0) = 0$, $y_t(x,0) = x$

8. $y_{tt} = 4y_{xx}$, $0 < x < \pi$, $t > 0$; $y(0,t) = y(\pi,t) = 0$,
$y(x,0) = \sin x$, $y_t(x,0) = 1$

9. $y_{tt} = 4y_{xx}$, $0 < x < 1$, $t > 0$; $y(0,t) = y(1,t) = 0$,
$y(x,0) = 0$, $y_t(x,0) = x(1-x)$

10. $y_{tt} = 25y_{xx}$, $0 < x < \pi$, $t > 0$; $y(0,t) = y(\pi,t) = 0$,
$y(x,0) = y_t(x,0) = \sin^2 x$

11. Suppose that a string 2 ft long weighs $\frac{1}{32}$ oz and is subjected to a tension of 32 lb. Find the fundamental frequency with which it vibrates and the velocity with which the vibration waves travel along it.

12. Show that the amplitude of the oscillations of the midpoint of the string of Example 3 is

$$y\left(\frac{L}{2}, \frac{L}{2a}\right) = \frac{4v_0 L}{\pi^2 a} \sum_{n \text{ odd}} \frac{1}{n^2} = \frac{v_0 L}{2a}.$$

If the string is the string of Problem 11 and the impact speed of the pickup truck is 60 mi/h, show that this amplitude is approximately 1 in.

13. Suppose that the function $F(x)$ is twice differentiable for all x. Use the chain rule to verify that the functions

$$y(x,t) = F(x+at) \quad \text{and} \quad y(x,t) = F(x-at)$$

satisfy the equation $y_{tt} = a^2 y_{xx}$.

14. Given the differentiable odd period $2L$ function $F(x)$, show that the function

$$y(x,t) = \tfrac{1}{2}[F(x+at) + F(x-at)]$$

satisfies the conditions $y(0,t) = y(L,t) = 0$, $y(x,0) = F(x)$, and $y_t(x,0) = 0$.

15. If $y(x,0) = 0$, then Eq. (36) implies (why?) that

$$y(x,t) = \tfrac{1}{2} \int_0^t G(x + a\tau)\, d\tau + \tfrac{1}{2} \int_0^t G(x - a\tau)\, d\tau.$$

Make appropriate substitutions in these integrals to derive Eqs. (37) and (38).

16. **(a)** Show that the substitutions $u = x + at$ and $v = x - at$ transform the equation $y_{tt} = a^2 y_{xx}$ into the equation $y_{uv} = 0$. **(b)** Conclude that every solution of $y_{tt} = a^2 y_{xx}$ is of the form

$$y(x,t) = F(x + at) + G(x - at),$$

which represents two waves traveling in opposite directions, each with speed a.

17. Suppose that

$$y(x,t) = \sum_{n=1}^{\infty} A_n \cos \frac{n\pi a t}{L} \sin \frac{n\pi x}{L}.$$

Square the derivatives y_t and y_x and then integrate termwise—applying the orthogonality of the sine and cosine functions—to verify that

$$E = \frac{1}{2} \int_0^L (\rho y_t^2 + T y_x^2)\, dx = \frac{\pi^2 T}{4L} \sum_{n=1}^{\infty} n^2 A_n^2.$$

18. Consider a stretched string, initially at rest; its end at $x = 0$ is fixed, but its end at $x = L$ is partially free—it is allowed to slide without friction along the vertical line $x = L$. The corresponding boundary value problem is

$$y_{tt} = a^2 y_{xx} \qquad (0 < x < L, \quad t > 0);$$
$$y(0,t) = y_x(L,t) = 0,$$
$$y(x,0) = f(x),$$
$$y_t(x,0) = 0.$$

Separate the variables and use the odd half-multiple sine series of $f(x)$, as in Problem 24 of Section 9.5, to derive the solution

$$y(x,t) = \sum_{n \text{ odd}} A_n \cos \frac{n\pi a t}{2L} \sin \frac{n\pi x}{2L},$$

where

$$A_n = \frac{2}{L} \int_0^L f(x) \sin \frac{n\pi x}{2L}\, dx.$$

Problems 19 and 20 deal with the vibrations of a string under the influence of the downward force $F(x) = -\rho g$ of gravity. According to Eq. (1), its displacement function satisfies the partial differential equation

$$\frac{\partial^2 y}{\partial t^2} = a^2 \frac{\partial^2 y}{\partial x^2} - g \tag{40}$$

with endpoint conditions $y(0,t) = y(L,t) = 0$.

19. Suppose first that the string hangs in a stationary position, so that $y = y(x)$ and $y_{tt} = 0$, and hence its differential equation of motion takes the simple form $a^2 y'' = g$. Derive the stationary solution

$$y(x) = \phi(x) = \frac{gx}{2a^2}(x - L).$$

20. Now suppose that the string is released from rest in equilibrium; consequently the initial conditions are $y(x,0) = 0$ and $y_t(x,0) = 0$. Define

$$v(x,t) = y(x,t) - \phi(x),$$

where $\phi(x)$ is the stationary solution of Problem 19. Deduce from Eq. (40) that $v(x,t)$ satisfies the boundary value problem

$$v_{tt} = a^2 v_{xx};$$
$$v(0,t) = v(L,t) = 0,$$
$$v(x,0) = -\phi(x),$$
$$v_t(x,0) = 0.$$

Conclude from Eqs. (22) and (23) that

$$y(x,t) - \phi(x) = \sum_{n=1}^{\infty} A_n \cos \frac{n\pi a t}{L} \sin \frac{n\pi x}{L},$$

where the coefficients $\{A_n\}$ are the Fourier sine coefficients of $f(x) = -\phi(x)$. Finally, explain why it follows that the string oscillates between the positions $y = 0$ and $y = 2\phi(x)$.

21. For a string vibrating in air with resistance proportional to velocity, the boundary value problem is

$$\begin{aligned} y_{tt} &= a^2 y_{xx} - 2h y_t; \\ y(0,t) &= y(L,t) = 0, \\ y(x,0) &= f(x), \\ y_t(x,0) &= 0. \end{aligned} \tag{41}$$

Assume that $0 < h < \pi a/L$. **(a)** Substitute

$$y(x,t) = X(x)T(t)$$

in (41) to obtain the equations

$$X'' + \lambda X = 0, \quad X(0) = X(L) = 0 \tag{42}$$

and

$$T'' + 2hT' + a^2 \lambda T = 0, \quad T'(0) = 0. \tag{43}$$

(b) The eigenvalues and eigenfunctions of (42) are

$$\lambda_n = \frac{n^2 \pi^2}{L^2} \quad \text{and} \quad X_n(x) = \sin \frac{n\pi x}{L}$$

(as usual). Show that the general solution with $\lambda = n^2 \pi^2 / L^2$ of the differential equation in (43) is

$$T_n(t) = e^{-ht}(A_n \cos \omega_n t + B_n \sin \omega_n t),$$

where $\omega_n = \sqrt{(n^2\pi^2 a^2/L^2) - h^2} < n\pi a/L$. **(c)** Show that $T_n'(0) = 0$ implies that $B_n = hA_n/\omega_n$, and hence that to within a constant multiplicative coefficient,

$$T_n(t) = e^{-ht}\cos(\omega_n t - \alpha_n)$$

where $\alpha_n = \tan^{-1}(h/\omega_n)$. **(d)** Finally, conclude that

$$y(x,t) = e^{-ht}\sum_{n=1}^{\infty} c_n \cos(\omega_n t - \alpha_n)\sin\frac{n\pi x}{L},$$

where

$$c_n = \frac{2}{L\cos\alpha_n}\int_0^L f(x)\sin\frac{n\pi x}{L}\,dx.$$

From this formula we see that the air resistance has three main effects: exponential damping of amplitudes, decreased frequencies $\omega_n < n\pi a/L$, and the introduction of the phase delay angles α_n.

22. Rework Problem 21 as follows: First substitute $y(x,t) = e^{-ht}v(x,t)$ in Eq. (41) and then show that the boundary value problem for $v(x,t)$ is

$$v_{tt} = a^2 v_{xx} + h^2 v;$$
$$v(0,t) = v(L,t) = 0,$$
$$v(x,0) = f(x),$$
$$v_t(x,0) = hf(x).$$

Next show that the substitution $v(x,t) = X(x)T(t)$ leads to the equations

$$X'' + \lambda X = 0, \quad X(0) = X(L) = 0,$$
$$T'' + (\lambda a^2 - h^2)T = 0.$$

Proceed in this manner to derive the solution $y(x,t)$ given in part (d) of Problem 21.

The snapshots in Fig. 9.6.4 show successive positions of a vibrating string with length $L = \pi$ and $a = 1$ (so its period of oscillation is 2π). The string is initially at rest with fixed endpoints, and at time $t = 0$ it is set in motion with initial position function

$$f(x) = 2\sin^2 x = 1 - \cos 2x. \tag{44}$$

23. The most interesting snapshot is the one in Fig. 9.6.4(e), where it appears that the string exhibits a momentary "flat spot" at the instant $t = \pi/4$. Indeed, apply the d'Alembert formula in (30) to prove that the string's position function $y(x,t)$ satisfies the condition

$$y\left(x,\frac{\pi}{4}\right) = 1 \quad \text{for} \quad \frac{\pi}{4} \leq x \leq \frac{3\pi}{4}.$$

24. (a) Show that the position function $f(x)$ defined in Eq. (44) has inflection points $[f''(x) = 0]$ at $x = \pi/4$ and at $x = 3\pi/4$. **(b)** In snapshots (a)–(e) of Fig. 9.6.4 it appears that these two inflection points may remain fixed during some initial portion of the string's vibration. Indeed, apply the d'Alembert formula to show that if either $x = \pi/4$ or $x = 3\pi/4$, then $y(x,t) = 1$ for $0 \leq t \leq \pi/4$.

9.6 Application: Vibrating String Investigations

Here we describe a *Mathematica* implementation of the d'Alembert solution

$$y(x,t) = \tfrac{1}{2}[F(x+at) + F(x-at)] \tag{1}$$

of the vibrating string problem, and apply it to investigate graphically the motions that result from a variety of different initial positions of the string. *Maple* and MATLAB versions of this implementation are included in the applications manual that accompanies this text.

To plot the snapshots shown in Fig. 9.6.4, we began with the initial position function

```
f[x_] := 2*Sin[x]^2
```

To define the odd period 2π extension $F(x)$ of $f(x)$, we need the function $s(x)$ that shifts the point x by an integral multiple of π into the interval $[0, \pi]$.

```
s[x_] := Block[{k}, k = Floor[N[x/Pi]];
            If[EvenQ[k], (* k is even *)
            (* then *) N[x - k*Pi],
            (* else *) N[x - k*Pi - Pi]]]
```

Then the desired odd extension is defined by

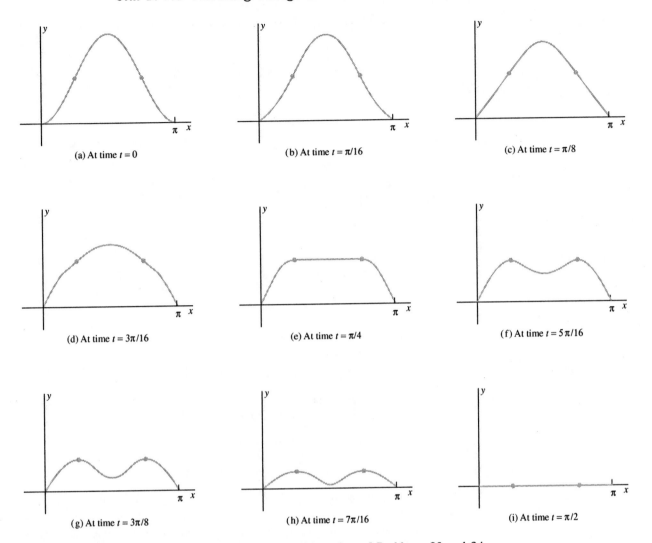

FIGURE 9.6.4. Successive snapshots of the vibrating string of Problems 23 and 24.

```
F[x_] := If[s[x] > 0, (* then *) f[s[x]],
                      (* else *)-f[-s[x]]]
```

Finally, the d'Alembert solution in (1) is

```
G[x_, t_] := ( F[x + t] + F[x - t] )/2
```

A snapshot of the position of the string at time *t* is defined by

```
stringAt[t_] := Plot[g[x,t], {x, 0, Pi} ];
```

For example, the command **stringAt[Pi/4]** plots the snapshot corresponding to $t = \pi/4$ shown in Fig. 9.6.4(e), which exhibits the apparent flat spot discussed in Problem 23. We can plot a whole sequence of shapshots at once:

```
snapshots = Table[ stringAt[t], {t, 0, Pi, Pi/12}]
```

These snapshots can be animated to show the vibrating string in motion, or we can exhibit simultaneously the successive positions of the string in a single composite figure (see Fig. 9.6.5) with the command **Show[snapshots]**.

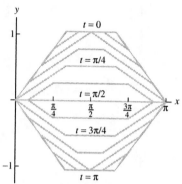

FIGURE 9.6.5. Successive positions of the vibrating string with initial position $f(x) = 2\sin^2 x$.

FIGURE 9.6.6. Successive positions of the vibrating string with triangular initial position.

FIGURE 9.6.7. Successive positions of the vibrating string with trapezoidal initial position.

The initial position function

```
f[x_] := If[x < Pi/2, (* then *) x,
               (* else *) Pi - x] // N
```

(corresponding to the triangular wave function of Fig. 9.2.4) generates in this way the composite picture shown in Fig. 9.6.6. Similarly, the initial position function

```
f[x_] := Which[ 0 <= x < Pi/3, x,
                Pi/3 <= x < 2*Pi/3, Pi/3,
                2*Pi/3 <= x <= Pi, Pi - x ] // N
```

(corresponding to the trapezoidal wave function of Fig. 9.2.5) produces the picture shown in Fig. 9.6.7.

You can test your implementation of d'Alembert's method by attempting to generate Figs. 9.6.6 and 9.6.7 for yourself. The initial position "bump function"

$$f(x) = \sin^{200} x, \quad 0 \leq x \leq \pi$$

generates traveling waves traveling (initially) in opposite directions, as indicated in Fig. 9.6.3 in the text. The initial position function

$$f(x) = \begin{cases} \sin^{200}\left(x + \frac{3}{2}\right) & \text{for } 0 < x < \pi/2, \\ 0 & \text{for } \pi/2 < x < \pi \end{cases}$$

generates a single wave that begins at $x = 0$ and (initially) travels to the right. (Think of a jump rope tied to a tree, whose free end is given a "snap" at time $t = 0$.)

After exploring some of the possibilities indicated previously, try some initial position functions of your own choice. Any continuous function f such that $f(0) = f(\pi) = 0$ is fair game. The more exotic the resulting vibration of the string, the better.

9.7 Steady-State Temperature and Laplace's Equation

We now consider the temperature in a two-dimensional plate, or lamina, that occupies a region R in the xy-plane bounded by a piecewise smooth curve C, as shown in Fig. 9.7.1. We assume that the faces of the plate are insulated, and that it is so thin that the temperature within it does not vary in the direction perpendicular to the xy-plane. We want to determine, under various conditions, the temperature $u(x, y, t)$ at the point (x, y) at time t.

Let the plate consist of material with density δ (mass per unit volume), specific heat c (per unit mass), and thermal conductivity K, all assumed constant throughout the plate. Under these assumptions, it can be shown (by a generalization of the derivation of the one-dimensional heat equation in Section 9.5) that the temperature function $u(x, y, t)$ satisfies the **two-dimensional heat equation**

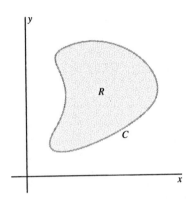

$$\frac{\partial u}{\partial t} = k\left(\frac{\partial^2 u}{\partial x^2} + \frac{\partial^2 u}{\partial y^2}\right). \tag{1}$$

As in Section 9.5, k denotes the thermal diffusivity,

$$k = \frac{K}{c\delta}, \tag{2}$$

FIGURE 9.7.1. A plane region R and its bounding curve C.

of the material of the plate. The sum of second derivatives on the right-hand side in (1) is the **Laplacian** of the function u, commonly denoted by

$$\nabla^2 u = \frac{\partial^2 u}{\partial x^2} + \frac{\partial^2 u}{\partial y^2}, \tag{3}$$

so the two-dimensional heat equation may be written as

$$\frac{\partial u}{\partial t} = k\nabla^2 u. \tag{1'}$$

In comparing Eq. (1′) with the one-dimensional heat equation $u_t = ku_{xx}$, we see that in passing from one to two dimensions, the second-order space derivative u_{xx} is replaced with the Laplacian $\nabla^2 u$. This is an instance of a general phenomenon. For instance, if a flexible stretched membrane occupies in equilibrium a region in the xy-plane and vibrates in the (perpendicular) z-direction, then its displacement function $z = z(x, y, t)$ satisfies the **two-dimensional wave equation**

$$\frac{\partial^2 z}{\partial t^2} = a^2\left(\frac{\partial^2 z}{\partial x^2} + \frac{\partial^2 z}{\partial y^2}\right) = a^2 \nabla^2 z. \tag{4}$$

This equation has the same relation to the one-dimensional wave equation $z_{tt} = a^2 z_{xx}$ (here writing $z(x, y)$ for the displacement of a string) as Eq. (1′) has to the one-dimensional heat equation.

In this section we confine our attention to the steady-state situation in which the temperature u does not vary with time, and so is a function only of x and y. Thus we are interested in the *steady-state temperature* of a plate. In this case $u_t = 0$, so Eq. (1) becomes the **two-dimensional Laplace equation**

$$\nabla^2 u = \frac{\partial^2 u}{\partial x^2} + \frac{\partial^2 u}{\partial y^2} = 0. \tag{5}$$

This important partial differential equation is also known as the **potential equation.** The three-dimensional Laplace equation $u_{xx} + u_{yy} + u_{zz} = 0$ is satisfied (in empty space) by electric and gravitational potential functions. It is also satisfied by the velocity potential function for the steady irrotational flow of an incompressible and inviscid liquid.

Dirichlet Problems

A particular solution of Laplace's equation in a bounded plane region R is determined by appropriate boundary conditions. For example, it is plausible on physical grounds that the steady-state temperature $u(x, y)$ in a plate is determined if we know that $u(x, y)$ agrees with a given function $f(x, y)$ at each point of the boundary curve C of the plate. To find the steady-state temperature in a plate with assigned boundary values, we need to solve the boundary value problem

$$\frac{\partial^2 u}{\partial x^2} + \frac{\partial^2 u}{\partial y^2} = 0 \qquad \text{(within } R\text{)};$$

$$u(x, y) = f(x, y) \qquad \text{(if } (x, y) \text{ is on } C\text{)}.$$

(6)

Such a problem, finding a solution of Laplace's equation in a region R with given boundary values, is called a **Dirichlet problem.** It is known that if the boundary curve C and the boundary value function f are reasonably well behaved, then there exists a unique solution of the Dirichlet problem in (6).

FIGURE 9.7.2. A rectangular plate with given boundary values.

Figure 9.7.2 shows a rectangular plate with indicated boundary values along its four edges. The corresponding Dirichlet problem is

$$u_{xx} + u_{yy} = 0 \qquad \text{(within } R\text{)};$$
$$u(x, 0) = f_1(x), \quad u(x, b) = f_2(x) \qquad (0 < x < a),$$
$$u(0, y) = g_1(y), \quad u(a, y) = g_2(y) \qquad (0 < y < b).$$

(7)

Because there are four nonhomogeneous conditions (rather than one), this boundary value problem is not directly susceptible to the method of separation of variables. In Section 9.6, when confronted with this difficulty, we split the problem of the vibrating string with both nonzero initial position and nonzero initial velocity into problems with a single nonhomogeneous condition each. In a similar way, the boundary value problem in (7) can be split into *four* problems, each with a single nonhomogeneous boundary condition. For each of these problems, $u(x, y)$ will be zero along three edges of the rectangle and will have assigned values on the fourth. Each of these four boundary values can be solved by the method of separation of variables, and the sum of the four solutions is the solution of the original problem in (7). In the following example we solve one of these four problems—the one illustrated in Fig. 9.7.3.

Example 1   Solve the boundary value problem

$$u_{xx} + u_{yy} = 0;$$
$$u(0, y) = u(a, y) = u(x, b) = 0,$$
$$u(x, 0) = f(x)$$

(8)

for the rectangle in Fig. 9.7.3.

Solution   Substitution of $u(x, y) = X(x)Y(y)$ gives $X''Y + XY'' = 0$, so

$$\frac{X''}{X} = -\frac{Y''}{Y} = -\lambda$$

(9)

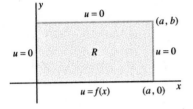

for some constant λ. Thus $X(x)$ must satisfy the familiar eigenvalue problem

$$X'' + \lambda X = 0,$$
$$X(0) = X(a) = 0.$$

FIGURE 9.7.3. The boundary value problem of Example 1.

The eigenvalues and associated eigenfunctions are

$$\lambda_n = \frac{n^2 \pi^2}{a^2}, \quad X_n(x) = \sin \frac{n\pi x}{a}$$

(10)

for $n = 1, 2, 3, \ldots$. From Eq. (9) with $\lambda = n^2\pi^2/a^2$ and the remaining homogeneous boundary conditions in (8), we get

$$Y_n'' - \frac{n^2\pi^2}{a^2} Y_n = 0, \quad Y_n(b) = 0.$$

(11)

The general solution of the differential equation in (11) is

$$Y_n(y) = A_n \cosh \frac{n\pi y}{a} + B_n \sinh \frac{n\pi y}{a},$$

and the condition

$$Y_n(b) = A_n \cosh \frac{n\pi b}{a} + B_n \sinh \frac{n\pi b}{a} = 0$$

implies that $B_n = -[A_n \cosh(n\pi b/a)]/[\sinh(n\pi b/a)]$, so

$$Y_n(y) = A_n \cosh \frac{n\pi y}{a} - \frac{A_n \cosh(n\pi b/a)}{\sinh(n\pi b/a)} \sinh \frac{n\pi y}{a}$$

$$= \frac{A_n}{\sinh(n\pi b/a)} \left(\sinh \frac{n\pi b}{a} \cosh \frac{n\pi y}{a} - \cosh \frac{n\pi b}{a} \sinh \frac{n\pi y}{a} \right).$$

Therefore,

$$Y_n(y) = c_n \sinh \frac{n\pi(b - y)}{a}$$

(12)

where $c_n = A_n / \sinh(n\pi b/a)$. From (10) and (12) we obtain the formal series solution

$$u(x, y) = \sum_{n=1}^{\infty} X_n(x) Y_n(y) = \sum_{n=1}^{\infty} c_n \sin \frac{n\pi x}{a} \sinh \frac{n\pi(b - y)}{a}. \tag{13}$$

It remains only to choose the coefficients $\{c_n\}$ to satisfy the nonhomogeneous condition

$$u(x, 0) = \sum_{n=1}^{\infty} \left(c_n \sinh \frac{n\pi b}{a} \right) \sin \frac{n\pi x}{a} = f(x).$$

For this purpose we want

$$c_n \sinh \frac{n\pi b}{a} = b_n = \frac{2}{a} \int_0^a f(x) \sin \frac{n\pi x}{a}\, dx,$$

so

$$c_n = \frac{2}{a \sinh(n\pi b/a)} \int_0^a f(x) \sin \frac{n\pi x}{a}\, dx. \tag{14}$$

With this choice of coefficients, the series in (13) is a formal series solution of the Dirichlet problem in (8). ∎

For instance, suppose that

$$f(x) \equiv T_0 = \frac{4T_0}{\pi} \sum_{n \text{ odd}} \frac{1}{n} \sin \frac{n\pi x}{a}$$

if $0 < x < a$, so that $b_n = 4T_0/(\pi n)$ for n odd and $b_n = 0$ for n even. Then the formulas in (13) and (14) yield

$$u(x, y) = \frac{4T_0}{\pi} \sum_{n \text{ odd}} \frac{\sin(n\pi x/a) \sinh(n\pi[b - y]/a)}{n \sinh(n\pi b/a)} \tag{15}$$

for the steady-state temperature in a rectangular plate with its base held at temperature T_0 and its other three edges at temperature zero. In particular, suppose that $T_0 = 100$ and that $a = b = 10$. Then from Eq. (15) we find that the temperature at the center of the plate is

$$u(5, 5) = \frac{400}{\pi} \sum_{n \text{ odd}} \frac{\sin(n\pi/2) \sinh(n\pi/2)}{n \sinh n\pi}$$

$$\approx 25.3716 - 0.3812 + 0.0099 - 0.0003;$$

that is, $u(5, 5)$ is approximately 25.00.

Remark 1: Can you supply an argument—perhaps using symmetry—that proves (without using the series solution) that $u(5, 5)$ is exactly 25?

Remark 2: In practice, engineers use solutions like the one in Eq. (15) to plot the variation of temperature within a plate or piece of machinery; they are particularly interested in any "hot spots" that may appear. Such information is often presented by constructing *level curves* on which the temperature function $u(x, y)$ is constant. Figure 9.7.4 shows typical level curves for the function $u(x, y)$ in (15) with $a = b = 10$ and $T_0 = 100$.

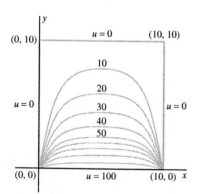

FIGURE 9.7.4. Typical level curves of the function $u(x, y)$ in Eq. (15).

Example 2   Let R be the "semi-infinite" strip shown in Fig. 9.7.5. Solve the boundary value problem

$$u_{xx} + u_{yy} = 0 \qquad \text{(in } R\text{)};$$
$$u(x,0) = u(x,b) = 0 \qquad (0 < x < \infty),$$
$$u(x,y) \text{ is bounded as } x \to +\infty,$$
$$u(0,y) = g(y). \tag{16}$$

Solution   The condition that $u(x,y)$ is bounded as $x \to +\infty$ plays the role of a homogeneous boundary condition associated with the "missing" right edge of the "rectangle"; this is typical of Dirichlet problems for unbounded regions. With $u(x,y) = X(x)Y(y)$, the actual homogeneous conditions give $Y(0) = Y(b) = 0$. Hence it is $Y(y)$ that will satisfy an eigenvalue problem. We therefore write the separation in (9) as

$$\frac{Y''}{Y} = -\frac{X''}{X} = -\lambda, \tag{17}$$

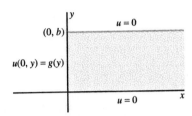

FIGURE 9.7.5. The "semi-infinite" strip of Example 2.

changing the sign of λ to get the familiar eigenvalue problem

$$Y'' + \lambda Y = 0, \quad Y(0) = Y(b) = 0$$

with eigenvalues and associated eigenfunctions

$$\lambda_n = \frac{n^2 \pi^2}{b^2}, \quad Y_n(y) = \sin \frac{n\pi y}{b}. \tag{18}$$

The general solution of

$$X_n'' - \frac{n^2 \pi^2}{b^2} X_n = 0$$

is $X_n(x) = A_n \exp(n\pi x/b) + B_n \exp(-n\pi x/b)$. We write the solution in exponential form because then the condition that $u(x,y)$, and hence $X(x)$, is bounded as $x \to +\infty$ immediately implies that $A_n = 0$ for all n. Suppressing the constant, this leaves

$$X_n(x) = \exp\left(-\frac{n\pi x}{b}\right). \tag{19}$$

From Eqs. (18) and (19) we get the formal series solution

$$\blacktriangleright \qquad u(x,y) = \sum_{n=1}^{\infty} b_n X_n(x) Y_n(y) = \sum_{n=1}^{\infty} b_n \exp\left(-\frac{n\pi x}{b}\right) \sin \frac{n\pi y}{b} \tag{20}$$

that satisfies the homogeneous boundary conditions and the boundedness condition. In order also to satisfy the nonhomogeneous condition

$$u(0,y) = \sum_{n=1}^{\infty} b_n \sin \frac{n\pi y}{b} = g(y),$$

we choose b_n to be the Fourier sine coefficient

$$\blacktriangleright \qquad b_n = \frac{2}{b} \int_0^b g(y) \sin \frac{n\pi y}{b} \, dy \tag{21}$$

of the function $g(y)$ on $[0, b]$.

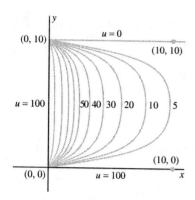

FIGURE 9.7.6. Typical level curves of the function $u(x, y)$ of Example 2.

For instance, if

$$g(y) = T_0 = \frac{4T_0}{\pi} \sum_{n \text{ odd}} \frac{1}{n} \sin \frac{n\pi y}{b}$$

for $0 < y < b$, then Eqs. (20) and (21) yield

$$u(x, y) = \frac{4T_0}{\pi} \sum_{n \text{ odd}} \frac{1}{n} \exp\left(-\frac{n\pi x}{b}\right) \sin \frac{n\pi y}{b}.$$

Figure 9.7.6 shows some typical level curves of the temperature function defined by this formula with $b = 10$ and $T_0 = 100$. ∎

The Dirichlet Problem for a Circular Disk

We now investigate the steady-state temperature in a circular disk of radius a with insulated faces and with given boundary temperatures. Obviously we should accommodate the geometry of the circle by expressing $u = u(r, \theta)$ in terms of polar coordinates r and θ, with $x = r\cos\theta$ and $y = r\sin\theta$. When these equations are used to transform the Laplacian, the result is **Laplace's equation in polar coordinates:**

$$\blacktriangleright \qquad \nabla^2 u = \frac{\partial^2 u}{\partial r^2} + \frac{1}{r}\frac{\partial u}{\partial r} + \frac{1}{r^2}\frac{\partial^2 u}{\partial \theta^2} = 0. \qquad (22)$$

We prescribe assigned boundary temperatures (as indicated in Fig. 9.7.7) by requiring that

$$\blacktriangleright \qquad u(a, \theta) = f(\theta), \qquad (23)$$

where the function $f(\theta)$ of period 2π is given. In addition, because (r, θ) and $(r, \theta + 2\pi)$ are the polar coordinates of the same point, we impose on u the periodicity condition

$$\blacktriangleright \qquad u(r, \theta) = u(r, \theta + 2\pi) \qquad (24)$$

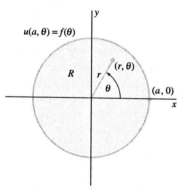

FIGURE 9.7.7. The Dirichlet problem for a circular disk.

for $r < a$ and all θ; this will play the role of a homogeneous boundary condition.

To solve the boundary value problem in Eqs. (22) through (24), we substitute $u(r, \theta) = R(r)\Theta(\theta)$ in Eq. (22); the result is

$$R''\Theta + \frac{1}{r}R'\Theta + \frac{1}{r^2}R\Theta'' = 0.$$

Division by $R\Theta/r^2$ gives

$$\frac{r^2 R'' + rR'}{R} + \frac{\Theta''}{\Theta} = 0,$$

so it follows that

$$\frac{r^2 R'' + rR'}{R} = -\frac{\Theta''}{\Theta} = \lambda$$

for some constant λ. This yields the two ordinary differential equations

$$r^2 R'' + r R' - \lambda R = 0 \qquad (25)$$

and

$$\Theta'' + \lambda \Theta = 0. \qquad (26)$$

The general solution of Eq. (26) is

$$\Theta(\theta) = A \cos \alpha \theta + B \sin \alpha \theta \quad \text{if } \lambda = \alpha^2 > 0, \qquad (27\text{a})$$
$$\Theta(\theta) = A + B\Theta \qquad\qquad \text{if } \lambda = 0, \qquad (27\text{b})$$
$$\Theta(\theta) = A e^{\alpha \theta} + B e^{-\alpha \theta} \qquad \text{if } \lambda = -\alpha^2 < 0. \qquad (27\text{c})$$

Now we apply the condition in (24), which implies that $\Theta(\theta) = \Theta(\theta + 2\pi)$; that is, that $\Theta(\theta)$ has period 2π. In Problems 22 and 23 we ask you to show that this is so only if $\lambda = n^2$ (n an integer) in (27a) or if $\lambda = 0$ and $B = 0$ in (27b). Thus we have the eigenvalues and associated eigenfunctions

$$\lambda_0 = 0, \quad \Theta_0(\theta) = 1; \qquad (28\text{a})$$
$$\lambda_n = n^2, \quad \Theta_n(\theta) = A_n \cos n\theta + B_n \sin n\theta \qquad (28\text{b})$$

for $n = 1, 2, 3, \ldots$.

Next we turn our attention to Eq. (25). With $\lambda_0 = 0$ it reduces to the equation $r^2 R_0'' + r R_0' = 0$ with general solution

$$R_0(r) = C_0 + D_0 \ln r. \qquad (29)$$

Of course we want $u(r, \theta)$, and hence $R(r)$, to be continuous at $r = 0$; this requires that $D_0 = 0$ in Eq. (29), so $R_0(r) = C_0$. Then, with $\lambda = \lambda_n = n^2$, Eq. (25) is

$$r^2 R_n'' + r R_n' - n^2 R_n = 0.$$

On substituting the trial solution $R(r) = r^k$, we find that $k = \pm n$, so the general solution of the previous equation is

$$R_n(r) = C_n r^n + \frac{D_n}{r^n}. \qquad (30)$$

Continuity at $r = 0$ then requires that $D_n = 0$, so $R_n(r) = C_n r^n$.

Finally we combine the results in Eqs. (28) through (30) with $D_n \equiv 0$ to obtain a formal series solution of the form

$$u(r, \theta) = \sum_{n=0}^{\infty} R_n(r) \Theta_n(\theta);$$

that is,

$$u(r, \theta) = \frac{a_0}{2} + \sum_{n=1}^{\infty} (a_n \cos n\theta + b_n \sin n\theta) r^n. \qquad (31)$$

In order that the boundary condition $u(a, \theta) = f(\theta)$ be satisfied, we want

$$u(a, \theta) = \frac{a_0}{2} + \sum_{n=1}^{\infty} (a_n a^n \cos n\theta + b_n a^n \sin n\theta)$$

to be the Fourier series of $f(\theta)$ on $[0, 2\pi]$. Hence we choose

$$a_n = \frac{1}{\pi a^n} \int_0^{2\pi} f(\theta) \cos n\theta \, d\theta \qquad (n = 0, 1, 2, \ldots) \qquad (32\text{a})$$

and

$$b_n = \frac{1}{\pi a^n} \int_0^{2\pi} f(\theta) \sin n\theta \, d\theta \qquad (n = 1, 2, 3, \dots). \qquad (32b)$$

Example 3 For instance, if $F(\theta) = T_0$ for $0 < \theta < \pi$ and $F(\theta) = -T_0$ for $\pi < \theta < 2\pi$, so that

$$F(\theta) = \frac{4T_0}{\pi} \sum_{n \text{ odd}} \frac{1}{n} \sin n\theta,$$

then $a_n = 0$ for all $n \geq 0$, $b_n = 0$ for n even, and $b_n = 4T_0/(\pi n a^n)$ for n odd. So Eqs. (31) and (32) yield

$$u(r, \theta) = \frac{4T_0}{\pi} \sum_{n \text{ odd}} \frac{r^n}{na^n} \sin n\theta. \qquad \blacksquare$$

> **Note:** In the Dirichlet problems of this section, we have concentrated on temperature functions with preassigned boundary values. In the case of a plate with an *insulated* edge—across which no heat can flow—the boundary condition is that the derivative of $u(x, y)$ in the direction normal to this edge vanishes. For instance, consider the rectangular plate in Fig. 9.7.2. If the edge $x = 0$ is insulated, then $u_x(0, y) \equiv 0$, whereas if the edge $y = b$ is insulated, then $u_y(x, b) \equiv 0$.

9.7 Problems

In Problems 1 through 3, solve the Dirichlet problem for the rectangle $0 < x < a$, $0 < y < b$ consisting of Laplace's equation $u_{xx} + u_{yy} = 0$ and the given boundary value conditions.

1. $u(x, 0) = u(x, b) = u(0, y) = 0$, $u(a, y) = g(y)$
2. $u(x, 0) = u(x, b) = u(a, y) = 0$, $u(0, y) = g(y)$
3. $u(x, 0) = u(0, y) = u(a, y) = 0$, $u(x, b) = f(x)$
4. Consider the boundary value problem

$$u_{xx} + u_{yy} = 0;$$
$$u_x(0, y) = u_x(a, y) = u(x, 0) = 0,$$
$$u(x, b) = f(x)$$

corresponding to a rectangular plate $0 < x < a$, $0 < y < b$ with the edges $x = 0$ and $x = a$ insulated. Derive the solution

$$u(x, y) = \frac{a_0 y}{2b} + \sum_{n=1}^{\infty} a_n \left(\cos \frac{n\pi x}{a} \right) \left(\frac{\sinh(n\pi y/a)}{\sinh(n\pi b/a)} \right),$$

where

$$a_n = \frac{2}{a} \int_0^a f(x) \cos \frac{n\pi x}{a} \, dx \qquad (n = 0, 1, 2, \dots).$$

(*Suggestion:* Show first that λ_0 is an eigenvalue with $X_0(x) \equiv 1$ and $Y_0(y) = y$.)

In Problems 5 and 6, find a solution of Laplace's equation $u_{xx} + u_{yy} = 0$ in the rectangle $0 < x < a$, $0 < y < b$ that satisfies the given boundary conditions (see Problem 4).

5. $u_y(x, 0) = u_y(x, b) = u(a, y) = 0$, $u(0, y) = g(y)$
6. $u_x(0, y) = u_x(a, y) = u_y(x, 0) = 0$, $u(x, b) = f(x)$

In Problems 7 and 8, find a solution of Laplace's equation in the semi-infinite strip $0 < x < a$, $y > 0$ that satisfies the given boundary conditions and the additional condition that $u(x, y)$ is bounded as $y \to +\infty$.

7. $u(0, y) = u(a, y) = 0$, $\quad u(x, 0) = f(x)$
8. $u_x(0, y) = u_x(a, y) = 0$, $\quad u(x, 0) = f(x)$
9. Suppose that $a = 10$ and $f(x) = 10x$ in Problem 8. Show that

$$u(x, y) = 50 - \frac{400}{\pi^2} \sum_{n \text{ odd}} \frac{1}{n^2} e^{-n\pi y/10} \cos \frac{n\pi x}{10}.$$

Then compute (with two-decimal-place accuracy) the values $u(0, 5)$, $u(5, 5)$, and $u(10, 5)$.

10. The edge $x = a$ of the rectangular plate $0 < x < a$, $0 < y < b$ is insulated, the edges $x = 0$ and $y = 0$ are held at temperature zero, and $u(x, b) = f(x)$. Use the odd half-multiple sine series of Problem 21 of Section 9.3 to derive a solution of the form

$$u(x, y) = \sum_{n \text{ odd}} c_n \sin \frac{n\pi x}{2a} \sinh \frac{n\pi y}{2a}.$$

Then give a formula for c_n.

11. The edge $y = 0$ of the rectangular plate $0 < x < a$, $0 < y < b$ is insulated, the edges $x = a$ and $y = b$ are held at temperature zero, and $u(0, y) = g(y)$. Use the odd half-multiple cosine series of Problem 22 of Section 9.3 to find $u(x, y)$.

12. A vertical cross section of a long high wall 30 cm thick has the shape of the semi-infinite strip $0 < x < 30$, $y > 0$. The face $x = 0$ is held at temperature zero, but the face $x = 30$ is insulated. Given $u(x, 0) = 25$, derive the formula

$$u(x, y) = \frac{100}{\pi} \sum_{n \text{ odd}} \frac{1}{n} e^{-n\pi y/60} \sin \frac{n\pi x}{60}$$

for the steady-state temperature within the wall.

Problems 13 through 15 deal with the semicircular plate of radius a shown in Fig. 9.7.8. The circular edge has a given temperature $u(a, \theta) = f(\theta)$. In each problem, derive the given series for the steady-state temperature $u(r, \theta)$ satisfying the given boundary conditions along $\theta = 0$ and $\theta = \pi$, and give the formula for the coefficients c_n.

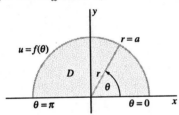

FIGURE 9.7.8. The semicircular plate of Problems 13 through 15.

13. $u(r, 0) = u(r, \pi) = 0$;

$$u(r, \theta) = \sum_{n=1}^{\infty} c_n r^n \sin n\theta$$

14. $u_\theta(r, 0) = u_\theta(r, \pi) = 0$;

$$u(r, \theta) = \frac{c_0}{2} + \sum_{n=1}^{\infty} c_n r^n \cos n\theta$$

15. $u(r, 0) = u_\theta(r, \pi) = 0$;

$$u(r, \theta) = \sum_{n \text{ odd}} c_n r^{n/2} \sin \frac{n\theta}{2}$$

16. Consider Dirichlet's problem for the region *exterior* to the circle $r = a$. You want to find a solution of

$$r^2 u_{rr} + r u_r + u_{\theta\theta} = 0$$

such that $u(a, \theta) = f(\theta)$ and $u(r, \theta)$ is bounded as $r \to +\infty$. Derive the series

$$u(r, \theta) = \frac{a_0}{2} + \sum_{n=1}^{\infty} \frac{1}{r^n} (a_n \cos n\theta + b_n \sin n\theta),$$

and give formulas for the coefficients $\{a_n\}$ and $\{b_n\}$.

17. The velocity potential function $u(r, \theta)$ for steady flow of an ideal fluid around a cylinder of radius $r = a$ satisfies the boundary value problem

$$r^2 u_{rr} + r u_r + u_{\theta\theta} = 0 \quad (r > a);$$
$$u_r(a, \theta) = 0, \qquad u(r, \theta) = u(r, -\theta),$$
$$\lim_{r \to \infty} [u(r, \theta) - U_0 r \cos \theta] = 0.$$

(a) By separation of variables, derive the solution

$$u(r, \theta) = \frac{U_0}{r} (r^2 + a^2) \cos \theta.$$

(b) Hence show that the velocity components of the flow are

$$u_x = \frac{\partial u}{\partial x} = \frac{U_0}{r^2} (r^2 - a^2 \cos 2\theta)$$

and

$$u_y = \frac{\partial u}{\partial y} = -\frac{U_0}{r^2} a^2 \sin 2\theta.$$

The streamlines for this fluid flow around the cylinder are shown in Fig. 9.7.9.

FIGURE 9.7.9. Streamlines for ideal fluid flow around a cylinder.

Comment: The streamlines in Fig. 9.7.9 are the level curves of the function $\psi(x, y)$ given in part (b) of Problem 18. It is troublesome to write a computer program to plot such level curves. It is far easier to plot some solutions of the differential equation $dy/dx = u_y/u_x$. We did so with initial conditions $x_0 = -5$, $y_0 = -2.7, -2.5, -2.3, \ldots, 2.5, 2.7$. The solutions were obtained numerically using the improved Euler method (Section 2.5) with step size 0.02.

18. **(a)** Show that the velocity potential in part (a) of Problem 17 can be written in rectangular coordinates as

$$u(x, y) = U_0 x \left(1 + \frac{a^2}{x^2 + y^2} \right).$$

(b) The stream function for the flow is

$$\psi(x, y) = U_0 y \left(\frac{a^2}{x^2 + y^2} - 1 \right).$$

Show that $\nabla u \cdot \nabla \psi \equiv 0$. Because $\mathbf{v} = \nabla u$ is the velocity vector, this shows that the streamlines of the flow are the level curves of $\psi(x, y)$.

Problems 19 through 21 deal with a solid spherical ball of radius $r = a$ with initial temperature T_0 throughout. At time $t = 0$ it is packed in ice, so its temperature at the surface $r = a$ is zero thereafter. Its temperature then depends only on time t and the distance r from the center of the ball, so we write $u = u(r, t)$.

19. (a) The heat content of the spherical shell with inner radius r and outer radius $r + \Delta r$ is

$$Q(t) = \int_r^{r+\Delta r} c\delta u(x,t) \cdot 4\pi s^2 \, ds.$$

Show that $Q'(t) = 4\pi c\delta r^2 u_t(\bar{r}, t)$ for some $\bar{r}$ in the interval $(r, r + \Delta r)$. **(b)** The radial heat flux is $\phi = -Ku_r$ across the bounding spherical surfaces of the shell in part (a). Conclude that

$$Q'(t) = 4\pi K \left[(r + \Delta r)^2 u_r(r + \Delta r, t) - r^2 u_r(r, t) \right].$$

(c) Equate the values of $Q'(t)$ in parts (a) and (b); then take the limit as $\Delta r \to 0$ to get the equation

$$\frac{\partial u}{\partial t} = \frac{k}{r^2} \frac{\partial}{\partial r} \left(r^2 \frac{\partial u}{\partial r} \right).$$

(d) Finally, show that this last equation is equivalent to

$$\frac{\partial}{\partial t}(ru) = k \frac{\partial^2}{\partial r^2}(ru).$$

20. It follows from part (d) of Problem 19 that $u(r, t)$ satisfies the boundary value problem

$$\frac{\partial}{\partial t}(ru) = k \frac{\partial^2}{\partial r^2}(ru) \qquad (r < a);$$

$$u(a, t) = 0, \quad u(r, 0) = T_0.$$

Show that the new function $v(r, t) = ru(r, t)$ satisfies a familiar boundary value problem (in Section 9.5), and thus

derive the solution

$$u(r,t) = \frac{2aT_0}{\pi} \sum_{n=1}^{\infty} \frac{(-1)^{n+1}}{nr} \exp\left(-\frac{n^2 \pi^2 kt}{a^2} \right) \sin \frac{n\pi r}{a}.$$

21. (a) Deduce from the solution to Problem 20 that the temperature at the center of the ball at time t is

$$u(0,t) = 2T_0 \sum_{n=1}^{\infty} (-1)^{n+1} \exp\left(-\frac{n^2 \pi^2 kt}{a^2} \right).$$

(b) Let $a = 30$ cm and $T_0 = 100°$C. Compute $u(0, t)$ after 15 min if the ball is made of iron with $k = 0.15$ cgs. (*Answer*: Approximately 45°C.) **(c)** If you have access to a programmable calculator, repeat part (b) for a ball made of concrete with $k = 0.005$ in cgs units. About 15 terms are required to show that $u = 100.00°$C accurate to two decimal places.

22. In the discussion of the Dirichlet problem for a circular disk in this section, we obtained the ordinary differential equation $\Theta'' + \lambda\Theta = 0$ with the periodicity condition $\Theta(\theta) = \Theta(\theta + 2\pi)$. **(a)** Suppose that $\lambda = \alpha^2 > 0$. Show that the general solution

$$\Theta(\theta) = A \cos \alpha\theta + B \sin \alpha\theta$$

has period 2π only if $\lambda = n^2$ with n an integer. **(b)** In the case $\lambda = 0$, show that the general solution

$$\Theta(\theta) = A\theta + B$$

is periodic only if $A = 0$.

23. If $\lambda = -\alpha^2 < 0$ in Problem 22, then the general solution of the differential equation is

$$\Theta(\theta) = Ae^{\alpha\theta} + Be^{-\alpha\theta}.$$

Show that this function is not periodic unless $A = B = 0$.

ANSWERS TO SELECTED PROBLEMS

Chapter 7

Section 7.1

1. $1/s^2$, $s > 0$

2. $2/s^3$, $s > 0$

3. $e/(s-3)$, $s > 3$

4. $s/(s^2+1)$, $s > 0$

5. $1/(s^2-1)$, $s > 1$

6. $\frac{1}{2}[1/s - s/(s^2+4)]$, $s > 0$

7. $(1-e^{-s})/s$, $s > 0$

8. $(e^{-s} - e^{-2s})/s$, $s > 0$

9. $(1 - e^{-s} - se^{-s})/s^2$, $s > 0$

10. $(s - 1 + e^{-s})/s^2$, $s > 0$

11. $\frac{1}{2}\sqrt{\pi}s^{-3/2} + 3s^{-2}$, $s > 0$

12. $(45\pi - 192s^{3/2})/(8s^{7/2})$, $s > 0$

13. $s^{-2} - 2(s-3)^{-1}$, $s > 3$

14. $3\sqrt{\pi}/(4s^{5/2}) + 1/(s+10)$, $s > 0$

15. $s^{-1} + s(s^2 - 25)^{-1}$, $s > 5$

16. $(s+2)/(s^2+4)$, $s > 0$

17. $\cos^2 2t = \frac{1}{2}(1 + \cos 4t)$; $\frac{1}{2}[s^{-1} + s/(s^2 + 16)]$, $s > 0$

18. $3/(s^2 + 36)$, $s > 0$

19. $s^{-1} + 3s^{-2} + 6s^{-3} + 6s^{-4}$, $s > 0$

20. $1/(s-1)^2$, $s > 1$

21. $(s^2 - 4)/(s^2 + 4)^2$, $s > 0$

22. $\frac{1}{2}[s/(s^2 - 36) - s^{-1}]$

23. $\frac{1}{2}t^3$

24. $2\sqrt{t/\pi}$

25. $1 - \frac{8}{3}t^{3/2}\pi^{-1/2}$

26. e^{-5t}

27. $3e^{4t}$

28. $3\cos 2t + \frac{1}{2}\sin 2t$

29. $\frac{5}{3}\sin 3t - 3\cos 3t$

30. $-\cosh 2t - \frac{9}{2}\sinh 2t$

31. $\frac{3}{5}\sinh 5t - 10\cosh 5t$

32. $2u(t-3)$

37. $f(t) = 1 - u(t-a)$. Your figure should indicate that the graph of f contains the point $(a, 0)$, but not the point $(a, 1)$.

38. $f(t) = u(t-a) - u(t-b)$. Your figure should indicate that the graph of f contains the points $(a, 1)$ and $(b, 0)$, but not the points $(a, 0)$ and $(b, 1)$.

39. Figure 7.2.8 shows the graph of the unit staircase function.

Section 7.2

1. $x(t) = 5\cos 2t$

2. $x(t) = 3\cos 3t + \frac{4}{3}\sin 3t$

3. $x(t) = \frac{2}{3}(e^{2t} - e^{-t})$

4. $x(t) = \frac{1}{2}(7e^{-3t} - 3e^{-5t})$

5. $x(t) = \frac{1}{3}(2\sin t - \sin 2t)$

6. $x(t) = \frac{1}{3}(\cos t - \cos 2t)$

7. $x(t) = \frac{1}{8}(9\cos t - \cos 3t)$

8. $x(t) = \frac{1}{9}(1 - \cos 3t)$

9. $x(t) = \frac{1}{6}(2 - 3e^{-t} + e^{-3t})$

10. $x(t) = \frac{1}{4}(2t - 3 + 12e^{-t} - 9e^{-2t})$

11. $x(t) = 1$, $y(t) = -2$

12. $x(t) = \frac{2}{9}(e^{2t} - e^{-t} - 3te^{-t})$, $y(t) = \frac{1}{9}(e^{2t} - e^{-t} + 6te^{-t})$

13. $x(t) = -(2/\sqrt{3})\sinh(t/\sqrt{3})$,
$y(t) = \cosh(t/\sqrt{3}) + (1/\sqrt{3})\sinh(t/\sqrt{3})$

14. $x(t) = \frac{1}{4}(2t - 3\sin 2t)$, $y(t) = -\frac{1}{8}(2t + 3\sin 2t)$

15. $x(t) = \frac{1}{3}\left(2 + e^{-3t/2}\left[\cos(rt/2) + r\sin(rt/2)\right]\right)$,
$y(t) = \frac{1}{21}\left(28 - 9e^{t} + 2e^{-3t/2}\left[\cos(rt/2) + 4r\sin(rt/2)\right]\right)$ where $r = \sqrt{3}$

16. $x(t) = \cos t + \sin t$, $y(t) = e^{t} - \cos t$, $z(t) = -2\sin t$

17. $f(t) = \frac{1}{3}(e^{3t} - 1)$

18. $f(t) = \frac{3}{5}(1 - e^{-5t})$

19. $f(t) = \frac{1}{4}(1 - \cos 2t) = \frac{1}{2}\sin^2 t$

20. $f(t) = \frac{1}{9}(6\sin 3t - \cos 3t + 1)$

21. $f(t) = t - \sin t$

22. $f(t) = \frac{1}{9}(-1 + \cosh 3t)$

23. $f(t) = -t + \sinh t$

24. $f(t) = \frac{1}{2}(e^{-2t} - 2e^{-t} + 1)$

Section 7.3

1. $24/(s-\pi)^5$

2. $\frac{3}{4}\sqrt{\pi}(s+4)^{-5/2}$

3. $3\pi/[(s+2)^2 + 9\pi^2]$

4. $\sqrt{2}(2s+5)/(4s^2 + 4s + 17)$

5. $\frac{3}{2}e^{2t}$

6. $(t - t^2)e^{-t}$

7. te^{-2t}

8. $e^{-2t}\cos t$

9. $e^{3t}\left(3\cos 4t + \frac{7}{2}\sin 4t\right)$

10. $\frac{1}{36}e^{2t/3}\left(8\cos\frac{4}{3}t - 5\sin\frac{4}{3}t\right)$

11. $\frac{1}{2}\sinh 2t$

12. $2 + 3e^{3t}$

13. $3e^{-2t} - 5e^{-5t}$

14. $2 + e^{2t} - 3e^{-t}$

15. $\frac{1}{25}(e^{5t} - 1 - 5t)$

16. $\frac{1}{125}[e^{2t}(5t - 2) + e^{-3t}(5t + 2)]$

17. $\frac{1}{16}(\sinh 2t - \sin 2t)$

18. $e^{4t}\left(1 + 12t + 24t^2 + \frac{32}{3}t^3\right)$

19. $\frac{1}{3}(2\cos 2t + 2\sin 2t - 2\cos t - \sin t)$

20. $\frac{1}{32}[e^{2t}(2t - 1) + e^{-2t}(2t + 1)]$

21. $\frac{1}{2}e^{-t}(5\sin t - 3t\cos t - 2t\sin t)$

22. $\frac{1}{64}e^{t/2}[(4t + 8)\cos t + (4 - 3t)\sin t]$

27. $\frac{1}{4}e^{-3t}(8\cos 4t + 9\sin 4t)$

28. $\frac{1}{4}(1 - 2e^{2t} + e^{4t})$

29. $\frac{1}{8}(-6t + 3\sinh 2t)$

30. $\frac{1}{10}[2e^{-t} - e^{-2t}(2\cos 2t + \sin 2t)]$

31. $\frac{1}{15}(6e^{2t} - 5 - e^{-3t})$

32. $\frac{1}{2}(\cosh t + \cos t)$

33. $x(t) = r(\cosh rt \sin rt - \sinh rt \cos rt)$ where $r = 1/\sqrt{2}$

34. $\frac{1}{2}\sin 2t + \frac{1}{3}\sin 3t$

35. $\frac{1}{16}(\sin 2t - 2t\cos 2t)$

36. $\frac{1}{50}[2e^{2t} + (10t - 2)\cos t - (5t + 14)\sin t]$

37. $\frac{1}{50}[(5t - 1)e^{-t} + e^{-2t}(\cos 3t + 32\sin 3t)]$

38. $\frac{1}{510}e^{-3t}(489\cos 3t + 307\sin 3t) + \frac{1}{170}(7\cos 2t + 6\sin 2t)$

39.

Section 7.4

1. $\frac{1}{2}t^2$

2. $(e^{at} - at - 1)/a^2$

3. $\frac{1}{2}(\sin t - t \cos t)$

4. $2(t - \sin t)$

5. te^{at}

6. $(e^{at} - e^{bt})/(a - b)$

7. $\frac{1}{3}(e^{3t} - 1)$

8. $\frac{1}{4}(1 - \cos 2t)$

9. $\frac{1}{54}(\sin 3t - 3t \cos 3t)$

10. $(kt - \sin kt)/k^3$

11. $\frac{1}{4}(\sin 2t + 2t \cos 2t)$

12. $\frac{1}{5}[1 - e^{-2t}(\cos t + 2 \sin t)]$

13. $\frac{1}{10}(3e^{3t} - 3\cos t + \sin t)$

14. $\frac{1}{3}(\cos t - \cos 2t)$

15. $6s/(s^2 + 9)^2,\ s > 0$

16. $(2s^3 - 24s)/(s^2 + 4)^3,\ s > 0$

17. $(s^2 - 4s - 5)/(s^2 - 4s + 13)^2,\ s > 0$

18. $\dfrac{2(3s^2 + 6s + 7)}{(s + 1)^2(s^2 + 2s + 5)^2},\ s > 0$

19. $\frac{1}{2}\pi - \arctan s = \arctan(1/s),\ s > 0$

20. $\frac{1}{2}\ln(s^2 + 4) - \ln s,\ s > 0$

21. $\ln s - \ln(s - 3),\ s > 3$

22. $\ln(s + 1) - \ln(s - 1),\ s > 1$

23. $-(2 \sinh 2t)/t$

24. $2(\cos 2t - \cos t)/t$

25. $e^{-2t} + e^{3t} - 2\cos t/t$

26. $(e^{-2t} \sin 3t)/t$

27. $2(1 - \cos t)/t$

28. $\frac{1}{8}(t \sin t - t^2 \cos t)$

29. $(s + 1)X'(s) + 4X(s) = 0;\ x(t) = Ct^3e^{-t},\ C \neq 0$

30. $X(s) = A/(s + 3)^3;\ x(t) = Ct^2e^{-3t},\ C \neq 0$

31. $(s - 2)X'(s) + 3X(s) = 0;\ x(t) = Ct^2e^{2t},\ C \neq 0$

32. $(s^2 + 2s)X'(s) + (4s + 4)X(s) = 0;$
$x(t) = C(1 - t - e^{-2t} - te^{-2t}),\ C \neq 0$

33. $(s^2 + 1)X'(s) + 4sX(s) = 0;\ x(t) = C(\sin t - t \cos t),\ C \neq 0$

34. $x(t) = Ce^{-2t}(\sin 3t - 3t \cos 3t),\ C \neq 0$

Section 7.5

1. $f(t) = u(t - 3) \cdot (t - 3)$

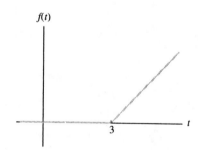

2. $f(t) = (t - 1)u(t - 1) - (t - 3)u(t - 3)$

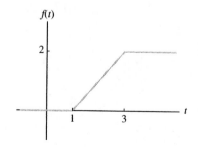

3. $f(t) = u(t - 1) \cdot e^{-2(t-1)}$

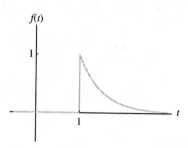

4. $f(t) = e^{t-1}u(t - 1) - e^2e^{t-2}u(t - 2)$

5. $f(t) = u(t - \pi) \cdot \sin(t - \pi) = -u(t - \pi)\sin t$

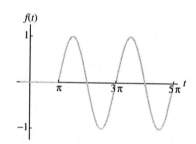

6. $f(t) = u(t - 1) \cdot \cos \pi(t - 1) = -u(t - 1)\cos \pi t$

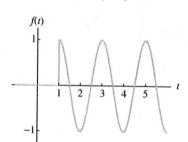

7. $f(t) = \sin t - u(t - 2\pi)\sin(t - 2\pi) = [1 - u(t - 2\pi)]\sin t$

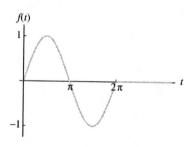

8. $f(t) = \cos \pi t - u(t-2)\cos \pi(t-2) = [1 - u(t-2)]\cos \pi t$

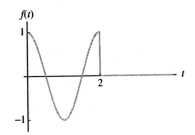

9. $f(t) = \cos \pi t + u(t-3)\cos \pi(t-3) = [1 - u(t-3)]\cos \pi t$

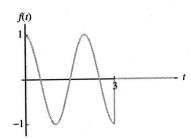

10. $f(t) = 2u(t-\pi)\cos 2(t-\pi) - 2u(t-2\pi)\cos 2(t-2\pi)$
$\quad\quad = 2[u(t-\pi) - u(t-2\pi)]\cos 2t$

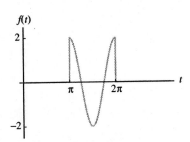

11. $f(t) = 2[1 - u_3(t)];\quad F(s) = 2(1 - e^{-3s})/s$

12. $F(s) = (e^{-s} - e^{-4s})/s$

13. $F(s) = (1 - e^{-2\pi s})/(s^2 + 1)$

14. $F(s) = s(1 - e^{-2s})/(s^2 + \pi^2)$

15. $F(s) = (1 + e^{-3\pi s})/(s^2 + 1)$

16. $F(s) = 2(e^{-\pi s} - e^{-2\pi s})/(s^2 + 4)$

17. $F(s) = \pi(e^{-2s} + e^{-3s})/(s^2 + \pi^2)$

18. $F(s) = 2\pi(e^{-3s} + e^{-5s})/(4s^2 + \pi^2)$

19. $F(s) = e^{-s}(s^{-1} + s^{-2})$

20. $F(s) = (1 - e^{-s})/s^2$

21. $F(s) = (1 - 2e^{-s} + e^{-2s})/s^2$

28. $F(s) = (1 - e^{-as} - ase^{-as})/[s^2(1 - e^{-2as})]$

31. $x(t) = \frac{1}{2}[1 - u(t-\pi)]\sin^2 t$

32. $x(t) = g(t) - u(t-2)g(t-2)$ where
$\quad\quad g(t) = \frac{1}{12}(3 - 4e^{-t} + e^{-4t}).$

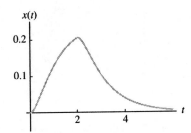

33. $x(t) = \frac{1}{8}[1 - u(t-2\pi)]\left(\sin t - \frac{1}{3}\sin 3t\right)$

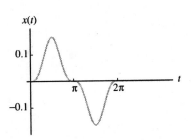

34. $x(t) = g(t) - u(t-1)[g(t-1) + h(t-1)]$ where
$\quad\quad g(t) = t - \sin t$ and $h(t) = 1 - \cos t.$

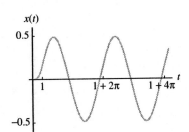

35. $x(t) = \frac{1}{4}\left\{-1 + t + (t+1)e^{-2t} + u(t-2)\left[1 - t + (3t-5)e^{-2(t-2)}\right]\right\}$

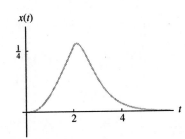

36. $i(t) = e^{-10t} - u(t-1)e^{-10(t-1)}$

37. $i(t) = [1 - u(t-2\pi)]\sin 100t$

38. $i(t) = \frac{10}{99}[1 - (u-\pi)](\cos 10t - \cos 100t)$

39. $i(t) = \frac{1}{50}\left[(1 - e^{-50t})^2 - u(t-1)(1 + 98e^{-50(t-1)} - 99e^{-100(t-1)})\right]$

40. $i(t) = \frac{1}{50}\left[(1 - e^{-50t} - 50te^{-50t}) - u(t-1)(1 - e^{-50(t-1)}\right.$
$\quad\quad\left. + 2450te^{-50(t-1)})\right]$

41. $x(t) = 2|\sin t| \sin t$

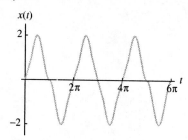

42. $x(t) = g(t) + 2\sum_{n=1}^{\infty} (-1)^n u(t - n\pi) g(t - n\pi)$ where

$g(t) = 1 - \frac{1}{3} e^{-t} (3\cos 3t + \sin 3t)$

Section 7.6

1. $x(t) = \frac{1}{2} \sin 2t$

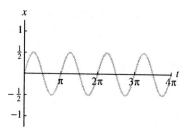

2. $x(t) = \frac{1}{2}[1 + u(t - \pi)] \sin 2t$

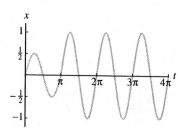

3. $x(t) = \frac{1}{4}[1 - e^{-2t} - 2te^{-2t}] + u(t - 2)(t - 2)e^{-2(t-2)}$

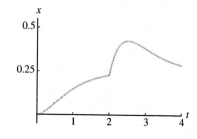

4. $x(t) = -2 + t + 2e^{-t} + 3te^{-t}$

5. $x(t) = 2u(t - \pi)e^{-(t-\pi)} \sin(t - \pi)$

6. $x(t) = \frac{1}{6}(t - 2u(t - 3\pi)) \sin 3t$

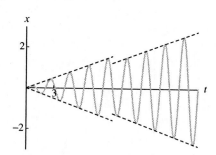

7. $x(t) = \left[2 - e^{2\pi}u(t - \pi) + e^{4\pi}u(t - 2\pi)\right] e^{-2t} \sin t$

8. $x(t) = (2 + 5t)e^{-t} - u(t - 2)(t - 2)e^{-(t-2)}$

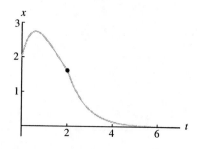

9. $x(t) = \int_0^t \frac{1}{2}(\sin 2\tau) f(t-\tau) \, d\tau$

10. $x(t) = \int_0^t \tau e^{-3\tau} f(t-\tau) \, d\tau$

11. $x(t) = \int_0^t (e^{-3\tau} \sinh \tau) f(t-\tau) \, d\tau$

12. $x(t) = \int_0^t (e^{-2\tau} \sin 2\tau) f(t-\tau) \, d\tau$

13. (a) $mx_\epsilon(t) = p[t^2 - u_\epsilon(t)(t-\epsilon)^2]/(2\epsilon)$;
  (b) If $t > \epsilon$, then $mx_\epsilon(t) = p(2\epsilon t - \epsilon^2)/(2\epsilon)$, and hence
  $mx_\epsilon(t) \to pt$ as $\epsilon \to 0$;
  (c) $mv = (mx)' = (pt)' = 0$.

15. The transform of each of the two given initial value problems is $(ms^2 + k)X(s) = mv_0 = p_0$.

17. (b) $i(t) = e^{-100(t-1)}u_1(t) - e^{-100(t-2)}u_2(t)$.
  If $t > 2$, then $i(t) = -(e^{100} - 1)e^{100(1-t)} < 0$.

18. $i(t) = [1 - u(t-\pi)] \sin 10t$

19. $i(t) = \sum_{n=0}^{\infty} u(t - n\pi/10) \sin 10t$

20. $i(t) = \sum_{n=0}^{\infty} (-1)^n u(t - n\pi/5) \sin 10t$

21. $i(t) = \sum_{n=0}^{\infty} u(t - n\pi/10) e^{3n\pi} e^{-30t} \sin t$

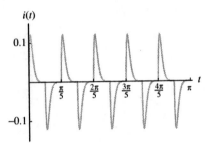

22. $x(t) = \sum_{n=0}^{\infty} u(t - 2n\pi) \sin t$

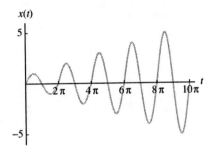

Chapter 8

Section 8.1

1. $y(x) = c_0\left(1 + x + \frac{x^2}{2} + \frac{x^3}{3!} + \cdots\right) = c_0 e^x; \; \rho = +\infty$

2. $y(x) = c_0\left(1 + \frac{4x}{1!} + \frac{4^2 x^2}{2!} + \frac{4^3 x^3}{3!} + \frac{4^4 x^4}{4!} + \cdots\right) = c_0 e^{4x};$
  $\rho = \infty$

3. $y(x) = c_0\left(1 - \frac{3x}{2} + \frac{(3x)^2}{2!2^2} - \frac{(3x)^3}{3!2^3} + \frac{(3x)^4}{4!2^4} - \cdots\right) = c_0 e^{-3x/2};$
  $\rho = +\infty$

4. $y(x) = c_0\left(1 - \frac{x^2}{1!} + \frac{x^4}{2!} - \frac{x^6}{3!} + \cdots\right) = c_0 e^{-x^2}; \; \rho = \infty$

5. $y(x) = c_0\left(1 + \frac{x^3}{3} + \frac{x^6}{2!3^2} + \frac{x^9}{3!3^3} + \cdots\right) = c_0 \exp\left(\frac{1}{3}x^3\right);$
  $\rho = +\infty$

6. $y(x) = c_0\left(1 + \frac{x}{2} + \frac{x^2}{4} + \frac{x^3}{8} + \frac{x^4}{16} + \cdots\right) = \frac{2c_0}{2-x}; \; \rho = 2$

7. $y(x) = c_0(1 + 2x + 4x^2 + 8x^3 + \cdots) = \frac{c_0}{1 - 2x}; \; \rho = \frac{1}{2}$

8. $y(x) = c_0\left(1 + \frac{x}{2} - \frac{x^2}{8} + \frac{x^3}{16} - \frac{5x^4}{128} + \cdots\right) = c_0\sqrt{1+x}; \; \rho = 1$

9. $y(x) = c_0(1 + 2x + 3x^2 + 4x^3 + \cdots) = \frac{c_0}{(1-x)^2}; \; \rho = 1$

10. $y(x) = c_0\left(1 - \frac{3x}{2} + \frac{3x^2}{8} + \frac{x^3}{16} + \frac{3x^4}{128} + \cdots\right) = c_0(1-x)^{3/2};$
  $\rho = 1$

11. $y(x) = c_0\left(1 + \frac{x^2}{2!} + \frac{x^4}{4!} + \frac{x^6}{6!} + \cdots\right) +$
  $c_1\left(x + \frac{x^3}{3!} + \frac{x^5}{5!} + \frac{x^7}{7!} + \cdots\right)$
  $= c_0 \cosh x + c_1 \sinh x; \; \rho = +\infty$

12. $y(x) = c_0\left(1 + \frac{(2x)^2}{2!} + \frac{(2x)^4}{4!} + \frac{(2x)^6}{6!} + \cdots\right) +$
  $\frac{c_1}{2}\left((2x) + \frac{(2x)^3}{3!} + \frac{(2x)^5}{5!} + \frac{(2x)^7}{7!} + \cdots\right) =$
  $c_0 \cosh 2x + \frac{c_1}{2} \sinh 2x; \; \rho = \infty$

13. $y(x) = c_0\left(1 - \frac{(3x)^2}{2!} + \frac{(3x)^4}{4!} - \frac{(3x)^6}{6!} + \cdots\right) +$
  $\frac{c_1}{3}\left(3x - \frac{(3x)^3}{3!} + \frac{(3x)^5}{5!} - \frac{(3x)^7}{7!} + \cdots\right)$
  $= c_0 \cos 3x + \frac{1}{3}c_1 \sin 3x; \; \rho = +\infty$

14. $y(x) = x + c_0\left(1 - \frac{x^2}{2!} + \frac{x^4}{4!} - \frac{x^6}{6!} + \cdots\right)$
  $+ (c_1 - 1)\left(x - \frac{x^3}{3!} + \frac{x^5}{5!} - \frac{x^7}{7!} + \cdots\right)$
  $= x + c_0 \cos x + (c_1 - 1) \sin x; \; \rho = \infty$

15. $(n+1)c_n = 0$ for all $n \geq 0$, so $c_n = 0$ for all $n \geq 0$.

16. $2nc_n = c_n$ for all $n \geq 0$, so $c_n = 0$ for all $n \geq 0$.

17. $c_0 = c_1 = 0$ and $c_{n+1} = -nc_n$ for $n \geq 1$, thus $c_n = 0$ for all $n \geq 0$.

18. $c_n = 0$ for all $n \geq 0$

19. $(n+1)(n+2)c_{n+2} = -4c_n;$
  $y(x) = \frac{3}{2}\left[(2x) - \frac{(2x)^3}{3!} + \frac{(2x)^5}{5!} - \frac{(2x)^7}{7!} + \cdots\right] = \frac{3}{2} \sin 2x$

20. $(n+1)(n+2)c_{n+2} = 4c_n;$
  $y(x) = 2\left[1 + \frac{(2x)^2}{2!} + \frac{(2x)^4}{4!} + \frac{(2x)^6}{6!} + \cdots\right] = 2 \cosh 2x$

21. $n(n+1)c_{n+1} = 2nc_n - c_{n-1};$
  $y(x) = x + x^2 + \frac{x^3}{2!} + \frac{x^4}{3!} + \frac{x^5}{4!} + \cdots = xe^x$

22. $n(n+1)c_{n+1} = -nc_n + 2c_{n-1}; \; y = e^{-2x}$

23. As $c_0 = c_1 = 0$ and $(n^2 - n + 1)c_n + (n-1)c_{n-1} = 0$ for $n \geq 2$, $c_n = 0$ for all $n \geq 0$

Section 8.2

1. $c_{n+2} = c_n$; $y(x) = c_0 \sum_{n=0}^{\infty} x^{2n} + c_1 \sum_{n=0}^{\infty} x^{2n+1} = \dfrac{c_0 + c_1 x}{1 - x^2}$; $\rho = 1$

2. $c_{n+2} = -\frac{1}{2}c_n$; $\rho = 2$;
$$y(x) = c_0 \sum_{n=0}^{\infty} \frac{(-1)^n x^{2n}}{2^n} + c_1 \sum_{n=0}^{\infty} \frac{(-1)^n x^{2n+1}}{2^n}$$

3. $(n+2)c_{n+2} = -c_n$; $y(x) = c_0 \sum_{n=0}^{\infty} \frac{(-1)^n x^{2n}}{n! 2^n} + c_1 \sum_{n=0}^{\infty} \frac{(-1)^n x^{2n+1}}{(2n+1)!!}$;
$\rho = +\infty$

4. $(n+2)c_{n+2} = -(n+4)c_n$; $\rho = 1$;
$$y(x) = c_0 \sum_{n=0}^{\infty} (-1)^n (n+1)x^{2n} + \frac{1}{3}c_1 \sum_{n=0}^{\infty} (-1)^n (2n+3)x^{2n+1}$$

5. $3(n+2)c_{n+2} = nc_n$; $\rho = \sqrt{3}$; $y(x) = c_0 + c_1 \sum_{n=0}^{\infty} \frac{x^{2n+1}}{(2n+1)3^n}$

6. $(n+1)(n+2)c_{n+2} = (n-3)(n-4)c_n$; $\rho = \infty$;
$y(x) = c_0(1 + 6x^2 + x^4) + c_1(x + x^3)$

7. $3(n+1)(n+2)c_{n+2} = -(n-4)^2 c_n$; $y(x) = c_0 \left(1 - \frac{8x^2}{3} + \frac{8x^4}{27}\right) +$
$c_1\left(x - \frac{x^3}{2} + \frac{x^5}{120} + 9 \sum_{n=3}^{\infty} \frac{(-1)^n(2n-5)!! x^{2n+1}}{(2n+1)! 3^n}\right)$

8. $2(n+1)(n+2)c_{n+2} = (n-4)(n+4)c_n$; $y(x) = c_0(1 - 4x^2 +$
$2x^4) + c_1\left(x - \frac{5x^3}{4} + \frac{7x^5}{32} + \sum_{n=3}^{\infty} \frac{(2n-5)!!(2n+3)!! x^{2n+1}}{(2n+1)! 2^n}\right)$

9. $(n+1)(n+2)c_{n+2} = (n+3)(n+4)c_n$; $\rho = 1$;
$$y(x) = c_0 \sum_{n=0}^{\infty} (n+1)(2n+1)x^{2n} + \frac{c_1}{3} \sum_{n=0}^{\infty} (n+1)(2n+3)x^{2n+1}$$

10. $3(n+1)(n+2)c_{n+2} = -(n-4)c_n$; $y(x) = c_0\left(1 + \frac{2x^2}{3} + \frac{x^4}{27}\right) +$
$c_1\left(x + \frac{x^3}{6} + \frac{x^5}{360} + 3\sum_{n=3}^{\infty} \frac{(-1)^n(2n-5)!! x^{2n+1}}{(2n+1)! 3^n}\right)$

11. $5(n+1)(n+2)c_{n+2} = 2(n-5)c_n$; $y(x) = c_1\left(x - \frac{4x^3}{15} + \frac{4x^5}{375}\right) +$
$c_0\left(1 - x^2 + \frac{x^4}{10} + \frac{x^6}{750} + 15\sum_{n=4}^{\infty} \frac{(2n-7)!! \, 2^n x^{2n}}{(2n)! 5^n}\right)$

12. $c_2 = 0$; $(n+2)c_{n+3} = c_n$;
$$y(x) = c_0\left(1 + \sum_{n=1}^{\infty} \frac{x^{3n}}{2 \cdot 5 \cdots (3n-1)}\right) + c_1 \sum_{n=0}^{\infty} \frac{x^{3n+1}}{n! 3^n}$$

13. $c_2 = 0$; $(n+3)c_{n+3} = -c_n$;
$$y(x) = c_0 \sum_{n=0}^{\infty} \frac{(-1)^n x^{3n}}{n! 3^n} + c_1 \sum_{n=0}^{\infty} \frac{(-1)^n x^{3n+1}}{1 \cdot 4 \cdots (3n+1)}$$

14. $c_2 = 0$; $(n+2)(n+3)c_{n+3} = -c_n$;
$$y(x) = c_0\left(1 + \sum_{n=1}^{\infty} \frac{(-1)^n x^{3n}}{3^n \cdot n! \cdot 2 \cdot 5 \cdots (3n-1)}\right) +$$
$$c_1 \sum_{n=0}^{\infty} \frac{(-1)^n x^{3n+1}}{3^n \cdot n! \cdot 1 \cdot 4 \cdots (3n+1)}$$

15. $c_2 = c_3 = 0$; $(n+3)(n+4)c_{n+4} = -c_n$;
$$y(x) = c_0\left(1 + \sum_{n=1}^{\infty} \frac{(-1)^n x^{4n}}{4^n \cdot n! \cdot 3 \cdot 7 \cdots (4n-1)}\right) +$$
$$c_1 \sum_{n=0}^{\infty} \frac{(-1)^n x^{4n+1}}{4^n \cdot n! \cdot 5 \cdot 9 \cdots (4n+1)}$$

16. $y(x) = x$

17. $y(x) = 1 + x^2$

18. $y(x) = 2 \sum_{n=0}^{\infty} \frac{(-1)^n(x-1)^{2n}}{n! 2^n}$; converges for all x

19. $y(x) = \frac{1}{3} \sum_{n=0}^{\infty} (2n+3)(x-1)^{2n+1}$; converges if $0 < x < 2$

20. $y(x) = 2 - 6(x-3)^2$; converges for all x

21. $y(x) = 1 + 4(x+2)^2$; converges for all x

22. $y(x) = 2x + 6$

23. $2c_2 + c_0 = 0$; $(n+1)(n+2)c_{n+2} + c_n + c_{n-1} = 0$ for $n \geq 1$;
$y_1(x) = 1 - \frac{x^2}{2} - \frac{x^3}{6} + \cdots$; $y_2(x) = x - \frac{x^3}{6} - \frac{x^4}{12} + \cdots$

24. $y_1(x) = 1 + \frac{x^3}{3} + \frac{x^5}{5} + \frac{x^6}{45} + \cdots$; $y_2(x) = x + \frac{x^3}{3} + \frac{x^4}{6} + \frac{x^5}{5} + \cdots$

25. $c_2 = c_3 = 0$, $(n+3)(n+4)c_{n+4} + (n+1)c_{n+1} + c_n = 0$ for $n \geq 0$;
$y_1(x) = 1 - \frac{x^4}{12} + \frac{x^7}{126} + \cdots$; $y_2(x) = x - \frac{x^4}{12} - \frac{x^5}{20} + \cdots$

26. $y(x) = c_0\left(1 - \frac{x^6}{30} + \frac{x^9}{72} + \cdots\right) + c_1\left(x - \frac{x^7}{42} + \frac{x^{10}}{90} + \cdots\right)$

27. $y(x) = 1 - x - \frac{x^2}{2} + \frac{x^3}{3} - \frac{x^4}{24} + \frac{x^5}{30} + \frac{29x^6}{720} + \frac{13x^7}{630} - \frac{143x^8}{40320} + \cdots$;
$y(0.5) \approx 0.4156$

28. $y(x) = c_0\left(1 - \frac{x^2}{2} + \frac{x^3}{6} + \cdots\right) + c_1\left(x - \frac{x^3}{6} + \frac{x^4}{12} + \cdots\right)$

29. $y_1(x) = 1 - \frac{1}{2}x^2 + \frac{1}{720}x^6 + \cdots$; $y_2(x) = x - \frac{1}{6}x^3 - \frac{1}{60}x^5 + \cdots$

30. $y(x) = c_0\left(1 - \frac{x^2}{2} + \frac{x^3}{6} + \cdots\right) + c_1\left(x - \frac{x^2}{2} + \frac{x^4}{18} + \cdots\right)$

33. The following figure shows the interlaced zeros of the 4th and 5th Hermite polynomials.

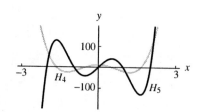

34. The figure below results when we use $n = 40$ terms in each summation. But with $n = 50$ we get the same picture as Fig. 8.2.3 in the text.

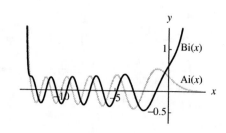

Section 8.3

1. Ordinary point

2. Ordinary point

3. Irregular singular point

4. Irregular singular point

5. Regular singular point; $r_1 = 0$, $r_2 = -1$

6. Regular singular point; $r_1 = 1$, $r_2 = -2$

7. Regular singular point; $r = -3$, -3

8. Regular singular point; $r = \frac{1}{2}$, -3

9. Regular singular point $x = 1$

10. Regular singular point $x = 1$

11. Regular singular points $x = 1$, -1

12. Irregular singular point $x = 2$

13. Regular singular points $x = 2$, -2

14. Irregular singular points $x = 3$, -3

15. Regular singular point $x = 2$

16. Irregular singular point $x = 0$, regular singular point $x = 1$

17. $y_1(x) = \cos\sqrt{x}$, $y_2(x) = \sin\sqrt{x}$

18. $y_1(x) = \sum_{n=0}^{\infty} \frac{x^n}{n!(2n+1)!!}$, $y_2(x) = x^{-1/2}\sum_{n=0}^{\infty} \frac{x^n}{n!(2n-1)!!}$

19. $y_1(x) = x^{3/2}\left(1 + 3\sum_{n=1}^{\infty} \frac{x^n}{n!(2n+3)!!}\right)$,

$y_2(x) = 1 - x - \sum_{n=2}^{\infty} \frac{x^n}{n!(2n-3)!!}$

20. $y_1(x) = x^{1/3}\sum_{n=0}^{\infty} \frac{(-1)^n 2^n x^n}{n! \cdot 4 \cdot 7 \cdots (3n+1)}$,

$y_2(x) = \sum_{n=0}^{\infty} \frac{(-1)^n 2^n x^n}{n! \cdot 2 \cdot 5 \cdots (3n-1)}$

21. $y_1(x) = x\left(1 + \sum_{n=1}^{\infty} \frac{x^{2n}}{n! \cdot 7 \cdot 11 \cdots (4n+3)}\right)$,

$y_2(x) = x^{-1/2}\left(1 + \sum_{n=1}^{\infty} \frac{x^{2n}}{n! \cdot 1 \cdot 5 \cdots (4n-3)}\right)$

22. $y_1(x) = x^{3/2}\left(1 + \sum_{n=1}^{\infty} \frac{(-1)^n x^{2n}}{n! \cdot 9 \cdot 13 \cdots (4n+5)}\right)$,

$y_2(x) = x^{-1}\left(1 + \sum_{n=1}^{\infty} \frac{(-1)^{n-1} x^{2n}}{n! \cdot 3 \cdot 7 \cdots (4n-1)}\right)$

23. $y_1(x) = x^{1/2}\left(1 + \sum_{n=1}^{\infty} \frac{x^{2n}}{2^n \cdot n! \cdot 19 \cdot 31 \cdots (12n+7)}\right)$,

$y_2(x) = x^{-2/3}\left(1 + \sum_{n=1}^{\infty} \frac{x^{2n}}{2^n \cdot n! \cdot 5 \cdot 17 \cdots (12n-7)}\right)$

24. $y_1(x) = x^{1/3}\left(1 + \sum_{n=1}^{\infty} \frac{(-1)^n x^{2n}}{2^n \cdot n! \cdot 7 \cdot 13 \cdots (6n+1)}\right)$,

$y_2(x) = 1 + \sum_{n=1}^{\infty} \frac{(-1)^n x^{2n}}{2^n \cdot n! \cdot 5 \cdot 11 \cdots (6n-1)}$

25. $y_1(x) = x^{1/2}\sum_{n=0}^{\infty} \frac{(-1)^n x^n}{n! \cdot 2^n} = x^{1/2}e^{-x/2}$,

$y_2(x) = 1 + \sum_{n=1}^{\infty} \frac{(-1)^n x^n}{(2n-1)!!}$

26. $y_1(x) = x^{1/2}\sum_{n=0}^{\infty} \frac{x^{2n}}{n! \cdot 2^n} = x^{1/2}\exp\left(\frac{1}{2}x^2\right)$,

$y_2(x) = 1 + \sum_{n=1}^{\infty} \frac{2^n x^{2n}}{3 \cdot 7 \cdots (4n-1)}$

27. $y_1(x) = \frac{1}{x}\cos 3x$, $y_2(x) = \frac{1}{x}\sin 3x$

28. $y_1(x) = \frac{1}{x}\cosh 2x$, $y_2(x) = \frac{1}{x}\sinh 2x$

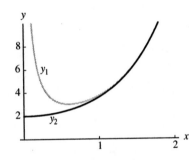

29. $y_1(x) = \frac{1}{x}\cos\frac{x}{2}$, $y_2(x) = \frac{1}{x}\sin\frac{x}{2}$

30. $y_1(x) = \cos x^2$, $y_2(x) = \sin x^2$

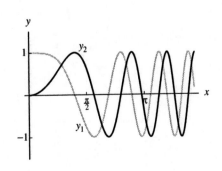

31. $y_1(x) = x^{1/2} \cosh x$, $y_2(x) = x^{1/2} \sinh x$

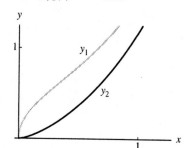

32. $y_1(x) = x + \dfrac{x^2}{5}$,

$y_2(x) = x^{-1/2} \left(1 - \dfrac{5x}{2} - \dfrac{15x^2}{8} - \dfrac{5x^3}{48} + \cdots \right)$

33. $y_1(x) = x^{-1} \left(1 + 10x + 5x^2 + \dfrac{10x^3}{9} + \cdots \right)$,

$y_2(x) = x^{1/2} \left(1 + \dfrac{11x}{20} - \dfrac{11x^2}{224} + \dfrac{671x^3}{24192} + \cdots \right)$

34. $y_1(x) = x \left(1 - \dfrac{x^2}{42} + \dfrac{x^4}{1320} + \cdots \right)$,

$y_2(x) = x^{-1/2} \left(1 - \dfrac{7x^2}{24} + \dfrac{19x^4}{3200} + \cdots \right)$

Section 8.4

1. $y_1(x) = \dfrac{1+x}{x^2}$, $y_2(x) = 1 + 2 \displaystyle\sum_{n=1}^{\infty} \dfrac{x^n}{(n+2)!}$

2. $y_1(x) = \dfrac{1}{x^2} \left(1 + x + \dfrac{x^2}{2} + \dfrac{x^3}{6} \right)$, $y_2(x) = 1 + 24 \displaystyle\sum_{n=1}^{\infty} \dfrac{x^n}{(n+4)!}$

3. $y_1(x) = \dfrac{1}{x^4} \left(1 - 3x + \dfrac{9x^2}{2} - \dfrac{9x^3}{2} \right)$,

$y_2(x) = 1 + 24 \displaystyle\sum_{n=1}^{\infty} \dfrac{(-1)^n 3^n x^n}{(n+4)!}$

4. $y_1(x) = \dfrac{1}{x^5} \left(1 - \dfrac{3x}{5} + \dfrac{9x^2}{50} - \dfrac{9x^3}{250} + \dfrac{27x^4}{5000} \right)$,

$y_2(x) = 1 + 120 \displaystyle\sum_{n=1}^{\infty} \dfrac{(-1)^n 3^n x^n}{(n5)! \cdot 5^n}$

5. $y_1(x) = 1 + \dfrac{3x}{4} + \dfrac{x^2}{4} + \dfrac{x^3}{24}$,

$y_2(x) = x^5 \left(1 + 120 \displaystyle\sum_{n=1}^{\infty} \dfrac{(n+1)x^n}{(n+5)!} \right)$

6. $y_1(x) = x^4 \left(1 + \dfrac{8}{5} \displaystyle\sum_{n=1}^{\infty} \dfrac{(2n+5)!! x^n}{n!\,(n+4)!\,2^n} \right)$

7. $y_1(x) = \dfrac{1}{x^2}(2 - 6x + 9x^2)$, $y_2(x) = \displaystyle\sum_{n=1}^{\infty} \dfrac{(-1)^{n-1} 3^n x^n}{(n+2)!}$

8. $y_1(x) = 3 + 2x + x^2$, $y_2(x) = \dfrac{x^4}{(1-x)^2}$

9. $y_1(x) = 1 + \dfrac{x^2}{2^2} + \dfrac{x^4}{2^2 \cdot 4^2} + \dfrac{x^6}{2^2 \cdot 4^2 \cdot 6^2} + \cdots$,

$y_2(x) = y_1(x) \cdot \left(\ln x - \dfrac{x^2}{4} + \dfrac{5x^4}{128} - \dfrac{23x^6}{3456} + \cdots \right)$

10. $y_1(x) = x \left(1 - \dfrac{x^2}{2^2} + \dfrac{x^4}{2^2 \cdot 4^2} - \dfrac{x^6}{2^2 \cdot 4^2 \cdot 6^2} + \cdots \right)$,

$y_2(x) = y_1(x) \cdot \left(\ln x + \dfrac{x^2}{4} + \dfrac{5x^4}{128} + \dfrac{23x^6}{3456} + \cdots \right)$

11. $y_1(x) = x^2 \left(1 - 2x + \dfrac{3x^2}{2} - \dfrac{2x^3}{3} + \cdots \right)$,

$y_2(x) = y_1(x) \cdot \left(\ln x + 3x + \dfrac{11x^2}{4} + \dfrac{49x^3}{18} + \cdots \right)$

12. $y_1(x) = x^2 \left(1 - \dfrac{x}{2} + \dfrac{3x^2}{20} - \dfrac{x^3}{30} + \dfrac{x^4}{168} - \cdots \right)$,

$y_2(x) = y_1(x) \cdot \left(-\dfrac{1}{3x^3} + \dfrac{1}{20x} + \dfrac{x}{700} + \cdots \right)$

13. $y_1(x) = x^3 \left(1 - 2x + 2x^2 - \dfrac{4x^3}{3} + \cdots \right)$,

$y_2(x) = y_1(x) \cdot \left(2 \ln x - \dfrac{1}{2x^2} - \dfrac{2}{x} + \dfrac{4x}{3} + \cdots \right)$

14. $y_1(x) = x^2 \left(1 - \dfrac{2x}{5} + \dfrac{x^2}{10} - \dfrac{2x^3}{105} + \dfrac{x^4}{336} - \cdots \right)$,

$y_2(x) = y_1(x) \cdot \left(-\dfrac{1}{4x^4} + \dfrac{1}{15x^3} + \dfrac{1}{100x^2} - \dfrac{13}{1750x} + \cdots \right)$;

$y_2(x)$ contains no logarithmic term.

16. $y_1(x) = x^{3/2} \left(1 + \displaystyle\sum_{n=1}^{\infty} \dfrac{(-1)^n x^{2n}}{2^n \cdot n! \cdot 5 \cdot 7 \cdots (2n+3)} \right)$,

$y_2(x) = x^{-3/2} \left(1 + \displaystyle\sum_{n=1}^{\infty} \dfrac{(-1)^n x^{2n}}{2^n \cdot n! \cdot (-1) \cdot 1 \cdot 3 \cdots (2n-3)} \right)$

Section 8.5

2.

4.

5. $J_4(x) = \dfrac{1}{x^2}(x^2 - 24)J_0(x) + \dfrac{8}{x^3}(6 - x^2)J_1(x)$

12. The following figure corroborates the calculated value $y(0) = 3$.

13. $x^2 J_1(x) + x J_1(x) - \displaystyle\int J_0(x)\, dx + C$

14. $(x^3 - 4x)J_1(x) + 2x^2 J_0(x) + C$

15. $(x^4 - 9x^2)J_1(x) + (3x^3 - 9x)J_0(x) + 9 \displaystyle\int J_0(x)\, dx + C$

16. $-x J_1(x) + \displaystyle\int J_0(x)\, dx + C$

17. $2x J_1(x) - x^2 J_0(x) + C$

18. $3x^2 J_1(x) + (3x - x^3)J_0(x) - 3 \displaystyle\int J_0(x)\, dx + C$

19. $(4x^3 - 16x)J_1(x) + (8x^2 - x^4)J_0(x) + C$

20. $-2J_1(x) + \int J_0(x)\,dx + C$

21. $J_0(x) - \dfrac{4}{x}J_1(x) + C$

26.

Section 8.6

1. $y(x) = x\left[c_1 J_0(x) + C_2 Y_0(x)\right]$

2. $y(x) = \dfrac{1}{x}\left[c_1 J_1(x) + c_2 Y_1(x)\right]$

3. $y(x) = x\left[c_1 J_{1/2}(3x^2) + c_2 J_{-1/2}(3x^2)\right]$

4. $y(x) = x^3\left[c_1 J_2(2x^{1/2}) + c_2 Y_2(2x^{1/2})\right]$

5. $y(x) = x^{-1/3}\left[c_1 J_{1/3}\left(\tfrac{1}{3}x^{3/2}\right) + c_2 J_{-1/3}\left(\tfrac{1}{3}x^{3/2}\right)\right]$

6. $y(x) = x^{-1/4}\left[c_1 J_0(2x^{3/2}) + c_2 Y_0(2x^{3/2})\right]$

7. $y(x) = x^{-1}\left[c_1 J_0(x) + c_2 Y_0(x)\right]$

8. $y(x) = x^2\left[c_1 J_1(4x^{1/2}) + c_2 Y_1(4x^{1/2})\right]$

9. $y(x) = x^{1/2}\left[c_1 J_{1/2}(2x^{3/2}) + c_2 J_{-1/2}(2x^{3/2})\right]$

10. $y(x) = x^{-1/4}\left[c_1 J_{3/2}\left(\tfrac{2}{5}x^{5/2}\right) + c_2 J_{-3/2}\left(\tfrac{2}{5}x^{5/2}\right)\right]$

11. $y(x) = x^{1/2}\left[c_1 J_{1/6}\left(\tfrac{1}{3}x^3\right) + c_2 J_{-1/6}\left(\tfrac{1}{3}x^3\right)\right]$

12. $y(x) = x^{1/2}\left[c_1 J_{1/5}\left(\tfrac{4}{5}x^{5/2}\right) + c_2 J_{-1/5}\left(\tfrac{4}{5}x^{5/2}\right)\right]$

Chapter 9

Section 9.1

1. $\tfrac{2}{3}\pi$

2. 1

3. $\tfrac{4}{3}\pi$

4. 6

5. π

6. $\tfrac{1}{2}$

7. Not periodic

8. Not periodic

9. π

10. $\frac{1}{3}\pi$

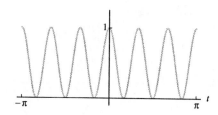

11. $a_0 = 2$; $a_n = b_n = 0$ for $n \geqq 1$

12. $-\frac{12}{\pi}\left(\sin t + \frac{1}{3}\sin 3t + \frac{1}{5}\sin 5t + \cdots\right)$

13. $\frac{1}{2} + \frac{2}{\pi}\left(\sin t + \frac{1}{3}\sin 3t + \frac{1}{5}\sin 5t + \cdots\right)$

14. $\frac{1}{2} - \frac{10}{\pi}\left(\sin t + \frac{1}{3}\sin 3t + \frac{1}{5}\sin 5t + \cdots\right)$

15. $2\left(\sin t - \frac{1}{2}\sin 2t + \frac{1}{3}\sin 3t - \cdots\right)$

16. $\pi - 2\left(\sin t + \frac{1}{2}\sin 2t + \frac{1}{3}\sin 3t + \cdots\right)$

17. $\frac{\pi}{2} - \frac{4}{\pi}\left(\cos t + \frac{1}{9}\cos 3t + \frac{1}{25}\cos 5t + \cdots\right)$

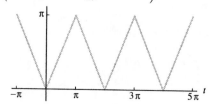

18. $\frac{\pi}{2} + \frac{4}{\pi}\left(\cos t + \frac{1}{9}\cos 3t + \frac{1}{25}\cos 5t + \cdots\right)$

19. $a_0 = \frac{\pi}{4}$; $a_n = \frac{1-(-1)^n}{n^2\pi}$ for $n \geqq 1$; $b_n = -\frac{1}{n}$ for $n \geqq 1$.

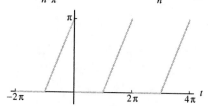

20. $\frac{1}{2} + \frac{2}{\pi}\left(\cos t - \frac{1}{3}\cos 3t + \frac{1}{5}\cos 5t - \cdots\right)$

21. $\frac{1}{3}\pi^2 - 4\left(\cos t - \frac{1}{4}\cos 2t + \frac{1}{9}\cos 3t - \cdots\right)$

22. $a_0 = \frac{8}{3}\pi^2$; $a_n = \frac{4}{n}$ for $n \geq 1$; $b_n = -\frac{4\pi}{n}$ for $n \geq 1$.

23. $a_0 = \frac{1}{3}\pi^2$; $a_n = \frac{2 \cdot (-1)^n}{n^2}$ for $n \geq 1$;

$b_n = 2 \cdot \frac{(-1)^n - 1}{\pi n^3} - \pi \cdot \frac{(-1)^n}{n}$ for $n \geq 1$

24. $b_n = 0$ for $n \geq 1$; $a_n = 0$ if n is odd;

$a_n = -\frac{4}{\pi(n^2 - 1)}$ for $n = 0, 2, 4, \ldots$.

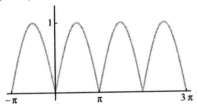

25. $a_0 = 1$, $a_4 = \frac{1}{2}$, and all other coefficients are zero.

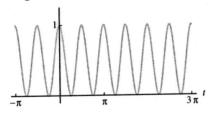

26. $\frac{1}{2}\sin t + \frac{1}{\pi} - \frac{2}{\pi}\left(\frac{1}{1 \cdot 3}\cos 2t + \frac{1}{3 \cdot 5}\cos 4t + \frac{1}{5 \cdot 7}\cos 6t + \cdots\right)$

Section 9.2

1. $\frac{8}{\pi}\left(\sin\frac{\pi t}{3} + \frac{1}{3}\sin\frac{3\pi t}{3} + \frac{1}{5}\sin\frac{5\pi t}{3} + \cdots\right)$

2. $\frac{1}{2} + \frac{2}{\pi}\left(\sin\frac{\pi t}{5} + \frac{1}{3}\sin\frac{3\pi t}{5} + \frac{1}{5}\sin\frac{5\pi t}{5} + \cdots\right)$

3. $\frac{1}{2} - \frac{6}{\pi}\left(\sin\frac{t}{2} + \frac{1}{3}\sin\frac{3t}{2} + \frac{1}{5}\sin\frac{5t}{2} + \cdots\right)$

4. $\frac{4}{\pi}\left(\sin\frac{\pi t}{2} - \frac{1}{2}\sin\frac{2\pi t}{2} + \frac{1}{3}\sin\frac{3\pi t}{2} - \cdots\right)$

5. $4\left(\sin\frac{t}{2} - \frac{1}{2}\sin\frac{2t}{2} + \frac{1}{3}\sin\frac{3t}{2} - \cdots\right)$

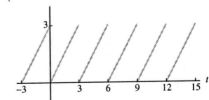

6. $\frac{3}{2} - \frac{3}{\pi}\left(\sin\frac{2\pi t}{3} + \frac{1}{2}\sin\frac{4\pi t}{3} + \frac{1}{3}\sin\frac{6\pi t}{3} + \cdots\right)$

7. $\frac{1}{2} - \frac{4}{\pi^2}\left(\cos \pi t + \frac{1}{9}\cos 3\pi t + \frac{1}{25}\cos 5\pi t + \cdots\right)$

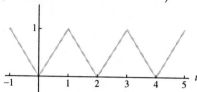

8. $\frac{1}{3} - \frac{\sqrt{3}}{\pi}\left(\cos \frac{2\pi t}{3} - \frac{1}{2}\cos \frac{4\pi t}{3} + \frac{1}{4}\cos \frac{8\pi t}{3} - \frac{1}{5}\cos \frac{10\pi t}{3} + \cdots\right)$

9. $\frac{1}{3} - \frac{4}{\pi^2}\left(\cos \pi t - \frac{1}{4}\cos 2\pi t + \frac{1}{9}\cos 3\pi t - \cdots\right)$

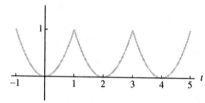

10. $\frac{2}{3} - \frac{8}{\pi^2}\left(\cos \frac{\pi t}{2} - \frac{1}{4}\cos \frac{2\pi t}{2} + \frac{1}{9}\cos \frac{3\pi t}{2} - \cdots\right) +$
$\frac{4}{\pi}\left(\sin \frac{\pi t}{2} - \frac{1}{2}\sin \frac{2\pi t}{2} + \frac{1}{3}\sin \frac{3\pi t}{2} - \cdots\right) -$
$\frac{16}{\pi^3}\left(\sin \frac{\pi t}{2} + \frac{1}{27}\sin \frac{3\pi t}{2} + \frac{1}{125}\sin \frac{5\pi t}{2} + \cdots\right)$

11. $a_0 = \frac{4}{\pi}$; $a_n = \frac{4 \cdot (-1)^{n+1}}{\pi(4n^2 - 1)}$; $b_n = 0$ for all $n \geqq 1$.

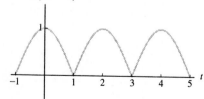

12. $L = \frac{1}{2}$; $a_0 = \frac{4}{\pi}$; $a_n = -\frac{4}{\pi(4n^2 - 1)}$ for $n \geqq 1$;
$b_n = 0$ for all $n \geqq 1$.

13. $a_0 = \frac{2}{\pi}$; $a_1 = 0$; $a_n = -\frac{1 + (-1)^n}{\pi(n^2 - 1)}$ for $n \geqq 2$;
$b_1 = \frac{1}{2}$; $b_n = 0$ if $n \geqq 2$.

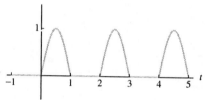

14. $\frac{1}{2}\sin t + \frac{4}{\pi}\left(\frac{1}{3}\cos \frac{t}{2} - \frac{1}{5}\cos \frac{3t}{2} - \frac{1}{21}\cos \frac{5t}{2} - \cdots\right)$

15.

16.

17.

18.

19.

20.

21.

24.

25.

Section 9.3

1. Cosine series: $f(t) = 1$

Sine series:
$$f(t) = \frac{4}{\pi} \left(\sin t + \frac{1}{3} \sin 3t + \frac{1}{5} \sin 5t + \frac{1}{7} \sin 7t + \cdots \right)$$

2. Cosine series:
$$f(t) = \frac{1}{2} + \frac{4}{\pi^2} \left(\cos \pi t + \frac{\cos 3\pi t}{3^2} + \frac{\cos 5\pi t}{5^2} + \frac{\cos 7\pi t}{7^2} + \cdots \right)$$

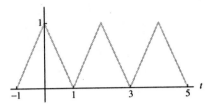

Sine series:
$$f(t) = \frac{2}{\pi} \left(\sin \pi t + \frac{\sin 2\pi t}{2} + \frac{\sin 3\pi t}{3} + \frac{\sin 4\pi t}{4} + \cdots \right)$$

3. Cosine series: $f(t) =$
$$\frac{8}{\pi^2} \left(\cos \frac{\pi t}{2} + \frac{1}{3^2} \cos \frac{3\pi t}{2} + \frac{1}{5^2} \cos \frac{5\pi t}{2} + \frac{1}{7^2} \cos \frac{7\pi t}{2} + \cdots \right)$$

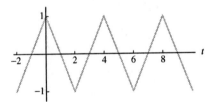

Sine series:
$$f(t) = \frac{4}{\pi} \left(\frac{\sin \pi t}{2} + \frac{\sin 2\pi t}{4} + \frac{\sin 3\pi t}{6} + \frac{\sin 4\pi t}{8} + \cdots \right)$$

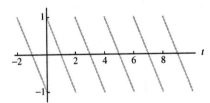

4. Cosine series:
$$f(t) = 1 - \frac{16}{\pi^2} \left(\frac{\cos \pi t}{2^2} + \frac{\cos 3\pi t}{6^2} + \frac{\cos 5\pi t}{10^2} + \frac{\cos 7\pi t}{14^2} + \cdots \right)$$

Sine series: $f(t) =$
$$\frac{8}{\pi^2}\left(\sin\frac{\pi t}{2} - \frac{1}{3^2}\sin\frac{3\pi t}{2} + \frac{1}{5^2}\sin\frac{5\pi t}{2} - \frac{1}{7^2}\sin\frac{7\pi t}{2} + \cdots\right)$$

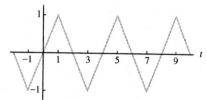

5. Cosine series: $f(t) = \dfrac{1}{3} - \dfrac{2\sqrt{3}}{\pi}\left(\dfrac{1}{2}\cos\dfrac{2\pi t}{3} - \dfrac{1}{4}\cos\dfrac{4\pi t}{3} + \dfrac{1}{8}\cos\dfrac{8\pi t}{3} - \dfrac{1}{10}\cos\dfrac{10\pi t}{3} + \cdots\right)$

Sine series:
$$f(t) = \frac{2}{\pi}\left(\sin\frac{\pi t}{3} - \frac{2}{3}\sin\frac{3\pi t}{3} + \frac{1}{5}\sin\frac{5\pi t}{3} + \frac{1}{7}\sin\frac{7\pi t}{3} - \frac{2}{9}\sin\frac{9\pi t}{3} + \frac{1}{11}\sin\frac{11\pi t}{3} + \cdots\right)$$

6. Cosine series:
$$f(t) = \frac{\pi^2}{3} - 4\left(\cos t - \frac{1}{2^2}\cos 2t + \frac{1}{3^2}\cos 3t + \frac{1}{4^2}\cos 4t + \cdots\right)$$

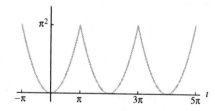

Sine series:
$$f(t) = 2\pi\left(\sin t - \frac{1}{2}\sin 2t + \frac{1}{3}\sin 3t - \frac{1}{4}\sin 4t + \cdots\right) - \frac{8}{\pi}\left(\sin t + \frac{1}{3^2}\sin 3t + \frac{1}{5^3}\sin 5t + \frac{1}{7^3}\sin 7t + \cdots\right)$$

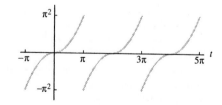

7. Cosine series:
$$f(t) = \frac{\pi^2}{6} - 4\left(\frac{\cos 2t}{2^2} + \frac{\cos 4t}{4^2} + \frac{\cos 6t}{6^2} + \frac{\cos 8t}{8^2} + \cdots\right)$$

Sine series: $f(t) = \dfrac{8}{\pi}\left(\sin t + \dfrac{\sin 3t}{3^3} + \dfrac{\sin 5t}{5^3} + \dfrac{\sin 7t}{7^3} + \cdots\right)$

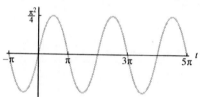

8. Cosine series:
$$f(t) = \frac{1}{6} - \frac{4}{\pi^2}\left(\frac{\cos 2\pi t}{2^2} + \frac{\cos 4\pi t}{4^2} + \frac{\cos 6\pi t}{6^2} + \frac{\cos 8\pi t}{8^2} + \cdots\right)$$
Sine series:
$$f(t) = \frac{8}{\pi^3}\left(\sin\pi t + \frac{\sin 3\pi t}{3^3} + \frac{\sin 5\pi t}{5^3} + \frac{\sin 7\pi t}{7^3} + \cdots\right)$$
The graphs of these two series look precisely the same as those in Problem 7, except with a scale of -1 to 5 (rather than $-\pi$ to 5π) on the t-axis, and with arches of height 1/4 (rather than $\pi^2/4$).

9. Cosine series:
$$f(t) = \frac{2}{\pi} - \frac{4}{\pi^2}\left(\frac{\cos 2t}{3} + \frac{\cos 4t}{15} + \frac{\cos 6t}{35} + \frac{\cos 8t}{63} + \cdots\right)$$
Sine series: $f(t) = \sin t$
The graphs of these two series look essentially the same as those in Problem 7, except with sine arches rather than quadratic arches.

10. Cosine series:
$$f(t) = \frac{1}{\pi} - \frac{4}{\pi}\left(-\frac{1}{3}\cos\frac{t}{2} + \frac{1}{5}\cos\frac{3t}{2} + \frac{2}{12}\cos\frac{4t}{2} + \frac{1}{21}\cos\frac{5t}{2} + \frac{1}{45}\cos\frac{7t}{2} + \frac{2}{60}\cos\frac{8t}{2} + \cdots\right)$$

Sine series:
$$f(t) = \frac{1}{2}\sin t - \frac{4}{\pi}\left(\frac{1}{3}\sin\frac{t}{2} + \frac{1}{5}\sin\frac{3t}{2} - \frac{1}{21}\sin\frac{5t}{2} + \frac{1}{45}\sin\frac{7t}{2} - \frac{1}{77}\sin\frac{9t}{2} + \cdots\right)$$

11. $x(t) = \dfrac{4}{\pi} \sum\limits_{n \text{ odd}} \dfrac{\sin nt}{n(2 - n^2)} =$

$\dfrac{4}{\pi} \left(\sin t - \dfrac{\sin 3t}{21} - \dfrac{\sin 5t}{115} - \dfrac{\sin 7t}{329} - \cdots \right)$

12. $x(t) = -\dfrac{4}{\pi} \left[\dfrac{\sin t}{5} + \dfrac{\sin 3t}{39} + \dfrac{\sin 5t}{145} + \dfrac{\sin 7t}{371} + \cdots \right]$

13. $x(t) = \dfrac{2}{\pi} \sum\limits_{n=1}^{\infty} \dfrac{(-1)^n \sin n\pi t}{n(n^2 \pi^2 - 1)}$

14. $x(t) = \dfrac{16}{\pi} \sum\limits_{n=1}^{\infty} \dfrac{(-1)^n \sin(n\pi t/2)}{n(n^2 \pi^2 - 8)}$

15. $x(t) = \dfrac{\pi}{4} + \dfrac{4}{\pi} \sum\limits_{n \text{ odd}} \dfrac{\cos nt}{n^2(n^2 - 2)} =$

$\dfrac{\pi}{4} + \dfrac{4}{\pi} \left(-\cos t + \dfrac{\cos 3t}{63} + \dfrac{\cos 5t}{575} + \dfrac{\cos 7t}{2303} + \cdots \right)$

17. *Suggestion:* Substitute $u = -t$ in the left-hand integral.

Section 9.4

1. $x_{sp}(t) = \dfrac{12}{\pi} \sum\limits_{n \text{ odd}} \dfrac{\sin nt}{n(5 - n^2)} =$

$\dfrac{12}{\pi} \left(\dfrac{\sin t}{4} - \dfrac{\sin 3t}{12} - \dfrac{\sin 5t}{100} - \dfrac{\sin 7t}{308} - \cdots \right).$

2. $x_{sp}(t) = \dfrac{48}{\pi} \sum\limits_{n \text{ odd}} \dfrac{(-1)^{(n-1)/2}}{n(40 - \pi^2 n^2)} \cos \dfrac{n\pi t}{2}.$

3. $x_{sp}(t) = 4 \sum\limits_{n=1}^{\infty} \dfrac{(-1)^{n-1} \sin nt}{n(3 - n^2)} =$

$4 \left(\dfrac{\sin t}{2} + \dfrac{\sin 2t}{2} - \dfrac{\sin 3t}{18} + \dfrac{\sin 4t}{52} - \cdots \right).$

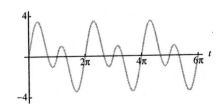

4. $x_{sp} = \dfrac{1}{2} - \dfrac{64}{\pi^2} \sum\limits_{n \text{ odd}} \dfrac{\cos n\pi t/2}{\pi^2 n^2(16 - \pi^2 n^2)}.$

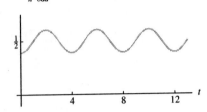

5. $x_{sp}(t) = \dfrac{8}{\pi^3} \sum\limits_{n \text{ odd}} \dfrac{\sin n\pi t}{n^3(10 - n^2 \pi^2)}$

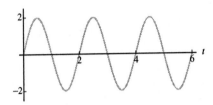

6. $x_{sp} = \dfrac{4}{\pi} - \dfrac{4}{\pi} \sum\limits_{n \text{ even}} \dfrac{\cos nt}{(n^2 - 1)(n^2 - 2)}$

$= \dfrac{4}{\pi} \left(1 - \dfrac{\cos 2t}{6} - \dfrac{\cos 4t}{210} - \dfrac{\cos 6t}{1190} - \cdots \right).$

7. The Fourier series $F(t) = \dfrac{4}{\pi} \sum\limits_{n \text{ odd}} \dfrac{\sin nt}{n}$ contains a $\sin 3t$ term, so resonance does occur.

8. No resonance occurs.

9. The Fourier series $F(t) = \dfrac{4}{\pi} \sum\limits_{n \text{ odd}} \dfrac{\sin nt}{n}$ contains no $\sin 2t$ term, so no resonance occurs.

10. Resonance does occur.

11. The Fourier series $F(t) = \dfrac{\pi}{2} - \dfrac{4}{\pi} \sum\limits_{n \text{ odd}} \dfrac{\cos nt}{n^2}$ contains no $\cos 4t$ term, so no resonance occurs.

12. Resonance does occur.

13. $x_{sp}(t) \approx (1.2725) \sin(t - 0.0333) + (0.2542) \sin(3t - 3.0817) + (0.0364) \sin(5t - 3.1178) + \cdots$

14. $x_{sp}(t) \approx (0.2500) \sin(t - 0.0063) - (0.2000) \sin(2t - 0.0200) + (4.444) \sin(3t - 1.5708) - (0.0714) \sin(4t - 3.1130) + \cdots$

15. $x_{sp}(t) \approx (0.08150) \sin(\pi t - 1.44692) + (0.00004) \sin(3\pi t - 3.10176) + \cdots$

16. $x_{sp}(t) \approx 0.5000 + 1.0577 \cos(\pi t/2 - 0.0103) - 0.0099 \cos(3\pi t/2 - 3.1390) - 0.0011 \cos(5\pi t/2 - 3.1402) \cdots$

17. (a) $x_{sp}(t) \approx (0.5687) \sin(\pi t - 0.0562) + (0.4721) \sin(3\pi t - 0.3891) + (0.01396) \sin(5\pi t - 2.7899) + (0.0318) \sin(7\pi t - 2.9874) + \cdots$

18. $x_{sp}(t) \approx 0.0531 \sin(t - 0.0004) - 0.0088 \sin(3t - 0.0019) + 1.0186 \sin(5t - 1.5708) - 0.0011 \sin(7t - 3.1387) + \cdots$

Section 9.5

1. $u(x,t) = 4e^{-12t} \sin 2x$

2. $u(x,t) \equiv 7$

3. $u(x,y) = 5\exp(-2\pi^2 t)\sin \pi x - \frac{1}{5}\exp(-18\pi^2 t)\sin 3\pi x$

4. $u(x,t) = 2e^{-4t}\sin 2x + 2e^{-36t}\sin 6x$

5. $u(x,t) =$
$$4\exp\left(-\frac{8\pi^2 t}{9}\right)\cos\left(\frac{2\pi x}{3}\right) - 2\exp\left(-\frac{32\pi^2 t}{9}\right)\cos\left(\frac{4\pi x}{3}\right)$$

6. $u(x,t) = \exp(-2\pi^2 t)\sin 2\pi x + \frac{1}{2}\exp(-8\pi^2 t)\sin 4\pi x$

7. $u(x,t) = \frac{1}{2} + \frac{1}{2}\exp\left(-\frac{16\pi^2 t}{3}\right)\cos 4\pi x$

8. $u(x,t) = 5\exp(-4\pi^2 t)\cos 2\pi x + 5\exp(-16\pi^2 t)\cos 4\pi x$

9. $u(x,t) = \frac{100}{\pi}\sum_{n \text{ odd}}\frac{1}{n}\exp\left(-\frac{n^2\pi^2 t}{250}\right)\sin\frac{n\pi x}{5}$

10. $u(x,t) = \frac{80}{\pi}\sum_{n=1}^{\infty}\frac{(-1)^{n+1}}{n}\exp\left(-\frac{n^2\pi^2 t}{500}\right)\sin\frac{n\pi x}{10}$

11. $u(x,t) = 20 - \frac{160}{\pi^2}\sum_{n \text{ odd}}\frac{1}{n^2}\exp\left(-\frac{n^2\pi^2 t}{500}\right)\cos\frac{n\pi x}{10}$

12. $u(x,t) = \frac{80000}{\pi^3}\sum_{n \text{ odd}}\frac{1}{n^3}\exp\left(-\frac{n^2\pi^2 t}{10000}\right)\sin\frac{n\pi x}{100}$

13. (a) $u(x,t) = \frac{400}{\pi}\sum_{n \text{ odd}}\frac{1}{n}\exp\left(-\frac{n^2\pi^2 kt}{1600}\right)\sin\frac{n\pi x}{40}$;
    (b) with $k = 1.15$, $u(20,300) \approx 15.16°C$;
    (c) about 19 h 16 min

14. (b) $u(10,60) \approx 25.15°C$; (c) 6 min 54.3 s

16. (b) 15 h

Section 9.6

1. $y(x,t) = \frac{1}{10}\cos 4t \sin 2x$

2. $y(x,t) = \frac{1}{10}\cos \pi t \sin \pi x - \frac{1}{20}\cos 3\pi t \sin 3\pi x$

3. $y(x,t) = \frac{1}{10}\left(\cos\frac{t}{2} + 2\sin\frac{t}{2}\right)\sin x$

4. $y(x,y) = \frac{1}{10}\cos \pi t \sin 2\pi x$

5. $y(x,t) = \frac{1}{4}\cos 5\pi t \sin \pi x + \frac{1}{\pi}\sin 10\pi t \sin 2\pi x$

6. $y(x,t) = \sum_{n \text{ odd}}\frac{8}{\pi n^3}\cos 10nt \sin nx$

7. $y(x,t) = \sum_{n=1}^{\infty}\frac{(-1)^{n+1}}{5\pi^2 n^2}\sin 10n\pi t \sin n\pi x$

8. $y(x,t) = \cos 2t \sin x + \frac{4}{\pi}\sum_{n \text{ odd}}\frac{\sin 2nt \sin nx}{n}$.

9. $y(x,t) = \frac{4}{\pi^4}\sum_{n \text{ odd}}\frac{\sin 2n\pi t \sin n\pi x}{n^4}$.

10. $y(x,t) = \frac{8}{5\pi}\sum_{n \text{ odd}}\frac{(5n\cos 5nt + \sin 5nt)}{n^2(4-n^2)}$.

11. Fundamental frequency: 256 Hz; velocity: 1024 ft/s

Section 9.7

1. $u(x,y) = \sum_{n=1}^{\infty}c_n \sinh\frac{n\pi x}{b}\sin\frac{n\pi y}{b}$ where
$$c_n = \frac{2}{b\sinh(n\pi a/b)}\int_0^b g(y)\sin\frac{n\pi y}{b}\,dy$$

2. $u(x,y) = \sum_{n=1}^{\infty}c_n \sinh\frac{n\pi(a-x)}{b}\sin\frac{n\pi y}{b}$ where
$$c_n = \frac{2}{b\sinh(n\pi a/b)}\int_0^b g(y)\sin\frac{n\pi y}{b}\,dy$$

3. $u(x,y) = \sum_{n=1}^{\infty}c_n \sin\frac{n\pi x}{a}\sinh\frac{n\pi y}{a}$ where
$$c_n = \frac{2}{a\sinh(n\pi b/a)}\int_0^a f(x)\sin\frac{n\pi x}{a}\,dx$$

4. $u(x,y) = b_0 y + \sum_{n=1}^{\infty}b_n \cos\frac{n\pi x}{a}\sinh\frac{n\pi y}{a}$ where $b_0 = a_0/2b$, $b_n = a_n/(\sinh n\pi b/a)$ and $\{a_n\}_0^{\infty}$ are the Fourier cosine coefficients of $f(x)$ on the interval $0 \le x \le a$.

5. $u(x,y) = \frac{a_0}{2a}(a-x) + \sum_{n=1}^{\infty}a_n \frac{\sinh(n\pi[a-x]/b)}{\sinh(n\pi a/b)}\cos\frac{n\pi y}{b}$, where
$$a_n = \frac{2}{b}\int_0^b g(y)\cos\frac{n\pi y}{b}\,dy$$

6. $u(x,y) = A_0 + \sum_{n=1}^{\infty}A_n \cos\frac{n\pi x}{a}\cosh\frac{n\pi y}{a}$ where $A_0 = a_0/2$, $A_n = a_n/(\cosh n\pi b/a)$ and $\{a_n\}_0^{\infty}$ are the Fourier cosine coefficients of $f(x)$ on the interval $0 \le x \le a$.

7. $u(x,y) = \sum_{n=1}^{\infty}b_n \exp\left(-\frac{n\pi y}{a}\right)\sin\frac{n\pi x}{a}$
    where $b_n = \frac{2}{a}\int_0^a f(x)\sin\frac{n\pi x}{a}\,dx$

8. $u(x,y) = \frac{a_0}{2} + \sum_{n=1}^{\infty}a_n e^{-n\pi y/a}\cos\frac{n\pi x}{a}$ where $\{a_n\}_0^{\infty}$ are the Fourier cosine coefficients of $f(x)$ on the interval $0 \le x \le a$.

9. $u(0,5) \approx 41.53$; $u(5,5) \approx 50$; $u(10,5) \approx 58.47$

11. $u(x,y) = \sum_{n \text{ odd}}c_n \sinh\frac{n\pi(a-x)}{2b}\cos\frac{n\pi y}{2b}$ where
$$c_n = \frac{2}{b\sinh(n\pi a/(2b))}\int_0^b g(y)\cos\frac{n\pi y}{2b}\,dy$$

13. $c_n = \frac{2}{\pi a^n}\int_0^{\pi}f(\theta)\sin n\theta\,d\theta$

14. $c_n = \frac{2}{\pi a^n}\int_0^{\pi}f(\theta)\cos n\theta\,d\theta$

15. $c_n = \frac{2}{\pi a^{n/2}}\int_0^{\pi}f(\theta)\sin\frac{n\theta}{2}\,d\theta$

Appendix

1. $y_0 = 3$, $y_1 = 3 + 3x$, $y_2 = 3 + 3x + \frac{3}{2}x^2$,
    $y_3 = 3 + 3x + \frac{3}{2}x^2 + \frac{1}{2}x^3$,
    $y_4 = 3 + 3x + \frac{3}{2}x^2 + \frac{1}{2}x^3 + \frac{1}{8}x^4$; $y(x) = 3e^x$

3. $y_0 = 1$, $y_1 = 1 - x^2$, $y_2 = 1 - x^2 + \frac{1}{2}x^4$,
    $y_3 = 1 - x^2 + \frac{1}{2}x^4 - \frac{1}{6}x^6$,
    $y_4 = 1 - x^2 + \frac{1}{2}x^4 - \frac{1}{6}x^6 + \frac{1}{24}x^8$; $y(x) = \exp(-x^2)$

5. $y_0 = 0$, $y_1 = 2x$, $y_2 = 2x + 2x^2$,
    $y_3 = 2x + 2x^2 + \frac{4}{3}x^3$,
    $y_4 = 2x + 2x^2 + \frac{4}{3}x^3 + \frac{2}{3}x^4$; $y(x) = e^{2x} - 1$

7. $y_0 = 0$, $y_1 = x^2$, $y_2 = x^2 + \frac{1}{2}x^4$, $y_3 = x^2 + \frac{1}{2}x^4 + \frac{1}{6}x^6$,

$y_4 = x^2 + \frac{1}{2}x^4 + \frac{1}{6}x^6 + \frac{1}{24}x^8$; $y(x) = \exp(x^2) - 1$

9. $y_0 = 1$, $y_1 = (1 + x) + \frac{1}{2}x^2$, $y_2 = (1 + x + x^2) + \frac{1}{6}x^3$,

$y_3 = \left(1 + x + x^2 + \frac{1}{3}x^3\right) + \frac{1}{24}x^4$;

$y(x) = 2e^x - 1 - x = 1 + x + x^2 + \frac{1}{3}x^3 + \cdots$

11. $y_0 = 1$, $y_1 = 1 + x$, $y_2 = (1 + x + x^2) + \frac{1}{3}x^3$,

$y_3 = (1 + x + x^2 + x^3) + \frac{2}{3}x^4 + \frac{1}{3}x^5 + \frac{1}{9}x^6 + \frac{1}{63}x^7$;

$y(x) = \dfrac{1}{1 - x} = 1 + x + x^2 + x^3 + x^4 + x^5 + \cdots$

12. $y_0 = 1$, $y_1 = 1 + \frac{1}{2}x$, $y_2 = 1 + \frac{1}{2}x + \frac{3}{8}x^3 + \frac{1}{8}x^3 + \frac{1}{64}x^4$,

$y_3 = 1 + \frac{1}{2}x + \frac{3}{8}x^2 + \frac{5}{16}x^3 + \frac{13}{64}x^4 + \cdots$; $y(x) = (1 - x)^{-1/2}$

13. $\begin{bmatrix} x_0 \\ y_0 \end{bmatrix} = \begin{bmatrix} 1 \\ -1 \end{bmatrix}$, $\begin{bmatrix} x_1 \\ y_1 \end{bmatrix} = \begin{bmatrix} 1 + 3t \\ -1 + 3t \end{bmatrix}$,

$\begin{bmatrix} x_2 \\ y_2 \end{bmatrix} = \begin{bmatrix} 1 + 3t + \frac{1}{2}t^2 \\ -1 + 5t - \frac{1}{2}t^2 \end{bmatrix}$,

$\begin{bmatrix} x_3 \\ y_3 \end{bmatrix} = \begin{bmatrix} 1 + 3t + \frac{1}{2}t^2 + \frac{1}{3}t^3 \\ -1 + 5t - \frac{1}{2}t^2 + \frac{5}{6}t^3 \end{bmatrix}$

14. $x(t) = \begin{bmatrix} e^t + te^t \\ e^t \end{bmatrix}$ **16.** $y_3(1) \approx 0.350185$

INDEX

Boldface page numbers indicate where terms are defined.

UNIT C

ADVANCED ENGINEERING MATHEMATICS

Second Edition

Michael D. Greenberg

CHAPTER

Selected Sections

17

17.9 Fourier Integral

If a function f defined on $-\infty < x < \infty$ is periodic (and sufficiently well-behaved), then it can be represented by a Fourier series. We have begun to see, and will continue to see in Chapters 18–20, that Fourier series representation is of great importance. Sometimes we work with functions, defined on $-\infty < x < \infty$, that are not periodic, such as $f(x) = e^{-x^2}$, the graph of which is given in Fig. 1. Evidently, we cannot expand such functions in Fourier series if they are not periodic. Yet, we can think of f as periodic but with an infinite period.

Thus, to extend the Fourier series concept to nonperiodic functions we will now consider the limiting case of the classical Fourier series*

$$f(x) = \sum_{n=0}^{\infty} \left(a_n \cos \frac{n\pi x}{\ell} + b_n \sin \frac{n\pi x}{\ell} \right) \tag{1a}$$

where

$$a_0 = \frac{1}{2\ell} \int_{-\ell}^{\ell} f(x)\,dx, \qquad a_n = \frac{1}{\ell} \int_{-\ell}^{\ell} f(x) \cos \frac{n\pi x}{\ell}\,dx,$$

$$b_n = \frac{1}{\ell} \int_{-\ell}^{\ell} f(x) \sin \frac{n\pi x}{\ell}\,dx, \tag{1b}$$

FIGURE 1. Graph of $f(x) = e^{-x^2}$.

as $\ell \to \infty$. We cannot simply set $\ell = \infty$ in (1), as that would yield nonsense. Rather one needs to carry out a careful limit process, as ℓ *tends* to ∞.

First, note that the $n\pi/\ell$'s in (1a) are the *frequencies* — spatial or temporal, depending on whether x is a space variable or time. The set of all of the frequencies,

$$0, \frac{\pi}{\ell}, \frac{2\pi}{\ell}, \frac{3\pi}{\ell}, \cdots$$

---
* Although we usually split out the a_0 term, here we include it in the sum, merely to increase the resemblance between (1a) and (2a), below.

is called the **frequency spectrum**. To see what happens to the frequency spectrum as ℓ increases, consider the cases where $\ell = \pi, 2\pi,$ and 10π. The corresponding frequency spectra are as follows:

$$\ell = \pi : \qquad n\pi/\ell = 0, 1, 2, 3, 4, \ldots$$
$$\ell = 2\pi : \qquad n\pi/\ell = 0, 0.5, 1.0, 1.5, 2.0, \ldots$$
$$\ell = 10\pi : \qquad n\pi/\ell = 0, 0.1, 0.2, 0.3, 0.4, \ldots$$

Observe that as ℓ increases the discrete spectrum becomes more and more dense, and approaches a *continuous spectrum* (from 0 to ∞) as $\ell \to \infty$. Therefore, we can expect that as $\ell \to \infty$ the summation in (1a), on the discrete variable n, will give way to an integration on a continuous variable, say ω. In fact, if f is sufficiently well-behaved (e.g., see Theorem 17.9.1 below) one can show that

$$f(x) = \int_0^\infty [a(\omega) \cos \omega x + b(\omega) \sin \omega x]\, d\omega, \qquad (2a)$$

where*

$$a(\omega) = \frac{1}{\pi} \int_{-\infty}^\infty f(x) \cos \omega x\, dx,$$
$$b(\omega) = \frac{1}{\pi} \int_{-\infty}^\infty f(x) \sin \omega x\, dx. \qquad (2b)$$

The right-hand side of (2a) is called the **Fourier integral** of f, which we denote as FI f, and (2a) is called the Fourier integral representation of f.

THEOREM 17.9.1: Fourier Integral Theorem

Let f be defined on $-\infty < x < \infty$, let f and f' be piecewise continuous on every finite interval $[-\ell, \ell]$ (i.e., for ℓ arbitrarily large), and let $\int_{-\infty}^\infty |f(x)|dx$ be convergent. Then the Fourier integral of f converges to $f(x)$ at every point x at which f is continuous, and to the mean value $[f(x+) + (f(x-)]/2$ at every point x at which f is discontinuous.

Proof: Rigorous proof of this theorem is well beyond our present scope, and the following is put forward only as a heuristic derivation. If we change the dummy integration variable to ξ in (1b), to distinguish it from the fixed point x in (1a),

---

*Normally, a singular integral of the form $\int_{-\infty}^\infty F(x)dx$ is understood to mean

$$\int_{-\infty}^\infty F(x)\, dx = \lim_{A \to \infty, B \to \infty} \int_{-A}^B F(x)\, dx,$$

where A and B tend to infinity independently. However, the integrals in (2b) are to be understood in the more forgiving sense.

$$\int_{-\infty}^\infty F(x)\, dx = \lim_{A \to \infty} \int_{-A}^A F(x)\, dx.$$

To see that the latter is "more forgiving" than the former, observe that if $F(x) = x$, for instance, then with the former interpretation the integral is divergent but with the latter interpretation it converges to zero.

insert (1b) into (1a), and use the identity $\cos A \cos B + \sin A \sin B = \cos(A - B)$ for greater compactness, then the right-hand side of (1a), namely, FS f, becomes

$$\text{FS } f = \frac{1}{2\ell} \int_{-\ell}^{\ell} f(\xi)\, d\xi + \sum_{n=1}^{\infty} \frac{1}{\ell} \int_{-\ell}^{\ell} f(\xi) \cos \frac{n\pi}{\ell}(\xi - x)\, d\xi. \tag{3}$$

Denote the two terms on the right-hand side as I and J, respectively. For I we have

$$|I| = \left| \frac{1}{2\ell} \int_{-\ell}^{\ell} f(\xi)\, d\xi \right| \leq \frac{1}{2\ell} \int_{-\infty}^{\infty} |f(\xi)|\, d\xi \to 0 \tag{4}$$

as $\ell \to \infty$ because $\int_{-\infty}^{\infty} |f(\xi)|\, d\xi$ is finite, by assumption, and $1/(2\ell) \to 0$ as $\ell \to \infty$. Thus, $I \to 0$ as $\ell \to \infty$. In J, let $\pi/\ell \equiv \Delta\omega$. Then

$$J = \frac{1}{\pi} \sum_{n=1}^{\infty} \left[\int_{-\ell}^{\ell} f(\xi) \cos n\Delta\omega(\xi - x)\, d\xi \right] \Delta\omega$$

$$\to \frac{1}{\pi} \int_{0}^{\infty} \left[\int_{-\infty}^{\infty} f(\xi) \cos \omega(\xi - x)\, d\xi \right] d\omega \tag{5}$$

as $\ell \to \infty$. To understand the last step, observe that the sum in (5) is a Riemann sum, and as $\Delta\omega \to 0$ (i.e., as $\ell \to \infty$, because $\Delta\omega = \pi/\ell$) it yields a Riemann integral. That is, we partition the interval $0 < \omega < \infty$ into equal parts, of dimension $\Delta\omega = \pi/\ell$, and call $\omega_1 = \pi/\ell$, $\omega_2 = 2\pi/\ell$, $\omega_3 = 3\pi/\ell$, and so on, and use the general Riemann integral formula

$$\lim_{\Delta\omega \to 0} \sum_{n=1}^{\infty} F(n\Delta\omega)\Delta\omega = \lim_{\Delta\omega \to 0} \sum_{n=1}^{\infty} F(\omega_n)\Delta\omega = \int_{0}^{\infty} F(\omega)\, d\omega. \tag{6}$$

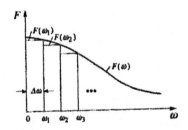

FIGURE 2.   Riemann sum.

(See Fig. 2.) Finally, expressing $\cos \omega(\xi - x) = \cos \omega\xi \cos \omega x + \sin \omega\xi \sin \omega x$, we have

$$\text{FS} f = I + J$$

$$\to 0 + \int_{0}^{\infty} \left[\frac{1}{\pi} \int_{-\infty}^{\infty} f(\xi) \cos \omega\xi\, d\xi \right] \cos \omega x\, d\omega$$

$$+ \int_{0}^{\infty} \left[\frac{1}{\pi} \int_{-\infty}^{\infty} f(\xi) \sin \omega\xi\, d\xi \right] \sin \omega x\, d\omega$$

$$= \int_{0}^{\infty} [a(\omega) \cos \omega x + b(\omega) \sin \omega x]\, d\omega \tag{7}$$

as $\ell \to \infty$. That is, as $\ell \to \infty$ the Fourier series tends to the Fourier integral. We reiterate that our approach has been heuristic, not rigorous. ■

Example 1   *Rectangular Pulse.* Let f be the rectangular pulse shown in Fig. 3. This f does satisfy the conditions of the theorem. According to (2b),

$$a(\omega) = \frac{1}{\pi} \int_{-\infty}^{\infty} f(x) \cos \omega x\, dx = \frac{1}{\pi} \int_{-1}^{1} \cos \omega x\, dx = \frac{2}{\pi} \frac{\sin \omega}{\omega} \tag{8a}$$

FIGURE 3. Rectangular pulse.

and

$$b(\omega) = \frac{1}{\pi} \int_{-\infty}^{\infty} f(x) \sin \omega x \, dx = 0 \qquad (8b)$$

because the integrand $f(x) \sin \omega x$ is an odd function (recall that even × odd = odd). Thus, the Fourier integral representation of f is, from (2) and (8),

$$f(x) = \frac{2}{\pi} \int_{0}^{\infty} \frac{\sin \omega}{\omega} \cos \omega x \, d\omega. \qquad (9)$$

Just as it was illuminating to plot the *partial sums* $s_n(x)$ of Fourier series, it should be illuminating to see how the *partial integral*

$$f_\Omega(x) = \frac{2}{\pi} \int_{0}^{\Omega} \frac{\sin \omega}{\omega} \cos \omega x \, dx \qquad (10)$$

converges to $f(x)$ as $\Omega \to \infty$. Though the latter integral is not elementary, it can be evaluated in terms of the **sine integral** function

$$\boxed{Si(x) = \int_{0}^{x} \frac{\sin t}{t} \, dt, \qquad (11)}$$

either analytically (Exercise 1) or using computer software. Using *Maple*, for instance, the command

$$\text{int}((2/\text{Pi}) * (1/y) * \sin(y) * \cos(y * x), \ y = 0..z);$$

(where z is used in place of Ω) gives

$$f_\Omega(x) = \frac{1}{\pi} \{ Si[\Omega(x+1)] - Si[\Omega(x-1)] \}, \qquad (12)$$

which we've plotted in Fig. 4 for $\Omega = 4, 16,$ and 128. Evidently $f_\Omega(x)$ does converge to the pulse $f(x)$, but the convergence is slow near the jump discontinuities; the limiting case as $\Omega \to \infty$ is left for Exercise 3. As in the case of Fourier series, the Fourier integral exhibits the Gibbs phenomenon at such discontinuities.

FIGURE 4. Convergence of $f_\Omega(x)$ to $f(x)$ as $\Omega \to \infty$.

FIGURE 5. Harmonic content, $a(\omega)$.

It is also interesting to plot the Fourier coefficient $a(\omega)$, given by (8a), since $a(\omega)$ tells us the harmonic content of f, that is, the amplitude or "amount" of each $\cos \omega x$ harmonic present (Fig. 5).   ■

Example 2

Infinite Beam on Elastic Foundation. As a physical application of the Fourier integral let us consider the same problem as contained in Example 4 of Section 17.3 (which we urge you to review), but instead of the periodic loading suppose we have the nonperiodic rectangular pulse loading shown here in Fig. 6. Recall that the beam's deflection $u(x)$ is governed by the differential equation

w_0 newtons / meter

FIGURE 6. Infinite beam on elastic foundation.

$$EIu'''' + ku = w(x), \tag{13}$$

where E, I, k are physical constants, and

$$w(x) = \begin{cases} w_0, & |x| < 1 \\ 0, & |x| > 1 \end{cases} \tag{14}$$

is the rectangular pulse applied load distribution. Proceeding essentially as in Example 4 of Section 17.3, we first express $w(x)$ in Fourier integral form. Since $w(x)$ is merely $f(x)$ in Example 1, scaled by w_0, we conclude from (9) that

$$w(x) = \frac{2w_0}{\pi} \int_0^\infty \frac{\sin \omega}{\omega} \cos \omega x \, d\omega. \tag{15}$$

Next, we seek $u(x)$ in the Fourier integral form

$$u(x) = \int_0^\infty a(\omega) \cos \omega x \, d\omega, \tag{16}$$

where $a(\omega)$ remains to be determined. We have omitted the $b(\omega) \sin \omega x$ since $u(x)$ will evidently be a symmetric (even) function of x; that is, if we did include that term we would find that $b(\omega) = 0$.

Formally differentiating (16) under the integral sign four times, and putting that result and (15) and (16) into (13) gives

$$\int_0^\infty (EI\omega^4 + k)a(\omega) \cos \omega x \, d\omega = \frac{2w_0}{\pi} \int_0^\infty \frac{\sin \omega}{\omega} \cos \omega x \, d\omega. \tag{17}$$

Then, formally equating the coefficients of each cosine harmonic gives

$$(EI\omega^4 + k)a(\omega) = \frac{2w_0}{\pi} \frac{\sin \omega}{\omega} \tag{18}$$

or

$$a(\omega) = \frac{2w_0}{\pi} \frac{\sin \omega}{\omega} \frac{1}{(EI\omega^4 + k)}, \tag{19}$$

so that (16) becomes

$$u(x) = \frac{2w_0}{\pi} \int_0^\infty \frac{\sin\omega}{\omega} \frac{\cos\omega x}{(EI\omega^4 + k)} d\omega. \tag{20}$$

This integral can be evaluated analytically using complex variable techniques (the residue theorem), but for our present purposes it will suffice to let (20) stand as it is. ∎

Closure. We obtain the Fourier integral representation of nonperiodic functions defined on $-\infty < x < \infty$ by taking the limit of the Fourier series formula as the period tends to infinity. We limit discussion to two examples because we plan to use the Fourier integral only as a stepping stone to the *Fourier transform*. The latter is more highly developed as a methodology, like the Laplace transform, and is the subject of the next section.

17.9 Problems

1. Use (11) to derive (12) from (10).

2. Derive the Fourier integral representations of the following functions. At which points, if any, does the Fourier integral fail to converge of $f(x)$? To what value does the integral converge at those points?

(a) $f(x) = \begin{cases} 100, & 0 \le x \le 2 \\ 0, & x < 0, \ x > 2 \end{cases}$

(b) $f(x) = \begin{cases} x, & 0 \le x < L \\ 0, & x < 0, \ x \ge L \end{cases}$

(c) $f(x) = \begin{cases} x, & |x| \le L \\ 0, & |x| > L \end{cases}$

(d) $f(x) = \begin{cases} -x, & -5 < x \le 0 \\ 0, & x \le -5, \ x > 0 \end{cases}$

(e) $f(x) = \begin{cases} |x|, & -1 < x < 2 \\ 0, & x \le -1, \ x \ge 2 \end{cases}$

(f) $f(x) = \begin{cases} 10, & 0 \le x \le 3 \\ 5, & 6 \le x \le 9 \\ 0, & x < 0, \ 3 < x < 6, \ x > 9 \end{cases}$

(g) $f(x) = \begin{cases} e^{-x}, & x \ge 0 \\ 0, & x < 0 \end{cases}$

(h) $f(x) = \begin{cases} e^x, & x \ge 0 \\ 0, & x < 0 \end{cases}$

(i) $f(x) = e^{-|x|}$

3. (a) Show that $Si(x)$ is an odd function of x.

(b) Using the known integral

$$Si(\infty) = \int_0^\infty \frac{\sin t}{t} dt = \frac{\pi}{2}$$

and recalling (11), show that

$$\lim_{\Omega \to \infty} f_\Omega(x) = \begin{cases} 1, & |x| < 1 \\ 1/2, & |x| = 1 \\ 0, & |x| > 1 \end{cases}$$

so that the Fourier integral (9) does converge to the rectangular pulse and (in accordance with Theorem 17.9.1) to the average values at the two jump discontinuities.

4. Comparing (2) with the classical Fourier series (1), it might appear that $a(0)$ is analogous to the a_0 term in the Fourier series and represents the average value of f. Is it true that $a(0)$ is the average value of f where, by the average value of f we mean $\lim_{A \to \infty} \frac{1}{2A} \int_{-A}^A f(x)dx$? Explain.

17.10 Fourier Transform

Our purpose in this section is to recast the Fourier integral representation of a function f as a pair of formulas, the first giving the so-called Fourier transform of f, and the second giving the inverse of that transform. Once the transform and its inverse are derived, in Section 17.10.1, discussion will closely parallel our discussion, in Chapter 5, of the Laplace transform.

Transition from Fourier integral to Fourier transform

Our starting point is the Fourier integral formula

$$f(x) = \int_0^\infty [a(\omega)\cos\omega x + b(\omega)\sin\omega x]d\omega, \tag{1a}$$

where

$$a(\omega) = \frac{1}{\pi} \int_{-\infty}^{\infty} f(x) \cos \omega x \, dx,$$

$$b(\omega) = \frac{1}{\pi} \int_{-\infty}^{\infty} f(x) \sin \omega x \, dx. \tag{1b}$$

Just as one can express a Fourier series in complex exponential form (Section 17.3.4), one can express the Fourier integral (1) in complex exponential form. To obtain that form put (1b) into (1a). [First we change the dummy integration variable x in (1b) to ξ, say, to avoid confusing that variable with the x's occurring in (1a), which denote the fixed point at which $f(x)$ is being computed.] Thus,

$$
\begin{aligned}
f(x) &= \frac{1}{\pi} \int_0^{\infty} \left\{ \int_{-\infty}^{\infty} f(\xi)[\cos \omega \xi \cos \omega x + \sin \omega \xi \sin \omega x] d\xi \right\} d\omega \\
&= \frac{1}{\pi} \int_0^{\infty} \int_{-\infty}^{\infty} f(\xi) \cos \omega (\xi - x) d\xi \, d\omega,
\end{aligned}
\tag{2}
$$

since $\cos(A - B) = \cos A \cos B + \sin A \sin B$. To introduce complex exponentials, re-express (2) as

$$
\begin{aligned}
f(x) &= \frac{1}{\pi} \int_0^{\infty} \int_{-\infty}^{\infty} f(\xi) \frac{e^{i\omega(\xi-x)} + e^{-i\omega(\xi-x)}}{2} d\xi \, d\omega \\
&= \frac{1}{2\pi} \int_0^{\infty} \int_{-\infty}^{\infty} f(\xi) e^{i\omega(\xi-x)} d\xi \, d\omega + \frac{1}{2\pi} \int_0^{\infty} \int_{-\infty}^{\infty} f(\xi) e^{-i\omega(\xi-x)} d\xi \, d\omega.
\end{aligned}
$$

To combine the two terms on the right-hand side, let us change the dummy integration variable from ω to $-\omega$ in the first. Thus,

$$
\begin{aligned}
f(x) &= \frac{1}{2\pi} \int_0^{-\infty} \int_{-\infty}^{\infty} f(\xi) e^{-i\omega(\xi-x)} d\xi \, (-d\omega) \\
&\quad + \frac{1}{2\pi} \int_0^{\infty} \int_{-\infty}^{\infty} f(\xi) e^{-i\omega(\xi-x)} d\xi \, d\omega \\
&= \frac{1}{2\pi} \int_{-\infty}^0 \int_{-\infty}^{\infty} f(\xi) e^{-i\omega(\xi-x)} d\xi \, d\omega + \frac{1}{2\pi} \int_0^{\infty} \int_{-\infty}^{\infty} f(\xi) e^{-i\omega(\xi-x)} d\xi \, d\omega,
\end{aligned}
$$

so

$$
\begin{aligned}
f(x) &= \frac{1}{2\pi} \int_{-\infty}^{\infty} \int_{-\infty}^{\infty} f(\xi) e^{-i\omega(\xi-x)} d\xi \, d\omega \\
&= \frac{1}{2\pi} \int_{-\infty}^{\infty} \left[\int_{-\infty}^{\infty} f(\xi) e^{-i\omega\xi} d\xi \right] e^{i\omega x} d\omega.
\end{aligned}
\tag{3}
$$

The latter can be split apart as

$$f(x) = a \int_{-\infty}^{\infty} c(\omega) e^{i\omega x} d\omega \tag{4a}$$

and

$$c(\omega) = b \int_{-\infty}^{\infty} f(\xi) e^{-i\omega\xi} d\xi, \tag{4b}$$

if the constants a, b are such that $ab = 1/2\pi$. We can make (4) resemble (1) more closely by choosing $a = 1$ and $b = 1/2\pi$, but we will choose $a = 1/2\pi$ and $b = 1$.* There is no longer a need to distinguish x and ξ, because the x's are confined to (4a) and the ξ's to (4b). Thus, to minimize nomenclature and to mimic the form of (1), we write

$$f(x) = \frac{1}{2\pi} \int_{-\infty}^{\infty} c(\omega) e^{i\omega x} d\omega, \tag{5a}$$

$$c(\omega) = \int_{-\infty}^{\infty} f(x) e^{-i\omega x} dx. \tag{5b}$$

Rather than thinking of (5a) as the Fourier integral of f and (5b) as giving (give or take the factor of $1/2\pi$) the Fourier coefficients $c(\omega)$, we can think of (5a,b) as a transform pair: (5b) defines the **Fourier transform** $c(\omega)$ of the given function $f(x)$, and (5a) is called the **inversion formula** because putting $c(\omega)$ in and integrating gives us back $f(x)$. It is standard to use the notation $\hat{f}(\omega)$, in place of $c(\omega)$, for the transform, so we rewrite (5) in final form as

$$F\{f(x)\} = \hat{f}(\omega) = \int_{-\infty}^{\infty} f(x) e^{-i\omega x} dx, \tag{6a}$$

and

$$F^{-1}\{\hat{f}(\omega)\} = f(x) = \frac{1}{2\pi} \int_{-\infty}^{\infty} \hat{f}(\omega) e^{i\omega x} d\omega. \tag{6b}$$

Thus, the Fourier transform and inversion formulas are not mysterious; together, they simply amount to the Fourier integral representation, expressed in complex exponential form, and conditions imposed on f are the same as in Theorem 17.9.1.

Let us illustrate the calculation of the transform $\hat{f}(\omega)$ of $f(x)$.

Example 1

Rectangular Pulse. Consider the rectangular pulse $f(x) = H(x+1) - H(x-1)$, where H denotes the Heaviside function. The graph of f is given in Fig. 1. Using (6a), the Fourier transform of f is

$$\hat{f}(\omega) = \int_{-\infty}^{\infty} [H(x+1) - H(x-1)] e^{-i\omega x} dx = \int_{-1}^{1} e^{-i\omega x} dx$$

$$= \frac{e^{-i\omega x}}{-i\omega} \bigg|_{-1}^{1} = 2\frac{\sin\omega}{\omega}. \tag{7}$$

FIGURE 1. Rectangular pulse.

Comment   We could illustrate the inversion formula as well, by putting $\hat{f}(\omega) = (2\sin\omega)/\omega$ into the integrand of (6b), integrating, and showing that the result is the rectangular pulse f that we started with. In fact, that integral can be evaluated by using the residue theorem of the complex integral calculus, but we won't study that theorem until Chapter 24.   ∎

Example 2

Evaluate the Fourier transform of

$$f(x) = H(x) e^{-ax}, \quad (a > 0) \tag{8}$$

FIGURE 2. $f(x) = H(x)e^{-ax}$.

FIGURE 3. Modulus of z.

the graph of which is given in Fig. 2. From (6a),

$$\hat{f}(\omega) = \int_{-\infty}^{\infty} H(x)e^{-ax}e^{-i\omega x}dx = \int_{0}^{\infty} e^{-(a+i\omega)x}dx$$

$$= -\frac{e^{-(a+i\omega)x}}{a+i\omega}\Big|_{0}^{\infty} = \frac{1}{a+i\omega} - \frac{1}{a+i\omega}\lim_{x\to\infty}e^{-(a+i\omega)x}$$

$$= \frac{1}{a+i\omega}. \tag{9}$$

To explain the last step in (9), recall that the magnitude (or modulus) $|z|$ of a complex number $z = x + iy$ (Fig. 3) is $|z| = \sqrt{x^2 + y^2}$, and that the modulus of a product is the product of the moduli ($|z_1 z_2| = |z_1||z_2|$). Then

$$\left|e^{-(a+i\omega)x}\right| = \left|e^{-ax}e^{-i\omega x}\right| = \left|e^{-ax}\right|\left|e^{-i\omega x}\right|$$

$$= e^{-ax}|\cos\omega x - i\sin\omega x|$$

$$= e^{-ax}\sqrt{\cos^2\omega x + \sin^2\omega x}$$

$$= e^{-ax} \to 0 \tag{10}$$

as $x \to \infty$.   ■

As with the Laplace transform, it is convenient to use tables for both the transform and its inverse, insofar as possible. The table provided here, in Appendix D, is brief, but will suffice for present purposes. Much more extensive tables are available,* as well as powerful computer software; the relevant commands, using *Maple*, are given at the end of this section.

Properties and applications

The Fourier transform admits a number of useful properties, our discussion of which will closely parallel our analogous discussion for the Laplace transform, given in Chapter 5. We will assume, without reiteration, that the functions being transformed satisfy the conditions given in Theorem 17.9.1.

Linearity of the transform and its inverse. For any scalars α and β, and any functions f and g,

$$\boxed{F\{\alpha f + \beta g\} = \alpha F\{f\} + \beta F\{g\}} \tag{11}$$

and

$$\boxed{F^{-1}\{\alpha\hat{f} + \beta\hat{g}\} = \alpha F^{-1}\{\hat{f}\} + \beta F^{-1}\{\hat{g}\}.} \tag{12}$$

Of course, $F^{-1}\{\hat{f}\}$ is f and $F^{-1}\{\hat{g}\}$ is g. Proofs of (11) and (12) follow the same lines as the proofs of Theorems 5.3.1. and 5.3.2, respectively.

Transform of nth derivative. If $f(x), f'(x), \ldots, f^{n-1}(x)$ all tend to zero as $x \to \pm\infty$, and $\int_{-\infty}^{\infty}|f^{(j)}(x)|dx$ converges for each $j = 0, 1, \ldots, n$, then

$$\boxed{F\{f^{(n)}(x)\} = (i\omega)^n\hat{f}(\omega). \qquad (n = 0, 1, 2, \ldots)} \tag{13}$$

---

* Some authors, perhaps out of a greater sense of fair play, choose $a = b = 1/\sqrt{2\pi}$.

* See, for example, A. Erdèlyi (ed.), *Tables of Integral transforms*, Vols. 1 and 2 (New York: McGraw-Hill, 1954). Volume 1 contains Fourier, Laplace, and Mellin transforms, and volume 2 contains Hankel and various other transforms.

Proof: Let us prove (13) by induction. First, observe that (13) holds for $n = 0$, by definition. To complete the proof by induction we need to establish that if it holds for $n = k$ then it also holds for $n = k + 1$. To do so, integrate by parts:

$$
\begin{aligned}
F\{f^{(k+1)}(x)\} &= \int_{-\infty}^{\infty} f^{(k+1)}(x)e^{-i\omega x}dx \\
&= [f^{(k)}(x)e^{-i\omega x}]\Big|_{-\infty}^{\infty} + i\omega \int_{-\infty}^{\infty} f^{(k)}(x)e^{-i\omega x}dx \\
&= [f^{(k)}(x)e^{-i\omega x}]\Big|_{-\infty}^{\infty} + i\omega[(i\omega)^k \hat{f}(\omega)] \\
&= [f^{(k)}(x)e^{-i\omega x}]\Big|_{-\infty}^{\infty} + (i\omega)^{k+1}\hat{f}(\omega),
\end{aligned}
\tag{14}
$$

the third equality following from the assumption that (13) holds for $n = k$. Now, $|f^{(k)}(x)e^{-i\omega x}| = |f^{(k)}(x)||e^{-i\omega x}| = |f^{(k)}(x)|$, and since $f^{(k)}(x) \to 0$ as $x \to \pm\infty$, by assumption, the boundary term in (14) drops out. Thus $F\{f^{(k+1)}(x)\} = (i\omega)^{k+1}\hat{f}(\omega)$ so (13) does hold for $n = k + 1$, which result completes out proof by induction. ▲

Fourier convolution. We denote the **Fourier convolution** of functions f and g as $f * g$. It too is a function of x, defined as

$$
\boxed{(f * g)(x) \equiv \int_{-\infty}^{\infty} f(x - \xi)g(\xi)d\xi.}
\tag{15}
$$

Then the **Fourier convolution theorem** states that

$$
\boxed{F\{f * g\} = \hat{f}(\omega)\hat{g}(\omega),}
\tag{16}
$$

or, equivalently, that

$$
\boxed{F^{-1}\{\hat{f}\hat{g}\} = f * g.}
\tag{17}
$$

Proof: It suffices to prove (16) or (17), because of their equivalence. Let us prove (16). We have

$$
\begin{aligned}
F\{f * g\} &= \int_{-\infty}^{\infty}\left\{\int_{-\infty}^{\infty} f(x - \xi)g(\xi)d\xi\right\}e^{-i\omega x}dx \\
&= \int_{-\infty}^{\infty} g(\xi)d\xi \int_{-\infty}^{\infty} f(x - \xi)e^{-i\omega x}dx \\
&= \int_{-\infty}^{\infty} g(\xi)d\xi \int_{-\infty}^{\infty} f(\eta)e^{-i\omega(\xi+\eta)}d\eta \\
&= \left(\int_{-\infty}^{\infty} g(\xi)e^{-i\omega\xi}d\xi\right)\left(\int_{-\infty}^{\infty} f(\eta)e^{-i\omega\eta}d\eta\right) \\
&= \hat{g}(\omega)\hat{f}(\omega),
\end{aligned}
\tag{18}
$$

as was to be shown. In the second equality we reversed the order of integration,* and the third equality follows from the change of variables $x - \xi = \eta$. ▲

---

* Sufficient conditions for the validity of this reversal are that f and g both be **absolutely integrable**, i.e., that $\int_{-\infty}^{\infty} |f(x)|dx$ and $\int_{-\infty}^{\infty} |g(x)|dx$ both converge. But these conditions have already been assumed. For detailed discussion, see T. M. Apostol, *Mathematical Analysis* (Reading, MA: Addison-Wesley, 1957), p.491.

It is easy to show that the Fourier convolution is commutative,

$$f * g = g * f, \tag{19}$$

proof of which is left for the exercises. That is, it doesn't matter whether we take the argument of f to be $x - \xi$ and the argument of g to be ξ, in (15), or visa versa.

Translation formulas, x-shift and ω-shift. It is also easy to derive the shift (or translation) formulas

$$\boxed{F\{f(x - a)\} = e^{-ia\omega}\hat{f}(\omega)} \tag{20}$$

and

$$\boxed{F^{-1}\{\hat{f}(\omega - a)\} = e^{iax}f(x),} \tag{21}$$

proofs of which are left for the exercises.

Each of the properties (11), (12), (13), (16), (17), (20), and (21) and corresponds to an analogous property of the Laplace transform. Properties (11) and (12) are identical to the corresponding properties of the Laplace transform. The derivative property (13) is similar to the property

$$L\{f^{(n)}(t)\} = s^n\overline{f}(s) - s^{n-1}f(0) - s^{n-2}f'(0) - \cdots - f^{(n-1)}(0), \tag{22}$$

but does not include any boundary values analogous to the initial conditions $f(0), \ldots, f^{(n-1)}(0)$ in (22), because the boundaries are at $x = \pm\infty$, and it is assumed that $f(x), f'(x), \ldots, f^{(n-1)}(x)$ all tend to zero as $x \to \pm\infty$. The convolution properties (16) and (17) are identical to the corresponding ones for the Laplace transform, but keep in mind that the Fourier and Laplace convolutions are not quite the same; in contrast with the Fourier convolution (15), the Laplace convolution was defined as

$$(f * g)(t) \equiv \int_0^t f(t - \tau)g(\tau)\,d\tau. \tag{23}$$

That is, the integration limits are different.

In the examples to follow, we illustrate the use of these various properties and the table in Appendix D.

Example 3 Given

$$f(x) = 4e^{-|x|} - 5e^{-3|x+2|}, \tag{24}$$

evaluate its transform $\hat{f}(\omega)$. First, the linearity property (11) gives

$$F\{4e^{-|x|} - 5e^{-3|x+2|}\} = 4F\{e^{-|x|}\} - 5F\{e^{-3|x+2|}\}. \tag{25}$$

Next, entry 4 in Appendix D gives

$$F\{e^{-|x|}\} = \frac{2}{\omega^2 + 1}, \tag{26}$$

and entry 11 (with $a = 3$ and $b = 6$)gives

$$
\begin{aligned}
F\{e^{-3|x+2|}\} &= F\{e^{-|3x+6|}\} \\
&= \frac{1}{3}e^{i6\omega/3}\left(F\{e^{-|x|}\}\right)\Big|_{\omega\to\omega/3} \\
&= \frac{1}{3}e^{i2\omega}\left(\frac{2}{\omega^2+1}\right)\Big|_{\omega\to\omega/3} \\
&= \frac{1}{3}e^{i2\omega}\frac{2}{\left(\dfrac{\omega}{3}\right)^2+1}.
\end{aligned}
\tag{27}
$$

From(25)–(27), it follows that

$$
\begin{aligned}
\hat{f}(\omega) &= 4\frac{2}{\omega^2+1} - 5\left(\frac{2}{3}\right)\frac{e^{i2\omega}}{\left(\dfrac{\omega}{3}\right)^2+1} \\
&= \frac{8}{\omega^2+1} - \frac{30e^{i2\omega}}{\omega^2+9}. \qquad\blacksquare
\end{aligned}
$$

Example 4 Given

$$
f(x) = xe^{-4x^2},
\tag{28}
$$

evaluate $\hat{f}(\omega)$. First,

$$
\begin{aligned}
F\{e^{-4x^2}\} &= F\{e^{-(2x)^2}\} \\
&= \frac{1}{2}\left(F\{e^{-x^2}\}\right)\Big|_{\omega\to\omega/2} \qquad (\text{entry}11, a=2, b=0) \\
&= \frac{1}{2}\sqrt{\pi}e^{-\omega^2/4}\Big|_{\omega\to\omega/2} \qquad (\text{entry 5}) \\
&= \frac{\sqrt{\pi}}{2}e^{-\omega^2/16}.
\end{aligned}
\tag{29}
$$

Next, entry 17 (with $n = 1$) gives

$$
\hat{f}(\omega) = i\frac{d}{d\omega}\left(\frac{\sqrt{\pi}}{2}e^{-\omega^2/16}\right) = -i\frac{\sqrt{\pi}}{16}\omega e^{-\omega^2/16}. \qquad\blacksquare
$$

Example 5 Given $\hat{f}(\omega) = e^{-2|\omega|}$, evaluate $f(x)$. With $a = 2$, entry 1 gives

$$
F^{-1}\left\{\frac{\pi}{2}e^{-2|\omega|}\right\} = \frac{1}{x^2+4}.
\tag{30}
$$

Then it follows from the linearity property (12), with $\alpha = \pi/2$ and $\beta = 0$, that (30) can be re-expressed as

$$
\frac{\pi}{2}F^{-1}\left\{e^{-2|\omega|}\right\} = \frac{1}{x^2+4},
\tag{31}
$$

so

$$
F^{-1}\left\{e^{-2|\omega|}\right\} = \frac{2}{\pi}\frac{1}{x^2+4},
\tag{32}
$$

is the desired inverse function $f(x)$. $\qquad\blacksquare$

Example 6   Evaluate

$$F^{-1}\left\{\frac{1}{\omega^2 + 4\omega + 13}\right\}. \tag{33}$$

First, completing the square, write $\omega^2 + 4\omega = (\omega^2 + 4\omega + 4) - 4 = (\omega + 2)^2 - 4$, so (33) becomes

$$F^{-1}\left\{\frac{1}{(\omega + 2)^2 + 9}\right\}. \tag{34}$$

Now, entry 4 (with $a = 3$) and linearity give

$$F^{-1}\left\{\frac{1}{\omega^2 + 9}\right\} = \frac{1}{6}e^{-3|x|}. \tag{35}$$

Finally, from entry 12, with $a = 1$ and $b = 2$, and (35), we have

$$F^{-1}\left\{\frac{1}{(\omega + 2)^2 + 9}\right\} = e^{-i2x}\left(\frac{1}{6}e^{-3|x|}\right) \tag{36}$$

as the desired result.

    Comment   Alternatively, we could have used partial fractions, as follows. Solving $\omega^2 + 4\omega + 13 = 0$ gives $\omega = -2 \pm 3i$. Thus,

$$\begin{aligned}
\frac{1}{\omega^2 + 4\omega + 13} &= \frac{1}{(\omega + 2 - 3i)(\omega + 2 + 3i)} \\
&= \frac{1}{6i}\frac{1}{\omega + 2 - 3i} - \frac{1}{6i}\frac{1}{\omega + 2 + 3i} \\
&= \frac{1}{6}\frac{1}{i\omega + (3 + 2i)} - \frac{1}{6}\frac{1}{i\omega + (-3 + 2i)} \\
&= \frac{1}{6}\frac{1}{i\omega + (3 + 2i)} + \frac{1}{6}\frac{1}{-i\omega + (3 - 2i)}. \tag{37}
\end{aligned}$$

Observe that the first term after the third equal sign can be inverted by entry 2, because Re $(3 + 2i) = 3 > 0,$* but the second cannot, because Re $(-3 + 2i) = -3 < 0$. Thus, in the final step we rearranged that term so that it can be inverted by entry 3, because Re $(3 - 2i) = 3 > 0$. Finally, using the linearity property (12), together with entries 2 and 3 gives

$$\begin{aligned}
F^{-1}\left\{\frac{1}{\omega^2 + 4\omega + 13}\right\} &= \frac{1}{6}H(x)e^{-(3+2i)x} + \frac{1}{6}H(-x)e^{(3-2i)x} \\
&= \frac{1}{6}e^{-i2x}[H(x)e^{-3x} + H(-x)e^{3x}] \\
&= \frac{1}{6}e^{-i2x}e^{-3|x|}, \tag{38}
\end{aligned}$$

as obtained in (36).   ■

---

* If $z = x + iy$ is a complex number, then x and y are called the **real** and **imaginary parts** of z, and are denoted as Re z and Im z, respectively.

Example 7   Evaluate

$$F^{-1}\left\{\frac{1}{\omega^2 + 1}\right\}.\qquad(39)$$

The latter can be evaluated directly from entry 4 (together with the linearity property), as $e^{-|x|}/2$. However, for pedagogical purposes let us use this example to illustrate the convolution property. First, factor $1/(\omega^2 + 1)$ as

$$\frac{1}{\omega^2 + 1} = \frac{1}{(\omega + i)(\omega - i)} = \frac{1}{(1 - i\omega)(1 + i\omega)},\qquad(40)$$

the final form in (40) being more convenient than the intermediate form because each factor can be inverted, using entries 3 and 2, respectively:

$$F^{-1}\left\{\frac{1}{1 - i\omega}\right\} = H(-x)e^x,\qquad(41a)$$

$$F^{-1}\left\{\frac{1}{1 + i\omega}\right\} = H(x)e^{-x}.\qquad(41b)$$

Then the Fourier convolution formula (17) gives

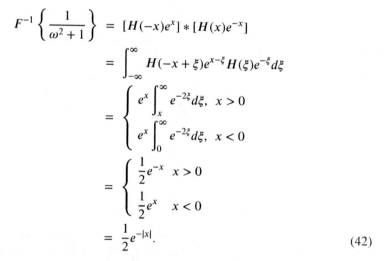

$$
\begin{aligned}
F^{-1}\left\{\frac{1}{\omega^2 + 1}\right\} &= [H(-x)e^x] * [H(x)e^{-x}] \\
&= \int_{-\infty}^{\infty} H(-x + \xi)e^{x-\xi} H(\xi)e^{-\xi} d\xi \\
&= \begin{cases} e^x \int_x^{\infty} e^{-2\xi} d\xi, & x > 0 \\ e^x \int_0^{\infty} e^{-2\xi} d\xi, & x < 0 \end{cases} \\
&= \begin{cases} \dfrac{1}{2}e^{-x} & x > 0 \\ \dfrac{1}{2}e^{x} & x < 0 \end{cases} \\
&= \frac{1}{2}e^{-|x|}. \qquad(42)
\end{aligned}
$$

FIGURE 4. $H(\xi - x)$ and $H(\xi)$.

To understand the third equality in (42), it is useful to plot $H(\xi - x)$ and $H(\xi)$, both for $x > 0$ and for $x < 0$, as we have in Fig. 4. Namely, we see from Fig. 4 that their product $H(\xi - x)H(\xi)$ is $H(\xi - x)$ if $x > 0$, and $H(\xi)$ if $x < 0$.

    Comment   Alternatively, we could have applied partial fractions to the right-hand side of (40) and proceeded as in the comment in Example 6. ∎

Example 8   *Infinite Beam on Elastic Foundation, Revisited.* In Example 2 in Section 17.9 we investigated the deflection $u(x)$ of an infinitely long beam resting on an elastic foundation and subjected to a load $w(x)$ newtons per meter (Fig. 5), governed by the differential equation

$$EIu'''' + ku = w(x),\qquad(43)$$

FIGURE 5. Beam on elastic foundation.

where E, I, and k are physical constants. There we used the Fourier integral method, whereby $w(x)$ was expanded in a Fourier integral, and $u(x)$ was sought in the form of a Fourier integral. Here, we use the Fourier transform instead.

Taking the Fourier transform of (43) (i.e., multiplying each term by $e^{-i\omega x}dx$ and integrating from $x = -\infty$ to $x = +\infty$), we have

$$F\{EIu'''' + ku\} = F\{w\}. \tag{44}$$

It follows that

$$EIF\{u''''\} + kF\{u\} = F\{w\} \tag{45}$$

by the linearity property (11), and

$$EI(i\omega)^4\hat{u} + k\hat{u} = \hat{w} \tag{46}$$

by (13), assuming that u, u', u'', u''' all tend to zero as $x \to \pm\infty$ and that $\int_{-\infty}^{\infty} |u^{(j)}(x)|dx$ coverges for $j = 0, 1, 2, 3, 4$. Now solving (46) for $\hat{u}$,

$$\hat{u} = \frac{\hat{w}}{EI\omega^4 + k}. \tag{47}$$

To invert (47), let us write the right-hand side in the more suggestive product form

$$\hat{u} = \left(\frac{1}{EI\omega^4 + k}\right)(\hat{w}). \tag{48}$$

The inverse of the product is not the product of the two inverses, but is the Fourier convolution of the two inverses,

$$u(x) = F^{-1}\left\{\frac{1}{EI\omega^4 + k}\right\} * F^{-1}\{\hat{w}\}. \tag{49}$$

From entry 8 in Appendix D, and the linearity of F^{-1}, we obtain

$$F^{-1}\left\{\frac{1}{EI\omega^4 + k}\right\} = \frac{\alpha}{\sqrt{2}k}e^{-\alpha|x|}\sin(\alpha|x| + \frac{\pi}{4}), \tag{50}$$

where $\alpha = [k/(4EI)]^{1/4}$, and of course $F^{-1}\{\hat{w}\} = w(x)$, so (49) gives

$$u(x) = \frac{\alpha}{\sqrt{2}k}\int_{-\infty}^{\infty} e^{-\alpha|x-\xi|}\sin(\alpha|x - \xi| + \frac{\pi}{4})w(\xi)d\xi \tag{51}$$

as the desired solution.

Comment 1 It is always important to check our results. An excellent partial check of a result is provided by any special case for which the exact solution is known. In the present example, such a special case is provided by the case where $w(x) = $ constant $\equiv W$, for then surely the solution $u(x)$ will be a constant too. Specifically, with $w(x) = W$, and u a constant, (43) gives $u(x) = W/k$. If we set $w(\xi) = W$ in (51), and integrate, do we obtain the same result? Yes, but we leave that calculation for the exercises.

In fact, observe that the correctness of (51) for the case where $w(x)$ is a constant is a surprise since some of the assumptions that were built into our solution are violated in that case. For instance, the transform $\hat{w}$ of $w(x) = W$ does not even exist, because the transform integral does not converge. That is,

$$\hat{w} = \int_{-\infty}^{\infty} W e^{-i\omega x} dx = W \lim_{A \to \infty} \int_{-A}^{A} e^{-i\omega x} dx$$
$$= \frac{2W}{\omega} \lim_{A \to \infty} \sin \omega A, \tag{52}$$

FIGURE 6. Response to a point unit load at $x = 0$.

which limit does not exist. Without elaborating, we state that (51) ends up being correct, for this case, even though (44) is not (since $F\{w\} = \hat{w}$ does not exist), thanks to the interchange in the order of integration that underlies the convolution property.* In any case, the moral is that it is often best to proceed formally to a solution. If we can verify that the solution thus obtained does satisfy all of the specified requirements (such as a differential equation and boundary conditions), then there is no need to worry about any lack of rigor in the intermediate steps.

Comment 2 If w is a delta function, $w(x) = \delta(x)$, then $u(x)$ is the response to a unit load at $x = 0$ (Fig. 6).[†] Remember that

$$\int_{-\infty}^{\infty} f(x)\delta(x)dx = f(0) \tag{53}$$

if f is continuous, by the definition of the delta function. Thus, if $w(x) = \delta(x)$ in (51) then we obtain the response

$$u(x) = \frac{\alpha}{\sqrt{2}k} e^{-\alpha|x|} \sin(\alpha|x| + \frac{\pi}{4}), \tag{54}$$

which is plotted in Fig. 6 for the representative case where $\alpha = 1$.

Comment 3 Let us re-express (51) in the compact form

$$u(x) = \int_{-\infty}^{\infty} K(x - \xi)\omega(\xi)d\xi. \tag{55}$$

That is, the output function u is given by the action of an integral operator on the input function w, the operator being multiplication by K followed by integration from $-\infty$ to ∞. We have written $K(x-\xi)$ rather than $K(\xi, x)$ to show that K depends only on the difference between x and ξ. We call K the **kernel** of the integral operator.* Since K is a function of the difference $x - \xi$, we call it a **difference kernel**. The physical significance of K is revealed by the fact that if the loading $w(\xi)$ in (51) is a point unit load $\delta(\xi)$ at the origin, then the resulting deflection $u(x)$ is, according to (53),

$$u(x) = \int_{-\infty}^{\infty} K(x - \xi)\delta(\xi)d\xi = K(x). \tag{56}$$

---

*See our proof of the convolution formula, following (17).
[†] A *unit* load because $\int_{-\infty}^{\infty} w(x)dx = \int_{-\infty}^{\infty} \delta(x)dx = 1$.
*To further illustrate the idea of the kernel of an integral operator, we note that the kernel of the Laplace transform operator is e^{-st}.

FIGURE 7. Incremental deflection du, due to load $w(\xi)d\xi$.

That is, $K(x)$ is the response function (54), the graph of which is shown in Fig. 6 (for $\alpha = 1$), so $K(x-\xi)$ in (55) is the deflection due to a point unit load a ξ. If the load between ξ and $\xi+d\xi$ is $w(\xi)d\xi$ rather than unity (Fig. 7), then the contribution du to the deflection u, due to that bit of loading, is $K(x-\xi)$ scaled by $w(\xi)d\xi$,

$$d(u) = K(x-\xi)\omega(\xi)d\xi. \tag{57}$$

Adding all of these du's gives the integral in (55). Thus, we can now understand (55) as a *superposition* principle, whereby $u(x)$ is the sum, or superposition, of the individual contributions du due to each point load $w(\xi)d\xi$. That superposition result is a consequence of the linearity of (43). ∎

Additional physical ODE (ordinary differential equation) applications, to the deflection of a loaded string and to the steady-state concentration distribution in a stream subjected to an input of pollutant are given to the exercises. We urge you to at least read through those exercises even if you do not work them.

Closure. We have seen that the Fourier transform and the corresponding inversion formula are actually just a restatement of the Fourier integral representation of a nonperiodic function defined on $-\infty < x < \infty$. We have also seen that the Fourier transform methodology is analogous, and in some aspects identical, to the Laplace transform methodology studied in Chapter 5. Given that similarity, the important question arises, as to which of the two transform methods to use in a given ODE application. The general guideline is as follows:

- The **Laplace transform** is tailored to **initial-value problems** on a **semi-infinite interval** $0 < t < \infty$.
- The **Fourier transform** is tailored is tailored to **boundary-value problems** on an **infinite interval** $-\infty < x < \infty$.

The independent variables are usually t (time) and x (linear dimension), but not always. Further, there does exist a "bilateral" Laplace transform defined on an infinite interval, the Laplace transform can sometimes be used for boundary-value problems on finite intervals, and the Fourier transform can (and will, in Section 17.11) be adapted to boundary-value problems on a semi-infinite interval $0 < x < \infty$. But the guideline given about provides the general rule of thumb for selecting one transform or the other.

In closing, we note that to compute the Fourier transform $\hat{f}(\omega)$ of $f(x)$ requires an integration of f over $(-\infty, \infty)$. One can evaluate the integral numerically by sampling the integrand at discrete x points and obtain what is known as the **discrete Fourier transform**. Further, there exist algorithms known collectively as the **fast Fourier transform** (i.e., the **FFT**) that provide a more efficient method of calculating the sum in the discrete Fourier transform. For an introduction to these methods we refer the interested reader to Peter V. O'Neil's *Advanced Engineering Mathematics*, 3rd ed. (Belmont, CA: Wadsworth, 1991).

Computer software. To obtain the Fourier transform of $e^{-5|x|}$, say, using *Maple*, enter

readlib(fourier):

to access the Fourier transform and inverse transform commands. Then enter

fourier(exp($-5 *$ abs(x)), x, w);

and return. The result is

$$10\frac{1}{25 + w^2}$$

which agrees with entry 4 in Appendix D. To invert the latter, enter

$$\text{invfourier}(10/(25 + w^2), \ w, \ x);$$

and return. The result is

$$e^{-5x}\text{Heaviside}(x) + e^{5x}\text{Heaviside}(-x)$$

which does reduce to $e^{-5|x|}$.

17.10 Problems

1. Using (6a), derive the result

$$F\{H(x)e^{-ax}\} = \frac{1}{a + i\omega}$$

if Re $a > 0$. (This case was worked in Example 2, but there a was considered to be real. Here, allow for a to be complex, with Re $a > 0$.)

2. Using (6a), derive the result

$$F\{H(-x)e^{ax}\} = \frac{1}{a - i\omega}$$

if Re $a > 0$.

3. Using (6a), derive the result

$$F\{e^{-a|x|}\} = \frac{2a}{\omega^2 + a^2}$$

if $a > 0$.

4. Given $\hat{f}(\omega)$, use (6b) to evaluate the inverse, $f(x)$.

(a) $e^{-a|\omega|}$ $(a > 0)$
(b) $H(\omega + a) - H(\omega - a)$ $(a > 0)$
(c) $[H(\omega) - H(\omega - 1)]\omega$
(d) $H(\omega)e^{-a\omega}$ (Re $a > 0$)
(e) $[H(\omega + 1) - H(\omega - 1)]|\omega|$
(f) $\delta(\omega - a)$

5. Derive the following entry in Appendix D, by showing that the transform of the function given in the f column is the result given in the $\hat{f}$ column.

(a) Entry 10   (b) Entry 11
(c) Entry 12   (d) Entry 13
(e) Entry 14   (f) Entry 15

(a) Entry 17, by formally differentiating both sides of

$$\hat{f}(\omega) = \int_{-\infty}^{\infty} f(x)e^{-i\omega x} dx$$

a sufficient number of times, with respect of ω

(b) Entry 19, using integration by parts

6. Evaluate the following using Appendix D. You may need to use more than one entry. Cite, by number, any entries that you use.

(a) $F\{4x^2 e^{-3|x|}\}$ (b) $F\{xe^{-x^2}\}$

(c) $F\left\{\dfrac{\cos 3x}{x^2 + 2}\right\}$ (d) $F\left\{\dfrac{\sin 2x}{4x^2 + 3}\right\}$

(e) $F\left\{\dfrac{3}{2x^2 + 1} - 5e^{-|x|}\right\}$ (f) $F\left\{e^{-|x|} + e^{-3|x+2|}\right\}$

(g) $F^{-1}\left\{\dfrac{4\sin \omega}{\omega} - \dfrac{1}{\sqrt{|\omega|}}\right\}$ (h) $F^{-1}\left\{e^{-2|\omega - 3|}\right\}$

(i) $F^{-1}\left\{\dfrac{9}{2\omega + i}\right\}$ (j) $F^{-1}\left\{e^{-\omega^2 + 4\omega}\right\}$

(k) $F^{-1}\left\{e^{-|\omega|}\cos \omega\right\}$ (l) $F^{-1}\left\{\omega e^{-3\omega^2}\right\}$

(m) $F^{-1}\left\{\dfrac{1}{\omega^2 + i\omega + 2}\right\}$ (n) $F^{-1}\left\{\dfrac{\omega}{\omega^2 + 1}\right\}$

7. (a)–(n) Use computer software to obtain (if possible) the transform or inverse transform called for in the corresponding part of Exercise 6.

8. We claimed, in Comment 1 in Example 8, that if $w(x) = W$ then the integral on the right-hand side of (51) is W/k. Verify that claim by evaluating the integral. HINT: Break the integral into two parts, one from $-\infty$ to x and the other from x to ∞, then make a suitable change of variables in each.

9. (*Preservation of evenness and oddness*)

(a) Show that $f(x)$ is an even function of x if and only if $\hat{f}(\omega)$ is an even function of ω.

(b) Show that $f(x)$ is an odd function of x if and only if $\hat{f}(\omega)$ is an odd function of ω.

10. (*Extension of transform tables*) It follows from the results in Exercise 9 that the transform of the even and odd parts of $f(x)$ are the even and odd parts of $\hat{f}(\omega)$, respectively. This result can be used to obtain more information from a given transform table. For example, consider entry 2 in Appendix D. Breaking f and $\hat{f}$ into even and odd parts, show that

$$F\left\{e^{-a|x|}\right\} = \frac{2a}{\omega^2 + a^2} \qquad (10.1)$$

and

$$F\left\{(\text{sgn } x)e^{-a|x|}\right\} = -\frac{2i\omega}{\omega^2 + a^2}, \qquad (10.2)$$

where

$$\text{sgn } x \equiv \begin{cases} +1, & x > 0 \\ -1, & x < 0, \end{cases} \qquad (10.3)$$

which is read as "sign of x." Of these two results, observe that (10.1) is identical to entry 4, and that (10.2) is not contained in Appendix D.

11. (*Extension of transform tables*) Another idea that enables us to extend a given Fourier transform table is that of reciprocity, namely the reciprocity relations

$$F\{\hat{f}(x)\} = 2\pi f(-\omega) \qquad (11.1)$$

and

$$F^{-1}\{f(-\omega)\} = \frac{\hat{f}(x)}{2\pi}. \qquad (11.2)$$

(a) Derive the relations (11.1) and (11.2).

(b) To illustrate, use (11.1) and entry 4, in Appendix D, to show that

$$F\left\{\frac{2a}{x^2 + a^2}\right\} = 2\pi e^{-a|\omega|}, \qquad (a > 0)$$

or, equivalently,

$$F\left\{\frac{1}{x^2 + a^2}\right\} = \frac{\pi}{a}e^{-a|\omega|}, \qquad (a > 0)$$

(In this case the result does not extend our table since it already appears as Entry 1.)

(c) Use (11.1) and entry 9 to show that

$$F\left\{\frac{\sin ax}{x}\right\} = \pi[H(\omega + a) - H(\omega - a)]. \quad (a > 0)$$

(d) Use (11.1) and entry 3 to show that

$$F\left\{\frac{1}{a - ix}\right\} = 2\pi H(\omega)e^{-a\omega}. \quad (\text{Re } a > 0)$$

12. (*Deflection of loaded string*) Related to the problem of a beam on an elastic foundation is the analogous problem for a flexible string. Imagine a string (of negligible mass per unit length) stretched along the x axis, over $-\infty < x < \infty$, by a tension T newtons, and let $w(x)$ be an applied load distribution (newtons/meter), as sketched in the figure. If the displacement $u(x)$ of the string is resisted by a distributed spring of stiffness k (newtons per meter per meter), and the slope $u'(x)$ is sufficiently small over $-\infty < x < \infty$, then $u(x)$ is accurately governed by the differential equation $Tu'' - ku = -w$, or,

$$u'' - \alpha^2 u = -f(x), \quad (-\infty < x < \infty) \qquad (12.1)$$

where $\alpha^2 = k/T$ and $f(x) = w(x)/T$. (Here we consider the static deflection. In Chapter 20 we will derive the governing differential equation for the not-necessarily-static case.) Assume that $w(x)$ is sufficiently localized for $u(x)$ to satisfy the boundary conditions

$$u \to 0 \quad \text{and} \quad u' \to 0 \qquad (12.2)$$

as $x \to \pm\infty$, as well.

(a) Solving (12.1) and (12.2) using a Fourier transform, derive the solution

$$u(x) = \frac{1}{2\alpha} \int_{-\infty}^{\infty} e^{-\alpha|x - \xi|} f(\xi)d\xi. \qquad (12.3)$$

(b) Evaluate $u(x)$ from (12.3) for the case where $f(x)$ is a point unit load at the origin, $f(x) = \delta(x)$, and sketch the graph of u.

(c) Verify, by formally using the Leibniz rule, that (12.3) satisfies the differential equation (12.1).

13. (*Pollution in river*) Suppose that a manufacturing plant discharges a certain pollutant into an initially clear river at the rate Q grams/second. We wish to determine the resulting steady-state distribution of pollutant in the river, i.e., its concentration c (grams/meter^3). Measure x along the river, positive downstream, with origin at the plant site, as shown in the figure. The river flows with velocity U (meters/second), and has a cross-sectional area A, both of which, for simplicity, we assume to be constant. Also for simplicity, suppose that c is a function of x only; i.e, it is a constant over each cross section of the stream. This is evidently a poor approximation near the plant, where we expect appreciable across-stream and vertical variations in c, but it should suffice if we are concerned mostly with the concentration variation far upstream and downstream (for $|x|$ greater than several river widths, say).

Then it can be shown that $c(x)$ is governed by the differential equation

$$kc'' - Uc' - \beta c = -\frac{Q}{A}\delta(x), \qquad (13.1)$$

where k (meters^2/second) is a diffusion constant, β (grams per second per gram) is a chemical decay constant, and $\delta(x)$ is a delta function. [Physically, (13.1) expresses a mass balance between the *input* $Q\delta(x)/A$, the transport of pollutant by *diffusion*, kc'', the transport of pollutant by *convection* with the moving stream, Uc', and by disappearance through *chemical decay*, βc.]

(a) Applying the Fourier transform to (13.1), show that

$$c(x) = F^{-1}\left\{ \frac{Q}{A}\frac{1}{k\omega^2 + iU\omega + \beta} \right\}. \qquad (13.2)$$

(b) Expanding $1/(k\omega^2 + iU\omega + \beta)$ in partial fractions, and then using Appendix D, show that (13.2) gives

$$c(x) = \begin{cases} c_0 e^{-\Omega_- x}, & x < 0 \\ c_0 e^{-\Omega_+ x}, & x > 0 \end{cases} \qquad (13.3)$$

where

$$c_0 = \frac{Q}{A\sqrt{U^2 + 4k\beta}},$$

$$\Omega_\pm = \frac{1}{2k}(\pm\sqrt{U^2 + 4k\beta} - U).$$

(c) Sketch the graph of $c(x)$ and state the qualitative effect of increasing β.

17.11 Fourier Cosine and Sine Transforms, and Passage from Fourier Integral to Laplace Transform (Optional)

Cosine and sine transforms.

Recall from Section 17.4 that if a problem is defined on a finite interval, say $0 < x < L$, then the concepts of periodicity and Fourier series are not directly applicable. However, by fictitiously extending both the domain and the functions involved to the infinite interval $-\infty < x < \infty$, so that the extended functions are periodic, we are able to use Fourier series representations of those functions. Depending upon the symmetries and/or antisymmetries about $x = 0$ and $x = L$, we obtain half- or quarter-range cosine or sine expansions.

Similarly, we sometimes encounter problems defined on a semi-infinite interval, say $0 < x < \infty$. Fictitiously extending both the domain and the functions involved, to the infinite interval $-\infty < x < \infty$, we will be able to use Fourier integral representations of those functions. Specifically, given a function f defined on $0 < x < \infty$ (such as the one shown in Fig. 1a), we shall be interested in two particular extensions, one that is even and one that is odd, as indicated in Figs. 1b and 1c, respectively.

Denoting the extended functions as f_{ext}, consider first the even extension (Fig. 1b). Then the Fourier transform of f_{ext} is

FIGURE 1. Even and odd extensions of f.

$$\widehat{f_{\text{ext}}}(\omega) = \int_{-\infty}^{\infty} f_{\text{ext}}(x)e^{-i\omega x}dx$$

$$= \int_{-\infty}^{\infty} f_{\text{ext}}(x)(\cos\omega x - i\sin\omega x)dx = 2\int_{0}^{\infty} f_{\text{ext}}(x)\cos\omega x\, dx, \qquad (1a)$$

where the last equality holds because $f_{ext}(x)\cos\omega x$ is an even function of x and $f_{ext}\sin\omega(x)$ is odd, and the inversion formula gives

$$
\begin{aligned}
f_{ext}(x) &= \frac{1}{2\pi}\int_{-\infty}^{\infty}\widehat{f_{ext}}(\omega)e^{iwx}\,dw \\
&= \frac{1}{2\pi}\int_{-\infty}^{\infty}\widehat{f_{ext}}(\omega)(\cos wx + i\sin wx)\,dw \\
&= \frac{2}{2\pi}\int_{0}^{\infty}\widehat{f_{ext}}(\omega)\cos wx\,dw,
\end{aligned}
\tag{1b}
$$

where the last equality holds because $\widehat{f_{ext}}(\omega)$ is an even function of ω [as can be seen from (1a)] and $\sin\omega x$ is an odd function of ω, so that the term $\widehat{f_{ext}}(\omega)\sin\omega x$ in the integrand is odd. Putting (1a) into (1b) gives the single statement

$$
f_{ext}(x) = \int_{0}^{\infty}\left\{\frac{2}{\pi}\int_{0}^{\infty}f_{ext}(\xi)\cos\omega\xi\,d\xi\right\}\cos\omega x\,d\omega. \quad (-\infty < x < \infty) \tag{2}
$$

Since (2) holds on $-\infty < x < \infty$, it also holds on the original interval $0 < x < \infty$. For $0 < x < \infty$ we can drop the subscripted "ext" on the left-hand side, because on that interval $f_{ext}(x) = f(x)$. Further, we can drop the "ext" on the right-hand side because the ξ integral is on $0 < x < \infty$, not $-\infty < x < \infty$. Then (2) becomes

$$
f(x) = \frac{2}{\pi}\int_{0}^{\infty}\left\{\int_{0}^{\infty}f(\xi)\cos\omega\xi\,d\xi\right\}\cos\omega x\,d\omega, \quad (0 < x < \infty) \tag{3}
$$

which can be re-expressed, equivalently, as the **Fourier cosine transform**

$$
\boxed{F_C\{f(x)\} = \widehat{f}_C(\omega) = \int_{0}^{\infty}f(x)\cos\omega x\,dx} \tag{4a}
$$

and its inverse

$$
\boxed{F_C^{-1}\{\widehat{f}_S(\omega)\} = f(x) = \frac{2}{\pi}\int_{0}^{\infty}\widehat{f}_C(\omega)\sin\omega x\,d\omega,} \tag{4b}
$$

on $0 < x < \infty$.

Similarly, an odd extension of f gives the **Fourier sine transform**

$$
\boxed{F_S\{f(x)\} = \widehat{f}_S(\omega) = \int_{0}^{\infty}f(x)\sin\omega x\,dx} \tag{5a}
$$

and its inverse

$$
\boxed{F_S^{-1}\{\widehat{f}_S(\omega)\} = f(x) = \frac{2}{\pi}\int_{0}^{\infty}\widehat{f}S(\omega)\sin\omega x\,d\omega,} \tag{5b}
$$

on $0 < x < \infty$ (Exercise 1). Sufficient conditions on f, for (4) and (5) to hold, are that f and f' be piecewise continuous on $0 \le x < \infty$, and that $\int_{0}^{\infty}|f(x)|dx$ converge (i.e., that f be *absolutely integrable* on $0 < x < \infty$).

Next, we could derive that various properties of the cosine and sine transforms, that are analogous to those derived for the Fourier transforms. However, for brevity let it suffice to state that both the cosine and sine transforms, and their inverses, are linear, and that the transforms of the derivative f' are

$$\boxed{\begin{aligned} F_C\{f'(x)\} &= \omega \hat{f}_S(w) - f(0), \\ F_S\{f'(x)\} &= -\omega \hat{f}_C(w), \end{aligned}} \qquad (6a, b)$$

if we assume additionally that $f(x) \to 0$ as $x \to \infty$. Let us derive (6a) and leave (6b) for the exercises. Integrating by parts,

$$\begin{aligned} F_C\{f'(x)\} &= \int_0^\infty f'(x) \cos \omega x \, dx \\ &= [f(x) \cos \omega x]\Big|_0^\infty + \omega \int_0^\infty f(x) \sin \omega x \, d\omega \\ &= 0 - f(0) + \omega \hat{f}_S(\omega). \end{aligned} \qquad (7)$$

The transforms of higher-order derivatives can be obtained by repeated use of (6). For instrnace, replacing the function f by the function f' in (6) gives

$$F_C\{f''(x)\} = \omega F_S\{f'(x)\} - f'(0) = \omega[-\omega \hat{f}_C(\omega)] - f'(0) \qquad (8a)$$

and

$$F_S\{f''(x)\} = -\omega F_C\{f'(x)\} = -\omega[-\omega \hat{f}_S(\omega) - f'(0)], \qquad (8b)$$

so

$$\boxed{\begin{aligned} F_C\{f''(x)\} &= -w^2 \hat{f}_C(\omega) - f'(0), \\ F_S\{f''(x)\} &= -w^2 \hat{f}_S(\omega) - w f(0), \end{aligned}} \qquad (9a, b)$$

if f and f' tend to zero as $x \to \infty$. Similarly for higher-order derivatives. For convolution properties, see Exercise 10 and Appendix E.

Short Fourier cosine and sine transform tables are given in Appendix E.

Example 1 Consider the boundary-value problem

$$u'' - 9u = 50e^{-2x}, \quad (0 < x < \infty) \qquad (10a)$$

$$u(0) = u_0, \quad u(\infty) \text{ bounded.} \qquad (10b)$$

To solve (10) using an integral transform we need to choose among the Laplace, Fourier cosine, and Fourier sine transforms, all of these being candidates because they are semi-infinite transforms; that is, they apply when the domain is semi-infinite ($0 < x < \infty$ in this case). The Laplace transform will be inconvenient at best, because it is tailored to initial value problems whereas (10) is of boundary-value type. In choosing between the Fourier cosine and sine transforms, they key is in (9). Taking a cosine transform of (10a) we will, according to (9a), need to know $u'(0)$, yet the latter is not prescribed; taking a sine transform of (10a) we will, according to (9a), need to know $u(0)$, and the latter is prescribed.

Thus, take the Fourier sine transform of (10a), using the linearity of the transform property (9b), and entry $1S$ in Appendix E:

$$F_S\{u'' - 9u\} = F_S\{50e^{-2x}\}, \tag{11a}$$

$$F_S\{u''\} - 9F_S\{u\} = 50F_S\{e^{-2x}\}, \tag{11b}$$

$$-\omega^2 \hat{u}_s + \omega u_0 - 9\hat{u}_S = 50\frac{\omega}{\omega^2 + 4}. \tag{11c}$$

Solving this linear algebraic equation for $\hat{u}_S$ gives

$$\hat{u}S(\omega) = u_0 \frac{\omega}{\omega^2 + 9} - 50\frac{\omega}{(\omega^2 + 4)(\omega^2 + 9)}. \tag{12}$$

By partial fractions,

$$\frac{1}{(\omega^2 + 4)(\omega^2 + 9)} = \frac{1}{5}\frac{1}{(\omega^2 + 4)} - \frac{1}{5}\frac{1}{(\omega^2 + 9)}, \tag{13}$$

so

$$\hat{u}_S(\omega) = (u_0 + 10)\frac{\omega}{\omega^2 + 9} - 10\frac{\omega}{(w^2 + 4)}. \tag{14}$$

Then, using the linearity of the inverse transform and entry $1S$, gives

$$\begin{aligned}
u(x) &= F_S^{-1}\left\{(u_0 + 10)\frac{\omega}{\omega^2 + 9} - 10\frac{\omega}{\omega^2 + 4}\right\} \\
&= (u_0 + 10)F_S^{-1}\left\{\frac{\omega}{\omega^2 + 9}\right\} - 10F_S^{-1}\left\{\frac{\omega}{\omega^2 + 4}\right\} \\
&= (u_0 + 10)e^{-3x} - 10e^{-2x}. \tag{15}
\end{aligned}$$

Comment 1   Note that we used property (9b) tentatively since (9b) presupposes that both $u(x) \to 0$ and $u'(x) \to 0$ as $x \to \infty$. Now that $u(x)$ is in hand, in (15), we can check, and we see that these conditions are met. Or, more directly, we can simply verify that (15) does satisfy (10a) and (10b).

Comment 2   If $u'(0)$ were prescribed, in (10b), in place of $u(0)$, then we would use the Fourier cosine transform instead.   ∎

Passage from Fourier integral to Laplace transform

We have seen that the Fourier transform is merely a restatement of the Fourier integral, the Fourier integral is a limiting case of the Fourier series of a periodic function (as the period tends to infinity), and the Fourier series is as an eigenfunction expansion corresponding to a periodic Sturm–Liouville problem. On the other hand, the Laplace transform and its inversion formula were given in Chapter 5 without derivation and may seem unrelated to these Fourier methods. In this final subsection we will show that the Laplace transform and its inverse can be derived from the Fourier integral!

We begin with the Fourier integral in the complex exponential form given by equation (3) in Section 17.10.

$$F(t) = \frac{1}{2\pi}\int_{-\infty}^{\infty}\left\{\int_{-\infty}^{\infty} F(\tau)e^{-i\omega t}d\tau\right\}e^{-i\omega t}\,d\omega, \quad (-\infty < t < \infty) \tag{16}$$

where we use t in place of x because we will end up with the Laplace transform, in which the independent variable is traditionally taken to be t (because in applications it usually correcponds to the time). Further, it will be convenient to use F in place of f. In (16), let

$$F(t) = \begin{Bmatrix} e^{-\gamma t}f(t), & t > 0 \\ 0, & t < 0, \end{Bmatrix} \qquad (17)$$

where γ is a real constant which is sufficiently positive so that $e^{-\gamma t}$"clobbers" $f(t)$ as $t \to \infty$. Specifically, suppose that f is of exponential order (defined in section 5.2) as $t \to \infty$. Then a sufficiently positive γ can indeed be found such that $e^{-\gamma t}f(t)$ dies out exponentially fast as $t \to \infty$. Of course, whereas $e^{-\gamma t}$ helps as $t \to +\infty$, it hurts as $t \to -\infty$. Thus, we simply "shut off F" for $t < 0$ by defining it to be zero for $t < 0$, in (17). The resulting F easily satisfies the condition $\int_{-\infty}^{\infty}|F(t)|dt < \infty$ contained in the Fourier integral theorem.

Putting (17) into (16) gives

$$H(t)e^{-\gamma t}f(t) = \frac{1}{2\pi} = \int_{-\infty}^{\infty}\left\{\int_{0}^{\infty}e^{-\gamma \tau}f(\tau)e^{-i\omega t}d\tau\right\}e^{i\omega t}d\omega \qquad (18)$$

where H is the Heaviside function. Thus,

$$H(t)f(t) = \frac{1}{2\pi} = \int_{-\infty}^{\infty}\left\{\int_{0}^{\infty}e^{(-\gamma+i\omega)\tau}f(\tau)dt\right\}e^{(\gamma+i\omega)t}d\omega \qquad (19)$$

which form suggests changing variables from ω to s according to

$$s = \gamma + iw. \qquad (20)$$

Thus,

$$H(t)f(t) = \frac{1}{2\pi i} = \int_{\gamma-i\infty}^{\gamma+i\infty}\left\{\int_{0}^{\infty}e^{-s\tau}f(\tau)dt\right\}e^{st}ds, \qquad (21)$$

where $\int_{\gamma-i\infty}^{\gamma+i\infty}$ denotes an integration along a vertical line in a complex s plane (Fig. 2). If we define the **Laplace transform** of f as

$$\boxed{L\{f(t)\} = \overline{f}(s) = \int_{0}^{\infty}f(t)e^{-st}dt,} \qquad (22)$$

where we have changed the dummy integration variable from τ to t, then (21) gives the inversion formula as

$$\boxed{L^{-1}\{\overline{f}(s)\} = H(t)f(t) = \frac{1}{2\pi i}\int_{\gamma-i\infty}^{\gamma+i\infty}\overline{f}(s)e^{st}ds.} \qquad (23)$$

Normally we are interested only in $0 < t < \infty$, so we can replace $H(t)$ by 1 in (23). However, for completeness we observe that while the integral in (23) gives $f(t)$ for $t > 0$, it gives 0 for $t < 0$, which result is, after all, in accordance with our definition $F(t) = 0$ for $t < 0$, in (17).

Closure In this section we have combined two topics, each being too brief to justify a full section. First we introduced the Fourier cosine and sine transforms, for problems defined on the semi-infinite interval $0 < x < \infty$, which results are analogous to the half-range cosine and sine Fourier series. The Laplace transform is also a semi-infinite transform, but it is tailored to *initial-value* problems whereas the Fourier cosine and sine transforms are tailored to *boundary-value* problems, because

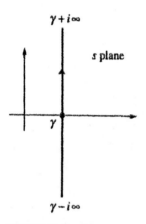

$\gamma + i\infty$

s plane

γ

$\gamma - i\infty$

FIGURE 2. Line of integration in s plane.

$L\{f(n)(t)\}$ involves values of $f, f', \ldots, f^{(n-1)}$ at $t = 0$, whereas $F_C\{f^{(n)}(x)\}$ and $F_S\{f^{(n)}(x)\}$ involve values both at $x = 0$ and at $x = \infty$. Whether to use a cosine transform or a sine transform, in solving a differential equation boundary-value problem, depends (as we saw in Example 1) on the type of boundary conditions prescribed at $x = 0$.

Finally, we used the complex exponential form of the Fourier integral to derive the Laplace transform and its inversion formula. Normally, in using the Laplace transform, we have the t domain of interest is $t > 0$. However, we noted that if one *were* to obtain an inverse Laplace transform by evaluating the inversion integral in (23), for $t < 0$, then one would inevitably find that the inverse function is identically zero for $t < 0$.

17.11 Problems

1. Derive the formulas (5a) and (5b) for the Fourier sine transform and its inverse, respectively
2. Derive (6b), that $F_S\{f'(x)\} = \omega \hat{f}_C(\omega)$.
3. Derive these results:

   (a) $F_C\{f''''(x)\} = \omega^4 \hat{f}_C(\omega) + \omega^2 f'(0) - f'''(0)$
   (b) $F_S\{f''''(x)\} = \omega^4 \hat{f}_S(\omega) - \omega^3 f(0) + \omega f''(0)$ if $f(x), f'(x), f''(x)$, and $f'''(x)$ all tend to zero as $x \to \infty$.

4. Given the rectangular pulse $f(x) = 50[1 - H(x-4)]$, evaluate $\hat{f}_C(\omega)$ and $\hat{f}_S(\omega)$.
5. Use computer software, such as the int command on *Maple*, to evaluate each, where $a > 0$. Show that your result agrees with the corresponding result obtained from Appendix E.

   (a) $F_C\{e^{-ax}\}$ (b) $F_S\{e^{-ax}\}$
   (c) $F_C\{xe^{-ax}\}$ (d) $F_S\{xe^{-ax}\}$
   (e) $F_C\{x^2 e^{-ax}\}$ (f) $F_S\{x^2 e^{-ax}\}$

   NOTE: Be careful, in using tables or software, to be clear on the author's definition of the transform. For instance, in contrast with our definitions (4) and (5) of the Fourier cosine and sine transforms, some authors use the more symmetric versions

   $$F_C\{f(x)\} = \sqrt{\frac{2}{\pi}} \int_0^\infty f(x) \cos \omega x \, dx \qquad (5.1)$$

   $$F_C^{-1}\{\hat{f}_C(\omega)\} = \sqrt{\frac{2}{\pi}} \int_0^\infty \hat{f}_C(\omega) \cos \omega x \, d\omega \qquad (5.2)$$

   and

   $$F_S\{f(x)\} = \sqrt{\frac{2}{\pi}} \int_0^\infty f(x) \sin \omega x \, dx \qquad (5.3)$$

   $$F_S^{-1}\{\hat{f}S(\omega)\} = \sqrt{\frac{2}{\pi}} \int_0^\infty \hat{f}_S(\omega) \sin \omega x \, d\omega. \qquad (5.4)$$

6. In Example 1 we avoided the Laplace transform because (10) is of boundary-value type, not of initial-value type. Show that the Laplace transform can be used nevertheless, and does give the solution (15), though not as conveniently. HINT: When you take the transform of u'' you will be faced with a $u'(0)$ term, which is not prescribed in (10b). Thus, call that quantity C, say, and evaluate it by imposing on your solution the condition that $u(\infty)$ be bounded, at the end.

7. We used a sine transform to solve Example 1. Try to solve (10) using a cosine transform instead, and explain why that methods does not work.

8. Modify (10) by changing $u(0) = u_0$ to $u'(0) = u'_0$, and solve by a cosine or sine transform.

9. Solve, using a cosine or sine tranform.

   (a) $u'' - 9u = 50e^{-3x}$, $(0 < x < \infty)$
   $u(0) = 0$, $u(\infty)$ bounded

   (b) $u'' - 9u = 50e^{-3x}$, $(0 < x < \infty)$
   $u'(0) = 0$, $u(\infty)$ bounded

10. (*Convolution Theorem*) As for the Fourier and Laplace transforms there are convolution theorems for the Fourier cosine and sine transforms, and these are given in Appendix E.

    (a) Prove the Fourier cosine transform convolution theorem (entry 7C), either by showing that the transform of the given integral is $\hat{f}_C(\omega)\hat{g}_S(\omega)$ or by showing that the inverse of $\hat{f}_C(\omega)\hat{g}_S(\omega)$ is the given integral.

    (b) Prove the Fourier sine transform convolution theorem (entry 7S).

    (c) Verify entry 7C for the case where $f(x) = e^{-x}$ and $g(x) = e^{-3x}$.

    (d) Verify entry 7S for the case where $f(x) = e^{-x}$ and $g(x) = e^{-3x}$.

APPENDIX D

Table of Fourier Transforms

$f(x)$	$\hat{f}(\omega) = \int_{-\infty}^{\infty} f(x)e^{-i\omega x}dx$
1. $\dfrac{1}{x^2 + a^2}$ $(a > 0)$	$\dfrac{\pi}{a}e^{-a|\omega|}$
2. $H(x)e^{-ax}$ $(\text{Re}\,a > 0)$	$\dfrac{1}{a + i\omega}$
3. $H(-x)e^{ax}$ $(\text{Re}\,a > 0)$	$\dfrac{1}{a - i\omega}$
4. $e^{-a|x|}$ $(a > 0)$	$\dfrac{2a}{\omega^2 + a^2}$
5. e^{-x^2}	$\sqrt{\pi}e^{-\omega^2/4}$
6. $\dfrac{1}{2a\sqrt{\pi}}e^{-x^2/(2a)^2}$ $(a > 0)$	$e^{-a^2\omega^2}$
7. $\dfrac{1}{\sqrt{|x|}}$	$\sqrt{\dfrac{2\pi}{|\omega|}}$
8. $e^{-a|x|/\sqrt{2}}\sin\left(\dfrac{a}{\sqrt{2}}|x| + \dfrac{\pi}{4}\right)$ $(a > 0)$	$\dfrac{2a^3}{\omega^4 + a^4}$
9. $H(x + a) - H(x - a)$	$\dfrac{2\sin\omega a}{\omega}$
10. $\delta(x - a)$	$e^{-i\omega a}$
11. $f(ax + b)$ $(a > 0)$	$\dfrac{1}{a}e^{ib\omega/a}\hat{f}\left(\dfrac{\omega}{a}\right)$
12. $\dfrac{1}{a}e^{-ibx/a}f\left(\dfrac{x}{a}\right)$ $(a > 0,\ b\ \text{real})$	$\hat{f}(a\omega + b)$
13. $f(ax)\cos cx$ $(a > 0,\ c\ \text{real})$	$\dfrac{1}{2a}\left[\hat{f}\left(\dfrac{\omega - c}{a}\right) + \hat{f}\left(\dfrac{\omega + c}{a}\right)\right]$
14. $f(ax)\sin cx$ $(a > 0,\ c\ \text{real})$	$\dfrac{1}{2ai}\left[\hat{f}\left(\dfrac{\omega - c}{a}\right) - \hat{f}\left(\dfrac{\omega + c}{a}\right)\right]$
15. $f(x + c) + f(x - c)$ $(c\ \text{real})$	$2\hat{f}(\omega)\cos\omega c$
16. $f(x + c) - f(x - c)$ $(c\ \text{real})$	$2i\hat{f}(\omega)\sin\omega c$
17. $x^n f(x)$ $(n = 1, 2, \ldots)$	$i^n\dfrac{d^n}{d\omega^n}\hat{f}(\omega)$

Linearity of transform and inverse:

| 18. $\alpha f(x) + \beta g(x)$ | $\alpha\hat{f}(\omega) + \beta\hat{g}(\omega)$ |

$f(x)$	$\hat{f}(\omega) = \int_{-\infty}^{\infty} f(x)e^{-i\omega x}\,dx$

Transform of derivative:

19. $f^{(n)}(x)$ $(i\omega)^n \hat{f}(\omega)$

Transform of integral:

20. $f(x) = \int_{-\infty}^{x} g(\xi)\,d\xi,$ $\hat{f}(\omega) = \dfrac{1}{i\omega}\hat{g}(\omega)$

         where $f(x) \to 0$ as $x \to \infty$

Fourier convolution theorem:

21. $(f * g)(x) = \int_{-\infty}^{\infty} f(x - \xi)g(\xi)\,d\xi$ $\hat{f}(\omega)\hat{g}(\omega)$

APPENDIX E

Table of Fourier Cosine and Sine Transforms

$f(x)$	$\hat{f}c(\omega) = \int_0^\infty f(x)\cos\omega x\,dx$
1C. e^{-ax} $(a > 0)$	$\dfrac{a}{\omega^2 + a^2}$
2C. $x^n e^{-ax}$ $(a > 0)$	$\dfrac{n!\,\text{Re}(a + i\omega)^{n+1}}{(\omega^2 + a^2)^{n+1}}$ (Re = real part)
3C. $\dfrac{1}{x^2 + a^2}$ $(a > 0)$	$\dfrac{\pi}{2a}e^{-a\omega}$

Linearity of transform and inverse:

4C. $\alpha f(x) + \beta g(x)$	$\alpha \hat{f}c(\omega) + \beta \hat{g}c(\omega)$

Transform of derivative:

5C. $f'(x)$	$\omega \hat{f}s(\omega) - f(0)$
6C. $f''(x)$	$-\omega^2 \hat{f}c(\omega) - f'(0)$

Convolution theorem:

7C. $\dfrac{1}{2}\int_0^\infty [f(\lvert x - \xi \rvert) + f(x + \xi)]g(\xi)d\xi$	$\hat{f}c(\omega)\hat{g}c(\omega)$

$f(x)$	$\hat{f}s(\omega) = \int_0^\infty f(x)\sin\omega x\,dx$
1S. e^{-ax} $(a > 0)$	$\dfrac{\omega}{\omega^2 + a^2}$
2S. $x^n e^{-ax}$ $(a > 0)$	$\dfrac{n!\,\text{Im}(a + i\omega)^{n+1}}{(\omega^2 + a^2)^{n+1}}$ (Im = imaginary part)
3S. $\dfrac{x}{x^2 + a^2}$ $(a > 0)$	$\dfrac{\pi}{2}e^{-a\omega}$

Linearity of transform and inverse:

4S. $\alpha f(x) + \beta g(x)$	$\alpha \hat{f}s(\omega) + \beta \hat{g}s(\omega)$

Transform of derivative:

5S. $f'(x)$	$-\omega \hat{f}c(\omega)$
6S. $f''(x)$	$-\omega^2 \hat{f}s(\omega) + \omega f(0)$

Convolution theorem:

7S. $\dfrac{1}{2}\int_0^\infty [f(\lvert x - \xi \rvert) - f(x + \xi)]g(\xi)d\xi$	$\hat{f}c(\omega)\hat{g}s(\omega)$

ANSWERS TO SELECTED PROBLEMS

Section 17.9

2. (a) $f(x) = (100/\pi)\int_0^\infty [\sin 2\omega \cos \omega x + (1 - \cos 2\omega)\sin \omega x]d\omega/\omega$ for all x expect $x = 0$ and $x = 2$: $f(0) = f(2) = 100$ but the Fourier integral of f converges to the average value 50. As a check, application of the *Maple* int command gives these values for the Fourier integral, integrating from 0 to 5000: $200 Si(5000)/\pi$ at $x = 1$ and $-100[Si(10,000) - Si(20,000)]/\pi$ at $x = 4$. Following the int command with evalf(") evaluates these quantities as 99.96 and -0.0043, respectively. (d) $f(x) = (1/\pi)\int_0^\infty [(\cos 5\omega + 5\omega \sin 5\omega - 1)\cos \omega x + (5\omega \cos 5\omega - \sin 5\omega)\sin \omega x]d\omega/\omega^2$ for all x except $x = -5$: $f(-5) = 0$ but the Fourier integral of f converges to 2.5.

Section 17.10

4. (a) $f(x) = a/[\pi(a^2 + x^2)]$ (b) $f(x) = \sin ax/(\pi x)$ **6.** (a) $F\{4x^2 e^{-3|x|}\} = 4i^2 \frac{d^2}{d\omega^2} F\{e^{-3|x|}\}$ (entry 17)

$= -4\frac{d^2}{d\omega^2}\left(\frac{6}{\omega^2+9}\right)$ (entry 4) $= 48\left[\frac{1}{(\omega^2+9)^2} - \frac{4\omega^2}{(\omega^2+9)^3}\right]$ (c) With $c = 3, a = 1, f(x) = 1/(x^2 + 2)$ in entry 13, and

$\hat{f} = (\pi/\sqrt{2})\exp(-\sqrt{2}|\omega|)$, we have $F\left\{\frac{\cos 3x}{x^2+2}\right\} = \frac{1}{2}[\hat{f}(\omega-3) + \hat{f}(\omega+3)] = \frac{\pi}{2\sqrt{2}}(e^{-\sqrt{2}|\omega-3|} + e^{-\sqrt{2}|\omega+3|})$ (e) $F\left\{\frac{3}{2x^2+1} - 5e^{-|x|}\right\}$

$= \frac{3}{2}F\left\{\frac{1}{x^2+1/2}\right\} - 5F\left\{e^{-|x|}\right\}$ (entry 18) $= \frac{3}{2}\pi\sqrt{2}e^{-|\omega|/\sqrt{2}} - 5\frac{2}{\omega^2+1}$ (entries 1, 4) $= \frac{3\pi}{\sqrt{2}}e^{-|\omega|/\sqrt{2}} - \frac{10}{\omega^2+1}$ (g) $F^{-1}\left\{\frac{4\sin\omega}{\omega} - \frac{1}{\sqrt{|\omega|}}\right\}$

$= 2F^{-1}\left\{\frac{2\sin\omega}{\omega}\right\} - \frac{1}{\sqrt{2\pi}}F^{-1}\left\{\sqrt{\frac{2\pi}{|\omega|}}\right\}$ (entry 18) $= 2[H(x+1) - H(x-1)] - \frac{1}{\sqrt{2\pi|x|}}$ (entries 9, 7) (i) $F^{-1}\left\{\frac{9}{2\omega+i}\right\} =$

$-\frac{9i}{2}F^{-1}\left\{\frac{1}{1/2-i\omega}\right\}$ (entry 18) $= -\frac{9i}{2}H(-x)e^{x/2}$ (entry 3) (k) $F^{-1}\{e^{-|\omega|}\cos\omega\} = \frac{1}{2\pi}F^{-1}\{2(\pi e^{-|\omega|})\cos\omega\}$ (entry 18)

$= \frac{1}{2\pi}\left[\frac{1}{(x+1)^2+1} + \frac{1}{(x-1)^2+1}\right]$ (entries 15, 1) (m) $F^{-1}\left\{\frac{1}{\omega^2+i\omega+2}\right\} = F^{-1}\left\{\frac{1}{3i}\left(\frac{1}{\omega-i} - \frac{1}{\omega+2i}\right)\right\} = F^{-1}\left\{\frac{1}{3}\left(\frac{1}{1+i\omega} - \frac{1}{-2+i\omega}\right)\right\} =$

$\frac{1}{3}F^{-1}\left\{\frac{1}{1+i\omega} + \frac{1}{2-i\omega}\right\}$ (entry 18) $= \frac{1}{3}[H(x)e^{-x} + H(-x)e^{2x}]$ (entries 2, 3)

Section 17.11

9. (a) Because $u(0)$ is given, use the sine transform. Obtain $\hat{u}_S = -50\frac{\omega}{(\omega^2+9)^2}$ and consider entry 2S with $a = 3$. Since

$Im(3 + i\omega)^2 = 6\omega$, write $\hat{u}_S = -\frac{50}{6}\frac{6\omega}{(\omega^2+9)^2} = -\frac{25}{3}\frac{Im(3+i\omega)^2}{(\omega^2+3^2)^2}$ so $u(x) = -\frac{25}{3}xe^{-3x}$.

INDEX

Boldface page numbers indicate where terms are defined.

AREA ELEMENT: If $x = x(u,v),\ y = y(u,v),\ z = z(u,v):\quad dA = \sqrt{EG - F^2}\, du\, dv,$

$$E = x_u^2 + y_u^2 + z_u^2,\quad F = x_u x_v + y_u y_v + z_u z_v,\quad G = x_v^2 + y_v^2 + z_v^2$$

If $z = f(x,y):\quad dA = \sqrt{1 + f_x^2 + f_y^2}\, dx\, dy$

VOLUME ELEMENT: $dV = \left| \dfrac{\partial(x,y,z)}{\partial(u,v,w)} \right| du\, dv\, dw = \left\| \begin{array}{ccc} x_u & x_v & x_w \\ y_u & y_v & y_w \\ z_u & z_v & z_w \end{array} \right\| du\, dv\, dw$

LEIBNIZ RULE: $\dfrac{d}{dt} \displaystyle\int_{a(t)}^{b(t)} f(x,t)dx = \int_{a(t)}^{b(t)} \dfrac{\partial f}{\partial t} dx + b'(t) f(b(t),t) - a'(t) f(a(t),t)$

FOURIER SERIES:

$f(x)2\ell$-periodic: $\quad f(x) = a_0 + \displaystyle\sum_{n=1}^{\infty} \left(a_n \cos \dfrac{n\pi x}{\ell} + b_n \sin \dfrac{n\pi x}{\ell} \right)$

$$a_0 = \dfrac{1}{2\ell} \int_{-\ell}^{\ell} f(x)dx, \quad a_n = \dfrac{1}{\ell} \int_{-\ell}^{\ell} f(x)\cos \dfrac{n\pi x}{\ell} dx, \quad b_n = \dfrac{1}{\ell} \int_{-\ell}^{\ell} f(x)\sin \dfrac{n\pi x}{\ell} dx$$

$f(x)$ defined only on $0 < x < L$:

HRC: $\quad f(x) = a_0 + \displaystyle\sum_{n=1}^{\infty} a_n \cos \dfrac{n\pi x}{L}, \qquad a_0 = \dfrac{1}{L} \int_0^L f(x)dx, \quad a_n = \dfrac{2}{L} \int_0^L f(x)\cos \dfrac{n\pi x}{L} dx$

HRC: $\quad f(x) = \displaystyle\sum_{n=1}^{\infty} b_n \sin \dfrac{n\pi x}{L}, \qquad b_n = \dfrac{2}{L} \int_0^L f(x)\sin \dfrac{n\pi x}{L} dx$

QRC: $\quad f(x) = \displaystyle\sum_{n=1,3,\ldots}^{\infty} a_n \cos \dfrac{n\pi x}{2L}, \qquad a_n = \dfrac{2}{L} \int_0^L f(x)\cos \dfrac{n\pi x}{2L} dx$

QRS: $\quad f(x) = \displaystyle\sum_{n=1,3,\ldots}^{\infty} b_n \sin \dfrac{n\pi x}{2L}, \qquad b_n = \dfrac{2}{L} \int_0^L f(x)\sin \dfrac{n\pi x}{2L} dx$

FOURIER INTEGRAL: $\quad f(x) = \displaystyle\int_0^{\infty} [a(\omega)\cos \omega x + b(\omega)\sin \omega x]dx \quad (-\infty < x < \infty)$

$$a(\omega) = \dfrac{1}{\pi} \int_{-\infty}^{\infty} f(x)\cos \omega x, \quad b(\omega) = \dfrac{1}{\pi} \int_{-\infty}^{\infty} f(x)\sin \omega x$$

FOURIER TRANSFORM: $\quad F\{f(x)\} = \hat{f}(\omega) = \displaystyle\int_{-\infty}^{\infty} f(x)e^{-i\omega x} dx$

$$F^{-1}\{\hat{f}(\omega)\} = f(x) = \dfrac{1}{2\pi} \int_{-\infty}^{\infty} \hat{f}(\omega)e^{i\omega x} d\omega$$

LAPLACE TRANSFORM: $\quad L\{f(t)\} = \overline{f}(s) = \displaystyle\int_0^{\infty} f(t)e^{-st} dt$

$$L^{-1}\{\overline{f}(s)\} = f(t) = \dfrac{1}{2\pi i} \int_{\gamma - i\infty}^{\gamma + i\infty} \overline{f}(s)e^{st} ds$$

Table of Integrals (cont.)

30. $\displaystyle\int \cos au \, \cos bu \, du = \frac{\sin(a-b)u}{2(a-b)} + \frac{\sin(a+b)u}{2(a+b)} + C \quad \text{if } a^2 \neq b^2$

31. $\displaystyle\int \sin au \, \cos bu \, du = -\frac{\cos(a-b)u}{2(a-b)} - \frac{\cos(a+b)u}{2(a+b)} + C \quad \text{if } a^2 \neq b^2$

32. $\displaystyle\int \sin^n u \, du = -\frac{1}{n} \sin^{n-1} u \, \cos u + \frac{n-1}{n} \int \sin^{n-2} u \, du$

33. $\displaystyle\int \cos^n u \, du = \frac{1}{n} \cos^{n-1} u \, \sin u + \frac{n-1}{n} \int \cos^{n-2} u \, du$

34. $\displaystyle\int \tan^n u \, du = \frac{1}{n-1} \tan^{n-1} u - \int \tan^{n-2} u \, du \quad \text{if } n \neq 1$

35. $\displaystyle\int \cot^n u \, du = -\frac{1}{n-1} \cot^{n-1} u - \int \cot^{n-2} u \, du \quad \text{if } n \neq 1$

36. $\displaystyle\int \sec^n u \, du = \frac{1}{n-1} \sec^{n-2} u \, \tan u + \frac{n-2}{n-1} \int \sec^{n-2} u \, du \quad \text{if } n \neq 1$

37. $\displaystyle\int \csc^n u \, du = -\frac{1}{n-1} \csc^{n-2} u \, \cot u + \frac{n-2}{n-1} \int \csc^{n-2} u \, du \quad \text{if } n \neq 1$

38. $\displaystyle\int u \, \sin u \, du = \sin u - u \cos u + C$

39. $\displaystyle\int u \, \cos u \, du = \cos u + u \sin u + C$

40. $\displaystyle\int u^n \, \sin u \, du = -u^n \cos u + n \int u^{n-1} \cos u \, du$

41. $\displaystyle\int u^n \, \cos u \, du = u^n \sin u - n \int u^{n-1} \sin u \, du$

FORMS INVOLVING $\sqrt{u^2 \pm a^2}$

42. $\displaystyle\int \sqrt{u^2 \pm a^2} \, du = \frac{u}{2} \sqrt{u^2 \pm a^2} \pm \frac{a^2}{2} \ln \left| u + \sqrt{u^2 \pm a^2} \right| + C$

43. $\displaystyle\int \frac{du}{\sqrt{u^2 \pm a^2}} = \ln \left| u + \sqrt{u^2 \pm a^2} \right| + C$

FORMS INVOLVING $\sqrt{a^2 - u^2}$

44. $\displaystyle\int \sqrt{a^2 - u^2} \, du = \frac{u}{2} \sqrt{a^2 - u^2} + \frac{a^2}{2} \sin^{-1} \frac{u}{a} + C$

45. $\displaystyle\int \frac{\sqrt{a^2 - u^2}}{u} \, du = \sqrt{a^2 - u^2} - a \ln \left| \frac{a + \sqrt{a^2 - u^2}}{u} \right| + C$

Table of Integrals (cont.)

EXPONENTIAL AND LOGARITHMIC FORMS

46. $\displaystyle\int ue^u\,du = (u-1)e^u + C$

47. $\displaystyle\int u^n e^u\,du = u^n e^u - n\int u^{n-1}e^u\,du$

48. $\displaystyle\int u^n \ln u\,du = \frac{u^{n+1}}{n+1}\ln u - \frac{u^{n+1}}{(n+1)^2} + C$

49. $\displaystyle\int e^{au}\sin bu\,du = \frac{e^{au}}{a^2+b^2}(a\sin bu - b\cos bu) + C$

50. $\displaystyle\int e^{au}\cos bu\,du = \frac{e^{au}}{a^2+b^2}(a\cos bu + b\sin bu) + C$

INVERSE TRIGONOMETRIC FORMS

51. $\displaystyle\int \sin^{-1}u\,du = u\sin^{-1}u + \sqrt{1-u^2} + C$

52. $\displaystyle\int \tan^{-1}u\,du = u\tan^{-1}u - \frac{1}{2}\ln(1+u^2) + C$

53. $\displaystyle\int \sec^{-1}u\,du = u\sec^{-1}u - \ln\left|u + \sqrt{u^2-1}\right| + C$

54. $\displaystyle\int u\sin^{-1}u\,du = \frac{1}{4}(2u^2-1)\sin^{-1}u + \frac{u}{4}\sqrt{1-u^2} + C$

55. $\displaystyle\int u\tan^{-1}u\,du = \frac{1}{2}(u^2+1)\tan^{-1}u - \frac{u}{2} + C$

56. $\displaystyle\int u\sec^{-1}u\,du = \frac{u^2}{2}\sec^{-1}u - \frac{1}{2}\sqrt{u^2-1} + C$

57. $\displaystyle\int u^n\sin^{-1}u\,du = \frac{u^{n+1}}{n+1}\sin^{-1}u - \frac{1}{n+1}\int \frac{u^{n+1}}{\sqrt{1-u^2}}\,du \quad \text{if } n \neq -1$

58. $\displaystyle\int u^n\tan^{-1}u\,du = \frac{u^{n+1}}{n+1}\tan^{-1}u - \frac{1}{n+1}\int \frac{u^{n+1}}{1+u^2}\,du \quad \text{if } n \neq -1$

59. $\displaystyle\int u^n\sec^{-1}u\,du = \frac{u^{n+1}}{n+1}\sec^{-1}u - \frac{1}{n+1}\int \frac{u^{n+1}}{\sqrt{u^2-1}}\,du \quad \text{if } n \neq -1$

OTHER USEFUL FORMULAS

60. $\displaystyle\int_0^\infty u^n e^{-u}\,du = \Gamma(n+1) = n! \quad (n \geq 0)$

61. $\displaystyle\int_0^\infty e^{-au^2}\,du = \frac{1}{2}\sqrt{\frac{\pi}{a}} \quad (a>0)$

62. $\displaystyle\int_0^{\pi/2}\sin^n u\,du = \int_0^{\pi/2}\cos^n u\,du = \begin{cases} \dfrac{1\cdot3\cdot5\cdots(n-1)}{2\cdot4\cdot6\cdots n}\cdot\dfrac{\pi}{2} & \text{if } n \text{ is an even integer and } n \geq 2 \\[2mm] \dfrac{2\cdot4\cdot6\cdots(n-1)}{3\cdot5\cdot7\cdots n} & \text{if } n \text{ is an odd integer and } n \geq 3 \end{cases}$